Showing Why Math Matters

Rockswold teaches algebra and trigonometry in context, answering the question, "Why am I learning this?"

Creating a Social Network

Although it may not be obvious, math is essential for social networks to operate properly. Matrices are used to keep track of relationships between people on Facebook, Twitter, or Spotify. Also, a matrix can be used to describe links to and from websites on the Internet. (See the Chapter 9 Opener on page 700, Example 2 on page 755, and Example 9 on page 762.)

Starting Up Your Own Company

If you are starting up a small business, you might be interested in a payment startup called Square that allows businesses to swipe credit cards on iPhones and Android devices. Square's dramatic growth during recent years can be analyzed with the aid of a linear inequality. (See the Introduction to Section 2.3 on page 104 and Example 3 on pages 107-108.)

Getting the Jitters?

The side effects of caffeine include either headaches or the jitters. However, with the aid of a system of linear inequalities, we can identify the levels of caffeine intake where neither side effect occurs. (See the Introduction to Section 9.2 on page 719.)

Determining a Margin of Error

Whether a person is being shot out of a cannon or manufacturing an iPhone, the concept of a margin of error is essential. To determine accurate margins of error, we need the concept of an absolute value inequality. (See the Introduction to Section 2.5 on page 134 and Example 7 on page 140.)

Modeling Half-Life of a Facebook Link

A typical Facebook link experiences half of its engagements, or hits, during the first 3 hours. By using exponential functions we can estimate how many hits a Facebook link might experience in a given period of time. (See the Chapter 5 Opener on page 348 and Example 12 in Section 5.3 on pages 390-391.)

Classifying Tornados

The intensity of a tornado is often classified using the Fujita scale: the greater the wind speed of a tornado, the greater its Fujita number. To use this scale we need the concept of a piecewise-constant function. (See the discussion in Section 2.4 on page 121.)

Diminishing Returns and Overfishing

If there are only a few fishing boats in a large body of water, each boat might catch its limit. However, as the number of boats increases, there is a point of diminishing returns, where each boat starts to catch fewer and fewer fish. We can analyze this situation with a piecewise-polynomial function. (See Example 7 in Section 4.2 on pages 250-251.)

Understanding Size in Biology

Larger animals tend to have slower heart rates and larger birds tend to have bigger wings. To understand size and physical characteristics in nature, we need to study power functions. (See the discussion and Example 10 in Section 4.8 on pages 326-328.)

Gary K. Rockswold • Terry A. Krieger • Jessica C. Rockswold

Algebra and Trigonometry with Modeling and Visualization

With
Algebraic Reasoning Activities Manual by Barbara Edwards

Fourth Custom Edition for Oregon State University

Math 103 ▪ Math 111

Taken from:
Algebra and Trigonometry with Modeling and Visualization, Fifth Edition
by Gary K. Rockswold, Terry A. Krieger, and Jessica C. Rockswold

Cover Art: Courtesy of EyeWire, Photodisc/Getty Images.

Taken from:

Algebra and Trigonometry with Modeling and Visualization, Fifth Edition
by Gary K. Rockswold, Terry A. Krieger, and Jessica C. Rockswold
Copyright © 2014, 2010, 2006 by Pearson Education, Inc.
Published by Pearson
Upper Saddle River, New Jersey 07458

Pearson Learning Solutions, 501 Boylston Street, Suite 900, Boston, MA 02116
A Pearson Education Company
www.pearsoned.com

Printed in the United States of America

2 3 4 5 6 7 8 9 10 V092 16 15 14 13

000200010271795843

SR

ISBN 10: 1-269-51667-1
ISBN 13: 978-1-269-51667-9

In memory of a kind man who said to me,

"Have joy wherever you go."

Marvin, 1914–2010

In today's dynamic society, students need to understand mathematics regardless of their major. However, at every level, students continue to have difficulty learning and retaining mathematics. In order to both learn and retain mathematics, students must see a connection between the concepts and their real-life experiences. *Algebra and Trigonometry with Modeling and Visualization,* Fifth Edition, addresses these issues by appropriately connecting applications, modeling, and visualization to mathematical concepts and skills. This text consistently gives meaning to the equations and demonstrates that mathematics *is* relevant. It allows students to learn mathematics in the context of their experiences. Students learn mathematics more fully when concepts are presented not only symbolically but also visually. By complementing a symbolic approach with an emphasis on visual presentations, this text allows students to absorb information faster and more intuitively.

The concept of a function is the unifying theme in this text with an emphasis on the rule of four (verbal, graphical, numerical, and symbolic representations). A flexible approach allows instructors to strike their own balance of skills, rule of four, applications, modeling, and technology. Rather than reviewing all of the necessary intermediate algebra skills in the first chapter, this text integrates required math skills seamlessly by referring students "just in time" to Chapter R, "Basic Concepts from Algebra and Geometry." Instructors are free to assign supplemental homework from this chapter. Students also have additional opportunities to review their skills in the MyMathLab® course when needed. Here personalized homework and quizzes are readily available on a wide variety of review topics.

Students frequently do not realize that mathematics is transforming our society. To communicate this fact, the author has established a website at www.garyrockswold.net. Here, several resources are available, including a number of invited addresses given by the author. These presentations are accessible to students and allow them to understand the big picture of how mathematics influences everyone's life.

Gary Rockswold

Contents

3 Quadratic Functions and Equations *155*

Algebraic Reasoning Activities Manual

by Barbara Edwards, Charisse Hake, Ching-chia Ko, Stephanie Bowers, Gulden Karakok, and Jessica Cohen

Preface

Changes to the Fifth Edition

The Fifth Edition has an exciting new look that makes mathematics more visual and easier for students to understand. The following changes are the result of suggestions made by students, instructors, and reviewers.

- Several features have been added that allow graphs and tables to be labeled in a way that explains topics visually with fewer words.
- Hundreds of new real-world applications that relate to students' lives have been added.
- Approximately 1000 examples and exercises have been replaced or modified to better meet student needs.
- Real-world data has been added and updated to be more current and meaningful to students.
- Chapter 1 has been streamlined from five to four sections at the request of reviewers. As a result, the first two chapters can be covered more efficiently. Also at the request of reviewers, the definition of increasing and decreasing has been modified.
- Chapter 2 has been reorganized so that it begins with equations of lines in Section 2.1. Now additional modeling with linear functions occurs in Section 2.4.
- Chapter 3 includes new visual presentations and explanations for quadratic equations, quadratic inequalities, and transformations of graphs. Rules for the order of transformations have also been included.
- Chapter 4 includes a new subsection covering radical functions and their transformations. Several visuals have been added to help students understand polynomial behavior and graphs of rational functions.
- Chapter 5 has increased emphasis on transformations of exponential and logarithmic functions. It includes more visual explanations of logarithms.
- Chapter 6 has new visuals to explain angular velocity and transformations of sinusoidal graphs. Additional material covering other inverse trigonometric functions has also been added.
- Chapter 7 has improved clarity for students when they verify identities, simplify expressions, find reference angles, and solve trigonometric equations.
- Chapter 8 has additional examples for solving triangles using the law of sines and the law of cosines. New visuals have been added to the topic of vectors to help students understand this important concept better.
- Chapter 9 has a new subsection on social networks and matrices. Several application topics that relate to students' lives, such as the Internet, have been included.
- Chapter 10 has several new visuals that help students understand conic sections.
- Chapter 11 has an increased emphasis on explaining the distinction between sequences and series. More explanation of conditional probability is also given.
- Appendix D is new and explains how percentages, constant percent change, and exponential functions are related. These topics are important to students in their everyday lives.

Features

NEW!

■ **See the Concept**

This new and exciting feature allows students to make important connections by walking them through detailed visualizations. Students use graphs, tables, and diagrams to learn new concepts in a concise and efficient way. This feature also promotes multiple learning styles and deepens every student's understanding of mathematics. (See pages 32, 109, 233, 290, and 373.)

NEW!

■ **Comment Boxes**

This new feature allows graphs, tables, and symbolic explanations to be labeled in such a way that a *concept is easier to understand.* The explanation is now tied closely to a graph, table, or equation. (See pages 26, 73, 214, 271, and 294.)

■ **Chapter and Section Introductions**

Many algebra and trigonometry students have little or no understanding of mathematics beyond basic computation. To motivate students, chapter and section introductions explain some of the reasons for studying mathematics. (See pages 1, 67, 134, and 232.)

■ **Now Try**

This feature occurs after each example. It suggests a similar exercise students can work to see if they understand the concept presented in the example. (See pages 17, 74, and 106.)

■ **Getting Started**

This feature occurs in selected examples that require multistep solutions. Getting Started helps students develop an overall problem-solving strategy before they begin writing a detailed solution. (See pages 6, 71, and 390.)

■ **Algebra and Geometry Review Notes**

Throughout the text, Algebra and Geometry Review Notes, located in the margins, direct students "just in time" to Chapter R, where important topics in algebra and geometry are reviewed. Instructors can use this chapter for extra review or refer students to it as needed. This feature *frees* instructors from having to frequently review material from intermediate algebra and geometry. (See pages 97 and 160.) In addition, quizzes and personalized homework on review skills are now embedded in MyMathLab.

■ **Calculator Help Notes**

The Calculator Help Notes in the margins direct students "just in time" to Appendix A, "Using the Graphing Calculator." This appendix shows students the keystrokes necessary to complete specific examples from the text. This feature *frees* instructors from having to teach the specifics of the graphing calculator and gives students a convenient reference written specifically for this text. (See pages 6, 20, and 93.)

■ **Class Discussion**

This feature, included in most sections, poses a question that can be used for either classroom discussion or homework. (See pages 47, 157, and 236.)

■ **Making Connections**

This feature, which occurs throughout the text, shows students how concepts covered previously are related to new concepts being presented. (See pages 29, 94, 110, 136, and 175.)

■ **Putting It All Together**

This helpful feature at the end of each section summarizes techniques and reinforces the mathematical concepts presented in the section. It is given in an easy-to-follow grid. (See pages 98–99, 331–332, and 392–393.)

■ **Checking Basic Concepts**

This feature, included after every two sections, provides a small set of exercises that can be used as mixed review. These exercises require about 15 or 20 minutes to complete and can be used for collaborative learning exercises if time permits. (See pages 104, 133, and 188.)

■ **Exercise Sets**

The exercise sets are the heart of any mathematics text, and this text includes a large variety of instructive exercises. Each set of exercises covers skill building, mathematical concepts, and applications. Graphical interpretation and tables of data are often used to extend students' understanding of mathematical concepts. The exercise sets are graded carefully and categorized according to topic, making it easy for an instructor to select appropriate assignments. (See pages 80–85 and 183–188.)

■ **Chapter Summaries**

Chapter summaries are presented in an easy-to-read grid. They allow students to quickly review key concepts from the chapter. (See pages 224–227 and 337–341.)

■ **Chapter Review Exercises**

This exercise set contains both skill-building and applied exercises. These exercises stress different techniques for solving problems and provide students with the review necessary to pass a chapter test. (See pages 63–66 and 341–345.)

■ **Extended and Discovery Exercises**

Extended and Discovery Exercises occur at the end of selected sections and at the end of every chapter. These exercises are usually more complex and challenging than the rest of the exercises and often require extension of a topic presented or exploration of a new topic. They can be used for either collaborative learning or extra homework assignments. (See pages 65–66, 230, and 344–345.)

■ **Cumulative Review Exercises**

These comprehensive exercise sets, which occur after every two chapters, give students an opportunity to review previous material. (See pages 152–154 and 345–347.)

Instructor Supplements

ANNOTATED INSTRUCTOR'S EDITION

- Includes sample homework assignments indicated by problem numbers underlined in blue within each end-of-section exercise set.
- Sample homework assignments assignable in MyMathLab.
- Includes Teaching Examples, an extra set of examples for instructors to present in class, doubling the number of examples available for instructors. Solutions and Power Point Slides are available for these.
- Includes Teaching Tips, helpful ideas about presenting topics or teaching from the text
- Includes all the answers to the exercise sets, usually right on the page where the exercise appears

ISBN: 0-321-83679-0 / 978-0-321-83679-3

INSTRUCTOR'S SOLUTIONS MANUAL

- By David Atwood, *Rochester Community and Technical College*
- Provides complete solutions to all text exercises, excluding Writing about Mathematics

ISBN: 0-321-82619-1 / 978-0-321-82619-0

INSTRUCTOR'S TESTING MANUAL (DOWNLOAD ONLY)

- By David Atwood, *Rochester Community and Technical College*
- Provides prepared tests for each chapter of the text, as well as answers
- Available in MyMathLab or downloadable from Pearson Education's online catalog.

TESTGEN® (DOWNLOAD ONLY)

- Enables instructors to build, edit, print, and administer tests using a computerized bank of questions that cover all the objectives of the text
- Using algorithmically based questions, allows instructors to create multiple but equivalent versions of the same question or test with the click of a button
- Lets instructors modify test bank questions or add new questions
- Provides printable or online tests
- Available in MyMathLab or downloadable from Pearson Education's online catalog

INSIDER'S GUIDE

- Includes resources to help faculty with course preparation and classroom management
- Provides helpful teaching tips correlated to the sections of text, as well as general teaching advice

ISBN: 0-321-57717-5 / 978-0-321-57717-7

POWERPOINT PRESENTATION (DOWNLOAD ONLY)

- Classroom presentation software correlated specifically to this textbook sequence
- Available for download within MyMathLab or from Pearson Education's online catalog

Student Supplements

STUDENT'S SOLUTIONS MANUAL

- By David Atwood, *Rochester Community and Technical College*
- Provides complete solutions to all odd-numbered text exercises, excluding Writing about Mathematics and Extended and Discovery Exercises

ISBN: 0-321-83307-4 / 978-0-321-83307-5

Technology Resources

MyMathLab® MyMathLab Online Course (access code required)

MyMathLab delivers **proven results** in helping individual students succeed.

- MyMathLab has a consistently positive impact on the quality of learning in higher education math instruction. MyMathLab can be successfully implemented in any environment—lab-based, hybrid, fully online, traditional—and demonstrates the quantifiable difference that integrated usage has on student retention, subsequent success, and overall achievement.

- MyMathLab's comprehensive online gradebook automatically tracks your students' results on tests, quizzes, homework, and in the study plan. You can use the gradebook to quickly intervene if your students have trouble or to provide positive feedback on a job well done. The data within MyMathLab is easily exported to a variety of spreadsheet programs, such as Microsoft Excel. You can determine which points of data you want to export and then analyze the results to determine success.

MyMathLab provides **engaging experiences** that personalize, stimulate, and measure learning for each student.

- **Exercises:** The homework and practice exercises in MyMathLab are correlated to the exercises in the textbook, and they regenerate algorithmically to give students unlimited opportunity for practice and mastery. The software offers immediate, helpful feedback when students enter incorrect answers.

- **Multimedia Learning Aids:** Exercises include guided solutions, sample problems, videos, and eText clips for extra help at point-of-use.

- **Expert Tutoring:** Although many students describe the whole of MyMathLab as "like having your own personal tutor," students using MyMathLab do have access to live tutoring from Pearson, from qualified math and statistics instructors.

And, MyMathLab comes from a **trusted partner** with educational expertise and an eye on the future.

- Knowing that you are using a Pearson product means knowing that you are using quality content. That means that our eTexts are accurate and our assessment tools work. Whether you are just getting started with MyMathLab, or have a question along the way, we're here to help you learn about our technologies and how to incorporate them into your course.

Rockswold's MyMathLab course engages students and keeps them thinking.

- Author designated preassigned homework assignments are provided.

- Integrated Review provides optional quizzes throughout the course that test prerequisite knowledge. After taking each quiz, students receive a personalized, just-in-time review assignment to help them refresh forgotten skills.

- Interactive figures are available, enabling users to manipulate figures to bring hard-to-convey math concepts to life.

- Section-Lecture Videos provide lectures for each section of the text to help students review important concepts and procedures 24/7. Assignable questions are available to check students' video comprehension.

To learn more about how MyMathLab combines proven learning applications with powerful assessment, visit www.mymathlab.com or contact your Pearson representative.

MyMathLab Ready to Go Course (access code required)

These new Ready to Go courses provide students with all the same great MyMathLab features, but make it easier for instructors to get started. Each course includes pre-assigned homework and quizzes to make creating a course even simpler.

Ask your Pearson representative about the details for this particular course or to see a copy of this course.

MyMathLab Plus/MyLabsPlus

MyLabsPlus combines proven results and engaging experiences from MyMathLab with convenient management tools and a dedicated services team. Designed to support growing math and statistics programs, it includes additional features such as

- **Batch Enrollment:** Your school can create the login name and password for every student and instructor, so everyone can be ready to start class on the first day. Automation of this process is also possible through integration with your school's Student Information System.

- **Login from your campus portal:** You and your students can link directly from your campus portal into your MyLabsPlus courses. A Pearson service team works with your institution to create a single sign-on experience for instructors and students.

- **Advanced Reporting:** MyLabsPlus's advanced reporting allows instructors to review and analyze students' strengths and weaknesses by tracking their performance on tests, assignments, and tutorials. Administrators can review grades and assignments across all courses on your MyLabsPlus campus for a broad overview of program performance.

- **24/7 Support:** Students and instructors receive 24/7 support, 365 days a year, by email or online chat.

MyLabsPlus is available to qualified adopters. For more information, visit our website at www.mylabsplus.com or contact your Pearson representative.

MathXL® MathXL Online Course (access code required)

MathXL is the homework and assessment engine that runs MyMathLab. (MyMathLab is MathXL plus a learning management system.)

With MathXL, instructors can
- Create, edit, and assign online homework and tests using algorithmically generated exercises correlated at the objective level to the textbook.
- Create and assign their own online exercises and import TestGen tests for added flexibility.
- Maintain records of all student work tracked in MathXL's online gradebook.

With MathXL, students can:
- Take chapter tests in MathXL and receive personalized study plans and/or personalized homework assignments based on their test results.
- Use the study plan and/or the homework to link directly to tutorial exercises for the objectives they need to study.
- Access supplemental animations and video clips directly from selected exercises.

MathXL is available to qualified adopters. For more information, visit our website at www.mathxl.com or contact your Pearson representative.

Acknowledgments

Many individuals contributed to the development of this textbook. I would like to thank the following reviewers, whose comments and suggestions were invaluable in preparing this edition of the text.

Dawit Aberra	*Fort Valley State University*
Dr. Josephine D. Davis	*Fort Valley State University*
Christy Dittmar	*Austin Community College*
Chi Giang	*Westchester Community College*
Christian Mason	*Virginia Commonwealth University*
Val Mohanakumar	*Hillsborough Community College*
Nancy Pevey	*Pellissippi State Community College*
Carolynn Reed	*Austin Community College*
Tracy Romesser	*Erie Community College North*
Jeffrey Saikali	*San Diego Miramar College*
Meredith Watts	*Massachusetts Bay Community College*
Cathleen Zucco-Teveloff	*Rowan University*

I would like to welcome Terry Krieger and Jessica Rockswold to the team for the fifth edition. They have provided invaluable help with developing new applications, visualizations, examples, and exercises. Terry and Jessica have contributed at all levels in the development of this new and exciting edition.

I would like to thank Paul Lorczak, Lynn Baker, Namyong Lee at Minnesota State University, Mankato, Mark Rockswold at Denver Community College, and David Atwood at Rochester Community and Technical College for their superb work with proofreading and accuracy checking.

Without the excellent cooperation from the professional staff at Pearson, this project would have been impossible. They are, without a doubt, the best. Thanks go to Greg Tobin for his support of this project. Particular recognition is due Anne Kelly and Christine O'Brien, who gave advice, support, assistance, and encouragement. The outstanding contributions of Sheila Spinney, Judith Garber, Heather Scott, Peggy Sue Lucas, Justine Goulart, and Joe Vetere are much appreciated. The outstanding work of Kathy Diamond was instrumental to the success of this project.

Thanks go to Wendy Rockswold, who gave invaluable assistance and encouragement throughout the project. She also supplied several of the photographs found throughout the text.

A special thank you goes to the many students and instructors who used the first four editions of this text. Their suggestions were insightful. Please feel free to contact me at either *gary.rockswold@mnsu.edu* or *www.garyrockswold.net* with your comments. Your opinion is important.

Gary Rockswold

1 Introduction to Functions and Graphs

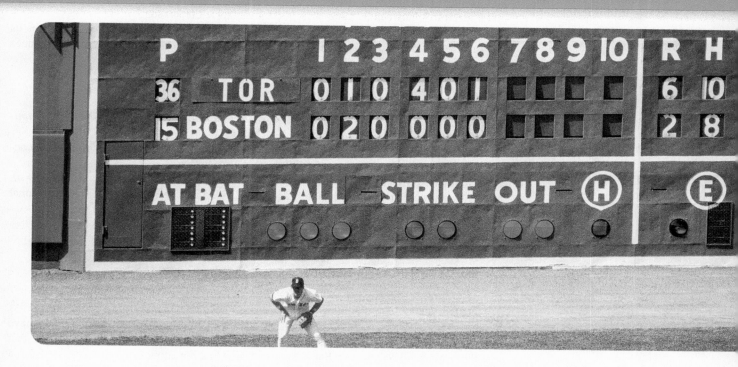

Have you ever thought about how we "live by the numbers"? Money, sports, digital televisions, speed limits, grade point averages, gas mileages, and temperatures are all based on numbers. When we are told what our weight, blood pressure, body mass index, and cholesterol levels are, it can even affect how we feel about ourselves. Numbers permeate our society.

Numbers are part of mathematics, but mathematics is *much more* than numbers. Mathematics also includes techniques to analyze these numbers and to guide our decisions about the future. Mathematics is used not only in science and technology; it is also used to describe almost every facet of life, including consumer behavior, social networks, and the Internet. Mathematics gives people the reasoning skills to solve problems from work and life.

In this chapter we discuss numbers and how functions are used to do computations with these numbers. Understanding numbers and mathematical concepts is essential to understanding and dealing with the many changes that will occur in our lifetimes. Mathematics makes life easier!

> The essence of mathematics is not to make simple things complicated, but to make complicated things simple.
> —Stanley Gudder

1.1 Numbers, Data, and Problem Solving

- Recognize common sets of numbers
- Evaluate expressions by applying the order of operations
- Learn scientific notation and use it in applications
- Apply problem-solving strategies

Introduction

Because society is becoming more complex and diverse, our need for mathematics is increasing dramatically each year. Numbers are essential to our everyday lives. For example, the iPhone 4Gs is 4.5 inches in height, 2.31 inches in width, and 0.37 inch in thickness. It has an 8-gigabyte flash drive and a 5-megapixel camera, and it can operate at temperatures between 32° and 95°F. (*Source:* Apple Corporation.)

Mathematics not only provides numbers to describe new products but also gives us problem-solving strategies. This section discusses basic sets of numbers and introduces some essential problem-solving strategies.

Sets of Numbers

One important set of numbers is the set of **natural numbers**. This set comprises the *counting numbers* $N = \{1, 2, 3, 4, \dots\}$.

The **integers** $I = \{\dots, -3, -2, -1, 0, 1, 2, 3, \dots\}$ are a set of numbers that contains the natural numbers, their additive inverses (negatives), and 0.

A **rational number** can be expressed as the *ratio* of two integers $\frac{p}{q}$, where $q \neq 0$. A rational number results when an integer is divided by a nonzero integer. Thus rational numbers include fractions and the integers. Examples of rational numbers are

$$\frac{2}{1}, \frac{1}{3}, -\frac{1}{4}, \frac{-50}{2}, \frac{22}{7}, 0, \sqrt{25}, \text{ and } 1.2.$$

Rational Numbers

Note that 0 and 1.2 are both rational numbers. They can be represented by the fractions $\frac{0}{1}$ and $\frac{12}{10}$. Because two fractions that look different can be equivalent, rational numbers have more than one form. A rational number can always be expressed in a decimal form that either *repeats* or *terminates*. For example, $\frac{2}{3} = 0.\overline{6}$, a repeating decimal, and $\frac{1}{4} = 0.25$, a terminating decimal. The overbar indicates that $0.\overline{6} = 0.6666666 \dots$.

CLASS DISCUSSION

The number 0 was invented well after the natural numbers. Many societies did not have a zero—for example, there is no Roman numeral for 0. Discuss some possible reasons for this.

Real numbers can be represented by decimal numbers. Since every rational number has a decimal form, real numbers include rational numbers. However, some real numbers cannot be expressed as a ratio of two integers. These numbers are called **irrational numbers**. The numbers $\sqrt{2}$, $\sqrt{15}$, and π are examples of irrational numbers. They can be represented by nonrepeating, nonterminating decimals. Note that for any positive integer a, if $\sqrt{a}$ is not an integer, then $\sqrt{a}$ is an irrational number.

Real numbers are either rational or irrational numbers and can always be *approximated* by a terminating decimal. Examples of real numbers include

$$2, -10, -131.3337, \frac{1}{3} = 0.\overline{3}, -\sqrt{5} \approx -2.2361, \text{ and } \sqrt{11} \approx 3.3166.$$

Real Numbers

NOTE The symbol $\approx$ means **approximately equal**. This symbol is used in place of an equals sign whenever two unequal quantities are close in value. For example, $\frac{1}{2} = 0.5$, whereas $\frac{1}{3} \approx 0.3333$.

Figure 1.1 illustrates how the different sets of numbers are related.

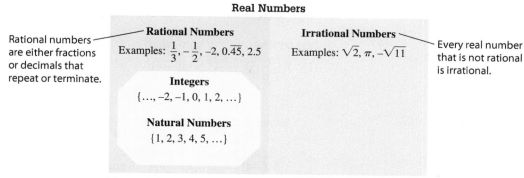

Figure 1.1

EXAMPLE 1 Classifying numbers

Classify each real number as one or more of the following: natural number, integer, rational number, or irrational number.

$$5, -1.2, \frac{13}{7}, -\sqrt{7}, -12, \sqrt{16}$$

SOLUTION

5: natural number, integer, and rational number

-1.2: rational number

$\frac{13}{7}$: rational number

$-\sqrt{7}$: irrational number

-12: integer and rational number

$\sqrt{16} = 4$: natural number, integer, and rational number

Now Try Exercise 7

Order of Operations

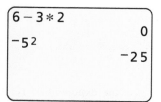

Figure 1.2

Does $6 - 3 \cdot 2$ equal 0 or 6? Does -5^2 equal 25 or -25? Figure 1.2 correctly shows that $6 - 3 \cdot 2 = 0$ and that $-5^2 = -25$. Because multiplication is performed before subtraction, $6 - 3 \cdot 2 = 0$. Similarly, because exponents are evaluated before performing negation, $-5^2 = -25$. It is essential that algebraic expressions be evaluated consistently, so the following rules have been established.

ORDER OF OPERATIONS

Using the following order of operations, perform all calculations within parentheses, square roots, and absolute value bars and above and below fraction bars. Then use the same order of operations to perform any remaining calculations.

1. Evaluate all exponents. Then do any negation *after* evaluating exponents.
2. Do all multiplication and division from *left to right*.
3. Do all addition and subtraction from *left to right*.

EXAMPLE 2 Evaluating arithmetic expressions by hand

Evaluate each expression by hand.

(a) $3(1-5)^2 - 4^2$ **(b)** $\dfrac{10-6}{5-3} - 4 - |7-2|$

SOLUTION

(a) $3(1-5)^2 - 4^2 = 3(-4)^2 - 4^2$

$= 3(16) - 16$

$= 48 - 16$

$= 32$

(b) $\dfrac{10-6}{5-3} - 4 - |7-2| = \dfrac{4}{2} - 4 - |5|$

$= 2 - 4 - 5$

$= -2 - 5$

$= -7$

NOTE $(-4)^2 = (-4)(-4) = 16$ and $-4^2 = -(4)(4) = -16$.

Now Try Exercises 19 and 21

Scientific Notation

Numbers that are large or small in absolute value are often expressed in scientific notation. Table 1.1 lists examples of numbers in **standard (decimal) form** and in **scientific notation**.

Applications of Scientific Notation

Standard Form	Scientific Notation	Application
93,000,000 mi	9.3×10^7 mi	Distance to the sun
256,000	2.56×10^5	Number of cell towers in 2010
9,000,000,000	9×10^9	Estimated world population in 2050
0.00000538 sec	5.38×10^{-6} sec	Time for light to travel 1 mile
0.000005 cm	5×10^{-6} cm	Size of a typical virus

Table 1.1

EXAMPLE 3 Writing a number in scientific notation

Write 0.000578 in scientific notation.

SOLUTION
To write 0.000578 in scientific notation, start by moving the decimal point to the right of the first nonzero digit, 5, to obtain 5.78.

Decimal Form   *Scientific Notation*

$0.\underset{1\ 2\ 3\ 4}{\underbrace{0\ 0\ 0\ 5}}.7\ 8 \quad \rightarrow \quad 5.78 \times 10^{-4}$ *Move the decimal point right.*

Since the decimal point was moved four places to the *right*, the exponent of 10 is *negative* 4, or -4. If the decimal point had been moved to the *left*, the exponent of 10 would be *positive* 4.

Now Try Exercise 35

Here is a formal definition of scientific notation.

SCIENTIFIC NOTATION

Calculator Help
To display numbers in scientific notation, see Appendix A (page AP-2).

A real number r is in **scientific notation** when r is written as $c \times 10^n$, where $1 \le |c| < 10$ and n is an integer.

An Application The next example demonstrates how scientific notation appears in the description of a new technology.

EXAMPLE 4 Analyzing the energy produced by your body

Nanotechnology is a technology of the very small: on the order of one billionth of a meter. Researchers are using nanotechnology to power tiny devices with energy from the human body. (*Source:* Z. Wang, "Self-Powered Nanotech," *Scientific American*, January 2008.)
(a) Write one billionth in scientific notation.
(b) While typing, a person's fingers generate about 2.2×10^{-3} watt of electrical energy. Write this number in standard (decimal) form.

SOLUTION
(a) One billionth can be written as $\frac{1}{1,000,000,000} = \frac{1}{10^9} = 1 \times 10^{-9}$.
(b) Move the decimal point in 2.2 three places to the left: $2.2 \times 10^{-3} = 0.0022$.

Now Try Exercise 77

The next example illustrates how to evaluate expressions in scientific notation.

EXAMPLE 5 Evaluating expressions by hand

Evaluate each expression. Write your result in scientific notation and standard form.
(a) $(3 \times 10^3)(2 \times 10^4)$ **(b)** $(5 \times 10^{-3})(6 \times 10^5)$ **(c)** $\dfrac{4.6 \times 10^{-1}}{2 \times 10^2}$

SOLUTION
(a)
$$\begin{aligned}
(3 \times 10^3)(2 \times 10^4) &= 3 \times 2 \times 10^3 \times 10^4 && \text{Commutative property}\\
&= 6 \times 10^{3+4} && \text{Add exponents.}\\
&= 6 \times 10^7 && \text{Scientific notation}\\
&= 60,000,000 && \text{Standard form}
\end{aligned}$$

(b)
$$\begin{aligned}
(5 \times 10^{-3})(6 \times 10^5) &= 5 \times 6 \times 10^{-3} \times 10^5 && \text{Commutative property}\\
&= 30 \times 10^2 && \text{Add exponents.}\\
&= 3 \times 10^3 && \text{Scientific notation}\\
&= 3000 && \text{Standard form}
\end{aligned}$$

Algebra Review
To review exponents, see Chapter R (page R-8).

(c)
$$\begin{aligned}
\frac{4.6 \times 10^{-1}}{2 \times 10^2} &= \frac{4.6}{2} \times \frac{10^{-1}}{10^2} && \text{Multiplication of fractions}\\
&= 2.3 \times 10^{-1-2} && \text{Subtract exponents.}\\
&= 2.3 \times 10^{-3} && \text{Scientific notation}\\
&= 0.0023 && \text{Standard form}
\end{aligned}$$

Now Try Exercises 53, 55, and 57

Calculators Calculators often use E to express powers of 10. For example, 4.2×10^{-3} might be displayed as 4.2E–3. On some calculators, numbers can be entered in scientific notation with the $\boxed{\text{EE}}$ key, which you can find by pressing $\boxed{\text{2nd}}\,\boxed{\,.\,}$.

EXAMPLE 6 Computing in scientific notation with a calculator

Approximate each expression. Write your answer in scientific notation.
(a) $\left(\dfrac{6 \times 10^3}{4 \times 10^6}\right)(1.2 \times 10^2)$ **(b)** $\sqrt{4500\pi}\left(\dfrac{103 + 450}{0.233}\right)^3$

SOLUTION
(a) The given expression is entered in two ways in Figure 1.3. Note that in both cases
$$\left(\frac{6 \times 10^3}{4 \times 10^6}\right)(1.2 \times 10^2) = 0.18 = 1.8 \times 10^{-1}.$$

```
(6*10^3)/(4*10^6
)*(1.2*10^2)
                .18
(6E3)/(4E6)*(1.2
E2)
                .18
```

Figure 1.3

Calculator Help
To enter numbers in scientific notation, see Appendix A (page AP-2).

(b) Be sure to insert parentheses around 4500π and around the numerator, $103 + 450$, in the expression $\sqrt{4500\pi}\left(\frac{103 + 450}{0.233}\right)^3$. From Figure 1.4 we can see that the result is approximately 1.59×10^{12}.

```
√(4500π)*((103+4
50)/.233)^3
      1.58960355E12
```

Figure 1.4

Now Try Exercises 61 and 63

EXAMPLE 7 Computing with a calculator

Use a calculator to evaluate each expression. Round answers to the nearest thousandth.

(a) $\sqrt[3]{131}$ **(b)** $\pi^3 + 1.2^2$ **(c)** $\frac{1 + \sqrt{2}}{3.7 + 9.8}$ **(d)** $|\sqrt{3} - 6|$

SOLUTION
(a) On some calculators the cube root can be found by using the MATH menu. If your calculator does not have a cube root key, enter $131^{\wedge}(1/3)$. From the first two lines in Figure 1.5, we see that $\sqrt[3]{131} \approx 5.079$.
(b) Do *not* use 3.14 for the value of π. Instead, use the built-in key to obtain a more accurate value of π. From the bottom two lines in Figure 1.5, $\pi^3 + 1.2^2 \approx 32.446$.
(c) When evaluating this expression be sure to include parentheses around the numerator and around the denominator. Most calculators have a special square root key that can be used to evaluate $\sqrt{2}$. From the first three lines in Figure 1.6, $\frac{1 + \sqrt{2}}{3.7 + 9.8} \approx 0.179$.
(d) The absolute value can be found on some calculators by using the MATH NUM menus. From the bottom two lines in Figure 1.6, $|\sqrt{3} - 6| \approx 4.268$.

Algebra Review
To review cube roots, see Chapter R (page R-37).

Calculator Help
To enter expressions such as $\sqrt[3]{131}$, $\sqrt{2}$, π, and $|\sqrt{3} - 6|$, see Appendix A (page AP-2).

```
3√(131)
        5.078753078
π^3+1.2²
        32.44627668
```

Figure 1.5

```
(1+√(2))/(3.7+9.
8)
        .1788306342
abs(√(3)−6)
        4.267949192
```

Figure 1.6

Now Try Exercises 67, 69, 71, and 73

Problem Solving

Many problem-solving strategies are used in algebra. However, in this subsection we focus on two important strategies that are used frequently: making a sketch and applying one or more formulas. These strategies are illustrated in the next two examples.

EXAMPLE 8 Finding the speed of Earth

Earth travels around the sun in an approximately circular orbit with an average radius of 93 million miles. If Earth takes 1 year, or about 365 days, to complete one orbit, estimate the orbital speed of Earth in miles per hour.

SOLUTION
Getting Started Speed S equals distance D divided by time T, $S = \frac{D}{T}$. We need to find the number of miles Earth travels in 1 year and then divide it by the number of hours in 1 year. ▶

Geometry Review
To find the circumference of a circle, see Chapter R (page R-2).

Earth's Orbit

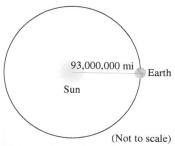

Figure 1.7

Distance Traveled Make a sketch of Earth orbiting the sun, as shown in Figure 1.7. In 1 year Earth travels the circumference of a circle with a radius of 93 million miles. The circumference of a circle is $2\pi r$, where r is the radius, so the distance D is

$$D = 2\pi r = 2\pi(93{,}000{,}000) \approx 584{,}300{,}000 \text{ miles.}$$

Hours in 1 Year The number of hours T in 1 year, or 365 days, equals

$$T = 365 \times 24 = 8760 \text{ hours.}$$

Speed of Earth $S = \dfrac{D}{T} = \dfrac{584{,}300{,}000}{8760} \approx 66{,}700$ miles per hour.

> **Now Try Exercise 79**

Many times in geometry we evaluate formulas to determine quantities, such as perimeter, area, and volume. In the next example we use a formula to determine the number of fluid ounces in a soda can.

A Soda Can

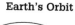

Figure 1.8

> **EXAMPLE 9** Finding the volume of a soda can

The volume V of the cylindrical soda can in Figure 1.8 is given by $V = \pi r^2 h$, where r is its radius and h is its height.
(a) If $r = 1.4$ inches and $h = 5$ inches, find the volume of the can in cubic inches.
(b) Could this can hold 16 fluid ounces? (*Hint:* 1 cubic inch equals 0.55 fluid ounce.)

SOLUTION
(a) $V = \pi r^2 h = \pi(1.4)^2(5) = 9.8\pi \approx 30.8$ cubic inches.
(b) To find the number of fluid ounces, multiply the number of cubic inches by 0.55.

$$30.8 \times 0.55 = 16.94$$

Yes, the can could hold 16 fluid ounces.

> **Now Try Exercise 85**

1.1 Putting It All Together

Numbers play a central role in our society. Without numbers, data could be described qualitatively but not quantitatively. For example, we could say that the day seems hot but would not be able to give an actual number for the temperature. Mathematics provides problem-solving strategies that are used in almost every facet of our lives.

CONCEPT	COMMENTS	EXAMPLES
Natural numbers	Sometimes referred to as the *counting numbers*	$1, 2, 3, 4, 5, \ldots$
Integers	Include the natural numbers, their opposites, and 0	$\ldots, -2, -1, 0, 1, 2, \ldots$
Rational numbers	Include integers; all fractions $\frac{p}{q}$, where p and q are integers with $q \neq 0$; all repeating and all terminating decimals	$\dfrac{1}{2}, -3, \dfrac{128}{6}, -0.335, 0,$ $0.25 = \dfrac{1}{4}, 0.\overline{33} = \dfrac{1}{3}$

continued on next page

CONCEPT	COMMENTS	EXAMPLES
Irrational numbers	Can be written as nonrepeating, nonterminating decimals; cannot be a rational number; if a square root of a positive integer is not an integer, it is an irrational number.	$\pi, \sqrt{2}, -\sqrt{5}, \sqrt[3]{7}, \pi^4$
Real numbers	Any number that can be expressed in standard (decimal) form Include the rational numbers and irrational numbers	$\pi, \sqrt{7}, -\dfrac{4}{7}, 0, -10, 1.237$ $0.\overline{6} = \dfrac{2}{3}, 1000, \sqrt{15}, -\sqrt{5}$
Order of operations	Using the following order of operations, perform all calculations within parentheses, square roots, and absolute value bars and above and below fraction bars. Then perform any remaining calculations. **1.** Evaluate all exponents. Then do any negation *after* evaluating exponents. **2.** Do all multiplication and division from *left to right*. **3.** Do all addition and subtraction from *left to right*.	$\begin{aligned} -4^2 - 12 \div 2 - 2 &= -16 - 12 \div 2 - 2 \\ &= -16 - 6 - 2 \\ &= -22 - 2 \\ &= -24 \end{aligned}$ $\begin{aligned} \dfrac{2 + 4^2}{3 - 3 \cdot 5} &= \dfrac{2 + 16}{3 - 15} \\ &= \dfrac{18}{-12} \\ &= -\dfrac{3}{2} \end{aligned}$
Scientific notation	A number in the form $c \times 10^n$, where $1 \le \lvert c \rvert < 10$ and n is an integer Used to represent numbers that are large or small in absolute value	$3.12 \times 10^4 = 31{,}200$ $-1.4521 \times 10^{-2} = -0.014521$ $5 \times 10^9 = 5{,}000{,}000{,}000$ $1.5987 \times 10^{-6} = 0.0000015987$

1.1   Exercises

Classifying Numbers

Exercises 1–6: Classify the number as one or more of the following: natural number, integer, rational number, or real number.

1. $\frac{21}{24}$ (Fraction of people in the United States completing at least 4 years of high school)

2. 695,000 (Number of Facebook status updates every 60 seconds)

3. 7.5 (Average number of gallons of water used each minute while taking a shower)

4. 8.4 (Neilsen rating of the TV show *Modern Family* the week of January 2, 2012)

5. $90\sqrt{2}$ (Distance in feet from home plate to second base on a baseball field)

6. −71 (Wind chill when the temperature is −30°F and the wind speed is 40 mi/hr)

Exercises 7–10: Classify each number as one or more of the following: natural number, integer, rational number, or irrational number.

7. $\pi, -3, \frac{2}{9}, \sqrt{9}, 1.\overline{3}, -\sqrt{2}$

8. $\frac{3}{1}, -\frac{5}{8}, \sqrt{7}, 0.\overline{45}, 0, 5.6 \times 10^3$

9. $\sqrt{13}, \frac{1}{3}, 5.1 \times 10^{-6}, -2.33, 0.\overline{7}, -\sqrt{4}$

10. $-103, \frac{21}{25}, \sqrt{100}, -\frac{5.7}{10}, \frac{2}{9}, -1.457, \sqrt{3}$

Exercises 11–16: For the measured quantity, state the set of numbers that most appropriately describes it. Choose from the natural numbers, integers, and rational numbers. Explain your answer.

11. Shoe sizes

12. Populations of states

13. Speed limits

14. Gallons of gasoline

15. Temperatures in a winter weather forecast in Montana

16. Numbers of compact disc sales

Order of Operations
Exercises 17–28: Evaluate by hand.

17. $|5 - 8 \cdot 7|$

18. $-2(16 - 3 \cdot 5) \div 2$

19. $-6^2 - 3(2 - 4)^4$

20. $(4 - 5)^2 - 3^2 - 3\sqrt{9}$

21. $\sqrt{9 - 5} - \dfrac{8 - 4}{4 - 2}$

22. $\dfrac{6 - 4^2 \div 2^3}{3 - 4}$

23. $\sqrt{13^2 - 12^2}$

24. $\dfrac{13 - \sqrt{9 + 16}}{|5 - 7|^2}$

25. $\dfrac{4 + 9}{2 + 3} - \dfrac{-3^2 \cdot 3}{5}$

26. $10 \div 2 \div \dfrac{5 + 10}{5}$

27. $-5^2 - 20 \div 4 - 2$

28. $5 - (-4)^3 - (4)^3$

Scientific Notation
Exercises 29–40: Write the number in scientific notation.

29. 40 (Percent of smartphones that run the Android operating system in 2012)

30. 11,700,000 (Number of U. S. cancer survivors in 2007)

31. 0.00365 (Proportion of cosmetic surgeries performed on 13–19 year olds)

32. 0.62 (Number of miles in 1 kilometer)

33. 2450

34. 105.6

35. 0.56

36. −0.00456

37. −0.0087

38. 1,250,000

39. 206.8

40. 0.00007

Exercises 41–52: Write the number in standard form.

41. 1×10^{-6} (Wavelength of visible light in meters)

42. 9.11×10^{-31} (Weight of an electron in kilograms)

43. 2×10^8 (Years required for the sun to orbit our galaxy)

44. 8×10^9 (Annual dollars spent in the United States on cosmetics)

45. 1.567×10^2

46. -5.68×10^{-1}

47. 5×10^5

48. 3.5×10^3

49. 0.045×10^5

50. -5.4×10^{-5}

51. 67×10^3

52. 0.0032×10^{-1}

Exercises 53–60: Evaluate the expression by hand. Write your result in scientific notation and standard form.

53. $(4 \times 10^3)(2 \times 10^5)$

54. $(3 \times 10^1)(3 \times 10^4)$

55. $(5 \times 10^2)(7 \times 10^{-4})$

56. $(8 \times 10^{-3})(7 \times 10^1)$

57. $\dfrac{6.3 \times 10^{-2}}{3 \times 10^1}$

58. $\dfrac{8.2 \times 10^2}{2 \times 10^{-2}}$

59. $\dfrac{4 \times 10^{-3}}{8 \times 10^{-1}}$

60. $\dfrac{2.4 \times 10^{-5}}{4.8 \times 10^{-7}}$

Exercises 61–66: Use a calculator to approximate the expression. Write your result in scientific notation.

61. $\dfrac{8.947 \times 10^7}{0.00095}(4.5 \times 10^8)$

62. $(9.87 \times 10^6)(3.4 \times 10^{12})$

63. $\left(\dfrac{101 + 23}{0.42}\right)^2 + \sqrt{3.4 \times 10^{-2}}$

64. $\sqrt[3]{(2.5 \times 10^{-8}) + 10^{-7}}$

65. $(8.5 \times 10^{-5})(-9.5 \times 10^7)^2$

66. $\sqrt{\pi(4.56 \times 10^4) + (3.1 \times 10^{-2})}$

Exercises 67–76: Use a calculator to evaluate the expression. Round your result to the nearest thousandth.

67. $\sqrt[3]{192}$

68. $\sqrt{(32 + \pi^3)}$

69. $|\pi - 3.2|$

70. $\dfrac{1.72 - 5.98}{35.6 + 1.02}$

71. $\dfrac{0.3 + 1.5}{5.5 - 1.2}$

72. $3.2(1.1)^2 - 4(1.1) + 2$

73. $\dfrac{1.5^3}{\sqrt{2 + \pi} - 5}$

74. $4.3^2 - \dfrac{5}{17}$

75. $15 + \dfrac{4 + \sqrt{3}}{7}$

76. $\dfrac{5 + \sqrt{5}}{2}$

Applications

77. Nanotechnology (Refer to Example 4.) During inhalation, the typical body generates 0.14 watt of electrical power, which could be used to power tiny electrical circuits. Write this number in scientific notation. (***Source:*** *Scientific American,* January 2008.)

78. Movement of the Pacific Plate The Pacific plate (the floor of the Pacific Ocean) near Hawaii is moving at about 0.000071 kilometer per year. This is about the speed at which a fingernail grows. Use scientific notation to determine how many kilometers the Pacific plate travels in 1 million years.

79. Orbital Speed (Refer to Example 8.) The planet Mars travels around the sun in a nearly circular orbit with a radius of 141 million miles. If it takes 1.88 years for Mars to complete one orbit, estimate the orbital speed of Mars in miles per hour.

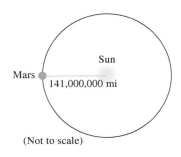

(Not to scale)

80. Size of the Milky Way The speed of light is about 186,000 miles per second. The Milky Way galaxy has an approximate diameter of 6×10^{17} miles. Estimate, to the nearest thousand, the number of years it takes for light to travel across the Milky Way. (**Source:** C. Ronan, *The Natural History of the Universe.*)

81. Living with Cancer The number of people living with cancer (cancer survivors) has increased dramatically from 1971 to 2007. (**Source:** CDC.)
(a) In 1971 the population of the United States was 208 million and the number living with cancer was 3,000,000. To the nearest tenth, approximate the percentage of the population living with cancer in 1971.

(b) In 2007 the population of the United States was 300 million and the number living with cancer was 11,700,000. To the nearest tenth, approximate the percentage of the population living with cancer in 2007.

82. Discharge of Water The Amazon River discharges water into the Atlantic Ocean at an average rate of 4,200,000 cubic feet per second, the highest rate of any river in the world. Is this more or less than 1 cubic mile of water per day? Explain your calculations. (**Source:** *The Guinness Book of Records 1993.*)

83. Analyzing Debt A 1-inch-high stack of $100 bills contains about 250 bills. In 2010 the gross federal debt was approximately 13.5 trillion dollars.
(a) If the entire federal debt were converted into a stack of $100 bills, how many feet high would it be?

(b) The distance between Los Angeles and New York is approximately 2500 miles. Could this stack of $100 bills reach between these two cities?

84. Volume of a Cone The volume V of a cone is given by $V = \frac{1}{3}\pi r^2 h$, where r is its radius and h is its height. Find V when $r = 4$ inches and $h = 1$ foot. Round your answer to the nearest hundredth.

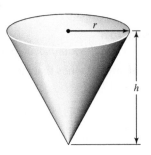

85. Size of a Soda Can (Refer to Example 9.) The volume V of a cylindrical soda can is given by $V = \pi r^2 h$, where r is its radius and h is its height.
(a) If $r = 1.3$ inches and $h = 4.4$ inches, find the volume of the can in cubic inches.

(b) Could this can hold 12 fluid ounces? (*Hint:* 1 cubic inch equals about 0.55 fluid ounce.)

86. Volume of a Sphere The volume of a sphere is given by $V = \frac{4}{3}\pi r^3$, where r is the radius of the sphere. Calculate the volume if the radius is 3 feet. Approximate your answer to the nearest tenth.

Writing about Mathematics

87. Describe some basic sets of numbers that are used in mathematics and where you find them in everyday life.

88. Suppose that a positive number a is written in scientific notation as $a = c \times 10^n$, where n is an integer and $1 \le c < 10$. Explain what n indicates about the size of a.

Extended and Discovery Exercise

Exercises 1–4: Measuring the thickness of a very thin layer of material can be difficult to do directly. For example, it would be difficult to measure the thickness of an oil film on water or a coat of paint with a ruler. However, it can be done indirectly using the following formula.

$$\text{Thickness} = \frac{\text{Volume}}{\text{Area}}$$

That is, the thickness of a thin layer equals the volume of the substance divided by the area that it covers. For example, if a volume of 1 cubic inch of paint is spread over an area of 100 square inches, then the thickness of the paint equals $\frac{1}{100}$ inch. Use this formula in the following exercises.

1. **Thickness of an Oil Film** A drop of oil measuring 0.12 cubic centimeter in volume is spilled onto a lake. The oil spreads out in a circular shape having a *diameter* of 23 centimeters. Approximate the thickness of the oil film.

2. **Thickness of Gold Foil** A flat, rectangular sheet of gold foil measures 20 centimeters by 30 centimeters and has a mass of 23.16 grams. If 1 cubic centimeter of gold has a mass of 19.3 grams, find the thickness of the gold foil. (***Source:*** U. Haber-Schaim, *Introductory Physical Science.*)

3. **Thickness of Cement** A 100-foot-long sidewalk is 5 feet wide. If 125 cubic feet of cement are evenly poured to form the sidewalk, find the thickness of the sidewalk.

4. **Depth of a Lake** A lake covers 2.5×10^7 square feet and contains 7.5×10^8 cubic feet of water. Find the average depth of the lake.

1.2 Visualizing and Graphing Data

- Analyze one-variable data
- Find the domain and range of a relation
- Graph in the *xy*-plane
- Calculate distance
- Find the midpoint
- Learn the standard equation of a circle
- Learn to graph equations with a calculator (optional)

Introduction

There is a wealth of information in data, but the challenge is to convert data into meaningful information that can be used to solve problems. Visualization can be a powerful tool to analyze data, as pictures and graphs are often easier to understand than a list of numbers. For example, looking at Table 1.2, it is difficult to identify trends in the data for *Popular Science* iPad subscriptions. On the other hand, the *line graph* in Figure 1.9 makes it easy to see that there is a sudden increase in subscriptions in October 2011. This increase could be an indicator for Apple that its new product Newsstand, which makes it easier to subscribe to magazines, is a success. Insights like this are important to businesses and therefore visualization is an effective business strategy.

Popular Science iPad Subscription Sales 2011

Date	Subscriptions
27 Feb	7,100
24 Apr	15,400
19 Jun	20,100
14 Aug	25,000
9 Oct	28,700
30 Oct	36,000
27 Nov	40,700

Table 1.2

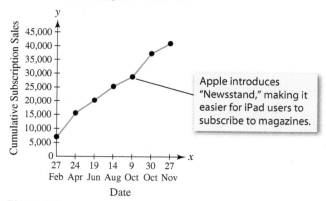

Apple introduces "Newsstand," making it easier for iPad users to subscribe to magazines.

Figure 1.9

One-Variable Data

Data often occur in the form of a list. A list of test scores without names is an example; the only variable is the score. Data of this type are referred to as **one-variable data.** If the values in a list are unique, they can be represented visually on a number line.

Means and medians can be found for one-variable data sets. To calculate the **mean** (or **average**) of a set of n numbers, we add the n numbers and then divide the sum by n. The **median** is equal to the value that is located in the middle of a *sorted* list. If there is an odd number of data items, the median is the middle data item. If there is an even number of data items, the median is the average of the two middle items.

EXAMPLE 1   Analyzing a list of temperatures

Table 1.3 lists the low temperatures T in degrees Fahrenheit that occurred in Minneapolis, Minnesota, for six consecutive nights during January 2012.

Low Temperatures in Minneapolis for Six Nights

T	-12	-4	-8	21	18	9

Table 1.3

(a) Plot these temperatures on a number line.
(b) Find the maximum and minimum of these temperatures.
(c) Determine the mean of these six temperatures.
(d) Find the median and interpret the result.

SOLUTION
(a) In Figure 1.10 the numbers in Table 1.3 are plotted on a number line.

Number Line Graph of Low Temperatures

$$\overset{\longleftarrow\,|\ \ \ \ |\ \ \bullet|\bullet\bullet\,|\ \ \ \ \bullet|\ \ \bullet|\bullet\ \ |\longrightarrow}{\underset{-30\ \ -20\ \ -10\ \ \ \ 0\ \ \ \ 10\ \ \ \ 20\ \ \ \ 30}{}}$$

Figure 1.10

(b) The maximum is 21°F and the minimum is -12°F.
(c) The mean temperature is calculated as follows:

$$\frac{-12 + (-4) + (-8) + 21 + 18 + 9}{6} = \frac{24}{6} = 4.$$

Thus the average low temperature was 4°F.
(d) In the ordered list $-12, -8, -4, 9, 18, 21$, the median is the average of the two middle temperatures, -4°F and 9°F. The median is $\frac{-4 + 9}{2} = 2.5$°F. This means that half of the temperatures are above 2.5°F and half are below.

Now Try Exercises 1 and 5

Two-Variable Data

Relations Sometimes a relationship exists between two lists of data. Table 1.4 lists the monthly average precipitation in inches for Portland, Oregon. In this table, 1 corresponds to January, 2 to February, and so on. We show the relationship between a month and its average precipitation by combining the two lists so that corresponding months and precipitations are visually paired.

This table forms a relation with ordered pairs in the form (month, precipitation).

Average Precipitation for Portland, Oregon

Month	1	2	3	4	5	6	7	8	9	10	11	12
Precipitation (inches)	6.2	3.9	3.6	2.3	2.0	1.5	0.5	1.1	1.6	3.1	5.2	6.4

Table 1.4

If *x* is the month and *y* is the precipitation in inches, then the **ordered pair** (x, y) represents the average amount of precipitation *y* during month *x*. For example, the ordered pair (5, 2.0) indicates that the average precipitation in May is 2.0 inches, whereas the ordered pair (2, 3.9) indicates that the average precipitation in February is 3.9 inches. *Order is important* in an ordered pair.

Since the data in Table 1.4 involve two variables, the month and precipitation, we refer to them as **two-variable data**. It is important to realize that a relation established by two-variable data is between two lists rather than within a single list. January is not related to August, and 6.2 inches of precipitation is not associated with 1.1 inches of precipitation. Instead, January is paired with 6.2 inches, and August is paired with 1.1 inches. We now define the mathematical concept of a relation.

> **RELATION**
>
> A **relation** is a set of ordered pairs.

If we denote the ordered pairs in a relation by (x, y), then the set of all *x*-values is called the **domain** of the relation and the set of all *y*-values is called the **range**. The relation shown in Table 1.4 has domain

$$D = \{1, 2, 3, 4, 5, 6, 7, 8, 9, 10, 11, 12\} \qquad x\text{-values}$$

The domain is the set of months.

and range

$$R = \{0.5, 1.1, 1.5, 1.6, 2.0, 2.3, 3.1, 3.6, 3.9, 5.2, 6.2, 6.4\}. \qquad y\text{-values}$$

The range is the set of average precipitations.

EXAMPLE 2   Finding the domain and range of a relation

A physics class measured the time *y* that it takes for an object to fall *x* feet, as shown in Table 1.5. The object was dropped twice from each height.

Falling Object

x (feet)	20	20	40	40
y (seconds)	1.2	1.1	1.5	1.6

Table 1.5

(a) Express the data as a relation *S*.
(b) Find the domain and range of *S*.

SOLUTION
(a) A relation is a set of ordered pairs, so we can write

$$S = \{(20, 1.2), (20, 1.1), (40, 1.5), (40, 1.6)\}.$$

(b) The domain is the set of *x*-values of the ordered pairs, or $D = \{20, 40\}$. The range is the set of *y*-values of the ordered pairs, or $R = \{1.1, 1.2, 1.5, 1.6\}$.

> **NOTE**   If an element in the domain or range occurs more than once in a data table, it is listed only once in the set for the domain or the range.

Now Try Exercise 13

Graphing Relations   To visualize a relation, we often use the **Cartesian (rectangular) coordinate plane**, or **xy-plane**. The horizontal axis is the **x-axis** and the vertical axis is the **y-axis**. The axes intersect at the **origin** and determine four regions called **quadrants**, numbered I, II, III, and IV, counterclockwise, as shown in Figure 1.11. We can plot the ordered pair (x, y) using the x- and y-axes. A grid is sometimes helpful when plotting points, as shown in Figure 1.12. A point lying on the x-axis or y-axis does not belong to any quadrant. The point $(-3, 0)$ is located on the x-axis, whereas the point $(0, -3)$ lies on the y-axis. Neither point belongs to a quadrant.

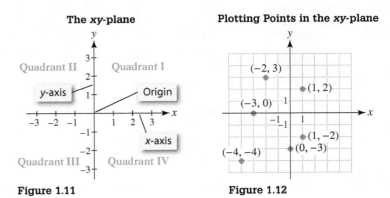

Figure 1.11   Figure 1.12

The term **scatterplot** is given to a graph in the xy-plane where distinct points are plotted. Figure 1.12 is an example of a scatterplot.

EXAMPLE 3   Graphing a relation

Complete the following for the relation

$$S = \{(5, 10), (5, -5), (-10, 10), (0, 15), (-15, -10)\}.$$

(a) Find the domain and range of the relation.
(b) Determine the maximum and minimum of the x-values and then of the y-values.
(c) Label appropriate scales on the xy-axes.
(d) Plot the relation as a scatterplot.

SOLUTION
(a) The elements of the domain D correspond to the first number in each ordered pair.

$$D = \{-15, -10, 0, 5\}$$

The elements of the range R correspond to the second number in each ordered pair.

$$R = \{-10, -5, 10, 15\}$$

(b) x-minimum: -15; x-maximum: 5; y-minimum: -10; y-maximum: 15
(c) An appropriate scale for both the x-axis and the y-axis might be -20 to 20, with each tick mark representing a distance of 5. This scale is shown in Figure 1.13.

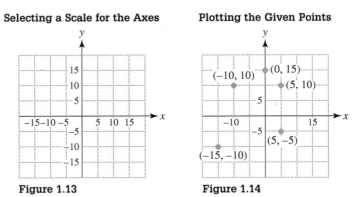

Figure 1.13   Figure 1.14

(d) The points in S are plotted in Figure 1.14.

Now Try Exercise 17

Sometimes it is helpful to connect consecutive data points in a scatterplot with straight-line segments. This type of graph, which visually emphasizes changes in the data, is called a **line graph**.

> **EXAMPLE 4** Making a scatterplot and a line graph
>
> Use Table 1.4 on page 12 to make a scatterplot of average monthly precipitation in Portland, Oregon. Then make a line graph.

SOLUTION

Use the x-axis for the months and the y-axis for the precipitation amounts. To make a scatterplot, simply graph the ordered pairs $(1, 6.2)$, $(2, 3.9)$, $(3, 3.6)$, $(4, 2.3)$, $(5, 2.0)$, $(6, 1.5)$, $(7, 0.5)$, $(8, 1.1)$, $(9, 1.6)$, $(10, 3.1)$, $(11, 5.2)$, and $(12, 6.4)$ in the xy-plane, as shown in Figure 1.15. Then connect consecutive data points to make a line graph, as shown in Figure 1.16.

Figure 1.15 Monthly Average Precipitation

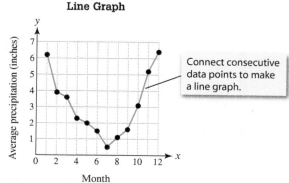

Connect consecutive data points to make a line graph.

Figure 1.16

> **Now Try Exercise 23**

Geometry Review
To review the Pythagorean theorem, see Chapter R (page R-2).

The Distance Formula

In the xy-plane, the length of a line segment with endpoints (x_1, y_1) and (x_2, y_2) can be calculated by using the **Pythagorean theorem**. See Figure 1.17.

The lengths of the legs of the right triangle are $|x_2 - x_1|$ and $|y_2 - y_1|$. The distance d is the hypotenuse of the right triangle. Applying the Pythagorean theorem to this triangle gives $d^2 = (x_2 - x_1)^2 + (y_2 - y_1)^2$. Because distance is nonnegative, we can solve this equation for d to get $d = \sqrt{(x_2 - x_1)^2 + (y_2 - y_1)^2}$.

Distance Between Two Points

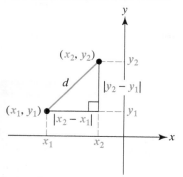

Figure 1.17

> **DISTANCE FORMULA**
>
> The **distance** d between the points (x_1, y_1) and (x_2, y_2) in the xy-plane is
> $$d = \sqrt{(x_2 - x_1)^2 + (y_2 - y_1)^2}.$$

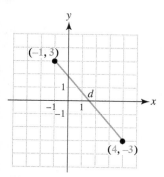

Figure 1.18

Figure 1.18 shows a line segment connecting the points $(-1, 3)$ and $(4, -3)$. Its length is

$$d = \sqrt{(4 - (-1))^2 + (-3 - 3)^2} \qquad \text{Distance formula}$$
$$= \sqrt{61} \qquad \text{Exact length}$$
$$\approx 7.81. \qquad \text{Approximate.}$$

EXAMPLE 5 Finding the distance between two points

Find the exact distance between $(3, -4)$ and $(-2, 7)$. Then approximate this distance to the nearest hundredth.

SOLUTION
In the distance formula, let (x_1, y_1) be $(3, -4)$ and (x_2, y_2) be $(-2, 7)$.

$$\sqrt{(x_2 - x_1)^2 + (y_2 - y_1)^2} = \sqrt{(-2 - 3)^2 + (7 - (-4))^2} \quad \text{Distance formula}$$
$$= \sqrt{(-5)^2 + 11^2} \quad \text{Subtract.}$$
$$= \sqrt{146} \quad \text{Simplify.}$$
$$\approx 12.08 \quad \text{Approximate.}$$

The *exact* distance is $\sqrt{146}$, and the *approximate* distance, rounded to the nearest hundredth, is 12.08. Note that we would obtain the same answer if we let (x_1, y_1) be $(-2, 7)$ and (x_2, y_2) be $(3, -4)$.

Now Try Exercise 27

In the next example the distance between two moving cars is found.

EXAMPLE 6 Finding the distance between two moving cars

Suppose that at noon car A is traveling south at 20 miles per hour and is located 80 miles north of car B. Car B is traveling east at 40 miles per hour.
(a) Let $(0, 0)$ be the initial coordinates of car B in the xy-plane, where units are in miles. Plot the location of each car at noon and at 1:30 P.M.
(b) Approximate the distance between the cars at 1:30 P.M.

Distance Between Two Cars

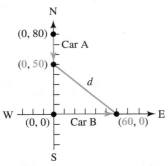

Figure 1.19

SOLUTION
(a) If the initial coordinates of car B are $(0, 0)$, then the initial coordinates of car A are $(0, 80)$, because car A is 80 miles north of car B. After 1 hour and 30 minutes, or 1.5 hours, car A has traveled $1.5 \times 20 = 30$ miles south, and so it is located 50 miles north of the initial location of car B. Thus its coordinates are $(0, 50)$ at 1:30 PM. Car B traveled $1.5 \times 40 = 60$ miles east, so its coordinates are $(60, 0)$ at 1:30 PM. See Figure 1.19, where these points are plotted.
(b) To find the distance between the cars at 1:30 P.M. we must find the distance d between the points $(0, 50)$ and $(60, 0)$.

$$d = \sqrt{(60 - 0)^2 + (0 - 50)^2} = \sqrt{6100} \approx 78.1 \text{ miles}$$

Now Try Exercise 43

The Midpoint Formula

A common way to make estimations is to average data values. For example, in 1995 the average cost of tuition and fees at public colleges and universities was about $4000, whereas in 2005 it was about $6000. One might estimate the cost of tuition and fees in 2000 to be $5000. This type of averaging is referred to as finding the midpoint. If a line segment is drawn between two data points, then its *midpoint* is the unique point on the line segment that is equidistant from the endpoints.

On a real number line, the midpoint M of two data points x_1 and x_2 is calculated by averaging their coordinates, as shown in Figure 1.20. For example, the midpoint of -3 and 5 is $M = \frac{-3 + 5}{2} = 1$.

Finding the Midpoint on a Number Line

Figure 1.20

Finding the Midpoint

Figure 1.21

The midpoint formula in the xy-plane is similar to the formula for the real number line, except that both coordinates are averaged. Figure 1.21 shows midpoint M located on the line segment connecting the two data points (x_1, y_1) and (x_2, y_2). The x-coordinate of the midpoint M is located halfway between x_1 and x_2 and is $\frac{x_1 + x_2}{2}$. Similarly, the y-coordinate of M is the average of y_1 and y_2. For example, if we let (x_1, y_1) be $(-3, 1)$ and (x_2, y_2) be $(-1, 3)$ in Figure 1.21, then the midpoint is computed by

$$\left(\frac{-3 + -1}{2}, \frac{1 + 3}{2} \right) = (-2, 2).$$

MIDPOINT FORMULA IN THE *XY*-PLANE

The **midpoint** of the line segment with endpoints (x_1, y_1) and (x_2, y_2) in the xy-plane is

$$\left(\frac{x_1 + x_2}{2}, \frac{y_1 + y_2}{2} \right).$$

EXAMPLE 7   Finding the midpoint

Find the midpoint of the line segment connecting the points $(6, -7)$ and $(-4, 6)$.

SOLUTION

In the midpoint formula, let (x_1, y_1) be $(6, -7)$ and (x_2, y_2) be $(-4, 6)$. Then the midpoint M can be found as follows.

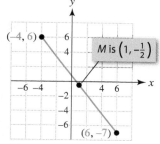

$$M = \left(\frac{x_1 + x_2}{2}, \frac{y_1 + y_2}{2} \right) \qquad \text{Midpoint formula}$$

$$= \left(\frac{6 + (-4)}{2}, \frac{-7 + 6}{2} \right) \qquad \text{Substitute.}$$

$$= \left(1, -\frac{1}{2} \right) \qquad \text{Simplify}$$

The midpoint M of this line segment is shown in Figure 1.22

Figure 1.22

Now Try Exercise 49

EXAMPLE 8   Estimating U.S. population

In 1990 the population of the United States was 249 million, and by 2010 it had increased to 308 million. Use the midpoint formula to estimate the population in 2000. (***Source:*** Bureau of the Census.)

SOLUTION

The U.S. populations in 1990 and 2010 are given by the points $(1990, 249)$ and $(2010, 308)$. The midpoint M of the line segment connecting these points is

$$M = \left(\frac{1990 + 2010}{2}, \frac{249 + 308}{2} \right) = (2000, 278.5).$$

The midpoint formula estimates a population of 278.5 million in 2000 (The actual population was 281 million.)

Now Try Exercise 45

Circles

Applying the Distance Formula to Circles   A **circle** consists of the set of points in a plane that are equidistant from a fixed point. The distance is called the **radius** of the circle, and the fixed point is called the **center**. If we let the center of the circle be (h, k), the radius be r, and (x, y) be any point on the circle, then the distance between (x, y) and (h, k) must equal r. See Figure 1.23. By the distance formula we have

$$\sqrt{(x - h)^2 + (y - k)^2} = r.$$

Squaring each side gives

$$(x - h)^2 + (y - k)^2 = r^2.$$

STANDARD EQUATION OF A CIRCLE

The circle with center (h, k) and radius r has equation

$$(x - h)^2 + (y - k)^2 = r^2.$$

Figure 1.23

> **NOTE** If the center of a circle is $(0, 0)$, then the equation simplifies to $x^2 + y^2 = r^2$. For example, the equation of the circle with center $(0, 0)$ and radius 7 is $x^2 + y^2 = 49$.

EXAMPLE 9 Finding the center and radius of a circle

Find the center and radius of the circle with the given equation. Graph each circle.
(a) $x^2 + y^2 = 9$ **(b)** $(x - 1)^2 + (y + 2)^2 = 4$

SOLUTION
(a) Because the equation $x^2 + y^2 = 9$ can be written as $(x - 0)^2 + (y - 0)^2 = 3^2$, the center is $(0, 0)$ and the radius is $\sqrt{9}$, or 3. The graph of this circle is shown in Figure 1.24.
(b) For $(x - 1)^2 + (y + 2)^2 = 4$, the center is $(1, -2)$ and the radius is $\sqrt{4}$, or 2. The graph is shown in Figure 1.25.

Figure 1.24

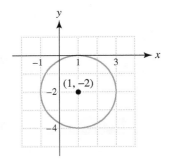

Figure 1.25

Now Try Exercises 59, 63, 81, and 83

EXAMPLE 10 Finding the equation of a circle

Find the equation of the circle that satisfies the conditions. Graph each circle.
(a) Radius 4, center $(-3, 5)$
(b) Center $(6, -3)$ with the point $(1, 2)$ on the circle

SOLUTION
(a) Let $r = 4$ and $(h, k) = (-3, 5)$. The equation of this circle is

$$(x - (-3))^2 + (y - 5)^2 = 4^2 \quad \text{or} \quad (x + 3)^2 + (y - 5)^2 = 16.$$

A graph of the circle is shown in Figure 1.26.
(b) First we must find the distance between the points $(6, -3)$ and $(1, 2)$ to determine r.

$$r = \sqrt{(6 - 1)^2 + (-3 - 2)^2} = \sqrt{50} \approx 7.1$$

Since $r^2 = 50$, the equation of the circle is $(x - 6)^2 + (y + 3)^2 = 50$. Its graph is shown in Figure 1.27.

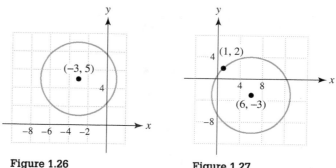

Figure 1.26   **Figure 1.27**

Now Try Exercises 71, 75, 85, and 87

EXAMPLE 11   Finding the equation of a circle

The diameter of a circle is shown in Figure 1.28. Find the standard equation of the circle.

SOLUTION

Getting Started First find the center of the circle, which is the midpoint of a diameter. Then find the radius by calculating the distance between the center and one of the given endpoints of the diameter. ▶

Find the center C of the circle by applying the midpoint formula to the endpoints of the diameter $(-3, 4)$ and $(5, 6)$.

$$C = \left(\frac{-3 + 5}{2}, \frac{4 + 6}{2} \right) = (1, 5)$$

Use the distance formula to find the radius, which equals the distance from the center $(1, 5)$ to the endpoint $(5, 6)$.

$$r = \sqrt{(5 - 1)^2 + (6 - 5)^2} = \sqrt{17}$$

Thus r^2 equals 17, and the standard equation is $(x - 1)^2 + (y - 5)^2 = 17$.

Now Try Exercise 79

Figure 1.28

Graphing with a Calculator (Optional)

Graphing calculators can be used to create tables, scatterplots, line graphs, and other types of graphs. The **viewing rectangle**, or **window**, on a graphing calculator is similar to the view finder in a camera. A camera cannot take a picture of an entire scene; it must be centered on a portion of the available scenery and then it can capture different views of the same scene by zooming in and out. Graphing calculators have similar capabilities. The calculator screen can show only a finite, rectangular region of the xy-plane, which is infinite. The viewing rectangle must be specified by setting minimum and maximum values for both the x- and y-axes before a graph can be drawn.

We will use the following terminology to describe a viewing rectangle. **Xmin** is the minimum x-value and **Xmax** is the maximum x-value along the x-axis. Similarly, **Ymin** is the minimum y-value and **Ymax** is the maximum y-value along the y-axis. Most graphs show an x-scale and a y-scale using tick marks on the respective axes. The distance represented by consecutive tick marks on the x-axis is called **Xscl**, and the distance represented by consecutive tick marks on the y-axis is called **Yscl**. See Figure 1.29. This information can be written concisely as

Identifying the Window Size

Figure 1.29

$$[\text{Xmin, Xmax, Xscl}] \text{ by } [\text{Ymin, Ymax, Yscl}].$$

For example, $[-10, 10, 1]$ by $[-10, 10, 1]$ means that $\text{Xmin} = -10$, $\text{Xmax} = 10$, $\text{Xscl} = 1$, $\text{Ymin} = -10$, $\text{Ymax} = 10$, and $\text{Yscl} = 1$. This setting is referred to as the **standard viewing rectangle**.

EXAMPLE 12 Setting the viewing rectangle

Show the standard viewing rectangle and the viewing rectangle given by $[-30, 40, 10]$ by $[-400, 800, 100]$ on your calculator.

SOLUTION
The required window settings and viewing rectangles are displayed in Figures 1.30–1.33. Notice that in Figure 1.31, there are 10 tick marks on the positive x-axis, since its length is 10 and the distance between consecutive tick marks is 1. Note that **Xres** is usually equal to 1.

The Standard Viewing Rectangle

$[-10, 10, 1]$ by $[-10, 10, 1]$

Calculator Help
To set a viewing rectangle or window, see Appendix A (page AP-3).

Figure 1.30

Figure 1.31

Setting a Different Window

$[-30, 40, 10]$ by $[-400, 800, 100]$

Figure 1.32

Figure 1.33

Now Try Exercise 93

EXAMPLE 13 Making a scatterplot with a graphing calculator

Plot the points $(-5, -5)$, $(-2, 3)$, $(1, -7)$, and $(4, 8)$ in the standard viewing rectangle.

SOLUTION
The standard viewing rectangle is given by $[-10, 10, 1]$ by $[-10, 10, 1]$. The points $(-5, -5)$, $(-2, 3)$, $(1, -7)$, and $(4, 8)$ are plotted in Figure 1.34.

$[-10, 10, 1]$ by $[-10, 10, 1]$

Figure 1.34

Calculator Help
To make the scatterplot in Figure 1.34, see Appendix A (page AP-3).

Now Try Exercise 101

EXAMPLE 14 Creating a line graph with a graphing calculator

Table 1.6 lists the percentage of music album sales accounted for by compact discs (CDs) from 1990 to 2010. Make a line graph of these sales in [1988, 2012, 2] by [0, 100, 20].

CD Album Sales

Year	1990	1995	2000	2005	2010
CDs (% share)	31	65	89	90	74

Source: Recording Industry Association of America.

Table 1.6

SOLUTION

Enter the data points (1990, 31), (1995, 65), (2000, 89), (2005, 90), and (2010, 74). A line graph can be created by selecting this option on your graphing calculator. The graph is shown in Figure 1.35.

Calculator Help

To make a line graph, see Appendix A (page AP-3).

[1988, 2012, 2] by [0, 100, 20]

Figure 1.35

Now Try Exercise 105

1.2 Putting It All Together

CONCEPT	EXPLANATION	EXAMPLES
Mean, or average	To find the mean, or average, of n numbers, divide their sum by n.	The mean of the four numbers $-3, 5, 6, 9$ is $$\frac{-3 + 5 + 6 + 9}{4} = 4.25.$$
Median	The median of a sorted list of numbers equals the value that is located in the middle of the list. Half the data are greater than or equal to the median, and half the data are less than or equal to the median.	The median of 2, 3, 6, 9, 11 is 6, the middle data item. The median of 2, 3, 6, 9 is the average of the two middle values: 3 and 6. Therefore the median is $\frac{3 + 6}{2} = 4.5$.
Relation, domain, and range	A relation is a set of ordered pairs (x, y). The set of x-values is called the domain, and the set of y-values is called the range.	The relation $S = \{(1, 3), (2, 5), (1, 6)\}$ has domain $D = \{1, 2\}$ and range $R = \{3, 5, 6\}$.
Distance formula	The distance between (x_1, y_1) and (x_2, y_2) is $$d = \sqrt{(x_2 - x_1)^2 + (y_2 - y_1)^2}.$$	The distance between $(2, -1)$ and $(-1, 3)$ is $$d = \sqrt{(-1 - 2)^2 + (3 - (-1))^2} = 5.$$

continued on next page

CONCEPT	EXPLANATION	EXAMPLES
Midpoint formula	The midpoint of the line segment connecting (x_1, y_1) and (x_2, y_2) is $$M = \left(\frac{x_1 + x_2}{2}, \frac{y_1 + y_2}{2} \right).$$	The midpoint of the line segment connecting $(4, 3)$ and $(-2, 5)$ is $$M = \left(\frac{4 + (-2)}{2}, \frac{3 + 5}{2} \right) = (1, 4).$$
Standard equation of a circle	The circle with center (h, k) and radius r has the equation $$(x - h)^2 + (y - k)^2 = r^2.$$	The circle with center $(-3, 4)$ and radius 5 has the equation $$(x + 3)^2 + (y - 4)^2 = 25.$$

The next table summarizes some basic concepts related to one-variable and two-variable data.

TYPE OF DATA	METHODS OF VISUALIZATION	COMMENTS
One-variable data	Number line, list, one-column or one-row table	The data items are the same type and can be described using x-values. Computations of the mean and median are performed on one-variable data.
Two-variable data	Two-column or two-row table, scatterplot, line graph or other type of graph in the xy-plane	Two types of data are related, can be described by using ordered pairs (x, y), and are often called a relation.

1.2 Exercises

Data Involving One Variable

Exercises 1–4: For the table of data, complete the following.

(a) Plot the numbers on a number line.
(b) Find the maximum and minimum of the data.
(c) Determine the mean of the data.

1.

3	−2	5	0	6	−1

2.

5	−3	4	−2	1	6

3.

−10	20	30	−20	0	10

4.

0.5	−1.5	2.0	4.5	−3.5	−1.0

Exercises 5–8: Sort the list of numbers from smallest to largest and display the result in a table.

(a) Determine the maximum and minimum values.
(b) Calculate the mean and median. Round each result to the nearest hundredth when appropriate.

5. −10, 25, 15, −30, 55, 61, −30, 45, 5

6. −1.25, 4.75, −3.5, 1.5, 2.5, 4.75, 1.5

7. $\sqrt{15}$, $2^{2.3}$, $\sqrt[3]{69}$, π^2, 2^{π}, 4.1

8. $\frac{22}{7}$, 3.14, $\sqrt[3]{28}$, $\sqrt{9.4}$, $4^{0.9}$, $3^{1.2}$

Exercises 9 and 10: **Geography** *The set of numbers contains data about geographic features of the world.*

(a) Plot the numbers on a number line.
(b) Calculate the mean and median for the set of numbers. Interpret your results.
(c) Try to identify the geographic feature associated with the largest number in the set.

9. $\{31.7, 22.3, 12.3, 26.8, 24.9, 23.0\}$ (Areas of largest freshwater lakes in thousands of square miles) (***Source:*** U.S. National Oceanic and Atmospheric Administration.)

10. $\{19.3, 18.5, 29.0, 7.31, 16.1, 22.8, 20.3\}$ (Highest elevations of the continents in thousands of feet) (***Source:*** National Geographic Atlas of the World.)

11. Designing a Data Set   Find a set of three numbers with a mean of 20 and a median of 18. Is your answer unique?

12. Designing a Data Set   Find a set of five numbers with a mean of 10 and a median of 9. Is your answer unique?

Data Involving Two Variables

Exercises 13–16: For the table of data, complete the following.

(a) *Express the data as a relation S.*
(b) *Find the domain and range of S.*

13.

x	−1	2	3	5	9
y	5	2	−1	−4	−5

14.

x	−2	0	2	4	6
y	−4	−2	−1	0	4

15.

x	1	4	5	4	1
y	5	5	6	6	5

16.

x	−1	0	3	−1	−2
y	$\frac{1}{2}$	1	$\frac{3}{4}$	3	$-\frac{5}{6}$

Exercises 17–22: Complete the following.

(a) *Find the domain and range of the relation.*
(b) *Determine the maximum and minimum of the x-values and then of the y-values.*
(c) *Label appropriate scales on the xy-axes.*
(d) *Plot the relation.*

17. $\{(0, 5), (−3, 4), (−2, −5), (7, −3), (0, 0)\}$

18. $\{(1, 1), (3, 0), (−5, −5), (8, −2), (0, 3)\}$

19. $\{(2, 2), (−3, 1), (−4, −1), (−1, 3), (0, −2)\}$

20. $\{(1, 1), (2, −3), (−1, −1), (−1, 2), (−1, 0)\}$

21. $\{(10, 50), (−35, 45), (0, −55), (75, 25), (−25, −25)\}$

22. $\{(−1.2, 1.5), (1.0, 0.5), (−0.3, 1.1), (−0.8, −1.3)\}$

Exercises 23 and 24: **Plotting Real Data**   *Use the table to make a scatterplot and line graph of the data.*

23. Global Cell Phone Subscribers (millions)

Year	1990	1995	2000	2005	2011
Subscribers	5	34	109	208	324

Source: CTIA–The Wireless Association.

24. Atmospheric CO_2 Levels (parts per million)

Year	1958	1975	1990	2005	2011
CO_2 Amounts	315	335	355	380	392

Source: Mauna Loa Observatory.

Distance Formula

Exercises 25–40: Find the exact distance between the two points. Where appropriate, also give approximate results to the nearest hundredth.

25. (2, −2), (5, 2)   **26.** (0, −3), (12, −8)

27. (7, −4), (9, 1)   **28.** (−1, −6), (−8, −5)

29. (3.6, 5.7), (−2.1, 8.7)   **30.** (−6.5, 2.7), (3.6, −2.9)

31. (−3, 2), (−3 , 10)   **32.** (7, 9), (−1 , 9)

33. $\left(\frac{1}{2}, -\frac{1}{2}\right), \left(\frac{3}{4}, \frac{1}{2}\right)$ **34.** $\left(-\frac{1}{3}, \frac{2}{3}\right), \left(\frac{1}{3}, -\frac{4}{3}\right)$

35. $\left(\frac{2}{5}, \frac{3}{10}\right), \left(-\frac{1}{10}, \frac{4}{5}\right)$ **36.** $\left(-\frac{1}{2}, \frac{2}{3}\right), \left(\frac{1}{3}, -\frac{5}{2}\right)$

37. (20, 30), (−30, −90)   **38.** (40, 6), (−20, 17)

39. $(a, 0), (0, −b)$ **40.** $(x, y), (1, 2)$

41. Geometry   An **isosceles triangle** has at least two sides of equal length. Determine whether the triangle with vertices (0, 0), (3, 4), (7, 1) is isosceles.

42. Geometry   An **equilateral triangle** has sides of equal length. Determine whether the triangle with vertices (−1, −1), (2, 3), (−4, 3) is equilateral.

43. Distance between Cars   (Refer to Example 6.) At 9:00 A.M. car A is traveling north at 50 miles per hour and is located 50 miles south of car B. Car B is traveling west at 20 miles per hour.
   (a) Let (0, 0) be the initial coordinates of car B in the *xy*-plane, where units are in miles. Plot the locations of each car at 9:00 A.M. and at 11:00 A.M.

   (b) Find the distance *d* between the cars at 11:00 A.M.

44. Distance between Ships   Two ships leave a harbor at the same time. The first ship heads north at 20 miles per hour, and the second ship heads west at 15 miles per hour. Write an expression that gives the distance *d* between the ships after *t* hours.

Midpoint Formula

Exercises 45–48: Use the midpoint formula for the following.

45. Nintendo Wii   Six months after Nintendo Wii was introduced it had sold 10 million units, and after 24 months it had sold 44 million units. Estimate the number of units sold 15 months after the Nintendo Wii was introduced. (The actual value was 25 million units.) (*Source:* Company Reports.)

46. World Population   In 1874 the world population was 1.24 billion. By 2050 this number is expected to be 9 billion. Estimate the world population in 1962. (The actual value was 3.14 billion.) (*Source:* United Nations Data.)

47. Olympic Times   In the Olympic Games, the 200-meter dash is run in approximately 19 seconds. Estimate the time to run the 100-meter dash.

48. Real Numbers   Between any two real numbers a and b there is always another real number. How could such a number be found?

Exercises 49–58: Find the midpoint of the line segment connecting the points.

49. $(1, 2), (5, -3)$ **50.** $(-6, 7), (9, -4)$

51. $(-30, 50), (50, -30)$ **52.** $(28, -33), (52, 38)$

53. $(1.5, 2.9), (-5.7, -3.6)$ **54.** $(9.4, -4.5), (-7.7, 9.5)$

55. $(\sqrt{2}, \sqrt{5}), (\sqrt{2}, -\sqrt{5})$

56. $(\sqrt{7}, 3\sqrt{3}), (-\sqrt{7}, -\sqrt{3})$

57. $(a, b), (-a, 3b)$ **58.** $(-a, b), (3a, b)$

Circles

Exercises 59–66: Find the center and radius of the circle.

59. $x^2 + y^2 = 25$ **60.** $x^2 + y^2 = 100$

61. $x^2 + y^2 = 7$ **62.** $x^2 + y^2 = 20$

63. $(x - 2)^2 + (y + 3)^2 = 9$

64. $(x + 1)^2 + (y - 1)^2 = 16$

65. $x^2 + (y + 1)^2 = 100$ **66.** $(x - 5)^2 + y^2 = 19$

Exercises 67–70: Find the standard equation of the circle.

67.

68.

69.

70.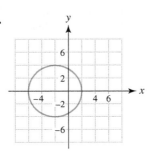

Exercises 71–78: Find the standard equation of a circle that satisfies the conditions.

71. Radius 8, center $(3, -5)$

72. Radius 5, center $(-1, 4)$

73. Radius 7, center $(3, 0)$

74. Radius 1, center $(0, 0)$

75. Center $(3, -5)$ with the point $(4, 2)$ on the circle

76. Center $(0, 0)$ with the point $(-3, -1)$ on the circle

77. Endpoints of a diameter $(-5, -7)$ and $(1, 1)$

78. Endpoints of a diameter $(-3, -2)$ and $(1, -4)$

Exercises 79 and 80: (Refer to Example 11.) Use the diameter to find the standard equation of the circle shown.

79.   **80.**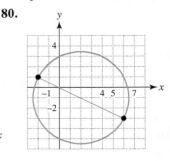

Exercises 81–90: Graph the equation.

81. $x^2 + y^2 = 25$ **82.** $x^2 + y^2 = 1$

83. $(x - 2)^2 + (y + 1)^2 = 25$

84. $(x + 2)^2 + (y + 3)^2 = 1$

85. $(x + 2)^2 + y^2 = 16$ **86.** $x^2 + (y - 2)^2 = 9$

87. $(x + 3)^2 + (y + 1)^2 = 9$

88. $(x - 1)^2 + (y - 2)^2 = 4$

89. $\left(x - \frac{1}{2}\right)^2 + (y - 1)^2 = 10$

90. $(x + 1)^2 + \left(y + \frac{3}{2}\right)^2 = 6$

Graphing Calculators

Exercises 91–96: Predict the number of tick marks on the positive x-axis and the positive y-axis. Then show the viewing rectangle on your graphing calculator.

91. Standard viewing rectangle

92. $[-4.7, 4.7, 1]$ by $[-3.1, 3.1, 1]$

93. $[0, 100, 10]$ by $[-50, 50, 10]$

94. $[-30, 30, 5]$ by $[-20, 20, 5]$

95. $[1980, 1995, 1]$ by $[12000, 16000, 1000]$

96. $[1800, 2000, 20]$ by $[5, 20, 5]$

Exercises 97–100: Match the settings for a viewing rectangle with the correct figure (a–d).

97. $[-9, 9, 1]$ by $[-6, 6, 1]$

98. $[-6, 6, 1]$ by $[-9, 9, 1]$

99. $[-2, 2, 0.5]$ by $[-4.5, 4.5, 0.5]$

100. $[-4, 8, 1]$ by $[-600, 600, 100]$

a.

b.

c.

d.

Exercises 101–104: Make a scatterplot of the relation.

101. $\{(1, 3), (-2, 2), (-4, 1), (-2, -4), (0, 2)\}$

102. $\{(6, 8), (-4, -10), (-2, -6), (2, -5)\}$

103. $\{(10, -20), (-40, 50), (30, 60), (-50, -80), (70, 0)\}$

104. $\{(-1.2, 0.6), (1.0, -0.5), (0.4, 0.2), (-2.8, 1.4)\}$

Exercises 105–108: The table contains real data.

(a) Determine the maximum and minimum values for each variable in the table.

(b) Use your results from part (a) to find an appropriate viewing rectangle.

(c) Make a scatterplot of the data.

(d) Make a line graph of the data.

105. Netflix Subscriptions (millions)

x	2006	2007	2008	2009	2010
y	6.1	7.3	9.1	11.9	19.4

Source: Company Reports.

106. Global Vehicle Sales That Are Electric/Hybrid

x	2011	2015	2019	2022	2025
y	0%	1%	2%	4.5%	8%

Source: *Business Insider* (projected).

107. MySpace U.S. Advertising Revenue ($ millions)

x	2006	2007	2008	2009	2010	2011
y	225	475	590	430	270	180

Source: eMarketer.

108. U.S. College Students Who Study Chinese (thousands)

x	1995	1998	2002	2006	2009
y	26	29	34	51	60

Source: Institute of International Education.

Writing about Mathematics

109. Give an example of a relation that has meaning in the real world. Give an example of an ordered pair (x, y) that is in your relation. Does the ordered pair (y, x) also have meaning? Explain your answers.

110. Do the mean and median represent the same thing? Explain your answer and give an example.

CHECKING BASIC CONCEPTS FOR SECTIONS 1.1 AND 1.2

1. Approximate each expression to the nearest hundredth.

(a) $\sqrt{4.2(23.1 + 0.5^3)}$ **(b)** $\dfrac{23 + 44}{85.1 - 32.9}$

2. Evaluate the expression by hand.
(a) $5 - (-4)^2 \cdot 3$ **(b)** $5 \div 5\sqrt{2} + 2$

3. Write each number using scientific notation.
(a) $348,500,000$ **(b)** -1237.4

(c) 0.00198

4. Find the exact distance between the points $(-3, 1)$ and $(3, -5)$. Then round this distance to the nearest hundredth.

5. Find the midpoint of the line segment connecting the points $(-2, 3)$ and $(4, 2)$.

6. Find the standard equation of a circle with center $(-4, 5)$ and radius 8.

7. The average depths in feet of four oceans are 13,215, 12,881, 13,002, and 3953. Calculate the mean and median of these depths.

8. Make a scatterplot and a line graph with the four points $(-5, -4), (-1, 2), (2, -2),$ and $(3, 6)$. State the quadrant in which each point lies.

1.3 Functions and Their Representations

- Learn function notation
- Represent a function four different ways
- Define a function formally
- Identify the domain and range of a function
- Use calculators to represent functions (optional)
- Identify functions
- Represent functions with diagrams and equations

Introduction

Because there are more than 300 million people in the United States who consume many natural resources, *going green* has become an important social and environmental issue. Figure 1.36 gives some information about U.S. consumption.

Population and Consumption in the United States

313,000,000 People	2,200 Napkins	40 Gallons H_2O	19.4 Pounds CO_2
in 2012	per person per year	per laundry load	per gallon of gas

Figure 1.36

The mathematical concept of a function can be used to analyze the impact of human consumption (see Exercises 101 and 102) and also to describe natural phenomena, such as lightning. This section introduces the important concept of a function, which is used throughout the course.

Basic Concepts

Although thunder is caused by lightning, we sometimes see a flash of lightning before we hear the thunder. The farther away lightning is, the greater the time lapse between seeing the flash of lightning and hearing the thunder. Table 1.7 lists the *approximate* distance y in miles between a person and a bolt of lightning when there is a time lapse of x seconds between seeing the lightning and hearing the thunder.

Time lapse between seeing lightning and hearing thunder

Distance from lightning

Distance from Lightning

x (seconds)	5	10	15	20	25
y (miles)	1	2	3	4	5

Divide x by 5 to get y.

Table 1.7

Table 1.7 established a special type of relation between x and y, called a *function*.

- Each x determines *exactly* one y, so we say that Table 1.7 *represents* or *defines* a function f.
- Function f *computes* the distance y between an observer and a lightning bolt, given the time lapse x. We say that y is a function of x.
- This computation is denoted $y = f(x)$, which is called **function notation** and is read "y equals f of x." It means that function f with input x produces output y. That is,

$$f(\text{Input}) = \text{Output}$$

or

$$f(\text{Time lapse in seconds}) = \text{Miles from lightning}.$$

We can represent the five values in Table 1.7 in function notation as

$$f(5) = 1, \ f(10) = 2, \ f(15) = 3, \ f(20) = 4, \ f(25) = 5,$$

A 5 second delay means the lightning bolt was about 1 mile away.

or more generally as,

$$f(x) = y.$$

The expression $f(x)$ represents the *output y* from f when the *input* is x.

Function f calculates a set of ordered pairs (x, y), where $y = f(x)$. From Table 1.7, the five ordered pairs $(5, 1)$, $(10, 2)$, $(15, 3)$, $(20, 4)$, and $(25, 5)$ belong to the relation computed by f. We can think of these ordered pairs as input-output pairs in the form (input, output).

A given x-value determines exactly one y-value. For example, if x equals 30 seconds, then y equals $\frac{30}{5} = 6$ miles. Thus the y-values (outputs) *depend* on the x-values (inputs). We call x the **independent variable** and y the **dependent variable**.

Computation Performed by Function f

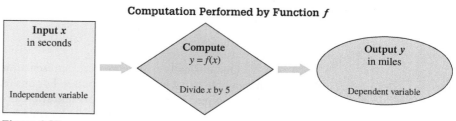

Figure 1.37

In Section 1.2 we discussed the domain and range of a relation. For a function, the set of valid or meaningful inputs x is called the **domain**, and the set of corresponding outputs y is the **range**. For example, suppose that a function f computes the height after x seconds of a ball that was thrown into the air. Then the domain of f consists of all times that the ball was in flight, and the range includes all heights attained by the ball.

This discussion about function notation is summarized as follows.

See the Concept: Function Notation

$y = f(x)$

Ⓐ Name
Ⓑ Output
Ⓒ Input

Ⓐ Common names are f, g, h.
Ⓑ The set of output values is the range.
Ⓒ The set of input values is the domain.

NOTE Every function is a *relation* that calculates *exactly* one output for each valid input.

Representations of Functions

Functions can be represented by verbal descriptions, tables, symbols, and graphs.

Verbal Representation (Words) If function f gives the distance between an observer and a bolt of lightning, then we can verbally describe f with the following sentence: "Divide x seconds by 5 to obtain y miles." We call this a **verbal representation** of f.

Sometimes when the computation performed by a function has meaning, we can interpret this computation verbally. For example, a verbal description of function f is "f calculates the number of miles from a lightning bolt when the delay between thunder and lightning is x seconds."

Numerical Representation (Table of Values)   Table 1.7 gave a numerical representation for the function f that calculates the distance between a lightning bolt and an observer. A **numerical representation** is a *table of values* that lists input-output pairs for a function. A different numerical representation for f is shown in Table 1.8.

Distance from a Bolt of Lightning

x (seconds)	1	2	3	4	5	6	7
y (miles)	0.2	0.4	0.6	0.8	1.0	1.2	1.4

Table 1.8

One difficulty with numerical representations is that it is often either inconvenient or impossible to list all possible inputs x. For this reason we sometimes refer to a table of this type as a **partial numerical representation** as opposed to a **complete numerical representation**, which would include all elements from the domain of a function. For example, many valid inputs do not appear in Table 1.8, such as $x = 11$ or $x = 0.75$.

Symbolic Representation (Formula)   A formula gives a **symbolic representation** of a function. The computation performed by f is expressed by

$$f(x) = \frac{x}{5},$$ Formula for f

where $y = f(x)$. We say that function f is *represented by*, *defined by*, or *given by* $f(x) = \frac{x}{5}$. For example, if the elapsed time is 6 seconds, we write $f(6) = \frac{6}{5} = 1.2$ miles. A formula is an efficient and complete, but less visual, way to define a function.

Graphical Representation (Graph)   A **graphical representation**, or **graph**, visually pairs an x-input with a y-output. In a graph of a function, the ordered pairs (x, y) are plotted in the xy-plane. The ordered pairs

$$(1, 0.2), (2, 0.4), (3, 0.6), (4, 0.8), (5, 1.0), (6, 1.2), \text{ and } (7, 1.4)$$

from Table 1.8 are plotted in Figure 1.38. This scatterplot suggests a line for the graph of f, as shown in Figure 1.39.

Figure 1.38

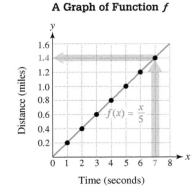

Figure 1.39

Evaluating f(a) Graphically

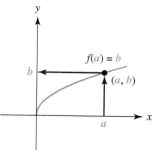

Figure 1.40

From Table 1.8 $f(5) = 1$, so the point $(5, 1)$ lies on the graph of f. Similarly, since $(7, 1.4)$ lies on the graph of f, it follows that $f(7) = 1.4$. See Figure 1.39 where the red arrows illustrate that $f(7) = 1.4$ because the point $(7, 1.4)$ lies on the graph of f.

MAKING CONNECTIONS

Functions, Points, and Graphs   If $f(a) = b$, then the point (a, b) lies on the graph of f. Conversely, if the point (a, b) lies on the graph of f, then $f(a) = b$. Thus each point on the graph of f can be written in the form $(a, f(a))$. See Figure 1.40.

The next example shows how we often use symbolic and numerical representations (formulas and tables) to graph a function by hand.

EXAMPLE 1   Graphing the absolute value function by hand

Graph $f(x) = |x|$ by hand.

SOLUTION

Getting Started Unless you already know what the graph of a given function looks like, a good technique to use when graphing by hand is to first make a table of values. Then plot the points in the table and sketch a smooth curve (or line) between these points. ▶

Start by selecting convenient x-values and then substitute them into $f(x) = |x|$, as shown in Table 1.9. For example, when $x = -2$, then $f(-2) = |-2| = 2$, so the point $(-2, 2)$ is located on the graph of $y = f(x)$.

Next, plot the points as shown in Figure 1.41. The points appear to be V-shaped, and the graph of f shown in Figure 1.42 results if all possible real number ordered pairs $(x, |x|)$ are plotted.

Make a Table

x	$|x|$
-2	2
-1	1
0	0
1	1
2	2

Table 1.9

Plot Points

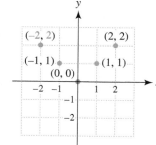

Figure 1.41

Sketch a Graph

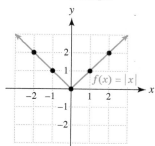

Figure 1.42

Now Try Exercise 13

MAKING CONNECTIONS

The Expressions f and f(x)   The italic letter f represents the *name* of a function, whereas the expression $f(x)$ represents the function f evaluated for input x. That is, $f(x)$ typically represents a formula for function f that can be used to evaluate f for various values of x.

The following See the Concept illustrates four representations for a function.

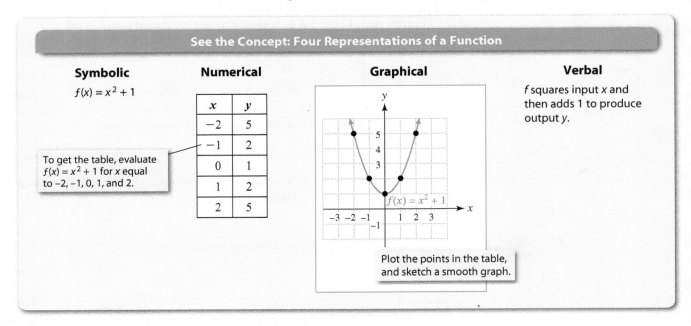

Formal Definition of a Function

Because the idea of a function is a fundamental concept in mathematics, it is important that we define a function precisely. This definition should allow for *all* representations of a function. The commonality among representations is the concept of an ordered pair. A relation is a set of ordered pairs, and a function is a special type of relation.

> **FUNCTION**
>
> A **function** is a relation in which *each* element in the domain corresponds to *exactly one* element in the range.

The set of ordered pairs for a function can be either finite or infinite.

$$f = \{(-3, 5), (0, 6), (3, 2)\} \qquad \textit{Finite Set}$$
$$h = \{(1, 2), (2, 4), (3, 6), (4, 8), \ldots\} \qquad \textit{Infinite Set}$$

A function given by $g(x) = x^2$, where x can be any real number, is another infinite set of ordered pairs of the form (x, x^2). Examples include $(-3, 9)$, $(4, 16)$, and $\left(\frac{1}{2}, \frac{1}{4}\right)$.

EXAMPLE 2 Finding the domain and range

Let a function f be defined by $f(-1) = 4$, $f(0) = 3$, $f(1) = 4$, and $f(2) = -2$. Write f as a set of ordered pairs. Give the domain and range.

SOLUTION
Because $f(-1) = 4$, the ordered pair $(-1, 4)$ is in the set. It follows that

$$f = \{(-1, 4), (0, 3), (1, 4), (2, -2)\}.$$

The domain D of f is the set of x-values, and the range R of f is the set of y-values. Thus

$$D = \{-1, 0, 1, 2\} \quad \text{and} \quad R = \{-2, 3, 4\}.$$

Now Try Exercise 21

EXAMPLE 3   Computing revenue of technology companies

The function f computes the revenue in dollars per unique user for different technology companies. This function is defined by $f(A) = 189$, $f(G) = 24$, $f(Y) = 8$, $f(F) = 4$, where A is Amazon, G is Google, Y is Yahoo, and F is Facebook. (**Source:** *Business Insider.*)
(a) Write f as a set of ordered pairs.
(b) Give the domain and range of f.

SOLUTION
(a) $f = \{(A, 189), (G, 24), (Y, 8), (F, 4)\}$
(b) The domain D and range R of f are

$$D = \{A, F, G, Y\} \quad \text{and} \quad R = \{4, 8, 24, 189\}.$$

Now Try Exercise 97

MAKING CONNECTIONS

Relations and Functions   Every function is a relation, whereas not every relation is a function. A function has exactly one output for each valid input.

Finding Domain, Range, and Function Values

Implied Domain   Unless stated otherwise, the domain of a function f is the set of all *real* numbers for which its symbolic representation (formula) is defined. The domain can be thought of as the set of all valid inputs that make sense in the expression for $f(x)$. In this case the domain is sometimes referred to as the **implied domain**.

When determining the domain of a function we must exclude values of x that result in division by 0. Division by 0 is *always* undefined. Also, unless stated otherwise, we will exclude values of x that result in taking the square root of a negative number. Examples of three functions and their domains D are the following.

The Domains D of Three Functions

1. $f(x) = 2x$

D is all real numbers because $2x$ is defined for all real numbers x.

2. $g(x) = \frac{1}{x}$

D is all real numbers except 0 $(x \neq 0)$.

3. $h(x) = \sqrt{x}$

D is all nonnegative real numbers $(x \geq 0)$.

EXAMPLE 4   Evaluating a function and finding its domain

Let $f(x) = \frac{x}{x-1}$.
(a) If possible, evaluate $f(2)$, $f(1)$, and $f(a + 1)$.   **(b)** Find the domain of f.

SOLUTION
(a) To evaluate $f(2)$, substitute 2 for x in the formula $f(x) = \frac{x}{x-1}$.

$$f(2) = \frac{2}{2-1} = 2 \qquad \textit{Let x = 2.}$$

To evaluate $f(1)$, let x be 1 in the formula.

$$f(1) = \frac{1}{1-1} = \frac{1}{0}, \qquad \textit{Division by 0 is undefined.}$$

which is undefined. Thus 1 is not in the domain of f.
To evaluate $f(a + 1)$, let x be $a + 1$ in the formula.

$$f(a + 1) = \frac{a+1}{a+1-1} = \frac{a+1}{a} \qquad \textit{Let x = a + 1.}$$

(b) The formula $f(x) = \frac{x}{x-1}$ is undefined whenever $x - 1$ equals 0. Thus we exclude 1 from the domain $(x \neq 1)$. In *set-builder notation* the domain is written $\{x \mid x \neq 1\}$.

Now Try Exercise 31

SET-BUILDER NOTATION

The expression $\{x \mid x \neq 1\}$ is written in **set-builder notation** and represents the set of all real numbers x such that x does not equal 1. Another example is $\{y \mid 1 < y < 5\}$, which represents the set of all real numbers y such that y is greater than 1 *and* less than 5.

EXAMPLE 5 Evaluating a function symbolically and graphically

A function g is given by $g(x) = x^2 - 2x$, and its graph is shown in Figure 1.43.
(a) Find the domain and range of g.
(b) Use $g(x)$ to evaluate $g(-1)$.
(c) Use the graph of g to evaluate $g(-1)$.

Figure 1.43

SOLUTION
(a) The domain for $g(x) = x^2 - 2x$ includes all real numbers because the formula is defined for all real number inputs x.

The minimum y-value on the graph is -1. The arrows on the graph point upward, so there is no maximum y-value. The range is all real numbers greater than or equal to -1, or $\{y \mid y \geq -1\}$.
(b) To evaluate $g(-1)$, substitute -1 for x in $g(x) = x^2 - 2x$.

$$g(-1) = (-1)^2 - 2(-1) = 1 + 2 = 3$$

(c) Refer to Figure 1.44 in the following See the Concept where $g(-1) = 3$.

See the Concept: Evaluating $g(-1) = 3$ Graphically

C Move horizontally to 3 on y-axis.

B Move up to graph of g.

A Find -1 on x-axis.

$g(x) = x^2 - 2x$

A To evaluate $g(-1)$, begin by finding $x = -1$ on the x-axis.

B Next, move upward until the graph of g is reached.

C Finally, move to the right until the y-axis is reached. The y-value corresponding to an x-value of -1 is 3. Thus $g(-1) = 3$.

Figure 1.44

Now Try Exercise 37

EXAMPLE 6 Finding the domain and range graphically

A graph of $f(x) = \sqrt{x - 2}$ is shown in Figure 1.45.
(a) Evaluate $f(1)$.
(b) Find the domain and range of f.

SOLUTION
(a) Start by finding 1 on the x-axis. Move up and down on the grid. Note that we do not intersect the graph of f. See Figure 1.46. Thus $f(1)$ is *undefined*.

Figure 1.45   **Figure 1.46**   **Figure 1.47**

(b) In Figure 1.45 the arrow on the graph of f indicates that both the x-values and the y-values increase without reaching a maximum value. In Figure 1.47 the domain and range of f have been labeled by an arrow on each axis. Note that points appear on the graph for all x greater than or equal to 2. Thus the domain is $D = \{x \mid x \geq 2\}$. The minimum y-value on the graph of f is 0 and it occurs at the point (2, 0). There is no maximum y-value on the graph, so the range is $R = \{y \mid y \geq 0\}$.

> **Now Try Exercise 45**

Graphing Calculators and Functions (Optional)

Graphing calculators can be used to create graphs and tables of a function—usually more efficiently and reliably than pencil-and-paper techniques. However, a graphing calculator uses the same basic method that we might use to draw a graph. For example, one way to sketch a graph of $y = x^2$ is to first make a table of values, such as Table 1.10.

Making a Table for $y = x^2$

x	-3	-2	-1	0	1	2	3
y	9	4	1	0	1	4	9

Table 1.10

We can plot these points in the xy-plane, as shown in Figure 1.48. Next we might connect the points with a smooth curve, as shown in Figure 1.49. A graphing calculator typically plots numerous points and connects them to make a graph. In Figure 1.50, a graphing calculator has been used to graph $y = x^2$.

Plotting Points   **Sketching a Graph**   **A Calculator Graph**

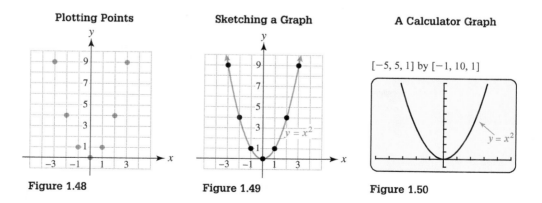

Figure 1.48   **Figure 1.49**   **Figure 1.50**

An Application In the next example we use a graphing calculator to represent a function that computes the decrease in air temperature as altitude increases.

EXAMPLE 7 Representing a function

When the relative humidity is less than 100%, air cools at a rate of 3.6°F for every 1000-foot increase in altitude. Give verbal, symbolic, graphical, and numerical representations of a function f that computes this change in temperature for an increase in altitude of x thousand feet. Let the domain of f be $0 \leq x \leq 6$. (***Source:*** L. Battan, *Weather in Your Life.*)

SOLUTION

Verbal Multiply the input x by -3.6 to obtain the change y in temperature.

Symbolic Let $f(x) = -3.6x$.

Graphical Since $f(x) = -3.6x$, enter $y_1 = -3.6x$, as shown in Figure 1.51. Graph y_1 in a viewing rectangle such as $[0, 6, 1]$ by $[-25, 10, 5]$, used in Figure 1.52.

Graphing with a Calculator

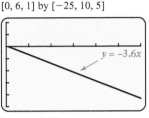

[0, 6, 1] by [−25, 10, 5]

Calculator Help
To enter a formula and create a graph, see Appendix A (pages AP-4 and AP-5).

Figure 1.51   **Figure 1.52**

Calculator Help
To create a table similar to Figure 1.54, see Appendix A (page AP-5).

Numerical It is impossible to list all inputs x, since $0 \leq x \leq 6$. However, Figures 1.53 and 1.54 show how to create a table for $y_1 = -3.6x$ with $x = 0, 1, 2, 3, 4, 5, 6$. Other values for x in the domain of f are possible.

Making a Table of Values

Figure 1.53   **Figure 1.54**

Now Try Exercise 103

NOTE Each of the four representations presented in Example 7 represent the *same* function f.

Identifying Functions

A function is a special type of relation where each valid input (x-value) produces exactly one output (y-value). We can use this concept to identify functions.

EXAMPLE 8 Determining if a set of ordered pairs is a function

Determine if each set of ordered pairs represents a function.
(a) $A = \{(-2, 3), (-1, 2), (0, -3), (-2, 4)\}$
(b) $B = \{(1, 4), (2, 5), (-3, -4), (-1, 7), (0, 4)\}$

SOLUTION
(a) Set A does not represent a function because input -2 results in two outputs: 3 and 4.
(b) Inputs 1 and 0 have the same output 4. However, set B represents a function because each input (x-value) results in one output (y-value).

Now Try Exercises 77 and 79

The following operations can be carried out by functions because they result in *one* output for each valid input.

- Calculating the square of a number x
- Finding the sale price when an item with regular price x is discounted 25%
- Naming the biological mother of person x

NOTE Not all computations can be done by functions. Suppose that we were given an eye color as an input and asked to output the name of each person in the class having this eye color. Typically we would *not* be computing a function. If, for example, several people in the class had brown eyes, there would not be a unique output (name) for each input (eye color).

Some tables do not represent a function. For example, Table 1.11 represents a relation but *not a function* because input 1 produces two outputs, 3 and 12.

A Relation That Is Not a Function

x	1	2	3	1	4
y	3	6	9	12	2

Table 1.11

Points on a Vertical Line Have the Same x-Values

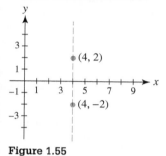

Figure 1.55

Not a Function

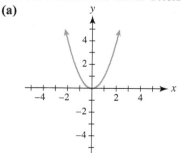

Figure 1.56

Vertical Line Test To conclude that a graph represents a function, we must be convinced that it is impossible for two distinct points with the same x-coordinate to lie on the graph. For example, the ordered pairs $(4, 2)$ and $(4, -2)$ are distinct points with the same x-coordinate. These two points could not lie on the graph of the same function because input 4 would result in two outputs: 2 and -2. When the points $(4, 2)$ and $(4, -2)$ are plotted, they lie on the same vertical line, as shown in Figure 1.55. A graph passing through these points intersects the line twice, as illustrated in Figure 1.56. Therefore the graph in Figure 1.56 does *not* represent a function.

To determine if a graph represents a function, simply visualize vertical lines in the xy-plane. If every vertical line intersects a graph at no more than one point, then it is a graph of a function. This procedure is called the **vertical line test** for a function.

VERTICAL LINE TEST

If every vertical line intersects a graph at no more than one point, then the graph represents a function.

NOTE If a vertical line intersects a graph more than once, then the graph does *not* represent a function.

EXAMPLE 9 Identifying a function graphically

Use the vertical line test to determine if the graph represents a function.

(a)   **(b)**

Function

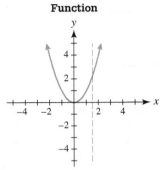

Figure 1.57

Not a Function

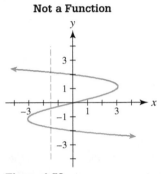

Figure 1.58

SOLUTION

(a) Note in Figure 1.57 that every vertical line that could be visualized would intersect the graph at most once. Therefore the graph represents a function.

(b) The graph in Figure 1.58 does not represent a function because it is possible for a vertical line to intersect the graph more than once.

> **Now Try Exercises 65 and 67**

Functions Represented by Diagrams and Equations

Thus far we have discussed four representations of a function: verbal, numerical, symbolic, and graphical. Two other ways that we can represent, or define, a function are with diagrams and equations.

Diagrammatic Representation (Diagram) Functions are sometimes represented using **diagrammatic representations,** or **diagrams.** Figure 1.59 is a diagram of a function with domain $D = \{5, 10, 15, 20\}$ and range $R = \{1, 2, 3,\}$. An arrow is used to show that input x produces output y. For example, in Figure 1.59 an arrow points from 5 to 1, so $f(5) = 1$ and the point $(5, 1)$ lies on the graph of f. Figure 1.60 shows a relation, but not a function.

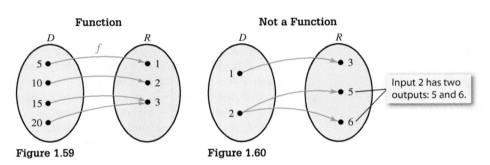

Figure 1.59   **Figure 1.60**

> **MAKING CONNECTIONS**
>
> **Functions as Mappings**   Functions are sometimes referred to as **mappings** between the domain and the range. If $f(5) = 1$, then we say that the range value 1 is the **image** of 5 and that the domain value 5 is the **preimage** of 1.

Functions Defined by Equations Equations can sometimes define functions. For example, the equation $x + y = 1$ defines a function f given by $f(x) = 1 - x$, where $y = f(x)$. Notice that for each input x, there is exactly one y output determined by $y = 1 - x$. In Figure 1.61 the graph passes the vertical line test. However, the graph of the equation $x^2 + y^2 = 4$ is a circle with center $(0, 0)$ and radius 2. Because a circle does not pass the vertical line test, this equation does not represent a function. See Figure 1.62.

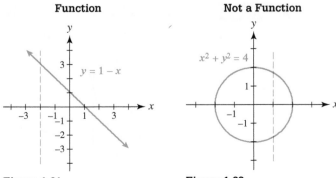

Figure 1.61   **Figure 1.62**

EXAMPLE 10　Identifying a function

Determine if y is a function of x.
(a) $x = y^2$
(b) $y = x^2 - 2$

SOLUTION
(a) For y to be a function of x in the equation $x = y^2$, each valid x-value must result in one y-value. If we let $x = 4$, then y could be either -2 or 2 since

$$4 = (-2)^2 \quad \text{and} \quad 4 = (2)^2. \qquad {\scriptstyle x = y^2}$$

Therefore y is not a function of x. A graph of $x = y^2$ is shown in Figure 1.63. Note that this graph fails the vertical line test.

(b) In the equation $y = x^2 - 2$ each x-value determines exactly one y-value, and so y is a function of x. A graph of this equation is shown in Figure 1.64. This graph passes the vertical line test.

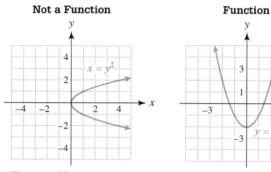

Figure 1.63　　　　　　**Figure 1.64**

> **Now Try Exercises 83 and 89**

1.3 Putting It All Together

CONCEPT	EXPLANATION	EXAMPLES
Function	A function is a *relation* in which each valid input results in one output. The *domain* of a function is the set of valid inputs (x-values), and the *range* is the set of resulting outputs (y-values).	$f = \{(1, 3), (2, 6), (3, 9), (4, 9)\}$ The domain is $D = \{1, 2, 3, 4\}$, and the range is $R = \{3, 6, 9\}$.
Implied domain	When a function is represented by a formula, its domain, unless otherwise stated, is the set of all valid inputs (x-values) that are defined or make sense in the formula.	$f(x) = \dfrac{1}{x + 4}$ Domain of f: $\{x \mid x \neq -4\}$
Identifying graphs of functions	*Vertical Line Test*: If every vertical line intersects a graph at no more than one point, then the graph represents a function. (Otherwise the graph does not represent a function.)	

continued on next page

CONCEPT	EXPLANATION	EXAMPLES
Verbal representation of a function	Words describe precisely what is computed.	A verbal representation of $f(x) = x^2$ is "Square the input x to obtain the output."
Symbolic representation of a function	Mathematical formula	The squaring function is given by $f(x) = x^2$, and the square root function is given by $g(x) = \sqrt{x}$.
Numerical representation of a function	Table of values	A *partial* numerical representation of $f(x) = 3x$ is shown. | x	0	1	2	3
---	---	---	---	---
$f(x)$	0	3	6	9	
Graphical representation of a function	Graph of ordered pairs (x, y) that satisfy $y = f(x)$	Each point on the graph satisfies $y = 2x$.

1.3 Exercises

Evaluating and Representing Functions

1. If $f(-2) = 3$, identify a point on the graph of f.

2. If $f(3) = -9.7$, identify a point on the graph of f.

3. If $(7, 8)$ lies on the graph of f, then $f(\underline{}) = \underline{}$.

4. If $(-3, 2)$ lies on the graph of f, then $f(\underline{}) = \underline{}$.

Exercises 5–20: Graph $y = f(x)$ by hand by first plotting points to determine the shape of the graph.

5. $f(x) = 3$

6. $f(x) = -2$

7. $f(x) = 2x$

8. $f(x) = x + 1$

9. $f(x) = 4 - x$

10. $f(x) = 3 + 2x$

11. $f(x) = \frac{1}{2}x - 2$

12. $f(x) = 2 - 2x$

13. $f(x) = |x - 1|$

14. $f(x) = |0.5x|$

15. $f(x) = |3x|$

16. $f(x) = |2x - 1|$

17. $f(x) = \frac{1}{2}x^2$

18. $f(x) = 2x^2$

19. $f(x) = x^2 - 2$

20. $f(x) = x^2 + 1$

Exercises 21–26: A function g is defined.
(a) Write g as a set of ordered pairs.
(b) Give the domain and range of g.

21. $g(-1) = 0, g(2) = -2, g(5) = 7$

22. $g(-2) = 5, g(3) = 9, g(4) = -4$

23. $g(1) = 8, g(2) = 8, g(3) = 8$

24. $g(-5) = 0, g(0) = -5, g(5) = 0$

25. $g(-1) = 2, g(0) = 4, g(1) = -3, g(2) = 2$

26. $g(-4) = 5, g(0) = -5, g(4) = 5, g(8) = 0$

Exercises 27–36: Complete the following.

(a) Find f(x) for the indicated values of x, if possible.
(b) Find the domain of f.

27. $f(x) = x^3$ for $x = -2, 5$

28. $f(x) = 2x - 1$ for $x = 8, -1$

29. $f(x) = \sqrt{x}$ for $x = -1, a + 1$

30. $f(x) = \sqrt{1 - x}$ for $x = -2, a + 2$

31. $f(x) = 6 - 3x$ for $x = -1, a + 1$

32. $f(x) = -7$ for $x = 6, a - 1$

33. $f(x) = \dfrac{3x - 5}{x + 5}$ for $x = -1, a$

34. $f(x) = x^2 - x + 1$ for $x = 1, -2$

35. $f(x) = \dfrac{1}{x^2}$ for $x = 4, -7$

36. $f(x) = \dfrac{1}{x - 9}$ for $x = 4, a + 9$

Exercises 37–42: (Refer to Example 5.) Use the graph to complete the following.

(a) Estimate the domain and range of g.
(b) Use the formula to evaluate $g(-1)$ and $g(2)$.
(c) Use the graph of g to evaluate $g(-1)$ and $g(2)$.

37.

38.

39.

40.

41.

42.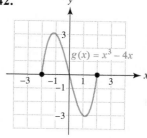

Exercises 43–48: Use the graph of the function f to estimate its domain and range. Evaluate $f(0)$.

43.

44.

45.

46.

47.

48.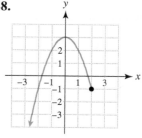

Exercises 49 and 50: **Diagrams** *Complete the following.*

(a) Evaluate $f(2)$.
(b) Write f as a set of ordered pairs.
(c) Find the domain and range of f.

49.

50.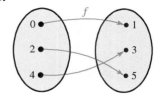

Exercises 51–54: Graph $y = f(x)$ in the viewing rectangle $[-4.7, 4.7, 1]$ by $[-3.1, 3.1, 1]$.

(a) *Use the graph to evaluate $f(2)$.*

(b) *Evaluate $f(2)$ symbolically.*

(c) *Let $x = -3, -2, -1, 0, 1, 2, 3$ and make a table of values for $f(x)$.*

51. $f(x) = 0.25x^2$ **52.** $f(x) = 3 - 1.5x^2$

53. $f(x) = \sqrt{x + 2}$ **54.** $f(x) = |1.6x - 2|$

Exercises 55–62: Use $f(x)$ to determine verbal, graphical, and numerical representations. For the numerical representation use a table with $x = -2, -1, 0, 1, 2$. Evaluate $f(2)$.

55. $f(x) = x^2$ **56.** $f(x) = 2x - 5$

57. $f(x) = |2x + 1|$ **58.** $f(x) = 8$

59. $f(x) = 5 - x$ **60.** $f(x) = |x|$

61. $f(x) = \sqrt{x + 1}$ **62.** $f(x) = x^2 - 1$

63. Cost of Driving In 2012 the average cost of driving a new car was about 50 cents per mile. Give symbolic, graphical, and numerical representations of the cost in dollars of driving x miles. For the numerical representation use a table with $x = 1, 2, 3, 4, 5, 6$. (*Source:* Associated Press.)

64. Counterfeit Money It is estimated that nine out of every one million bills are counterfeit. Give a numerical representation (table) of the predicted number of counterfeit bills in a sample of x million bills where $x = 0, 1, 2, \ldots, 6$. (*Source:* Department of the Treasury.)

Identifying Functions

Exercises 65–70: Does the graph represent a function? If so, determine the function's domain and range.

65.   **66.**

67.   **68.**

69.   **70.**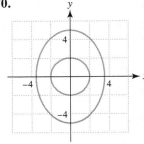

Exercises 71–74: Complete the following.

(a) *Determine if the following can be calculated with a function.*

(b) *Explain your answer.*

71. Input is a real number x; output is its real cube root.

72. Input is a Social Security number x; output is the age of the person with Social Security number x.

73. Input x is a score on a math exam; output is the ID numbers for all students having score x.

74. Input is a Social Security number x; output is the full names of the children of the person with Social Security number x.

75. Identification Numbers A relation takes a student's identification number at your college as input and outputs the student's name. Does this relation compute a function? Explain.

76. Heights A relation takes a height rounded to the nearest inch as input and outputs the name of a student with that height. Does this relation typically compute a function? Explain.

Exercises 77–82: Determine if S is a function.

77. $S = \{(1, 2), (2, 3), (4, 5), (1, 3)\}$

78. $S = \{(-3, 7), (-1, 7), (3, 9), (6, 7), (10, 0)\}$

79. $S = \{(a, 2), (b, 3), (c, 3), (d, 3), (e, 2)\}$

80. $S = \{(a, 2), (a, 3), (b, 5), (-b, 7)\}$

81. S is given by the table.

x	1	3	1
y	10.5	2	-0.5

82. S is given by the table.

x	1	2	3
y	1	1	1

Exercises 83–90: Determine if y is a function of x.

83. $x = y^4$

84. $y^2 = x + 1$

85. $\sqrt{x + 1} = y$

86. $x^2 = y - 7$

87. $x^2 + y^2 = 70$

88. $(x - 1)^2 + y^2 = 1$

89. $x + y = 2$

90. $y = |x|$

Exercises 91–96: **Formulas** *Write a symbolic representation (formula) for a function g that calculates the given quantity. Then evaluate g(10) and interpret the result.*

91. The number of inches in x feet

92. The number of quarts in x gallons

93. The number of dollars in x quarters

94. The number of quarters in x dollars

95. The number of seconds in x days

96. The number of feet in x miles

Applications

97. **DVD Video Rentals** (Refer to Example 3.) The function V computes the percent share of disc DVD rentals accounted for by various companies. This function is defined by $V(R) = 37$, $V(N) = 30$, and $V(S) = 17$, where R is Redbox, N is Netflix, and S is rental stores. (*Source: Business Insider.*)

(a) Write V as a set of ordered pairs.

(b) Give the domain and range of V.

98. **Food Insecurity** Function P computes the percentage of U.S. households that were food insecure during a selected year. This function is defined by $P(2006) = 10.9$, $P(2007) = 11.1$, $P(2008) = 14.6$, $P(2009) = 14.7$, and $P(2010) = 14.5$. (*Source:* U.S. Census Bureau.)

(a) Write P as a set of ordered pairs.

(b) Give the domain and range of P.

99. **Electronic Waste** As technology advances there are more and more obsolete electronic devices that need to be disposed of. The function $f(x) = 40x$ estimates the millions of tons of electronic waste that will accumulate

worldwide after x years. Evaluate $f(5)$ and interpret the result. (*Source: Environmental Protection Agency.*)

100. **Portion Size** If the average American always ordered the larger portion while eating out, then $W(x) = 8x$ would estimate the resulting weight gain in pounds after x years. Evaluate $W(3)$ and interpret the result. (*Source:* FDA.)

101. **Going Green** The average person uses 2200 paper napkins in one year. Write the formula for a function N that calculates the number of paper napkins that the average person uses in x years. Evaluate $N(3)$ and interpret your result.

102. **Going Green** The average top-loading washing machine uses about 40 gallons of water per load of clothes. Write the formula for a function W that calculates the number of gallons of water used while washing x loads of clothes. Evaluate $W(30)$ and interpret your result.

103. **Air Temperature** When the relative humidity is 100%, air cools 5.8°F for every 1-mile increase in altitude. Give verbal, symbolic, graphical, and numerical representations of a function f that computes this change in temperature for an increase in altitude of x miles for $0 \le x \le 3$. (*Source:* L. Battan.)

104. **Crutch Length** Each year 15 million people have foot and ankle problems. Many times they need crutches. The formula $f(x) = 0.72x + 2$ calculates the appropriate crutch length in inches for a person with a height of x inches. (*Source: Journal of the American Physical Therapy Association.*)

(a) Find the crutch length for a person 6 feet 3 inches tall.

(b) For each 1-inch increase in height, by how much does the recommended crutch length increase?

Writing about Mathematics

105. Explain how you could use a complete numerical representation (table) for a function to determine its domain and range.

106. Explain in your own words what a function is. How is a function different from a relation?

1.4 Types of Functions and Their Rates of Change

- Identify linear functions
- Interpret slope as a rate of change
- Identify nonlinear functions
- Identify where a function is increasing or decreasing
- Use interval notation
- Use and interpret average rate of change
- Calculate the difference quotient

Introduction

Functions are used to describe, or *model*, everything from weather to new product "specs," global warming, and U.S. population. New functions are created each day in the *dynamic field* of mathematics. Finding new functions, such as one that calculates memory requirements for an iPod (Example 3), requires creativity. This section discusses two basic types of functions: *linear* and *nonlinear*. We also discuss *constant* functions, which are a special type of linear function.

Linear Functions

A car is initially located 30 miles north of the Texas border and is traveling north on Interstate 35 at 60 miles per hour. The distances between the automobile and the border are listed in Table 1.12 for various times. A scatterplot of the data is shown in Figure 1.65. It suggests that a line that rises from left to right might model these data.

Distance from Texas Border

Elapsed time (hours)	0	1	2	3	4	5
Distance (miles)	30	90	150	210	270	330

Increases by 60 miles each hour

Table 1.12

A Scatterplot of Table 1.12

Initially 30 miles from border

Figure 1.65

A Linear Model

$f(x) = 60x + 30$

Figure 1.66

If the car travels for x hours, the distance traveled can be found by multiplying 60 times x and adding the initial distance of 30 miles. This computation can be expressed as $f(x) = 60x + 30$. For example, $f(1.5) = 60(1.5) + 30 = 120$ means that the car is 120 miles from the border after 1.5 hours. The formula is valid for nonnegative x. The graph of $f(x) = 60x + 30$ is a *line* (ray), shown in Figure 1.66. We call f a *linear function*.

> **LINEAR FUNCTION**
>
> A function f represented by $f(x) = mx + b$, where m and b are constants, is a **linear function**.

Recognizing Linear Functions In the example of the moving car, $f(x) = 60x + 30$, so $m = 60$ and $b = 30$. The value of m represents the speed of the car, and b is the initial distance of the car from the border.

A distinguishing feature of a linear function f is that each time x increases by one unit, the value of $f(x)$ always changes by an amount equal to m. That is, a linear function has a **constant rate of change**. (The constant rate of change m is equal to the slope of the graph of f.) The following applications are modeled by linear functions. Try to determine the value of the constant m in each case.

- The wages earned by an individual working x hours at \$9.25 per hour
- The amount of tuition and fees due when registering for x credits if each credit costs \$350 and the fees are fixed at \$560

Constant Functions If $m = 0$, then a linear function can be written as $f(x) = b$. In this case, f is a *constant function*.

> **CONSTANT FUNCTION**
>
> A function f represented by $f(x) = b$, where b is a constant (fixed number), is a **constant function.**

For example, if $f(x) = 2$, then every input x always results in an output of 2. Thus every point on the graph of f has a y-coordinate of 2 and its graph is a horizontal line. See Table 1.13 and Figure 1.67.

A Constant Function

For every input x, the output y is always 2.

x	y
-2	2
-1	2
1	2
2	2

Table 1.13

Graph is a horizontal line.

Figure 1.67

Slope as a Rate of Change

The graph of a linear function is a line. The slope m is a real number that measures the "tilt" of a line in the xy-plane. If the input x to a linear function increases by 1 unit, then the output y changes by a constant amount that is equal to the slope of its graph. In Figure 1.68 a line passes through the points (x_1, y_1) and (x_2, y_2). The *change in y* is $y_2 - y_1$, and the *change in x* is $x_2 - x_1$. The ratio of the change in y to the change in x is called the *slope*. We sometimes denote the change in y by Δy (delta y) and the change in x by Δx (delta x). That is, $\Delta y = y_2 - y_1$ and $\Delta x = x_2 - x_1$.

Finding Slope Given Two Points

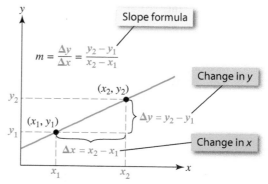

Slope formula

$$m = \frac{\Delta y}{\Delta x} = \frac{y_2 - y_1}{x_2 - x_1}$$

(x_2, y_2)

Change in y

(x_1, y_1)

$\Delta y = y_2 - y_1$

$\Delta x = x_2 - x_1$

Change in x

Figure 1.68

The following is a definition of slope.

> **SLOPE**
>
> The **slope** m of the line passing through the points (x_1, y_1) and (x_2, y_2) is
>
> $$m = \frac{\Delta y}{\Delta x} = \frac{y_2 - y_1}{x_2 - x_1}, \quad \text{where } x_1 \neq x_2.$$

Figures 1.69–1.72 summarize some basic concepts about slope.

Positive Slope
(Rises from left to right)

Rises 2 units for each unit increase in x

Figure 1.69

Negative Slope
(Falls from left to right)

Falls $\frac{1}{2}$ unit for each unit increase in x

Figure 1.70

Zero Slope
(Horizontal line)

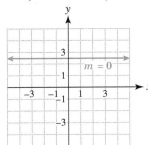

Figure 1.71

Undefined Slope
(Vertical line)

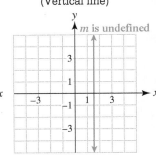

m is undefined

Figure 1.72

Given two points on a line we can calculate the slope of the line, as illustrated in Example 1.

EXAMPLE 1 Calculating the slope of a line

Find the slope of the line passing through the points $(-2, 3)$ and $(1, -2)$. Plot these points together with the line. Explain what the slope indicates about the line.

SOLUTION
Let $(x_1, y_1) = (-2, 3)$ and $(x_2, y_2) = (1, -2)$. The slope is

$$m = \frac{y_2 - y_1}{x_2 - x_1} = \frac{-2 - 3}{1 - (-2)} = -\frac{5}{3}.$$

A line passing through these two points is shown in Figure 1.73. The change in y is $\Delta y = -5$ and the change in x is $\Delta x = 3$, so $m = \frac{\Delta y}{\Delta x} = -\frac{5}{3}$ indicates that the line falls $\frac{5}{3}$ units for each unit increase in x, or equivalently, the line falls 5 units for each 3-unit increase in x.

Now Try Exercise 5

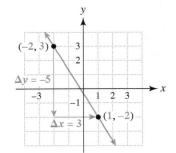

Figure 1.73

Linear Functions and Slope The graph of $f(x) = mx + b$ is a line that has slope m. We can verify this as follows. Since $f(0) = b$ and $f(1) = m + b$, the graph of f passes through the points $(0, b)$ and $(1, m + b)$. The slope of this line is

$$\frac{y_2 - y_1}{x_2 - x_1} = \frac{m + b - b}{1 - 0} = \frac{m}{1} = m.$$

Interpreting Slope In applications involving linear functions, slope sometimes is interpreted as a *(constant) rate of change* as in the next two examples.

EXAMPLE 2 Interpreting slope and going green

The function given by $P(x) = 19.4x$ calculates the pounds of CO_2 (carbon dioxide) released into the atmosphere by a car burning x gallons of gasoline.
(a) Calculate $P(5)$ and interpret the result.
(b) Find the slope of the graph of P. Interpret this slope as a rate of change.

SOLUTION
(a) $P(5) = 19.4(5) = 97$, so burning 5 gallons of gasoline releases 97 pounds of CO_2.
(b) The slope of the graph of P is 19.4. This means that 19.4 pounds of CO_2 are released for every gallon of gasoline burned by a car.

> **Now Try Exercise 27**

EXAMPLE 3 Interpreting slope and iPod memory

Figure 1.74 shows the (approximate) number of songs that can be stored on x gigabytes of Classic iPod memory. (***Source:*** Apple Corporation.)
(a) Why is it reasonable for the graph to pass through the origin?
(b) Find the slope of the line segment.
(c) Interpret the slope as a rate of change.

Figure 1.74

SOLUTION
(a) Because 0 songs require no memory, the graph passes through the point (0, 0).
(b) The graph passes through the points (0, 0) and (80, 20,000). The slope of the line is

$$m = \frac{20,000 - 0}{80 - 0} = 250.$$

(c) An iPod holds 250 songs per gigabyte.

> **Now Try Exercise 25**

> ⌐ **MAKING CONNECTIONS** ¬
>
> **Units for Rates of Change**   The units for a rate of change can be found from a graph by placing the units from the vertical axis over the units from the horizontal axis. For example, in Figure 1.74 the units on the y-axis are *songs* and the units on the x-axis are *gigabytes*. Thus the units for the slope, or rate of change, are *songs per gigabyte*.

Representations of Linear Functions   Any linear function can be written as $f(x) = mx + b$, where m equals the slope of the graph of f. Also, because $f(0) = m(0) + b = b$, the point $(0, b)$ lies on the graph of f and the value of b is the **y-intercept** of the graph of f. A function can have at most one y-intercept because $f(0)$ can have at most one value.

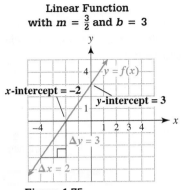

Linear Function
with $m = \frac{3}{2}$ and $b = 3$

Figure 1.75

Consider the graph of the linear function f shown in Figure 1.75. The graph is a line that intersects each axis once. From the graph we can see that when y increases by 3 units, x increases by 2 units. Thus the change in y is $\Delta y = 3$, the change in x is $\Delta x = 2$, and the slope is $\frac{\Delta y}{\Delta x} = \frac{3}{2}$. The graph f intersects the y-axis at the point $(0, 3)$, and so the y-intercept is 3. We can write the formula for f as:

$$f(x) = \frac{3}{2}x + 3.$$

slope   y-intercept

The graph of f in Figure 1.75 intersects the x-axis at the point $(-2, 0)$. We say that the **x-intercept** on the graph of f is -2. When we evaluate $f(-2)$, we obtain

$$f(-2) = \frac{3}{2}(-2) + 3 = 0.$$

An x-intercept corresponds to an input that results in an output of 0. We also say that -2 is a *zero* of the function f, since $f(-2) = 0$. A **zero** of a function f corresponds to an x-intercept on the graph of f. If the slope of the graph of a linear function f is not 0, then the graph of f has exactly one x-intercept.

The following See the Concept shows four representations of a linear function.

See the Concept: Four Representations of a Linear Function f

Verbal	**Symbolic**	**Numerical**	**Graphical**

Verbal

Multiply input x by $\frac{3}{2}$ and add 3 to get the output y.

Symbolic

$f(x) = \frac{3}{2}x + 3$

or

$f(x) = 1.5x + 3$

Numerical

x	y
-2	0
-1	1.5
0	3
1	4.5
2	6

1 → ← 1.5
1 → ← 1.5
1 → ← 1.5
1 → ← 1.5

If x-values increase by 1, the y-values increase by 1.5, or $\frac{3}{2}$.

Graphical

$f(x) = \frac{3}{2}x + 3$

EXAMPLE 4   Finding a formula from a graph

Use the graph of a linear function f in Figure 1.76 to complete the following.
(a) Find the slope, y-intercept, and x-intercept.
(b) Write a formula for f.
(c) Find any zeros of f.

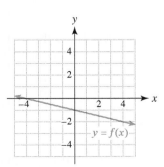

$y = f(x)$

Figure 1.76

SOLUTION

(a) The line falls 1 unit each time the x-values increase by 4 units. Therefore the slope is $-\frac{1}{4}$. The graph intersects the y-axis at the point $(0, -1)$ and intersects the x-axis at the point $(-4, 0)$. Therefore the y-intercept is -1, and the x-intercept is -4.

(b) Because the slope is $-\frac{1}{4}$ and the y-intercept is -1, it follows that

$$f(x) = -\frac{1}{4}x - 1.$$

(c) Zeros of f correspond to x-intercepts, so the only zero is -4.

> **Now Try Exercise 43**

Nonlinear Functions

We have discussed linear and constant functions. *Nonlinear functions* are another type of function.

Recognizing Nonlinear Functions   If a function is not linear, then it is called a **nonlinear function**. *The graph of a nonlinear function is not a (straight) line.* With a nonlinear function, it is possible for the input x to increase by 1 unit and the output y to change by different amounts. Nonlinear functions *cannot* be written in the form $f(x) = mx + b$.

One example of a nonlinear function is $f(x) = x^2$. In Figure 1.77 (below), its graph is *not* a line. In Table 1.14 we see that $f(x)$ does not increase by a constant amount for each unit increase in x.

The time required to drive 100 miles depends on the average speed x. Let $f(x)$ compute this time, given x as input. For example, $f(50) = 2$, because it would take 2 hours to travel 100 miles at an average speed of 50 miles per hour. Find a formula for f. Is f linear or nonlinear?

The Function $f(x) = x^2$

x	0	1	2	3	4
$f(x)$	0	1	4	9	16

Table 1.14

1   3   5   7

The increase in $f(x)$ is not the same for each unit increase in x, so $f(x) = x^2$ is nonlinear.

Increase is not constant.

Real-world phenomena often are modeled by using nonlinear functions. The following are two examples of quantities that can be described by nonlinear functions.

- The monthly average temperature in Chicago (Monthly average temperatures increase and decrease throughout the year.)
- The height of a child between the ages of 2 and 18 (A child grows faster at certain ages.)

Graphs of Nonlinear Functions   There are many nonlinear functions. In Figures 1.77–1.80 graphs and formulas are given for four common nonlinear functions. Note that each graph is not a line. See Appendix B for more examples of functions.

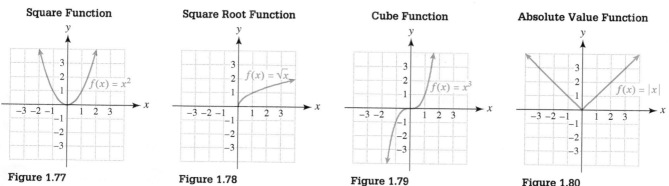

Square Function

$f(x) = x^2$

Figure 1.77

Square Root Function

$f(x) = \sqrt{x}$

Figure 1.78

Cube Function

$f(x) = x^3$

Figure 1.79

Absolute Value Function

$f(x) = |x|$

Figure 1.80

Increasing and Decreasing Functions

Sales of rock music have not remained constant during the past two decades. In 1990, rock music accounted for 36% of all U.S. music sales. This percentage decreased to a low of 24% in 2001 and then increased to 34% in 2006. (**Source:** Recording Industry Association of America.)

A linear function cannot be used to describe these data because the graph of a (nonconstant) linear function either always rises or always falls. The concepts of increasing and decreasing are important to nonlinear functions. Figure 1.81 illustrates the concepts of an increasing and decreasing function *f* that models rock music sales.

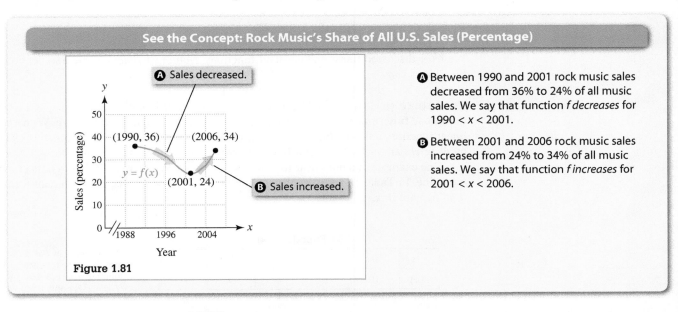

See the Concept: Rock Music's Share of All U.S. Sales (Percentage)

Ⓐ Sales decreased.

(1990, 36) (2006, 34)

y = f(x)

(2001, 24) Ⓑ Sales increased.

Ⓐ Between 1990 and 2001 rock music sales decreased from 36% to 24% of all music sales. We say that function *f decreases* for 1990 < x < 2001.

Ⓑ Between 2001 and 2006 rock music sales increased from 24% to 34% of all music sales. We say that function *f increases* for 2001 < x < 2006.

Figure 1.81

NOTE The inequality $a < x < b$ means that $x > a$ and $x < b$.

EXAMPLE 5 Recognizing increasing and decreasing graphs

The graphs of three functions are shown in Figure 1.82. Determine intervals where each function is increasing or decreasing.

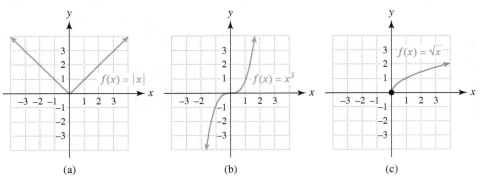

(a) (b) (c)

Figure 1.82

SOLUTION

(a) Moving from *left to right*, the graph of $f(x) = |x|$ is decreasing for $x < 0$ and increasing for $x > 0$.

(b) Moving from *left to right*, the graph of $f(x) = x^3$ is increasing for all real numbers x. Note that the y-values always increase as the x-values increase.

(c) The graph of $f(x) = \sqrt{x}$ is increasing for $x > 0$.

Now Try Exercises 65, 66, and 67

The concepts of increasing and decreasing are defined as follows.

> **INCREASING AND DECREASING FUNCTIONS**
>
> Suppose that a function f is defined over an *open* interval I on the number line. If x_1 and x_2 are in I,
> **(a)** f **increases** on I if, whenever $x_1 < x_2$, $f(x_1) < f(x_2)$;
> **(b)** f **decreases** on I if, whenever $x_1 < x_2$, $f(x_1) > f(x_2)$.

Figures 1.83–1.85 in See the Concept illustrate increasing and decreasing functions.

See the Concept: Increasing and Decreasing Functions

f Is Increasing

Ⓑ $f(x_1) < f(x_2)$.

Figure 1.83

Ⓐ Moving from left to right, …

Ⓑ the graph of f is uphill.

f Is Decreasing

Ⓓ $f(x_1) > f(x_2)$.

Figure 1.84

Ⓒ Moving from left to right, …

Ⓓ the graph of f is downhill.

f Decreases and Increases

Ⓔ Downhill   **Ⓕ** Uphill

Figure 1.85

Ⓔ Walking left to right the graph decreases …

Ⓕ and then increases.

> **NOTE** When stating where a function is increasing and where it is decreasing, it is important to give x-intervals and not y-intervals. These x-intervals do *not* include the endpoints.

Interval Notation

To describe intervals where functions are increasing or decreasing, a number line graph is sometimes used. The set $\{x \mid x > 2\}$, which includes all real numbers greater than 2, is graphed in Figure 1.86. Note that a parenthesis at $x = 2$ indicates that the endpoint *is not included*. The set $\{x \mid -1 \le x \le 4\}$ is shown in Figure 1.87 and the set $\{x \mid -\frac{7}{2} < x < -\frac{1}{2}\}$ is shown in Figure 1.88. Note that brackets, either $[$ or $]$, are used when endpoints *are included*.

$x > 2$

Figure 1.86

$-1 \le x \le 4$

Figure 1.87

$-\frac{7}{2} < x < -\frac{1}{2}$

Figure 1.88

A convenient notation is called **interval notation**. Instead of drawing the entire number line, as in Figure 1.87, we can express this set of real numbers as $[-1, 4]$. Because

Points and Intervals The expression (2, 5) has two possible meanings. It may represent the ordered pair (2, 5), which can be plotted as a point on the xy-plane, or it may represent the open interval $2 < x < 5$. To alleviate confusion, phrases like "the point (2, 5)" or "the interval (2, 5)" may be used.

the set includes the endpoints -1 and 4, the interval is a **closed interval** and brackets are used. A set that included all real numbers satisfying $-\frac{7}{2} < x < -\frac{1}{2}$ would be expressed as the **open interval** $\left(-\frac{7}{2}, -\frac{1}{2}\right)$. Parentheses indicate that the endpoints are not included in the set. An example of a **half-open interval** is [0, 4), which represents the set of real numbers satisfying $0 \le x < 4$.

Table 1.15 provides some examples of interval notation. The symbol ∞ refers to **infinity**; it does not represent a real number. The notation $(1, \infty)$ means $\{x \mid x > 1\}$, or simply $x > 1$. Since this interval has no maximum x-value, ∞ is used in the position of the right endpoint. A similar interpretation holds for the symbol $-\infty$, which represents **negative infinity**.

NOTE An inequality in the form $x < 1$ or $x > 3$ indicates the set of real numbers that are either less than 1 or greater than 3. The **union symbol** $\cup$ can be used to write this inequality in interval notation as $(-\infty, 1) \cup (3, \infty)$.

Interval Notation

Inequality	Interval Notation	Graph
$-2 < x < 2$	$(-2, 2)$ open interval	
$-1 < x \le 3$	$(-1, 3]$ half-open interval	
$-3 \le x \le 2$	$[-3, 2]$ closed interval	
$x > -3$	$(-3, \infty)$ infinite interval	
$x \le 1$	$(-\infty, 1]$ infinite interval	
$x \le -2$ or $x > 1$	$(-\infty, -2] \cup (1, \infty)$ infinite intervals	
$-\infty < x < \infty$ (entire number line)	$(-\infty, \infty)$ infinite interval	

Table 1.15

EXAMPLE 6   Determining where a function is increasing or decreasing

Use the graph of $f(x) = 4x - \frac{1}{3}x^3$ (shown in Figure 1.89) and interval notation to identify where f is increasing or decreasing.

SOLUTION Moving from left to right on the graph of f, the y-values decrease until $x = -2$, increase until $x = 2$, and decrease thereafter. Thus $f(x) = 4x - \frac{1}{3}x^3$ is decreasing on $(-\infty, -2)$, increasing on $(-2, 2)$, and decreasing again on $(2, \infty)$.

Now Try Exercise 69

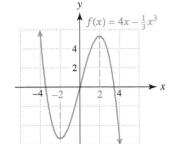

Figure 1.89

Average Rate of Change

The graphs of nonlinear functions are not lines, so there is no notion of a single slope. The slope of the graph of a linear function gives its constant rate of change. With a nonlinear function, we speak instead of an *average* rate of change. Suppose that the points (x_1, y_1) and (x_2, y_2) lie on the graph of a nonlinear function f. See Figure 1.90. The slope of the line L passing through these two points represents the *average rate of change of f from x_1 to x_2*. The line L is referred to as a **secant line**. If different values for x_1 and x_2 are selected, then a different secant line and a different average rate of change (slope) usually result.

Slope of *L* Is Average Rate of Change

Distance Traveled by a Car

Figure 1.90

Figure 1.91

The average rate of change of *f* from x_1 to x_2 equals the slope of red secant line *L*.

$y = f(x)$

L

(x_2, y_2)

(x_1, y_1)

The average speed of the car from 0.5 to 1 hour is 38 miles per hour.

$m = 38$

$y = f(x)$

$(1, 21)$

$(0.5, 2)$

In applications the average rate of change measures how fast a quantity is changing over an interval of its domain, *on average*. For example, suppose the graph of the function *f* in Figure 1.91 represents the distance *y* in miles that a car has traveled on a straight highway (under construction) after *x* hours. The points $(0.5, 2)$ and $(1, 21)$ lie on this graph. Thus after 0.5 hour the car has traveled 2 miles and after 1 hour the car has traveled 21 miles. The slope of the red line passing through these two points is

$$m = \frac{y_2 - y_1}{x_2 - x_1} = \frac{21 - 2}{1 - 0.5} = 38.$$

This means that during the half hour from 0.5 to 1 hour the average rate of change, or average *speed*, is 38 miles per hour.

> ### AVERAGE RATE OF CHANGE
>
> Let (x_1, y_1) and (x_2, y_2) be distinct points on the graph of a function *f*. The **average rate of change of *f* from x_1 to x_2** is
>
> $$\frac{y_2 - y_1}{x_2 - x_1}.$$
>
> That is, the average rate of change from x_1 to x_2 equals the slope of the line passing through (x_1, y_1) and (x_2, y_2).

NOTE If $y = f(x)$, then average rate of change equals $\frac{f(x_2) - f(x_1)}{x_2 - x_1}$.

EXAMPLE 7   Finding an average rate of change

Let $f(x) = 2x^2$. Find the average rate of change from $x = 1$ to $x = 3$.

SOLUTION   First calculate $f(1) = 2(1)^2 = 2$ and $f(3) = 2(3)^2 = 18$. The average rate of change equals the slope of the line passing through the points $(1, 2)$ and $(3, 18)$.

$$\text{Average rate of change } = \frac{18 - 2}{3 - 1} = \frac{16}{2} = 8.$$

The average rate of change from $x = 1$ to $x = 3$ is 8.

Now Try Exercise 97

NOTE If *f* is a constant function, its average rate of change is always 0. For a linear function defined by $f(x) = mx + b$, the average rate of change is always *m*, the slope of its graph. The average rate of change for a nonlinear function varies.

EXAMPLE 8 Calculating and interpreting average rates of change

Table 1.16 lists the U.S. population in millions for selected years.
(a) Calculate the average rates of change in the U.S. population from 1800 to 1840 and from 1900 to 1940.
(b) Illustrate your results from part (a) graphically. Interpret the results.

U.S. Population (millions)

Year	Population
1800	5
1840	17
1900	76
1940	132

Table 1.16

SOLUTION
(a) In 1800 the population was **5** million, and in 1840 it was **17** million. Therefore the average rate of change in the population from 1800 to 1840 was

$$\frac{17 - 5}{1840 - 1800} = 0.3.$$

In 1900 the population was **76** million, and in 1940 it was **132** million. Therefore the average rate of change in the population from 1900 to 1940 was

$$\frac{132 - 76}{1940 - 1900} = 1.4.$$

(b) These average rates of change are illustrated graphically and interpreted in Figure 1.92.

Interpreting Average Rate of Change

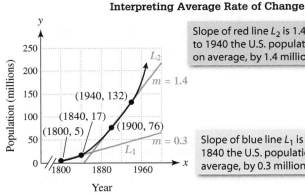

Slope of red line L_2 is 1.4, so from 1900 to 1940 the U.S. population increased, on average, by 1.4 million per year

Slope of blue line L_1 is 0.3, so from 1800 to 1840 the U.S. population increased, on average, by 0.3 million (300,000) per year

Figure 1.92

Now Try Exercise 99

The Difference Quotient

The difference quotient is often used in calculus to calculate rates of change and is explained in the following See the Concept. In Figure 1.93, the red secant line L passes through two points, $(x, f(x))$ and $(x + h, f(x + h))$, on the graph of $y = f(x)$. (In Figure 1.93, we assume that $h > 0$.)

See the Concept: Understanding the Difference Quotient

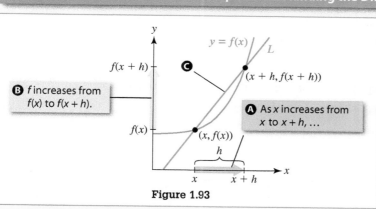

Ⓐ As x increases from x to $x + h$, …

Ⓑ f increases from $f(x)$ to $f(x + h)$.

Ⓒ The slope of the red line L represents the average rate of change of f from x to $x + h$.

The slope of L is $\dfrac{f(x + h) - f(x)}{(x + h) - x}$ and this

formula simplifies to the *difference quotient* of f.

Figure 1.93

The following box gives a definition of the difference quotient.

DIFFERENCE QUOTIENT

The **difference quotient of a function f** is an expression of the form

$$\frac{f(x + h) - f(x)}{h}, \qquad \text{where } h \neq 0.$$

EXAMPLE 9   Finding a difference quotient

Let $f(x) = 3x - 2$.

(a) Find $f(x + h)$.

(b) Find the difference quotient of f and simplify the result.

SOLUTION

(a) To find $f(x + h)$, substitute $(x + h)$ for x in the expression $3x - 2$.

$$f(x + h) = 3(x + h) - 2 \qquad f(x) = 3x - 2$$
$$= 3x + 3h - 2 \qquad \text{Distributive property}$$

(b) The difference quotient can be calculated as follows.

> Include parentheses when $f(x)$ is more than one term.

$$\frac{f(x + h) - f(x)}{h} = \frac{(3x + 3h - 2) - (3x - 2)}{h} \qquad \text{Substitute.}$$

Difference quotient

$$= \frac{3x + 3h - 2 - 3x + 2}{h} \qquad \text{Distributive property}$$

$$= \frac{3h}{h} \qquad \text{Combine like terms.}$$

$$= 3 \qquad \text{Simplify.}$$

NOTE   The difference quotient for a linear function $f(x) = mx + b$ always equals the slope m of the graph of f.

Now Try Exercise 107

EXAMPLE 10 Calculating a difference quotient

Let $f(x) = x^2 - 2x$.
(a) Find $f(x + h)$.
(b) Find the difference quotient of f and simplify the result.

SOLUTION
(a) To calculate $f(x + h)$, substitute $(x + h)$ for x in the expression $x^2 - 2x$.

$$f(x + h) = (x + h)^2 - 2(x + h) \qquad f(x) = x^2 - 2x$$
$$= x^2 + 2xh + h^2 - 2x - 2h \qquad \text{Square the binomial; distributive property.}$$

Algebra Review
To square a binomial, see Chapter R (page R-17)

(b) The difference quotient can be calculated as follows.

$$\frac{f(x + h) - f(x)}{h} = \frac{x^2 + 2xh + h^2 - 2x - 2h - (x^2 - 2x)}{h} \qquad \text{Substitute.}$$
$$= \frac{2xh + h^2 - 2h}{h} \qquad \text{Combine like terms.}$$
$$= \frac{h(2x + h - 2)}{h} \qquad \text{Factor out } h.$$
$$= 2x + h - 2 \qquad \text{Simplify.}$$

Now Try Exercise 109

1.4 Putting It All Together

CONCEPT	FORMULA	EXAMPLES
Slope of a line passing through (x_1, y_1) and (x_2, y_2)	$m = \dfrac{\Delta y}{\Delta x} = \dfrac{y_2 - y_1}{x_2 - x_1}$ $\Delta y = y_2 - y_1$ denotes the change in y. $\Delta x = x_2 - x_1$ denotes the change in x.	A line passing through $(-1, 3)$ and $(1, 7)$ has slope $m = \dfrac{7 - 3}{1 - (-1)} = \dfrac{4}{2} = 2$. This slope indicates that the line rises 2 units for each unit increase in x.
Constant function	$f(x) = b$, where b is a fixed number, or constant.	$f(x) = 12$, $g(x) = -2.5$, and $h(x) = 0$. Every constant function is also linear.
Linear function	$f(x) = mx + b$, where m and b are constants. The graph of f has slope m.	$f(x) = 3x - 1$, $g(x) = -5$, and $h(x) = \frac{1}{2} - \frac{3}{4}x$. Their graphs have slopes 3, 0, and $-\frac{3}{4}$.
Nonlinear function	A nonlinear function cannot be expressed in the form $f(x) = mx + b$.	$f(x) = \sqrt{x + 1}$, $g(x) = 4x^3$, and $h(x) = x^{1.01} + 2$.

CONCEPT	CONSTANT FUNCTION	LINEAR FUNCTION	NONLINEAR FUNCTION
Slope of graph	Always zero	Always constant	No notion of one slope
Graph	Horizontal line	Nonvertical line	Not a line
Examples			

CONCEPT	EXPLANATION	EXAMPLES
Interval notation	An efficient notation for writing inequalities	$x \le 6$ is equivalent to $(-\infty, 6\,]$. $x > 3$ is equivalent to $(3, \infty)$. $2 < x \le 5$ is equivalent to $(2, 5\,]$.
Increasing and decreasing	f increases on an *open* interval if, whenever $x_1 < x_2$, then $f(x_1) < f(x_2)$. f decreases on an *open* interval if, whenever $x_1 < x_2$, then $f(x_1) > f(x_2)$.	 f is increasing on $(-\infty, -2)$ and on $(2, \infty)$. f is decreasing on $(-2, 2)$.
Average rate of change of f from x_1 to x_2	If (x_1, y_1) and (x_2, y_2) are distinct points on the graph of f, then the average rate of change from x_1 to x_2 equals $$\frac{y_2 - y_1}{x_2 - x_1}.$$	If $f(x) = 3x^2$, then the average rate of change from $x = 1$ to $x = 3$ is $$\frac{27 - 3}{3 - 1} = 12$$ because $f(3) = 27$ and $f(1) = 3$. This means that, on average, $f(x)$ increases by 12 units for each unit increase in x from 1 to 3.
Difference quotient	Calculates average rate of change of f from x to $x + h$. $$\frac{f(x + h) - f(x)}{h}, h \ne 0$$	If $f(x) = 2x$, then the difference quotient equals $$\frac{2(x + h) - 2x}{h} = \frac{2h}{h} = 2.$$

1.4 Exercises

Formulas for Linear Functions

Exercises 1–4: A linear function f can be written in the form $f(x) = mx + b$. *Identify m and b for the given f(x).*

1. $f(x) = 5 - 2x$ **2.** $f(x) = 3 - 4x$

3. $f(x) = -8x$ **4.** $f(x) = -6$

Slope

Exercises 5–18: If possible, find the slope of the line passing through each pair of points.

5. $(4, 6), (2, 5)$ **6.** $(-8, 5), (-3, -7)$

7. $(-1, 4), (5, -2)$ **8.** $(10, -4), (-15, 7)$

9. $(12, -8), (7, -8)$ **10.** $(8, -5), (8, 2)$

11. $(0.2, -0.1), (-0.3, 0.4)$ **12.** $(-0.3, 0.6), (-0.2, 1.1)$

13. $(-0.5, 9.2), (-0.3, 7.6)$ **14.** $(1.6, 12), (1.6, 5)$

15. $(-5, 6), (-5, 8)$ **16.** $(17, 7), (19, 7)$

17. $\left(\frac{1}{3}, -\frac{3}{5}\right), \left(-\frac{5}{6}, \frac{7}{10}\right)$ **18.** $\left(-\frac{13}{15}, -\frac{7}{8}\right), \left(\frac{1}{10}, \frac{3}{16}\right)$

Exercises 19–24: State the slope of the graph of f. Explain what the slope indicates about the graph.

19. $f(x) = 2x + 7$ **20.** $f(x) = 6 - x$

21. $f(x) = -\frac{3}{4}x$ **22.** $f(x) = \frac{2}{3}x$

23. $f(x) = 9 - x$ **24.** $f(x) = 23$

Slope as a Rate of Change

25. Price of Carpet The graph shows the price of x square feet of carpeting.

   (a) Why is it reasonable for the graph to pass through the origin?

   (b) Find the slope of the graph.

   (c) Interpret the slope as a rate of change.

26. Landscape Rock The figure shows the price of x tons of landscape rock.

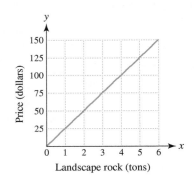

   (a) Why is it reasonable for the graph to pass through the origin?

   (b) Find the slope of the graph.

   (c) Interpret the slope as a rate of change.

27. Velocity of a Train The distance D in miles that a train is from a station after x hours is given by the formula $D(x) = 150 - 20x$.

   (a) Calculate $D(5)$ and interpret the result.

   (b) Find the slope of the graph of D. Interpret this slope as a rate of change.

28. Cost of Paint The cost C in dollars of purchasing x gallons of paint is given by $C(x) = 29x$.

   (a) Evaluate $C(5)$ and interpret your result.

   (b) Find the slope of the graph of C. Interpret this slope as a rate of change.

29. Velocity of a Car A driver's distance D in miles from a rest stop after x hours is given by $D(x) = 75x$.

   (a) How far is the driver from the rest stop after 2 hours?

   (b) Find the slope of the graph of D. Interpret this slope as a rate of change.

30. Age in the United States The median age of the U.S. population for each year t between 1970 and 2010 can be approximated by the formula $A(t) = 0.243t - 450.8$. (***Source:*** Bureau of the Census.)

   (a) Compute the median ages in 1980 and 2000.

   (b) What is the slope of the graph of A? Interpret the slope.

Linear and Nonlinear Functions

Exercises 31–38: Determine if f is a linear or nonlinear function. If f is a linear function, determine if f is a constant function. Support your answer by graphing f.

31. $f(x) = -2x + 5$ **32.** $f(x) = 3x - 2$

33. $f(x) = 1$ **34.** $f(x) = -2$

35. $f(x) = |x + 1|$ **36.** $f(x) = |2x - 1|$

37. $f(x) = x^2 - 1$ **38.** $f(x) = \sqrt{x - 1}$

Recognizing Linear Data

Exercises 39–42: Decide whether a line can pass through the data points. If it can, determine the slope of the line.

39.

x	0	1	2	3	4
y	-1	3	7	11	15

40.

x	-4	-2	0	2	4
y	1	$-\frac{1}{2}$	-2	$-\frac{7}{2}$	-5

41.

x	-5	-3	1	3	5
y	-5	-2	1	4	7

42.

x	10	20	25	35	40
y	40	190	300	600	790

Linear Functions

Exercises 43–46: The graph of a linear function f is shown.

(a) *Identify the slope, y-intercept, and x-intercept.*
(b) *Write a formula for f.*
(c) *Estimate the zero of f.*

43.

44.

45.

46.
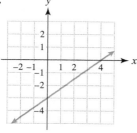

Exercises 47–50: Write a formula for a linear function f whose graph satisfies the conditions.

47. Slope $-\frac{3}{4}$, y-intercept $\frac{1}{3}$

48. Slope -122, y-intercept 805

49. Slope 15, passing through the origin

50. Slope 1.68, passing through $(0, 1.23)$

Interval Notation

Exercises 51–64: Express each of the following in interval notation.

51. $x \geq 5$

52. $x < 100$

53. $4 \leq x < 19$

54. $-4 < x < -1$

55. $\{x \mid -1 \leq x\}$

56. $\{x \mid x \leq -3\}$

57. $\{x \mid x < 1 \text{ or } x \geq 3\}$

58. $\{x \mid x \leq -2 \text{ or } x \geq 0\}$

59.

60.

61.

62. (number line)

63. (number line)

64. (number line)

Increasing and Decreasing Functions

Exercises 65–72: Use the graph of f to determine intervals where f is increasing and where f is decreasing.

65.

66.

67.

68.

69.

70.

71.
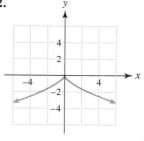

72. (graph)

Exercises 73–88: Identify where f is increasing and where f is decreasing. (Hint: Consider the graph $y = f(x)$.)

73. $f(x) = 2x - 1$ **74.** $f(x) = 4 - x$

75. $f(x) = x^2 - 2$ **76.** $f(x) = -\frac{1}{2}x^2$

77. $f(x) = 2x - x^2$ **78.** $f(x) = x^2 - 4x$

79. $f(x) = \sqrt{x - 1}$ **80.** $f(x) = -\sqrt{x + 1}$

81. $f(x) = |x + 3|$ **82.** $f(x) = |x - 1|$

83. $f(x) = x^3$ **84.** $f(x) = \sqrt[3]{x}$

85. $f(x) = \frac{1}{3}x^3 - 4x$ **86.** $f(x) = x^3 - 3x$

87. $f(x) = -\frac{1}{4}x^4 + \frac{1}{3}x^3 + x^2$

88. $f(x) = \frac{1}{4}x^4 - 2x^2$

Exercises 89 and 90: **Tides** *The graph gives the tides at Clearwater Beach, Florida, x hours after midnight on a particular day, where $0 \le x \le 27$.* (*Source:* Tide/Current Predictor.)

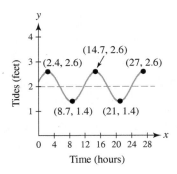

89. When were water levels increasing?

90. When were water levels decreasing?

Average Rates of Change

Exercises 91 and 92: Find the average rates of change of f from −3 to −1 and from 1 to 3.

91. $f(x) = -0.3x^2 + 4$ **92.** $f(x) = 0.3x^2 - 4$

 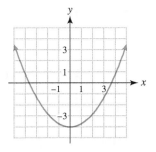

Exercises 93 and 94: (Refer to Examples 7 and 8.) Use the given f(x) to complete the following.

(a) Calculate the average rate of change of f from $x = 1$ to $x = 2$.

(b) Illustrate your result from part (a) graphically.

93. $f(x) = x^2$ **94.** $f(x) = 4 - x^2$

Exercises 95–98: Compute the average rate of change of f from x_1 to x_2. Round your answer to two decimal places when appropriate.

95. $f(x) = 7x - 2, x_1 = 1,$ and $x_2 = 4$

96. $f(x) = -8x + 5, x_1 = -2,$ and $x_2 = 0$

97. $f(x) = \sqrt{2x - 1}, x_1 = 1,$ and $x_2 = 3$

98. $f(x) = 0.5x^2 - 5, x_1 = -1,$ and $x_2 = 4$

99. U.S. Cigarette Consumption The following table lists the number of cigarettes in billions consumed in the United States for selected years.

Year	1900	1940	1980	2010
Cigarettes	3	182	632	315

Source: Department of Health and Human Services.

(a) Find the average rate of change during each time period.

(b) Interpret the results.

100. Torricelli's Law A cylindrical tank contains 100 gallons of water. A plug is pulled from the bottom of the tank and the amount of water in gallons remaining in the tank after x minutes is given by

$$A(x) = 100\left(1 - \frac{x}{5}\right)^2.$$

(a) Calculate the average rate of change of A from 1 to 1.5 and from 2 to 2.5. Interpret your results.

(b) Are the two average rates of change the same or different? Explain why.

Curve Sketching

Exercises 101 and 102: Sketch a graph that illustrates the motion of the person described. Let the x-axis represent time and the y-axis represent distance from home. Be sure to label each axis.

101. A person drives a car away from home for 2 hours at 50 miles per hour and then stops for 1 hour.

102. A person drives to a nearby park at 25 miles per hour for 1 hour, rests at the park for 2 hours, and then drives home at 50 miles per hour.

Exercises 103 and 104: **Critical Thinking** *Do not use a graphing calculator.*

103. On the same coordinate axes, sketch the graphs of a constant function f and a nonlinear function g that intersect exactly twice.

104. Sketch a graph of a function that has only positive average rates of change for $x \geq 1$ and only negative average rates of change for $x \leq 1$.

The Difference Quotient

Exercises 105–116: (Refer to Examples 9 and 10.) Complete the following for the given $f(x)$.
(a) Find $f(x + h)$.
(b) Find the difference quotient of f and simplify.

105. $f(x) = 3$ **106.** $f(x) = -5$

107. $f(x) = 2x + 1$ **108.** $f(x) = -3x + 4$

109. $f(x) = 3x^2 + 1$ **110.** $f(x) = x^2 - 2$

111. $f(x) = -x^2 + 2x$ **112.** $f(x) = -4x^2 + 1$

113. $f(x) = 2x^2 - x + 1$ **114.** $f(x) = x^2 + 3x - 2$

115. $f(x) = x^3$ **116.** $f(x) = 1 - x^3$

117. **Speed of a Car** Let the distance in feet that a car travels in t seconds be given by $d(t) = 8t^2$ for $0 \leq t \leq 6$.
 (a) Find $d(t + h)$.
 (b) Find the difference quotient for d and simplify.
 (c) Evaluate the difference quotient when $t = 4$ and $h = 0.05$. Interpret your result.

118. **Draining a Pool** Let the number of gallons G of water in a pool after t hours be given by $G(t) = 4000 - 100t$ for $0 \leq t \leq 40$.
 (a) Find $G(t + h)$.
 (b) Find the difference quotient. Interpret your result.

Writing about Mathematics

119. What does the average rate of change represent for a linear function? What does it represent for a nonlinear function? Explain your answers.

120. Suppose you are given a graphical representation of a function f. Explain how you would determine whether f is constant, linear, or nonlinear. How would you determine the type if you were given a numerical or symbolic representation? Give examples.

121. Suppose that a function f has a positive average rate of change from 1 to 4. Is it correct to assume that function f only increases on the interval $(1, 4)$? Make a sketch to support your answer.

122. If $f(x) = mx + b$, what does the difference quotient for function f equal? Explain your reasoning.

Extended and Discovery Exercise

1. **Geometry** Suppose that the radius of a circle on a computer monitor is increasing at a constant rate of 1 inch per second.
 (a) Does the circumference of the circle increase at a constant rate? If it does, find this rate.
 (b) Does the area of the circle increase at a constant rate? Explain.

2. **Velocity** If the distance in feet run by a racehorse in t seconds is given by $d(t) = 2t^2$, then the difference quotient for d is $4t + 2h$. How could you estimate the velocity of the racehorse at exactly 7 seconds?

CHECKING BASIC CONCEPTS FOR SECTIONS 1.3 AND 1.4

1. Give symbolic, numerical, and graphical representations of a function f that computes the number of feet in x miles. For the numerical representation use a table and let $x = 1, 2, 3, 4, 5$.

2. Let $f(x) = \frac{2x}{x - 4}$.
 (a) Find $f(2)$ and $f(a + 4)$.
 (b) Find the domain of f.

3. Find the slope of the line passing through the points $(-2, 4)$ and $(4, -5)$.

4. Identify each function f as constant, linear, or nonlinear.
 (a) $f(x) = -1.4x + 5.1$
 (b) $f(x) = 25$
 (c) $f(x) = 2x^2 - 5$

5. Write each expression in interval notation.
 (a) $x \leq 5$ (b) $1 \leq x < 6$

6. Determine where $f(x) = x^2 - 2$ is increasing and where it is decreasing.

7. Find the average rate of change of $f(x) = x^2 - 3x$ from $x = -3$ to $x = -1$.

8. Find the difference quotient for $f(x) = 4x^2$.

1 Summary

CONCEPT	EXPLANATION AND EXAMPLES

Section 1.1 Numbers, Data, and Problem Solving

Sets of Numbers

Natural numbers: $N = \{1, 2, 3, 4, \dots\}$

Integers: $I = \{\dots, -3, -2, -1, 0, 1, 2, 3, \dots\}$

Rational numbers: $\frac{p}{q}$, where p and q are integers with $q \neq 0$; includes fractions, repeating and terminating decimals

Irrational numbers: Includes nonrepeating, nonterminating decimals

Real numbers: Any number that can be expressed in decimal form; includes rational and irrational numbers

Order of Operations

Using the following order of operations, perform all calculations within parentheses, square roots, and absolute value bars and above and below fraction bars. Then use the same order of operations to perform any remaining calculations.

1. Evaluate all exponents. Then do any negation *after* evaluating exponents.
2. Do all multiplication and division from *left to right*.
3. Do all addition and subtraction from *left to right*.

Example: $5 + 3 \cdot 2^3 = 5 + 3 \cdot 8 = 5 + 24 = 29$

Scientific Notation

A real number r is written as $c \times 10^n$, where $1 \leq |c| < 10$.

Examples: $1234 = 1.234 \times 10^3$ $0.054 = 5.4 \times 10^{-2}$

Section 1.2 Visualizing and Graphing Data

Mean (Average) and Median

The mean represents the average of a set of numbers, and the median represents the middle of a sorted list.

Example: $4, 6, 9, 13, 15$;   Mean $= \dfrac{4 + 6 + 9 + 13 + 15}{5} = 9.4$;   Median $= 9$

Relation, Domain, and Range

A relation S is a set of ordered pairs. The domain D is the set of x-values, and the range R is the set of y-values.

Example: $S = \{(-1, 2), (4, -5), (5, 9)\}$; $D = \{-1, 4, 5,\}, R = \{-5, 2, 9\}$

Cartesian (Rectangular) Coordinate System, or xy-Plane

The xy-plane has four quadrants and is used to graph ordered pairs.

The xy-Plane

CONCEPT	EXPLANATION AND EXAMPLES

Section 1.2 Visualizing and Graphing Data (CONTINUED)

Distance Formula

The distance d between the points (x_1, y_1) and (x_2, y_2) is
$$d = \sqrt{(x_2 - x_1)^2 + (y_2 - y_1)^2}.$$

Example: The distance between $(-3, 5)$ and $(2, -7)$ is
$$d = \sqrt{(2 - (-3))^2 + (-7 - 5)^2} = \sqrt{5^2 + (-12)^2} = 13.$$

Midpoint Formula

The midpoint M of the line segment with endpoints (x_1, y_1) and (x_2, y_2) is
$$M = \left(\frac{x_1 + x_2}{2}, \frac{y_1 + y_2}{2}\right).$$

Example: The midpoint of the line segment connecting $(1, 2)$ and $(-3, 5)$ is
$$M = \left(\frac{1 + (-3)}{2}, \frac{2 + 5}{2}\right) = \left(-1, \frac{7}{2}\right).$$

Standard Equation of a Circle

The circle with center (h, k) and radius r has the equation
$$(x - h)^2 + (y - k)^2 = r^2.$$

Example: A circle with center $(-2, 5)$ and radius 6 has the equation
$$(x + 2)^2 + (y - 5)^2 = 36.$$

Scatterplot and Line Graph

A scatterplot consists of a set of ordered pairs plotted in the xy-plane. When consecutive points are connected with line segments, a line graph results.

Section 1.3 Functions and Their Representations

Function

A function computes exactly one output for each valid input. The set of valid inputs is called the domain D, and the set of outputs is called the range R.

Examples: $f(x) = \sqrt{1 - x}$
$$D = \{x \mid x \leq 1\}, R = \{y \mid y \geq 0\}$$
$$g = \{(-1, 0.5), (0, 4), (2, 4), (6, \pi)\}$$
$$D = \{-1, 0, 2, 6\}, R = \{0.5, \pi, 4\}$$

Function Notation

Examples: $f(x) = x^2 - 4; f(3) = 3^2 - 4 = 5$ and
$$f(a + 1) = (a + 1)^2 - 4 = a^2 + 2a - 3$$

Representations of Functions

A function can be represented symbolically (formula), graphically (graph), numerically (table of values), and verbally (words). Other representations are possible.

Symbolic Representation $f(x) = x^2 - 1$

CONCEPT	EXPLANATION AND EXAMPLES

Section 1.3 Functions and Their Representations (CONTINUED)

Representations of Functions

Numerical Representation

x	y
−2	3
−1	0
0	−1
1	0
2	3

Graphical Representation

$f(x) = x^2 - 1$

Verbal Representation f computes the square of the input x and then subtracts 1.

Vertical Line Test

If every vertical line intersects a graph at most once, then the graph represents a function.

Section 1.4 Types of Functions and Their Rates of Change

Slope

The slope m of the line passing through (x_1, y_1) and (x_2, y_2) is

$$m = \frac{\Delta y}{\Delta x} = \frac{y_2 - y_1}{x_2 - x_1}.$$

Example: The slope of the line passing through $(1, -1)$ and $(-2, 3)$ is

$$m = \frac{3 - (-1)}{-2 - 1} = -\frac{4}{3}.$$

Constant Function

Given by $f(x) = b$, where b is a constant; its graph is a horizontal line.

Linear Function

Given by $f(x) = mx + b$; its graph is a nonvertical line; the slope of its graph is equal to m, which is also equal to its constant rate of change.

Examples: The graph of $f(x) = -8x + 100$ has slope -8.
If $G(t) = -8t + 100$ calculates the number of gallons of water in a tank after t minutes, then water is *leaving* the tank at 8 gallons per minute.

Nonlinear Function

A nonlinear function *cannot* be written as $f(x) = mx + b$ and its graph is not a line.

Examples: $f(x) = x^2 - 4$; $g(x) = \sqrt[3]{x} - 2$; $h(t) = \dfrac{1}{t + 1}$

Interval Notation

A concise way to express intervals on the number line

Example: $x < 4$ is expressed as $(-\infty, 4)$.
$-3 \le x < 1$ is expressed as $[-3, 1)$.
$x \le 2$ or $x \ge 5$ is expressed as $(-\infty, 2] \cup [5, \infty)$.

Increasing/Decreasing

f increases on an *open* interval I if, whenever $x_1 < x_2$, $f(x_1) < f(x_2)$.
f decreases on an *open* interval I if, whenever $x_1 < x_2$, $f(x_1) > f(x_2)$.

Example: $f(x) = |x|$ increases on $(0, \infty)$ and decreases on $(-\infty, 0)$.

CONCEPT	EXPLANATION AND EXAMPLES

Section 1.4 Types of Functions and Their Rates of Change (CONTINUED)

Average Rate of Change

If (x_1, y_1) and (x_2, y_2) are distinct points on the graph of f, then the average rate of change from x_1 to x_2 equals the slope of the line passing through these two points, given by

$$\frac{y_2 - y_1}{x_2 - x_1}.$$

Example: $f(x) = x^2$; because $f(2) = 4$ and $f(3) = 9$, the graph of f passes through the points $(2, 4)$ and $(3, 9)$, and the average rate of change from 2 to 3 is given by $\frac{9 - 4}{3 - 2} = 5$.

Difference Quotient

The difference quotient of a function f is an expression of the form

$$\frac{f(x + h) - f(x)}{h}, \quad \text{where } h \neq 0,$$

and is the average rate of change from x to $x + h$.

Example: Let $f(x) = x^2$. The difference quotient of f is

$$\frac{(x + h)^2 - x^2}{h} = \frac{x^2 + 2xh + h^2 - x^2}{h} = 2x + h.$$

1 Review Exercises

Exercises 1 and 2: Classify each number listed as one or more of the following: natural number, integer, rational number, or real number.

1. $-2, \frac{1}{2}, 0, 1.23, \sqrt{7}, \sqrt{16}$

2. $55, 1.5, \frac{104}{17}, 2^3, \sqrt{3}, -1000$

Exercises 3 and 4: Write each number in scientific notation.

3. $1,891,000$

4. 0.0001001

Exercises 5 and 6: Write each number in standard form.

5. 1.52×10^4

6. -7.2×10^{-3}

7. Evaluate each expression with a calculator. Round answers to the nearest hundredth.

(a) $\sqrt[3]{1.2} + \pi^3$

(b) $\dfrac{3.2 + 5.7}{7.9 - 4.5}$

(c) $\sqrt{5^2 + 2.1}$

(d) $1.2(6.3)^2 + \dfrac{3.2}{\pi - 1}$

8. Evaluate each expression. Write your answer in scientific notation and in standard form.

(a) $(4 \times 10^3)(5 \times 10^{-5})$

(b) $\dfrac{3 \times 10^{-5}}{6 \times 10^{-2}}$

Exercises 9 and 10: Evaluate by hand.

9. $4 - 3^2 \cdot 5$

10. $3 \cdot 3^2 \div \dfrac{3 - 5}{6 + 2}$

Exercises 11 and 12: Sort the list of numbers from smallest to largest and display the result in a table.

(a) Determine the maximum and minimum values.

(b) Calculate the mean and median.

11. $-5, 8, 19, 24, -23$

12. $8.9, -1.2, -3.8, 0.8, 1.7, 1.7$

Exercises 13 and 14: Complete the following.

(a) Express the data as a relation S.

(b) Find the domain and range of S.

13.

x	-15	-10	0	5	20
y	-3	-1	1	3	5

14.

x	-0.6	-0.2	0.1	0.5	1.2
y	10	20	25	30	80

Exercises 15 and 16: Make a scatterplot of the relation. Determine if the relation is a function.

15. $\{(10, 13), (-12, 40), (-30, -23), (25, -22), (10, 20)\}$

16. $\{(1.5, 2.5), (0, 2.1), (-2.3, 3.1), (0.5, -0.8), (-1.1, 0)\}$

Exercises 17 and 18: Find the distance between the points.

17. $(-4, 5), (2, -3)$

18. $(1.2, -4), (0.2, 6)$

Exercises 19 and 20: Find the midpoint of the line segment with the given endpoints.

19. $(24, -16), (-20, 13)$ **20.** $\left(\frac{1}{2}, \frac{5}{4}\right) \left(\frac{1}{2}, -\frac{5}{2}\right)$

21. Determine if the triangle with vertices $(1, 2), (-3, 5)$, and $(0, 9)$ is isosceles.

22. Find the standard equation of a circle with center $(-5, 3)$ and radius 9.

23. A diameter of a circle has endpoints $(-2, 4)$ and $(6, 6)$. Find the standard equation of the circle.

24. Use the graph to determine the domain and range of each function. Evaluate $f(-2)$.

(a)   **(b)**

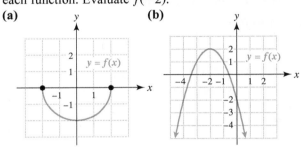

Exercises 25–32: Graph $y = f(x)$ by first plotting points to determine the shape of the graph.

25. $f(x) = -2$ **26.** $f(x) = 3x$

27. $f(x) = -x + 1$ **28.** $f(x) = 2x - 3$

29. $f(x) = 4 - 2x^2$ **30.** $f(x) = \frac{1}{2}x^2 - 1$

31. $f(x) = |x + 3|$ **32.** $f(x) = \sqrt{3 - x}$

Exercises 33 and 34: Use the verbal representation to express the function f symbolically, graphically, and numerically. Let $y = f(x)$ with $0 \le x \le 100$. For the numerical representation, use a table with $x = 0, 25, 50, 75, 100$.

33. To convert x pounds to y ounces, multiply x by 16.

34. To find the area y of a square, multiply the length x of a side by itself.

Exercises 35–40: Complete the following for the function f.
(a) Evaluate $f(x)$ at the indicated values of x.
(b) Find the domain of f.

35. $f(x) = 5$ for $x = -3, 1.5$

36. $f(x) = 4 - 5x$ for $x = -5, 6$

37. $f(x) = x^2 - 3$ for $x = -10, a + 2$

38. $f(x) = x^3 - 3x$ for $x = -10, a + 1$

39. $f(x) = \frac{1}{x - 4}$ for $x = -3, a + 1$

40. $f(x) = \sqrt{x + 3}$ for $x = 1, a - 3$

41. Determine if y is a function of x in $x = y^2 + 5$.

42. Write $5 \le x < 10$ in interval notation.

Exercises 43 and 44: The graph of a linear function f is shown.
(a) Identify the slope, y-intercept, and x-intercept.
(b) Write a formula for f.
(c) Find any zeros of f.

43.   **44.**

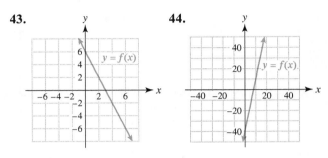

Exercises 45 and 46: Determine if the graph represents a function.

45.   **46.**

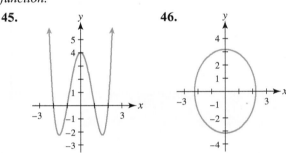

Exercises 47 and 48: Determine if S represents a function.

47. $S = \{(-3, 4), (-1, 2), (3, -5), (4, 2)\}$

48. $S = \{(-1, 3), (0, 2), (-1, 7), (3, -3)\}$

Exercises 49 and 50: State the slope of the graph of f.

49. $f(x) = 7$ **50.** $f(x) = \frac{1}{3}x - \frac{2}{3}$

Exercises 51–54: If possible, find the slope of the line passing through each pair of points.

51. $(-1, 7), (3, 4)$ **52.** $(1, -4), (2, 10)$

53. $(8, 4), (-2, 4)$ **54.** $\left(-\frac{1}{3}, \frac{2}{3}\right), \left(-\frac{1}{3}, -\frac{5}{6}\right)$

Exercises 55–58: Decide whether the function f is constant, linear, or nonlinear.

55. $f(x) = 8 - 3x$ **56.** $f(x) = 2x^2 - 3x - 8$

57. $f(x) = |x + 2|$ **58.** $f(x) = 6$

59. Sketch a graph for a 2-hour period showing the distance between two cars meeting on a straight highway, each traveling 60 miles per hour. Assume that the cars are initially 120 miles apart.

60. Determine where the graph of $f(x) = |x - 3|$ is increasing and where it is decreasing.

61. Determine if a line passes through every point in the table. If it does, give its slope.

x	−2	0	2	4
y	50	42	34	26

62. Find the average rate of change of $f(x) = x^2 - x + 1$ from $x_1 = 1$ to $x_2 = 3$.

Exercises 63 and 64: Find the difference quotient for f(x).

63. $f(x) = 5x + 1$ **64.** $f(x) = 3x^2 - 2$

Applications

65. **Speed of Light** The average distance between the planet Mars and the sun is approximately 228 million kilometers. Estimate the time required for sunlight, traveling at 300,000 kilometers per second, to reach Mars. (***Source:*** C. Ronan, *The Natural History of the Universe*.)

66. **Geometry** Suppose that 0.25 cubic inch of paint is applied to a circular piece of plastic with a diameter of 20 inches. Estimate the thickness of the paint. (*Hint:* Thickness equals volume divided by area.)

67. **Enclosing a Pool** A rectangular swimming pool that is 25 feet by 50 feet has a 6-foot-wide sidewalk around it.
(a) How much fencing would be needed to enclose the sidewalk?

(b) Find the area of the sidewalk.

68. **Distance** A driver's distance D in miles from a rest stop after t hours is given by $D(t) = 280 - 70t$.
(a) How far is the driver from the rest stop after 2 hours?

(b) Find the slope of the graph of D. Interpret this slope as a rate of change.

69. **Survival Rates** The survival rates for song sparrows are shown in the table. The values listed are the numbers of song sparrows that attain a given age from 100 eggs. For example, 6 sparrows reach an age of 2 years from 100 eggs laid in the wild. (***Source:*** S. Kress, *Bird Life*.)

Age	0	1	2	3	4
Number	100	10	6	3	2

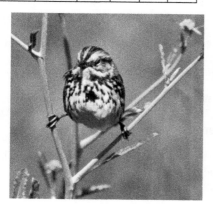

(a) Make a line graph of the data. Interpret the data.

(b) Does this line graph represent a function?

(c) Calculate and interpret the average rate of change for each 1-year period.

70. **Cost of Tuition** The graph shows the cost of taking x credits at a university.
(a) Why is it reasonable for the graph to pass through the origin?

(b) Find the slope of the graph.

(c) Interpret the slope as a rate of change.

71. **Average Rate of Change** Let $f(x) = 0.5x^2 + 50$ represent the outside temperature in degrees Fahrenheit at x P.M., where $1 \le x \le 5$.
(a) Graph f. Is f linear or nonlinear?

(b) Calculate the average rate of change of f from 1 P.M. to 4 P.M.

(c) Interpret this average rate of change.

72. **Distance** At noon car A is traveling north at 30 miles per hour and is located 20 miles north of car B. Car B is traveling west at 50 miles per hour. Approximate the distance between the cars at 12:45 P.M. to the nearest mile.

Extended and Discovery Exercises

Because a parabolic curve becomes sharp gradually, as shown in the first figure on the next page, curves designed by engineers for highways and railroads frequently have parabolic, rather than circular, shapes. If railroad tracks changed abruptly from straight to circular, the momentum of the locomotive could cause a derailment. The second figure on the next page illustrates straight tracks connecting to a circular curve. (***Source:*** F. Mannering and W. Kilareski, *Principles of Highway Engineering and Traffic Analysis*.)

In order to design a curve and estimate its cost, engineers determine the distance around the curve before it is built. In the third figure on the next page the distance along a parabolic curve from A to C is approximated by two line segments AB and BC. The distance formula can be used to calculate the length of each segment. The sum of these two lengths gives a crude estimate of the length of the curve.

A better estimate can be made using four line segments, as shown in the fourth figure. As the number of segments increases, so does the accuracy of the approximation.

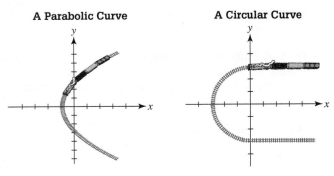

A Parabolic Curve   **A Circular Curve**

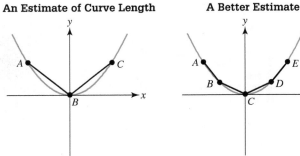

An Estimate of Curve Length   **A Better Estimate**

1. **Curve Length** Suppose that a curve designed for railroad tracks is represented by the equation $y = 0.2x^2$, where the units are in kilometers. The points $(-3, 1.8)$, $(-1.5, 0.45)$, $(0, 0)$, $(1.5, 0.45)$, and $(3, 1.8)$ lie on the graph of $y = 0.2x^2$. Approximate the length of the curve from $x = -3$ to $x = 3$ by using line segments connecting these points.

Exercises 2–5: **Curve Length** *Use three line segments connecting the four points to estimate the length of the curve on the graph of f from $x = -1$ to $x = 2$. Graph f and a line graph of the four points in the indicated viewing rectangle.*

2. $f(x) = x^2$; $(-1, 1)$, $(0, 0)$, $(1, 1)$, $(2, 4)$;
   $[-4.5, 4.5, 1]$ by $[-1, 5, 1]$

3. $f(x) = \sqrt[3]{x}$; $(-1, -1)$, $(0, 0)$, $(1, 1)$, $(2, \sqrt[3]{2})$;
   $[-3, 3, 1]$ by $[-2, 2, 1]$

4. $f(x) = 0.5x^3 + 2$; $(-1, 1.5)$, $(0, 2)$, $(1, 2.5)$, $(2, 6)$;
   $[-4.5, 4.5, 1]$ by $[0, 6, 1]$

5. $f(x) = 2 - 0.5x^2$; $(-1, 1.5)$, $(0, 2)$, $(1, 1.5)$, $(2, 0)$;
   $[-3, 3, 1]$ by $[-1, 3, 1]$

6. The distance along the curve of $y = x^2$ from $(0, 0)$ to $(3, 9)$ is about 9.747. Use this fact to estimate the distance along the curve of $y = 9 - x^2$ from $(0, 9)$ to $(3, 0)$.

7. Estimate the distance along the curve of $y = \sqrt{x}$ from $(1, 1)$ to $(4, 2)$. (The actual value is approximately 3.168.)

8. **Endangered Species** The Florida scrub-jay is an endangered species that prefers to live in open landscape with short vegetation. NASA has attempted to create a habitat for these birds near Kennedy Space Center. The following table lists their population for selected years, where $x = 0$ corresponds to 1980, $x = 1$ to 1981, $x = 2$ to 1982, and so on.

x (1980 $\leftrightarrow$ 0)	0	5	9
y (population)	3697	2512	2176

x (1980 $\leftrightarrow$ 0)	11	15	19
y (population)	2100	1689	1127

Source: Mathematics Explorations II, NASA–AMATYC–NSF.

(a) Make a scatterplot of the data.

(b) Find a linear function f that models the data.

(c) Graph the data and f in the same viewing rectangle.

(d) Estimate the scrub-jay population in 1987 and in 2003.

9. **Rise in Sea Level** If the global climate were to warm significantly, the Arctic ice cap would melt. It is estimated that this ice cap contains the equivalent of 680,000 cubic miles of water. Over 200 million people currently live on soil that is less than 3 feet above sea level. In the United States, several large cities have low average elevations, such as Boston (14 feet), New Orleans (4 feet), and San Diego (13 feet). (*Sources:* Department of the Interior, Geological Survey.)

(a) Devise a plan to determine how much sea level would rise if the Arctic cap melted. (*Hint:* The radius of Earth is 3960 miles and 71% of its surface is covered by oceans.)

(b) Use your plan to estimate this rise in sea level.

(c) Discuss the implications of your calculation.

(d) Estimate how much sea level would rise if the 6,300,000 cubic miles of water in the Antarctic ice cap melted.

10. Prove that $\sqrt{2}$ is irrational by assuming that $\sqrt{2}$ is rational and arriving at a contradiction.

Linear Functions and Equations

> The human mind has never invented a labor-saving device greater than algebra.
>
> —J.W. Gibbs

For over two centuries people have been transferring carbon from below the surface of the earth into the atmosphere. In 2006, the burning of coal, oil, and natural gas released 7 billion tons of carbon into the atmosphere. If the rate of growth continues, the amount could double to 14 billion tons by 2056. This increase is modeled by a linear function C in the figure on the left below. The green horizontal line $y = 7$ represents the 2006 level of emissions, and the red horizontal line $y = 14$ represents a doubling of carbon emissions. Their points of intersection with the graph of C represent when these levels of emission could

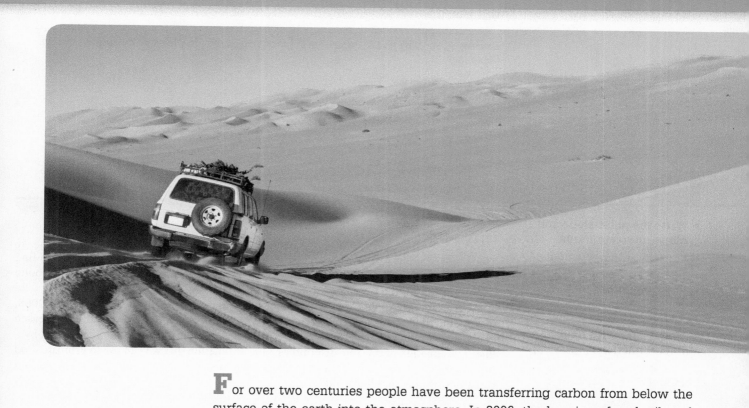

No Restrictions on Carbon Emissions

Restrictions on Carbon Emissions

occur. The figure on the right illustrates what might happen if levels of carbon emission could be held at 7 billion tons per year for the next 50 years. In this case, emissions are expected to decline after 50 years. This graph, made up of line segments, is called a *piecewise-linear function*.

Whatever your point of view, mathematics plays an essential role in understanding the future of carbon emissions; without mathematical support, predictions lack credibility. To model carbon emissions, we need constant, linear, and piecewise-defined functions. All of these important concepts are discussed in this chapter.

Source: R. Socolow and S. Pacala, "A Plan to Keep Carbon in Check," *Scientific American*, September, 2006.

2.1 Equations of Lines

- Write the point-slope and slope-intercept forms
- Find the intercepts of a line
- Write equations for horizontal, vertical, parallel, and perpendicular lines
- Model data with lines and linear functions (optional)
- Use linear regression to model data (optional)

Introduction

The graph of a linear function is a line. One way to determine a linear function is to find the equation of this line. Once this equation is known, we can easily write the symbolic representation for the linear function.

For example, Apple Corporation sold approximately 55 million iPods in fiscal 2008, making the iPod the fastest-selling music player in history. However, sales then decreased to about 43 million in 2011. (*Source:* Apple Corporation.) This decline can be modeled by a line. The equation of this line determines a linear function that we can use to estimate iPod sales for other years. See Example 4. This section discusses how to use data points to find equations of lines and linear functions.

Forms for Equations of Lines

Point-Slope Form   Suppose that a nonvertical line with slope m passes through the point (x_1, y_1). If (x, y) is any point on this *nonvertical* line with $x \neq x_1$, then the change in y is $\Delta y = y - y_1$, the change in x is $\Delta x = x - x_1$, and the slope is $m = \frac{\Delta y}{\Delta x} = \frac{y - y_1}{x - x_1}$, as illustrated in Figure 2.1.

Two Points Determine a Line

The slope formula is used to write the point-slope form of a line.

Figure 2.1

With this slope formula, the equation of the line can be found.

$$m = \frac{y - y_1}{x - x_1} \qquad \text{Slope formula}$$

$$y - y_1 = m(x - x_1) \qquad \text{Cross multiply.}$$

$$y = m(x - x_1) + y_1 \qquad \text{Add } y_1 \text{ to each side.}$$

The equation $y - y_1 = m(x - x_1)$ is traditionally called the *point-slope form* of the equation of a line. Since we think of y as being a function of x, written $y = f(x)$, the equivalent form $y = m(x - x_1) + y_1$ will also be referred to as the point-slope form. The point-slope form is not unique, as any point on the line can be used for (x_1, y_1). However, these point-slope forms are *equivalent*, meaning their graphs are identical.

POINT-SLOPE FORM

The line with slope m passing through the point (x_1, y_1) has an equation

$$y = m(x - x_1) + y_1, \quad \text{or} \quad y - y_1 = m(x - x_1),$$

the **point-slope form** of the equation of a line.

In the next example we find the equation of a line given two points.

EXAMPLE 1 Determining a point-slope form

Find an equation of the line passing through the points $(-2, -3)$ and $(1, 3)$. Plot the points and graph the line by hand.

SOLUTION Begin by finding the slope of the line.

$$m = \frac{3 - (-3)}{1 - (-2)} = \frac{6}{3} = 2$$

Substituting $(x_1, y_1) = (1, 3)$ and $m = 2$ into the point-slope form results in

First point-slope form ▸ $y = 2(x - 1) + 3.$ $y = m(x - x_1) + y_1$

If we use the point $(-2, -3)$, the point-slope form is

Second point-slope form ▸ $y = 2(x + 2) - 3.$ Note that $(x - (-2)) = (x + 2)$.

This line and the two points are shown in Figure 2.2.

Now Try Exercise 1

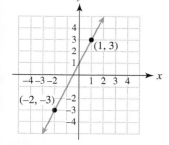

Figure 2.2

Slope-Intercept Form The two point-slope forms found in Example 1 are equivalent.

First point-slope form	**Second point-slope form**	
$y = 2(x - 1) + 3$	$y = 2(x + 2) - 3$	Point-slope form
$y = 2x - 2 + 3$	$y = 2x + 4 - 3$	Distributive property
$y = 2x + 1$	$y = 2x + 1$	Simplify.

Both point-slope forms simplify to the same equation.

The form $y = mx + b$ is called the *slope-intercept form.* Unlike the point-slope form, the slope-intercept form is *unique.* The real number m represents the slope and the real number b represents the y-intercept, as illustrated in Figure 2.3.

Slope-Intercept Form
$$y = mx + b$$

Slope: m
y-intercept: b

Figure 2.3

SLOPE-INTERCEPT FORM

The line with slope m and y-intercept b is given by

$$y = mx + b,$$

the **slope-intercept form** of the equation of a line.

EXAMPLE 2 Finding equations of lines

Find the point-slope form for the line that satisfies the conditions. Then convert this equation into slope-intercept form and write the formula for a function f whose graph is the line.

(a) Slope $-\frac{1}{2}$, passing through the point $(-3, -7)$

(b) x-intercept -4, y-intercept 2

SOLUTION

(a) Let $m = -\frac{1}{2}$ and $(x_1, y_1) = (-3, -7)$ in the point-slope form.

$$y = m(x - x_1) + y_1 \qquad \text{Point-slope form}$$

$$y = -\frac{1}{2}(x + 3) - 7 \qquad \text{Substitute.}$$

The slope-intercept form can be found by simplifying.

$$y = -\frac{1}{2}(x + 3) - 7 \qquad \text{Point-slope form}$$

$$y = -\frac{1}{2}x - \frac{3}{2} - 7 \qquad \text{Distributive property}$$

$$y = -\frac{1}{2}x - \frac{17}{2} \qquad \text{Slope-intercept form}$$

Thus $f(x) = -\frac{1}{2}x - \frac{17}{2}$ is the formula for the function whose graph is this line.

(b) The line passes through the points $(-4, 0)$ and $(0, 2)$. Its slope is

$$m = \frac{2 - 0}{0 - (-4)} = \frac{1}{2}.$$

Thus a point-slope form for the line is $y = \frac{1}{2}(x + 4) + 0$, where the point $(-4, 0)$ is used for (x_1, y_1). The slope-intercept form is $y = \frac{1}{2}x + 2$ and $f(x) = \frac{1}{2}x + 2$ is the formula for the function whose graph is this line.

Now Try Exercises 5 and 9

The next example demonstrates how to find the slope-intercept form of a line without first finding the point-slope form.

EXAMPLE 3 Finding slope-intercept form

Find the slope-intercept form of the line passing through the points $(-2, 1)$ and $(2, 3)$.

SOLUTION

Getting Started We need to determine m and b in the slope-intercept form, $y = mx + b$. First find the slope m. Then substitute *either* point into the equation and determine b. ▶

$$m = \frac{3 - 1}{2 - (-2)} = \frac{2}{4} = \frac{1}{2}$$

Thus $y = \frac{1}{2}x + b$. To find b, we substitute $(2, 3)$ in this equation.

$$3 = \frac{1}{2}(2) + b \qquad \text{Let } x = 2 \text{ and } y = 3.$$
$$3 = 1 + b \qquad \text{Multiply.}$$
$$2 = b \qquad \text{Determine } b.$$

Thus $y = \frac{1}{2}x + 2$.

Now Try Exercise 21

An Application In the next example we model the data about iPods discussed in the introduction to this section.

EXAMPLE 4   Estimating iPod sales

Apple Corporation sold approximately 55 million iPods in fiscal 2008 and 43 million iPods in fiscal 2011.
(a) Find the point-slope form of the line passing through $(2008, 55)$ and $(2011, 43)$. Interpret the slope of the line as a rate of change.
(b) Sketch a graph of the data and the line connecting these points.
(c) Estimate sales in 2010 and compare the estimate to the true value of 50 million.
(d) Estimate sales in 2023. Discuss the accuracy of your answers.

SOLUTION

Getting Started First find the slope m of the line connecting the data points, and then substitute this value for m and either of the two data points in the point-slope form. We can use this equation to estimate sales by substituting the required year for x in the equation. ▶

(a) The slope of the line passing through $(2008, 55)$ and $(2011, 43)$ is

$$m = \frac{43 - 55}{2011 - 2008} = -4.$$

Thus sales of iPods decreased, on average, by 4 million iPods per year from 2008 to 2011. If we substitute -4 for m and $(2008, 55)$ for (x_1, y_1), the point-slope form is

$$y = -4(x - 2008) + 55.$$

iPod Sales

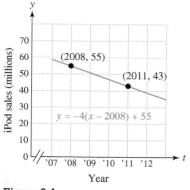

Figure 2.4

(b) The requested line passing through the data points is shown in Figure 2.4.
(c) If $x = 2010$, then $y = -4(2010 - 2008) + 55 = 47$ million. This estimated value is 3 million lower than the true value of 50 million.
(d) We can use the equation to estimate 2023 sales as follows.

$$y = -4(2023 - 2008) + 55 = -5 \text{ million} \qquad \text{Let } x = 2023.$$

The 2023 value is clearly incorrect because sales cannot be negative.

Now Try Exercise 81

Finding Intercepts

The point-slope form and the slope-intercept form are not the only forms for the equation of a line. An equation of a line is in **standard form** when it is written as

$$ax + by = c,$$

where a, b, and c are constants and a and b are not *both* zero. By using standard form, we can write the equation of any line, including vertical lines (which are discussed later in this section). Examples of equations of lines in standard form include the following.

Equations in Standard Form: $ax + by = c$

$$2x - 3y = -6, \quad y = \frac{1}{4}, \quad x = -3, \quad \text{and} \quad -3x + y = \frac{1}{2}$$

$a = 0 \qquad b = 0$

The following box gives an example of how to find the intercepts for a line given in standard form.

See the Concept : Finding Intercepts for $3x + 4y = 12$

A y-intercept: let $x = 0$ and solve for y.

B x-intercept: let $y = 0$ and solve for x.

$3x + 4y = 12$

A $3(0) + 4y = 12$, or $y = 3$, so the y-intercept is 3.

B $3x + 4(0) = 12$, or $x = 4$, so the x-intercept is 4.

NOTE To solve $ax = b$, divide each side by a to obtain $x = \frac{b}{a}$. Thus $3x = 12$ implies that $x = \frac{12}{3} = 4$. Linear equations are solved in general in the next section.

FINDING INTERCEPTS

To find any x-intercepts, let $y = 0$ in the equation and solve for x.
To find any y-intercepts, let $x = 0$ in the equation and solve for y.

EXAMPLE 5 Finding intercepts

Locate the x- and y-intercepts for the line whose equation is $4x + 3y = 6$. Use the intercepts to graph the equation.

SOLUTION To locate the x-intercept, let $y = 0$ in the equation.

$$4x + 3(0) = 6 \qquad \text{Let } y = 0.$$
$$x = 1.5 \qquad \text{Divide each side by 4.}$$

The x-intercept is 1.5. To find the y-intercept, substitute $x = 0$ into the equation.

$$4(0) + 3y = 6 \qquad \text{Let } x = 0.$$
$$y = 2 \qquad \text{Divide each side by 3.}$$

The y-intercept is 2. Therefore the line passes through the points $(1.5, 0)$ and $(0, 2)$, as shown in Figure 2.5.

Now Try Exercise 57

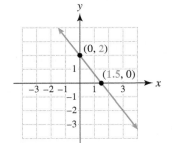

Figure 2.5

Horizontal, Vertical, Parallel, and Perpendicular Lines

Horizontal and Vertical Lines The graph of a constant function f, defined by the formula $f(x) = b$, is a *horizontal line* having slope 0 and y-intercept b.

A *vertical line* cannot be represented by a function because distinct points on a vertical line have the same x-coordinate. In fact, this is the distinguishing feature of points on a vertical line—they all have the same x-coordinate. See Figures 2.6 and 2.7.

CLASS DISCUSSION

Why do you think that a vertical line sometimes is said to have "infinite slope?" What are some problems with taking this phrase too literally?

Equations of Vertical Lines

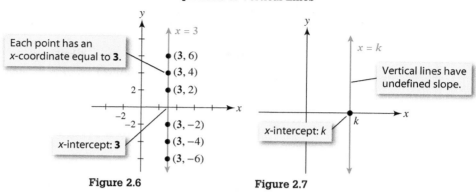

Figure 2.6   **Figure 2.7**

EQUATIONS OF HORIZONTAL AND VERTICAL LINES

An equation of the horizontal line with y-intercept b is $y = b$. An equation of the vertical line with x-intercept k is $x = k$.

EXAMPLE 6   Finding equations of horizontal and vertical lines

Find equations of vertical and horizontal lines passing through the point $(8, 5)$. If possible, for each line write a formula for a linear function whose graph is the line.

SOLUTION   The x-coordinate of the point $(8, 5)$ is 8. The vertical line $x = 8$ passes through every point in the xy-plane with an x-coordinate of 8, including the point $(8, 5)$. Similarly, the horizontal line $y = 5$ passes through every point with a y-coordinate of 5, including $(8, 5)$. See Figure 2.8, where each line is shown.

Vertical and Horizontal Lines

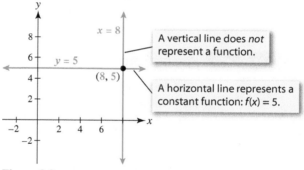

Figure 2.8

The horizontal line $y = 5$ represents the constant function $f(x) = 5$. The vertical line $x = 8$ does *not* represent a function because it does *not* pass the vertical line test.

Now Try Exercises 49 and 51

Parallel Lines   Two nonvertical parallel lines have equal slopes.

PARALLEL LINES

Two lines with slopes m_1 and m_2, neither of which is vertical, are parallel if and only if their slopes are equal; that is, $m_1 = m_2$.

NOTE   The phrase "if and only if" is used when two statements are mathematically equivalent. If two nonvertical lines are parallel, then $m_1 = m_2$. Conversely, if two nonvertical lines have equal slopes, then they are parallel. Either condition implies the other.

EXAMPLE 7   Finding parallel lines

Find the slope-intercept form of a line parallel to $y = -2x + 5$, passing through $(4, 3)$.

SOLUTION   The line $y = -2x + 5$ has slope -2, so any parallel line also has slope $m = -2$. The line passing through $(4, 3)$ with slope -2 is determined as follows.

$$y = -2(x - 4) + 3 \qquad \text{Point-slope form}$$
$$y = -2x + 8 + 3 \qquad \text{Distributive property}$$
$$y = -2x + 11 \qquad \text{Slope-intercept form}$$

Now Try Exercise 35

Perpendicular Lines   Two lines are perpendicular if the product of their slopes is equal to -1.

> **PERPENDICULAR LINES**
>
> Two lines with nonzero slopes m_1 and m_2 are perpendicular if and only if their slopes have product -1; that is, $m_1 m_2 = -1$.

For perpendicular lines, m_1 and m_2 are *negative reciprocals*. That is, $m_1 = -\frac{1}{m_2}$ and $m_2 = -\frac{1}{m_1}$. Table 2.1 shows some slopes of perpendicular lines.

Slopes of Perpendicular Lines

Slope of first line — m_1	$\frac{1}{2}$	$\frac{6}{5}$	5	-1	$-\frac{2}{3}$
Slope of second line — m_2	-2	$-\frac{5}{6}$	$-\frac{1}{5}$	1	$\frac{3}{2}$
Product always equals –1 — $m_1 m_2$	-1	-1	-1	-1	-1

Table 2.1

EXAMPLE 8   Finding perpendicular lines

Find the slope-intercept form of the line perpendicular to $y = -\frac{2}{3}x + 2$, passing through the point $(-2, 1)$. Graph the lines.

Perpendicular Lines

Figure 2.9

SOLUTION   The line $y = -\frac{2}{3}x + 2$ has slope $-\frac{2}{3}$. The negative reciprocal of $m_1 = -\frac{2}{3}$ is $m_2 = \frac{3}{2}$. The slope-intercept form of a line having slope $\frac{3}{2}$ and passing through $(-2, 1)$ can be found as follows.

$$y = m(x - x_1) + y_1 \qquad \text{Point-slope form}$$

$$y = \frac{3}{2}(x + 2) + 1 \qquad \text{Let } m = \tfrac{3}{2}, \, x_1 = -2, \text{ and } y_1 = 1.$$

$$y = \frac{3}{2}x + 3 + 1 \qquad \text{Distributive property}$$

$$y = \frac{3}{2}x + 4 \qquad \text{Slope-intercept form}$$

Figure 2.9 shows graphs of these perpendicular lines.

Now Try Exercise 41

Calculator Help

To set a square viewing rectangle, see Appendix A (page AP-5).

NOTE   If a graphing calculator is used to graph these lines, a square viewing rectangle must be used for the lines to appear perpendicular.

EXAMPLE 9   Determining a rectangle

In Figure 2.10 a rectangle is outlined by four lines denoted y_1, y_2, y_3, and y_4. Find the equation of each line.

CLASS DISCUSSION

Check the results from Example 9 by graphing the four equations in the same viewing rectangle. How does your graph compare with Figure 2.10? Why is it important to use a square viewing rectangle?

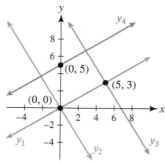

Figure 2.10

SOLUTION

Line y_1: This line passes through the points $(0, 0)$ and $(5, 3)$, so $m = \frac{3}{5}$ and the y-intercept is 0. Its equation is $y_1 = \frac{3}{5}x$.

Line y_2: This line passes through the point $(0, 0)$ and is perpendicular to y_1, so its slope is given by $m = -\frac{5}{3}$ and the y-intercept is 0. Its equation is $y_2 = -\frac{5}{3}x$.

Line y_3: This line passes through the point $(5, 3)$ and is parallel to y_2, so its slope is given by $m = -\frac{5}{3}$. In a point-slope form, its equation is $y_3 = -\frac{5}{3}(x - 5) + 3$, which is equivalent to $y_3 = -\frac{5}{3}x + \frac{34}{3}$.

Line y_4: This line passes through the point $(0, 5)$, so its y-intercept is 5. It is parallel to y_1, so its slope is given by $m = \frac{3}{5}$. Its equation is $y_4 = \frac{3}{5}x + 5$.

Now Try Exercise 95

Interpolation and Extrapolation

In 2005 about \$350 million was spent on U.S. digital music single downloads. This amount reached \$1350 million in 2010. (*Source:* RIAA.) These data can be modeled with a line, and the slope of this line is

$$m = \frac{1350 - 350}{2010 - 2005} = 200.$$

This value means that the increase in the amount spent on U.S. music downloads was, on average, \$200 million per year from 2005 to 2010.

A point-slope form of the line passing through $(2005, 350)$ with slope 200 is

$$y = 200(x - 2005) + 350.$$

We can easily write a formula for a linear function

$$D(x) = 200(x - 2005) + 350,$$

whose graph is this line. See Figure 2.11.

This formula can be used to estimate the value of downloads in 2008 as follows.

$$D(2008) = 200(2008 - 2005) + 350 = 950$$

Thus $D(x)$ estimates that the value of digital music single downloads was \$950 million in 2008. (The actual value was \$1000 million.) Because 2008 is *between* 2005 and 2010, we say that this estimation involves **interpolation.** Interpolation occurs when we estimate between given data points. However, if we use $D(x)$ to estimate this value in 2003 we obtain the following.

$$D(2003) = 200(2003 - 2005) + 350 = -50$$

U.S. Digital Single Download Sales

$D(x) = 200(x - 2005) + 350$

$(2010, 1350)$

$(2005, 350)$

Downloads (\$ millions)

2004 2006 2008 2010 2012

Year

Figure 2.11

This estimate is incorrect because sales cannot be negative. Because 2003 is *not between* 2005 and 2010, we say that this estimation involves **extrapolation.** Extrapolation occurs when we estimate "outside" of the given data. Interpolation is usually more accurate than extrapolation.

Modeling Data (Optional)

Point-slope form can sometimes be useful when modeling real data. In the next example we model how investments in cloud computing have increased. Cloud computing allows people to use files and applications on the Internet.

EXAMPLE 10   Modeling investments for cloud computing

Table 2.2 lists the investments in billions of dollars for cloud computing for selected years.

Investments in Cloud Computing ($ billions)

Year	2005	2006	2007	2008	2009
Investments	26	113	195	299	374

Source: Thomson Reuters.

Table 2.2

(a) Make a scatterplot of the data.
(b) Find a formula in point-slope form for a linear function f that models the data.
(c) Graph the data and $y = f(x)$ in the same xy-plane.
(d) Interpret the slope of the graph of $y = f(x)$.
(e) Estimate the investment in cloud computing in 2014. Does your answer involve interpolation or extrapolation?

Calculator Help

To make a scatterplot, see Appendix A (page AP-3). To plot data and graph an equation, see Appendix A (page AP-6).

[2004, 2010, 1] by [0, 500, 100]

Figure 2.12

Modeling Cloud Investments

[2004, 2010, 1] by [0, 500, 100]

$y = 87(x - 2005) + 26$

Figure 2.13

SOLUTION
(a) See Figure 2.12
(b) Because the data are nearly linear, we could require that the line pass through the first data point (2005, 26) and the last data point (2009, 374). The slope of this line is

$$m = \frac{374 - 26}{2009 - 2005} = 87. \qquad Slope = \frac{y_2 - y_1}{x_2 - x_1}$$

Thus we can write a formula for f as

$$f(x) = 87(x - 2005) + 26.$$

NOTE   When modeling real data, answers for $f(x)$ may vary, depending on the points that are used to determine the line.

(c) See Figure 2.13
(d) Slope 87 indicates that investments increased, on average, by $87 billion per year between 2005 and 2009.
(e) To estimate the investment amount in 2014, we can evaluate $f(2014)$.

$$f(2014) = 87(2014 - 2005) + 26 = 809$$

This model predicts an $809 billion investment in cloud computing during 2014. This result involves extrapolation because 2014 is "outside" of 2005 and 2009.

Now Try Exercise 87

Linear Regression (Optional)

We have used linear functions to model data involving the variables x and y. Problems where one variable is used to predict the behavior of a second variable are called **regression** problems. If a linear function or line is used to approximate the data, then the technique is referred to as **linear regression.**

We have already solved problems by selecting a line that *visually* fits the data in a scatterplot. See Example 10. However, this technique has some disadvantages. First, it does not produce a unique line. Different people may arrive at different lines to fit the same data. Second, the line is not determined automatically by a calculator or computer. A statistical method used to determine a unique linear function or line is based on the method of **least squares**.

Correlation Coefficient   Most graphing calculators have the capability to calculate the least-squares regression line automatically. When determining the least-squares line, calculators often compute a real number r, called the **correlation coefficient**, where $-1 \leq r \leq 1$. When r is positive and near 1, low x-values correspond to low y-values and high x-values correspond to high y-values. For example, there is a positive correlation between years of education x and income y. More years of education correlate with higher income. When r is near -1, the reverse is true. Low x-values correspond to high y-values and high x-values correspond to low y-values. If $r \approx 0$, then there is little or no correlation between the data points. In this case, a linear function does not provide a suitable model. A summary of these concepts is shown in the following.

Correlation Coefficient r ($-1 \leq r \leq 1$)

Value of r	Comments	Sample Scatterplot
$r = 1$	There is an exact linear fit. The line passes through all data points and has a positive slope.	
$r = -1$	There is an exact linear fit. The line passes through all data points and has a negative slope.	
$0 < r < 1$	There is a positive correlation. As the x-values increase, so do the y-values. The fit is not exact.	
$-1 < r < 0$	There is a negative correlation. As the x-values increase, the y-values decrease. The fit is not exact.	
$r = 0$	There is no correlation. The data has no tendency toward being linear. A regression line predicts poorly.	

MAKING CONNECTIONS

Correlation and Causation
When geese begin to fly north, summer is coming and the weather becomes warmer. Geese flying north correlate with warmer weather. However, geese flying north clearly do not *cause* warmer weather. It is important to remember that correlation does not always indicate causation.

Calculator Help
To find a line of least-squares fit, see
Appendix A (page AP-6).

In the next example we use a graphing calculator to find the line of least-squares fit that models three data points.

EXAMPLE 11 Determining a line of least-squares fit

Find the line of least-squares fit for the data points (1, 1), (2, 3), and (3, 4). What is the correlation coefficient? Plot the data and graph the line.

SOLUTION Begin by entering the three data points into the STAT EDIT menu. Refer to Figures 2.14–2.17. Select the LinReg (ax + b) option from the STAT CALC menu. From the home screen we can see that the line (linear function) of least squares is given by the formula $y = \frac{3}{2}x - \frac{1}{3}$. The correlation coefficient is $r \approx 0.98$. Since $r \neq 1$, the line does not provide an *exact* model of the data.

Enter Data into Two Lists

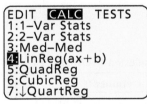

Figure 2.14

Select Linear Regression

Figure 2.15

Equation for Regression Line

Figure 2.16

Data and Regression Line
[0, 5, 1] by [0, 5, 1]

Figure 2.17

Now Try Exercise 99

An Application In the next example, we find the regression line that models the cloud computing data found in Example 10.

EXAMPLE 12 Modeling data with a regression line

Refer to the data from Table 2.2 in Example 10.
(a) Find the least-squares regression line that models this data.
(b) Compare the regression line with the one that was found in Example 10 by writing both lines in slope-intercept form.

SOLUTION
(a) Figures 2.18–2.21 show how to find this regression line. Its equation is

$$y = 88.2x - 176{,}816.$$

Enter Data into Two Lists

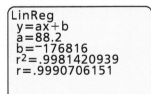

Figure 2.18

Select Linear Regression

Figure 2.19

Equation for Regression Line

Figure 2.20

Data and Regression Line
[2004, 2010, 1] by [0, 500, 100]

Figure 2.21

(b) The equation of the line found in Example 10 can be written in slope-intercept form as follows.

Calculator Help
To copy the regression equation directly
into Y₁, see Appendix A (page AP-11).

$$y = 87(x - 2005) + 26 \quad \text{Example 10 equation}$$
$$y = 87x - 174{,}435 + 26 \quad \text{Distributive property}$$
$$y = 87x - 174{,}409$$

Notice that the slope-intercept forms for these two lines are not exactly alike. However, both lines model the data reasonably well, as shown in Figures 2.13 and 2.21.

Now Try Exercise 107

2.1 Putting It All Together

$\mathbf{T}$he following table summarizes three forms for equations of a line and how to find the intercepts.

CONCEPT	COMMENTS	EXAMPLES
Point-slope form $$y = m(x - x_1) + y_1$$ or $$y - y_1 = m(x - x_1)$$	Used to find the equation of a line, given two points or one point and the slope	Given two points $(5, 1)$ and $(4, 3)$, first compute $m = \frac{3 - 1}{4 - 5} = -2$. An equation of this line is $$y = -2(x - 5) + 1.$$
Slope-intercept form $$y = mx + b$$	A unique equation for a line, determined by the slope m and the y-intercept b	An equation of the line with slope 5 and y-intercept -4 is $y = 5x - 4$.
Standard form $$ax + by = c$$	Any line can be written in this form.	$3x + 5y = 15$ $\qquad x = -4$ *Vertical line* $\qquad y = 7$ *Horizontal line*
Finding intercepts	1. To find x-intercepts, let $y = 0$ and solve for x. 2. To find y-intercepts, let $x = 0$ and solve for y.	1. In $3x + 5y = 15$ let $y = 0$ to obtain $3x = 15$, or $x = 5$. The x-intercept is 5. 2. In $3x + 5y = 15$ let $x = 0$ to obtain $5y = 15$, or $y = 3$. The y-intercept is 3.

The following table summarizes special types of lines.

CONCEPT	EQUATION(S)	EXAMPLES
Horizontal line	$y = b$, where b is a constant	A horizontal line with y-intercept 7 has the equation $y = 7$.
Vertical line	$x = k$, where k is a constant	A vertical line with x-intercept -8 has the equation $x = -8$.
Parallel lines	$y = m_1 x + b_1$ and $y = m_2 x + b_2$, where $m_1 = m_2$	The lines given by $y = -3x - 1$ and $y = -3x + 5$ are parallel because they both have slope -3.
Perpendicular lines	$y = m_1 x + b_1$ and $y = m_2 x + b_2$, where $m_1 m_2 = -1$	The lines $y = 2x - 5$ and $y = -\frac{1}{2}x + 2$ are perpendicular because $m_1 m_2 = 2\left(-\frac{1}{2}\right) = -1$.

continued on next page

The following table summarizes linear regression.

CONCEPT	DESCRIPTION
Correlation coefficient r	The values of r satisfy $-1 \leq r \leq 1$, where a line fits the data better if r is near -1 or 1. A value near 0 indicates a poor fit.
Least-squares regression line	The line of least-squares fit for the points (1, 3), (2, 5), and (3, 6) is $y = \frac{3}{2}x + \frac{5}{3}$ and $r \approx 0.98$. Try verifying this with a calculator.

2.1 Exercises

Equations of Lines

Exercises 1–4: Find the point-slope form of the line passing through the given points. Use the first point as (x_1, y_1). Plot the points and graph the line by hand.

1. $(1, 2), (3, -2)$ **2.** $(-2, 3), (1, 0)$

3. $(-3, -1), (1, 2)$ **4.** $(-1, 2), (-2, -3)$

Exercises 5–10: Find a point-slope form of the line satisfying the conditions. Use the first point given for (x_1, y_1). Then convert the equation to slope-intercept form, and write the formula for a function f whose graph is the line.

5. Slope -2.4, passing through (4, 5)

6. Slope 1.7, passing through $(-8, 10)$

7. Passing through $(1, -2)$ and $(-9, 3)$

8. Passing through $(-6, 10)$ and $(5, -12)$

9. x-intercept 4, y-intercept -3

10. x-intercept -2, y-intercept 5

Exercises 11–14: Find the slope-intercept form for the line in the figure.

11.

12.

13.

14.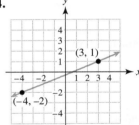

Exercises 15–20: **Concepts** *Match the given equation to its graph (a–f) shown.*

15. $y = m(x - x_1) + y_1, m > 0$

16. $y = m(x - x_1) + y_1, m < 0$

17. $y = mx, m > 0$

18. $y = mx + b, m < 0$ and $b > 0$

19. $x = k, k > 0$

20. $y = b, b < 0$

(a)   **(b)**

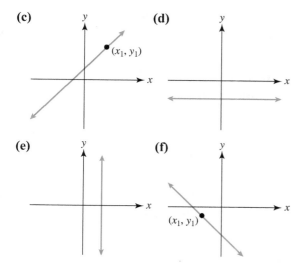

(c) **(d)** **(e)** **(f)**

Exercises 21–48: Find the slope-intercept form for the line satisfying the conditions.

21. Passing through $(-1, -4)$ and $(1, 2)$

22. Passing through $(-1, 6)$ and $(2, -3)$

23. Passing through $(4, 5)$ and $(1, -3)$

24. Passing through $(8, -2)$ and $(-2, 3)$

25. y-intercept 5, slope -7.8

26. y-intercept -155, slope 5.6

27. y-intercept 45, x-intercept 90

28. x-intercept -6, y-intercept -8

29. Slope -3, passing through $(0, 5)$

30. Slope $\frac{1}{3}$, passing through $\left(\frac{1}{2}, -2\right)$

31. Passing through $(0, -6)$ and $(4, 0)$

32. Passing through $\left(\frac{3}{4}, -\frac{1}{4}\right)$ and $\left(\frac{5}{4}, \frac{7}{4}\right)$

33. Passing through $\left(\frac{1}{2}, \frac{3}{4}\right)$ and $\left(\frac{1}{5}, \frac{2}{3}\right)$

34. Passing through $\left(-\frac{7}{3}, \frac{5}{3}\right)$ and $\left(\frac{5}{6}, -\frac{7}{6}\right)$

35. Parallel to $y = 4x + 16$, passing through $(-4, -7)$

36. Parallel to the line $y = -\frac{3}{4}(x - 100) - 99$, passing through $(1, 3)$

37. Perpendicular to the line $y = -\frac{2}{3}(x - 1980) + 5$, passing through $(1980, 10)$

38. Perpendicular to $y = 6x - 10$, passing through $(15, -7)$

39. Parallel to $y = \frac{2}{3}x + 3$, passing through $(0, -2.1)$

40. Parallel to $y = -4x - \frac{1}{4}$, passing through $(2, -5)$

41. Perpendicular to $y = -2x$, passing through $(-2, 5)$

42. Perpendicular to $y = -\frac{6}{7}x + \frac{3}{7}$, passing through $(3, 8)$

43. Perpendicular to $x + y = 4$, passing through $(15, -5)$

44. Parallel to $2x - 3y = -6$, passing through $(4, -9)$

45. Passing through $(5, 7)$ and parallel to the line passing through $(1, 3)$ and $(-3, 1)$

46. Passing through $(1990, 4)$ and parallel to the line passing through $(1980, 3)$ and $(2000, 8)$

47. Passing through $(-2, 4)$ and perpendicular to the line passing through $\left(-5, \frac{1}{2}\right)$ and $\left(-3, \frac{2}{3}\right)$

48. Passing through $\left(\frac{3}{4}, \frac{1}{4}\right)$ and perpendicular to the line passing through $(-3, -5)$ and $(-4, 0)$

Horizontal and Vertical Lines

Exercises 49–56: Find an equation of the line satisfying the conditions. If possible, for each line write a formula for a linear function whose graph is the line.

49. Vertical, passing through $(-5, 6)$

50. Vertical, passing through $(1.95, 10.7)$

51. Horizontal, passing through $(-5, 6)$

52. Horizontal, passing through $(1.95, 10.7)$

53. Perpendicular to $y = 15$, passing through $(4, -9)$

54. Perpendicular to $x = 15$, passing through $(1.6, -9.5)$

55. Parallel to $x = 4.5$, passing through $(19, 5.5)$

56. Parallel to $y = -2.5$, passing through $(1985, 67)$

Finding Intercepts

Exercises 57–68: Determine the x- and y-intercepts on the graph of the equation. Graph the equation.

57. $4x - 5y = 20$

58. $-3x - 5y = 15$

59. $x - y = 7$

60. $15x - y = 30$

61. $6x - 7y = -42$

62. $5x + 2y = -20$

63. $y - 3x = 7$

64. $4x - 3y = 6$

65. $0.2x + 0.4y = 0.8$

66. $\frac{2}{3}y - x = 1$

67. $y = 8x - 5$

68. $y = -1.5x + 15$

*Exercises 69–72: The **intercept form of a line** is $\frac{x}{a} + \frac{y}{b} = 1$. Determine the x- and y-intercepts on the graph of the equation. Draw a conclusion about what the constants a and b represent in this form.*

69. $\dfrac{x}{5} + \dfrac{y}{7} = 1$ **70.** $\dfrac{x}{2} + \dfrac{y}{3} = 1$

71. $\dfrac{2x}{3} + \dfrac{4y}{5} = 1$ **72.** $\dfrac{5x}{6} - \dfrac{y}{2} = 1$

Exercises 73 and 74: (Refer to Exercises 69–72.) Write the intercept form for the line with the given intercepts.

73. x-intercept 5, y-intercept 9

74. x-intercept $\frac{2}{3}$, y-intercept $-\frac{5}{4}$

Interpolation and Extrapolation

Exercises 75–78: The table lists data that are exactly linear.

(a) Find the slope-intercept form of the line that passes through these data points.

(b) Predict y when x = −2.7 and 6.3. Decide if these calculations involve interpolation or extrapolation.

75.

x	−3	−2	−1	0	1
y	−7.7	−6.2	−4.7	−3.2	−1.7

76.

x	−2	−1	0	1	2
y	10.2	8.5	6.8	5.1	3.4

77.

x	5	23	32	55	61
y	94.7	56.9	38	−10.3	−22.9

78.

x	−11	−8	−7	−3	2
y	−16.1	−10.4	−8.5	−0.9	8.6

79. iPhone Revenues   The percentage of smartphone revenues that were due to iPhones is shown in the table.

Year	2008	2009	2010	2011
Percentage	3	10	16	24

Source: Business Insider.

(a) Find a linear function f that models these data. Does f model these data exactly or approximately?

(b) Use f to estimate this percentage in 2007.

(c) Did your answer use interpolation or extrapolation? Comment on your result.

80. Deaths on School Grounds   Deaths on school grounds nationwide for school years ending in year x are shown in the table.

x (year)	1998	1999	2000
y (deaths)	43	26	9

Source: FBI.

(a) Find a linear function f that models these data. Is f exact or approximate?

(b) Use f to estimate the number of deaths on school grounds in 2003. Compare your answer to the actual value of 49. Did your estimate involve interpolation or extrapolation?

Applications

81. Projected Cost of College   In 2003 the average annual cost of attending a private college or university, including tuition, fees, room, and board, was $25,000. This cost rose to about $37,000 in 2010, as illustrated in the figure. (*Source:* Cerulli Associates.)

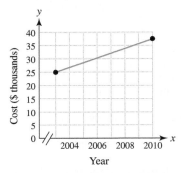

(a) Find a point-slope form of the line passing through the points (2003, 25,000) and (2010, 37,000). Interpret the slope.

(b) Use the equation to estimate the cost of attending a private college in 2007.

82. Distance   A person is riding a bicycle. The graph shows the rider's distance y in miles from an interstate highway after x hours.

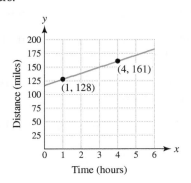

(a) How fast is the bicyclist traveling?

(b) Find the slope-intercept form of the line.

(c) How far was the bicyclist from the interstate highway initially?

(d) How far was the bicyclist from the interstate highway after 1 hour and 15 minutes?

83. Water in a Tank   The graph shows the amount of water in a 100-gallon tank after x minutes have elapsed.

(a) Is water entering or leaving the tank? How much water is in the tank after 3 minutes?

(b) Find the x- and y-intercepts. Interpret each intercept.

(c) Find the slope-intercept form of the equation of the line. Interpret the slope.

(d) Use the graph to estimate the x-coordinate of the point $(x, 50)$ that lies on the line.

84. Cost of Driving   The cost of driving a car includes both fixed costs and mileage costs. Assume that insurance and car payments cost $350 per month and gasoline, oil, and routine maintenance cost $0.29 per mile.
(a) Find a linear function f that gives the *annual* cost of driving this car x miles.

(b) What does the y-intercept on the graph of f represent?

85. U.S. Music Sales   In 1999 music sales from vinyl, CDs, and downloads were $15 billion and in 2013 they were $9 billion. (*Source:* RIAA.)
(a) Find the point-slope form for a line passing through the points (1999, 15) and (2013, 9).

(b) Interpret the slope of this line.

(c) Estimate sales in 2008 and compare them with the true value of $10.4 billion. Did your answer use interpolation or extrapolation?

86. Toyota Vehicle Sales   In 1998 Toyota sold 1.4 million vehicles and in 2007 it sold 2.3 million vehicles. (*Source:* Toyota Motor Division.)
(a) Find the point-slope form for a line passing through the points (1998, 1.4) and (2007, 2.3).

(b) Interpret the slope of this line.

(c) Estimate sales in 2004 and compare them with the true value of 2.0 million vehicles. Did your answer use interpolation or extrapolation?

87. Bankruptcies   The table lists the number of bankruptcies filed in thousands for selected years.

Year	2006	2007	2008	2009	2010
Bankruptcies	160	220	290	380	425

Source: Administrative Office of the United States.

(a) Make a scatterplot of the data.

(b) Find a formula in point-slope form for a linear function f that models the data.

(c) Graph the data and $y = f(x)$ in the same xy-plane.

(d) Interpret the slope of the graph of $y = f(x)$.

(e) Estimate the number of bankruptcies in 2014. Did your answer involve interpolation or extrapolation?

88. College Tuition   The table lists average tuition and fees in dollars at private colleges for selected years.

Year	1995	2000	2005	2010
Cost	12,432	16,233	21,235	26,273

Source: The College Board.

(a) Make a scatterplot of the data.

(b) Find a formula in point-slope form for a linear function f that models the data.

(c) Graph the data and $y = f(x)$ in the same xy-plane.

(d) Interpret the slope of the graph of $y = f(x)$.

(e) Estimate the cost in 2014. Did your answers involve interpolation or extrapolation?

89. Hours Worked in Europe   The table lists the annual hours worked by the average worker in Europe for selected years.

Year	1970	1980	1990	2000	2010
Hours	2000	1860	1750	1690	1590

Source: Gallup Research.

continued on next page

(a) Let x represent the number of years *after* 1970. Find a formula in slope-intercept form for a linear function f that models the data.

(b) Interpret the slope of the graph of $y = f(x)$.

(c) Estimate the annual hours worked in 2014.

90. **Green Building Material** The table lists U.S. demand for green building materials in billions of dollars for selected years.

Year	2010	2011	2012	2013
Demand	65	70	75	80

Source: Freedonia Group.

(a) Let x represent the number of years *after* 2010. Find a formula in slope-intercept form for a linear function f that models the data.

(b) Interpret the slope of the graph of $y = f(x)$.

(c) Estimate the demand in 2020.

Perspectives and Viewing Rectangles

91. Graph $y = \frac{1}{1024}x + 1$ in [0, 3, 1] by [−2, 2, 1].
   (a) Is the graph a horizontal line?

   (b) Why does the calculator screen appear as it does?

92. Graph $y = 1000x + 1000$ in the standard window.
   (a) Is the graph a vertical line?

   (b) Explain why the calculator screen appears as it does.

93. **Square Viewing Rectangle** Graph the lines $y = 2x$ and $y = -\frac{1}{2}x$ in the standard viewing rectangle.
   (a) Do the lines appear to be perpendicular?

   (b) Graph the lines in the following viewing rectangles.
      i. [−15, 15, 1] by [−10, 10, 1]
      ii. [−10, 10, 1] by [−3, 3, 1]
      iii. [−3, 3, 1] by [−2, 2, 1]
      Do the lines appear to be perpendicular in any of these viewing rectangles?

   (c) Determine the viewing rectangles where perpendicular lines will appear perpendicular. (Answers may vary.)

94. **Square Viewing Rectangle** Continuing with Exercise 93, make a conjecture about which viewing rectangles result in the graph of a circle with radius 5 and center at the origin appearing circular.
   i. [−9, 9, 1] by [−6, 6, 1]
   ii. [−5, 5, 1] by [−10, 10, 1]
   iii. [−5, 5, 1] by [−5, 5, 1]
   iv. [−18, 18, 1] by [−12, 12, 1]
   Test your conjecture by graphing this circle in each viewing rectangle. (*Hint:* Graph $y_1 = \sqrt{25 - x^2}$ and $y_2 = -\sqrt{25 - x^2}$ to create the circle.)

Finding a Rectangle

Exercises 95–98: (Refer to Example 9.) A rectangle is determined by the stated conditions. Find the slope-intercept form of the four lines that outline the rectangle.

95. Vertices (0, 0), (2, 2), and (1, 3)

96. Vertices (1, 1), (5, 1), and (5, 5)

97. Vertices (4, 0), (0, 4), (0, −4), and (−4, 0)

98. Vertices (1, 1) and (2, 3); the point (3.5, 1) lies on a side of the rectangle.

Linear Regression

Exercises 99 and 100: Find the line of least-squares fit for the given data points. What is the correlation coefficient? Plot the data and graph the line.

99. (−2, 2), (1, 0), (3, −2)

100. (−1, −1), (1, 4), (2, 6)

Exercises 101–104: Complete the following.

(a) Conjecture whether the correlation coefficient r for the data will be positive, negative, or zero.

(b) Use a calculator to find the equation of the least-squares regression line and the value of r.

(c) Use the regression line to predict y when $x = 2.4$.

101.

x	−1	0	1	2	3
y	−5.7	−2.6	1.1	3.9	7.3

102.

x	−4	−2	0	2	4
y	1.2	2.8	5.3	6.7	9.1

103.

x	1	3	5	7	10
y	5.8	-2.4	-10.7	-17.8	-29.3

104.

x	-4	-3	-1	3	5
y	37.2	33.7	27.5	16.4	9.8

105. Distant Galaxies In the late 1920s Edwin P. Hubble (1889–1953) determined both the distance to several galaxies and the velocity at which they were receding from Earth. Four galaxies with their distances in light-years and velocities in miles per second are listed in the table.

Galaxy	Distance	Velocity
Virgo	50	990
Ursa Minor	650	9,300
Corona Borealis	950	15,000
Bootes	1700	25,000

Source: A. Sharov and 1. Novikov, Edwin Hubble: The Discoverer of the Big Bang Universe.

(a) Let x be distance and y be velocity. Plot the points in $[-100, 1800, 100]$ by $[-1000, 28000, 1000]$.

(b) Find the least-squares regression line.

(c) If the galaxy Hydra is receding at a speed of 37,000 miles per second, estimate its distance.

106. Airline Travel The table at the top of the next column lists the numbers of airline passengers in millions at some of the largest airports in the United States during 2002 and 2006.

(a) Graph the data by using the 2002 data for x-values and the corresponding 2006 data for y-values. Predict whether the correlation coefficient will be positive or negative.

(b) Use a calculator to find the linear function f based on least-squares regression that models the data. Graph $y = f(x)$ and the data in the same viewing rectangle.

(c) In 2002 Newark International Airport had 29.0 million passengers. Assuming that this airport followed a trend similar to that of the five airports listed in the table, use $f(x)$ to estimate the number of passengers at Newark International in 2006. Compare this result to the actual value of 36.7 million passengers.

Airport	2002	2006
Atlanta (Hartsfield)	76.9	84.4
Chicago (O'Hare)	66.5	77.0
Los Angeles (LAX)	56.2	61.0
Dallas/Fort Worth	52.8	60.2
Denver	35.7	47.3

Source: Airports Association Council International.

107. Passenger Travel The table shows the number of miles (in trillions) traveled by passengers of all types x years after 1970.

Year (1970 ↔ 0)	0	10	20	30	40
Miles (trillions)	2.2	2.8	3.7	4.7	5.5

Source: Department of Transportation.

(a) Make a scatterplot of the data. Predict whether the correlation coefficient will be positive or negative.

(b) Use least-squares regression to find $f(x) = ax + b$ so that f models the data.

(c) Graph f and the data. Interpret the slope.

(d) Predict the number of passenger miles in 2015.

108. High School Enrollment The table lists the number of students (in millions) attending U.S. public school (grades 9–12) x years after 2000.

x (year)	0	3	5	7
y (students)	13.5	14.3	14.8	15.1

Source: National Center for Education Statistics.

(a) Use least-squares regression to find $f(x) = ax + b$ so that f models the data.

(b) Graph f and the data. Interpret the slope.

(c) Estimate enrollment in 2002 and compare the estimate to the actual value of 14.1 million.

Writing about Mathematics

109. Compare the slope-intercept form with the point-slope form. Give examples of each.

110. Explain how you would find the equation of a line passing through two points. Give an example.

2.2 Linear Equations

- Learn about equations and recognize a linear equation
- Solve linear equations symbolically
- Solve linear equations graphically and numerically
- Solve problems involving percentages
- Apply problem-solving strategies

Introduction

In Example 4 of Section 2.1, we modeled iPod sales y in millions during year x with the equation of a line, or *linear function*, given by

$$f(x) = -4(x - 2008) + 55.$$

To predict the year when iPod sales might decrease to 27 million, we could set the formula for $f(x)$ equal to 27 and solve the following *linear equation* for x.

$$27 = -4(x - 2008) + 55 \qquad \text{Linear equation}$$

This section discusses linear equations and their solutions. See Example 5 in this section.

Equations

An **equation** is a statement that two mathematical expressions are equal. Equations always contain an equals sign.

Equations with Zero, One, or Two Variables

$$x + 15 = 9x - 1, \quad x^2 - 2x + 1 = 2x, \quad z + 5 = 0,$$

$$xy + x^2 = y^3 + x, \quad \text{and} \quad 1 + 2 = 3$$

One variable

Two variables

Zero variables

We will concentrate on equations with one variable.

To **solve** an equation means to find all values for the variable that make the equation a true statement. Such values are called **solutions.** The set of all solutions is the **solution set.** For example, the solutions to the equation $x^2 - 1 = 0$ are 1 or -1, written as ± 1. Either value for x **satisfies** the equation. The solution set is $\{-1, 1\}$. Two equations are **equivalent** if they have the same solution set. For example, the equations $x + 2 = 5$ and $x = 3$ are equivalent.

If an equation has no solutions, then its solution set is empty and the equation is called a **contradiction.** The equation $x + 2 = x$ has no solutions and is a contradiction. However, if every (meaningful) value for the variable is a solution, then the equation is an **identity.** The equation $x + x = 2x$ is an identity because every value for x makes the equation true. Any equation that is satisfied by some but not all values of the variable is a **conditional equation.** The equation $x^2 - 1 = 0$ is a conditional equation. Only the values -1 and 1 for x make this equation a true statement.

Like functions, equations can be either *linear* or *nonlinear.* A linear equation is one of the simplest types of equations.

LINEAR EQUATION IN ONE VARIABLE

A **linear equation** in one variable is an equation that can be written in the form

$$ax + b = 0,$$

where a and b are constants with $a \neq 0$.

If an equation is not linear, then we say that it is a **nonlinear equation.** The following gives examples of linear and nonlinear equations.

Example	Explanation
$2x + 5 = 0$	*Linear:* Is written as $ax + b = 0$ with $a = 2$ and $b = 5$
$3x = -7$	*Linear:* Can be written as $3x + 7 = 0$
$5(x - 1) = 4$	*Linear:* Can be written as $5x - 9 = 0$
$x^2 + 2x = 1$	*Nonlinear:* Contains x^2
$\sqrt{x} = 7$	*Nonlinear:* Contains $\sqrt{x}$

Symbolic Solutions

A linear equation can be solved symbolically, and the solution is *always exact.* To solve a linear equation symbolically, we usually apply the *properties of equality* to the given equation and transform it into an equivalent equation that is simpler.

PROPERTIES OF EQUALITY

Addition Property of Equality

If a, b, and c are real numbers, then

$$a = b \quad \text{is equivalent to} \quad a + c = b + c.$$

Multiplication Property of Equality

If a, b, and c are real numbers with $c \neq 0$, then

$$a = b \quad \text{is equivalent to} \quad ac = bc.$$

Loosely speaking, the addition property states that "if equals are added to equals, the results are equal." For example, if $x + 5 = 15$, then we can add -5 to each side of the equation, or equivalently subtract 5 from each side, to obtain the following.

Equivalent equations
$$x + 5 = 15 \qquad \text{Given equation}$$
$$x + 5 - 5 = 15 - 5 \qquad \text{Subtract 5 from each side.}$$
$$x = 10 \qquad \text{Simplify.}$$

Similarly, the multiplication property states that "if equals are multiplied by nonzero equals, the results are equal." For example, if $5x = 20$, then we can multiply each side by $\frac{1}{5}$, or equivalently divide each side by 5, to obtain the following.

Equivalent equations
$$5x = 20 \qquad \text{Given equation}$$
$$\frac{5x}{5} = \frac{20}{5} \qquad \text{Divide each side by 5.}$$
$$x = 4 \qquad \text{Simplify.}$$

These two properties along with the distributive property are applied in the next two examples. We also check our answers.

EXAMPLE 1   Solving a linear equation symbolically

Solve the equation $3(x - 4) = 2x - 1$. Check your answer.

SOLUTION

Getting Started First we apply the distributive property: $a(b - c) = ab - ac$. Thus

$$3(x - 4) = 3 \cdot x - 3 \cdot 4 = 3x - 12. \blacktriangleright$$

Algebra Review
To review the distributive properties, see
Chapter R (page R-15).

Solving the given equation results in the following.

$$3(x - 4) = 2x - 1 \qquad \text{Given equation}$$

$$3x - 12 = 2x - 1 \qquad \text{Distributive property}$$

$$3x - 2x - 12 + 12 = 2x - 2x - 1 + 12 \qquad \text{Subtract 2x and add 12.}$$

$$3x - 2x = 12 - 1 \qquad \text{Simplify.}$$

$$x = 11 \qquad \text{Simplify.}$$

The solution is 11. We can check our answer as follows.

$$3(x - 4) = 2x - 1 \qquad \text{Given equation}$$

$$3(11 - 4) \stackrel{?}{=} 2 \cdot 11 - 1 \qquad \text{Let } x = 11.$$

$$21 = 21 \ \checkmark \qquad \text{The answer checks.}$$

> **Now Try Exercise 23**

EXAMPLE 2   Solving a linear equation symbolically

Solve $3(2x - 5) = 10 - (x + 5)$. Check your answer.

SOLUTION
Getting Started In this problem subtraction must be distributed over the quantity $(x + 5)$.
Thus

$$10 - (x + 5) = 10 - 1(x + 5) = 10 - x - 5. \blacktriangleright$$

Solving the given equation results in the following.

$$3(2x - 5) = 10 - (x + 5) \qquad \text{Given equation}$$

$$6x - 15 = 10 - x - 5 \qquad \text{Distributive property}$$

$$6x - 15 = 5 - x \qquad \text{Simplify.}$$

$$7x - 15 = 5 \qquad \text{Add x to each side.}$$

$$7x = 20 \qquad \text{Add 15 to each side.}$$

$$x = \frac{20}{7} \qquad \text{Divide each side by 7.}$$

The solution is $\frac{20}{7}$. To check this answer, let $x = \frac{20}{7}$ and simplify.

$$3(2x - 5) = 10 - (x + 5) \qquad \text{Given equation}$$

$$3\left(2 \cdot \frac{20}{7} - 5\right) \stackrel{?}{=} 10 - \left(\frac{20}{7} + 5\right) \qquad \text{Let } x = \frac{20}{7}.$$

$$3\left(\frac{5}{7}\right) \stackrel{?}{=} 10 - \frac{55}{7} \qquad \text{Simplify.}$$

$$\frac{15}{7} = \frac{15}{7} \ \checkmark \qquad \text{The answer checks.}$$

> **Now Try Exercise 27**

Fractions and Decimals When fractions or decimals appear in an equation, we sometimes can make our work simpler by multiplying each side of the equation by the least common denominator (LCD) or a common denominator of all fractions in the equation. This method is illustrated in the next two examples.

EXAMPLE 3   Eliminating fractions

Solve each linear equation.

(a) $\dfrac{x}{3} + 1 = \dfrac{2}{3}$ (b) $\dfrac{t-2}{4} - \dfrac{1}{3}t = 5 - \dfrac{1}{12}(3-t)$

SOLUTION

(a) To eliminate fractions, multiply each side (or term in the equation) by the LCD, 3.

$$\dfrac{x}{3} + 1 = \dfrac{2}{3} \qquad \textit{Given equation}$$

$$3 \cdot \dfrac{x}{3} + 3 \cdot 1 = 3 \cdot \dfrac{2}{3} \qquad \textit{Multiply each side (term) by 3.}$$

$$x + 3 = 2 \qquad \textit{Simplify.}$$

$$x + 3 - 3 = 2 - 3 \qquad \textit{Subtract 3 from each side.}$$

$$x = -1 \qquad \textit{Simplify.}$$

The solution is -1.

Algebra Review

To review least common multiples and least common denominators, see Chapter R (page R-30).

(b) To eliminate fractions, multiply each side (or term in the equation) by the LCD, 12.

$$\dfrac{t-2}{4} - \dfrac{1}{3}t = 5 - \dfrac{1}{12}(3-t) \qquad \textit{Given equation}$$

$$\dfrac{12(t-2)}{4} - \dfrac{12}{3}t = 12(5) - \dfrac{12}{12}(3-t) \qquad \textit{Multiply each side (term) by 12.}$$

$$3(t-2) - 4t = 60 - (3-t) \qquad \textit{Simplify.}$$

$$3t - 6 - 4t = 60 - 3 + t \qquad \textit{Distributive property}$$

$$-t - 6 = 57 + t \qquad \textit{Combine like terms on each side.}$$

$$-2t = 63 \qquad \textit{Add } -t \textit{ and 6 to each side.}$$

$$t = -\dfrac{63}{2} \qquad \textit{Divide each side by } -2.$$

The solution is $-\dfrac{63}{2}$.

Now Try Exercises 29 and 33

EXAMPLE 4   Eliminating decimals

Solve each linear equation.

(a) $5.1x - 2 = 3.7$ (b) $0.03(z - 3) - 0.5(2z + 1) = 0.23$

SOLUTION

(a) To eliminate decimals, multiply each side (or term in the equation) by 10.

$$5.1x - 2 = 3.7 \qquad \textit{Given equation}$$

$$10(5.1x) - 10(2) = 10(3.7) \qquad \textit{Multiply each side (term) by 10.}$$

$$51x - 20 = 37 \qquad \textit{Simplify.}$$

$$51x - 20 + 20 = 37 + 20 \qquad \textit{Add 20 to each side.}$$

$$51x = 57 \qquad \textit{Simplify.}$$

$$x = \dfrac{57}{51} \text{ or } \dfrac{19}{17} \qquad \textit{Divide each side by 51; simplify.}$$

The solution is $\dfrac{19}{17}$.

(b) To eliminate decimals, multiply each side (or term in the equation) by 100.

$$0.03(z - 3) - 0.5(2z + 1) = 0.23 \qquad \text{Given equation}$$
$$3(z - 3) - 50(2z + 1) = 23 \qquad \text{Multiply each side (term) by 100.}$$
$$3z - 9 - 100z - 50 = 23 \qquad \text{Distributive property}$$
$$-97z - 59 = 23 \qquad \text{Combine like terms.}$$
$$-97z = 82 \qquad \text{Add 59 to each side.}$$
$$z = -\frac{82}{97} \qquad \text{Divide each side by } -97.$$

The solution is $-\frac{82}{97}$.

Now Try Exercises 35 and 37

An Application   In the next example we solve the equation presented in the introduction to this section.

EXAMPLE 5 Analyzing iPod sales

The linear function defined by $f(x) = -4(x - 2008) + 55$ estimates iPod sales (in millions of units) during fiscal year x. Use $f(x)$ to estimate when iPod sales could reach 27 million.

SOLUTION   We need to find the year x when iPod sales, given by $f(x)$, equal 27 million.

$$-4(x - 2008) + 55 = 27 \qquad \text{Given equation}$$
$$-4(x - 2008) + 55 - 55 = 27 - 55 \qquad \text{Subtract 55 from each side.}$$
$$-4(x - 2008) = -28 \qquad \text{Simplify.}$$
$$\frac{-4(x - 2008)}{-4} = \frac{-28}{-4} \qquad \text{Divide each side by } -4.$$
$$x - 2008 = 7 \qquad \text{Simplify.}$$
$$x = 2015 \qquad \text{Add 2008 to each side.}$$

> Rather than dividing by –4, the distributive property could be used.

This model predicts that iPod sales could decrease to 27 million in 2015.

Now Try Exercise 97

Contradictions, Identities, and Conditional Equations   The next example illustrates how an equation can have no solutions (contradiction), one solution (conditional equation), or infinitely many solutions (identity).

EXAMPLE 6 Identifying contradictions, identities, and conditional equations

Identify each equation as a contradiction, identity, or conditional equation.
(a) $7 + 6x = 2(3x + 1)$ **(b)** $2x - 5 = 3 - (1 + 2x)$
(c) $2(5 - x) - 25 = 3(x - 5) - 5x$

SOLUTION
(a)
$$7 + 6x = 2(3x + 1) \qquad \text{Given equation}$$
$$7 + 6x = 6x + 2 \qquad \text{Distributive property}$$
$$7 = 2 \qquad \text{Subtract 6x from each side.}$$

The statement $7 = 2$ is false and there are *no* solutions. The equation is a contradiction.

(b)

$$2x - 5 = 3 - (1 + 2x) \qquad \textit{Given equation}$$
$$2x - 5 = 3 - 1 - 2x \qquad \textit{Distributive property}$$
$$4x = 7 \qquad \textit{Add 2x and 5 to each side.}$$
$$x = \frac{7}{4} \qquad \textit{Divide each side by 4.}$$

There is one solution: $\frac{7}{4}$. This is a conditional equation.

(c)

$$2(5 - x) - 25 = 3(x - 5) - 5x \qquad \textit{Given equation}$$
$$10 - 2x - 25 = 3x - 15 - 5x \qquad \textit{Distributive property}$$
$$-2x - 15 = -2x - 15 \qquad \textit{Simplify each side.}$$
$$0 = 0 \qquad \textit{Add 2x and 15 to each side.}$$

The statement $0 = 0$ is true and the solution set includes *all real numbers*. The equation is an identity.

> **Now Try Exercises 39, 41, and 43**

Graphical and Numerical Solutions

Graphical Solutions   The equation $f(x) = g(x)$ results whenever the formulas for two functions f and g are set equal to each other. A solution to this equation corresponds to the x-coordinate of a point where the graphs of f and g intersect. We call this graphical technique the **intersection-of-graphs** method and it is used to solve the linear equation $2x + 1 = -x + 4$ in the following box.

See the Concept: Intersection-of-Graphs Method

STEP 1: Set y_1 equal to the left side and y_2 equal to the right side of the given equation.

$$2x + 1 = -x + 4$$

$$y_1 = 2x + 1 \qquad y_2 = -x + 4$$

STEP 2: Graph y_1 and y_2 in the same xy-plane.

The only point of intersection is (1, 3).

$y_1 = 2x + 1$

$(1, 3)$

$y_2 = -x + 4$

STEP 3: Find all points of intersection. The x-coordinates are the solutions to the equation.

$(1, 3)$

The only solution is **1**.

We can check our work from the example above by substituting 1 for x in the given equation.

$$2x + 1 = -x + 4 \qquad \textit{Given equation}$$
$$2(1) + 1 \stackrel{?}{=} -(1) + 4 \qquad \textit{Let x = 1.}$$
$$3 = 3 \checkmark \qquad \textit{It checks.}$$

Notice that the point of intersection is $(1, 3)$, and that when we substitute 1 for x, each side of the equation evaluates to 3.

EXAMPLE 7 Solving an equation graphically and symbolically

Solve $2x - 1 = \frac{1}{2}x + 2$ graphically and symbolically.

SOLUTION

Graphical Solution Graph $y_1 = 2x - 1$ and $y_2 = \frac{1}{2}x + 2$. Their graphs intersect at the point $(2, 3)$, as shown in Figure 2.22, so the solution is 2. Figure 2.23 shows these graphs as created by a graphing calculator.

Intersection-of-Graphs Method

The graphs intersect at $(2, 3)$, so 2 is the solution.

$[-6, 8, 2]$ by $[-6, 8, 2]$

Figure 2.22 **Figure 2.23**

Symbolic Solution

$$2x - 1 = \frac{1}{2}x + 2 \qquad \text{Given equation}$$

$$2x = \frac{1}{2}x + 3 \qquad \text{Add 1 to each side.}$$

$$\frac{3}{2}x = 3 \qquad \text{Subtract } \frac{1}{2}x \text{ from each side.}$$

$$\frac{2}{3} \cdot \frac{3}{2}x = \frac{2}{3} \cdot 3 \qquad \text{Multiply each side by } \frac{2}{3}.$$

$$x = 2 \qquad \text{Multiply fractions.}$$

The solution is 2 and agrees with the graphical solution.

Now Try Exercise 53

EXAMPLE 8 Applying the intersection-of-graphs method

During the 1990s, compact discs were a new technology that replaced cassette tapes. The percentage share of music sales (in dollars) held by compact discs from 1987 to 1998 could be modeled by $f(x) = 5.91x + 13.7$. During the same time period the percentage share of music sales held by cassette tapes could be modeled by $g(x) = -4.71x + 64.7$. In these formulas $x = 0$ corresponds to 1987, $x = 1$ to 1988, and so on. Use the intersection-of-graphs method to estimate the year when the percentage share of CDs equaled the percentage share of cassettes. (*Source:* Recording Industry Association of America.)

SOLUTION We must solve the linear equation $f(x) = g(x)$, or equivalently,

$$5.91x + 13.7 = -4.71x + 64.7.$$

Graph $y_1 = 5.91x + 13.7$ and $y_2 = -4.71x + 64.7$, as in Figure 2.24. In Figure 2.25 their graphs intersect near the point $(4.8, 42.1)$. Since $x = 0$ corresponds to 1987 and $1987 + 4.8 \approx 1992$, it follows that in 1992 sales of CDs and cassette tapes were approximately equal. Each had about 42.1% of the sales in 1992.

Calculator Help

To find the point of intersection in Figure 2.25, see Appendix A (page AP-7).

Determining When Sales Were Equal

[0, 12, 2] by [0, 100, 10]   [0, 12, 2] by [0, 100, 10]

Figure 2.24   **Figure 2.25**

Now Try Exercise 99

Numerical Solutions   Sometimes it is also possible to find a numerical solution to an equation by using a table of values. When the solution is an integer or a convenient fraction, we can usually find it by using the table feature on a graphing calculator. However, when the solution is a fraction with a repeating decimal representation or an irrational number, a numerical method gives only an approximate solution. The formula

$$f(x) = 755.7(x - 1985) + 6121 \qquad \textit{Tuitions and fees after 1985}$$

can be used to model tuition and fees at private colleges and universities during year x. See Exercise 98. To determine when tuition and fees were about \$23,500, we could solve the equation

$$755.7(x - 1985) + 6121 = 23{,}500$$

for x by making a table of values for $f(x)$, as shown in Figure 2.26. By scrolling through the x-values, we can see that tuition and fees at private schools were about \$23,500 in 2008.

NOTE   Regardless of whether we use a symbolic, graphical, or numerical method to solve an equation, we should find the same solution set. However, our answers may differ slightly because of rounding.

A numerical technique is used in the next example, where a sequence of tables are generated to obtain an increasingly accurate answer.

$f(2008) \approx 23{,}500$

X	Y1
2005	21235
2006	21991
2007	22746
	23502
2009	24258
2010	25014
2011	25769
X=2008	

Figure 2.26

Calculator Help

To make a table of values, see Appendix A (page AP-5).

EXAMPLE 9   **Solving an equation numerically**

Solve $\sqrt{3}(2x - \pi) + \frac{1}{3}x = 0$ numerically to the nearest tenth.

SOLUTION   Make a table of $y_1 = \sqrt{3}(2x - \pi) + \frac{1}{3}x$, incrementing x, as shown in Figures 2.27–2.29. The solution to $y_1 = 0$, lies between x-values where y_1 changes from negative to positive. This process shows that the solution is 1.4 (to the nearest tenth).

Increment x by 1

X	Y1
−3	−16.83
−2	−13.04
−1	−9.239
0	−5.441
1	−1.644
2	2.1535
3	5.9509
X=2	

$y_1 < 0$

$y_1 > 0$

$y_1 = 0$ between 1 and 2.

Figure 2.27

Increment x by 0.1

X	Y1
1	−1.644
1.1	−1.264
1.2	−.8845
1.3	−.5047
1.4	−.125
1.5	.25475
1.6	.6345
X=1.5	

$y_1 < 0$

$y_1 > 0$

$y_1 = 0$ between 1.4 and 1.5.

Figure 2.28

Increment x by 0.01

X	Y1
1.4	−.125
1.41	−.087
1.42	−.049
1.43	−.0111
1.44	.02691
1.45	.06488
1.46	.10286
X=1.44	

$y_1 < 0$

$y_1 > 0$

$y_1 = 0$ between 1.43 and 1.44.

Figure 2.29

To the nearest tenth, the solution is 1.4.

Now Try Exercise 71

MAKING CONNECTIONS

Symbolic, Graphical, and Numerical Solutions Linear equations can be solved symbolically, graphically, and numerically. Symbolic solutions to linear equations are *always exact*, whereas graphical and numerical solutions are *sometimes approximate*. The following example illustrates how to solve the equation $2x - 1 = 3$ with each method.

Symbolic Solution	Graphical Solution	Numerical Solution

Symbolic Solution

$$2x - 1 = 3$$
$$2x = 4$$
$$x = 2$$

Check:

$$2(2) - 1 \stackrel{?}{=} 3$$
$$3 = 3 \checkmark$$

It checks.

Graphical Solution

Graphs intersect at (2, 3).

The solution is 2.

Numerical Solution

x	0	1	2	3
$2x - 1$	-1	1	3	5

Because $2x - 1$ equals **3** when $x = $ **2**, the solution to $2x - 1 = 3$ is **2**.

Percentages Applications involving percentages often result in linear equations because percentages can be computed by linear functions. A function for taking P percent of x is given by $f(x) = \frac{P}{100}x$, where $\frac{P}{100}$ is the decimal form for P percent. For example, to calculate 35% of x, let $f(x) = 0.35x$. Then 35% of $150 is $f(150) = 0.35(150) = 52.5$, or $52.50.

EXAMPLE 10 Solving an application involving percentages

A survey found that 76% of bicycle riders do not wear helmets. (**Source:** Opinion Research Corporation for Glaxo Wellcome, Inc.)
(a) Find a formula $f(x)$ for a function that computes the number of people who do not wear helmets among x bicycle riders.
(b) There are approximately 38.7 million riders of all ages who do not wear helmets. Find the total number of bicycle riders.

SOLUTION
(a) A function f that computes 76% of x is given by $f(x) = 0.76x$.
(b) We must find the x-value for which $f(x) = 38.7$ million, or solve the equation $0.76x = 38.7$. Solving gives $x = \frac{38.7}{0.76} \approx 50.9$ million bike riders.

Now Try Exercise 105

Solving for a Variable

The circumference C of a circle is given by $C = 2\pi r$, where r is the radius. This equation is *solved* for C. That is, given r, we can easily calculate C. For example, if $r = 4$, then $C = 2\pi(4)$, or $C = 8\pi$. However, if we are given C, then it is more work to calculate r. Solving the equation for r makes it simpler to calculate r.

$$C = 2\pi r \qquad \text{Given equation}$$

$$\frac{C}{2\pi} = r \qquad \text{Divide each side by } 2\pi.$$

The equation $r = \frac{C}{2\pi}$ is solved for r.

EXAMPLE 11   Solving for a variable

The area of a trapezoid with bases a and b and height h is given by $A = \frac{1}{2}h(a + b)$. Solve this equation for b.

SOLUTION

Getting Started If we multiply each side by 2 and divide each side by h, the right side of the equation becomes $a + b$. Subtracting a from each side isolates b. ►

$$A = \frac{1}{2}h(a + b) \qquad \textit{Given equation}$$

$$2A = h(a + b) \qquad \textit{Multiply each side by 2.}$$

$$\frac{2A}{h} = a + b \qquad \textit{Divide each side by h.}$$

$$\frac{2A}{h} - a = b \qquad \textit{Subtract a from each side.}$$

The equation $b = \frac{2A}{h} - a$ is solved for b.

Now Try Exercise 85

Problem-Solving Strategies

To become more proficient at solving problems, we need to establish a procedure to guide our thinking. The following steps may be helpful in solving application problems.

SOLVING APPLICATION PROBLEMS

STEP 1: Read the problem and make sure you understand it. Assign a variable to what you are being asked to find. If necessary, write other quantities in terms of this variable.

STEP 2: Write an equation that relates the quantities described in the problem. You may need to sketch a diagram and refer to known formulas.

STEP 3: Solve the equation and determine the solution.

STEP 4: Look back and check your solution. Does it seem reasonable?

These steps are applied in the next four examples.

EXAMPLE 12   Working together

A large pump can empty a tank of gasoline in 5 hours, and a smaller pump can empty the same tank in 9 hours. If both pumps are used to empty the tank, how long will it take?

SOLUTION

STEP 1: We are asked to find the time it takes for *both* pumps to empty the tank. Let this time be t.

$$t: \text{Time to empty the tank}$$

STEP 2: In 1 hour the large pump will empty $\frac{1}{5}$ of the tank and the smaller pump will empty $\frac{1}{9}$ of the tank. The fraction of the tank that they will empty together in 1 hour is given by $\frac{1}{5} + \frac{1}{9}$. In 2 hours the large pump will empty $\frac{2}{5}$ of the tank and the smaller pump will empty $\frac{2}{9}$ of the tank. The fraction of the tank that they will empty together in 2 hours is $\frac{2}{5} + \frac{2}{9}$. Similarly, in t hours the fraction of the tank that the two pumps can empty is $\frac{t}{5} + \frac{t}{9}$. Since the tank is empty when this fraction reaches 1, we must solve the following equation.

$$\frac{t}{5} + \frac{t}{9} = 1$$

STEP 3: Multiply by the LCD, 45, to eliminate fractions.

$$\frac{45t}{5} + \frac{45t}{9} = 45 \qquad \text{Multiply by LCD.}$$

$$9t + 5t = 45 \qquad \text{Simplify.}$$

$$14t = 45 \qquad \text{Add like terms.}$$

$$t = \frac{45}{14} \approx 3.21 \qquad \text{Divide by 14 and approximate.}$$

Working together, the two pumps can empty the tank in about 3.21 hours.

STEP 4: This sounds reasonable. Working together the two pumps should be able to empty the tank faster than the large pump working alone, but not twice as fast. Note that $\frac{3.21}{5} + \frac{3.21}{9} \approx 1$.

Now Try Exercise 107

EXAMPLE 13 Solving an application involving motion

In 1 hour an athlete traveled 10.1 miles by running first at 8 miles per hour and then at 11 miles per hour. How long did the athlete run at each speed?

SOLUTION

STEP 1: We are asked to find the time spent running at each speed. If we let x represent the time in hours spent running at 8 miles per hour, then $1 - x$ represents the time spent running at 11 miles per hour because the total running time was 1 hour.

x: Time spent running at 8 miles per hour

$1 - x$: Time spent running at 11 miles per hour

STEP 2: Distance d equals rate r times time t, that is, $d = rt$. In this example we have two rates (or speeds) and two times. The total distance must sum to 10.1 miles.

$$d = r_1 t_1 + r_2 t_2 \qquad \text{General equation}$$

$$10.1 = 8x + 11(1 - x) \qquad \text{Substitute.}$$

STEP 3: We can solve this equation symbolically.

$$10.1 = 8x + 11 - 11x \qquad \text{Distributive property}$$

$$10.1 = 11 - 3x \qquad \text{Combine like terms.}$$

$$3x = 0.9 \qquad \text{Add 3x; subtract 10.1.}$$

$$x = 0.3 \qquad \text{Divide by 3.}$$

The athlete runs 0.3 hour (18 minutes) at 8 miles per hour and 0.7 hour (42 minutes) at 11 miles per hour.

STEP 4: We can check this solution as follows.

$$8(0.3) + 11(0.7) = 10.1 \checkmark \qquad \text{It checks.}$$

This sounds reasonable. The runner's average speed was 10.1 miles per hour, so the runner must have run longer at 11 miles per hour than at 8 miles per hour.

Now Try Exercise 109

Geometry Review
To review similar triangles, see Chapter R
(page R-5).

Similar triangles are often used in applications involving geometry and are used to solve the next application.

EXAMPLE 14   Solving an application involving similar triangles

A person 6 feet tall stands 17 feet from the base of a streetlight, as illustrated in Figure 2.30. If the person's shadow is 8 feet, estimate the height of the streetlight.

SOLUTION

STEP 1: We are asked to find the height of the streetlight in Figure 2.30. Let x represent this height.

$$x: \text{Height of the streetlight}$$

STEP 2: In Figure 2.31, triangle ACD is similar to triangle BCE. Thus ratios of corresponding sides are equal.

$$\frac{AD}{BE} = \frac{DC}{EC} \qquad \text{Similar triangles}$$

$$\frac{x}{6} = \frac{17 + 8}{8}$$

STEP 3: We can solve this equation symbolically.

$$\frac{x}{6} = \frac{25}{8} \qquad \text{Simplify.}$$

$$x = \frac{6 \cdot 25}{8} \qquad \text{Multiply by 6.}$$

$$x = 18.75 \qquad \text{Simplify.}$$

The height of the streetlight is 18.75 feet.

STEP 4: One way to check this answer is to form a different proportion. Note that x is to $17 + 8$ in triangle ADC as 6 is to 8 in triangle BEC. If $x = 18.75$, then $\frac{18.75}{25} = \frac{6}{8}$, which is true, and our answer checks.

Now Try Exercise 113

Figure 2.30

Figure 2.31

EXAMPLE 15   Mixing acid in chemistry

Pure water is being added to 153 milliliters of a 30% solution of hydrochloric acid. How much water should be added to dilute the solution to a 13% mixture?

SOLUTION

STEP 1: We are asked to find the amount of water that should be added to 153 milliliters of 30% acid to make a 13% solution. Let this amount of water be equal to x. See Figure 2.32.

$$x: \text{Amount of pure water to be added}$$

$$x + 153: \text{Final volume of 13\% solution}$$

STEP 2: Since only water is added, the total amount of acid in the solution after the water is added must equal the amount of acid before the water is added. The volume of pure acid after the water is added equals 13% of $x + 153$ milliliters, and the volume of pure acid before the water is added equals 30% of 153 milliliters. We must solve the following equation.

$$0.13(x + 153) = 0.30(153) \qquad \begin{array}{l}\text{Pure acid after equals} \\ \text{pure acid before.}\end{array}$$

Figure 2.32

STEP 3: Begin by dividing each side by 0.13.

$$0.13(x + 153) = 0.30(153) \qquad \text{\textit{Equation to solve}}$$

$$x + 153 = \frac{0.30(153)}{0.13} \qquad \text{\textit{Divide by 0.13.}}$$

$$x = \frac{0.30(153)}{0.13} - 153 \qquad \text{\textit{Subtract 153.}}$$

$$x \approx 200.08 \qquad \text{\textit{Approximate.}}$$

We should add about 200 milliliters of pure water.

STEP 4: Initially the solution contains $0.30(153) = 45.9$ milliliters of pure acid. If we add 200 milliliters of water to the 153 milliliters, the final solution is 353 milliliters, which includes 45.9 milliliters of pure acid. Its concentration is $\frac{45.9}{353} \approx 0.13$, or about 13%.

> **Now Try Exercise 117**

2.2 Putting It All Together

A general four-step procedure for solving applications is given in this section. The following table summarizes some of the important concepts.

CONCEPT	EXPLANATION	EXAMPLES
Linear equation	A linear equation can be written as $ax + b = 0$, $a \neq 0$.	$4x + 5 = 0$ $3x - 1 = x + 2$
Addition property	$a = b$ is equivalent to $a + c = b + c$.	$x - 7 = 25$ $x - 7 + 7 = 25 + 7$ $x = 32$
Multiplication property	$a = b$ is equivalent to $ac = bc$, $c \neq 0$.	$\frac{1}{2}x = 4$ $2 \cdot \frac{1}{2}x = 4 \cdot 2$ $x = 8$
Distributive property	$a(b + c) = ab + ac$ $a(b - c) = ab - ac$	$2(5 + x) = 10 + 2x$ $-(2 - x) = -1(2 - x) = -2 + x$
Identity	An equation that is true for all (meaningful) values of the variable	$3(x - 2) = 3x - 6$ $2x + 3x = (2 + 3)x = 5x$
Contradiction	An equation that has no solutions	$x + 5 = x$ $2x - 2x = 5$
Conditional equation	An equation that is satisfied by some, but not all, of the values of the variable	$2x - 1 = 5$ *Given equation* $2x = 6$ *Add 1.* $x = 3$ *Divide by 2.*
Percentages	P percent of x equals $\frac{P}{100}x$, where $\frac{P}{100}$ is the decimal form for P percent.	35% of x is calculated by $f(x) = \frac{35}{100}x$, or $f(x) = 0.35x$.

The following example illustrates three ways to solve $5x - 1 = 3$.

Symbolic Solution

$$5x - 1 = 3$$
$$5x = 4$$
$$x = \frac{4}{5}$$

Check:
$$5\left(\tfrac{4}{5}\right) - 1 \overset{?}{=} 3$$
$$4 - 1 \overset{?}{=} 3$$
$$3 \overset{?}{=} 3 \checkmark$$

It checks.

Graphical Solution

$[-9, 9, 1]$ by $[-6, 6, 1]$

Graphs intersect at $(0.8, 3)$.

The solution is 0.8.

Numerical Solution

In the table, $y_1 = 3$ when $x = 0.8$.

2.2 **Exercises**

Concepts about Linear Equations

1. How many solutions are there to $ax + b = 0$ with $a \neq 0$?

2. How many times does the graph of $y = ax + b$ with $a \neq 0$ intersect the x-axis?

3. Apply the distributive property to $4 - (5 - 4x)$.

4. What property is used to solve $15x = 5$?

5. If $f(x) = ax + b$ with $a \neq 0$, how are the zero of f and the x-intercept of the graph of f related?

6. Distinguish between a contradiction and an identity.

Identifying Linear and Nonlinear Equations

Exercises 7–12: Determine whether the equation is linear or nonlinear by trying to write it in the form $ax + b = 0$.

7. $3x - 1.5 = 7$

8. $100 - 23x = 20x$

9. $2\sqrt{x} + 2 = 1$

10. $4x^3 - 7 = 0$

11. $7x - 5 = 3(x - 8)$

12. $2(x - 3) = 4 - 5x$

Solving Linear Equations Symbolically

Exercises 13–38: Solve the equation and check your answer.

13. $2x - 8 = 0$

14. $4x - 8 = 0$

15. $-5x + 3 = 23$

16. $-9x - 3 = 24$

17. $4(z - 8) = z$

18. $-3(2z - 1) = 2z$

19. $-5(3 - 4t) = 65$

20. $6(5 - 3t) = 66$

21. $k + 8 = 5k - 4$

22. $2k - 3 = k + 3$

23. $2(1 - 3x) + 1 = 3x$

24. $5(x - 2) = -2(1 - x)$

25. $-5(3 - 2x) - (1 - x) = 4(x - 3)$

26. $-3(5 - x) - (x - 2) = 7x - 2$

27. $-4(5x - 1) = 8 - (x + 2)$

28. $6(3 - 2x) = 1 - (2x - 1)$

29. $\frac{2}{7}n + 2 = \frac{4}{7}$

30. $\frac{6}{11} - \frac{2}{33}n = \frac{5}{11}n$

31. $\frac{1}{2}(d - 3) - \frac{2}{3}(2d - 5) = \frac{5}{12}$

32. $\frac{7}{3}(2d - 1) - \frac{2}{5}(4 - 3d) = \frac{1}{5}d$

33. $\frac{x - 5}{3} + \frac{3 - 2x}{2} = \frac{5}{4} - 2(1 - x)$

34. $\frac{3x - 1}{5} - 2 = \frac{2 - x}{3}$

35. $0.1z - 0.05 = -0.07z$

36. $1.1z - 2.5 = 0.3(z - 2)$

37. $0.15t + 0.85(100 - t) = 0.45(100)$

38. $0.35t + 0.65(10 - t) = 0.55(10)$

Exercises 39–48: Complete the following.

(a) Solve the equation symbolically.

(b) Classify the equation as a contradiction, an identity, or a conditional equation.

39. $5x - 1 = 5x + 4$

40. $7 - 9z = 2(3 - 4z) - z$

41. $3(x - 1) = 5$ **42.** $22 = -2(2x + 1.4)$

43. $0.5(x - 2) + 5 = 0.5x + 4$

44. $\frac{1}{2}x - 2(x - 1) = -\frac{3}{2}x + 2$

45. $\frac{t + 1}{2} = \frac{3t - 2}{6}$ **46.** $\frac{2x + 1}{3} = \frac{2x - 1}{3}$

47. $\frac{1 - 2x}{4} = \frac{3x - 1.5}{-6}$

48. $0.5(3x - 1) + 0.5x = 2x - 0.5$

Solving Linear Equations Graphically

Exercises 49 and 50: A linear equation is solved by using the intersection-of-graphs method. Find the solution by interpreting the graph. Assume that the solution is an integer.

49.   **50.**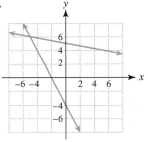

Exercises 51 and 52: Use the graph of $y = f(x)$ to solve each equation.

(a) $f(x) = -1$ (b) $f(x) = 0$ (c) $f(x) = 2$

51.   **52.**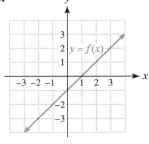

Exercises 53–58: Use the intersection-of-graphs method to solve the equation. Then solve symbolically.

53. $x + 4 = 1 - 2x$ **54.** $2x = 3x - 1$

55. $-x + 4 = 3x$ **56.** $1 - 2x = x + 4$

57. $2(x - 1) - 2 = x$ **58.** $-(x + 1) - 2 = 2x$

Exercises 59–66: Solve the linear equation with the intersection-of-graphs method. Approximate the solution to the nearest thousandth whenever appropriate.

59. $5x - 1.5 = 5$ **60.** $8 - 2x = 1.6$

61. $3x - 1.7 = 1 - x$ **62.** $\sqrt{2}x = 4x - 6$

63. $3.1(x - 5) = \frac{1}{5}x - 5$ **64.** $65 = 8(x - 6) - 5.5$

65. $\frac{6 - x}{7} = \frac{2x - 3}{3}$

66. $\pi(x - \sqrt{2}) = 1.07x - 6.1$

Solving Linear Equations Numerically

Exercises 67–74: Use tables to solve the equation numerically to the nearest tenth.

67. $2x - 7 = -1$ **68.** $1 - 6x = 7$

69. $2x - 7.2 = 10$ **70.** $5.8x - 8.7 = 0$

71. $\sqrt{2}(4x - 1) + \pi x = 0$

72. $\pi(0.3x - 2) + \sqrt{2}x = 0$

73. $0.5 - 0.1(\sqrt{2} - 3x) = 0$

74. $\sqrt{5} - \pi(\pi + 0.3x) = 0$

Solving Linear Equations by More Than One Method

Exercises 75–82: Solve the equation (to the nearest tenth)

(a) symbolically,

(b) graphically, and

(c) numerically.

75. $5 - (x + 1) = 3$ **76.** $7 - (3 - 2x) = 1$

77. $x - 3 = 2x + 1$ **78.** $3(x - 1) = 2x - 1$

79. $\sqrt{3}(2 - \pi x) + x = 0$

80. $3(\pi - x) + \sqrt{2} = 0$

81. $6x - 8 = -7x + 18$

82. $5 - 8x = 3(x - 7) + 37$

Solving for a Variable

Exercises 83–90: Solve the equation for the specified variable.

83. $A = LW$ for W

84. $E = IR + 2$ for R

85. $P = 2L + 2W$ for L

86. $V = 2\pi rh + \pi r^2$ for h

87. $3x + 2y = 8$ for y

88. $5x - 4y = 20$ for y

89. $y = 3(x - 2) + x$ for x

90. $y = 4 - (8 - 2x)$ for x

Exercises 91–96: The equation of a line is written in standard form.

(a) Solve the equation for y.
(b) Write a formula f(x) for a function whose graph is the given line.

91. $2x + y = 8$

92. $3x - y = 5$

93. $2x - 4y = -1$

94. $7x + 3y = -4$

95. $-9x + 8y = 9$

96. $-2x - 6y = 3$

Applications

97. **Income** The per capita (per person) income from 1980 to 2010 can be modeled by

$$f(x) = 1000(x - 1980) + 10,000,$$

where x is the year. Determine the year when the per capita income was $19,000. (**Source:** Bureau of the Census.)

98. **Tuition and Fees** Tuition and fees during year x at private colleges can be modeled by

$$f(x) = 755.7(x - 1985) + 6121.$$

Use $f(x)$ to determine when tuition and fees might reach $28,000.

99. **Vinyl and CD Sales** During the 1980s, sales of compact discs surpassed vinyl record sales. From 1985 to 1990, sales of compact discs in millions can be modeled by the formula $f(x) = 51.6(x - 1985) + 9.1$, whereas sales of vinyl LP records in millions can be modeled by $g(x) = -31.9(x - 1985) + 167.7$. Approximate the year x when sales of LP records and compact discs were equal by using the intersection-of-graphs method. (**Source:** Recording Industry Association of America.)

100. **Median Age** The median age A in the United States during year x, where $2000 \le x \le 2050$, is projected to be

$$A(x) = 0.07(x - 2000) + 35.3.$$

Use $A(x)$ to estimate when the median age may reach 37 years. (**Source:** Bureau of the Census.)

101. **Legalize of Not?** The attitudes toward legalization of marijuana changed between 1995 and 2012. The formula $A(x) = -1.6x + 3265$ gives the percentage of people in year x who were against legalization, and the formula $F(x) = 1.5x - 2968$ gives the percentage of people in year x who were in favor of legalization. (**Source:** Gallup Poll.)

(a) Interpret the slope of the graphs of A and F.

(b) Estimate the year when the percentages for and against were equal.

102. **Population Density** In 2000 the population density of the United States was 80 people per square mile, and in 2011 it was 88 people per square mile. Use a linear function to estimate when the U.S. population density will reach 91 people per square mile.

103. **Sale Price** A store is discounting all regularly priced merchandise by 25%. Find a function f that computes the sale price of an item having a regular price of x. If an item normally costs $56.24, what is its sale price?

104. **Sale Price** Continuing Exercise 103, use f to find the regular price of an item that costs $19.62 on sale.

105. **Skin Cancer** Approximately 4.8% of all cancer cases diagnosed in 2011 were skin cancer. (**Source:** American Cancer Society.)
(a) If x cases of cancer were diagnosed, how many of these were skin cancer?

(b) There were 76,000 cases of skin cancer diagnosed in 2011. Find the total number of cancer cases in 2011.

106. **Grades** In order to receive an A in a college course it is necessary to obtain an average of 90% correct on three 1-hour exams of 100 points each and on one final exam of 200 points. If a student scores 82, 88, and 91 on the 1-hour exams, what is the minimum score that the person can receive on the final exam and still earn an A?

107. **Working Together** Suppose that a lawn can be raked by one gardener in 3 hours and by a second gardener in 5 hours.
(a) Mentally estimate how long it will take the two gardeners to rake the lawn working together.

(b) Solve part (a) symbolically.

108. **Pumping Water** Suppose that a large pump can empty a swimming pool in 50 hours and a small pump can empty the pool in 80 hours. How long will it take to empty the pool if both pumps are used?

109. **Motion** A car went 372 miles in 6 hours, traveling part of the time at 55 miles per hour and part of the time at 70 miles per hour. How long did the car travel at each speed?

110. **Mixing Candy** Two types of candy sell for $2.50 per pound and $4.00 per pound. A store clerk is trying to make a 5-pound mixture worth $17.60. How much of each type of candy should be included in the mixture?

111. **Running** At 2:00 P.M. a runner heads north on a highway, jogging at 10 miles per hour. At 2:30 P.M. a driver heads north on the same highway to pick up the runner. If the car travels at 55 miles per hour, how long will it take the driver to catch the runner?

112. **Investments** A total of $5000 was invested in two accounts. One pays 5% annual interest, and the second pays 7% annual interest. If the first-year interest is $325, how much was invested in each account?

113. **Height of a Tree** In the accompanying figure, a person 5 feet tall casts a shadow 4 feet long. A nearby tree casts a shadow 33 feet long. Find the height of the tree by solving a linear equation.

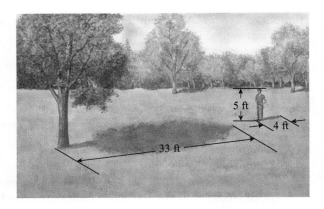

114. **Shadow Length** A person 66 inches tall is standing 15 feet from a streetlight. If the person casts a shadow 84 inches long, how tall is the streetlight?

115. **Conical Water Tank** A water tank in the shape of an inverted cone has a height of 11 feet and a radius of 3.5 feet, as illustrated in the figure. If the volume of the cone is $V = \frac{1}{3}\pi r^2 h$, find the volume of the water in the tank when the water is 7 feet deep. (*Hint:* Consider using similar triangles.)

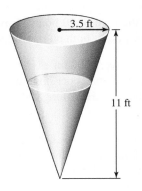

116. **Dimension of a Cone** (Refer to Exercise 115.) A conical water tank holds 100 cubic feet of water and has a diameter of 6 feet. Estimate its height to the nearest tenth of a foot.

117. **Chemistry** Determine how much pure water should be mixed with 5 liters of a 40% solution of sulfuric acid to make a 15% solution of sulfuric acid.

118. **Mixing Antifreeze** A radiator holds 5 gallons of fluid. If it is full with a 15% solution, how much fluid should be drained and replaced with a 65% antifreeze mixture to result in a 40% antifreeze mixture?

119. **Window Dimensions** A rectangular window has a length that is 18 inches more than its width. If its perimeter is 180 inches, find its dimensions.

120. **Sales of CRT and LCD Screens** In 2002, 75 million CRT (cathode ray tube) monitors were sold and 29 million flat LCD (liquid crystal display) monitors were sold. In 2006 the numbers were 45 million for CRT monitors and 88 million for LCD monitors. (*Source:* International Data Corporation.)
    (a) Find a linear function C that models these data for CRT monitors and another linear function L that models these data for LCD monitors. Let x be the year.
    (b) Interpret the slopes of the graphs of C and of L.
    (c) Determine graphically the year when sales of these two types of monitors were equal.
    (d) Solve part (c) symbolically.
    (e) Solve part (c) numerically.

121. **Online Shopping** In 2011 online sales were $192 billion, and in 2014 they are predicted to be $249 billion. (*Source:* Forrestor Forecast.)
    (a) Find a linear function S that models these data. Write $S(x)$ in slope-intercept form.
    (b) Interpret the slope of the graph of S.
    (c) Determine when online sales were $230 billion.

122. **Geometry** A 174-foot-long fence is being placed around the perimeter of a rectangular swimming pool that has a 3-foot-wide sidewalk around it. The actual swimming pool without the sidewalk is twice as long as it is wide. Find the dimensions of the pool without the sidewalk.

123. **Temperature Scales** The Celsius and Fahrenheit scales are related by the equation $C = \frac{5}{9}(F - 32)$. These scales have the same temperature reading at a unique value where $F = C$. Find this temperature.

124. Business A company manufactures compact discs with recorded music. The master disc costs $2000 to produce and copies cost $0.45 each. If a company spent $2990 producing compact discs, how many copies did the company manufacture?

125. Two-Cycle Engines Two-cycle engines, used in snowmobiles, chain saws, and outboard motors, require a mixture of gasoline and oil. For certain engines the amount of oil in pints that should be added to x gallons of gasoline is computed by $f(x) = 0.16x$. (*Source:* Johnson Outboard Motor Company.)

(a) Why is it reasonable to expect f to be linear?

(b) Evaluate $f(3)$ and interpret the answer.

(c) How much gasoline should be mixed with 2 pints of oil?

126. Perimeter Find the length of the longest side of the rectangle if its perimeter is 25 feet.

2x

5x − 1

Modeling Data with Linear Functions

Exercises 127 and 128: The following data can be modeled by a linear function. Estimate the value of x when y = 2.99.

127.

x	2	4	6	8
y	0.51	1.23	1.95	2.67

128.

x	1	2	3	4
y	−1.66	2.06	5.78	9.50

Writing about Mathematics

129. Describe a basic graphical method used to solve a linear equation. Give an example.

130. Describe verbally how to solve $ax + b = 0$. What assumptions have you made about the value of a?

Extended and Discovery Exercises

1. Geometry Suppose that two rectangles are similar and the sides of the first rectangle are twice as long as the corresponding sides of the second rectangle.

(a) Is the perimeter of the first rectangle twice the perimeter of the second rectangle? Explain.

(b) Is the area of the first rectangle twice the area of the second rectangle? Explain.

2. Geometry Repeat the previous exercise for an equilateral triangle. Try to make a generalization. (*Hint:* The area of an equilateral triangle is $A = \frac{\sqrt{3}}{4}x^2$, where x is the length of a side.) What will happen to the circumference of a circle if the radius is doubled? What will happen to its area?

3. Indoor Air Pollution Formaldehyde is an indoor air pollutant formerly found in plywood, foam insulation, and carpeting. When concentrations in the air reach 33 micrograms per cubic foot ($\mu g/ft^3$), eye irritation can occur. One square foot of new plywood could emit 140 μg per hour. (*Source:* A. Hines, *Indoor Air Quality & Control.*)

(a) A room has 100 square feet of new plywood flooring. Find a linear function f that computes the amount of formaldehyde in micrograms that could be emitted in x hours.

(b) The room contains 800 cubic feet of air and has no ventilation. Determine how long it would take for concentrations to reach 33 $\mu g/ft^3$.

4. Temperature and Volume The table shows the relationship between the temperature of a sample of helium and its volume.

Temperature (°C)	0	25	50	75	100
Volume (in³)	30	32.7	35.4	38.1	40.8

(a) Make a scatterplot of the data.

(b) Write a formula for a function f that receives the temperature x as input and outputs the volume y of the helium.

(c) Find the volume when the temperature is 65°C.

(d) Find the temperature if the volume is 25 cubic inches. Did your answer involve interpolation or extrapolation? Do you believe that your answer is accurate?

CHECKING BASIC CONCEPTS FOR SECTIONS 2.1 AND 2.2

1. Find an equation of the line passing through the points $(-3, 4)$ and $(5, -2)$. Give equations of lines that are parallel and perpendicular to this line.

2. Find equations of horizontal and vertical lines that pass through the point $(-4, 7)$.

3. Write the slope-intercept form of the line.

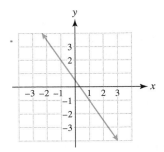

4. Find the x- and y-intercepts of the graph of the equation $-3x + 2y = -18$.

5. Solve $5x + 2 = 2x - 3$ and check your answer.

6. Solve each equation.
   (a) $\frac{3x}{4} + 2 = \frac{2x}{3}$

   (b) $-4.1x + 5.45 = 1.05(5 - 2x)$

7. Solve the linear equation $4(x - 2) = 2(5 - x) - 3$ by using each method. Compare your results.
   (a) Graphical

   (b) Numerical

   (c) Symbolic

2.3   Linear Inequalities

- **Understand basic terminology related to inequalities**
- **Solve linear inequalities symbolically**
- **Solve linear inequalities graphically and numerically**
- **Solve compound inequalities**

Introduction

Twitter cofounder Jack Dorsey has started another company called Square. Square is a payment startup that allows businesses to swipe credit cards on their iPhones and Android devices. During a 12-month period from March 2011 to March 2012, Square's *daily* payment volume grew from $1 million to $11 million. In Example 3 we make estimations about this growth by using linear inqualities.   (***Source:*** Business Insider.)

Inequalities

Inequalities result whenever the equals sign in an equation is replaced with any one of the symbols $<$, $\leq$, $>$, or $\geq$.

Inequalities with Zero, One, and Two Variables

$$x + 15 < 9x - 1, \qquad x^2 - 2x + 1 \geq 2x, \qquad z + 5 > 0,$$
$$xy + x^2 \leq y^3 + x, \qquad \text{and} \qquad 2 + 3 > 1$$

One variable

Two variables

No variables

We will concentrate on inequalities with one variable.

To **solve** an inequality means to find all values for the variable that make the inequality a true statement. Such values are **solutions**, and the set of all solutions is the **solution set** to the inequality. Two inequalities are **equivalent** if they have the same solution set. It is common for an inequality to have infinitely many solutions. For instance, the inequality $x - 1 > 0$ has infinitely many solutions because any real number x satisfying $x > 1$ is a solution. The solution set is $\{x \mid x > 1\}$.

Like functions and equations, inequalities in one variable can be classified as *linear* or *nonlinear*.

> **LINEAR INEQUALITY IN ONE VARIABLE**
>
> A **linear inequality** in one variable is an inequality that can be written in the form
>
> $$ax + b > 0,$$
>
> where $a \neq 0$. (The symbol $>$ may be replaced by $\geq$, $<$, or $\leq$.)

Linear Inequalities

$$3x - 4 < 0, \qquad 7x + 5 \geq x, \qquad x + 6 > 23, \qquad \text{and} \qquad 7x + 2 \leq -3x + 6.$$

Using techniques from algebra, we can transform these inequalities into one of the forms $ax + b > 0$, $ax + b \geq 0$, $ax + b < 0$, or $ax + b \leq 0$. For example, by subtracting x from each side of $7x + 5 \geq x$, we obtain the equivalent inequality $6x + 5 \geq 0$. If an inequality is not a linear inequality, it is called a **nonlinear inequality**.

> **PROPERTIES OF INEQUALITIES**
>
> Let a, b, and c be real numbers.
> 1. $a < b$ and $a + c < b + c$ are equivalent.
>   (The same number may be added to or subtracted from each side of an inequality.)
> 2. If $c > 0$, then $a < b$ and $ac < bc$ are equivalent.
>   (Each side of an inequality may be multiplied or divided by the same *positive* number.)
> 3. If $c < 0$, then $a < b$ and $ac > bc$ are equivalent.
>   (Each side of an inequality may be multiplied or divided by the same *negative* number provided the inequality symbol is *reversed*.)
>
> Replacing $<$ with $\leq$ and $>$ with $\geq$ results in similar properties.

The following examples illustrate each property.

Property 1: To solve $x - 5 < 6$, add 5 to each side to obtain $x < 11$.

Property 2: To solve $5x < 10$, divide each side by 5 to obtain $x < 2$.

Property 3: To solve $-5x < 10$, divide each side by -5 to obtain $x > -2$. (Whenever you multiply or divide an inequality by a *negative* number, *reverse* the inequality symbol.)

> **MAKING CONNECTIONS**
>
> **Linear Functions, Equations, and Inequalities**   These concepts are closely related.
>
> $$f(x) = ax + b \qquad \text{Linear function } (a = m)$$
> $$ax + b = 0, a \neq 0 \qquad \text{Linear equation}$$
> $$ax + b > 0, a \neq 0 \qquad \text{Linear inequality}$$

Review of Interval Notation   In Section 1.4 interval notation was introduced as an efficient way to express intervals on the real number line. For example, the interval $3 \leq x \leq 5$ is written as $[3, 5]$, whereas the interval $3 < x < 5$ is written as $(3, 5)$. A bracket, [or], is used when an endpoint is included, and a parenthesis, (or), is used when an endpoint is not included. The interval $x \geq 2$ is written as $[2, \infty)$, where ∞ denotes infinity, and the interval $x < 2$ is written as $(-\infty, 2)$

Symbolic Solutions   In the next example we solve linear inequalities symbolically and express the solution set in both set-builder and interval notation.

EXAMPLE 1   Solving linear inequalities symbolically

Solve each inequality. Write the solution set in set-builder and interval notation.

(a) $2x - 3 < \dfrac{x + 2}{-3}$

(b) $-3(4z - 4) \geq 4 - (z - 1)$

SOLUTION

(a) Use Property 3 by multiplying each side by -3 to clear fractions.

$2x - 3 < \dfrac{x + 2}{-3}$	*Given inequality*
$-3(2x - 3) > -3\left(\dfrac{x + 2}{-3}\right)$	*Property 3: Multiply by −3 and reverse the inequality symbol.*
$-6x + 9 > x + 2$	*Distributive property; simplify.*
$9 < 7x + 2$	*Property 1: Add 6x.*
$7 > 7x$	*Property 1: Add −2 (or subtract 2).*
$1 > x$	*Property 2: Divide by 7.*

Reverse < to > when multiplying by a negative.

The solution set is $\{x \mid x < 1\}$, and in interval notation it is written as $(-\infty, 1)$.

(b) Begin by applying the distributive property.

$-3(4z - 4) \geq 4 - (z - 1)$	*Given inequality*
$-12z + 12 \geq 4 - z + 1$	*Distributive property*
$-12z + 12 \geq -z + 5$	*Simplify.*
$-12z + z \geq 5 - 12$	*Property 1: Add z and −12.*
$-11z \geq -7$	*Simplify.*
$z \leq \dfrac{7}{11}$	*Property 3: Divide by −11 and reverse inequality symbol.*

The solution set is $\left\{z \mid z \leq \frac{7}{11}\right\}$, and in interval notation it is written as $\left(-\infty, \frac{7}{11}\right]$.

Now Try Exercises 15 and 17

Graphical Solutions   The intersections-of-graphs method can be extended to solve inequalities. The following box shows the actual and projected percentages of college degrees conferred to females F and to males M.   (***Source:*** Bureau of Labor Statistics.)

See the Concept: Solving an Inequality Graphically

College Degrees Conferred, 1975–2017 (Female versus Male)

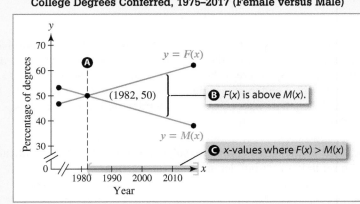

A In 1982 half, or 50%, of all college degrees conferred were given to females.

B There are more female graduates after 1982.

C $F(x) > M(x)$ when **1982 < x ≤ 2017**.

The preceding box illustrates how we can solve the inequality $F(x) > M(x)$ graphically. This graphical technique is used in the next example.

EXAMPLE 2   Solving a linear inequality graphically

Graph $y_1 = \frac{1}{2}x + 2$ and $y_2 = 2x - 1$ by hand. Use the graph to solve the linear inequality $\frac{1}{2}x + 2 > 2x - 1$.

SOLUTION The graphs of $y_1 = \frac{1}{2}x + 2$ and $y_2 = 2x - 1$ are shown in Figure 2.33. The graphs intersect at the point $(2, 3)$. The graph of $y_1 = \frac{1}{2}x + 2$ is above the graph of $y_2 = 2x - 1$ to the left of the point of intersection, or when $x < 2$. Thus the solution set to the inequality $\frac{1}{2}x + 2 > 2x - 1$ is $\{x \mid x < 2\}$, or $(-\infty, 2)$.

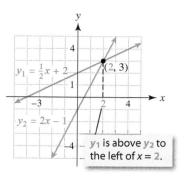

Figure 2.33

Now Try Exercise 39

An Application   In the next example we use graphical and symbolic techniques to analyze the growth of Square, which is discussed in the introduction to this section.

EXAMPLE 3   Analyzing the growth of Square

The *daily* payment processing volume for the company Square grew from \$1 million in March 2011 to \$11 million in March 2012. Its growth was approximately linear.
(a) Write a formula $S(x)$ for a linear function that models this growth in millions of dollars, where x represents months after March 2011. Assume that $0 \leq x \leq 12$.
(b) Determine symbolically and graphically when Square's daily volume was \$8.5 million or less.

SOLUTION
(a) The graph of S must pass through the point $(0, 1)$ and $(12, 11)$. The slope of this graph is

$$m = \frac{11 - 1}{12 - 0} = \frac{10}{12} = \frac{5}{6}.$$

The graph passes through $(0, 1)$, so the y-intercept is 1. Thus $S(x) = \frac{5}{6}x + 1$.

(b) *Symbolic Solution* We must determine when $S(x) \leq 8.5$.

$$\frac{5}{6}x + 1 \leq 8.5 \qquad \text{Substitute for } S(x).$$

$$\frac{5}{6}x \leq 7.5 \qquad \text{Subtract 1 from each side.}$$

$$x \leq 9 \qquad \text{Multiply each side by } \frac{6}{5}, \text{ or } 1.2.$$

The daily payment processing volume for Square was \$8.5 million or less from March 2011 to December 2011. (Note that $x = 0$ corresponds to March 2011.)

Graphical Solution A graphical solution to $\frac{5}{6}x + 1 \leq 8.5$ is shown in Figure 2.34.

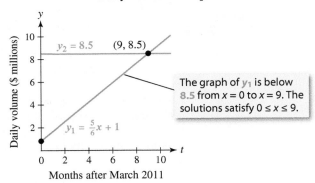

Daily Volume for Square

Figure 2.34

Now Try Exercise 89

***x*-Intercept Method** If a linear inequality can be written as $y_1 > 0$, where $>$ may be replaced by $\geq$, $\leq$, or $<$, then we can solve this inequality by using the ***x*-intercept method**. To apply this method for $y_1 > 0$, graph y_1 and find the *x*-intercept. The solution set includes *x*-values where the graph of y_1 is above the *x*-axis.

EXAMPLE 4 **Applying the *x*-intercept method**

Solve the inequality $1 - x > \frac{1}{2}x - 2$ by using the *x*-intercept method. Write the solution set in set-builder and interval notation.

SOLUTION

Graphing by Hand First, use properties of inequalities to rewrite the given inequality so that 0 is on the right side.

$$1 - x > \frac{1}{2}x - 2 \qquad \textit{Given inequality}$$

$$1 - x - \frac{1}{2}x + 2 > 0 \qquad \textit{Subtract } \tfrac{1}{2}x \textit{ and add 2.}$$

$$3 - \frac{3}{2}x > 0 \qquad \textit{Simplify.}$$

Next, graph $y_1 = 3 - \frac{3}{2}x$ and locate the *x*-intercept 2. From Figure 2.35(a), $y_1 > 0$ when $x < 2$ and the solution set is $\{x \mid x < 2\}$, or $(-\infty, 2)$.

Graphing with a Calculator With a calculator graph $y_1 = 1 - x - \frac{1}{2}x + 2$ without simplifying further, as shown in Figure 2.35(b). The calculator can locate the zero, or *x*-intercept, of 2.

Calculator Help

To locate a zero or *x*-intercept on the graph of a function, see Appendix A (page AP-7).

x-Intercept Method

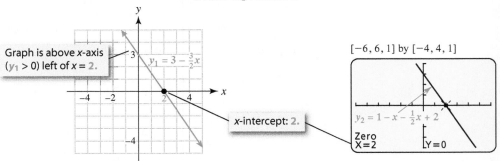

Graph is above *x*-axis ($y_1 > 0$) left of $x = 2$.

$y_1 = 3 - \frac{3}{2}x$

x-intercept: 2.

$[-6, 6, 1]$ by $[-4, 4, 1]$

$y_2 = 1 - x - \frac{1}{2}x + 2$

Zero
X=2   Y=0

Figure 2.35(a)   **Figure 2.35(b)**

Now Try Exercise 51

> ┌─────────────────────┐
> │ **MAKING CONNECTIONS** │
> └─────────────────────┘
> **Equations and Inequalities**   In mathematics a lot of time is spent solving equations and determining equality. One reason is that equality is frequently a boundary between *greater than* and *less than*. The solution set to an inequality often can be found by first locating where two expressions are equal. Since equality and inequality are closely connected, many of the techniques used to solve equations can also be applied to inequalities.

Visualizing Solutions   We can visualize the solution set to the linear inequality $ax + b > 0$ with $a \neq 0$, as shown in the following See the Concept. (The inequality $ax + b < 0$ can be solved similarly.)

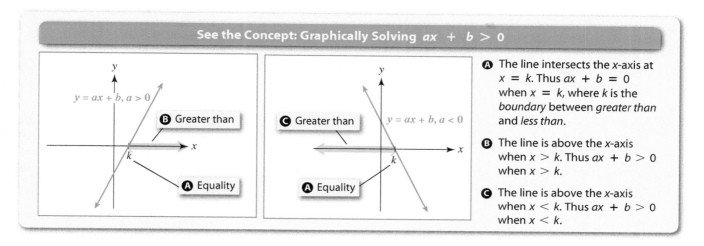

See the Concept: Graphically Solving $ax + b > 0$

A The line intersects the *x*-axis at $x = k$. Thus $ax + b = 0$ when $x = k$, where *k* is the *boundary* between *greater than* and *less than*.

B The line is above the *x*-axis when $x > k$. Thus $ax + b > 0$ when $x > k$.

C The line is above the *x*-axis when $x < k$. Thus $ax + b > 0$ when $x < k$.

Numerical Solutions   Suppose that it costs a company $5x + 200$ dollars to produce x earbuds and the company receives $15x$ dollars for selling x earbuds. Then the profit P from selling x earbuds is $P = 15x - (5x + 200) = 10x - 200$. A value of $x = 20$ results in $P = 0$, and so $x = 20$ is called the **boundary number** because selling 20 earbuds represents the boundary between making money and losing money (the break-even point). To make money, the profit P must be positive, and the inequality

$$10x - 200 > 0$$

must be satisfied. The table of values for $y_1 = 10x - 200$ in Table 2.3 shows the boundary number $x = 20$ along with several **test values**. The test values of $x = 17$, 18, and 19 result in a loss. The test values of $x = 21$, 22, and 23 result in a profit. Therefore the solution set to $10x - 200 > 0$ is $\{x \mid x > 20\}$.

Profit from Sales

x	17	18	19	20	21	22	23
$10x - 200$	-30	-20	-10	0	10	20	30

Table 2.3   Less than 0   Greater than 0
                                              Boundary number

┌─────────────┐
│ **EXAMPLE 5** │   **Solving a linear inequality with test values**
└─────────────┘

Solve $3(6 - x) + 5 - 2x < 0$ numerically.

SOLUTION Make a table of $y_1 = 3(6 - x) + 5 - 2x$ as shown in Figure 2.36 on the next page. The boundary number for this inequality lies between $x = 4$ and $x = 5$. Changing the increment from 1 to 0.1 in Figure 2.37 shows that the boundary number for the inequality is $x = 4.6$. The test values of $x = 4.7, 4.8$, and 4.9 indicate that when $x > 4.6$, the inequality $y_1 < 0$ is true. The solution set to $3(6 - x) + 5 - 2x < 0$ is $\{x \mid x > 4.6\}$.

Incrementing x by 1

X	Y1	
1	18	
2	13	Greater
3	8	than 0
4	3	
5	−2	Less
6	−7	than 0
7	−12	

X=4

Figure 2.36

Incrementing x by 0.1

X	Y1	
4.3	1.5	
4.4	1	Greater
4.5	.5	than 0
4.6	0	
4.7	−.5	Less
4.8	−1	than 0
4.9	−1.5	

X=4.6

Figure 2.37

Now Try Exercise 71

MAKING CONNECTIONS

Symbolic, Graphical, and Numerical Solutions   Each method is used to solve the inequality $3 - (x + 2) > 0$.

Symbolic Solution

$$3 - (x + 2) > 0$$
$$-(x + 2) > -3$$
$$x + 2 < 3$$
$$x < 1$$

Graphical Solution

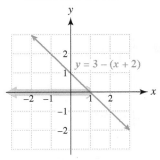

The graph of $y = 3 - (x + 2)$ is above the x-axis when $x < 1$.

Numerical Solution

x	3 − (x + 2)	
−2	3	
−1	2	Greater than 0
0	1	
1	0	Equals 0
2	−1	Less than 0
3	−2	

The values of $3 - (x + 2)$ are greater than 0 when $x < 1$.

Compound Inequalities

Sometimes a variable must satisfy two inequalities. For example, on a freeway there may be a minimum speed limit of 40 miles per hour and a maximum speed limit of 70 miles per hour. If x represents the speed of a vehicle, then x must satisfy the compound inequality

$$x \geq 40 \quad \text{and} \quad x \leq 70.$$

A **compound inequality** occurs when two inequalities are connected by the word *and* or *or*. When the word *and* connects two inequalities, the two inequalities can sometimes be written as a **three-part inequality**. For example, the previous compound inequality may be written as the three-part inequality

$$40 \leq x \leq 70.$$

Compound inequalities involving the word *or* are discussed in the next section.

EXAMPLE 6   Solving a three-part inequality symbolically

Solve the inequality. Write the solution set in set-builder and interval notation.

(a) $-4 \leq 5x + 1 < 21$ **(b)** $\dfrac{1}{2} < \dfrac{1 - 2t}{4} < 2$

SOLUTION
(a) Use properties of inequalities to simplify the three-part inequality.

$$-4 \leq 5x + 1 < 21 \qquad \text{Given inequality}$$
$$-5 \leq 5x < 20 \qquad \text{Add −1 to each part.}$$
$$-1 \leq x < 4 \qquad \text{Divide each part by 5.}$$

The solution set is $\{x \mid -1 \leq x < 4\}$, or $[-1, 4)$.

(b) Begin by multiplying each part by 4 to clear fractions.

$$\frac{1}{2} < \frac{1 - 2t}{4} < 2 \qquad \text{Given inequality}$$

$$2 < 1 - 2t < 8 \qquad \text{Multiply each part by 4.}$$

$$1 < -2t < 7 \qquad \text{Add } -1 \text{ to each part.}$$

$$-\frac{1}{2} > t > -\frac{7}{2} \qquad \text{Divide by } -2; \text{ reverse inequalities.}$$

$$-\frac{7}{2} < t < -\frac{1}{2} \qquad \text{Rewrite the inequality.}$$

The solution set is $\left\{ t \mid -\frac{7}{2} < t < -\frac{1}{2} \right\}$, or $\left(-\frac{7}{2}, -\frac{1}{2} \right)$.

> **Now Try Exercises 23 and 35**

NOTE In Example 6, it is correct to write a three-part inequality as either $-\frac{1}{2} > t > -\frac{7}{2}$ or $-\frac{7}{2} < t < -\frac{1}{2}$. However, we usually write the smaller number on the left side and the larger number on the right side.

Three-part inequalities occur in many applications and can often be solved symbolically and graphically. This is demonstrated in the next example.

EXAMPLE 7   Modeling sunset times

In Boston, on the 82nd day (March 22) the sun set at 7:00 P.M., and on the 136th day (May 15) the sun set at 8:00 P.M. Use a linear function S to estimate the days when the sun set between 7:15 P.M. and 7:45 P.M., inclusive. Do not consider any days of the year after May 15. (***Source:*** R. Thomas, *The Old Farmer's 2012 Almanac.*)

SOLUTION

Getting Started First find a linear function S whose graph passes through the points $(82, 7)$ and $(136, 8)$. Then solve the compound inequality $7.25 \leq S(x) \leq 7.75$. Note that 7.25 hours past noon corresponds to 7:15 P.M. and 7.75 hours past noon corresponds to 7:45 P.M. ▶

Symbolic Solution   The slope of the line passing through $(82, 7)$ and $(136, 8)$ is given by $\frac{8 - 7}{136 - 82} = \frac{1}{54}$. The point-slope form of the line passing through $(82, 7)$ with slope $\frac{1}{54}$ is

$$S(x) = \frac{1}{54}(x - 82) + 7. \qquad \text{Point-slope form}$$

Now solve the following compound inequality.

$$7.25 \leq \frac{1}{54}(x - 82) + 7 \leq 7.75 \qquad \text{Given inequality}$$

$$0.25 \leq \frac{1}{54}(x - 82) \leq 0.75 \qquad \text{Subtract 7 from each part.}$$

$$13.5 \leq x - 82 \leq 40.5 \qquad \text{Multiply each part by 54.}$$

$$95.5 \leq x \leq 122.5 \qquad \text{Add 82 to each part.}$$

If we round 95.5 and 122.5 up to 96 and 123, then this model predicts that the sun set between 7:15 P.M. and 7:45 P.M. from the 96th day (April 5) to the 123rd day (May 2). (Note that the actual days were April 5 and May 1.)

[80, 150, 10] by [6.5, 8.5, 1]

Figure 2.38

[80, 150, 10] by [6.5, 8.5, 1]

Figure 2.39

Graphical Solution Graph $y_1 = 7.25$, $y_2 = \frac{1}{54}(x - 82) + 7$, and $y_3 = 7.75$ and determine their points of intersection, $(95.5, 7.25)$ and $(122.5, 7.75)$, as shown in Figures 2.38 and 2.39. The graph of y_2 is between the graphs of y_1 and y_3 for $95.5 \le x \le 122.5$. This agrees with the symbolic solution. A different graph showing this solution appears in Figure 2.40.

Modeling Sunset Times in Boston

Figure 2.40

Now Try Exercise 93

EXAMPLE 8 Solving inequalities symbolically

Solve the linear inequalities symbolically. Express the solution set using interval notation.

(a) $-\dfrac{x}{2} + 1 \le 3$ **(b)** $-8 < \dfrac{3x - 1}{2} \le 5$ **(c)** $5(x - 6) < 2x - 2(1 - x)$

SOLUTION

(a) Simplify the inequality as follows.

> Reverse the inequality when multiplying by a negative.

$$-\frac{x}{2} + 1 \le 3 \qquad \text{Given inequality}$$

$$-\frac{x}{2} \le 2 \qquad \text{Add } -1, \text{ or subtract } 1.$$

$$x \ge -4 \qquad \text{Multiply by } -2.$$

In interval notation the solution set is $[-4, \infty)$.

(b) The parts of this compound inequality can be solved simultaneously.

$$-8 < \frac{3x - 1}{2} \le 5 \qquad \text{Given inequality}$$

$$-16 < 3x - 1 \le 10 \qquad \text{Multiply by 2.}$$

$$-15 < 3x \le 11 \qquad \text{Add 1.}$$

$$-5 < x \le \frac{11}{3} \qquad \text{Divide by 3.}$$

The solution set is $\left(-5, \frac{11}{3}\right]$.

(c) Start by applying the distributive property to each side of the inequality.

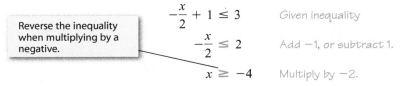

$$5(x - 6) < 2x - 2(1 - x) \qquad \text{Given inequality}$$

$$5x - 30 < 2x - 2 + 2x \qquad \text{Distributive property}$$

$$5x - 30 < 4x - 2 \qquad \text{Simplify.}$$

$$x - 30 < -2 \qquad \text{Subtract } 4x.$$

$$x < 28 \qquad \text{Add 30.}$$

The solution set is $(-\infty, 28)$.

Now Try Exercises 13, 27, and 33

2.3 Putting It All Together

$\mathbf{A}$ny linear inequality can be written as $ax + b > 0$ with $a \neq 0$, where $>$ can be replaced by $\geq$, $<$, or $\leq$. The following table includes methods for solving linear inequalities.

CONCEPT	EXPLANATION	EXAMPLES
Compound inequality	Two inequalities connected by the word *and* or *or*	$x \leq 4$ or $x \geq 10$ $x \geq -3$ and $x < 4$ $x > 5$ and $x \leq 20$ can be written as the three-part inequality $5 < x \leq 20$.
Symbolic method	Use properties of inequalities to simplify $f(x) > g(x)$ to either $x > k$ or $x < k$ for some real number k.	$\dfrac{1}{2}x + 1 > 3 - \dfrac{3}{2}x$ Given inequality $2x + 1 > 3$ Add $\frac{3}{2}x$. $2x > 2$ Subtract 1. $x > 1$ Divide by 2.
Intersection-of-graphs method	To solve $f(x) > g(x)$, graph $y_1 = f(x)$ and $y_2 = g(x)$. Find the point of intersection. The solution set includes x-values where the graph of y_1 is above the graph of y_2.	$\dfrac{1}{2}x + 1 > 3 - \dfrac{3}{2}x$ Graph $y_1 = \frac{1}{2}x + 1$ and $y_2 = 3 - \frac{3}{2}x$. The solution set for $y_1 > y_2$ is $\{x \mid x > 1\}$.
The x-intercept method	Write the inequality as $h(x) > 0$. Graph $y_1 = h(x)$. Solutions occur where the graph is above the x-axis.	$\dfrac{1}{2}x + 1 > 3 - \dfrac{3}{2}x$ Graph $y_1 = \frac{1}{2}x + 1 - \left(3 - \frac{3}{2}x\right)$. The solution set for $y_1 > 0$ is $\{x \mid x > 1\}$.
Numerical method	Write the inequality as $h(x) > 0$. Create a table for $y_1 = h(x)$ and find the boundary number $x = k$ such that $h(k) = 0$. Use the test values in the table to determine if the solution set is $x > k$ or $x < k$.	$\dfrac{1}{2}x + 1 > 3 - \dfrac{3}{2}x$ Table $y_1 = \frac{1}{2}x + 1 - \left(3 - \frac{3}{2}x\right)$. The solution set for $y_1 > 0$ is $\{x \mid x > 1\}$. <table> <tr><td>x</td><td>−1</td><td>0</td><td>1</td><td>2</td><td>3</td></tr> <tr><td>y_1</td><td>−4</td><td>−2</td><td>0</td><td>2</td><td>4</td></tr> </table> Less than 0 Greater than 0

2.3   Exercises

Review of Interval Notation

Exercises 1–8: Express the following in interval notation.

1. $x < 2$

2. $x > -3$

3. $x \geq -1$

4. $x \leq 7$

5. $\{x \mid 1 \leq x < 8\}$

6. $\{x \mid -2 < x \leq 4\}$

7. $\{x \mid x \leq 1\}$

8. $\{x \mid x > 5\}$

Solving Linear Inequalities Symbolically

Exercises 9–38: Solve the inequality symbolically. Express the solution set in set-builder or interval notation.

9. $2x + 6 \geq 10$

10. $-4x - 3 < 5$

11. $-2(x - 10) + 1 > 0$

12. $3(x + 5) \leq 0$

13. $\dfrac{t + 2}{3} \geq 5$

14. $\dfrac{2 - t}{6} < 0$

15. $4x - 1 < \dfrac{3 - x}{-3}$

16. $\dfrac{x + 5}{-10} > 2x + 3$

17. $-3(z - 4) \geq 2(1 - 2z)$

18. $-\dfrac{1}{4}(2z - 6) + z \geq 5$

19. $\dfrac{1 - x}{4} < \dfrac{2x - 2}{3}$

20. $\dfrac{3x}{4} < x - \dfrac{x + 2}{2}$

21. $2x - 3 > \dfrac{1}{2}(x + 1)$

22. $5 - (2 - 3x) \leq -5x$

23. $5 < 4t - 1 \leq 11$

24. $-1 \leq 2t \leq 4$

25. $3 \leq 4 - x \leq 20$

26. $-5 < 1 - 2x < 40$

27. $-7 \leq \dfrac{1 - 4x}{7} < 12$

28. $0 < \dfrac{7x - 5}{3} \leq 4$

29. $5 > 2(x + 4) - 5 > -5$

30. $\dfrac{8}{3} \geq \dfrac{4}{3} - (x + 3) \geq \dfrac{2}{3}$

31. $3 \leq \dfrac{1}{2}x + \dfrac{3}{4} \leq 6$

32. $-4 \leq 5 - \dfrac{4}{5}x < 6$

33. $5x - 2(x + 3) \geq 4 - 3x$

34. $3x - 1 < 2(x - 3) + 1$

35. $\dfrac{1}{2} \leq \dfrac{1 - 2t}{3} < \dfrac{2}{3}$

36. $-\dfrac{3}{4} < \dfrac{2 - t}{5} < \dfrac{3}{4}$

37. $\dfrac{1}{2}z + \dfrac{2}{3}(3 - z) - \dfrac{5}{4}z \geq \dfrac{3}{4}(z - 2) + z$

38. $\dfrac{2}{3}(1 - 2z) - \dfrac{3}{2}z + \dfrac{5}{6}z \geq \dfrac{2z - 1}{3} + 1$

Solving Linear Inequalities Graphically

Exercises 39–46: (Refer to Example 2.) Solve the inequality graphically. Use set-builder notation.

39. $x + 2 \geq 2x$

40. $2x - 1 \leq x$

41. $\dfrac{2}{3}x - 2 > -\dfrac{4}{3}x + 4$

42. $-2x \geq -\dfrac{5}{3}x + 1$

43. $-1 \leq 2x - 1 \leq 3$

44. $-2 < 1 - x < 2$

45. $-3 < x - 2 \leq 2$

46. $-1 \leq 1 - 2x < 5$

Exercises 47–50: Use the given graph of $y = ax + b$ to solve each equation and inequality. Write the solution set to each inequality in set-builder or interval notation.

(a) $ax + b = 0$ (b) $ax + b < 0$ (c) $ax + b \geq 0$

47.

48.

49.

50.
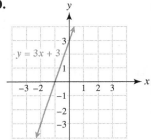

*Exercises 51–54: **x-Intercept Method** (Refer to Example 4.) Use the x-intercept method to solve the inequality. Write the solution set in set-builder or interval notation. Then check your answer by solving the inequality symbolically.*

51. $x - 3 \leq \dfrac{1}{2}x - 2$

52. $x - 2 \leq \dfrac{1}{3}x$

53. $2 - x < 3x - 2$

54. $\dfrac{1}{2}x + 1 > \dfrac{3}{2}x - 1$

Exercises 55–60: Solve the linear inequality graphically. Write the solution set in set-builder notation. Approximate endpoints to the nearest hundredth whenever appropriate.

55. $5x - 4 > 10$

56. $-3x + 6 \leq 9$

57. $-2(x - 1990) + 55 \geq 60$

58. $\sqrt{2}x > 10.5 - 13.7x$

59. $\sqrt{5}(x - 1.2) - \sqrt{3}x < 5(x + 1.1)$

60. $1.238x + 0.998 \le 1.23(3.987 - 2.1x)$

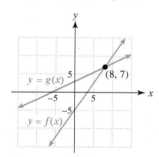 *Exercises 61–66; Solve the compound linear inequality graphically. Write the solution set in set-builder or interval notation, and approximate endpoints to the nearest tenth whenever appropriate.*

61. $3 \le 5x - 17 < 15$

62. $-4 < \dfrac{55 - 3.1x}{4} < 17$

63. $1.5 \le 9.1 - 0.5x \le 6.8$ **64.** $0.2x < \dfrac{2x - 5}{3} < 8$

65. $x - 4 < 2x - 5 < 6$ **66.** $-3 \le 1 - x \le 2x$

67. The graphs of two linear functions f and g are shown.
   (a) Solve the equation $g(x) = f(x)$.

   (b) Solve the inequality $g(x) > f(x)$.

68. Use the figure to solve each equation or inequality.
   (a) $f(x) = g(x)$ **(b)** $g(x) = h(x)$

   (c) $f(x) < g(x) < h(x)$ **(d)** $g(x) > h(x)$

Solving Linear Inequalities Numerically

Exercises 69 and 70: Assume y_1 represents a linear function with the set of real numbers for its domain. Use the table to solve the inequalities. Use set-builder notation.

69. $y_1 > 0, y_1 \le 0$ **70.** $y_1 < 0, y_1 \ge 0$

X	Y1
0	220
1	165
2	110
3	55
4	0
5	-55
6	-110
X=0	

X	Y1
-5	-32
-4	-16
-3	0
-2	16
-1	32
0	48
1	64
X=-5	

Exercises 71–78: Solve each inequality numerically. Write the solution set in set-builder or interval notation, and approximate endpoints to the nearest tenth when appropriate.

71. $-4x - 6 > 0$ **72.** $1 - 2x \ge 9$

73. $1 \le 3x - 2 \le 10$ **74.** $-5 < 2x - 1 < 15$

75. $-\dfrac{3}{4} < \dfrac{2 - 5x}{3} \le \dfrac{3}{4}$ **76.** $\dfrac{3x - 1}{5} < 15$

77. $(\sqrt{11} - \pi)x - 5.5 \le 0$

78. $1.5(x - 0.7) + 1.5x < 1$

You Decide the Method

Exercises 79–82: Solve the inequality. Approximate the end-points to the nearest thousandth when appropriate.

79. $2x - 8 > 5$ **80.** $5 < 4x - 2.5$

81. $\pi x - 5.12 \le \sqrt{2}x - 5.7(x - 1.1)$

82. $5.1x - \pi \ge \sqrt{3} - 1.7x$

Applications

83. Distance Between Cars Cars A and B are both traveling in the same direction. Their distances in miles north of St. Louis after x hours are computed by the functions f_A and f_B, respectively. The graphs of f_A and f_B are shown in the figure for $0 \le x \le 10$.
   (a) Which car is traveling faster? Explain.

   (b) How many hours elapse before the two cars are the same distance from St. Louis? How far are they from St. Louis when this occurs?

   (c) During what time interval is car B farther from St. Louis than car A?

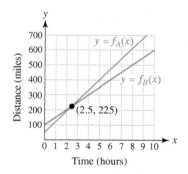

84. Distance Function f computes the distance y in miles between a car and the city of Omaha after x hours, where $0 \le x \le 6$. The graphs of f and the horizontal lines $y = 100$ and $y = 200$ are shown in the figure on the next page.
   (a) Is the car moving toward or away from Omaha? Explain.

   (b) Determine the times when the car is 100 miles and 200 miles from Omaha.

(c) Determine when the car is from 100 to 200 miles from Omaha.

(d) When is the car's distance from Omaha greater than 100 miles?

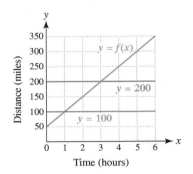

85. Clouds and Temperature As the altitude increases, both the air temperature and the dew point decrease. As long as the air temperature is greater than the dew point, clouds will not form. Typically, the air temperature T cools at 19°F for each 1-mile increase in altitude and the dew point D decreases by 5.8°F for each 1-mile increase in altitude. (**Source:** A. Miller and R. Anthes, *Meteorology.*)

(a) Suppose the air temperature at ground level is 65°F. Write a formula for a linear function T that gives the air temperature at x miles high.

(b) Suppose the dew point at ground level is 50°F. Write a formula for a linear function D that gives the dew point at x miles high.

(c) Determine symbolically altitudes where clouds will not form.

(d) Solve part (c) graphically.

86. Temperature and Altitude Suppose the Fahrenheit temperature x miles above ground level is given by the formula $T(x) = 85 - 19x$.

(a) Use the intersection-of-graphs method to estimate the altitudes where the temperature is below freezing. Assume that the domain of T is $0 \le x \le 6$.

(b) What does the x-intercept on the graph of $y = T(x)$ represent?

(c) Solve part (a) symbolically.

87. U.S. Social Gaming Social gaming revenues (via the Internet) in billions of dollars from 2010 to 2015 are projected to be modeled by $R(x) = 0.86x + 1.2$, where x represents years after 2010. (**Source:** BI Intelligence.)

(a) Interpret the slope of the graph of R.

(b) Estimate when this revenue is expected to be more than $3 billion.

88. Overweight Americans If trends continue, the past and future percentages of the population who are overweight can be estimated by $W(x) = x + 45$, where x represents years after 1980. (**Source:** New York Times.)

(a) Interpret the slope of the graph of W.

(b) Estimate when this percentage was between 70% and 77%.

89. Facebook Users The number of active Facebook users increased from 100 million in 2008 to 1 billion in 2012. (**Source:** Business Insider.)

(a) Find a formula for a linear function U that models this growth in millions of users, where x is years after 2008.

(b) Estimate when the number of users was 550 million or more.

90. Cost of Education The cost of K–12 education per student was $2200 in 1978 and increased to $10,300 in 2008. (**Source:** Department of Education.)

(a) Find a formula for a linear function C that models this cost in dollars, where x is years after 1978.

(b) Estimate when this cost was from $4900 to $7600.

91. Video Sharing In 2006 about 33% of Americans reported watching online videos via sharing sites such as YouTube and Vimeo. By 2011 this number increased to 71% (**Source:** Column Five.)

(a) Find a formula for a linear function V that models the data, where x represents the year.

(b) Estimate when this percentage was between 40% and 55%.

92. Consumer Spending In 2005 consumers used credit and debit cards to pay for 40% of all purchases. This percentage was 55% in 2011. (*Source:* Bloomburg.)

(a) Find a linear function P that models the data.

(b) Estimate when this percentage was between 45% and 50%.

93. Modeling Sunrise Times In Boston, on the 90th day (March 30) the sun rose at 6:30 A.M., and on the 129th day (May 8) the sun rose at 5:30 A.M. Use a linear function to estimate the days when the sun rose between 5:45 A.M. and 6:00 A.M. Do not consider days after May 8. (*Source:* R Thomas.)

94. Modeling Sunrise Times In Denver, on the 77th day (March 17) the sun rose at 7:00 A.M., and on the 112th day (April 21) the sun rose at 6:00 A.M. Use a linear function to estimate the days when the sun rose between 6:10 A.M. and 6:40 A.M. Do not consider days after April 21. (*Source:* R. Thomas.)

95. Error Tolerances Suppose that an aluminum can is manufactured so that its radius r can vary from 1.99 inches to 2.01 inches. What range of values is possible for the circumference C of the can? Express your answer by using a three-part inequality.

96. Error Tolerances Suppose that a square picture frame has sides that vary between 9.9 inches and 10.1 inches. What range of values is possible for the perimeter P of the picture frame? Express your answer by using a three-part inequality.

97. Modeling Data The following data are exactly linear.

x	0	2	4	6
y	−1.5	4.5	10.5	16.5

(a) Find a linear function f that models the data.

(b) Solve the inequality $f(x) > 2.25$.

98. Modeling Data The following data are exactly linear.

x	1	2	3	4	5
y	0.4	3.5	6.6	9.7	12.8

(a) Find a linear function f that models the data.

(b) Solve the inequality $2 \leq f(x) \leq 8$.

Linear Regression

99. Female College Graduates The table in the next column lists the percentage P of the female population who had college degrees in selected years.

x	1980	1990	2000	2010
$P(\%)$	12.8	18.4	23.6	33.0

Source: Bureau of the Census.

(a) Find a linear function P that models the data.

(b) Estimate when this percentage was between 18% and 28.5%.

(c) Did your estimate involve interpolation or extrapolation?

100. Tablet Sales The table lists the actual and projected number N of tablets, such as the iPad, sold worldwide in millions for selected years x.

x	2011	2012	2013	2014	2015
N	90	165	250	340	470

Source: Business Insider.

(a) Find a linear function N that models the data.

(b) Estimate when this number is expected to be more than 637 million.

(c) Did your estimate involve interpolation or extrapolation?

Writing about Mathematics

101. Suppose the solution to the equation $ax + b = 0$ with $a > 0$ is $x = k$. Discuss how the value of k can be used to help solve the linear inequalities $ax + b > 0$ and $ax + b < 0$. Illustrate this process graphically. How would the solution sets change if $a < 0$?

102. Describe how to numerically solve the linear inequality $ax + b \leq 0$. Give an example.

103. If you multiply each part of a three-part inequality by the same negative number, what must you make sure to do? Explain by using an example.

104. Explain how a linear function, a linear equation, and a linear inequality are related. Give an example.

Extended and Discovery Exercises

1. Arithmetic Mean The **arithmetic mean** of two numbers a and b is given by $\frac{a + b}{2}$. Use properties of inequalities to show that if $a < b$, then $a < \frac{a + b}{2} < b$.

2. Geometric Mean The **geometric mean** of two numbers a and b is given by $\sqrt{ab}$. Use properties of inequalities to show that if $0 < a < b$, then $a < \sqrt{ab} < b$.

2.4 More Modeling with Functions

- **Model data with a linear function**
- **Evaluate and graph piecewise-defined functions**
- **Evaluate and graph the greatest integer function**
- **Use direct variation to solve problems**

Introduction

Throughout history, people have attempted to explain the world around them by creating models. A model is based on observations. It can be a diagram, a graph, an equation, a verbal expression, or some other form of communication. Models are used in diverse areas such as economics, chemistry, astronomy, religion, and mathematics. Regardless of where it is used, a **model** is an *abstraction* with the following two characteristics:

1. A model is able to explain present phenomena. It should not contradict data and information already known to be correct.
2. A model is able to make predictions about data or results. It should use current information to forecast phenomena or create new information.

Mathematical models are used to forecast business trends, design social networks, estimate ecological trends, control highway traffic, describe the Internet, predict weather, and discover new information when human knowledge is inadequate.

Modeling with Linear Functions

Linear functions can be used to model things that change at a constant rate. For example, the distance traveled by a car can be modeled by a linear function *if* the car is traveling at a constant speed.

MODELING WITH A LINEAR FUNCTION

To model a quantity that is changing at a constant rate with $f(x) = mx + b$, the following formula may be used.

$$f(x) = (\text{constant rate of change})\, x + (\text{initial amount})$$

The constant rate of change corresponds to the slope of the graph of f, and the initial amount corresponds to the y-intercept.

This method is illustrated in the next two examples.

EXAMPLE 1 Writing formulas for functions

Write the formula for a linear function that models each situation. Choose both an appropriate name and an appropriate variable for the function. State what the input variable represents and the domain of the function.

(a) In 2011 the average cost of attending a public college was $8200, and it is projected to increase, on average, by $600 per year until 2014. (*Source:* The College Board.)
(b) A car's speed is 50 miles per hour, and it begins to slow down at a constant rate of 10 miles per hour each second.

SOLUTION
(a) Getting Started To model cost with a linear function, we need to find two quantities: the initial amount and the rate of change. In this example the initial amount is $8200 and the rate of change is $600 per year. ▶

Let C be the name of the function and x be the number of years after 2011. Then

$$C(x) = (\textbf{constant rate of change})x + (\textbf{initial amount})$$
$$= 600x + 8200$$

models the cost in dollars of attending a public college x years after 2011. Because this projection is valid only until 2014, or for 3 years past 2011, the domain D of function C is

$$D = \{x \mid x = 0, 1, 2, \text{ or } 3\}.$$

Note that x represents a year, so it may be most appropriate to restrict the domain to integer values for x.

(b) Let S be the name of the function and t be the elapsed time in seconds that the car has been slowing down. Then

$$S(t) = (\text{constant rate of change})t + (\text{initial speed})$$
$$= -10t + 50$$

models the speed of the car after an elapsed time of t seconds. Because the car's initial speed is 50 miles per hour and it slows at 10 miles per hour per second, the car can slow down for at most 5 seconds before it comes to a stop. Thus the domain D of S is

$$D = \{t \mid 0 \le t \le 5\}.$$

Note that t represents time in seconds and does not need to be restricted to an integer.

Now Try Exercises 11 and 13

EXAMPLE 2   **Finding a symbolic representation**

A 100-gallon tank, initially full of water, is being drained at a rate of 5 gallons per minute.
(a) Write a formula for a linear function f that models the number of gallons of water in the tank after x minutes.
(b) How much water is in the tank after 4 minutes?
(c) Graph f. Identify the x- and y-intercepts and interpret each.
(d) Discuss the domain of f.

SOLUTION
(a) The amount of water in the tank is *decreasing* at 5 gallons per minute, so the constant rate of change is −5. The initial amount of water is 100 gallons.

$$f(x) = (\text{constant rate of change})x + (\text{initial amount})$$
$$= -5x + 100$$

(b) After 4 minutes the tank contains $f(4) = -5(4) + 100 = 80$ gallons.
(c) $f(x) = -5x + 100$, so the graph has y-intercept 100 and slope −5. See Figure 2.41.

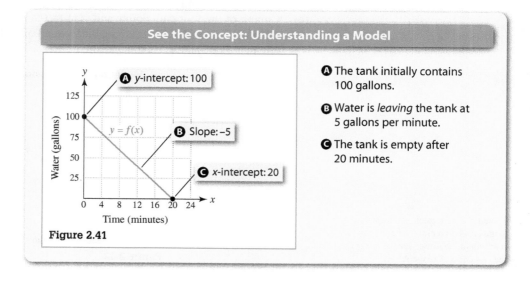

See the Concept: Understanding a Model

Ⓐ *y*-intercept: 100

Ⓑ Slope: −5

Ⓒ *x*-intercept: 20

$y = f(x)$

Water (gallons)

Time (minutes)

Ⓐ The tank initially contains 100 gallons.

Ⓑ Water is *leaving* the tank at 5 gallons per minute.

Ⓒ The tank is empty after 20 minutes.

Figure 2.41

(d) From the graph we see that the domain of f must be restricted to $0 \le x \le 20$. For example, 21 is not in the domain of f because $f(21) = -5(21) + 100 = -5$; the tank cannot hold -5 gallons. Similarly, -1 is not in the domain of f because $f(-1) = -5(-1) + 100 = 105$; the tank holds *at most* 100 gallons.

Now Try Exercise 17

If the slopes between consecutive pairs of data points are always the same, the data can be modeled exactly by a linear function. If the slopes between consecutive pairs of data points are nearly the same, then the data can be modeled approximately by a linear function. In the next example we model data approximately.

EXAMPLE 3 Modeling airliner CO_2 emissions

Airliners emit carbon dioxide into the atmosphere when they burn jet fuel. Table 2.4 shows the *average* number y of pounds of carbon dioxide (CO_2) emitted by an airliner for each passenger who flies a distance of x miles.

Carbon Dioxide Emissions

x (miles)	240	360	680	800
y (pounds)	150	230	435	510

Source: E. Rogers and T. Kostigen, *The Green Book.*

Table 2.4

(a) Calculate the slopes of the line segments that connect consecutive data points.
(b) Find a linear function f that models the data.
(c) Graph f and the data. What does the slope of the graph of f indicate?
(d) Calculate $f(1000)$ and interpret the result.

SOLUTION
(a) The slopes of the lines passing through the points (240, 150), (360, 230), (680, 435), and (800, 510) are as follows.

$$m_1 = \frac{230 - 150}{360 - 240} \approx 0.67, \quad m_2 = \frac{435 - 230}{680 - 360} \approx 0.64, \quad \text{and}$$

$$m_3 = \frac{510 - 435}{800 - 680} \approx 0.63$$

(b) One possibility for m is to find the average of m_1, m_2, and m_3. The average of 0.67, 0.64, and 0.63 is 0.65, rounded to the nearest hundredth. Because traveling 0 miles produces 0 pounds of carbon dioxide, let the graph of f pass through (0, 0). Thus the y-intercept is 0 and $f(x) = 0.65x + 0$.

(c) A graph of the four data points and $f(x) = 0.65x$ is shown in Figure 2.42. The slope of 0.65 indicates that, on average, 0.65 pound of carbon dioxide is produced for each mile that a person travels in an airliner.

Modeling CO$_2$ Emissions

Figure 2.42

Calculator Help

To make a scatterplot, see Appendix A (page AP-3). To plot data and graph an equation in the same viewing rectangle, see Appendix A (page AP-6).

(d) $f(1000) = 0.65(1000) = 650$; thus 650 pounds of carbon dioxide are emitted into the atmosphere, on average, when a person flies 1000 miles.

Now Try Exercise 23

MAKING CONNECTIONS

Slope and Approximately Linear Data · Another way to obtain an initial value for m is to calculate the slope between the first and last data point in the table. The value for m can then be adjusted visually by graphing f and the data. In Example 3 this would have resulted in

$$m = \frac{510 - 150}{800 - 240} \approx 0.64,$$

which compares favorably with our decision to let $m = 0.65$.

Piecewise-Defined Functions

When a function f models data, there may not be one formula for $f(x)$ that works. In this case, the function is sometimes defined on pieces of its domain and is therefore called a **piecewise-defined function**. If each piece is linear, the function is a **piecewise-linear function**. An example of a piecewise-defined function is the *Fujita scale,* which classifies tornadoes by intensity. If a tornado has wind speeds between 40 and 72 miles per hour, it is an F1 tornado. Tornadoes with wind speeds *greater than* 72 miles per hour but not more than 112 miles per hour are F2 tornadoes. The Fujita scale is represented by the following function F, where the input x represents the maximum wind speed of a tornado and the output is the F-scale number from 1 to 5.

Fujita Scale ($F1 \rightarrow F5$)

$$F(x) = \begin{cases} 1 & \text{if } 40 \leq x \leq 72 \\ 2 & \text{if } 72 < x \leq 112 \\ 3 & \text{if } 112 < x \leq 157 \\ 4 & \text{if } 157 < x \leq 206 \\ 5 & \text{if } 206 < x \leq 260 \end{cases}$$

F is defined in five pieces over intervals of its domain.

$F(180) = 4$

For example, if the maximum wind speed is 180 miles per hour, then $F(180) = 4$ because 180 is between 157 and 206; that is, $157 < 180 \leq 206$. Thus a tornado with a maximum wind speed of 180 miles per hour is an F4 tornado.

A graph of $y = f(x)$ is shown in Figure 2.43. It is composed of horizontal line segments. Because each piece is constant, F is sometimes called a **piecewise-constant function** or a **step function**. A solid dot occurs at the point $(72, 1)$ and an open circle occurs at the point $(72, 2)$, because technically a tornado with 72-mile-per-hour winds is an F1 tornado, not an F2 tornado.

Tornado Intensities

An open circle indicates that this point is not included in the graph of *F.*

$y = F(x)$ — Piecewise-constant function

Figure 2.43

Continuous Functions The graph of a **continuous function** can be sketched without picking up the pencil. There are no breaks in the graph of a continuous function. Because there are breaks in the graph shown in Figure 2.43, function F is not continuous; rather it is **discontinuous** at $x = 72$, 112, 157, and 206.

An Application The housing market peaked in 2005. Shortly after, the housing bubble burst and continued to plummet, hitting a low in 2011. In the next example we use a piecewise-defined function to model housing starts from 2005 to 2011.

EXAMPLE 4 Analyzing housing starts

Table 2.5 lists numbers of single residential homes built during selected years.

Housing Starts in Millions

Year	2000	2005	2011	2012
Homes	1.3	1.7	0.4	0.5

Source: Bureau of the Census.

Table 2.5

(a) Plot a line graph of these data. Let this graph define a function H.
(b) Find and interpret the slope of each line segment.
(c) Is H continuous on its domain?
(d) Identify where H is increasing, decreasing, or constant.
(e) Write a piecewise-defined formula for H.

SOLUTION
(a) Plot the points (2000, 1.3), (2005, 1.7), (2011, 0.4), and (2012, 0.5). Connect these points with three line segments as shown in Figure 2.44. (*Source:* Bureau of the Census.)

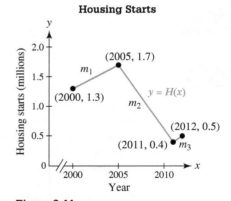

Housing Starts

Figure 2.44

(b) The first line segment passes through (2000, 1.3) and (2005, 1.7) with slope

$$m_1 = \frac{1.7 - 1.3}{2005 - 2000} = \frac{0.4}{5} = \frac{2}{25} = 0.08.$$

Housing starts increased, on average, by 0.08 million (80,000) per year from 2000 to 2005. The other two slopes are $m_2 = -\frac{13}{60} \approx -0.22$ and $m_3 = \frac{1}{10}$ and can be interpreted similarly.
(c) There are no breaks in the graph so H is continuous on its domain, [2000, 2012].
(d) Function H is increasing on the intervals (2000, 2005) and (2011, 2012). It is decreasing on (2005, 2011) and is never constant.
(e) **Getting Started** We must determine three equations for the lines that represent the three line segments. Given the slope and one point we can write the point-slope form of each line. ▶

The first line segment passes through $(2000, 1.3)$ and has slope $\frac{2}{25}$. Therefore $H(x) = \frac{2}{25}(x - 2000) + 1.3$, if $2000 \leq x \leq 2005$. Continuing in this manner, we can write a piecewise-defined formula for $H(x)$.

$$H(x) = \begin{cases} \frac{2}{25}(x - 2000) + 1.3, & \text{if } 2000 \leq x \leq 2005 \\ -\frac{13}{60}(x - 2005) + 1.7, & \text{if } 2005 < x \leq 2011 \\ \frac{1}{10}(x - 2011) + 0.4, & \text{if } 2011 < x \leq 2012 \end{cases}$$

Now Try Exercise 43

EXAMPLE 5 Evaluating and graphing a piecewise-defined function

Use $f(x)$ to complete the following.

$$f(x) = \begin{cases} x - 1 & \text{if } -4 \leq x < 2 \\ -2x & \text{if } 2 \leq x \leq 4 \end{cases}$$

(a) What is the domain of f?
(b) Evaluate $f(-3)$, $f(2)$, $f(4)$, and $f(5)$.
(c) Sketch a graph of f.
(d) Is f a continuous function on its domain?

SOLUTION
(a) Function f is defined for x-values satisfying either $-4 \leq x < 2$ or $2 \leq x \leq 4$. Thus the domain of f is $D = \{x \mid -4 \leq x \leq 4\}$, or $[-4, 4]$.
(b) For x-values satisfying $-4 \leq x < 2$, $f(x) = x - 1$ and so $f(-3) = -4$. Similarly, if $2 \leq x \leq 4$, then $f(x) = -2x$. Thus $f(2) = -4$ and $f(4) = -8$. The expression $f(5)$ is undefined because 5 is not in the domain of f.
(c) **Getting Started** Because each piece of $f(x)$ is linear, the graph of $y = f(x)$ consists of two line segments. Therefore we can find the endpoints of each line segment and then sketch the graph. ▶

Graph the First Piece

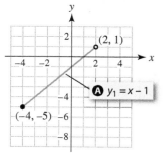

Figure 2.45

Graph the Second Piece

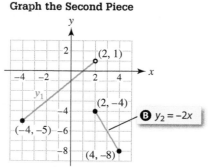

Figure 2.46

Ⓐ Evaluate $y_1 = x - 1$ at $x = -4$ and $x = 2$. Place a dot at $(-4, -5)$ and an open circle at $(2, 1)$, because $y_1 = x - 1$ applies for $x < 2$. Sketch a line segment between these points.

Ⓑ Evaluate $y_2 = -2x$ at $x = 2$ and $x = 4$. Place dots at $(2, -4)$ and $(4, -8)$. Sketch a line segment between these points.

(d) The function f is *not* continuous because in Figure 2.46 there is a break in its graph at $x = 2$.

Now Try Exercise 33

The Greatest Integer Function

A common piecewise-defined function used in mathematics is the greatest integer function, denoted $f(x) = [x]$. The **greatest integer function** is defined as follows.

$[x]$ is the greatest integer less than or equal to x.

Some examples of the evaluation of $[x]$ include

$$[6.7] = 6, \quad [3] = 3, \quad [-2.3] = -3, \quad [-10] = -10, \quad \text{and} \quad [-\pi] = -4.$$

The graph of $y = [\![x]\!]$ is shown in Figure 2.47. The greatest integer function is both a piecewise-constant function and a step function.

The Greatest Integer Function

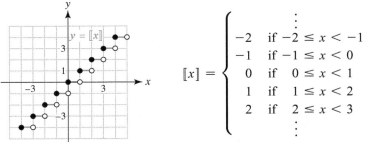

$$[\![x]\!] = \begin{cases} \vdots \\ -2 & \text{if } -2 \leq x < -1 \\ -1 & \text{if } -1 \leq x < 0 \\ 0 & \text{if } 0 \leq x < 1 \\ 1 & \text{if } 1 \leq x < 2 \\ 2 & \text{if } 2 \leq x < 3 \\ \vdots \end{cases}$$

Figure 2.47

Calculator Help

To access the greatest integer function or to set a calculator in dot mode, see Appendix A (pages AP-6 and AP-8).

In some applications, fractional parts are either not allowed or ignored. Framing lumber for houses is measured in 2-foot multiples, and mileage charges for rental cars may be calculated to the mile.

Suppose a car rental company charges $31.50 per day plus $0.25 for each mile driven, where fractions of a mile are ignored. The function given by $f(x) = 0.25[\![x]\!] + 31.50$ calculates the cost of driving x miles in one day. For example, the cost of driving 100.4 miles is

$$f(100.4) = 0.25[\![100.4]\!] + 31.50 = 0.25(100) + 31.50 = \$56.50.$$

On some calculators and computers, the greatest integer function is denoted int(X). A graph of $Y_1 = 0.25*\text{int}(X) + 31.5$ is shown in Figure 2.48.

Dot Mode

[0, 10, 1] by [31, 35, 1]

$y = 0.25[\![x]\!] + 31.5$

Figure 2.48

MAKING CONNECTIONS

Connected and Dot Modes   Graphing calculators often connect points to make a graph look continuous. However, if a graph has breaks in it, a graphing calculator may connect points where there should be breaks. In *dot mode*, points are plotted but not connected. Figure 2.49 is the same graph shown in Figure 2.48, except that it is plotted in *connected mode*. Note that connected mode generates an inaccurate graph of this step function.

Connected Mode

[0, 10, 1] by [31, 35, 1]

$y = 0.25[\![x]\!] + 31.5$

Inaccurate graph

Figure 2.49

Direct Variation

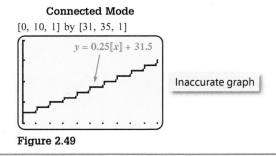

When a change in one quantity causes a proportional change in another quantity, the two quantities are said to *vary directly* or to *be directly proportional*. For example, if we work for $8 per hour, our pay is proportional to the number of hours that we work. Doubling the hours doubles the pay, tripling the hours triples the pay, and so on.

DIRECT VARIATION

Let x and y denote two quantities. Then y is **directly proportional** to x, or y **varies directly** with x, if there exists a nonzero number k such that

$$y = kx.$$

The number k is called the **constant of proportionality** or the **constant of variation**.

If a person earns $\$57.75$ working for 7 hours, the constant of proportionality k is the hourly pay rate. If y represents the pay in dollars and x the hours worked, then k is found by substituting values for x and y into the equation $y = kx$ and solving for k. That is,

$$57.75 = k(7), \quad \text{or} \quad k = \frac{57.75}{7} = 8.25,$$

so the hourly pay rate is $\$8.25$ and, in general, $y = 8.25x$.

An Application   Hooke's law states that the distance that an elastic spring stretches beyond its natural length is *directly* proportional to the amount of weight hung on the spring, as illustrated in Figure 2.50. This law is valid whether the spring is stretched or compressed. The constant of proportionality is called the **spring constant**. Thus if a weight or force F is applied and the spring stretches a distance x beyond its natural length, then the equation $F = kx$ models this situation, where k is the spring constant.

A Spring Being Stretched

Figure 2.50

EXAMPLE 6   Working with Hooke's law

A 12-pound weight is hung on a spring, and it stretches 2 inches.
(a) Find the spring constant.
(b) Determine how far the spring will stretch when a 19-pound weight is hung on it.

SOLUTION
(a) Let $F = kx$, given that $F = 12$ pounds and $x = 2$ inches. Thus

$$12 = k(2), \quad \text{or} \quad k = 6,$$

and the spring constant equals 6.
(b) If $F = 19$ and $F = 6x$, then $19 = 6x$, or $x = \frac{19}{6} \approx 3.17$ inches.

Now Try Exercise 63

The following four-step method can often be used to solve variation problems.

SOLVING A VARIATION PROBLEM

When solving a variation problem, the following steps can be used.

STEP 1: Write the general equation for the type of variation problem that you are solving.

STEP 2: Substitute given values in this equation so the constant of variation k is the only unknown value in the equation. Solve for k.

STEP 3: Substitute the value of k in the general equation in Step 1.

STEP 4: Use this equation to find the requested quantity.

EXAMPLE 7   Solving a direct variation problem

Let T vary directly with x, and suppose that $T = 33$ when $x = 5$. Find T when $x = 31$.

SOLUTION
STEP 1: The equation for direct variation is $T = kx$.
STEP 2: Substitute 33 for T and 5 for x. Then solve for k.

$$T = kx \qquad \text{Direct variation equation}$$
$$33 = k(5) \qquad \text{Let } T = 33 \text{ and } x = 5.$$
$$\frac{33}{5} = k \qquad \text{Divide each side by 5.}$$

STEP 3: Thus $T = \frac{33}{5}x$, or $T = 6.6x$.
STEP 4: When $x = 31$, we have $T = 6.6(31) = 204.6$.

Now Try Exercise 51

Suppose that, for each point (x, y) in a data set, the ratios $\frac{y}{x}$ are equal to some constant k. That is, $\frac{y}{x} = k$ for each data point. Then $y = kx$, so y varies directly with x and the constant of variation is k. In addition, the data points (x, y) all lie on the line $y = kx$, which has slope k and passes through the origin. These concepts are used in the next example.

EXAMPLE 8 Modeling memory requirements

Table 2.6 lists the megabytes (MB) x needed to record y seconds of music.

Recording Digital Music

x (MB)	0.23	0.49	1.16	1.27
y (sec)	10.7	22.8	55.2	60.2

Table 2.6

(a) Compute the ratios $\frac{y}{x}$ for the four data points. Does y vary directly with x? If it does, what is the constant of variation k?

(b) Estimate the seconds of music that can be stored on 5 megabytes.

(c) Graph the data in Table 2.6 and the line $y = kx$.

SOLUTION

(a) The four ratios $\frac{y}{x}$ from Table 2.6 are

$$\frac{10.7}{0.23} \approx 46.5, \quad \frac{22.8}{0.49} \approx 46.5, \quad \frac{55.2}{1.16} \approx 47.6, \quad \text{and} \quad \frac{60.2}{1.27} \approx 47.4.$$

Because the ratios are nearly equal, it is reasonable to say that y is directly proportional to x. The constant of proportionality is about 47, the average of the four ratios. This means that $y = 47x$ and we can store about 47 seconds of music per megabyte.

(b) Let $x = 5$ in the equation $y = 47x$, to obtain $y = 47(5) = 235$ seconds.

(c) Graphs of the data and the line $y = 47x$ are shown in Figure 2.51.

Now Try Exercise 65

Music and Memory Requirements
[0, 1.5, 0.5] by [0, 70, 10]

$y = 47x$

Figure 2.51

2.4 Putting It All Together

The following table summarizes important concepts.

CONCEPT	DESCRIPTION
Models	A good model describes and explains current data. It should also make predictions and forecast phenomena.
Linear model	If a quantity experiences a constant rate of change, then it can be modeled by a linear function in the form $f(x) = mx + b$. $$f(x) = (\text{constant rate of change})x + (\text{initial value})$$
Piecewise-defined function	A function is piecewise-defined if it has different formulas on different intervals of its domain. Many times the domain is restricted. $$f(x) = \begin{cases} 2x - 3 & \text{if } -3 \leq x < 1 \\ x + 5 & \text{if } 1 \leq x \leq 5 \end{cases}$$ When $x = 2$ then $f(x) = x + 5$, so $f(2) = 2 + 5 = 7$. The domain of f is $[-3, 5]$.

CONCEPT	DESCRIPTION
The greatest integer function	$[\![x]\!]$ is the greatest integer less than or equal to x. $[\![-5.9]\!] = -6, \quad [\![8.7]\!] = 8, \quad$ and $\quad [\![-5]\!] = -5$
Direct variation	The variable y is directly proportional to x or varies directly with x if $y = kx$ for some nonzero constant k. Constant k is the constant of proportionality or the constant of variation.

2.4 Exercises

Modeling with Linear Functions

Exercises 1 and 2: Write a symbolic representation (formula) for a function f that computes the following.

1. (a) The number of pounds in x ounces

   (b) The number of dimes in x dollars

   (c) The monthly electric bill in dollars if x kilowatt-hours are used at 6 cents per kilowatt-hour and there is a fee of $6.50

   (d) The cost of skiing x times with a $500 season pass

2. (a) The distance traveled by a car moving at 50 miles per hour for x hours

   (b) The total number of hours in day x

   (c) The distance in miles between a runner and home after x hours if the runner starts 1 mile from home and jogs *away* from home at 6 miles per hour

   (d) A car's speed in feet per second after x seconds if its tires are 2 feet in diameter and rotating 14 times per second

Exercises 3–6: Find the formula for a linear function f that models the data in the table exactly.

3.

x	-2	0	4
$f(x)$	4	3	1

4.

x	-6	0	3
$f(x)$	-5	-1	1

5.

x	1	2	3
$f(x)$	7	9	11

6.

x	15	30	45
$f(x)$	40	30	20

Exercises 7–10: Match the situation with the graph (a–d) that models it best, where x-values represent time.

7. Height of the Empire State Building from 1990 to 2010

8. Average cost of a new car from 1980 to 2010

9. Distance between a runner in a race and the finish line

10. Amount of money earned after x hours when working at an hourly rate of pay

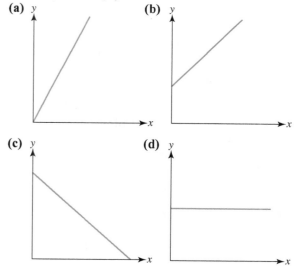

Exercises 11–16: Write a formula for a linear function that models the situation. Choose both an appropriate name and an appropriate variable for the function. State what the input variable represents and the domain of the function. Assume that the domain is an interval of the real numbers.

11. **U.S. Homes with Broadband** In 2010 about 27% of U.S. homes had broadband Internet access. This percentage is expected to increase, on average, by 1.2 percentage points per year for the next 4 years. (*Source:* Bureau of the Census.)

12. **Velocity of a Falling Object** A stone is dropped from a water tower and its velocity increases at a rate of 32 feet per second. The stone hits the ground with a velocity of 96 feet per second.

13. **Text Messages** In the first month of 2010 about 0.4 trillion text messages were sent. The number of text messages being sent during 2010 grew by 0.5 trillion per month. (*Source:* CTIA.)

14. **Speed of a Car** A car is traveling at 30 miles per hour, and then it begins to slow down at a constant rate of 6 miles per hour every 4 seconds.

15. **Population Density** In 1900 the average number of people per square mile in the United States was 21.5, and it increased, on average, by 6 people every 10 years until 2011. (*Source:* Bureau of the Census.)

16. **Injury Rate** In 1992 the number of injury cases recorded in private industry per 100 full-time workers was 8.3, and it decreased, on average, by 0.27 injury every year until 2010. (*Source:* Bureau of Labor Statistics.)

17. **Draining a Water Tank** A 300-gallon tank is initially full of water and is being drained at a rate of 10 gallons per minute.
    (a) Write a formula for a function W that gives the number of gallons of water in the tank after t minutes.
    (b) How much water is in the tank after 7 minutes?
    (c) Graph W and identify and interpret the intercepts.
    (d) Find the domain of W.

18. **Filling a Tank** A 500-gallon tank initially contains 200 gallons of fuel oil. A pump is filling the tank at a rate of 6 gallons per minute.
    (a) Write a formula for a linear function f that models the number of gallons of fuel oil in the tank after x minutes.
    (b) Graph f. What is an appropriate domain for f?
    (c) Identify the y-intercept and interpret it.
    (d) Does the x-intercept of the graph of f have any physical meaning in this problem? Explain.

19. **Living with HIV/AIDS** In 2007 there were 1.2 million people in the United States who had been infected with HIV. At that time the infection rate was 40,000 people per year. (*Source:* CDC.)
    (a) Write a formula for a linear function f that models the total number of people in millions who were living with HIV/AIDS x years after 2007.
    (b) Estimate the number of people who may have been infected by the year 2014.

20. **Birth Rate** In 1990 the number of births per 1000 people in the United States was 16.7 and decreasing, on average, at 0.136 birth per 1000 people each year. (*Source:* National Center for Health Statistics.)
    (a) Write a formula for a linear function f that models the birth rate x years after 1990.
    (b) Estimate the birth rate in 2012 and compare this estimate to the actual value of 13.7.

21. **Ice Deposits** A roof has a 0.5-inch layer of ice on it from a previous storm. Another ice storm begins to deposit ice at a rate of 0.25 inch per hour.
    (a) Find a formula for a linear function f that models the thickness of the ice on the roof x hours after the second ice storm started.
    (b) How thick is the ice after 2.5 hours?

22. **Rainfall** Suppose that during a storm rain is falling at a rate of 1 inch per hour. The water coming from a circular roof with a radius of 20 feet is running down a downspout that can accommodate 400 gallons of water per hour. See the figure.
    (a) Determine the number of cubic inches of water falling on the roof in 1 hour.
    (b) One gallon equals about 231 cubic inches. Write a formula for a function g that computes the gallons of water landing on the roof in x hours.
    (c) How many gallons of water land on the roof during a 2.5-hour rain storm?
    (d) Will one downspout be sufficient to handle this type of rainfall? How many downspouts should there be?

Exercises 23 and 24: **Modeling Fuel Consumption** *The table shows the distance y in miles traveled by a vehicle using x gallons of gasoline.*

(a) *Calculate the slopes of the line segments that connect consecutive points.*
(b) *Find a linear function that models the data.*
(c) *Graph f and the data together. What does the slope indicate?*
(d) *Evaluate $f(30)$ and interpret the result.*

23.

x (gallons)	5	10	15	20
y (miles)	84	169	255	338

24.

x (gallons)	5	10	15	20
y (miles)	194	392	580	781

Piecewise-Defined Functions

25. Speed Limits The graph of $y = f(x)$ gives the speed limit y along a rural highway x miles from its starting point.

(a) What are the maximum and minimum speed limits along this stretch of highway?

(b) Estimate the miles of highway with a speed limit of 55 miles per hour.

(c) Evaluate $f(4)$, $f(12)$, and $f(18)$.

(d) At what x-values is the graph discontinuous? Interpret each discontinuity.

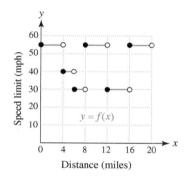

26. ATM The graph of $y = f(x)$ depicts the amount of money y in dollars in an automatic teller machine (ATM) after x minutes.

(a) Determine the initial and final amounts of money in the ATM.

(b) Evaluate $f(10)$ and $f(50)$. Is f continuous?

(c) How many *withdrawals* occurred?

(d) When did the largest withdrawal occur? How much was it?

(e) How much was deposited into the machine?

27. First-Class Mail In January 2012, the retail flat rate in dollars for first-class mail weighing up to 5 ounces could be computed by the piecewise-constant function P, where x is the number of ounces.

$$P(x) = \begin{cases} 0.90 & \text{if } 0 < x \le 1 \\ 1.10 & \text{if } 1 < x \le 2 \\ 1.30 & \text{if } 2 < x \le 3 \\ 1.50 & \text{if } 3 < x \le 4 \\ 1.70 & \text{if } 4 < x \le 5 \end{cases}$$

(a) Evaluate $P(1.5)$ and $P(3)$. Interpret your results.

(b) Sketch a graph of P. What is the domain of P?

(c) Where is P discontinuous on its domain?

28. Swimming Pool Levels The graph of $y = f(x)$ shows the amount of water y in thousands of gallons remaining in a swimming pool after x days.

(a) Estimate the initial and final amounts of water in the pool.

(b) When did the amount of water in the pool remain constant?

(c) Approximate $f(2)$ and $f(4)$.

(d) At what rate was water being drained from the pool when $1 \le x \le 3$?

Exercises 29 and 30: An individual is driving a car along a straight road. The graph shows the driver's distance from home after x hours.

(a) Use the graph to evaluate $f(1.5)$ and $f(4)$.

(b) Interpret the slope of each line segment.

(c) Describe the motion of the car.

(d) Identify where f is increasing, decreasing, or constant.

29.

30.

Exercises 31–36: Complete the following for f(x).

(a) Determine the domain of f.
(b) Evaluate f(−2), f(0), and f(3).
(c) Graph f.
(d) Is f continuous on its domain?

31. $f(x) = \begin{cases} 2 & \text{if } -5 \le x \le -1 \\ x + 3 & \text{if } -1 < x \le 5 \end{cases}$

32. $f(x) = \begin{cases} 2x + 1 & \text{if } -3 \le x < 0 \\ x - 1 & \text{if } 0 \le x \le 3 \end{cases}$

33. $f(x) = \begin{cases} 3x & \text{if } -1 \le x < 1 \\ x + 1 & \text{if } 1 \le x \le 2 \end{cases}$

34. $f(x) = \begin{cases} -2 & \text{if } -6 \le x < -2 \\ 0 & \text{if } -2 \le x < 0 \\ 3x & \text{if } 0 \le x \le 4 \end{cases}$

35. $f(x) = \begin{cases} x & \text{if } -3 \le x \le -1 \\ 1 & \text{if } -1 < x < 1 \\ 2 - x & \text{if } 1 \le x \le 3 \end{cases}$

36. $f(x) = \begin{cases} 3 & \text{if } -4 \le x \le -1 \\ x - 2 & \text{if } -1 < x \le 2 \\ 0.5x & \text{if } 2 < x \le 4 \end{cases}$

Exercises 37 and 38: Graph f.

37. $f(x) = \begin{cases} -\frac{1}{2}x + 1 & \text{if } -4 \le x \le -2 \\ 1 - 2x & \text{if } -2 < x \le 1 \\ \frac{2}{3}x + \frac{4}{3} & \text{if } 1 < x \le 4 \end{cases}$

38. $f(x) = \begin{cases} \frac{3}{2} - \frac{1}{2}x & \text{if } -3 \le x < -1 \\ -2x & \text{if } -1 \le x \le 2 \\ \frac{1}{2}x - 5 & \text{if } 2 < x \le 3 \end{cases}$

39. Use $f(x)$ to complete the following.

$$f(x) = \begin{cases} 3x - 1 & \text{if } -5 \le x < 1 \\ 4 & \text{if } 1 \le x \le 3 \\ 6 - x & \text{if } 3 < x \le 5 \end{cases}$$

(a) Evaluate f at $x = -3, 1, 2$, and 5.

(b) On what interval is f constant?

(c) Sketch a graph of f. Is f continuous on its domain?

40. Use $g(x)$ to complete the following.

$$g(x) = \begin{cases} -2x - 6 & \text{if } -8 \le x \le -2 \\ x & \text{if } -2 < x < 2 \\ 0.5x + 1 & \text{if } 2 \le x \le 8 \end{cases}$$

(a) Evaluate g at $x = -8, -2, 2$, and 8.

(b) For what x-values is g increasing?

(c) Sketch a graph of g. Is g continuous on its domain?

Exercises 41 and 42: Use the graph of $y = f(x)$ to write a piecewise-defined formula for f. Write each piece in slope-intercept form.

41.

42.

43. Housing Market One way to describe the housing market is to divide the population of the United States by the number of new housing starts. This ratio is listed in the following table for selected years.

Year	2000	2005	2009	2011
Ratio	225	180	700	727

Source: Bureau of the Census.

(a) Plot a line graph of these data. Let this graph be function R.

(b) Evaluate $R(2009)$ and interpret the result. Do small or large values indicate a strong housing market?

(c) Is R continuous on its domain?

(d) Identify where R is increasing, decreasing, or constant.

(e) Write a piecewise-defined formula for R.

44. **High School Dropouts** The table lists the percentage of the population that did not have a high school diploma for selected years.

Year	1960	1980	2000	2010
Percentage	28	14	11	8

Source: Bureau of the Census.

(a) Plot a line graph of these data. Let this graph be function D.

(b) Interpret the slope of each line segment.

(c) Is D continuous on its domain?

(d) Identify where D is increasing, decreasing, or constant.

(e) Write a piecewise-defined formula for D.

Greatest Integer Function

Exercises 45–48: Complete the following.

(a) *Use dot mode to graph the function f in the standard viewing rectangle.*
(b) *Evaluate $f(-3.1)$ and $f(1.7)$.*
45. $f(x) = [\![2x - 1]\!]$ 46. $f(x) = [\![x + 1]\!]$

47. $f(x) = 2[\![x]\!] + 1$ 48. $f(x) = [\![-x]\!]$

49. **Lumber Costs** The lumber used to frame walls of houses is frequently sold in multiples of 2 feet. If the length of a board is not exactly a multiple of 2 feet, there is often no charge for the additional length. For example, if a board measures at least 8 feet but less than 10 feet, then the consumer is charged for only 8 feet.
(a) Suppose that the cost of lumber is $0.80 for every 2 feet. Find a formula for a function f that computes the cost of a board x feet long for $6 \le x \le 18$.

(b) Graph f.

(c) Determine the costs of boards with lengths of 8.5 feet and 15.2 feet.

50. **Cost of Carpet** Each foot of carpet purchased from a 12-foot-wide roll costs $36. If a fraction of a foot is purchased, a customer does not pay for the extra amount. For example, if a customer wants 14 feet of carpet and the salesperson cuts off 14 feet 4 inches, the customer does not pay for the extra 4 inches.
(a) How much does 9 feet 8 inches of carpet from this roll cost?

(b) Using the greatest integer function, write a formula for the price P of x feet of carpet.

Direct Variation

Exercises 51–54: Let y be directly proportional to x. Complete the following.

51. Find y when $x = 5$, if $y = 7$ when $x = 14$.

52. Find y when $x = 2.5$, if $y = 13$ when $x = 10$.

53. Find y when $x = \frac{1}{2}$, if $y = \frac{3}{2}$ when $x = \frac{2}{3}$.

54. Find y when $x = 1.3$, if $y = 7.2$ when $x = 5.2$.

Exercises 55–58: Find the constant of proportionality k and the undetermined value in the table if y is directly proportional to x.

55.

x	3	5	6	8
y	7.5	12.5	15	?

56.

x	1.2	4.3	5.7	?
y	3.96	14.19	18.81	23.43

57. Sales tax y on a purchase of x dollars

x	$25	$55	?
y	$1.50	$3.30	$5.10

58. Cost y of buying x compact discs at the same price

x	3	4	5
y	$41.97	$55.96	?

59. **Cost of Tuition** The cost of tuition is directly proportional to the number of credits taken. If 11 credits cost $720.50, find the cost of taking 16 credits. What is the constant of proportionality?

60. **Strength of a Beam** The maximum load that a horizontal beam can carry is directly proportional to its width. If a beam 1.5 inches wide can support a load of 250 pounds, find the load that a beam of the same type can support if its width is 3.5 inches.

61. **Antarctic Ozone Layer** Stratospheric ozone occurs in the atmosphere between altitudes of 12 and 18 miles. Ozone in the stratosphere is frequently measured in Dobson units, where 300 Dobson units corresponds to an ozone layer 3 millimeters thick. In 1991 the reported minimum in the Antarctic *ozone hole* was about 110 Dobson units. (***Source:*** R. Huffman, *Atmospheric Ultraviolet Remote Sensing.*)
(a) The thickness y of the ozone layer is directly proportional to the number of Dobson units x. Find the constant of proportionality k.

(b) How thick was the ozone layer in 1991?

62. Weight on Mars The weight of an object on Earth is directly proportional to the weight of an object on Mars. If a 25-pound object on Earth weighs 10 pounds on Mars, how much would a 195-pound astronaut weigh on Mars?

63. Hooke's Law Suppose a 15-pound weight stretches a spring 8 inches, as shown in the figure.

8 in.

15 lb

(a) Find the spring constant.

(b) How far will a 25-pound weight stretch this spring?

64. Hooke's Law If an 80-pound force compresses a spring 3 inches, how much force must be applied to compress the spring 7 inches?

65. Force of Friction The table lists the force F needed to push a cargo box weighing x pounds on a wood floor.

x (lb)	150	180	210	320
F (lb)	26	31	36	54

(a) Compute the ratio $\frac{F}{x}$ for each data pair in the table. Interpret these ratios.

(b) Approximate a constant of proportionality k satisfying $F = kx$. (k is the *coefficient of friction*.)

(c) Graph the data and the equation together.

(d) Estimate the force needed to push a 275-pound cargo box on the floor.

66. Electrical Resistance The electrical resistance of a wire varies directly with its length. If a 255-foot wire has a resistance of 1.2 ohms, find the resistance of 135 feet of the same type of wire. Interpret the constant of proportionality in this situation.

Linear Regression

67. Ring Size The table lists ring size S for a finger with circumference x in centimeters.

x (cm)	4.65	5.40	5.66	6.41
S (size)	4	7	8	11

Source: Overstock.

(a) Find a linear function S that models the data.

(b) Find the circumference of a finger with a ring size of 6.

68. Hat Size The table lists hat size H for a head with circumference x in inches.

x (in.)	$21\frac{1}{8}$	$21\frac{7}{8}$	$22\frac{5}{8}$	25
S (size)	$6\frac{3}{4}$	7	$7\frac{1}{4}$	8

(a) Find a linear function S that models the data.

(b) Find the circumference of a head with a hat size of $7\frac{1}{2}$.

69. Super Bowl Ads The table lists the cost in millions of dollars for a 30-second Super Bowl commercial for selected years.

Year	1994	1998	2004	2008	2012
Cost	1.2	1.6	2.3	2.7	3.5

Source: MSNBC.

(a) Find a linear function f that models the data.

(b) Estimate the cost in 2009 and compare the estimate to the actual value of $3.0 million. Did your estimate involve interpolation or extrapolation?

(c) Use f to predict the year when the cost could reach $4.0 million.

70. Women in Politics The table lists the percentage P of women in state legislatures during year x.

x	1993	1997	2001	2005	2007
P	20.5	21.6	22.4	22.7	23.5

Source: National Women's Political Caucus.

(a) Find a linear function P that models the data.

(b) Estimate this percentage in 2003 and compare the estimate to the actual value of 22.4%. Did your estimate involve interpolation or extrapolation?

(c) Use P to predict the year when this percentage could reach 25%.

Writing about Mathematics

71. Explain what a piecewise-defined function is and why it is used. Sketch a graph of a continuous piecewise-linear function f that increases, decreases, and is constant. Let the domain of f be $-4 \leq x \leq 4$.

72. Find a real data set on the Internet that can be modeled by a linear function. Find the linear modeling function. Is your model exact or approximate? Explain.

73. How can you recognize a symbolic representation (formula) of a linear function? How can you recognize a graph or table of values of a linear function?

74. Explain how you determine whether a linear function is increasing, decreasing, or constant. Give an example of each.

Extended and Discovery Exercises

Exercises 1 and 2: **Estimating Populations** *Biologists sometimes use direct variation to estimate the number of fish in small lakes. They start by tagging a small number of fish and then releasing them. They assume that over a period of time, the tagged fish distribute themselves evenly throughout the lake. Later, they collect a second sample. The total number of fish and the number of tagged fish in the second sample are counted. To determine the total population of fish in the lake, biologists assume that the proportion of tagged fish in the second sample is equal to the proportion of tagged fish in the entire lake. This technique can also be used to count other types of animals, such as birds, when they are not migrating.*

1. Eighty-five fish are tagged and released into a pond. A later sample of 94 fish from the pond contains 13 tagged fish. Estimate the number of fish in the pond.

2. Sixty-three blackbirds are tagged and released. Later it is estimated that out of a sample of 32 blackbirds, only 8 are tagged. Estimate the population of blackbirds in the area.

3. **Height and Shoe Size** In this exercise you will determine if there is a relationship between height and shoe size.

   (a) Have classmates write their sex, shoe size, and height in inches on a slip of paper. When you have enough information, complete the following table—one for adult males and one for adult females.

Height (inches)				
Shoe size				

   (b) Make a scatterplot of each table, with height on the *x*-axis and shoe size on the *y*-axis. Is there any relationship between height and shoe size? Explain.

   (c) Try to find a linear function that models each data set.

Exercises 4 and 5: **Linear Approximation** *Graph the function f in the standard viewing rectangle.*

(a) *Choose any curved portion of the graph of f and repeatedly zoom in. Describe how the graph appears. Repeat this process on different portions of the graph.*

(b) *Under what circumstances could a linear function be used to accurately model a nonlinear graph?*

4. $f(x) = 4x - x^3$

5. $f(x) = x^4 - 5x^2$

CHECKING BASIC CONCEPTS FOR SECTIONS 2.3 AND 2.4

1. Solve the inequality $2(x - 4) > 1 - x$. Express the solution set in set-builder notation.

2. Solve the compound inequality $-2 \leq 1 - 2x \leq 3$. Use set-builder or interval notation.

3. Use the graph to solve each equation and inequality. Then solve each part symbolically. Use set-builder or interval notation when possible.

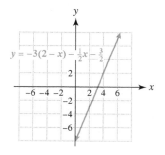

(a) $-3(2 - x) - \frac{1}{2}x - \frac{3}{2} = 0$

(b) $-3(2 - x) - \frac{1}{2}x - \frac{3}{2} > 0$

(c) $-3(2 - x) - \frac{1}{2}x - \frac{3}{2} \leq 0$

4. The death rate from heart disease for people ages 15 through 24 is 2.7 per 100,000 people.

   (a) Write a function f that models the number of deaths in a population of x million people 15 to 24 years old.

   (b) There are about 39 million people in the United States who are 15 to 24 years old. Estimate the number of deaths from heart disease in this age group.

5. A driver of a car is initially 50 miles south of home, driving 60 miles per hour south. Write a function f that models the distance between the driver and home.

2.5 Absolute Value Equations and Inequalities

- **Evaluate and graph the absolute value function**
- **Solve absolute value equations**
- **Solve absolute value inequalities**

Introduction

A margin of error can be very important in many aspects of life, including being fired out of a cannon. The most dangerous part of the feat, first done by a human in 1875, is to land squarely on a net. For a human cannonball who wants to fly 180 feet in the air and then land in the center of a net with a 60-foot-long safe zone, there is a margin of error of ± 30 feet. That is, the horizontal distance D traveled by the human cannonball can vary between $180 - 30 = 150$ feet and $180 + 30 = 210$ feet. (***Source:*** Ontario Science Center.)

This margin of error can be expressed mathematically by using the *absolute value inequality*

$$|D - 180| \leq 30.$$

The absolute value is necessary because D can be either less than or greater than 180, but by not more than 30 feet.

The Absolute Value Function

The absolute value function is defined by $f(x) = |x|$. The following See the Concept describes many of the properties of this function.

See the Concept: The Absolute Value Function

x	$\|x\|$
-2	2
-1	1
0	0
1	1
2	2

$y = -x$, when $x < 0$ $y = x$, when $x \geq 0$

Domain: All real numbers

Range: $y \geq 0$

Increasing: $x > 0$

Decreasing: $x < 0$

Symbolic Representations (Formulas) The graph of the absolute value function suggests that the absolute value function can be defined symbolically using the following piecewise-linear function.

$$|x| = \begin{cases} -x & \text{if } x < 0 \\ x & \text{if } x \geq 0 \end{cases} \qquad \textit{Piecewise-linear function}$$

There is another formula for $|x|$. Consider the following examples.

$$\sqrt{3^2} = \sqrt{9} = 3 \quad \text{and} \quad \sqrt{(-3)^2} = \sqrt{9} = 3$$
$$\sqrt{7^2} = \sqrt{49} = 7 \quad \text{and} \quad \sqrt{(-7)^2} = \sqrt{49} = 7$$

That is, regardless of whether a real number x is positive or negative, the expression $\sqrt{x^2}$ equals the *absolute value* of x. This statement is summarized by

$$\sqrt{x^2} = |x| \qquad \text{for all real numbers } x.$$

For example, $\sqrt{y^2} = |y|$, $\sqrt{(x-1)^2} = |x-1|$, and $\sqrt{(2x)^2} = |2x|$.

Calculator Help

To access the absolute value function, see Appendix A (page AP-8).

EXAMPLE 1   Analyzing the graph of $y = |ax + b|$

Graph $y = f(x)$ and $y = |f(x)|$ separately. Discuss how the absolute value affects the graph of f.

(a) $f(x) = x + 2$ (b) $f(x) = -2x + 4$

SOLUTION

(a) The line $y = x + 2$ is shown in Figure 2.52. The graph of $y = |x + 2|$ in Figure 2.53 is V-shaped and *never* dips below the x-axis because an absolute value is *never* negative.

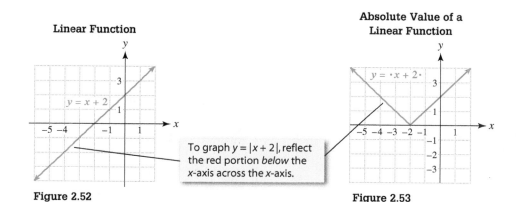

Figure 2.52

Figure 2.53

(b) The graphs of $y_1 = -2x + 4$ and $y_2 = |-2x + 4|$ are shown in Figures 2.54 and 2.55, respectively.

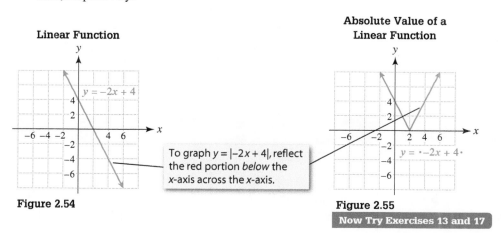

Figure 2.54

Figure 2.55

Now Try Exercises 13 and 17

NOTE Example 1 illustrates the fact that the graph of $y = |ax + b|$ with $a \neq 0$ is V-shaped and is never located below the x-axis. The vertex (or point) of the V-shaped graph corresponds to the x-intercept, which can be found by solving the linear equation $ax + b = 0$.

Graphs and the Absolute Value In general, the graph of $y = |f(x)|$ is a reflection of the graph of $y = f(x)$ across the x-axis whenever $f(x) < 0$. Otherwise (whenever $f(x) > 0$), their graphs are identical. The following graphs illustrate this connection.

The Effect of the Absolute Value on a Graph

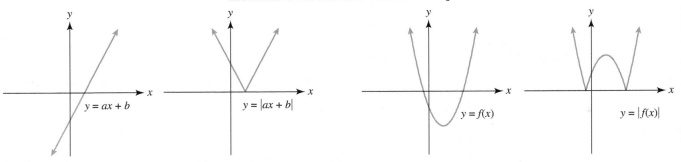

Absolute Value Equations

The equation $|x| = 5$ has two solutions: ± 5. This fact is shown visually in Figure 2.56, where the graph of $y = |x|$ intersects the horizontal line $y = 5$ at the points $(\pm 5, 5)$. In general, the solutions to $|x| = k$ with $k > 0$ are given by $x = \pm k$. See Figure 2.57.

Solving $|x| = 5$ Graphically

Two solutions: $-5, 5$

Figure 2.56

Solving $|x| = k$ Graphically

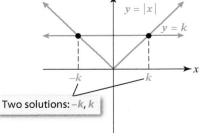

Two solutions: $-k, k$

Figure 2.57

The absolute value equation $|ax + b| = k$ can be solved graphically. In the following box, the V-shaped graph of $y = |ax + b|$ intersects the horizontal line ($y = k$) two, one, or zero times, depending on the value of k.

See the Concept: Solving $|ax + b| = k$ Graphically

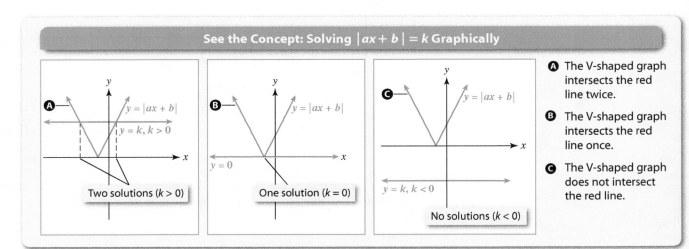

Two solutions ($k > 0$)

One solution ($k = 0$)

No solutions ($k < 0$)

Ⓐ The V-shaped graph intersects the red line twice.

Ⓑ The V-shaped graph intersects the red line once.

Ⓒ The V-shaped graph does not intersect the red line.

Because the solution to $|x| = k$ are given by $x = \pm k$, it follows that the solutions to $|ax + b| = k$ are given by $ax + b = \pm k$. This concept is used to solve absolute value equations symbolically.

ABSOLUTE VALUE EQUATIONS

Let k be a positive number. Then

$$|ax + b| = k \quad \text{is equivalent to} \quad ax + b = \pm k.$$

EXAMPLE 2 Solving absolute value equations

Solve each equation.
(a) $\left|\frac{3}{4}x - 6\right| = 15$ **(b)** $|1 - 2x| = -3$ **(c)** $|3x - 2| - 5 = -2$

SOLUTION
(a) The equation $\left|\frac{3}{4}x - 6\right| = 15$ is satisfied when $\frac{3}{4}x - 6 = \pm 15$.

$$\frac{3}{4}x - 6 = 15 \qquad \text{or} \qquad \frac{3}{4}x - 6 = -15 \qquad \textit{Equations to solve}$$
$$\frac{3}{4}x = 21 \qquad \text{or} \qquad \frac{3}{4}x = -9 \qquad \textit{Add 6 to each side.}$$
$$x = 28 \qquad \text{or} \qquad x = -12 \qquad \textit{Multiply by } \frac{4}{3}.$$

The solutions are -12 and 28.

No Solutions

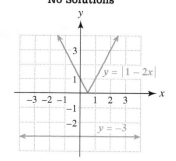

Figure 2.58

(b) Because an absolute value is never negative, $|1 - 2x| \geq 0$ for all x and can never equal -3. There are no solutions. This is illustrated graphically in Figure 2.58.

(c) Because the right side of the equation is a negative number, it might appear at first glance that there were no solutions. However, if we add 5 to each side of the equation,

$$|3x - 2| - 5 = -2 \quad \text{becomes} \quad |3x - 2| = 3.$$

This equation is equivalent to $3x - 2 = \pm 3$ and has two solutions.

$$3x - 2 = 3 \qquad \text{or} \qquad 3x - 2 = -3 \qquad \textit{Equations to solve}$$
$$3x = 5 \qquad \text{or} \qquad 3x = -1 \qquad \textit{Add 2 to each side.}$$
$$x = \frac{5}{3} \qquad \text{or} \qquad x = -\frac{1}{3} \qquad \textit{Divide by 3.}$$

The solutions are $-\frac{1}{3}$ and $\frac{5}{3}$.

> **Now Try Exercises 21, 29, and 31**

EXAMPLE 3 Solving an equation with technology

Solve the equation $|2x + 5| = 2$ graphically, numerically, and symbolically.

SOLUTION
Graphical Solution Graph $y_1 = |2x + 5|$ and $y_2 = 2$. The V-shaped graph of y_1 intersects the horizontal line at the points $(-3.5, 2)$ and $(-1.5, 2)$, as shown in Figures 2.59 and 2.60. The solutions are -3.5 and -1.5.

Numerical Solution Table y_1 and y_2, as shown in Figure 2.61. The solutions to $y_1 = y_2$ are -3.5 and -1.5.

Calculator Help
To find a point of intersection, see Appendix A (page AP-7).

First Graphical Solution

$[-9, 9, 1]$ by $[-6, 6, 1]$

Figure 2.59

Second Graphical Solution

$[-9, 9, 1]$ by $[-6, 6, 1]$

Figure 2.60

Numerical Solutions

Figure 2.61

Symbolic Solution The equation $|2x + 5| = 2$ is satisfied when $2x + 5 = \pm 2$.

$2x + 5 = 2$	or	$2x + 5 = -2$	Equations to solve
$2x = -3$	or	$2x = -7$	Subtract 5 from each side.
$x = -\dfrac{3}{2}$	or	$x = -\dfrac{7}{2}$	Divide by 2.

> Now Try Exercises 45(a), (b), (c)

EXAMPLE 4 Describing speed limits with absolute values

The maximum and minimum lawful speeds S on an interstate highway satisfy the equation $|S - 55| = 15$. Find the maximum and minimum speed limits.

SOLUTION The equation $|S - 55| = 15$ is equivalent to $S - 55 = \pm 15$.

$S - 55 = 15$	or	$S - 55 = -15$	Equations to solve
$S = 70$	or	$S = 40$	Add 55 to each side.

The maximum speed limit is 70 miles per hour and the minimum is 40 miles per hour.

> Now Try Exercise 73

An Equation with Two Absolute Values Sometimes more than one absolute value sign occurs in an equation. For example, an equation might be in the form

$$|ax + b| = |cx + d|.$$

In this case there are two possibilities:

either $\quad ax + b = cx + d \quad$ or $\quad ax + b = -(cx + d)$.

This symbolic technique is demonstrated in the next example.

EXAMPLE 5 Solving an equation involving two absolute values

Solve the equation $|x - 2| = |1 - 2x|$.

SOLUTION We must solve both of the following equations.

$x - 2 = 1 - 2x$	or	$x - 2 = -(1 - 2x)$
$3x = 3$	or	$x - 2 = -1 + 2x$
$x = 1$	or	$-1 = x$

There are two solutions: -1 and 1.

> Now Try Exercise 35

Absolute Value Inequalities

The solution set to an absolute value inequality can be understood graphically, as shown in the following See the Concept.

See the Concept: Solving $|ax + b| < k$ and $|ax + b| > k$ Graphically

Ⓐ The V-shaped graph is *below* the red line between s_1 and s_2. The solutions to $|ax + b| < k$ satisfy $s_1 < x < s_2$.

Ⓑ The V-shaped graph is *above* the red line to the left of s_1 and to the right of s_2. The solutions to $|ax + b| > k$ satisfy $x < s_1$ or $x > s_2$.

NOTE In both of the above figures, equality (determined by s_1 and s_2) is the boundary between *greater than* and *less than*. For this reason, s_1 and s_2 are called *boundary numbers*.

ABSOLUTE VALUE INEQUALITIES

Let the solutions to $|ax + b| = k$ be s_1 and s_2, where $s_1 < s_2$ and $k > 0$.

1. $|ax + b| < k$ is equivalent to $s_1 < x < s_2$.
2. $|ax + b| > k$ is equivalent to $x < s_1$ or $x > s_2$.

Similar statements can be made for inequalities involving $\leq$ or $\geq$.

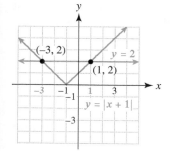

Figure 2.62

For example, the graphs of $y = |x + 1|$ and $y = 2$ are shown in Figure 2.62. These graphs intersect at the points $(-3, 2)$ and $(1, 2)$. It follows that the two solutions to

$$|x + 1| = 2$$

are $s_1 = -3$ and $s_2 = 1$. The solutions to $|x + 1| < 2$ lie between $s_1 = -3$ and $s_2 = 1$, which can be written as $-3 < x < 1$. Furthermore, the solutions to $|x + 1| > 2$ lie "outside" $s_1 = -3$ and $s_2 = 1$. This can be written as $x < -3$ or $x > 1$.

NOTE The **union symbol** $\cup$ may be used to write $x < s_1$ or $x > s_2$ in interval notation. For example, $x < -3$ or $x > 1$ is written as $(-\infty, -3) \cup (1, \infty)$ in interval notation. This indicates that the solution set includes all real numbers in either $(-\infty, -3)$ or $(1, \infty)$.

EXAMPLE 6 Solving inequalities involving absolute values symbolically

Solve each inequality symbolically. Write the solution set in interval notation.
(a) $|2x - 5| \leq 6$ **(b)** $|5 - x| > 3$

SOLUTION
(a) Begin by solving $|2x - 5| = 6$, or equivalently, $2x - 5 = \pm 6$.

$$2x - 5 = 6 \qquad \text{or} \qquad 2x - 5 = -6$$
$$2x = 11 \qquad \text{or} \qquad 2x = -1$$
$$x = \frac{11}{2} \qquad \text{or} \qquad x = -\frac{1}{2}$$

The solutions to $|2x - 5| = 6$ are $-\frac{1}{2}$ and $\frac{11}{2}$. The solution set for the inequality $|2x - 5| \leq 6$ includes all real numbers x satisfying $-\frac{1}{2} \leq x \leq \frac{11}{2}$. In interval notation this is written as $\left[-\frac{1}{2}, \frac{11}{2}\right]$.

(b) To solve $|5 - x| > 3$, begin by solving $|5 - x| = 3$, or equivalently, $5 - x = \pm 3$.

$$5 - x = 3 \qquad \text{or} \qquad 5 - x = -3$$
$$-x = -2 \qquad \text{or} \qquad -x = -8$$
$$x = 2 \qquad \text{or} \qquad x = 8$$

The solutions to $|5 - x| = 3$ are 2 and 8. Thus $|5 - x| > 3$ is equivalent to $x < 2$ or $x > 8$. In interval notation this is written as $(-\infty, 2) \cup (8, \infty)$.

Now Try Exercises 55 and 63

Error Tolerances The iPhone 4s is 4.5 inches in height. However, it would be impossible to make every iPhone 4s *exactly* 4.5 inches high. Instead there is typically an error tolerance, where the height of an actual iPhone must be within a certain range.

Suppose that the actual height of a particular phone is A inches, but it is specified that this phone should be S inches high. If the maximum error tolerance is E, then Figure 2.63 illustrates this situation.

Distance Between A and S Must Be Less Than E

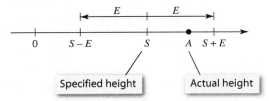

Figure 2.63

The value of A must be located between $S - E$ and $S + E$ on the number line. That is, the distance between A and S must be less than the error tolerance E, and this statement can be written as $|A - S| < E$.

EXAMPLE 7 Finding error tolerances on the iPhone 4s

The iPhone 4s is 4.5 inches high. Suppose that the actual height A of any particular iPhone has a maximum error tolerance that is less than 0.005 inch.
(a) Write an absolute value statement that describes this situation.
(b) Solve this inequality for A and interpret your result.

SOLUTION
(a) The distance between A and 4.5 on the number line must be less than 0.005. This statement can be written as $|A - 4.5| < 0.005$.
(b) To solve this inequality, we first solve $|A - 4.5| = 0.005$.

$$A - 4.5 = -0.005 \quad \text{or} \quad A - 4.5 = 0.005 \qquad \textit{First solve equality.}$$
$$A = 4.495 \quad \text{or} \qquad A = 4.505 \qquad \textit{Add 4.5 to each side.}$$

Thus $4.495 < A < 4.505$. The actual height must be greater than 4.495 inches *and* less than 4.505 inches.

Now Try Exercise 83

An Alternative Method There is a second symbolic method that can be used to solve absolute value inequalities. This method is often used in advanced mathematics courses, such as calculus. It is based on the following two properties.

> **ABSOLUTE VALUE INEQUALITIES (ALTERNATIVE METHOD)**
>
> Let k be a positive number.
> 1. $|ax + b| < k$ is equivalent to $-k < ax + b < k$.
> 2. $|ax + b| > k$ is equivalent to $ax + b < -k$ or $ax + b > k$.
>
> Similar statements can be made for inequalities involving $\leq$ or $\geq$.

EXAMPLE 8   Using an alternative method

Solve each absolute value inequality. Write your answer in interval notation.
(a) $|4 - 5x| \leq 3$
(b) $|-4x - 6| > 2$

SOLUTION
(a) $|4 - 5x| \leq 3$ is equivalent to the following three-part inequality.

$$-3 \leq 4 - 5x \leq 3 \qquad \text{Equivalent inequality}$$

$$-7 \leq -5x \leq -1 \qquad \text{Subtract 4 from each part.}$$

$$\frac{7}{5} \geq x \geq \frac{1}{5} \qquad \text{Divide each part by } -5; \text{ reverse the inequality.}$$

In interval notation the solution is $\left[\frac{1}{5}, \frac{7}{5}\right]$.

(b) $|-4x - 6| > 2$ is equivalent to the following compound inequality.

$-4x - 6 < -2$	or	$-4x - 6 > 2$	Equivalent compound inequality
$-4x < 4$	or	$-4x > 8$	Add 6 to each side.
$x > -1$	or	$x < -2$	Divide each by -4; reverse the inequality.

In interval notation the solution set is $(-\infty, -2) \cup (-1, \infty)$.

Now Try Exercises 57 and 61

> **CLASS DISCUSSION**
>
> Sketch the graphs of $y = ax + b$, $y = |ax + b|$, $y = -k$, and $y = k$ on one xy-plane. Now use these graphs to explain why the alternative method for solving absolute value inequalities is correct.

2.5 Putting It All Together

The following table summarizes some important concepts from this section.

CONCEPT	EXPLANATION	EXAMPLES
Absolute value function	$f(x) = |x|$: The output from the absolute value function is never negative. $|x|$ is equivalent to $\sqrt{x^2}$. $|x| = \begin{cases} -x & \text{if } x < 0 \\ x & \text{if } x \geq 0 \end{cases}$	$f(-2) = |-2| = 2$

continued on next page

CONCEPT	EXPLANATION	EXAMPLES
Absolute value equations	**1.** If $k > 0$, then $\lvert ax + b \rvert = k$ has two solutions, given by $ax + b = \pm k$.	**1.** Solve $\lvert 3x - 5 \rvert = 4$. $3x - 5 = -4$ or $3x - 5 = 4$ $3x = 1$ or $3x = 9$ $x = \frac{1}{3}$ or $x = 3$
	2. If $k = 0$, then $\lvert ax + b \rvert = k$ has one solution, given by $ax + b = 0$.	**2.** Solve $\lvert x - 1 \rvert = 0$. $x - 1 = 0$ implies $x = 1$.
	3. If $k < 0$, then $\lvert ax + b \rvert = k$ has no solutions.	**3.** $\lvert 4x - 9 \rvert = -2$ has no solutions.
Absolute value inequalities	To solve $\lvert ax + b \rvert < k$ or $\lvert ax + b \rvert > k$ with $k > 0$, first solve $\lvert ax + b \rvert = k$. Let these solutions be s_1 and s_2, where $s_1 < s_2$.	To solve $\lvert x - 5 \rvert < 4$ or $\lvert x - 5 \rvert > 4$, first solve $\lvert x - 5 \rvert = 4$ to obtain the solutions $s_1 = 1$ and $s_2 = 9$.
	1. $\lvert ax + b \rvert < k$ is equivalent to $s_1 < x < s_2$.	**1.** $\lvert x - 5 \rvert < 4$ is equivalent to $1 < x < 9$.
	2. $\lvert ax + b \rvert > k$ is equivalent to $x < s_1$ or $x > s_2$.	**2.** $\lvert x - 5 \rvert > 4$ is equivalent to $x < 1$ or $x > 9$.
Alternative method	**1.** $\lvert ax + b \rvert < k$ with $k > 0$ is equivalent to $-k < ax + b < k$.	**1.** $\lvert x - 1 \rvert < 5$ is solved as follows. $-5 < x - 1 < 5$ $-4 < x < 6$
	2. $\lvert ax + b \rvert > k$ with $k > 0$ is equivalent to $ax + b < -k$ or $ax + b > k$.	**2.** $\lvert x - 1 \rvert > 5$ is solved as follows. $x - 1 < -5$ or $x - 1 > 5$ $x < -4$ or $x > 6$

2.5 Exercises

Basic Concepts

Exercises 1–8: Let $a \neq 0$.

1. Solve $\lvert x \rvert = 3$.

2. Solve $\lvert x \rvert \leq 3$.

3. Solve $\lvert x \rvert > 3$.

4. Solve $\lvert ax + b \rvert \leq -2$.

5. Describe the graph of $y = \lvert ax + b \rvert$.

6. Solve $\lvert ax + b \rvert = 0$.

7. Rewrite $\sqrt{36a^2}$ by using an absolute value.

8. Rewrite $\sqrt{(ax + b)^2}$ by using an absolute value.

Absolute Value Graphs

Exercises 9–12: Graph by hand.

(a) Find the x-intercept.

(b) Determine where the graph is increasing and where it is decreasing.

9. $y = \lvert x + 1 \rvert$

10. $y = \lvert 1 - x \rvert$

11. $y = \lvert 2x - 3 \rvert$

12. $y = \lvert \frac{1}{2}x + 1 \rvert$

Exercises 13–18: (Refer to Example 1.) Do the following.

(a) Graph $y = f(x)$.

(b) Use the graph of $y = f(x)$ to sketch a graph of the equation $y = \lvert f(x) \rvert$.

(c) Determine the x-intercept for the graph of $y = \lvert f(x) \rvert$.

13. $y = 2x$

14. $y = \frac{1}{2}x$

15. $y = 3x - 3$

16. $y = 2x - 4$

17. $y = 6 - 2x$

18. $y = 2 - 4x$

Absolute Value Equations and Inequalities

Exercises 19–40: Solve the absolute value equation.

19. $|-2x| = 4$

20. $|3x| = -6$

21. $|5x - 7| = 2$

22. $|-3x - 2| = 5$

23. $|3 - 4x| = 5$

24. $|2 - 3x| = 1$

25. $|-6x - 2| = 0$

26. $|6x - 9| = 0$

27. $|7 - 16x| = 0$

28. $|-x - 4| = 0$

29. $|17x - 6| = -3$

30. $|-8x - 11| = -7$

31. $|1.2x - 1.7| - 5 = -1$

32. $|3 - 3x| - 2 = 2$

33. $|4x - 5| + 3 = 2$

34. $|4.5 - 2x| + 1.1 = 9.7$

35. $|2x - 9| = |8 - 3x|$

36. $|x - 3| = |8 - x|$

37. $\left|\frac{3}{4}x - \frac{1}{4}\right| = \left|\frac{3}{4} - \frac{1}{4}x\right|$

38. $\left|\frac{1}{2}x + \frac{3}{2}\right| = \left|\frac{3}{2}x - \frac{7}{2}\right|$

39. $|15x - 5| = |35 - 5x|$

40. $|20x - 40| = |80x - 20|$

Exercises 41 and 42. The graphs of f and g are shown. Solve each equation and inequality.

41. **(a)** $f(x) = g(x)$

    (b) $f(x) < g(x)$

    (c) $f(x) > g(x)$

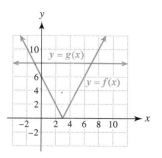

42. **(a)** $f(x) = g(x)$

    (b) $f(x) \le g(x)$

    (c) $f(x) \ge g(x)$

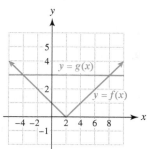

Exercises 43 and 44: Solve each equation or inequality.

43. **(a)** $|2x - 3| = 1$

    (b) $|2x - 3| < 1$

    (c) $|2x - 3| > 1$

44. **(a)** $|5 - x| = 2$

    (b) $|5 - x| \le 2$

    (c) $|5 - x| \ge 2$

Exercises 45–48: Solve the equation

(a) *graphically,*

(b) *numerically, and*

(c) *symbolically.*

Then solve the related inequality.

45. $|2x - 5| = 10,$ $|2x - 5| < 10$

46. $|3x - 4| = 8,$ $|3x - 4| \le 8$

47. $|5 - 3x| = 2,$ $|5 - 3x| > 2$

48. $|4x - 7| = 5,$ $|4x - 7| \ge 5$

Exercises 49–54: Solve the equation symbolically. Then solve the related inequality.

49. $|2.1x - 0.7| = 2.4,$ $|2.1x - 0.7| \ge 2.4$

50. $\left|\frac{1}{2}x - \frac{3}{4}\right| = \frac{7}{4},$ $\left|\frac{1}{2}x - \frac{3}{4}\right| \le \frac{7}{4}$

51. $|3x| + 5 = 6,$ $|3x| + 5 > 6$

52. $|x| - 10 = 25,$ $|x| - 10 < 25$

53. $\left|\frac{2}{3}x - \frac{1}{2}\right| = -\frac{1}{4},$ $\left|\frac{2}{3}x - \frac{1}{2}\right| \le -\frac{1}{4}$

54. $|5x - 0.3| = -4,$ $|5x - 0.3| > -4$

You Decide the Method

Exercises 55–66: Solve the inequality. Write the solution in interval notation.

55. $|3x - 1| < 8$

56. $|15 - x| < 7$

57. $|7 - 4x| \le 11$

58. $|-3x + 1| \le 5$

59. $|0.5x - 0.75| < 2$

60. $|2.1x - 5| \le 8$

61. $|2x - 3| > 1$

62. $|5x - 7| > 2$

63. $|-3x + 8| \ge 3$

64. $|-7x - 3| \ge 5$

65. $|0.25x - 1| > 3$

66. $|-0.5x + 5| \ge 4$

Domain and Range

67. If $f(k) = -6$, what is the value of $|f(k)|$?

68. If $f(k) = 17$, what is the value of $|f(k)|$?

69. If the domain of $f(x)$ is given by $[-2, 4]$, what is the domain of $|f(x)|$?

70. If the domain of $f(x)$ is given by $(-\infty, 0]$, what is the domain of $|f(x)|$?

71. If the range of $f(x)$ is given by $(-\infty, 0]$, what is the range of $|f(x)|$?

72. If the range of $f(x)$ is given by $(-4, 5)$, what is the range of $|f(x)|$?

Applications

73. Speed Limits The maximum and minimum lawful speeds S on an interstate highway satisfy the equation $|S - 57.5| = 17.5$. Find the maximum and minimum speed limits.

74. Human Cannonball A human cannonball plans to travel 180 feet and land squarely on a net with a 70-foot-long safe zone.
(a) What distances D can this performer travel and still land safely on the net?

(b) Use an absolute value inequality to describe the restrictions on D.

75. Temperature and Altitude Air temperature decreases as altitude increases. If the ground temperature is 80°F, then the air temperature x miles high is $T = 80 - 19x$.
(a) Determine the altitudes x where the air temperature T is between 0°F and 32°F, inclusive.

(b) Use an absolute value inequality to describe these altitudes.

76. Dew Point and Altitude The dew point decreases as altitude increases. If the dew point on the ground is 80°F, then the dew point x miles high is $D = 80 - \frac{29}{5}x$.
(a) Determine the altitudes x where the dew point D is between 50°F and 60°F, inclusive.

(b) Use an absolute value inequality to describe these altitudes.

Exercises 77–82: **Average Temperatures** *The inequality describes the range of monthly average temperatures T in degrees Fahrenheit at a certain location.*
(a) Solve the inequality.
(b) If the high and low monthly average temperatures satisfy equality, interpret the inequality.
77. $|T - 43| \leq 24$, Marquette, Michigan

78. $|T - 62| \leq 19$, Memphis, Tennessee

79. $|T - 50| \leq 22$, Boston, Massachusetts

80. $|T - 10| \leq 36$, Chesterfield, Canada

81. $|T - 61.5| \leq 12.5$, Buenos Aires, Argentina

82. $|T - 43.5| \leq 8.5$, Punta Arenas, Chile

83. Classic iPod Dimensions The classic iPod is 10.5 millimeters thick. Suppose that the actual thickness T of any particular iPod has a maximum error tolerance that is less than 0.05 millimeter.
(a) Write an absolute value statement that describes this situation.

(b) Solve this inequality for T and interpret your result.

84. Error In Measurements An aluminum can should have a diameter D of 3 inches with a maximum error tolerance that is less than 0.004 inch.
(a) Write an absolute value statement that describes this situation.

(b) Solve this inequality for D and interpret your result.

85. Machine Parts A part for a machine must fit into a hole and must have a diameter D that is less than or equal to 2.125 inches. The diameter D cannot be less than this maximum diameter of 2.125 inches by more than 0.014 inch.
(a) Write an absolute value statement that describes this situation.

(b) Solve this inequality for D and interpret your result.

86. Error in Measurements Suppose that a 12-inch ruler must have the correct length L to within 0.0002 inch.
(a) Write an absolute value inequality for L that describes this requirement.

(b) Solve this inequality and interpret the results.

87. Relative Error If a quantity is measured to be Q and its exact value is A, then the relative error in Q is

$$\left| \frac{Q - A}{A} \right|.$$

If the exact value is $A = 35$ and you want the relative error in Q to be less than or equal to 0.02 (or 2%), what values for Q are possible?

88. Relative Error (Refer to Exercise 87.) The exact perimeter P of a square is 50 feet. What measured lengths are possible for the side S of the square to have relative error in the perimeter that is less than or equal to 0.04 (or 4%)?

Writing about Mathematics

89. Explain how to solve $|ax + b| = k$ with $k > 0$ symbolically. Give an example.

90. Explain how you can use the solutions to $|ax + b| = k$ with $k > 0$ to solve the inequalities $|ax + b| < k$ and $|ax + b| > k$. Give an example.

Extended and Discovery Exercises

1. Let δ be a positive number and let x and c be real numbers. Write an absolute value inequality that expresses that the distance between x and c on the number line is less than δ.

2. Let ε be a positive number, L be a real number, and f be a function. Write an absolute value inequality that expresses that the distance between $f(x)$ and L on the number line is less than ε.

CHECKING BASIC CONCEPTS FOR SECTION 2.5

1. Rewrite $\sqrt{4x^2}$ by using an absolute value.

2. Graph $y = |3x - 2|$ by hand.

3. (a) Solve the equation $|2x - 1| = 5$.

(b) Use part (a) to solve the absolute value inequalities $|2x - 1| \le 5$ and $|2x - 1| > 5$.

4. Solve each equation or inequality. For each inequality, write the solution set in interval notation.

(a) $|2 - 5x| - 4 = -1$

(b) $|3x - 5| \le 4$

(c) $\left|\frac{1}{2}x - 3\right| > 5$

5. Solve $|x + 1| = |2x|$.

2 Summary

CONCEPT	EXPLANATION AND EXAMPLES
Section 2.1 Equations of Lines	
Point-Slope Form	If a line with slope m passes through (x_1, y_1), then $$y = m(x - x_1) + y_1 \quad \text{or} \quad y - y_1 = m(x - x_1).$$ **Example:** $y = -\frac{3}{4}(x + 4) + 5$ has slope $-\frac{3}{4}$ and passes through $(-4, 5)$.
Slope-Intercept Form	If a line has slope m and y-intercept b, then $y = mx + b$. **Example:** $y = 3x - 4$ has slope 3 and y-intercept -4.
Determining Intercepts	To find the x-intercept(s), let $y = 0$ in the equation and solve for x. To find the y-intercept(s), let $x = 0$ in the equation and solve for y. **Examples:** The x-intercept on the graph of $3x - 4y = 12$ is 4 because $3x - 4(0) = 12$ implies that $x = 4$. The y-intercept on the graph of $3x - 4y = 12$ is -3 because $3(0) - 4y = 12$ implies that $y = -3$.
Horizontal and Vertical Lines	A horizontal line passing through the point (a, b) is given by $y = b$, and a vertical line passing through (a, b) is given by $x = a$. **Examples:** The horizontal line $y = -3$ passes through $(6, -3)$. The vertical line $x = 4$ passes through $(4, -2)$.
Parallel and Perpendicular Lines	Parallel lines have equal slopes satisfying $m_1 = m_2$, and perpendicular lines have slopes satisfying $m_1 m_2 = -1$, provided neither line is vertical. **Examples:** The lines $y_1 = 3x - 1$ and $y_2 = 3x + 4$ are parallel. The lines $y_1 = 3x - 1$ and $y_2 = -\frac{1}{3}x + 4$ are perpendicular.

CONCEPT	EXPLANATION AND EXAMPLES

Section 2.1 Equations of Lines (CONTINUED)

Linear Regression

One way to determine a linear function or a line that models data is to use the method of least squares. This method determines a unique line that can be found with a calculator. The correlation coefficient r $(-1 \leq r \leq 1)$ measures how well a line fits the data.

Example: The line of least squares modeling the data $(1, 1)$, $(3, 4)$, and $(4, 6)$ is given by $y \approx 1.643x - 0.714$, with $r \approx 0.997$.

Section 2.2 Linear Equations

Linear Equation

Can be written as $ax + b = 0$ with $a \neq 0$ and has one solution

Example: The solution to $2x - 4 = 0$ is 2 because $2(2) - 4 = 0$.

Properties of Equality

Addition: $a = b$ is equivalent to $a + c = b + c$.
Multiplication: $a = b$ is equivalent to $ac = bc$, provided $c \neq 0$.

Example:

$\dfrac{1}{2}x - 4 = 3$ Given equation

$\dfrac{1}{2}x = 7$ Addition property; add 4.

$x = 14$ Multiplication property; multiply by 2.

Contradiction, Identity, and Conditional Equation

A contradiction has no solutions, an identity is true for all (meaningful) values of the variable, and a conditional equation is true for some, but not all, values of the variable.

Examples:

$3(1 - 2x) = 3 - 6x$ Identity

$x + 5 = x$ Contradiction

$x - 1 = 4$ Conditional equation

Intersection-of-Graphs and *x*-Intercept Methods

Intersection-of-graphs method: Set y_1 equal to the left side of the equation and set y_2 equal to the right side. The x-coordinate of a point of intersection is a solution.

Example: The graphs of $y_1 = 2x$ and $y_2 = x + 1$ intersect at $(1, 2)$, so the solution to the linear equation $2x = x + 1$ is 1. See the figure below on the left.

x-intercept method: Move all terms to the left side of the equation. Set y_1 equal to the left side of the equation. The solutions are the x-intercepts. (See Section 2.3.)

Example: Write $2x = x + 1$ as $2x - (x + 1) = 0$. Graph $y_1 = 2x - (x + 1)$. The only x-intercept is 1, as shown in the figure on the right.

Point of Intersection (1, 2)   x-intercept: 1

CONCEPT	EXPLANATION AND EXAMPLES

Section 2.2 Linear Equations (CONTINUED)

Problem-Solving Strategies

STEP 1: Read the problem and make sure you understand it. Assign a variable to what you are being asked to find. If necessary, write other quantities in terms of this variable.

STEP 2: Write an equation that relates the quantities described in the problem. You may need to sketch a diagram and refer to known formulas.

STEP 3: Solve the equation and determine the solution.

STEP 4: Look back and check your solution. Does it seem reasonable?

Section 2.3 Linear Inequalities

Linear Inequality

Can be written as $ax + b > 0$ with $a \neq 0$, where $>$ can be replaced by $<$, $\leq$, or $\geq$. If the solution to $ax + b = 0$ is k, then the solution to the linear inequality $ax + b > 0$ is either the interval $(-\infty, k)$ or the interval (k, ∞).

Example: $3x - 1 < 2$ is linear since it can be written as $3x - 3 < 0$. The solution set is $\{x \mid x < 1\}$, or $(-\infty, 1)$.

Properties of Inequalities

Addition: $a < b$ is equivalent to $a + c < b + c$.
Multiplication: $a < b$ is equivalent to $ac < bc$ when $c > 0$.
$a < b$ is equivalent to $ac > bc$ when $c < 0$.

Example: $-3x - 4 < 14$ *Given equation*

$-3x < 18$ *Addition property; add 4.*

$x > -6$ *Multiplication property; divide by -3. Reverse the inequality symbol.*

Compound Inequality

Example: $x \geq -2$ and $x \leq 4$ is equivalent to $-2 \leq x \leq 4$. This is called a three-part inequality.

Section 2.4 More Modeling with Functions

Linear Model

If a quantity increases or decreases by a constant amount for each unit increase in x, then it can be modeled by a linear function given by

$$f(x) = (\text{constant rate of change})x + (\text{initial amount}).$$

Example: If water is pumped from a full 100-gallon tank at 7 gallons per minute, then $A(t) = 100 - 7t$ gives the gallons of water in the tank after t minutes.

Piecewise-Defined Function

A function defined by more than one formula on its domain

Examples: Step function, greatest integer function, absolute value function, and

$$f(x) = \begin{cases} 4 - x & \text{if } -4 \leq x < 1 \\ 3x & \text{if } 1 \leq x \leq 5 \end{cases}$$

It follows that $f(2) = 6$ because if $1 \leq x \leq 5$ then $f(x) = 3x$. Note that f is continuous on its domain of $[-4, 5]$.

CONCEPT	EXPLANATION AND EXAMPLES

Section 2.4 More Modeling with Functions (CONTINUED)

Direct Variation

A quantity y is directly proportional to a quantity x, or y varies directly with x, if $y = kx$, where $k \neq 0$. If data vary directly, the ratios $\frac{y}{x}$ are equal to the constant of variation k.

Example: If a person works for \$8 per hour, then that person's pay P is directly proportional to, or varies directly with, the number of hours H that the person works by the equation $P = 8H$, where the constant of variation is $k = 8$.

Section 2.5 Absolute Value Equations and Inequalities

Absolute Value Function

An absolute value function is defined by $f(x) = |x|$. Its graph is V-shaped. An equivalent formula is $f(x) = \sqrt{x^2}$.

Examples: $f(-9) = |-9| = 9$; $\sqrt{(2x + 1)^2} = |2x + 1|$

Absolute Value Equations

$|ax + b| = k$ with $k > 0$ is equivalent to $ax + b = \pm k$.

Example: $|2x - 3| = 4$ is equivalent to $2x - 3 = 4$ or $2x - 3 = -4$.

The solutions are $\frac{7}{2}$ and $-\frac{1}{2}$.

Absolute Value Inequalities

Let the solutions to $|ax + b| = k$ be s_1 and s_2, where $s_1 < s_2$ and $k > 0$.

1. $|ax + b| < k$ is equivalent to $s_1 < x < s_2$.

2. $|ax + b| > k$ is equivalent to $x < s_1$ or $x > s_2$.

Similar statements can be made for inequalities involving $\leq$ or $\geq$.

Example: The solutions to $|2x + 1| = 5$ are given by $x = -3$ and $x = 2$.
The solutions to $|2x + 1| < 5$ are given by $-3 < x < 2$.
The solutions to $|2x + 1| > 5$ are given by $x < -3$ or $x > 2$.

2 Review Exercises

Exercises 1 and 2: Find the point-slope form of the line passing through the given points. Use the first point as (x_1, y_1).

1. $(-3, 4)$, $(2, 5)$ **2.** $(1, -6)$, $(-7, 5)$

Exercises 3–6: Find the point-slope form of the line passing through the given points. Use the first point as (x_1, y_1). Then convert the equation to slope-intercept form and write a formula for a function f whose graph is the line.

3. Slope $-\frac{7}{5}$, passing through $(-5, 6)$

4. Passing through $(-4, -7)$ and $(-2, 3)$

5. x-intercept 5, y-intercept -2

6. y-intercept 6, passing through $(8, -2)$

7. Write a formula for a linear function f whose graph has slope -2 and passes through $(-2, 3)$.

8. Find the average rate of change of $f(x) = -3x + 8$ from -2 to 3.

Exercises 9–14: Find the slope-intercept form of the equation of a line satisfying the conditions.

9. Slope 7, passing through $(-3, 9)$

10. Passing through $(2, -4)$ and $(7, -3)$

11. Passing through $(1, -1)$, parallel to $y = -3x + 1$

12. Passing through the point $(-2, 1)$, perpendicular to the line $y = 2(x + 5) - 22$

13. Parallel to the line segment connecting $(0, 3.1)$ and $(5.7, 0)$, passing through $(1, -7)$

14. Perpendicular to $y = -\frac{5}{7}x$, passing through $\left(\frac{6}{7}, 0\right)$

Exercises 15–20: Find an equation of the specified line.

15. Parallel to the y-axis, passing through $(6, -7)$

16. Parallel to the x-axis, passing through $(-3, 4)$

17. Horizontal, passing through $(1, 3)$

18. Vertical, passing through $(1.5, 1.9)$

19. Vertical with x-intercept 2.7

20. Horizontal with y-intercept -8

Exercises 21 and 22: Determine the x- and y-intercepts for the graph of the equation. Graph the equation.

21. $5x - 4y = 20$ **22.** $\dfrac{x}{3} - \dfrac{y}{2} = 1$

Exercises 23–28: Solve the linear equation either symbolically or graphically.

23. $5x - 22 = 10$ **24.** $5(4 - 2x) = 16$

25. $-2(3x - 7) + x = 2x - 1$

26. $5x - \frac{1}{2}(4 - 3x) = \frac{3}{2} - (2x + 3)$

27. $\pi x + 1 = 6$

28. $\dfrac{x - 4}{2} = x + \dfrac{1 - 2x}{3}$

Exercises 29 and 30: Use a table to solve each linear equation numerically to the nearest tenth.

29. $3.1x - 0.2 - 2(x - 1.7) = 0$

30. $\sqrt{7} - 3x - 2.1(1 + x) = 0$

Exercises 31–34: Complete the following.
(a) Solve the equation symbolically.
(b) Classify the equation as a contradiction, an identity, or a conditional equation.

31. $4(6 - x) = -4x + 24$

32. $\frac{1}{2}(4x - 3) + 2 = 3x - (1 + x)$

33. $5 - 2(4 - 3x) + x = 4(x - 3)$

34. $\dfrac{x - 3}{4} + \dfrac{3}{4}x - 5(2 - 7x) = 36x - \dfrac{43}{4}$

Exercises 35–38: Express the inequality in interval notation.

35. $x > -3$ **36.** $x \le 4$

37. $-2 \le x < \frac{3}{4}$ **38.** $x \le -2$ or $x > 3$

Exercises 39–44: Solve the linear inequality. Write the solution set in set-builder or interval notation.

39. $3x - 4 \le 2 + x$ **40.** $-2x + 6 \le -3x$

41. $\dfrac{2x - 5}{2} < \dfrac{5x + 1}{5}$

42. $-5(1 - x) > 3(x - 3) + \frac{1}{2}x$

43. $-2 \le 5 - 2x < 7$ **44.** $-1 < \dfrac{3x - 5}{-3} < 3$

Exercises 45 and 46: Solve the inequality graphically.

45. $2x > x - 1$ **46.** $-1 \le 1 + x \le 2$

47. The graphs of two linear functions f and g are shown in the figure. Solve each equation or inequality.
   (a) $f(x) = g(x)$
   (b) $f(x) < g(x)$
   (c) $f(x) > g(x)$

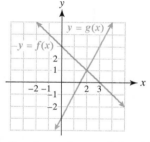

48. The graphs of three linear functions f, g, and h with domains $D = \{x \mid 0 \le x \le 7\}$ are shown in the figure. Solve each equation or inequality.
   (a) $f(x) = g(x)$
   (b) $g(x) = h(x)$
   (c) $f(x) < g(x) < h(x)$
   (d) $g(x) > h(x)$

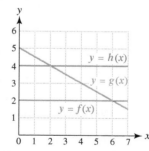

49. Use $f(x)$ to complete the following.
$$f(x) = \begin{cases} 8 + 2x & \text{if } -3 \le x \le -1 \\ 5 - x & \text{if } -1 < x \le 2 \\ x + 1 & \text{if } 2 < x \le 5 \end{cases}$$

   (a) Evaluate f at $x = -2, -1, 2,$ and 3.

   (b) Sketch a graph of f. Is f continuous on its domain?

   (c) Determine the x-value(s) where $f(x) = 3$.

50. If $f(x) = [\![2x - 1]\!]$, evaluate $f(-3.1)$ and $f(2.5)$.

Exercises 51–54: Solve the equation.

51. $|2x - 5| - 1 = 8$ **52.** $|3 - 7x| = 10$

53. $|6 - 4x| = -2$ **54.** $|9 + x| = |3 - 2x|$

Exercises 55–58: Solve the equation. Use the solutions to help solve the related inequality.

55. $|x| = 3$, $|x| > 3$

56. $|-3x + 1| = 2, |-3x + 1| < 2$

57. $|3x - 7| = 10$, $|3x - 7| > 10$

58. $|4 - x| = 6$, $|4 - x| \leq 6$

Exercises 59–62: Solve the inequality.

59. $|3 - 2x| < 9$ **60.** $|-2x - 3| > 3$

61. $|\frac{1}{3}x - \frac{1}{6}| \geq 1$ **62.** $|\frac{1}{2}x| - 3 \leq 5$

Applications

63. **U.S. Median Income** In 1980 the median family income was $17,700 and in 2010 it was $49,500. (**Source:** Bureau of the Census.)
  (a) Find a linear function f that models these data. Let x represent the number of years after 1980.

  (b) Interpret the slope and y-intercept for the graph of f.

  (c) Estimate the median income in 1992 and compare your answer with the true value of $30,600.

  (d) Predict the year when median income might reach $60,000. Did your answer involve interpolation or extrapolation?

64. **Course Grades** In order to receive a B grade in a college course, it is necessary to have an overall average of 80% correct on two 1-hour exams of 75 points each and one final exam of 150 points. If a person scores 55 and 72 on the 1-hour exams, what is the minimum score that the person can receive on the final exam and still earn a B?

65. **Medicare Spending** In 2010 Medicare spending was $524 billion and in 2020 it is projected to be $949 billion. (**Source:** Congressional Budget Office.)
  (a) Find a linear function f that models these data. Let x represent the number of years after 2010.

  (b) Interpret the slope and y-intercept for the graph of f.

  (c) Estimate Medicare spending in 2016. Did your answer involve interpolation or extrapolation?

  (d) Predict the years when Medicare spending could be between $694 billion and $864 billion.

66. **Temperature Scales** The table shows equivalent temperatures in degrees Celsius and degrees Fahrenheit.

°F	−40	32	59	95	212
°C	−40	0	15	35	100

  (a) Plot the data with Fahrenheit temperature on the x-axis and Celsius temperature on the y-axis. What type of relation exists between the data?

  (b) Find a function C that receives the Fahrenheit temperature x as input and outputs the corresponding Celsius temperature. Interpret the slope.

  (c) If the temperature is 83°F, what is it in degrees Celsius?

67. **Distance from Home** The graph depicts the distance y that a person driving a car on a straight road is from home after x hours. Interpret the graph. What speeds did the car travel?

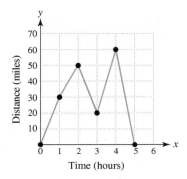

68. **Piecewise-Linear Function** Given the data points $(1, 2)$, $(4, 9)$, and $(6, 3)$, complete the following.
  (a) Write the formula for a piecewise-linear function f that passes through these data points whose domain is $1 \leq x \leq 6$.

  (b) Evaluate $f(5)$.

  (c) Is f continuous on its domain?

69. **Population Estimates** In 2008 the population of a city was 143,247, and in 2012 it was 167,933. Estimate the population in 2010.

70. **Distance** A driver of a car is initially 455 miles from home, traveling toward home on a straight freeway at 70 miles per hour.
  (a) Write a formula for a linear function f that models the distance between the driver and home after x hours.

  (b) Graph f. What is an appropriate domain?

  (c) Identify the x- and y-intercepts. Interpret each.

71. Working Together Suppose that one worker can shovel snow from a storefront sidewalk in 50 minutes and another worker can shovel it in 30 minutes. How long will it take if they work together?

72. Antifreeze Initially, a tank contains 20 gallons of a 30% antifreeze solution. How many gallons of an 80% antifreeze solution should be added to the tank in order to increase the concentration of the antifreeze in the tank to 50%?

73. Running An athlete traveled 13.5 miles in 1 hour and 48 minutes, jogging at 7 miles per hour and then at 8 miles per hour. How long did the runner jog at each speed?

74. Least-Squares Fit The table lists the actual annual cost y to drive a midsize car 15,000 miles per year for selected years x.

x	1970	1980	1990	2000	2010
y	\$1763	\$3176	\$5136	\$6880	\$8595

Source: Runzheimer International.

(a) Predict whether the correlation coefficient is positive, negative, or zero.

(b) Find a least-squares regression line that models these data. What is the correlation coefficient?

(c) Estimate the cost of driving a midsize car in 2005.

(d) Estimate the year when the cost to drive a car could reach \$10,000.

75. Modeling The table lists data that are exactly linear.

x	−3	−2	−1	1	2
y	6.6	5.4	4.2	1.8	0.6

(a) Determine the slope-intercept form of the line that passes through these data points.

(b) Predict y when $x = -1.5$ and 3.5. State whether these calculations involve interpolation or extrapolation.

(c) Predict x when $y = 1.3$.

76. Geometry A rectangle is twice as long as it is wide and has a perimeter of 78 inches. Find the width and length of this rectangle.

77. Flow Rates A water tank has an inlet pipe with a flow rate of 5 gallons per minute and an outlet pipe with a flow rate of 3 gallons per minute. A pipe can be either closed or completely open. The graph shows the number of gallons of water in the tank after x minutes have

elapsed. Use the concept of slope to interpret each piece of this graph.

78. Flow Rates (Refer to Exercise 77.) Suppose the tank is modified so that it has a second inlet pipe, which flows at a rate of 2 gallons per minute. Interpret the graph by determining when each inlet and outlet pipe is open or closed.

79. Air Temperature For altitudes up to 4 kilometers, moist air will cool at a rate of about 6°C per kilometer. If the ground temperature is 25°C, at what altitudes would the air temperature be from 5°C to 15°C? (*Source:* A. Miller and R. Anthes, *Meteorology.*)

80. Water Pollution At one time the Thames River in England supported an abundant community of fish. Pollution then destroyed all the fish in a 40-mile stretch near its mouth for a 45-year period beginning in 1915. Since then, improvement of sewage treatment facilities and other ecological steps have resulted in a dramatic increase in the number of different fish present. The number of species present from 1967 to 1978 can be modeled by $f(x) = 6.15x - 12{,}059$, where x is the year.

(a) Estimate the year when the number of species first exceeded 70.

(b) Estimate the years when the number of species was between 50 and 100.

81. Relative Error The actual length of a side of a building is 52.3 feet. How accurately must an apprentice carpenter measure this side to have the relative error in the measurement be less than 0.003 (0.3%)? (*Hint:* Use $\left|\frac{C - A}{A}\right|$, where C is the carpenter's measurement and A is the actual length.)

82. Brown Trout Due to acid rain, the percentage of lakes in Scandinavia that lost their population of brown trout increased dramatically between 1940 and 1975. Based on a sample of 2850 lakes, this percentage can be approximated by the following piecewise-linear function. (**Source:** C. Mason, *Biology of Freshwater Pollution.*)

$$f(x) = \begin{cases} \frac{11}{20}(x - 1940) + 7 & \text{if } 1940 \le x < 1960 \\ \frac{32}{15}(x - 1960) + 18 & \text{if } 1960 \le x \le 1975 \end{cases}$$

(a) Determine the percentage of lakes that lost brown trout by 1947 and by 1972.

(b) Sketch a graph of f.

(c) Is f a continuous function on its domain?

Extended and Discovery Exercises

1. **Archeology** It is possible for archeologists to estimate the height of an adult based only on the length of the humerus, a bone located between the elbow and the shoulder. The approximate relationship between the height y of an individual and the length x of the humerus is shown in the table for both males and females. All measurements are in inches. Although individual values may vary, tables like this are the result of measuring bones from many skeletons.

x	8	9	10	11
y (females)	50.4	53.5	56.6	59.7
y (males)	53.0	56.0	59.0	62.0

x	12	13	14
y (females)	62.8	65.9	69.0
y (males)	65.0	68.0	71.0

(a) Find the estimated height of a female with a 12-inch humerus.

(b) Plot the ordered pairs (x, y) for both sexes. What type of relation exists between the data?

(c) For each 1-inch increase in the length of the humerus, what are the corresponding increases in the heights of females and of males?

(d) Determine linear functions f and g that model these data for females and males, respectively.

(e) Suppose a humerus from a person of unknown sex is estimated to be between 9.7 and 10.1 inches long. Use f and g to approximate the range for the height of a female and a male.

2. **Archeology** Continuing with Exercise 1, have members of the class measure their heights and the lengths of their humeri (plural of *humerus*) in inches.
(a) Make a table of the results.

(b) Find regression lines that fit the data points for males and females.

(c) Compare your results with the table in Exercise 1.

3. **A Puzzle** Three people leave for a city 15 miles away. The first person walks 4 miles per hour, and the other two people ride in a car that travels 28 miles per hour. After some time, the second person gets out of the car and walks 4 miles per hour to the city while the driver goes back and picks up the first person. The driver takes the first person to the city. If all three people arrive in the city at the same time, how far did each person walk?

4. **Limit Notation** Let ε and δ be positive numbers; let x, c, and L be real numbers; and let f be a function. Consider the following: "If the distance between x and c is less than δ, then the distance between $f(x)$ and L is less than ε." Rewrite this sentence by using two absolute value inequalities.

1–2 Cumulative Review Exercises

1. Write 123,000 and 0.0051 in scientific notation.

2. Write 6.7×10^6 and 1.45×10^{-4} in standard form.

3. Evaluate $\dfrac{4 + \sqrt{2}}{4 - \sqrt{2}}$. Round your answer to the nearest hundredth.

4. The table represents a relation S.

x	-1	0	1	2	3
y	6	4	3	0	0

(a) Does S represent a function?

(b) Determine the domain and range of S.

5. Find the standard equation of a circle with center $(-2, 3)$ and radius 7.

6. Evaluate $-5^2 - 2 - \frac{10 - 2}{5 - 1}$ by hand.

7. Find the exact distance between $(-3, 5)$ and $(2, -3)$.

8. Find the midpoint of the line segment with endpoints $(5, -2)$ and $(-3, 1)$.

9. Find the domain and range of the function shown in the graph. Evaluate $f(-1)$.

(a)   **(b)**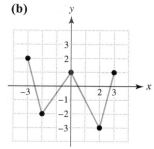

10. Graph f by hand.
   (a) $f(x) = 3 - 2x$ **(b)** $f(x) = |x + 1|$

Exercises 11 and 12: Complete the following.

(a) Evaluate $f(2)$ and $f(a - 1)$.
(b) Determine the domain of f.

11. $f(x) = 5x - 3$

12. $f(x) = \sqrt{2x - 1}$

13. Determine if the graph represents a function. Explain your answer.

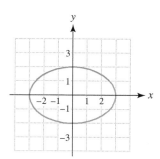

14. Write a formula for a function f that computes the cost of taking x credits if credits cost \$80 each and fees are fixed at \$89.

15. Find the average rate of change of $f(x) = x^2 - 2x + 1$ from $x = 1$ to $x = 2$.

16. Find the difference quotient for $f(x) = 2x^2 - x$.

Exercises 17 and 18: The graph of a linear function f is shown.

(a) Identify the slope, y-intercept, and x-intercept.
(b) Write a formula for f.
(c) Find any zeros of f.

17.   **18.**

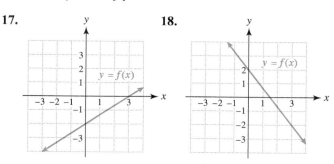

Exercises 19–24: Write an equation of a line satisfying the given conditions. Use slope-intercept form whenever possible.

19. Passing through $(1, -5)$ and $\left(-3, \frac{1}{2}\right)$

20. Passing through the point $(-3, 2)$ and perpendicular to the line $y = \frac{2}{3}x - 7$

21. Parallel to the y-axis and passing through $(-1, 3)$

22. Slope 30, passing through $(2002, 50)$

23. Passing through $(-3, 5)$ and parallel to the line segment connecting $(2.4, 5.6)$ and $(3.9, 8.6)$

24. Perpendicular to the y-axis and passing through the origin

Exercises 25 and 26: Determine the x- and y-intercepts on the graph of the equation. Graph the equation.

25. $-2x + 3y = 6$ **26.** $x = 2y - 3$

Exercises 27–30: Solve the equation.

27. $4x - 5 = 1 - 2x$ **28.** $\dfrac{2x - 4}{2} = \dfrac{3x}{7} - 1$

29. $\frac{2}{3}(x - 2) - \frac{4}{5}x = \frac{4}{15} + x$

30. $-0.3(1 - x) - 0.1(2x - 3) = 0.4$

31. Solve $x + 1 = 2x - 2$ graphically and numerically.

32. Solve $2x - (5 - x) = \frac{1 - 4x}{2} + 5(x - 2)$. Is this equation either an identity or a contradiction?

Exercises 33–36: Express each inequality in interval notation.

33. $x < 5$ **34.** $-2 \le x \le 5$

35. $x < -2$ or $x > 2$ **36.** $x \ge -3$

Exercises 37 and 38: Solve the inequality. Write the solution set in set-builder or interval notation.

37. $-3(1 - 2x) + x \le 4 - (x + 2)$

38. $\dfrac{1}{3} \le \dfrac{2 - 3x}{2} < \dfrac{4}{3}$

39. The graphs of two linear functions f and g are shown. Solve each equation or inequality.

(a) $f(x) = g(x)$

(b) $f(x) > g(x)$

(c) $f(x) \le g(x)$

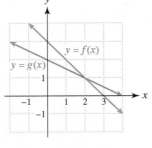

40. Graph f. Is f continuous on the interval $[-4, 4]$?

$$f(x) = \begin{cases} 2 - x & \text{if } -4 \le x < -2 \\ \frac{1}{2}x + 5 & \text{if } -2 \le x < 2 \\ 2x + 1 & \text{if } 2 \le x \le 4 \end{cases}$$

Exercises 41–44: Solve the equation.

41. $|d + 1| = 5$

42. $|3 - 2x| = 7$

43. $|2t| - 4 = 10$

44. $|11 - 2x| = |3x + 1|$

Exercises 45 and 46: Solve the inequality.

45. $|2t - 5| \le 5$

46. $|5 - 5t| > 7$

Applications

47. Cost A company's cost C in dollars for making x computers is $C(x) = 500x + 20{,}000$.

(a) Evaluate $C(1500)$. Interpret the result.

(b) Find the slope of the graph of C. Interpret the slope and y-intercept.

48. Distance At midnight car A is traveling north at 60 miles per hour and is located 40 miles south of car B. Car B is traveling west at 70 miles per hour. Approximate the distance between the cars at 1:15 A.M. to the nearest tenth of a mile.

49. Average Rate of Change On a warm summer day the Fahrenheit temperature x hours past noon is given by the formula $T(x) = 70 + \frac{3}{2}x^2$.

(a) Find the average rate of change of T from 2:00 P.M. to 4:00 P.M.

(b) Interpret this average rate of change.

50. Distance from Home A driver is initially 270 miles from home, traveling toward home on a straight interstate at 72 miles per hour.

(a) Write a formula for a function D that models the distance between the driver and home after x hours.

(b) What is an appropriate domain for D? Graph D.

(c) Identify the x- and y-intercepts. Interpret each.

51. Working Together Suppose one person can mow a large lawn in 5 hours with a riding mower and it takes another person 12 hours to mow the lawn with a push mower. How long will it take to mow the lawn if the two people work together?

52. Running An athlete traveled 15 miles in 1 hour and 45 minutes, running at 8 miles per hour and then 10 miles per hour. How long did the athlete run at each speed?

53. Chicken Consumption In 2001 Americans ate, on average, 56 pounds of chicken annually. This amount increased to 84 pounds in 2010. (*Source:* Department of Agriculture.)

(a) Determine a formula

$$f(x) = m(x - x_1) + y_1$$

that models these data. Let x be the year.

(b) Estimate the annual chicken consumption in 2015.

54. Income The table lists per capita income.

Year	1980	1990	2000	2010
Income	$10,183	$19,572	$29,760	$40,584

Source: Bureau of Economic Analysis.

(a) Find the least-squares regression line for the data.

(b) Estimate the per capita income in 1995. Did this calculation involve interpolation or extrapolation?

3

Quadratic Functions and Equations

> The work of mathematicians from even a millennium ago is still routinely used today, and the work of mathematicians from today will be part of the math of the future.
>
> —Terry Tao, Fields Medal 2006

The last basketball player in the NBA to shoot foul shots underhand was Rick Barry, who retired in 1980. On average, he was able to make about 9 out of 10 shots. Since then, every NBA player has used the overhand style of shooting foul shots—even though this style has often resulted in lower free-throw percentages.

According to Dr. Peter Brancazio, a physics professor emeritus from Brooklyn College and author of *Sports Science*, there are good reasons for shooting underhand. An underhand shot obtains a higher arc, and as the ball approaches the hoop, it has a better chance of going through the hoop than does a ball with a flatter arc. Lower release points require steeper arcs and increase the chances of the ball passing through the hoop. (See the Extended and

Rick Barry

Discovery Exercise at the end of this chapter to model the arc of a basketball.)

Mathematics plays an important role in analyzing applied problems such as shooting foul shots. Whether NBA players choose to listen to Professor Brancazio is another question, but mathematics tells us that steeper arcs are necessary for accurate foul shooting.

Source: Curtis Rist, "The Physics of Foul Shots," *Discover,* October 2000. (Photograph reprinted with permission.)

3.1 Quadratic Functions and Models

- **Learn basic concepts about quadratic functions and their graphs**
- **Complete the square and apply the vertex formula**
- **Graph a quadratic function by hand**
- **Solve applications and model data**
- **Use quadratic regression to model data (optional)**

Introduction

Sometimes when data lie on or nearly on a line, they can be modeled with a linear function ($f(x) = mx + b$) and are called *linear data*. Data that are not linear are called **nonlinear data** and must be modeled with a nonlinear function. One of the simplest types of nonlinear functions is a *quadratic function,* which can be used to model the flight of a baseball, an athlete's heart rate, or MySpace advertising revenue. Figures 3.1–3.3 illustrate three sets of nonlinear data that can be modeled by a quadratic function. Although the complete graph of a quadratic function is either $\cup$-shaped or $\cap$-shaped, we often use only one side or a portion of the graph to model real-world data.

Data Modeled with a Parabola

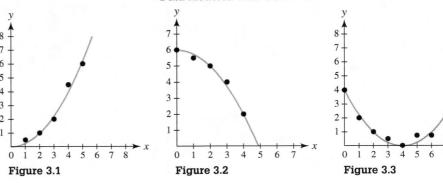

Figure 3.1 Figure 3.2 Figure 3.3

Basic Concepts

The formula for a quadratic function is different from that of a linear function because it contains an x^2-term. Examples of quadratic functions include the following.

Quadratic Functions

$$f(x) = 2x^2 - 4x - 1, \qquad g(x) = 4 - x^2, \qquad and \qquad h(x) = \frac{1}{3}x^2 + \frac{2}{3}x + 1$$

The following box defines a *general form* for a quadratic function.

QUADRATIC FUNCTION

Let a, b, and c be constants with $a \neq 0$. A function represented by

$$f(x) = ax^2 + bx + c$$

is a **quadratic function**.

The following are some basics of quadratic functions.

- The domain is *all* real numbers.
- The leading coefficient is a: $f(x) = ax^2 + bx + c$.

    Examples: $f(x) = 2x^2 - 4x - 1, \qquad g(x) = 4 - 1x^2, \qquad h(x) = \frac{1}{3}x^2 + \frac{2}{3}x + 1$

    $\boxed{a = 2}$ $\boxed{a = -1}$ $\boxed{a = \frac{1}{3}}$

- The graph is a **parabola**, or $\cup$-shaped, that opens upward if a is positive, and opens downward if a is negative.

See the Concept: Graphs of Quadratic Functions

$a > 0$: Opens Upward

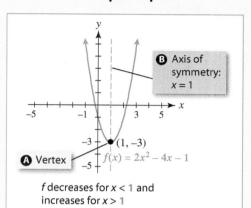

Ⓑ Axis of symmetry: $x = 1$

$(1, -3)$

$f(x) = 2x^2 - 4x - 1$

Ⓐ Vertex

f decreases for $x < 1$ and increases for $x > 1$

$a < 0$: Opens Downward

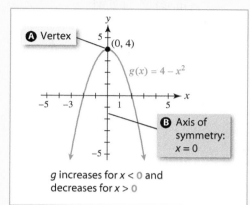

Ⓐ Vertex

$(0, 4)$

$g(x) = 4 - x^2$

Ⓑ Axis of symmetry: $x = 0$

g increases for $x < 0$ and decreases for $x > 0$

Ⓐ The highest point on a parabola that opens downward or the lowest point on a parabola that opens upward is called the **vertex.**

Ⓑ The vertical line passing through the vertex is called the **axis of symmetry.**

The leading coefficient a of a quadratic function not only determines whether its graph opens upward or downward but also controls the width of the parabola. This concept is illustrated in Figures 3.4 and 3.5.

The Effect of a on the Graph of $y = ax^2$

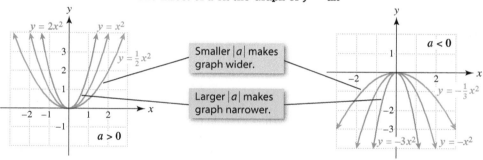

Smaller $|a|$ makes graph wider.

Larger $|a|$ makes graph narrower.

Figure 3.4

Figure 3.5

CLASS DISCUSSION

What does the graph of a quadratic function resemble if its leading coefficient is nearly 0?

EXAMPLE 1 Identifying quadratic functions

Identify the function as linear, quadratic, or neither. If it is quadratic, identify the leading coefficient and evaluate the function at $x = 2$.

(a) $f(x) = 3 - 2^2x$ **(b)** $g(x) = 5 + x - 3x^2$ **(c)** $h(x) = \dfrac{3}{x^2 + 1}$

SOLUTION

Getting Started The formula for a quadratic function always has an x^2-term and may have an x-term and a constant. It does not have a variable raised to any other power or a variable in a denominator. ▶

(a) Because $f(x) = 3 - 2^2x$ can be written as $f(x) = -4x + 3$, f is linear.
(b) Because $g(x) = 5 + x - 3x^2$ can be written as $g(x) = -3x^2 + x + 5$, g is a quadratic function with $a = -3$, $b = 1$, and $c = 5$. The leading coefficient is $a = -3$ and

$$g(2) = 5 + 2 - 3(2)^2 = -5.$$

(c) $h(x) = \dfrac{3}{x^2 + 1}$ cannot be written as $h(x) = ax + b$ or as $h(x) = ax^2 + bx + c$, so h is neither a linear nor a quadratic function.

Now Try Exercises 1, 3, and 5

EXAMPLE 2 Analyzing graphs of quadratic functions

Use the graph of each quadratic function to determine the sign of the leading coefficient a, the vertex, and the equation of the axis of symmetry. Give the intervals where the function is increasing and where it is decreasing. Give the domain and range.

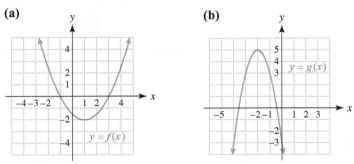

(a)

(b)

Figure 3.6   Figure 3.7

SOLUTION

(a) The graph of f in Figure 3.6 opens upward, so a is positive. The vertex is the lowest point on the graph and is $(1, -2)$. The axis of symmetry is a vertical line passing through the vertex with equation $x = 1$. Function f increases to the right of the vertex and decreases to the left of the vertex. Thus f is increasing for $x > 1$ and decreasing for $x < 1$. The domain includes all real numbers and the range is $R = \{y \mid y \geq -2\}$.

(b) The graph of g in Figure 3.7 opens downward, so a is negative. The vertex is $(-2, 5)$, and the axis of symmetry is given by $x = -2$. Function g is increasing for $x < -2$ and decreasing for $x > -2$. The domain includes all real numbers and the range is $R = \{y \mid y \leq 5\}$.

Now Try Exercises 7 and 9

Completing the Square and the Vertex Formula

When a quadratic function f is expressed as $f(x) = ax^2 + bx + c$, the coordinates of the vertex are not apparent. However, if f is written as $f(x) = a(x - h)^2 + k$, then the vertex is located at (h, k), as illustrated in Figure 3.8. For example, in Figure 3.9 the graph of $f(x) = -2(x - 1)^2 + 2$ opens downward with vertex $(1, 2)$.

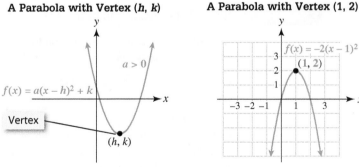

A Parabola with Vertex (h, k)   **A Parabola with Vertex (1, 2)**

Figure 3.8   Figure 3.9

To justify that the vertex is indeed (h, k), consider the following. If $a > 0$ in the form $f(x) = a(x - h)^2 + k$, then the term $a(x - h)^2$ is never negative and the minimum value of $f(x)$ is k. This value occurs when $x = h$ because

$$f(h) = a(h - h)^2 + k = 0 + k = k.$$

Thus the lowest point on the graph of $f(x) = a(x - h)^2 + k$ with $a > 0$ is (h, k), and because this graph is a parabola that opens upward, the vertex must be (h, k). A similar discussion can be used to justify that (h, k) is the vertex when $a < 0$.

The formula $f(x) = a(x - h)^2 + k$ is sometimes called the **standard form for a parabola with a vertical axis**. Because the vertex is apparent in this formula, we will call it simply the **vertex form**.

VERTEX FORM

The parabolic graph of $f(x) = a(x - h)^2 + k$ with $a \neq 0$ has vertex (h, k). Its graph opens upward when $a > 0$ and opens downward when $a < 0$.

The next example illustrates how to determine the vertex form given the graph of a parabola.

EXAMPLE 3 Writing the equation of a parabola

Find the vertex form for the graph shown in Figure 3.10.

SOLUTION

Getting Started We must determine a, h, and k in $f(x) = a(x - h)^2 + k$. The coordinates of the vertex correspond to the values of h and k. To find a, substitute the coordinates of a point on the graph in the equation and solve for a. ▶

From Figure 3.10, the vertex is $(2, 3)$. Thus $h = 2$ and $k = 3$ and $f(x) = a(x - 2)^2 + 3$. The point $(0, 1)$ lies on the graph, so $f(0) = 1$. (Any point on the graph of f other than the vertex could be used.)

Figure 3.10

$$f(x) = a(x - 2)^2 + 3 \qquad \text{Vertex form}$$
$$1 = a(0 - 2)^2 + 3 \qquad \text{Let } x = 0 \text{ and } f(0) = 1. \text{ Solve for } a.$$
$$1 = 4a + 3 \qquad \text{Simplify.}$$
$$-2 = 4a \qquad \text{Subtract 3 from each side.}$$
$$a = -\frac{1}{2} \qquad \text{Divide by 4 and rewrite equation.}$$

Thus $f(x) = -\frac{1}{2}(x - 2)^2 + 3$.

Now Try Exercise 25

EXAMPLE 4 Converting to $f(x) = ax^2 + bx + c$

Write $f(x) = 2(x - 1)^2 + 4$ in the form $f(x) = ax^2 + bx + c$.

SOLUTION Begin by expanding the expression $(x - 1)^2$.

$$2(x - 1)^2 + 4 = 2(x^2 - 2x + 1) + 4 \qquad \text{Square binomial.}$$
$$= 2x^2 - 4x + 2 + 4 \qquad \text{Distributive property}$$
$$= 2x^2 - 4x + 6 \qquad \text{Add terms.}$$

Algebra Review
To review squaring a binomial, see Chapter R (page R-17).

Thus $f(x) = 2x^2 - 4x + 6$.

Now Try Exercise 15

Completing the Square We can convert the general form $f(x) = ax^2 + bx + c$ to vertex form by **completing the square**. If a quadratic expression can be written as $x^2 + kx + \left(\frac{k}{2}\right)^2$, then it is a perfect square trinomial and can be factored as

$$x^2 + kx + \left(\frac{k}{2}\right)^2 = \left(x + \frac{k}{2}\right)^2.$$

Note that the k used to complete the square is different from the k found in the vertex form. (A variable can have different meanings in different situations.)

This technique of converting to vertex form by completing the square is illustrated in the next example.

EXAMPLE 5 Converting to vertex form

Write each formula in vertex form by completing the square. Identify the vertex.

(a) $f(x) = x^2 + 6x - 3$ (b) $f(x) = \frac{1}{3}x^2 - x + 2$

SOLUTION

(a) Start by letting $y = f(x)$.

$y = x^2 + 6x - 3$	Given formula
$y + 3 = x^2 + 6x$	Add 3 to each side.
$y + 3 + 9 = x^2 + 6x + 9$	Let $k = 6$; add $\left(\frac{k}{2}\right)^2 = \left(\frac{6}{2}\right)^2 = 9$.
$y + 12 = (x + 3)^2$	Factor perfect square trinomial.
$y = (x + 3)^2 - 12$	Subtract 12.

The required form is $f(x) = (x + 3)^2 - 12$. The vertex is $(-3, -12)$.

(b) Start by letting $y = f(x)$.

Algebra Review
To review perfect square trinomials, see Chapter R (page R-25).

$y = \frac{1}{3}x^2 - x + 2$	Given formula
Multiply each side by 3. $\quad 3y = x^2 - 3x + 6$	Make leading coefficient 1.
$3y - 6 = x^2 - 3x$	Subtract 6 from each side.
$3y - 6 + \frac{9}{4} = x^2 - 3x + \frac{9}{4}$	Let $k = -3$; add $\left(\frac{k}{2}\right)^2 = \left(\frac{-3}{2}\right)^2 = \frac{9}{4}$.
$3y - \frac{15}{4} = \left(x - \frac{3}{2}\right)^2$	Factor perfect square trinomial.
$3y = \left(x - \frac{3}{2}\right)^2 + \frac{15}{4}$	Add $\frac{15}{4}$ to each side.
$y = \frac{1}{3}\left(x - \frac{3}{2}\right)^2 + \frac{5}{4}$	Multiply each side by $\frac{1}{3}$.

The required form is $f(x) = \frac{1}{3}\left(x - \frac{3}{2}\right)^2 + \frac{5}{4}$. The vertex is $\left(\frac{3}{2}, \frac{5}{4}\right)$.

Now Try Exercises 29 and 35

Derivation of the Vertex Formula   The procedure above of completing the square can be done in general to derive a formula for determining the vertex of any parabola.

$y = ax^2 + bx + c$	General equation for a parabola
$\frac{y}{a} = x^2 + \frac{b}{a}x + \frac{c}{a}$	Divide each side by a to make leading coefficient 1.
$\frac{y}{a} - \frac{c}{a} = x^2 + \frac{b}{a}x$	Subtract $\frac{c}{a}$ from each side.
$\frac{y}{a} - \frac{c}{a} + \frac{b^2}{4a^2} = x^2 + \frac{b}{a}x + \frac{b^2}{4a^2}$	Add $\left(\frac{b/a}{2}\right)^2 = \frac{b^2}{4a^2}$.
$\frac{y}{a} + \frac{b^2 - 4ac}{4a^2} = \left(x + \frac{b}{2a}\right)^2$	Combine left terms; factor perfect square trinomial.
$\frac{y}{a} = \left(x + \frac{b}{2a}\right)^2 - \frac{b^2 - 4ac}{4a^2}$	Isolate y-term on the left side.
$y = a\left(x + \frac{b}{2a}\right)^2 - \frac{b^2 - 4ac}{4a}$	Multiply by a.
$y = a\left(x - \left(-\frac{b}{2a}\right)\right)^2 + \frac{4ac - b^2}{4a}$	Write $y = a(x - h)^2 + k$.

$\underbrace{\phantom{-\frac{b}{2a}}}_{h} \qquad \underbrace{\phantom{\frac{4ac - b^2}{4a}}}_{k}$

Because the coordinates of the vertex are (h, k), the x-coordinate is $-\frac{b}{2a}$. Note that it is *not* necessary to memorize the expression for k, because the y-coordinate can be found by evaluating $y = f(x)$ for $x = -\frac{b}{2a}$. This derivation of the *vertex formula* is now summarized.

> **VERTEX FORMULA**
>
> The *vertex* of the graph of $f(x) = ax^2 + bx + c$ with $a \neq 0$ is the point $\left(-\frac{b}{2a}, f\left(-\frac{b}{2a}\right)\right)$.

NOTE If a parabola has two x-intercepts, then the x-coordinate of the vertex is equal to the midpoint of these two x-intercepts. For example, the x-intercepts in Figure 3.9 on page 158 are 0 and 2. Their midpoint is $\frac{0 + 2}{2} = 1$, which is the x-coordinate of the vertex.

EXAMPLE 6 Converting to $f(x) = a(x - h)^2 + k$

Use the vertex formula to write $f(x) = 3x^2 + 12x + 7$ in vertex form.

SOLUTION Begin by finding the vertex. Let $a = 3$ and $b = 12$.

$$x = -\frac{b}{2a} = -\frac{12}{2(3)} = -2$$

Since $f(-2) = 3(-2)^2 + 12(-2) + 7 = -5$, the vertex is $(-2, -5)$. Because $a = 3$, $f(x)$ can be written as $f(x) = 3(x + 2)^2 - 5$.

Now Try Exercise 37

Graphing Quadratic Functions When sketching a parabola, it is important to determine the vertex, the axis of symmetry, and whether the parabola opens upward or downward. In the next example we sketch the graphs of two quadratic functions by hand.

EXAMPLE 7 Graphing quadratic functions by hand

Graph each quadratic function. Find the intervals where the function is increasing and where it is decreasing.

(a) $g(x) = 2(x - 1)^2 - 3$ **(b)** $h(x) = -\frac{1}{2}x^2 - x + 2$

SOLUTION

(a) The vertex is $(1, -3)$ and the axis of symmetry is $x = 1$. The parabola opens upward because $a = 2$ is positive. In Table 3.1 we list the vertex and a few other points located on either side of the vertex. Note the symmetry of the y-values on each side of the vertex. These points and a smooth $\cup$-shaped curve are plotted in Figure 3.11. When $x = 0$, $y = -1$, and so the y-intercept is -1. Function g is decreasing when $x < 1$ and increasing when $x > 1$.

x	y
-1	5
0	-1
1	-3
2	-1
3	5

Vertex → (row with $x = 1$)

Symmetric about the vertex

$(1, -3)$

$g(x) = 2(x - 1)^2 - 3$

Table 3.1   **Figure 3.11**

(b) The formula $h(x) = -\frac{1}{2}x^2 - x + 2$ is not in vertex form, but we can find the vertex.

$$x = -\frac{b}{2a} = -\frac{-1}{2\left(-\frac{1}{2}\right)} = -1$$

The y-coordinate of the vertex is $h(-1) = -\frac{1}{2}(-1)^2 - (-1) + 2 = \frac{5}{2}$. Thus the vertex is $\left(-1, \frac{5}{2}\right)$, the axis of symmetry is $x = -1$, and the parabola opens downward because $a = -\frac{1}{2}$ is negative. In Table 3.2 we list the vertex and a few other points located on either side of the vertex. These points and a smooth ∩-shaped curve are plotted in Figure 3.12. When $x = 0$, $y = 2$, and so the y-intercept is 2. Function h is increasing when $x < -1$ and decreasing when $x > -1$.

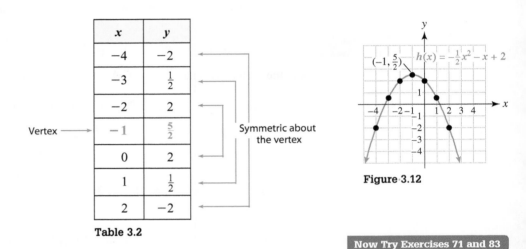

x	y
-4	-2
-3	$\frac{1}{2}$
-2	2
-1	$\frac{5}{2}$
0	2
1	$\frac{1}{2}$
2	-2

Vertex ⟶ (row -1)

Symmetric about the vertex

Table 3.2

Figure 3.12

Now Try Exercises 71 and 83

Applications and Models

Min-Max Values   Sometimes when a quadratic function f is used in applications, the vertex provides important information. The reason is that the y-coordinate of the vertex is the minimum value of $f(x)$ when its graph opens upward and is the maximum value of $f(x)$ when its graph opens downward. See Figure 3.13 and 3.14.

Minimum or Maximum y-Value of a Parabola

Figure 3.13

Figure 3.14

The process for finding a maximum for a quadratic function is applied in the next example.

EXAMPLE 8   Maximizing area

A rancher is fencing a rectangular area for cattle using the straight portion of a river as one side of the rectangle, as illustrated in Figure 3.15. If the rancher has 2400 feet of fence, find the dimensions of the rectangle that give the maximum area for the cattle.

SOLUTION

Getting Started Because the goal is to maximize the area, first write a formula for the area. If the formula is quadratic with $a < 0$ (parabola opening downward), then the maximum area will be the y-coordinate of the vertex. ▶

Let W be the width and L be the length of the rectangle. Because the 2400-foot fence does not go along the river, it follows that

$$W + L + W = 2400, \quad \text{or} \quad L = 2400 - 2W.$$

Area A of a rectangle equals length times width, so

$$
\begin{aligned}
A &= LW & &\text{Area of rectangle} \\
&= (2400 - 2W)W & &\text{Substitute for } L. \\
&= 2400W - 2W^2. & &\text{Distributive property}
\end{aligned}
$$

Thus the graph of $A = -2W^2 + 2400W$ is a parabola opening downward, and by the vertex formula, maximum area occurs when

$$W = -\frac{b}{2a} = -\frac{2400}{2(-2)} = 600 \text{ feet.}$$

The corresponding length is $L = 2400 - 2W = 2400 - 2(600) = 1200$ feet. The dimensions that maximize area are 600 feet by 1200 feet. The maximum area is 720,000 square feet.

Now Try Exercise 105

Modeling   Another application of quadratic functions occurs in projectile motion, such as when a baseball is hit up in the air. If air resistance is ignored, then the formula

$$s(t) = -16t^2 + v_0 t + h_0$$

calculates the height s of the object above the ground in feet after t seconds. In this formula h_0 represents the initial height of the object in feet and v_0 represents its initial *vertical* velocity in feet per second. If the initial velocity is upward, then $v_0 > 0$, and if the initial velocity is downward, then $v_0 < 0$.

EXAMPLE 9   Modeling the flight of a baseball

A baseball is hit straight up with an initial velocity of $v_0 = 80$ feet per second (or about 55 miles per hour) and leaves the bat with an initial height of $h_0 = 3$ feet, as shown in Figure 3.16.
(a) Write a formula $s(t)$ that models the height of the baseball after t seconds.
(b) How high is the baseball after 2 seconds?
(c) Find the maximum height of the baseball. Support your answer graphically.

Figure 3.15

3 ft

s

Figure 3.16

Calculator Help

To find a maximum or minimum point on a graph, see Appendix A (page AP-8).

SOLUTION

(a) Because $v_0 = 80$ and the initial height is $h_0 = 3$,

$$s(t) = -16t^2 + v_0 t + h_0 = -16t^2 + 80t + 3.$$

(b) $s(2) = -16(2)^2 + 80(2) + 3 = 99$, so the baseball is 99 feet high after 2 seconds.

(c) Because $a = -16$, the graph of s is a parabola opening downward. The vertex is the highest point on the graph, with a t-coordinate of

$$t = -\frac{b}{2a} = -\frac{80}{2(-16)} = 2.5.$$

The corresponding y-coordinate of the vertex is

$$s(2.5) = -16(2.5)^2 + 80(2.5) + 3 = 103 \text{ feet}.$$

Thus the vertex is $(2.5, 103)$ and the maximum height of the baseball is 103 feet after 2.5 seconds. Graphical support is shown in Figure 3.17, where the vertex is (2.5, 103).

Now Try Exercise 101

Height of a Baseball

[0, 5, 1] by [−20, 120, 20]

Figure 3.17

A well-conditioned athlete's heart rate can reach 200 beats per minute (bpm) during strenuous physical activity. Upon stopping an activity, a typical heart rate decreases rapidly at first and then gradually levels off, as shown in Table 3.3.

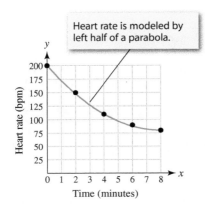

Heart rate is modeled by left half of a parabola.

Figure 3.18

Athlete's Heart Rate After Exercise

Time (min)	0	2	4	6	8
Heart rate (bpm)	200	150	110	90	80

Source: Adapted from: V. Thomas, *Science and Sport.*

Table 3.3

The data are not linear because for each 2-minute interval the heart rate does not decrease by a fixed amount. In Figure 3.18 the data are modeled with a nonlinear function. Note that the graph resembles the left half of a parabola that opens upward.

EXAMPLE 10 Modeling an athlete's heart rate

Find a quadratic function f expressed in vertex form that models the data in Table 3.3. Support your result by graphing f and the data in the same xy-plane. What is the domain of your function?

SOLUTION To model the data we use the left half of a parabola. Since the minimum heart rate of 80 beats per minute occurs when $x = 8$, let (8, 80) be the vertex and write

$$f(x) = a(x - 8)^2 + 80.$$

Next we must determine a value for the leading coefficient a. One possibility is to have the graph of f pass through the first data point $(0, 200)$, or equivalently, let $f(0) = 200$.

$$f(0) = 200 \qquad \text{Have the graph pass through (0, 200).}$$
$$a(0 - 8)^2 + 80 = 200 \qquad \text{Let } x = 0 \text{ in } f(x). \text{ Solve for } a.$$
$$a(0 - 8)^2 = 120 \qquad \text{Subtract 80.}$$
$$a = \frac{120}{64} \qquad \text{Divide by } (0 - 8)^2 = 64.$$
$$a = 1.875 \qquad \text{Write as a decimal.}$$

Thus $f(x) = 1.875(x - 8)^2 + 80$ can be used to model the athlete's heart rate. A graph of f and the data are shown in Figure 3.19, which is similar to Figure 3.18. Figure 3.20 shows a table of $f(x)$. Although the table in Figure 3.20 does not match Table 3.3 exactly, it gives reasonable approximations. (Note that formulas for $f(x)$ may vary. For example, if we had selected the point (2, 150) rather than (0, 200), then $a \approx 1.94$. You may wish to verify this result.)

The domain D of $f(x) = 1.875(x - 8)^2 + 80$ needs to be restricted to $0 \le x \le 8$ because this interval corresponds to the domain of the data in Table 3.3.

Calculator Help

To create a table similar to Figure 3.20, see Appendix A (page AP-9).

Modeling an Athlete's Heart Rate

$[-0.5, 8.5, 2]$ by $[0, 220, 20]$

Figure 3.19

Figure 3.20

> **Now Try Exercise 115**

MAKING CONNECTIONS

General Form, Vertex Form, and Modeling   When modeling quadratic data by hand, it is often easier to use the vertex form, $f(x) = a(x - h)^2 + k$, rather than the general form, $f(x) = ax^2 + bx + c$. Because (h, k) corresponds to the vertex of a parabola, it may be appropriate to let (h, k) correspond to either the highest data point or the lowest data point in the scatterplot. Then a value for a can be found by substituting a data point into the formula for $f(x)$. In the next subsection least-squares regression provides a quadratic modeling function in general form.

Quadratic Regression (Optional)

In Chapter 2 we discussed how a regression line could be found by the method of least squares. This method can also be applied to quadratic data; the process is illustrated next.

EXAMPLE 11   Finding a quadratic regression model

Table 3.4 lists MySpace U.S. advertising revenue in millions of dollars for 2006 through 2011, where x corresponds to years after 2006.
(a) Plot the data. Discuss reasons why a quadratic function might model the data.
(b) Find a least-squares function f given by $f(x) = ax^2 + bx + c$ that models the data.
(c) Graph f and the data in $[-2, 7, 1]$ by $[0, 1000, 100]$. Discuss the fit.

MySpace Ad Revenue ($ millions)

Year	0	1	2	3	4	5
Revenue	225	450	590	435	285	190

Table 3.4

$[-2, 7, 1]$ by $[0, 1000, 100]$

Figure 3.21

SOLUTION
(a) A plot of the data is shown in Figure 3.21. The y-values (ad revenue) first increase and then decrease as the year x increases. The data suggest a parabolic shape opening downward.

(b) Enter the data into your calculator, and then select quadratic regression from the menu, as shown in Figure 3.22 and Figure 3.23. In Figure 3.24 the modeling function f is given (approximately) by $f(x) = -49.29x^2 + 222.9x + 257$.

Figure 3.22

Figure 3.23

Figure 3.24

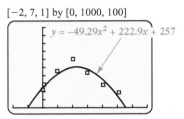

$[-2, 7, 1]$ by $[0, 1000, 100]$

Figure 3.25

Calculator Help

To find an equation of least-squares fit, see Appendix A (page AP-9).

(c) The graph of $y_1 = -49.29x^2 + 222.9x + 257$ with the data is shown in Figure 3.25. Although the model is not exact, the parabola describes the general trend in the data. The parabola opens downward because $a = -49.29$ is negative.

Now Try Exercise 125

3.1 Putting It All Together

The following table summarizes some important topics from this section.

CONCEPT	SYMBOLIC REPRESENTATION	COMMENTS AND EXAMPLES
Quadratic function	$f(x) = ax^2 + bx + c$, where a, b, and c are constants with $a \neq 0$ (general form)	It models data that are not linear. Its graph is a parabola ($\cup$-shaped) that opens either upward $(a > 0)$ or downward $(a < 0)$.
Parabola	The graph of $y = ax^2 + bx + c$, $a \neq 0$, is a parabola.	Vertex: (h, k); axis of symmetry: $x = h$ Maximum (or minimum) y-value: k

CONCEPT	SYMBOLIC REPRESENTATION	COMMENTS AND EXAMPLES
Completing the square to find vertex form	To complete the square for $x^2 + kx$, add $\left(\frac{k}{2}\right)^2$ to make a perfect square trinomial.	$y = x^2 - 2x + 3$ $y - 3 = x^2 - 2x \qquad k = -2$ $y - 3 + 1 = x^2 - 2x + 1 \quad$ Add $\left(\frac{-2}{2}\right)^2 = 1.$ $y - 2 = (x - 1)^2$ $y = (x - 1)^2 + 2$
Vertex formula	The vertex for $f(x) = ax^2 + bx + c$ is the point $$\left(-\frac{b}{2a}, f\left(-\frac{b}{2a}\right)\right).$$	If $f(x) = x^2 - 2x + 3$, then $$x = -\frac{-2}{2(1)} = 1.$$ y-value of vertex: $f(1) = 2$ Vertex: $(1, 2)$; axis of symmetry: $x = 1$
Vertex form (standard form for a parabola with vertical axis)	The vertex form for a quadratic function is $f(x) = a(x - h)^2 + k$, with vertex (h, k).	Let $f(x) = 2(x + 3)^2 - 5$. Parabola opens upward: $a > 0 \qquad a = 2$ Vertex: $(-3, -5)$ Axis of symmetry: $x = -3$ Minimum y-value on graph: -5

3.1 Exercises

Basics of Quadratic Functions

Exercises 1–6: Identify f as being linear, quadratic, or neither. If f is quadratic, identify the leading coefficient a and evaluate f(−2).

1. $f(x) = 1 - 2x + 3x^2$ **2.** $f(x) = -5x + 11$

3. $f(x) = \dfrac{1}{x^2 - 1}$ **4.** $f(x) = (x^2 + 1)^2$

5. $f(x) = \frac{1}{2} - \frac{3}{10}x$ **6.** $f(x) = \frac{1}{5}x^2$

Exercises 7–10: Use the graph to find the following.

(a) Sign of the leading coefficient
(b) Vertex
(c) Axis of symmetry
(d) Intervals where f is increasing and where f is decreasing
(e) Domain and range

7.

8.

9.

10.

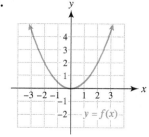

Exercises 11–14: The formulas for f(x) and g(x) are identical except for their leading coefficients a. Compare the graphs of f and g. You may want to support your answers by graphing f and g together.

11. $f(x) = x^2,$ $\qquad\qquad g(x) = 2x^2$

12. $f(x) = \frac{1}{2}x^2,$ $\qquad\quad g(x) = -\frac{1}{2}x^2$

13. $f(x) = 2x^2 + 1,$ $\qquad g(x) = -\frac{1}{3}x^2 + 1$

14. $f(x) = x^2 + x,$ $\qquad g(x) = \frac{1}{4}x^2 + x$

Vertex Formula

Exercises 15–20: Identify the vertex and leading coefficient. Then write the expression as $f(x) = ax^2 + bx + c$.

15. $f(x) = -3(x - 1)^2 + 2$

16. $f(x) = 5(x + 2)^2 - 5$

17. $f(x) = 5 - 2(x - 4)^2$ **18.** $f(x) = \frac{1}{2}(x + 3)^2 - 5$

19. $f(x) = \frac{3}{4}(x + 5)^2 - \frac{7}{4}$ **20.** $f(x) = -5(x - 4)^2$

Exercises 21–28: Use the graph of the quadratic function f to write its formula as $f(x) = a(x - h)^2 + k$.

21.

22.

23.

24.

25.

26.

27.

28.
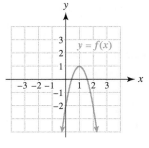

Exercises 29–40: Write the given expression in the form $f(x) = a(x - h)^2 + k$. Identify the vertex.

29. $f(x) = x^2 + 4x - 5$ **30.** $f(x) = x^2 + 10x + 7$

31. $f(x) = x^2 - 3x$ **32.** $f(x) = x^2 - 7x + 5$

33. $f(x) = 2x^2 - 5x + 3$ **34.** $f(x) = 3x^2 + 6x + 2$

35. $f(x) = \frac{1}{3}x^2 + x + 1$ **36.** $f(x) = -\frac{1}{2}x^2 - \frac{3}{2}x + 1$

37. $f(x) = 2x^2 - 8x - 1$ **38.** $f(x) = -\frac{1}{2}x^2 - x$

39. $f(x) = 2 - 9x - 3x^2$

40. $f(x) = 6 + 5x - 10x^2$

Exercises 41–52: Complete the following.
(a) Use the vertex formula to find the vertex.
(b) Find the intervals where f is increasing and where f is decreasing.

41. $f(x) = 6 - x^2$ **42.** $f(x) = 2x^2 - 2x + 1$

43. $f(x) = x^2 - 6x$ **44.** $f(x) = -2x^2 + 4x + 5$

45. $f(x) = 2x^2 - 4x + 1$ **46.** $f(x) = -3x^2 + x - 2$

47. $f(x) = \frac{1}{2}x^2 + 10$ **48.** $f(x) = \frac{9}{10}x^2 - 12$

49. $f(x) = -\frac{3}{4}x^2 + \frac{1}{2}x - 3$ **50.** $f(x) = -\frac{4}{5}x^2 - \frac{1}{5}x + 1$

51. $f(x) = 1.5 - 3x - 6x^2$ **52.** $f(x) = -4x^2 + 16x$

Min-Max

Exercises 53–58: Find the minimum y-value on the graph of $y = f(x)$.

53. $f(x) = x^2 + 4x - 2$ **54.** $f(x) = x^2 - 6x$

55. $f(x) = 3x^2 - 4x + 2$ **56.** $f(x) = 2x^2 + 6x$

57. $f(x) = x^2 + 3x + 5$ **58.** $f(x) = 2x^2 - x + 1$

Exercises 59–64: Find the maximum y-value on the graph of $y = f(x)$.

59. $f(x) = -x^2 + 3x - 2$ **60.** $f(x) = -x^2 + 4x + 5$

61. $f(x) = 5x - x^2$ **62.** $f(x) = -2x^2 - 2x - 5$

63. $f(x) = 2x - 3x^2$ **64.** $f(x) = -4x^2 + 6x - 9$

Graphing Quadratic Functions

Exercises 65–84: Sketch a graph of f.

65. $f(x) = x^2$ **66.** $f(x) = -2x^2$

67. $f(x) = -\frac{1}{2}x^2$ **68.** $f(x) = 4 - x^2$

69. $f(x) = x^2 - 3$ **70.** $f(x) = x^2 + 2$

71. $f(x) = (x - 2)^2 + 1$ **72.** $f(x) = (x + 1)^2 - 2$

73. $f(x) = -3(x + 1)^2 + 3$

74. $f(x) = -2(x - 1)^2 + 1$

75. $f(x) = x^2 - 2x - 2$ 76. $f(x) = x^2 - 4x$

77. $f(x) = -x^2 + 4x - 2$ 78. $f(x) = -x^2 + 2x + 1$

79. $f(x) = 2x^2 - 4x - 1$ 80. $f(x) = 3x^2 + 6x$

81. $f(x) = -3x^2 - 6x + 1$ 82. $f(x) = -2x^2 + 4x - 1$

83. $f(x) = -\frac{1}{2}x^2 + x + 1$ 84. $f(x) = \frac{1}{2}x^2 - 2x + 2$

Exercises 85 and 86: **Average Rate of Change** *Find the average rate of change of f from 1 to 3.*

85. $f(x) = -3x^2 + 5x$ 86. $f(x) = 4x^2 - 3x + 1$

Exercises 87 and 88: **Difference Quotient** *Find the difference quotient of f.*

87. $f(x) = 3x^2 - 2x$ 88. $f(x) = 5 - 4x^2$

Exercises 89 and 90: Find the formula for a quadratic function that satisfies the given conditions.

89. Axis of symmetry $x = 3$, passing through the points $(3, 1)$ and $(1, 9)$

90. Vertex $(-3, 4)$, passing through $(-2, 1)$

Graphs and Models

Exercises 91–94: Match the situation with the graph of the quadratic function (a–d) that models it best.

91. The height y of a stone thrown from ground level after x seconds

92. The number of people attending a popular movie x weeks after its opening

93. The temperature after x hours in a house where the furnace quits and a repair person fixes it

94. The cumulative number of reported AIDS cases in year x, where $1982 \le x \le 1994$

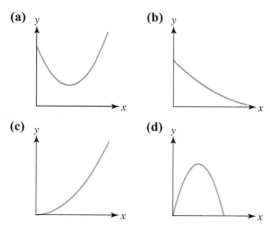

(a) **(b)** **(c)** **(d)**

Applications and Models

95. **Maximizing Area** A farmer has 1000 feet of fence to enclose a rectangular area. What dimensions for the rectangle result in the maximum area enclosed by the fence?

96. **Maximizing Area** A homeowner has 80 feet of fence to enclose a rectangular garden. What dimensions for the garden give the maximum area?

97. **Maximizing Revenue** Suppose the revenue R in thousands of dollars that a company receives from producing x thousand DVD players is given by the formula $R(x) = x(40 - 2x)$.
    (a) Evaluate $R(2)$ and interpret the result.

    (b) How many DVD players should the company produce to maximize its revenue?

    (c) What is the maximum revenue?

98. **Maximizing Revenue** A large hotel is considering giving the following group discount on room rates: the regular price of \$120 decreases by \$2 for each room rented. For example, one room costs \$118, two rooms cost $\$116 \times 2 = \$232$, three rooms cost $\$114 \times 3 = \$342$, and so on.
    (a) Write a formula for a function R that gives the revenue for renting x rooms.

    (b) Sketch a graph of R. What is a reasonable domain?

    (c) Determine the maximum revenue and the corresponding number of rooms rented.

99. **Minimizing Cost** A business that produces color copies is trying to minimize its average cost per copy (total cost divided by the number of copies). This average cost in cents is given by

    $$f(x) = 0.00000093x^2 - 0.0145x + 60,$$

    where x represents the total number of copies produced.
    (a) Describe the graph of f.

    (b) Find the minimum average cost per copy and the corresponding number of copies made.

100. **Minimizing Cost** A publisher is trying to minimize its average cost per book printed (total cost divided by the number of books printed). This average cost in dollars is given by

    $$f(x) = 0.000000015x^2 - 0.0007x + 26,$$

    where x represents the total number of books printed.
    (a) Describe the graph of f.

    (b) Find the minimum average cost per book and the corresponding number of books printed.

101. Hitting a Baseball A baseball is hit so that its height in feet after t seconds is $s(t) = -16t^2 + 44t + 4$.
(a) How high is the baseball after 1 second?

(b) Find the maximum height of the baseball. Support your answer graphically.

102. Flight of a Baseball (Refer to Example 9.) A baseball is hit straight up with an initial velocity of $v_0 = 96$ feet per second (about 65 miles per hour) and leaves the bat with an initial height of $h_0 = 2.5$ feet.
(a) Write a formula $s(t)$ that models the height after t seconds.

(b) How high is the baseball after 4 seconds?

(c) Find the maximum height of the baseball. Support your answer graphically.

103. Throwing a Stone (Refer to Example 9.) A stone is thrown *downward* with a velocity of 66 feet per second (45 miles per hour) from a bridge that is 120 feet above a river, as illustrated in the figure.
(a) Write a formula $s(t)$ that models the height of the stone after t seconds.

(b) Does the stone hit the water within the first 2 seconds? Explain.

104. Hitting a Golf Ball A golf ball is hit so that its height h in feet after t seconds is $h(t) = -16t^2 + 60t$.
(a) What is the initial height of the golf ball?

(b) How high is the golf ball after 1.5 seconds?

(c) Find the maximum height of the golf ball.

105. Maximizing Area (Refer to Example 8.) A farmer wants to fence a rectangular area by using the wall of a barn as one side of the rectangle and then enclosing the other three sides with 160 feet of fence. Find the dimensions of the rectangle that give the maximum area inside.

106. Maximizing Area A rancher plans to fence a rectangular area for cattle using the straight portion of a river as one side of the rectangle. If the farmer has P feet of fence, find the dimensions of the rectangle that give the maximum area for the cattle.

Exercises 107–110: **Maximizing Altitude** *If air resistance is ignored, the height h of a projectile above the ground after x seconds is given by $h(x) = -\frac{1}{2}gx^2 + v_0x + h_0$, where g is the acceleration due to gravity. This formula is also valid for other celestial bodies. Suppose a ball is thrown straight up at 88 feet per second from a height of 25 feet.*

(a) *For the given g, graphically estimate both the maximum height and the time when it occurs.*
(b) *Solve part (a) symbolically.*

107. $g = 32$ (Earth)   **108.** $g = 5.1$ (Moon)

109. $g = 13$ (Mars)   **110.** $g = 88$ (Jupiter)

111. Suspension Bridge The cables that support a suspension bridge, such as the Golden Gate Bridge, can be modeled by parabolas. Suppose that a 300-foot-long suspension bridge has at each end a tower that is 120 feet tall, as shown in the figure. If the cable comes within 20 feet of the road at the center of the bridge, find a function that models the height of the cable above the road a distance of x feet from the center of the bridge.

112. Suspension Bridge Repeat Exercise 111 for a suspension bridge that has 100-foot towers, a length of 200 feet, and a cable that comes within 15 feet of the road at the center of the bridge.

Exercises 113 and 114: Find $f(x) = a(x - h)^2 + k$ so that f models the data exactly.

113.

x	-1	0	1	2	3
y	5	-1	-3	-1	5

114.

x	-2	-1	0	1	2
y	2	4	2	-4	-14

115. Heart Rate The table shows the heart rate of an athlete upon stopping a moderate activity.

Time (min)	0	1	2	3	4
Heart rate (bpm)	122	108	98	92	90

(a) Model the data with $H(t) = a(t - h)^2 + k$. What is the domain of H?

(b) Approximate the athlete's heart rate for $t = 1.5$ minutes.

116. Heart Rate   The heart rate of an athlete while weight training is recorded for 4 minutes. The table lists the heart rate after x minutes.

Time (min)	0	1	2	3	4
Heart rate (bpm)	84	111	120	110	85

(a) Explain why the data are not linear.

(b) Find a quadratic function f that models the data.

(c) What is the domain of your function?

117. Slideshare   Slideshare is a social sharing site where users share professional materials such as PowerPoint presentations. The table shows the number of Slideshare visitors in millions for selected years, where x represents years after 2007.

Year	0	1	2	3	4
Visitors	1.5	6.1	17	33.2	60.1

Source: Business Insider.

(a) Model the data with $V(x) = a(x - h)^2 + k$.

(b) Approximate the number of visitors to Slideshare in 2012 if trends were to continue.

118. iPhone Sales   The table lists the number of iPhones sold in millions in the first 5 years on the market. Find a quadratic function f that models the data.

Year	1	2	3	4	5
Units sold	1	20	50	100	180

Source: Business Insider.

Exercises 119 and 120: **AIDS in America (1982–1994)**   *In the early years of AIDS, the numbers of both AIDS cases and AIDS deaths could be modeled with quadratic functions. The tables list cumulative numbers for selected years.*

(a)   *Find a quadratic function f that models the data.*
(b)   *Graph the data and f together.*
(c)   *Evaluate $f(1991)$ and interpret the result.*

119. Cumulative AIDS cases in thousands

Year	1982	1986	1990	1994
Cases	1.6	41.9	197	442

Source: Department of Health and Human Services.

120. Cumulative AIDS deaths in thousands

Year	1982	1986	1990	1994
Deaths	0.6	24.8	122	298

Source: Department of Health and Human Services.

Quadratic Regression

Exercises 121 and 122: **Quadratic Models**   *Use least-squares regression to find a quadratic function f that models the data given in the table. Estimate $f(3.5)$ to the nearest hundredth.*

121.

x	0	2	4	6
$f(x)$	-1	16	57	124

122.

x	10	20	30	40
$f(x)$	4.2	24.3	84.1	184

123. China's Rise   The economic rise of China has greatly increased American interest in learning Chinese. The following table lists the U.S. college and university enrollments in thousands to study Chinese.

Year	1980	1986	1995	2002	2009
Enrollment	11	17	27	34	61

Source: The Economist

(a) Find a quadratic function that models the data. Support your result graphically.

(b) Estimate the enrollment to study Chinese in 2006 and compare to the actual value of 51 thousand.

124. MySpace Visitors   The table lists the number of unique MySpace visitors per month in millions for various years.

Year	2006	2007	2008	2009	2010	2011
Visitors	55	70	77	65	55	35

Source: comScore

(a) Find a quadratic function that models the data. Support your result graphically.

(b) Estimate the number of MySpace visitors in 2012 if trends continued.

125. Head Start Enrollment   Head Start provides a wide range of services to children of low-income families. The table lists Head Start participation in thousands.

Year	1970	1980	1990	2006
Enrollment	447	376	541	909

Source: Department of Health and Human Services.

(a) Find a quadratic function that models the data.

(b) Estimate enrollment in 1985.

126. Photosynthesis In one study the efficiency of photosynthesis in an Antarctic species of grass was investigated. The table lists results for various temperatures. The temperature x is in degrees Celsius and the efficiency y is given as a percent. (*Source:* D. Brown and P. Rothery, *Models in Biology: Mathematics, Statistics and Computing.*)

x (°C)	−1.5	0	2.5	5	7	10	12
y (%)	33	46	55	80	87	93	95

x (°C)	15	17	20	22	25	27	30
y (%)	91	89	77	72	54	46	34

(a) Plot the data. Discuss reasons why a quadratic function might model the data.

(b) Find a least-squares quadratic function f given by $f(x) = ax^2 + bx + c$ that models the data.

(c) Graph f and the data in the window $[-5, 35, 5]$ by $[20, 110, 10]$. Discuss the fit.

Writing about Mathematics

127. How do the values of a, h, and k affect the graph of $f(x) = a(x - h)^2 + k$?

128. Explain why the vertex is important when you are trying to find either the maximum y-value or the minimum y-value on the graph of a quadratic function.

Extended and Discovery Exercises

Exercises 1–4: **Difference Quotient** *Complete the following.*

(a) Evaluate $f(x)$ for each x-value in the table.

x	1	2	3	4	5
$f(x)$					

(b) Calculate the average rate of change of f between consecutive data points in the table.

(c) Find the difference quotient for $f(x)$. Then let $h = 1$ in the difference quotient.

(d) Evaluate this difference quotient for $x = 1, 2, 3,$ and 4. Compare these results to your results in part (b).

1. $f(x) = x^2 - 3$

2. $f(x) = 2x - x^2$

3. $f(x) = -2x^2 + 3x - 1$

4. $f(x) = 3x^2 + x + 2$

3.2 Quadratic Equations and Problem Solving

- **Understand basic concepts about quadratic equations**
- **Use factoring, the square root property, completing the square, and the quadratic formula to solve quadratic equations**
- **Understand the discriminant**
- **Solve problems involving quadratic equations**

Introduction

In Example 10 of Section 3.1 we modeled an athlete's heart rate x minutes after exercise stopped by using $f(x) = 1.875(x - 8)^2 + 80$. This vertex form can easily be changed to *general form.*

$$f(x) = 1.875(x - 8)^2 + 80 \qquad \text{Vertex form}$$
$$= 1.875(x^2 - 16x + 64) + 80 \qquad \text{Square the binomial.}$$
$$= 1.875x^2 - 30x + 200 \qquad \text{General form}$$

To determine the length of time needed for the athlete's heart rate to slow from **200** beats per minute to **110** beats per minute, we can solve the *quadratic equation*

$$1.875x^2 - 30x + 200 = 110, \quad \text{or} \qquad \text{Quadratic equation}$$
$$1.875x^2 - 30x + 90 = 0 \qquad \text{Subtract 110 from each side.}$$

(See Example 7.) A quadratic equation results when the formula for a quadratic function is set equal to a constant.

Quadratic Equations

A quadratic equation can be defined as follows.

QUADRATIC EQUATION

A **quadratic equation** in one variable is an equation that can be written in the form
$$ax^2 + bx + c = 0,$$
where a, b, and c are constants with $a \neq 0$.

Examples of quadratic equations include

$$2x^2 - 3x - 4 = 0, \quad x^2 = 3, \quad -5x^2 + x = 0, \quad \text{and} \quad 3x + 1 = x^2.$$

The following See the Concept explains that quadratic equations can have zero, one, or two *real* solutions by showing that a parabola can intersect the x-axis zero, one, or two times. (Complex solutions are discussed in the next section.)

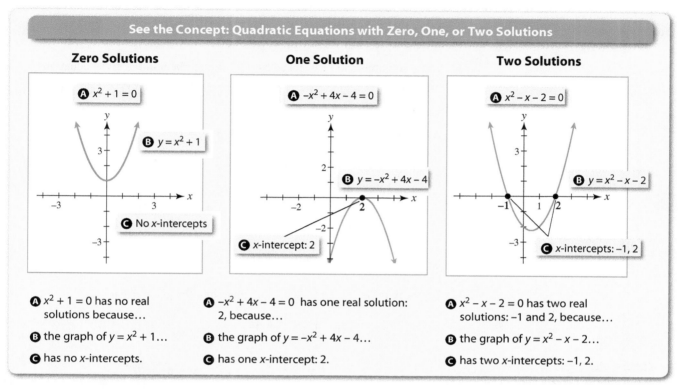

See the Concept: Quadratic Equations with Zero, One, or Two Solutions

Zero Solutions

Ⓐ $x^2 + 1 = 0$

Ⓑ $y = x^2 + 1$

Ⓒ No x-intercepts

One Solution

Ⓐ $-x^2 + 4x - 4 = 0$

Ⓑ $y = -x^2 + 4x - 4$

Ⓒ x-intercept: 2

Two Solutions

Ⓐ $x^2 - x - 2 = 0$

Ⓑ $y = x^2 - x - 2$

Ⓒ x-intercepts: −1, 2

Ⓐ $x^2 + 1 = 0$ has no real solutions because...

Ⓑ the graph of $y = x^2 + 1$...

Ⓒ has no x-intercepts.

Ⓐ $-x^2 + 4x - 4 = 0$ has one real solution: 2, because...

Ⓑ the graph of $y = -x^2 + 4x - 4$...

Ⓒ has one x-intercept: 2.

Ⓐ $x^2 - x - 2 = 0$ has two real solutions: −1 and 2, because...

Ⓑ the graph of $y = x^2 - x - 2$...

Ⓒ has two x-intercepts: −1, 2.

Quadratic equations can be solved symbolically by a variety of methods: factoring, the square root property, completing the square, and the quadratic formula. They can also be solved graphically and numerically; however, the exact solution can *always* be obtained symbolically.

Factoring

Factoring to solve an equation is based on the **zero-product property**, which states that if $ab = 0$, then $a = 0$ or $b = 0$ or both. It is important to remember that this property works only for 0. For example, if $ab = 1$, then this equation does *not* imply that either $a = 1$ or $b = 1$. For example, $a = \frac{1}{2}$ and $b = 2$ also satisfies $ab = 1$ and neither a nor b is 1.

EXAMPLE 1   Solving quadratic equations with factoring

Solve each quadratic equation. Check your results.
(a) $x^2 - 2x + 1 = 0$ **(b)** $2x^2 + 2x - 11 = 1$ **(c)** $12t^2 = t + 1$

SOLUTION
(a) Begin by factoring and applying the zero-product property.

$$x^2 - 2x + 1 = 0 \qquad \text{Given equation}$$
$$(x - 1)(x - 1) = 0 \qquad \text{Factor.}$$
$$x - 1 = 0 \quad \text{or} \quad x - 1 = 0 \qquad \text{Zero-product property}$$
$$x = 1 \quad \text{or} \quad x = 1 \qquad \text{Solve.}$$

The only solution is 1. We can check our answer.

$$(1)^2 - 2(1) + 1 = 0 \qquad \text{Let } x = 1.$$
$$0 = 0 \checkmark \qquad \text{It checks.}$$

Algebra Review
To review factoring trinomials, see Chapter R (pages R-22–R-23).

(b) Start by writing the equation in the form $ax^2 + bx + c = 0$.

$$2x^2 + 2x - 11 = 1 \qquad \text{Given equation}$$
$$2x^2 + 2x - 12 = 0 \qquad \text{Subtract 1 from each side.}$$
$$x^2 + x - 6 = 0 \qquad \text{Divide each side by 2.}$$
$$(x + 3)(x - 2) = 0 \qquad \text{Factor.}$$
$$x + 3 = 0 \quad \text{or} \quad x - 2 = 0 \qquad \text{Zero-product property}$$
$$x = -3 \quad \text{or} \quad x = 2 \qquad \text{Solve.}$$

These solutions can be checked by substituting them in the given equation.

$$2(-3)^2 + 2(-3) - 11 \stackrel{?}{=} 1 \qquad\qquad 2(2)^2 + 2(2) - 11 \stackrel{?}{=} 1$$
$$1 = 1 \checkmark \qquad\qquad\qquad\qquad 1 = 1 \checkmark$$

(c) Write the equation in the form $at^2 + bt + c = 0$.

$$12t^2 = t + 1 \qquad \text{Given equation}$$
$$12t^2 - t - 1 = 0 \qquad \text{Subtract } t \text{ and 1.}$$
$$(3t - 1)(4t + 1) = 0 \qquad \text{Factor.}$$
$$3t - 1 = 0 \quad \text{or} \quad 4t + 1 = 0 \qquad \text{Zero-product property}$$
$$t = \frac{1}{3} \quad \text{or} \quad t = -\frac{1}{4} \qquad \text{Solve.}$$

To check these solutions, substitute them into the given equation.

$$12\left(\frac{1}{3}\right)^2 = \frac{1}{3} + 1 \qquad 12\left(-\frac{1}{4}\right)^2 = -\frac{1}{4} + 1$$
$$\frac{4}{3} = \frac{4}{3} \checkmark \qquad\qquad \frac{3}{4} = \frac{3}{4} \checkmark$$

Now Try Exercises 1, 7, and 9

We can also use factoring to find the x-intercepts of the graph of a quadratic function, because the x-intercepts of the graph of $y = ax^2 + bx + c$ correspond to the solutions to $ax^2 + bx + c = 0$. The y-intercept is c, the value of y when $x = 0$.

EXAMPLE 2 Finding intercepts

Find the exact values for both the x-intercepts and the y-intercept shown in Figure 3.26.

SOLUTION From the graph it is difficult to determine the *exact* x-intercepts. However, they can be determined symbolically.

$$24x^2 + 7x - 6 = 0 \qquad \text{Set expression equal to 0.}$$
$$(3x + 2)(8x - 3) = 0 \qquad \text{Factor.}$$
$$3x + 2 = 0 \quad \text{or} \quad 8x - 3 = 0 \qquad \text{Zero-product property}$$
$$x = -\frac{2}{3} \quad \text{or} \quad x = \frac{3}{8} \qquad \text{Solve.}$$

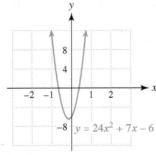

Figure 3.26

The x-intercepts are $-\frac{2}{3}$ and $\frac{3}{8}$.

To find the y-intercept, let $x = 0$ in $y = 24x^2 + 7x - 6$.

$$24(0)^2 + 7(0) - 6 = -6$$

The y-intercept is -6.

Now Try Exercise 33

Symbolic, Numerical, and Graphical Solutions   Quadratic equations can be solved symbolically, numerically, and graphically. The following example illustrates each technique for the equation $x(x - 2) = 3$. (Also, see Example 7.)

Symbolic Solution	Numerical Solution	Graphical Solution

Symbolic Solution

$$x(x - 2) = 3$$
$$x^2 - 2x = 3$$
$$x^2 - 2x - 3 = 0$$
$$(x + 1)(x - 3) = 0$$

The solutions are -1 and 3.

Numerical Solution

x	$x(x - 2)$
-2	8
-1	3
0	0
1	-1
2	0
3	3
4	8

Let $y = x(x - 2)$. In the table $y = 3$ when $x = -1$ or $x = 3$.

Graphical Solution

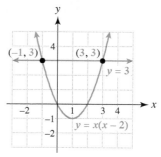

The graph of $y = x(x - 2)$ intersects the graph of $y = 3$ at $(-1, 3)$ and $(3, 3)$. The solutions are -1 and 3.

The Square Root Property

Algebra Review

To review square roots, see Chapter R (Page R-37).

Some quadratic equations can be written as $x^2 = k$, where k is a nonnegative number. The solutions are $\pm\sqrt{k}$. (Recall that the symbol $\pm$ represents *plus or minus*.) For example, $x^2 = 16$ has two solutions: ± 4. We refer to this as the **square root property**. See Extended and Discovery Exercise 7 in this section for a justification of this property.

> **SQUARE ROOT PROPERTY**
>
> Let k be a nonnegative number. Then the solutions to the equation
> $$x^2 = k$$
> are given by $x = \pm\sqrt{k}$.

EXAMPLE 3   Using the square root property

If a metal ball is dropped 100 feet from a water tower, its height h in feet above the ground after t seconds is given by $h(t) = 100 - 16t^2$. Determine how long it takes the ball to hit the ground.

SOLUTION   The ball strikes the ground when the equation $100 - 16t^2 = 0$ is satisfied.

$$100 - 16t^2 = 0$$

$$100 = 16t^2 \qquad \text{Add } 16t^2 \text{ to each side.}$$

$$t^2 = \frac{100}{16} \qquad \text{Divide each side by 16. Rewrite.}$$

$$t = \pm\sqrt{\frac{100}{16}} \qquad \text{Square root property}$$

$$t = \pm\frac{10}{4} \qquad \text{Simplify.}$$

In this example only positive values for time are valid, so the ball strikes the ground after $\frac{10}{4}$, or 2.5, seconds.

Now Try Exercise 105

Functions can be defined by formulas, graphs, tables, and diagrams. Functions can also be defined by equations. In the next example we use the square root property to solve equations for y and then determine if y is a function of x, where $y = f(x)$.

EXAMPLE 4 Determining if equations represent functions

Solve each equation for y. Determine if y is a function of x.

(a) $x^2 + (y - 1)^2 = 4$ (b) $2y = \dfrac{x + y}{2}$

SOLUTION

(a) Start by subtracting x^2 from each side of the equation.

$$(y - 1)^2 = 4 - x^2 \qquad \text{Subtract } x^2 \text{ from each side.}$$
$$y - 1 = \pm\sqrt{4 - x^2} \qquad \text{Square root property}$$
$$y = 1 \pm \sqrt{4 - x^2} \qquad \text{Add 1 to each side.}$$

There are two formulas, $y = 1 + \sqrt{4 - x^2}$ and $y = 1 - \sqrt{4 - x^2}$, which indicates that y is *not* a function of x. That is, one x-input can produce two y-outputs.

NOTE The equation $x^2 + (y - 1)^2 = 4$ is in standard form for a circle that has center $(0, 1)$ and radius 2. A circle does not pass the vertical line test, so the equation does not represent a function.

Algebra Review
To clear fractions, see Chapter R (page R-33).

(b) Clear fractions by multiplying each side of $2y = \dfrac{x + y}{2}$ by 2.

$$4y = x + y \qquad \text{Multiply each side by 2.}$$
$$3y = x \qquad \text{Subtract } y \text{ from each side.}$$
$$y = \frac{x}{3} \qquad \text{Divide each side by 3.}$$

The equation $y = \frac{x}{3}$ defines a linear function, $f(x) = \frac{1}{3}x$, so y is a function of x.

Now Try Exercises 71 and 73

Completing the Square

Another technique that can be used to solve a quadratic equation is *completing the square*. If a quadratic equation is written in the form $x^2 + kx = d$, where k and d are constants, then the equation can be solved using

$$x^2 + kx + \left(\frac{k}{2}\right)^2 = \left(x + \frac{k}{2}\right)^2.$$

Algebra Review
To review factoring perfect square trinomials, see Chapter R (page R-25)

For example, $k = 6$ in $x^2 + 6x = 7$, so add $\left(\frac{k}{2}\right)^2 = \left(\frac{6}{2}\right)^2 = 9$ to each side.

$$x^2 + 6x = 7 \qquad \text{Given equation}$$
$$x^2 + 6x + 9 = 7 + 9 \qquad \text{Add 9 to each side.}$$
$$(x + 3)^2 = 16 \qquad \text{Factor the perfect square.}$$
$$x + 3 = \pm 4 \qquad \text{Square root property}$$
$$x = -3 \pm 4 \qquad \text{Add } -3 \text{ to each side.}$$
$$x = 1 \quad \text{or} \quad x = -7 \qquad \text{Simplify.}$$

NOTE If the coefficient a of the x^2-term is not 1, we can divide each side of the equation by a so that it becomes 1. See Example 5(b).

Completing the square is useful when solving quadratic equations that do not factor easily.

EXAMPLE 5   Completing the square

Solve each equation.
(a) $x^2 - 8x + 9 = 0$ **(b)** $2x^2 - 8x = 7$

SOLUTION
(a) Start by writing the equation in the form $x^2 + kx = d$ with $k = -8$ and $d = -9$.

$$x^2 - 8x + 9 = 0 \qquad \text{Given equation}$$
$$x^2 - 8x = -9 \qquad \text{Subtract 9 from each side.}$$
$$x^2 - 8x + 16 = -9 + 16 \qquad \text{Add } \left(\tfrac{k}{2}\right)^2 = \left(\tfrac{-8}{2}\right)^2 = 16.$$
$$(x - 4)^2 = 7 \qquad \text{Factor the perfect square.}$$
$$x - 4 = \pm\sqrt{7} \qquad \text{Square root property}$$
$$x = 4 \pm \sqrt{7} \qquad \text{Add 4 to each side.}$$

(b) Divide each side by 2 to obtain a 1 for the leading coefficient.

$$2x^2 - 8x = 7 \qquad \text{Given equation}$$
$$x^2 - 4x = \tfrac{7}{2} \qquad \text{Divide each side by 2.}$$
$$x^2 - 4x + 4 = \tfrac{7}{2} + 4 \qquad \text{Add } \left(\tfrac{-4}{2}\right)^2 = 4 \text{ to each side.}$$
$$(x - 2)^2 = \tfrac{15}{2} \qquad \text{Factor the perfect square.}$$
$$x - 2 = \pm\sqrt{\tfrac{15}{2}} \qquad \text{Square root property}$$
$$x = 2 \pm \sqrt{\tfrac{15}{2}} \qquad \text{Add 2 to each side.}$$

Now Try Exercises 53 and 55

The Quadratic Formula

The quadratic formula can be used to find the solutions to *any* quadratic equation.

QUADRATIC FORMULA

The solutions to the quadratic equation $ax^2 + bx + c = 0$, where $a \neq 0$, are given by

$$x = \frac{-b \pm \sqrt{b^2 - 4ac}}{2a}.$$

EXAMPLE 6   Using the quadratic formula

Solve the equation $3x^2 - 6x + 2 = 0$.

SOLUTION   Let $a = 3$, $b = -6$, and $c = 2$.

$$x = \frac{-b \pm \sqrt{b^2 - 4ac}}{2a} \qquad \text{Quadratic formula}$$

$$x = \frac{-(-6) \pm \sqrt{(-6)^2 - 4(3)(2)}}{2(3)} \qquad \text{Substitute for } a, b, \text{ and } c.$$

$$x = \frac{6 \pm \sqrt{12}}{6} \qquad \text{Simplify.}$$

Algebra Review
To review simplifying square roots, see Chapter R (page R-43).

$$x = 1 \pm \frac{1}{6}\sqrt{12} \qquad \text{Divide: } \frac{a \pm b}{c} = \frac{a}{c} \pm \frac{b}{c}.$$

NOTE   Because $\sqrt{12} = \sqrt{4} \cdot \sqrt{3} = 2\sqrt{3}$, we can write $1 \pm \frac{1}{6}\sqrt{12}$ as $1 \pm \frac{1}{3}\sqrt{3}$.

Now Try Exercise 25

NOTE When solving quadratic equations, a common strategy is to first write the equation in the form $ax^2 + bx + c = 0$ and to then try to factor the left side of the equation. If the factors are not easily found, the quadratic formula is used.

EXAMPLE 7 Estimating an athlete's heart rate

An athlete's heart rate is given by $1.875x^2 - 30x + 200$. Determine when the heart rate was 110 beats per minute by solving the quadratic equation $1.875x^2 - 30x + 90 = 0$ symbolically, graphically, and numerically, where $0 \leq x \leq 8$. (This equation was discussed in the introduction to this section.)

SOLUTION

Symbolic Solution Let $a = 1.875$, $b = -30$, and $c = 90$ in the quadratic formula.

$$x = \frac{-b \pm \sqrt{b^2 - 4ac}}{2a} \qquad \text{Quadratic formula}$$

$$= \frac{-(-30) \pm \sqrt{(-30)^2 - 4(1.875)(90)}}{2(1.875)} \qquad a = 1.875, b = -30, \text{ and } c = 90$$

$$= \frac{30 \pm \sqrt{225}}{3.75} \qquad \text{Simplify.}$$

$$= 12 \text{ or } 4 \qquad \text{Simplify.}$$

The x-values are restricted to $0 \leq x \leq 8$, so the only valid solution is 4. Thus the athlete's heart rate reached 110 beats per minute 4 minutes after the athlete stopped exercising.

Graphical Solution To use the *x-intercept method* to solve this quadratic equation, graph $y_1 = 1.875x^2 - 30x + 90$ and locate the x-intercepts, as shown in Figures 3.27 and 3.28. The x-intercepts are 4 and 12, in agreement with the symbolic solution.

Numerical Solution Make a table of $y_1 = 1.875x^2 - 30x + 90$, as shown in Figure 3.29. The numerical solution agrees with the symbolic and graphical solutions because $y_1 = 0$ when $x = 4$ or $x = 12$.

Calculator Help

To find a zero, or *x*-intercept, see Appendix A (page AP-7).

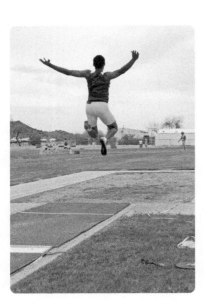

Graphical Solutions

$[0, 16, 4]$ by $[-125, 125, 25]$ $[0, 16, 4]$ by $[-125, 125, 25]$

Figure 3.27

Figure 3.28

Numerical Solutions

Figure 3.29

Now Try Exercise 107

The Discriminant

The quantity $b^2 - 4ac$ in the quadratic formula is called the **discriminant.** It provides information about the number of real solutions to a quadratic equation.

> **QUADRATIC EQUATIONS AND THE DISCRIMINANT**
>
> To determine the number of real solutions to $ax^2 + bx + c = 0$ with $a \neq 0$, evaluate the discriminant $b^2 - 4ac$.
>
> **1.** If $b^2 - 4ac > 0$, there are two real solutions.
> **2.** If $b^2 - 4ac = 0$, there is one real solution.
> **3.** If $b^2 - 4ac < 0$, there are no real solutions.

NOTE When $b^2 - 4ac < 0$, the solutions to a quadratic equation may be expressed as two complex numbers. Complex numbers are discussed in the next section.

In Example 6 the discriminant is $b^2 - 4ac = (-6)^2 - 4(3)(2) = 12$. Because the discriminant is positive, there are two real solutions.

EXAMPLE 8   Using the discriminant

Use the discriminant to find the number of solutions to $4x^2 - 12x + 9 = 0$. Then solve the equation by using the quadratic formula. Support your result graphically.

SOLUTION

Symbolic Solution   Let $a = 4$, $b = -12$, and $c = 9$. The discriminant is given by

$$b^2 - 4ac = (-12)^2 - 4(4)(9) = 0.$$

Since the discriminant is 0, there is one solution.

$$x = \frac{-b \pm \sqrt{b^2 - 4ac}}{2a} \qquad \text{Quadratic formula}$$

$$x = \frac{-(-12) \pm \sqrt{0}}{8} \qquad \text{Substitute.}$$

$$x = \frac{3}{2} \qquad \text{Simplify.}$$

The only solution is $\frac{3}{2}$.

Graphical Solution   A graph of $y = 4x^2 - 12x + 9$ is shown in Figure 3.30. The graph suggests that there is one solution because there is one x-intercept: $\frac{3}{2}$.

One Solution: $b^2 - 4ac = 0$

x-intercept: $\frac{3}{2}$

$y = 4x^2 - 12x + 9$

Figure 3.30

Now Try Exercise 87

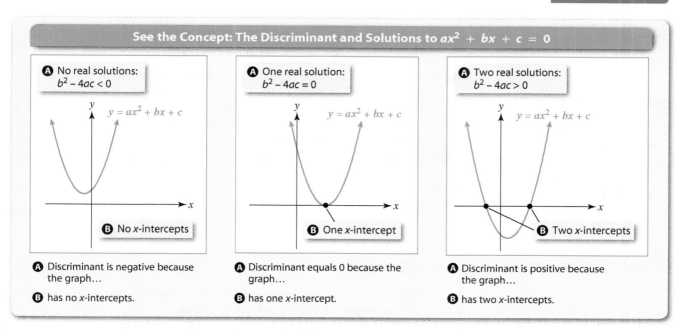

See the Concept: The Discriminant and Solutions to $ax^2 + bx + c = 0$

Ⓐ No real solutions:
$b^2 - 4ac < 0$

$y = ax^2 + bx + c$

Ⓑ No x-intercepts

Ⓐ One real solution:
$b^2 - 4ac = 0$

$y = ax^2 + bx + c$

Ⓑ One x-intercept

Ⓐ Two real solutions:
$b^2 - 4ac > 0$

$y = ax^2 + bx + c$

Ⓑ Two x-intercepts

Ⓐ Discriminant is negative because the graph...

Ⓑ has no x-intercepts.

Ⓐ Discriminant equals 0 because the graph...

Ⓑ has one x-intercept.

Ⓐ Discriminant is positive because the graph...

Ⓑ has two x-intercepts.

Factoring and the Discriminant   If a, b, and c are *integers* and $b^2 - 4ac$ is a perfect square, then the trinomial $ax^2 + bx + c$ can be factored using only integer coefficients. For example, if $6x^2 + x - 2 = 0$, then

$$b^2 - 4ac = 1^2 - 4(6)(-2) = 49,$$

which *is* a perfect square ($49 = 7^2$). Thus we can factor $6x^2 + x - 2$ as $(2x - 1)(3x + 2)$ to solve $6x^2 + x - 2 = 0$. However, if $3x^2 - x - 1 = 0$, then $b^2 - 4ac = 13$, which is *not* a perfect square. This trinomial cannot be factored (by using traditional methods with integer coefficients), so either the quadratic formula or completing the square should be used to solve $3x^2 - x - 1 = 0$. See Extended and Discovery Exercises 1–4 at the end of this section.

Problem Solving and Modeling

Many types of applications involve quadratic equations. To solve the next two problems, we use the steps for "Solving Application Problems" from Section 2.2.

EXAMPLE 9 Solving a construction problem

A box is being constructed by cutting 2-inch squares from the corners of a rectangular piece of cardboard that is 6 inches longer than it is wide, as illustrated in Figure 3.31. If the box is to have a volume of 224 cubic inches, find the dimensions of the piece of cardboard.

Figure 3.31

SOLUTION

Geometry Review
To review formulas related to boxes, see Chapter R (page R-3).

STEP 1: The rectangular piece of cardboard is 6 inches longer than it is wide. Let x be its width and $x + 6$ be its length.

$$x: \text{Width of the cardboard in inches}$$
$$x + 6: \text{Length of the cardboard in inches}$$

STEP 2: First make a drawing of the box with the appropriate labeling, as shown in Figure 3.32. The width of the *bottom* of the box is $x - 4$ inches, because two square corners with sides of 2 inches have been removed. Similarly, the length of the bottom of the box is $x + 2$ inches. Because the height times the width times the length must equal the volume, or 224 cubic inches, it follows that

$$2(x - 4)(x + 2) = 224, \quad \text{or} \quad (x - 4)(x + 2) = 112.$$

Figure 3.32

STEP 3: Write the quadratic equation in the form $ax^2 + bx + c = 0$ and factor.

$$x^2 - 2x - 8 = 112 \qquad \text{Equation to be solved}$$
$$x^2 - 2x - 120 = 0 \qquad \text{Subtract 112.}$$
$$(x - 12)(x + 10) = 0 \qquad \text{Factor.}$$
$$x = 12 \quad \text{or} \quad x = -10 \qquad \text{Zero-product property}$$

Since the dimensions cannot be negative, the width of the cardboard is 12 inches and the length is 6 inches more, or 18 inches.

STEP 4: After the 2-inch-square corners are cut out, the dimensions of the bottom of the box are $12 - 4 = 8$ inches by $18 - 4 = 14$ inches. The volume of the box is then $2 \cdot 8 \cdot 14 = 224$ cubic inches, which checks.

Now Try Exercise 111

When items are sold, a discount is sometimes given to a customer who makes a large order, which affects the revenue that a company receives. We discuss this situation in the next example.

EXAMPLE 10   Determining revenue

A company charges \$5 for earbud headphones, but it reduces this cost by \$0.05 for each additional pair ordered, up to a maximum of 50 earbuds. For example, the price for one pair is \$5, the price for two pair is 2(\$4.95) = \$9.90, the price for 3 pair is 3(\$4.90) = \$14.70, and so on. If the total price is \$95, how many earbuds were ordered?

SOLUTION

STEP 1: We are asked to find the number of earbuds that results in an order costing \$95. Let this number be x.

$$x: \text{ Number of earbuds ordered}$$

STEP 2: Revenue equals the number of earbuds sold times the price of each pair. If x earbuds are sold, then the price in dollars of each pair is $5 - 0.05(x - 1)$. (Note that when $x = 1$ the price is $5 - 0.05(1 - 1) = \$5$.) The revenue R is given by

$$R(x) = x(5 - 0.05(x - 1)),$$

Revenue = Number Sold × Price

[0, 100, 10] by [0, 150, 50]

$y_2 = 95$

$y_1 = x(5 - 0.05(x - 1))$

Intersection
X=25   Y=95

Figure 3.33

and we must solve the equation

$$x(5 - 0.05(x - 1)) = 95, \quad \text{or} \quad -0.05x^2 + 5.05x - 95 = 0.$$

STEP 3: We can solve $-0.05x^2 + 5.05x - 95$ by using the quadratic formula with $a = -0.05$, $b = 5.05$, and $c = -95$.

$$x = \frac{-5.05 \pm \sqrt{(5.05)^2 - 4(-0.05)(-95)}}{2(-0.05)} \quad \text{Quadratic formula}$$

$$= \frac{-5.05 \pm 2.55}{-0.1} \quad \text{Use a calculator.}$$

$$= 25 \text{ or } 76 \quad \text{Simplify.}$$

[0, 100, 10] by [0, 150, 50]

$y_2 = 95$

$y_1 = x(5 - 0.05(x - 1))$

Intersection
X=76   Y=95

Figure 3.34

This discount only applies to orders of 50 earbuds or fewer, so the answer is 25 earbuds. A graphical solution is shown in Figure 3.33 and 3.34.

STEP 4: If 25 earbuds are ordered, then the cost of each pair is $5 - 0.05(24) = \$3.80$ and the total revenue is $25(3.80) = \$95$.

Now Try Exercise 117

A Modeling Application   In Section 3.1 we learned that the height s of an object propelled into the air is modeled by $s(t) = -16t^2 + v_0 t + h_0$, where v_0 represents the object's initial (vertical) velocity in feet per second and h_0 represents the object's initial height in feet, as illustrated in Figure 3.35. In the next example we model the position of a projectile.

Figure 3.35

EXAMPLE 11   Modeling projectile motion

Table 3.5 shows the height of a projectile shot into the air.

Height of a Projectile

t (seconds)	0	2	4	6	8
$s(t)$ (feet)	96	400	576	624	544

Table 3.5

(a) Use $s(t) = -16t^2 + v_0 t + h_0$ to model the data.
(b) After how many seconds did the projectile strike the ground?

t (seconds)	$s(t)$ (feet)
0	96
2	400
4	576
6	624
8	544

Table 3.5 (repeated)

SOLUTION

Getting Started The value for h_0 can be determined by noting that $s(0) = 96$. The value for v_0 can be determined by using any other value in Table 3.5. We use $s(2) = 400$ to determine v_0. ▶

(a) Because $s(0) = 96$, $h_0 = 96$ and $s(t) = -16t^2 + v_0 t + 96$. Substituting $s(2) = 400$ gives the following result.

$$-16(2)^2 + v_0(2) + 96 = 400 \qquad s(2) = 400$$
$$2v_0 + 32 = 400 \qquad \text{Simplify.}$$
$$2v_0 = 368 \qquad \text{Subtract 32 from each side.}$$
$$v_0 = 184 \qquad \text{Divide each side by 2.}$$

Thus $s(t) = -16t^2 + 184t + 96$ models the height of the projectile.

(b) The projectile strikes the ground when $s(t) = 0$.

$$-16t^2 + 184t + 96 = 0 \qquad s(t) = 0; \text{ equation to be solved}$$
$$2t^2 - 23t - 12 = 0 \qquad \text{Divide each term by } -8.$$
$$(2t + 1)(t - 12) = 0 \qquad \text{Factor the trinomial.}$$
$$t = -\frac{1}{2} \quad \text{or} \quad t = 12 \qquad \text{Solve the equation.}$$

Thus the projectile strikes the ground after 12 seconds. The solution of $-\frac{1}{2}$ has no meaning in this problem because it corresponds to a time before the projectile is shot into the air.

Now Try Exercise 119

3.2 Putting It All Together

The following table summarizes important topics related to quadratic equations.

CONCEPT	EXPLANATION	EXAMPLES
Quadratic equation	$ax^2 + bx + c = 0$, where a, b, and c are constants with $a \neq 0$	A quadratic equation can have zero, one, or two real solutions. $x^2 = -5$ No real solutions $(x - 2)^2 = 0$ One real solution: 2 $x^2 - 4 = 0$ Two real solutions: ± 2
Factoring	A symbolic technique for solving equations, based on the zero-product property: if $ab = 0$, then either $a = 0$ or $b = 0$.	$x^2 - 3x = -2$ $x^2 - 3x + 2 = 0$ $(x - 1)(x - 2) = 0$ $x - 1 = 0$ or $x - 2 = 0$ $x = 1$ or $x = 2$

CONCEPT	EXPLANATION	EXAMPLES
Square root property	The solutions to $x^2 = k$ are $x = \pm\sqrt{k}$, where $k \geq 0$.	$x^2 = 9$ is equivalent to $x = \pm 3$. $x^2 = 11$ is equivalent to $x = \pm\sqrt{11}$.
Completing the square	To solve $x^2 + kx = d$ symbolically, add $\left(\frac{k}{2}\right)^2$ to each side to obtain a perfect square trinomial. Then apply the square root property.	$$x^2 - 6x = 1$$ $$x^2 - 6x + 9 = 1 + 9 \qquad \left(\frac{-6}{2}\right)^2 = 9$$ $$(x - 3)^2 = 10$$ $$x - 3 = \pm\sqrt{10}$$ $$x = 3 \pm \sqrt{10}$$
Quadratic formula	The solutions to $ax^2 + bx + c = 0$ are given by $$x = \frac{-b \pm \sqrt{b^2 - 4ac}}{2a}.$$ Always gives the *exact* solutions	To solve $2x^2 - x - 4 = 0$, let $a = 2$, $b = -1$, and $c = -4$. $$x = \frac{-(-1) \pm \sqrt{(-1)^2 - 4(2)(-4)}}{2(2)}$$ $$= \frac{1 \pm \sqrt{33}}{4} \approx 1.69 \text{ or } -1.19$$
Graphical solution	To use the *x-intercept method* to solve $ax^2 + bx + c = 0$, let y_1 equal the left side of the equation and graph y_1. The real solutions correspond to the *x*-intercepts. The *intersection-of-graphs* method can also be used when one side of the equation is *not* equal to 0. Let y_1 equal the left side of the equation and y_2 equal the right side of the equation. The real solutions correspond to the *x*-coordinates of any points of intersection.	To solve $x^2 + x - 2 = 0$, graph $y = x^2 + x - 2$. The solutions are -2 and 1. Solutions: $-2, 1$
Numerical solution	To solve $ax^2 + bx + c = 0$, let y_1 equal the left side of the equation and create a table for y_1. The zeros of y_1 are the real solutions. May *not* be a good method when solutions are fractions or irrational numbers	To solve $2x^2 + x - 1 = 0$, make a table. The solutions are -1 and 0.5.

Exercises

Quadratic Equations

Exercises 1–32: Solve the quadratic equation. Check your answers for Exercises 1–16.

1. $x^2 + x - 11 = 1$

2. $x^2 - 9x + 10 = -8$

3. $t^2 = 2t$

4. $t^2 - 7t = 0$

5. $3x^2 - 7x = 0$

6. $5x = 9x^2$

7. $2z^2 = 13z + 15$

8. $4z^2 = 7 - 27z$

9. $x^2 + 6x + 9 = 0$

10. $x^2 - 8x + 16 = 0$

11. $4x^2 + 1 = 4x$

12. $9x^2 + 4 = 12x$

13. $x(3x + 14) = 5$

14. $x(5x + 19) = 4$

15. $6x^2 + \frac{5}{2} = 8x$

16. $8x^2 + 63 = -46x$

17. $(t + 3)^2 = 5$

18. $(t - 2)^2 = 11$

19. $4x^2 - 13 = 0$

20. $9x^2 - 11 = 0$

21. $2(x - 1)^2 + 4 = 0$

22. $-3(x + 5)^2 - 6 = 0$

23. $\frac{1}{2}x^2 - 3x + \frac{1}{2} = 0$

24. $\frac{3}{4}x^2 + \frac{1}{2}x - \frac{1}{2} = 0$

25. $-3z^2 - 2z + 4 = 0$

26. $-4z^2 + z + 1 = 0$

27. $25k^2 + 1 = 10k$

28. $49k^2 + 4 = -28k$

29. $-0.3x^2 + 0.1x = -0.02$

30. $-0.1x^2 + 1 = 0.5x$

31. $2x(x + 2) = (x - 1)(x + 2)$

32. $(2x - 1)(x + 2) = (x + 3)(x + 1)$

Exercises 33–38: Find the exact values of all intercepts.

33.

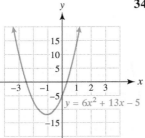

$y = 6x^2 + 13x - 5$

34.

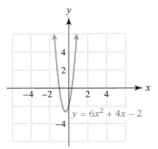

$y = 6x^2 + 4x - 2$

35.

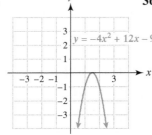

$y = -4x^2 + 12x - 9$

36.

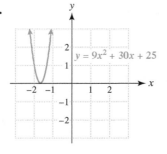

$y = 9x^2 + 30x + 25$

37.

$y = -3x^2 + 11x - 6$

38.

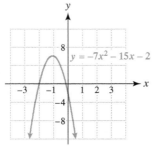

$y = -7x^2 - 15x - 2$

Graphical and Numerical Solutions

Exercises 39–46: Solve each quadratic equation (a) graphically, (b) numerically, and (c) symbolically. Express graphical and numerical solutions to the nearest tenth when appropriate.

39. $x^2 + 2x = 0$

40. $x^2 - 4 = 0$

41. $x^2 - x - 6 = 0$

42. $2x^2 + 5x - 3 = 0$

43. $2x^2 = 6$

44. $x^2 - 225 = 0$

45. $4x(x - 3) = -9$

46. $-4x(x - 1) = 1$

Exercises 47–50: Solve the quadratic equation graphically.

47. $20x^2 + 11x = 3$

48. $-2x^2 + 4x = 1.595$

49. $2.5x^2 = 4.75x - 2.1$

50. $x(x + 24) = 6912$

Completing the Square

Exercises 51–64: Solve the equation by completing the square.

51. $x^2 + 4x - 6 = 0$

52. $x^2 - 10x = 1$

53. $x^2 + 5x = 4$

54. $x^2 + 6x - 5 = 0$

55. $3x^2 - 6x = 2$

56. $2x^2 - 3x + 1 = 0$

57. $x^2 - 8x = 10$

58. $x^2 - 2x = 2$

59. $\frac{1}{2}t^2 - \frac{3}{2}t = 1$

60. $\frac{1}{3}t^2 + \frac{1}{2}t = 2$

61. $-2z^2 + 3z + 1 = 0$

62. $-3z^2 - 5z + 3 = 0$

63. $-\frac{3}{2}z^2 - \frac{1}{4}z + 1 = 0$

64. $-\frac{1}{5}z^2 - \frac{1}{2}z + 2 = 0$

Finding Domains

Exercises 65–68: Find the domain of the function. Write your answer in set-builder notation.

65. $f(x) = \dfrac{1}{x^2 - 5}$

66. $f(x) = \dfrac{4x}{7 - x^2}$

67. $g(t) = \dfrac{5 - t}{t^2 - t - 2}$

68. $g(t) = \dfrac{t + 1}{2t^2 - 11t - 21}$

Solving for a Variable

Exercises 69–76: (Refer to Example 4.) Solve the equation for y. Determine if y is a function of x.

69. $4x^2 + 3y = \dfrac{y + 1}{3}$

70. $\dfrac{x^2 + y}{2} = y - 2$

71. $3y = \dfrac{2x - y}{3}$

72. $\dfrac{5 - y}{3} = \dfrac{x + 3y}{4}$

73. $x^2 + (y - 3)^2 = 9$

74. $(x + 2)^2 + (y + 1)^2 = 1$

75. $3x^2 + 4y^2 = 12$

76. $x - 25y^2 = 50$

Exercises 77–84: Solve for the specified variable.

77. $V = \frac{1}{3}\pi r^2 h$ for r

78. $V = \frac{1}{2}gt^2 + h$ for t

79. $K = \frac{1}{2}mv^2$ for v

80. $W = I^2 R$ for I

81. $a^2 + b^2 = c^2$ for b

82. $S = 4\pi r^2 + x^2$ for r

83. $s = -16t^2 + 100t$ for t

84. $T^2 - kT - k^2 = 0$ for T

The Discriminant

Exercises 85–100: Complete the following.

(a) Write the equation as $ax^2 + bx + c = 0$ with $a > 0$.
(b) Calculate the discriminant $b^2 - 4ac$ and determine the number of real solutions.
(c) Solve the equation.

85. $3x^2 = 12$

86. $8x^2 - 2 = 14$

87. $x^2 - 2x = -1$

88. $6x^2 = 4x$

89. $4x = x^2$

90. $16x^2 + 9 = 24x$

91. $x^2 + 1 = x$

92. $2x^2 + x = 2$

93. $2x^2 + 3x = 12 - 2x$

94. $3x^2 + 3 = 5x$

95. $9x(x - 4) = -36$

96. $\frac{1}{4}x^2 + 3x = x - 4$

97. $x\left(\frac{1}{2}x + 1\right) = -\frac{13}{2}$

98. $4x = 6 + x^2$

99. $3x^2 = 1 - x$

100. $x(5x - 3) = 1$

Exercises 101–104: The graph of $f(x) = ax^2 + bx + c$ is shown in the figure.

(a) State whether $a > 0$ or $a < 0$.
(b) Solve the equation $ax^2 + bx + c = 0$.
(c) Is the discriminant positive, negative, or zero?

101.

102.

103.

104.

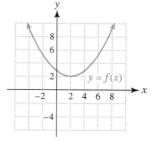

Applications and Models

105. Height of a Baseball   A baseball is dropped from a stadium seat that is 75 feet above the ground. Its height s in feet after t seconds is given by $s(t) = 75 - 16t^2$. Estimate to the nearest tenth of a second how long it takes for the baseball to strike the ground.

106. Height of a Baseball   A baseball is thrown *downward* with an initial velocity of 30 feet per second from a stadium seat that is 80 feet above the ground. Estimate to the nearest tenth of a second how long it takes for the baseball to strike the ground.

107. Facebook Visitors   The number of unique monthly visitors in millions to Facebook can be approximated by

$$V(x) = 16x^2 + 7x + 32,$$

where x is the number of years after 2008. Estimate the year when Facebook averaged 55 million unique monthly visitors.

108. U.S. AIDS Cases   From 1984 to 1994 the cumulative number of AIDS cases can be modeled by the equation

$$C(x) = 3034x^2 + 14{,}018x + 6400,$$

where x represents years after 1984. Estimate the year when 200,000 AIDS cases had been diagnosed.

109. Screen Dimensions   The width of a rectangular computer screen is 2.5 inches more than its height. If the area of the screen is 93.5 square inches, determine its dimensions symbolically, graphically, and numerically. Do your answers agree?

110. Maximizing Area   A rectangular pen for a pet is under construction using 100 feet of fence.
   (a) Find the dimensions that give an area of 576 square feet.

   (b) Find the dimensions that give maximum area.

111. Construction   (Refer to Example 9.) A box is being constructed by cutting 4-inch squares from the corners of a rectangular sheet of metal that is 10 inches longer than it is wide. If the box is to have a volume of 476 cubic inches, find the dimensions of the metal sheet.

112. **Construction** A box is being constructed by cutting 2-inch squares from the corners of a *square* sheet of metal. If the box is to have a volume of 1058 cubic inches, find the dimensions of the metal sheet.

113. **Geometry** A cylindrical aluminum can is being constructed to have a height h of 4 inches. If the can is to have a volume of 28 cubic inches, approximate its radius r. (*Hint:* $V = \pi r^2 h$.)

114. **Braking Distance** Braking distance for cars on level pavement can be approximated by $D(x) = \frac{x^2}{30k}$. The input x is the car's velocity in miles per hour and the output $D(x)$ is the braking distance in feet. The positive constant k is a measure of the traction of the tires. Small values of k indicate a slippery road or worn tires. (*Source:* L. Haefner, *Introduction to Transportation Systems.*)

    (a) Let $k = 0.3$. Evaluate $D(60)$ and interpret the result.

    (b) If $k = 0.25$, find the velocity x that corresponds to a braking distance of 300 feet.

115. **Window Dimensions** A window comprises a square with sides of length x and a semicircle with diameter x, as shown in the figure. If the total area of the window is 463 square inches, estimate the value of x to the nearest hundredth of an inch.

116. **Picture Frame** A frame for a picture is 2 inches wide. The picture inside the frame is 4 inches longer than it is wide. See the figure. If the area of the picture is 320 square inches, find the outside dimensions of the picture frame.

117. **Cost** (Refer to Example 10.) A company charges $20 to make one monogrammed shirt but reduces this cost by $0.10 per shirt for each *additional* shirt ordered up to 100 shirts. If the cost of an order is $989, how many shirts were ordered?

118. **Ticket Prices** The price of one airline ticket is $250. For each additional ticket sold to a group, the price of every ticket is reduced by $2. For example, 2 tickets cost $2 \cdot 248 = \$496$ and 3 tickets cost $3 \cdot 246 = \$738$.

    (a) Write a quadratic function that gives the total cost of buying x tickets.

    (b) What is the cost of 5 tickets?

    (c) How many tickets were sold if the cost is $5200?

    (d) What number of tickets sold gives the greatest cost?

Modeling Quadratic Data

119. **Projectile Motion** The table shows the height of a projectile that is shot into the air.

t (seconds)	0	1	2	3	4
s (feet)	32	176	288	368	416

    (a) Use $s(t) = -16t^2 + v_0 t + h_0$ to model the data.

    (b) After how long did the projectile strike the ground?

120. **Falling Object** The table lists the velocity and distance traveled by a falling object for various elapsed times.

Time (sec)	0	1	2	3	4
Velocity (ft/sec)	0	32	64	96	128
Distance (ft)	0	16	64	144	256

    (a) Make a scatterplot of the ordered pairs determined by (time, velocity) and (time, distance) in the same viewing rectangle $[-1, 5, 1]$ by $[-10, 280, 20]$.

    (b) Find a function v that models the velocity.

    (c) The distance is modeled by $d(x) = ax^2$. Find a.

    (d) Find the time when the distance is 200 feet. Find the velocity at this time.

121. Pedestrian and Bicycle Programs The Department of Transportation's budget for pedestrian and bicycle programs in millions of dollars for selected years is given in the table.

Year	1995	2001	2009
Budget	180	340	1200

Source: DOT.

(a) Determine a quadratic function B whose vertex is (1995, 180) and whose graph passes through the point (2009, 1200). Write $B(x)$ in vertex form.

(b) Use $B(x)$ to determine when the budget was $700 million.

122. Safe Runway Speed The taxiway used by an aircraft to exit a runway should not have sharp curves. The safe radius for any curve depends on the speed of the airplane. The table lists the minimum radius R of the exit curves, where the taxiing speed of the airplane is x miles per hour.

x(mi/hr)	10	20	30	40	50
R(ft)	50	200	450	800	1250

Source: Federal Aviation Administration.

(a) If the taxiing speed x of the plane doubles, what happens to the minimum radius R of the curve?

(b) The FAA used $R(x) = ax^2$ to compute the values in the table. Determine a.

(c) If $R = 500$, find x. Interpret your results.

Quadratic Regression

123. iPod Sales The table shows the number of iPods sold in millions of units for various years.

Year	2006	2007	2008	2009	2010	2011
Sales	39.4	51.6	54.8	54.1	50.3	42.6

Source: Apple Corporation.

(a) Use regression to find a quadratic function I that models the data. Let $x = 0$ correspond to 2006.

(b) Use I to estimate when sales were 28 million units.

124. Biology Some types of worms have a remarkable capacity to live without moisture. The table shows the number of worms y surviving after x days in one study.

x (days)	0	20	40	80	120	160
y (worms)	50	48	45	36	20	3

Source: D. Brown and P. Rothery, *Models in Biology.*

(a) Use regression to find a quadratic function f that models these data.

(b) Graph f and the data in the same window.

(c) Solve the quadratic equation $f(x) = 0$ graphically. Do both solutions have meaning? Explain.

125. Walmart Employees The table lists numbers of Walmart employees E in millions, x years after 1987.

x	0	5	10	15	20
E	0.20	0.38	0.68	1.4	2.2

Source: Walmart.

(a) Evaluate $E(15)$ and interpret the result.

(b) Find a quadratic function f that models these data.

(c) Graph the data and quadratic function f in the same xy-plane.

(d) Use f to estimate the year when the number of employees reached 3 million.

126. Women in the Workforce The number N of women in millions who were gainfully employed in the workforce in selected years is shown in the table.

Year	1900	1910	1920	1930	1940	1950
N	5.3	7.4	8.6	10.8	12.8	18.4

Year	1960	1970	1980	1990	2000	2010
N	23.2	31.5	45.5	56.6	65.6	74.8

Source: Department of Labor.

(a) Use regression to find a quadratic function f that models the data. Support your result graphically.

(b) Predict the number of women in the labor force in 2020.

Writing about Mathematics

127. Discuss three symbolic methods for solving a quadratic equation. Make up a quadratic equation and use each method to find the solution set.

128. Explain how to solve a quadratic equation graphically.

EXTENDED AND DISCOVERY EXERCISES

Exercises 1–4: **Discriminant and Factoring** *(Refer to pages 179 and 180.) For each equation, calculate the discriminant. Use the discriminant to decide whether the equation can be solved by factoring. If it can, solve the equation by factoring. Otherwise, use the quadratic formula.*

1. $8x^2 + 14x - 15 = 0$ **2.** $15x^2 - 17x - 4 = 0$

3. $5x^2 - 3x - 3 = 0$ **4.** $3x^2 - 2x - 4 = 0$

5. Quadratic Formula Prove the quadratic formula by completing the following.
   (a) Write $ax^2 + bx + c = 0$ as $x^2 + \frac{b}{a}x = -\frac{c}{a}$.

   (b) Complete the square to obtain $\left(x + \frac{b}{2a}\right)^2 = \frac{b^2 - 4ac}{4a^2}$.

   (c) Use the square root property and solve for x.

6. Difference Quotient If the difference quotient for the function $f(x) = ax^2 - bx + 1$ equals $2x + h - 4$, find values for a and b.

7. Square Root Property Use the fact that $\sqrt{x^2} = |x|$ to show that the solutions to $x^2 = k$ with $k > 0$ are given by $x = \pm\sqrt{k}$.

CHECKING BASIC CONCEPTS FOR SECTIONS 3.1 AND 3.2

1. Graph $f(x) = (x - 1)^2 - 4$. Identify the vertex, axis of symmetry, and x-intercepts.

2. A graph of $f(x) = ax^2 + bx + c$ is shown.
   (a) Is a positive, negative, or zero?

   (b) Find the vertex and axis of symmetry.

   (c) Solve $ax^2 + bx + c = 0$.

   (d) Is the discriminant positive, negative, or zero?

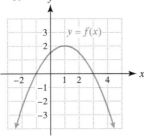

3. Use $f(x) = a(x - h)^2 + k$ to model the data exactly.

x	-3	-2	-1	0	1
$f(x)$	11	5	3	5	11

4. Find the vertex on the graph of $y = 3x^2 - 9x - 2$.

5. Write $f(x) = x^2 + 4x - 3$ as $f(x) = a(x - h)^2 + k$. What are the coordinates of the vertex? What is the minimum y-value of the graph of f?

6. Solve the quadratic equations.
   (a) $16x^2 = 81$ (b) $2x^2 + 3x = 2$

   (c) $x^2 = x - 3$ (d) $2x^2 = 3x + 4$

7. Dimensions of a Rectangle A rectangle is 4 inches longer than it is wide and has an area of 165 square inches. Find its dimensions.

8. Height of a Baseball The height s of a baseball in feet after t seconds is given by $s(t) = -16t^2 + 96t + 2$.
   (a) Find the height of the baseball after 1 second.

   (b) After how long is the baseball 142 feet high?

   (c) Find the maximum height of the baseball.

   (d) How long is the baseball in the air?

3.3 Complex Numbers

- **Perform arithmetic operations on complex numbers**
- **Solve quadratic equations having complex solutions**

Introduction

Throughout history, people have invented (or discovered) new numbers to solve equations and describe data. New numbers were often met with resistance and were seen as imaginary and useless. There was no Roman numeral for 0, as many skeptics probably wondered why a number was needed to represent nothing. Negative numbers also met strong resistance. After all, how could one possibly have -6 apples? Complex numbers were no different. In this section we introduce complex numbers and the "imaginary" unit i. Ultimately, complex numbers are no more imaginary than any other number. Society needs and uses complex numbers just as much as other numbers.

Basic Concepts

Graphing a quadratic equation is helpful only in finding the *real* solutions to the equation. Real solutions to the equation $x^2 + 1 = 0$ correspond to x-intercepts. See Figure 3.36. We can also solve this equation for real solutions symbolically, as shown next to Figure 3.36.

Solving $x^2 + 1 = 0$ Graphically and Symbolically

There are no
x-intercepts...

...and so there are
no real solutions.

$$x^2 + 1 = 0 \qquad \textit{Given equation}$$

$$x^2 = -1 \qquad \textit{Subtract 1.}$$

No real solutions; $x \geq 0$
for any real number x

Figure 3.36

Above we showed that there are no *real* solutions to the equation $x^2 + 1 = 0$. However, we can *invent* two solutions.

$$x^2 = -1, \quad \text{or} \quad x = \pm\sqrt{-1}$$

We now define a new number called the **imaginary unit**, denoted i.

PROPERTIES OF THE IMAGINARY UNIT i

$$i = \sqrt{-1}, \qquad i^2 = -1$$

Solving $x^2 + 1 = 0$ using the imaginary unit

$$x = \pm\sqrt{-1} \qquad \text{or}$$

$$x = \pm i$$

Using the real numbers and the imaginary unit i, complex numbers can be defined. A **complex number** can be written in **standard form** as $a + bi$, where a and b are real numbers. The **real part** is a and the **imaginary part** is b. Every real number a is also a complex number because it can be written as $a + 0i$. A complex number $a + bi$ with $b \neq 0$ is an **imaginary number**. A complex number $a + bi$ with $a = 0$ and $b \neq 0$ is sometimes called a **pure imaginary number**. Examples of pure imaginary numbers include $3i$ and $-i$. Table 3.6 lists several complex numbers with their real and imaginary parts.

Complex Numbers

Example	$a + bi$	a	b
5	$5 + 0i$	5	0
$-5 - 2i$	$-5 - 2i$	-5	-2
$-3i$	$0 - 3i$	0	-3
$4 + 6i$	$4 + 6i$	4	6

Table 3.6   Standard form   Real part   Imaginary part

Using the imaginary unit i, square roots of negative numbers can be written as complex numbers.

THE EXPRESSION $\sqrt{-a}$

If $a > 0$, then $\sqrt{-a} = i\sqrt{a}$.

EXAMPLE 1 Simplifying the expression $\sqrt{-a}$

Simplify each expression.

(a) $\sqrt{-16}$ **(b)** $\sqrt{-3}$ **(c)** $\dfrac{2 \pm \sqrt{-24}}{2}$

SOLUTION
(a) When $a > 0$, $\sqrt{-a} = i\sqrt{a}$. Thus $\sqrt{-16} = i\sqrt{16} = 4i$.
(b) $\sqrt{-3} = i\sqrt{3}$; we usually do not write $\sqrt{3}i$ because of the possibility of confusion about whether i is under the square root symbol.
(c) First note that $\sqrt{-24} = i\sqrt{24} = i\sqrt{4} \cdot \sqrt{6} = 2i\sqrt{6}$.

$$\frac{2 \pm \sqrt{-24}}{2} = \frac{2 \pm 2i\sqrt{6}}{2} \qquad \text{Simplify } \sqrt{-24}.$$

$$= \frac{2}{2} \pm \frac{2i\sqrt{6}}{2} \qquad \frac{a \pm b}{c} = \frac{a}{c} \pm \frac{b}{c}$$

$$= 1 \pm i\sqrt{6} \qquad \text{Simplify fractions.}$$

Now Try Exercises 1, 5, and 13

The property $\sqrt{a} \cdot \sqrt{b} = \sqrt{ab}$ is true only when *both* a and b are positive. When simplifying products containing square roots of negative numbers, it is important to first apply the property $\sqrt{-a} = i\sqrt{a}$, where $a > 0$. This technique is illustrated in the next example.

EXAMPLE 2 Simplifying complex expressions

Simplify each expression.
(a) $\sqrt{-3} \cdot \sqrt{-3}$ **(b)** $\sqrt{-2} \cdot \sqrt{-8}$

SOLUTION
(a) $\sqrt{-3} \cdot \sqrt{-3} = i\sqrt{3} \cdot i\sqrt{3} = i^2(\sqrt{3})^2 = -1(3) = -3$ $\qquad i^2 = -1$

NOTE $\sqrt{-3} \cdot \sqrt{-3} \neq \sqrt{(-3) \cdot (-3)} = \sqrt{9} = 3$

(b) $\sqrt{-2} \cdot \sqrt{-8} = i\sqrt{2} \cdot i\sqrt{8} = i^2\sqrt{16} = -1(4) = -4$

Now Try Exercises 15 and 17

Calculator Help
To perform arithmetic on complex numbers, see Appendix A (page AP-10).

Arithmetic Operations on Complex Numbers

Arithmetic operations are also defined for complex numbers.

Addition and Subtraction To add the complex numbers $(-2 + 3i)$ and $(4 - 6i)$, simply combine the real parts and the imaginary parts.

$$(-2 + 3i) + (4 - 6i) = -2 + 4 + 3i - 6i$$
$$= 2 - 3i$$

This same process works for subtraction.

$$(5 - 7i) - (8 + 3i) = 5 - 8 - 7i - 3i$$
$$= -3 - 10i$$

Figure 3.37

These operations are performed on a calculator in Figure 3.37.

Algebra Review
Before multiplying complex numbers, you may want to review multiplication of binomials in Chapter R (page R-15).

Multiplication   Two complex numbers can be multiplied. The property $i^2 = -1$ is applied when appropriate.

$$(-5 + i)(7 - 9i) = -5(7) + (-5)(-9i) + (i)(7) + (i)(-9i)$$
$$= -35 + 45i + 7i - 9i^2$$
$$= -35 + 52i - 9(-1)$$
$$= -26 + 52i$$

NOTE   Express your results in the standard form $a + bi$.

Division   The **conjugate** of $a + bi$ is $a - bi$. To find the conjugate, change the sign of the imaginary part b. Table 3.7 lists examples of complex numbers and their conjugates.

Complex Conjugates

Change the sign on b.

$a + bi$	$2 + 5i$	$6 - 3i$	$-2 + 7i$	$-1 - i$	5	$-4i$
$a - bi$	$2 - 5i$	$6 + 3i$	$-2 - 7i$	$-1 + i$	5	$4i$

Table 3.7

To simplify the quotient $\frac{3 + 2i}{5 - i}$, first multiply both the numerator and the denominator by the conjugate of the *denominator*.

$$\frac{3 + 2i}{5 - i} = \frac{(3 + 2i)(5 + i)}{(5 - i)(5 + i)}$$ Multiply by $\frac{conjugate}{conjugate}$.

$$= \frac{3(5) + (3)(i) + (2i)(5) + (2i)(i)}{(5)(5) + (5)(i) + (-i)(5) + (-i)(i)}$$ Expand.

$$= \frac{15 + 3i + 10i + 2i^2}{25 + 5i - 5i - i^2}$$ Simplify.

$$= \frac{15 + 13i + 2(-1)}{25 - (-1)}$$ $i^2 = -1$

$$= \frac{13 + 13i}{26}.$$ Simplify.

$$= \frac{1}{2} + \frac{1}{2}i$$ $\frac{a + bi}{c} = \frac{a}{c} + \frac{b}{c}i$

The last step expresses the quotient as a complex number in standard form. The evaluation of the previous multiplication and division examples is shown in Figure 3.38.

```
(-5+i)(7-9i)
             -26+52i
(3+2i)/(5-i)
             .5+.5i
Ans▶Frac
         1/2+1/2i
```

Figure 3.38

EXAMPLE 3   Performing complex arithmetic

Write each expression in standard form. Support your results using a calculator.
(a) $(-3 + 4i) + (5 - i)$ **(b)** $(-7i) - (6 - 5i)$

(c) $(-3 + 2i)^2$ **(d)** $\dfrac{17}{4 + i}$

SOLUTION
(a) $(-3 + 4i) + (5 - i) = -3 + 5 + 4i - i = 2 + 3i$
(b) $(-7i) - (6 - 5i) = -6 - 7i + 5i = -6 - 2i$
(c) $(-3 + 2i)^2 = (-3 + 2i)(-3 + 2i)$

$$= 9 - 6i - 6i + 4i^2$$
$$= 9 - 12i + 4(-1)$$
$$= 5 - 12i$$

(d) $\dfrac{17}{4+i} = \dfrac{17}{4+i} \cdot \dfrac{4-i}{4-i}$ *Multiply by $\dfrac{conjugate}{conjugate}$.*

$\qquad = \dfrac{68-17i}{16-i^2}$

$\qquad = \dfrac{68-17i}{17}$ $i^2 = -1$

$\qquad = 4 - i$

Standard forms can be found using a calculator. See Figures 3.39 and 3.40.

Figure 3.39   **Figure 3.40**

Now Try Exercises 23, 25, 35, and 39

MAKING CONNECTIONS

Complex, Real, and Imaginary Numbers   The following diagram illustrates the relationship among complex, real, and imaginary numbers, where a and b are real numbers. Note that complex numbers comprise two disjoint sets of numbers: the real numbers and the imaginary numbers.

Complex Numbers
$a + bi$

Real Numbers   **Imaginary Numbers**
$a + bi, \quad b = 0$ $a + bi, \quad b \neq 0$

NOTE   *Every* real number is a complex number.

Powers of i   We can simplify powers of i using the fact that $i^1 = i$ and $i^2 = -1$. In the next example we use these ideas.

EXAMPLE 4   Simplifying Powers of i

Simplify each power of i.
(a) i^8 **(b)** i^{19}

SOLUTION
(a) $i^8 = (i^2)^4 = (-1)^4 = 1$. Another way to simplify is the following.

$$i^8 = (i^2)(i^2)(i^2)(i^2) = (-1)(-1)(-1)(-1) = 1$$

(b) Write $i^{19} = i^{18} \cdot i$. Then $i^{19} = (i^2)^9 \cdot i = (-1)^9 i = -1 \cdot i = -i$.

Now Try Exercises 61 and 63

NOTE   In the Extended and Discovery Exercise in this section we discover a pattern for calculating the powers of i.

Quadratic Equations with Complex Solutions

We can use the quadratic formula to solve any quadratic equation $ax^2 + bx + c = 0$. If the discriminant $b^2 - 4ac$ is negative, then there are no real solutions, and the graph of

$y = ax^2 + bx + c$ does not intersect the *x*-axis. However, there are solutions that can be expressed as imaginary numbers. This is illustrated in the next example.

EXAMPLE 5 Solving quadratic equations with imaginary solutions

Solve the quadratic equation. Support your results graphically.

(a) $x^2 + 3x + 5 = 0$ **(b)** $\frac{1}{2}x^2 + 17 = 5x$ **(c)** $-2x^2 = 3$

SOLUTION

Getting Started Make sure each equation is in the form $ax^2 + bx + c = 0$, and then apply the quadratic formula, which always "works." ▶

(a) Let $a = 1$, $b = 3$, and $c = 5$ and apply the quadratic formula.

$$
\begin{aligned}
x &= \frac{-b \pm \sqrt{b^2 - 4ac}}{2a} \\
&= \frac{-3 \pm \sqrt{3^2 - 4(1)(5)}}{2(1)} \\
&= \frac{-3 \pm \sqrt{-11}}{2} \\
&= \frac{-3 \pm i\sqrt{11}}{2} \\
&= -\frac{3}{2} \pm \frac{i\sqrt{11}}{2}
\end{aligned}
$$

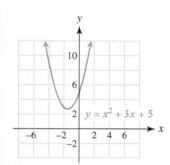

Figure 3.41

In Figure 3.41 the graph of $y_1 = x^2 + 3x + 5$ does not intersect the *x*-axis, which indicates that the equation $x^2 + 3x + 5 = 0$ has no real solutions. However, there are two complex solutions that are imaginary.

(b) Rewrite the equation as $\frac{1}{2}x^2 - 5x + 17 = 0$, and let $a = \frac{1}{2}$, $b = -5$, and $c = 17$.

$$
\begin{aligned}
x &= \frac{5 \pm \sqrt{(-5)^2 - 4(0.5)(17)}}{2(0.5)} \\
&= 5 \pm \sqrt{-9} \\
&= 5 \pm 3i
\end{aligned}
$$

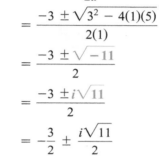

Figure 3.42

In Figure 3.42 the graphs of $y_1 = \frac{1}{2}x^2 + 17$ and $y_2 = 5x$ do not intersect, which indicates that the equation $\frac{1}{2}x^2 + 17 = 5x$ has no real solutions. However, there are two complex solutions that are imaginary.

(c) Rather than use the quadratic formula for this equation, we apply the square root property because the equation contains no *x*-term.

$$
\begin{aligned}
-2x^2 &= 3 && \text{\textcolor{gray}{Given equation}} \\
x^2 &= -\frac{3}{2} && \text{\textcolor{gray}{Divide each side by } -2.} \\
x &= \pm\sqrt{-\frac{3}{2}} && \text{\textcolor{gray}{Square root property}} \\
x &= \pm i\sqrt{\frac{3}{2}} && \text{\textcolor{gray}{$\sqrt{-a} = i\sqrt{a}$}}
\end{aligned}
$$

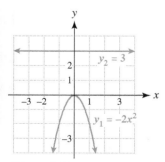

Figure 3.43

In Figure 3.43 the graphs of $y_1 = -2x^2$ and $y_2 = 3$ do not intersect, which indicates that the equation $-2x^2 = 3$ has no real solutions. However, there are two complex solutions that are imaginary.

Now Try Exercises 67, 73, and 75

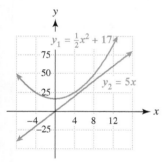

What is the result if the expression is evaluated? (See Example 5(a).)

$$\left(-\frac{3}{2} + \frac{i\sqrt{11}}{2}\right)^2 + 3\left(-\frac{3}{2} + \frac{i\sqrt{11}}{2}\right) + 5$$

3.3 Putting It All Together

Some of the important topics in this section are summarized in the following table.

CONCEPT	EXPLANATION	COMMENTS AND EXAMPLES
Imaginary unit	$i = \sqrt{-1}, i^2 = -1$	The imaginary unit i allows us to define the complex numbers.
The expression $\sqrt{-a}$ with $a > 0$	$\sqrt{-a} = i\sqrt{a}$	$\sqrt{-4} = 2i$ $\sqrt{-5} = i\sqrt{5}$ $\sqrt{-32} = i\sqrt{32} = i\sqrt{16}\sqrt{2} = 4i\sqrt{2}$ $\sqrt{-5}\sqrt{-20} = i\sqrt{5}\,i\sqrt{20} = i^2\sqrt{100} = -10$
Complex number	$a + bi$, where a and b are real numbers	Every real number is a complex number. $5 - 4i$, 5, $2 + i$, and $-9i$ are examples of complex numbers.
Standard form of a complex number	$a + bi$, where a and b are real numbers	Converting to standard form: $$\frac{3 \pm 4i}{2} = \frac{3}{2} + 2i \quad \text{or} \quad \frac{3}{2} - 2i$$
Conjugates	The conjugate of $a + bi$ is $a - bi$.	*Number* *Conjugate* $5 - 6i$ $5 + 6i$ $-12i$ $12i$ -7 -7 $2 + 3i$ $2 - 3i$
Arithmetic operations on complex numbers	Complex numbers may be added, subtracted, multiplied, or divided.	$(2 + 3i) + (-3 - i) = -1 + 2i$ $(5 + i) - (3 - i) = 2 + 2i$ $(1 + i)(5 - i) = 5 - i + 5i - i^2 = 6 + 4i$ $\dfrac{3 + i}{1 - i} = \dfrac{(3 + i)(1 + i)}{(1 - i)(1 + i)}$ $\qquad = 1 + 2i$
Powers of i	Use the fact that $i^2 = -1$ to simplify powers of i.	$i^{27} = i^{26} \cdot i$ $\qquad = (i^2)^{13} \cdot i$ $\qquad = (-1)^{13} \cdot i$ $\qquad = -i$

CONCEPT	EXPLANATION	COMMENTS AND EXAMPLES
Complex solutions to equations	Complex numbers $a + bi$ with $b \neq 0$ can be solutions to equations that cannot be solved with only real numbers.	$x^2 + 5 = 0$ implies $x^2 = -5$; there are no real solutions, but $x = \pm i\sqrt{5}$ are two complex solutions. Note that the graph of $y = x^2 + 5$ has no x-intercepts. The quadratic formula can be used to find complex solutions.

3.3 Exercises

Complex Numbers

Exercises 1–20: Simplify by using the imaginary unit i.

1. $\sqrt{-4}$

2. $\sqrt{-16}$

3. $\sqrt{-100}$

4. $\sqrt{-49}$

5. $\sqrt{-23}$

6. $\sqrt{-11}$

7. $\sqrt{-12}$

8. $\sqrt{-32}$

9. $\sqrt{-54}$

10. $\sqrt{-28}$

11. $\dfrac{4 \pm \sqrt{-16}}{2}$

12. $\dfrac{-2 \pm \sqrt{-36}}{6}$

13. $\dfrac{-6 \pm \sqrt{-72}}{3}$

14. $\dfrac{2 \pm \sqrt{-8}}{4}$

15. $\sqrt{-5} \cdot \sqrt{-5}$

16. $\sqrt{-8} \cdot \sqrt{-8}$

17. $\sqrt{-18} \cdot \sqrt{-2}$

18. $\sqrt{-20} \cdot \sqrt{-5}$

19. $\sqrt{-3} \cdot \sqrt{-6}$

20. $\sqrt{-15} \cdot \sqrt{-5}$

Exercises 21–48: Write the expression in standard form.

21. $3i + 5i$

22. $-7i + 5i$

23. $(3 + i) + (-5 - 2i)$

24. $(-4 + 2i) + (7 + 35i)$

25. $2i - (-5 + 23i)$

26. $(12 - 7i) - (-1 + 9i)$

27. $3 - (4 - 6i)$

28. $(7 + i) - (-8 + 5i)$

29. $(2)(2 + 4i)$

30. $(-5)(-7 + 3i)$

31. $(1 + i)(2 - 3i)$

32. $(-2 + i)(1 - 2i)$

33. $(-3 + 2i)(-2 + i)$

34. $(2 - 3i)(1 + 4i)$

35. $(-2 + 3i)^2$

36. $(2 - 3i)^2$

37. $2i(1 - i)^2$

38. $-i(5 - 2i)^2$

39. $\dfrac{1}{1 + i}$

40. $\dfrac{1 - i}{2 + 3i}$

41. $\dfrac{4 + i}{5 - i}$

42. $\dfrac{10}{1 - 4i}$

43. $\dfrac{2i}{10 - 5i}$

44. $\dfrac{3 - 2i}{1 + 2i}$

45. $\dfrac{3}{-i}$

46. $\dfrac{4 - 2i}{i}$

47. $\dfrac{-2 + i}{(1 + i)^2}$

48. $\dfrac{3}{(2 - i)^2}$

Exercises 49–54: Evaluate the expression with a calculator.

49. $(23 - 5.6i) + (-41.5 + 93i)$

50. $(-8.05 - 4.67i) + (3.5 + 5.37i)$

51. $(17.1 - 6i) - (8.4 + 0.7i)$

52. $\left(\frac{3}{4} - \frac{1}{10}i\right) - \left(-\frac{1}{8} + \frac{4}{25}i\right)$

53. $(-12.6 - 5.7i)(5.1 - 9.3i)$

54. $(7.8 + 23i)(-1.04 + 2.09i)$

Exercises 55 and 56: Evaluate with a calculator. Round values to the nearest thousandth.

55. $\dfrac{17 - 135i}{18 + 142i}$

56. $\dfrac{141 + 52i}{102 - 31i}$

Powers of *i*

Exercises 57–64: Simplify the powers of i.

57. i^{50}

58. i^{28}

59. i^{31}

60. i^{21}

61. i^{12}

62. i^{103}

63. i^{57}

64. i^{30}

Quadratic Equations with Complex Solutions

Exercises 65–82: Solve. Write answers in standard form.

65. $x^2 + 5 = 0$

66. $4x^2 + 3 = 0$

67. $5x^2 + 1 = 3x^2$

68. $x(3x + 1) = -1$

69. $3x = 5x^2 + 1$

70. $4x^2 = x - 1$

71. $x(x - 4) = -5$

72. $2x^2 + x + 1 = 0$

73. $x^2 = 3x - 5$

74. $3x - x^2 = 5$

75. $x^2 + 2x + 4 = 0$

76. $x(x - 4) = -8$

77. $3x^2 - 4x = x^2 - 3$

78. $2x^2 + 3 = 1 - x$

79. $2x(x - 2) = x - 4$

80. $3x^2 + x = x(5 - x) - 2$

81. $3x(3 - x) - 8 = x(x - 2)$

82. $-x(7 - 2x) = -6 - (3 - x)$

Zeros of Quadratic Functions

Exercises 83–88: The graph of a function is given.

(a) Use the graph to predict the number of real zeros and the number of imaginary zeros.

(b) Find these zeros using the quadratic formula.

83.

84.

85.

86.

87.

88.

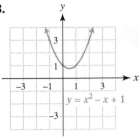

Applications

Exercises 89–94: **Electricity** *Complex numbers are used in the study of electrical circuits. Impedance Z (or the opposition to the flow of electricity), voltage V, and current I can all be represented by complex numbers. They are related by the equation* $Z = \frac{V}{I}$. *Find the value of the missing variable.*

89. $V = 50 + 98i$ $I = 8 + 5i$

90. $V = 30 + 60i$ $I = 8 + 6i$

91. $I = 1 + 2i$ $Z = 3 - 4i$

92. $I = \frac{1}{2} + \frac{1}{4}i$ $Z = 8 - 9i$

93. $Z = 22 - 5i$ $V = 27 + 17i$

94. $Z = 10 + 5i$ $V = 10 + 8i$

Writing about Mathematics

95. Could a quadratic function have one real zero and one imaginary zero? Explain.

96. Give an example of a quadratic function that has only real zeros and an example of one that has only imaginary zeros. How do their graphs compare? Explain how to determine from a graph whether a quadratic function has real zeros.

Extended and Discovery Exercise

1. Powers of *i* The properties of the imaginary unit are $i = \sqrt{-1}$ and $i^2 = -1$.

(a) Begin simplifying the expressions $i, i^2, i^3, i^4, i^5, \ldots$, until a simple pattern is discovered. For example, $i^3 = i \cdot i^2 = i \cdot (-1) = -i$.

(b) Summarize your findings by describing how to simplify i^n for any natural number n.

- **Understand basic concepts about quadratic inequalities**
- **Solve quadratic inequalities graphically**
- **Solve quadratic inequalities symbolically**

Introduction

Highway engineers often use quadratic functions to model safe stopping distances for cars. For example, $f(x) = \frac{1}{12}x^2 + \frac{11}{5}x$ is sometimes used to model the stopping distance for a car traveling at x miles per hour on dry, level pavement. If a driver can see only 200 feet ahead on a highway with a sharp curve, then safe driving speeds x satisfy the *quadratic inequality*

$$\frac{1}{12}x^2 + \frac{11}{5}x \le 200, \qquad \text{Quadratic inequality}$$

or equivalently,

$$\frac{1}{12}x^2 + \frac{11}{5}x - 200 \le 0. \qquad \text{Subtract 200.}$$

(See Example 4.) This section discusses methods for solving quadratic inequalities.

Basic Concepts

A quadratic equation can be written as $ax^2 + bx + c = 0$ with $a \ne 0$. If the equals sign is replaced by $>$, $\ge$, $<$, or $\le$, a **quadratic inequality** results. Examples of *quadratic equations* include

$$x^2 + 2x - 1 = 0, \qquad 4x^2 = 1, \qquad 2x^2 = 1 - 3x,$$

and examples of *quadratic inequalities* include

$$x^2 + 2x - 1 \ge 0, \qquad 4x^2 < 1, \quad \text{and} \quad 2x^2 \le 1 - 3x.$$

MAKING CONNECTIONS

Quadratic Function, Equation, and Inequality   The three concepts are closely related.

$$f(x) = ax^2 + bx + c, a \ne 0 \qquad \text{Quadratic function}$$
$$ax^2 + bx + c = 0, a \ne 0 \qquad \text{Quadratic equation}$$
$$ax^2 + bx + c > 0, a \ne 0 \qquad \text{Quadratic inequality}$$

Because equality is (usually) the boundary between *greater than* and *less than*, a first step in solving a quadratic inequality is to determine the x-values where equality occurs. These x-values are *boundary numbers*. We begin by discussing graphical solutions to quadratic inequalities.

Graphical and Numerical Solutions

Quadratic inequalities can be solved graphically, as illustrated in the next example.

EXAMPLE 1   Solving quadratic inequalities graphically

Solve each inequality graphically.
(a) $x^2 - 4 < 0$ **(b)** $x^2 - 4 > 0$

SOLUTION
(a) The graph of $y = x^2 - 4$ opens upward with x-intercepts -2 and 2, as shown in Figure 3.44 on the next page. Because the x-axis represents where $y = 0$, the solutions

to $x^2 - 4 < 0$ correspond to the red portion where the graph of $y = x^2 - 4$ is below the x-axis, which is between the x-intercepts ± 2. Thus the solution set is $\{x \mid -2 < x < 2\}$ or $(-2, 2)$.

Solving $x^2 - 4 < 0$ and $x^2 - 4 > 0$

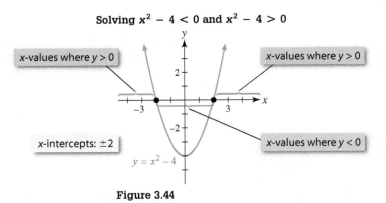

Figure 3.44

(b) From Figure 3.44 the green portions of the graph of $y = x^2 - 4$ are above the x-axis left of x-intercept -2 or right of x-intercept 2. Thus the solution set can be written as $\{x \mid x < -2 \text{ or } x > 2\}$, or $(-\infty, -2) \cup (2, \infty)$.

Now Try Exercise 1

The following steps summarize how to solve a quadratic inequality graphically.

SOLVING QUADRATIC INEQUALITIES GRAPHICALLY

STEP 1: If necessary, rewrite the inequality as $ax^2 + bx + c > 0$, where $>$ may be replaced by $<$, $\leq$, or $\geq$.

STEP 2: Graph $y = ax^2 + bx + c$ and determine any x-intercepts.

STEP 3: Depending on the inequality symbol, locate the x-values where the graph is either above or below the x-axis.

STEP 4: Use the information from Step 3 to solve the inequality.

In the next example we apply these steps to solve a quadratic inequality.

EXAMPLE 2 Solving a quadratic inequality graphically

Solve the inequality $2 + x \geq x^2$ graphically.

SOLUTION

STEP 1: Rewrite $2 + x \geq x^2$ as $-x^2 + x + 2 \geq 0$.

STEP 2: Figure 3.45 shows a graph of $y = -x^2 + x + 2$ where the x-intercepts are -1 and **2**. When graphing by hand, it may be helpful to locate the x-interecepts symbolically.

$$-x^2 + x + 2 = 0 \qquad \text{Let } y = 0 \text{ to find } x\text{-intercepts.}$$
$$x^2 - x - 2 = 0 \qquad \text{Multiply each side by } -1.$$
$$(x + 1)(x - 2) = 0 \qquad \text{Factor.}$$
$$x = -1 \quad \text{or} \quad x = 2 \qquad \text{Zero-product property.}$$

This confirms that the x-intercepts are -1 and 2.

STEP 3: The inequality symbol in $-x^2 + x + 2 \geq 0$ is $\geq$, so locate x-values where the parabola is above the x-axis. This occurs between the x-intercepts: -1, 2.

Solving $-x^2 + x + 2 \ge 0$ Graphically

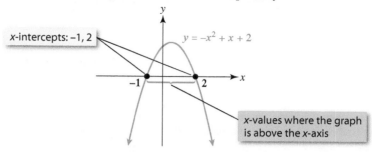

Figure 3.45

STEP 4: Because $\ge$ includes equality, the solution set includes -1 and 2 and can be written as $[-1, 2]$, or $\left\{ x \mid -1 \le x \le 2 \right\}$.

Now Try Exercise 35

In the next example we use symbolic, graphical, and numerical methods.

EXAMPLE 3   Solving quadratic equations and inequalities

Solve each equation or inequality.
(a) $2x^2 - 3x - 2 = 0$ **(b)** $2x^2 - 3x - 2 < 0$ **(c)** $2x^2 - 3x - 2 > 0$

SOLUTION
(a) *Symbolic Solution*   The equation $2x^2 - 3x - 2 = 0$ can be solved by factoring.

$$(2x + 1)(x - 2) = 0 \qquad \textit{Factor trinomial.}$$

$$x = -\frac{1}{2} \quad \text{or} \quad x = 2 \qquad \textit{Zero-product property}$$

The solutions are $-\frac{1}{2}$ and 2.

(b) *Graphical Solution*   The graph of $y = 2x^2 - 3x - 2$ is a parabola opening upward. Its x-intercepts are $-\frac{1}{2}$ and 2. See Figure 3.46. This parabola is below the x-axis $(y < 0)$ for x-values between $-\frac{1}{2}$ and 2, so the solution set is $\left(-\frac{1}{2}, 2\right)$, or $\left\{ x \mid -\frac{1}{2} < x < 2 \right\}$.

(c) *Graphical Solution*   In Figure 3.47, the graph of $y = 2x^2 - 3x - 2$ is above the x-axis $(y > 0)$ for x-values less than $-\frac{1}{2}$ or greater than 2, so the solution set is $\left(-\infty, -\frac{1}{2}\right) \cup (2, \infty)$, or $\left\{ x \mid x < -\frac{1}{2} \text{ or } x > 2 \right\}$.

Numerical Solution   The table of values in Figure 3.48 supports these graphical results. Note that $y_1 = 0$ for $x = -\frac{1}{2}$ and $x = 2$. For $-\frac{1}{2} < x < 2$, we see that $y_1 < 0$, and for $x < -\frac{1}{2}$ or $x > 2$, we see that $y_1 > 0$.

Graphical Solutions

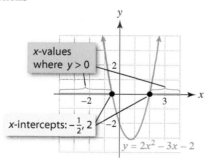

Figure 3.46

Figure 3.47

Numerical Solutions

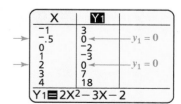

Figure 3.48

Now Try Exercise 7

NOTE *For a graphical solution, it is not necessary to graph the parabola precisely.* Instead you can simply *visualize* the parabola opening upward with *x*-intercepts $-\frac{1}{2}$ and 2.

The following box describes how to use the graph of $y = ax^2 + bx + c$ to solve either $ax^2 + bx + c > 0$ or $ax^2 + bx + c < 0$. The solution set depends on whether the graph opens upward or downward and on whether there are zero, one, or two intercepts.

SOLVING QUADRATIC INEQUALITIES GRAPHICALLY

Opens Upward $(y = ax^2 + bx + c$ with $a > 0)$

Zero *x*-intercepts

$y > 0$ for $(-\infty, \infty)$
$y < 0$: never

One *x*-intercept

$y > 0$ whenever $x \neq k$
$y < 0$: never

Two *x*-intercepts

$y > 0$ for $(-\infty, k_1) \cup (k_2, \infty)$
$y < 0$ for (k_1, k_2)

Opens Downward $(y = ax^2 + bx + c$ with $a < 0)$

Zero *x*-intercepts

$y > 0$: never
$y < 0$ for $(-\infty, \infty)$

One *x*-intercept

$y > 0$: never
$y < 0$ whenever $x \neq k$

Two *x*-intercepts

$y > 0$ for (k_1, k_2)
$y < 0$ for $(-\infty, k_1) \cup (k_2, \infty)$

CLASS DISCUSSION

Sketch a graph of $y = ax^2 + bx + c$ if the quadratic inequality $ax^2 + bx + c < 0$ satisfies the following conditions.
(a) $a > 0$, solution set: $\{x \mid -1 < x < 3\}$
(b) $a < 0$, solution set: $\{x \mid x \neq 1\}$
(c) $a < 0$, solution set: $\{x \mid x < -2 \text{ or } x > 2\}$

EXAMPLE 4 Determining safe speeds

In the introduction to this section the quadratic inequality

$$\frac{1}{12}x^2 + \frac{11}{5}x \leq 200$$

was explained. Solve this inequality to determine safe speeds on a curve where a driver can see the road ahead for only 200 feet. What might be a safe speed limit for this curve?

[−100, 100, 50] by [−300, 300, 100]

Intersection
X=37.536969 Y=200

Figure 3.49

SOLUTION Graph $y_1 = \frac{1}{12}x^2 + \frac{11}{5}x$ and $y_2 = 200$, as shown in Figure 3.49. Since we are interested in *positive* speeds, we need to locate only the point of intersection where x is positive. This is where $x \approx 37.5$. For positive x-values to the left of $x \approx 37.5$, $y_1 < 200$. Thus safe speeds are less than 37.5 miles per hour. A reasonable speed limit might be 35 miles per hour.

> **Now Try Exercise 67**

Symbolic Solutions

Although it is usually easier to solve a quadratic inequality graphically by visualizing a parabola and its x-intercepts, we can also solve a quadratic inequality symbolically without the aid of a graph. The symbolic method, which involves a table or a number line, is often used to solve more complicated inequalities. (See Section 4.7.)

SOLVING QUADRATIC INEQUALITIES SYMBOLICALLY

STEP 1: If necessary, write the inequality as $ax^2 + bx + c < 0$, where $<$ may be replaced by $>$, $\le$, or $\ge$.

STEP 2: Solve the equation $ax^2 + bx + c = 0$. The solutions are called boundary numbers.

STEP 3: Use the boundary numbers to separate the number line into disjoint open intervals. Note that on each open interval, $y = ax^2 + bx + c$ is either always positive or always negative.

STEP 4: To solve the inequality, choose a convenient test value (an x-value) from each disjoint interval in Step 3. Evaluate $y = ax^2 + bx + c$ at each test point. If the result is positive, then $y > 0$ over that interval. If the result is negative, then $y < 0$ over that interval. You may want to use either a number line or a table of values to organize your work.

Algebra Review
To review factoring, see Chapter R (pages R-22–R-23).

> **NOTE** Do not pick a boundary number for a test value, because the result will be $y = 0$.

For example, to solve $2x^2 - 5x - 12 < 0$ symbolically, replace $<$ with $=$ and solve the equation by factoring.

$$2x^2 - 5x - 12 = 0 \qquad \text{Quadratic equation}$$
$$(2x + 3)(x - 4) = 0 \qquad \text{Factor.}$$
$$2x + 3 = 0 \quad \text{or} \quad x - 4 = 0 \qquad \text{Zero-product property}$$
$$x = -\frac{3}{2} \quad \text{or} \quad x = 4 \qquad \text{Solve.}$$

$2x^2 - 5x - 12 = 0$

Figure 3.50

The boundary numbers $-\frac{3}{2}$ and 4 separate the number line into three disjoint intervals:

$$\left(-\infty, -\frac{3}{2}\right), \quad \left(-\frac{3}{2}, 4\right), \quad \text{and} \quad (4, \infty),$$

as illustrated in Figure 3.50.

The expression $2x^2 - 5x - 12$ is either always positive or always negative on a particular interval. To determine where $2x^2 - 5x - 12 < 0$, we can use the **test values** shown in Table 3.8.

Checking Test Values

Interval	Test Value x	$2x^2 - 5x - 12$	Positive or Negative?
$\left(-\infty, -\frac{3}{2}\right)$	-2	6	Positive
$\left(-\frac{3}{2}, 4\right)$	0	-12	Negative
$(4, \infty)$	6	30	Positive

Table 3.8

$2x^2 - 5x - 12$

Figure 3.51

For example, since the test value -2 lies in the interval $\left(-\infty, -\frac{3}{2}\right)$ and $2x^2 - 5x - 12$ evaluated at $x = -2$ equals 6, which is greater than 0, it follows that the expression $2x^2 - 5x - 12$ is always positive for $\left(-\infty, -\frac{3}{2}\right)$. This interval has $+$ signs on the number line in Figure 3.51. (See Table 3.8 on the previous page.)

See that the expression $2x^2 - 5x - 12$ equals -12 when $x = 0$, so it is always negative between the boundary numbers of $-\frac{3}{2}$ and 4. Negative signs are shown on the real number line in Figure 3.51 in the interval $\left(-\frac{3}{2}, 4\right)$.

Finally, when $x = 6$, the expression $2x^2 - 5x - 12$ equals 30, which is positive. Thus $+$ signs are placed along the x-axis in Figure 3.51 for $x > 4$. Therefore the solution set for $2x^2 - 5x - 12 < 0$ is $\left(-\frac{3}{2}, 4\right)$.

Note that it is important to choose one test value less than $-\frac{3}{2}$, one test value between $-\frac{3}{2}$ and 4, and one test value greater than 4. You do *not* need to use both a table and a number line.

EXAMPLE 5 Solving a quadratic inequality

Solve $x^2 \geq 2 - x$ symbolically. Write the solution set in interval notation.

SOLUTION

STEP 1: Rewrite the inequality as $x^2 + x - 2 \geq 0$.

STEP 2: Solve the quadratic equation $x^2 + x - 2 = 0$.

$$(x + 2)(x - 1) = 0 \qquad \text{Factor.}$$
$$x = -2 \quad \text{or} \quad x = 1 \qquad \text{Zero-product property}$$

$x^2 - x - 2$

Figure 3.52

STEP 3: These two boundary numbers separate the number line into three disjoint intervals:
$$(-\infty, -2), \quad (-2, 1), \quad \text{and} \quad (1, \infty).$$

STEP 4: We choose the test values $x = -3, x = 0$, and $x = 2$. From Table 3.9 or Figure 3.52 the expression $x^2 + x - 2$ is positive when $x = -3$ and $x = 2$. Thus the solution set is $(-\infty, -2] \cup [1, \infty)$. The boundary numbers, -2 and 1, are included because the inequality involves $\geq$ rather than $>$.

Interval	Test Value x	$x^2 + x - 2$	Positive or Negative?
$(-\infty, -2)$	-3	4	Positive
$(-2, 1)$	0	-2	Negative
$(1, \infty)$	2	4	Positive

Table 3.9

Now Try Exercise 61

3.4 Putting It All Together

The following table summarizes concepts related to solving quadratic inequalities.

CONCEPT	DESCRIPTION
Quadratic inequality	Can be written as $ax^2 + bx + c < 0$, where $<$ may be replaced by $>$, $\leq$, or $\geq$. **Example:** $-x^2 + x < -2$ is a quadratic inequality; it can be written as $-x^2 + x + 2 < 0$.

CONCEPT	DESCRIPTION
Graphical solution	Write the inequality as $ax^2 + bx + c < 0$, where $<$ may be $>$, $\leq$, or $\geq$. Graph $y = ax^2 + bx + c$, and use the x-intercepts, or boundary numbers, to determine x-values where the graph is below (above) the x-axis. In the figure, the inequality $-x^2 + x + 2 < 0$ is satisfied ($y < 0$) when either $x < -1$ or $x > 2$.
Symbolic solution	Write the inequality as $ax^2 + bx + c < 0$, where $<$ may be $>$, $\leq$, or $\geq$. Solve the equation $ax^2 + bx + c = 0$. To determine where $y = ax^2 + bx + c$ is positive or negative, use a table of test values or a number line. **Example:** Solve $-x^2 + x + 2 < 0$. Solving $-x^2 + x + 2 = 0$ results in $x = -1$ or $x = 2$. From the table the solution set is $\{x \mid x < -1 \text{ or } x > 2\}$ or $(-\infty, -1) \cup (2, \infty)$.

Interval	Test Value x	$-x^2 + x + 2$	Positive or Negative?
$(-\infty, -1)$	-2	-4	Negative
$(-1, 2)$	0	2	Positive
$(2, \infty)$	3	-4	Negative

3.4 Exercises

Quadratic Inequalities

Exercises 1–6: Solve each inequality.

1. (a) $x^2 - 1 > 0$ (b) $x^2 - 1 < 0$

2. (a) $x^2 - 9 < 0$ (b) $x^2 - 9 > 0$

3. (a) $x^2 - 16 \leq 0$ (b) $x^2 - 16 \geq 0$

4. (a) $x^2 - 25 \geq 0$ (b) $x^2 - 25 \leq 0$

5. (a) $4 - x^2 > 0$ (b) $4 - x^2 < 0$

6. (a) $\frac{1}{4} - x^2 < 0$ (b) $\frac{1}{4} - x^2 > 0$

Exercises 7–18: Solve each equation and inequality. Use set-builder or interval notation to write solution sets to the inequalities.

7. (a) $x^2 - x - 12 = 0$

   (b) $x^2 - x - 12 < 0$

   (c) $x^2 - x - 12 > 0$

8. (a) $x^2 - 8x + 12 = 0$

   (b) $x^2 - 8x + 12 < 0$

   (c) $x^2 - 8x + 12 > 0$

9. (a) $k^2 - 5 = 0$

   (b) $k^2 - 5 \leq 0$

   (c) $k^2 - 5 \geq 0$

10. (a) $n^2 - 17 = 0$

   (b) $n^2 - 17 \leq 0$

   (c) $n^2 - 17 \geq 0$

11. (a) $3x^2 + 8x = 0$

   (b) $3x^2 + 8x \leq 0$

   (c) $3x^2 + 8x \geq 0$

12. (a) $7x^2 - 4x = 0$

   (b) $7x^2 - 4x \leq 0$

   (c) $7x^2 - 4x \geq 0$

13. (a) $-4x^2 + 12x - 9 = 0$

   (b) $-4x^2 + 12x - 9 < 0$

   (c) $-4x^2 + 12x - 9 > 0$

14. (a) $x^2 + 2x + 1 = 0$

   (b) $x^2 + 2x + 1 < 0$

   (c) $x^2 + 2x + 1 > 0$

15. (a) $12z^2 - 23z + 10 = 0$

(b) $12z^2 - 23z + 10 \leq 0$

(c) $12z^2 - 23z + 10 \geq 0$

16. (a) $18z^2 + 9z - 20 = 0$

(b) $18z^2 + 9z - 20 \leq 0$

(c) $18z^2 + 9z - 20 \geq 0$

17. (a) $x^2 + 2x - 1 = 0$

(b) $x^2 + 2x - 1 < 0$

(c) $x^2 + 2x - 1 > 0$

18. (a) $x^2 + 4x - 3 = 0$

(b) $x^2 + 4x - 3 < 0$

(c) $x^2 + 4x - 3 > 0$

Exercises 19–24: The graph of $f(x) = ax^2 + bx + c$ is shown in the figure. Solve each inequality.

19. (a) $f(x) < 0$

(b) $f(x) \geq 0$

20. (a) $f(x) > 0$

(b) $f(x) < 0$

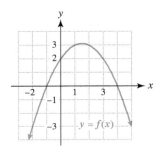

21. (a) $f(x) \leq 0$

(b) $f(x) > 0$

22. (a) $f(x) \geq 0$

(b) $f(x) \leq 0$

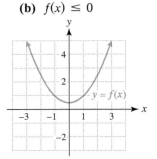

23. (a) $f(x) > 0$

(b) $f(x) < 0$

24. (a) $f(x) \geq 0$

(b) $f(x) < 0$

Exercises 25–28: Use the graph of $y = f(x)$ to solve each equation or inequality. Use set-builder or interval notation to write solution sets to the inequalities.

(a) $f(x) = 0$ (b) $f(x) < 0$ (c) $f(x) > 0$

25.

26.

27.

28.

Exercises 29–32: The table contains test values for a quadratic function $f(x) = ax^2 + bx + c$. Solve each inequality.

(a) $f(x) > 0$ (b) $f(x) \leq 0$

29.

x	-2	-1	0	1	2
$f(x)$	3	0	-1	0	3

30.

x	-6	-4	1	5	8
$f(x)$	-22	0	20	0	-36

31.

x	-6	-4	-2	0	2
$f(x)$	0	4	0	-12	-32

32.

x	-4	-2	0	2	4
$f(x)$	16	0	-8	-8	0

Exercises 33–58: Solve the inequality.

33. $2x^2 + 5x + 2 \leq 0$

34. $x^2 - 3x - 4 < 0$

35. $x^2 + x > 6$

36. $-3x \geq 9 - 12x^2$

37. $x^2 \leq 4$

38. $2x^2 > 16$

39. $x(x - 4) \geq -4$

40. $x^2 - 3x - 10 < 0$

41. $-x^2 + x + 6 \leq 0$

42. $-x^2 - 2x + 8 > 0$

43. $6x^2 - x < 1$

44. $5x^2 \leq 10 - 5x$

45. $(x + 4)(x - 10) \leq 0$

46. $(x - 3.1)(x + 2.7) > 0$

47. $2x^2 + 4x + 3 < 0$ **48.** $2x^2 + x + 4 < 0$

49. $9x^2 + 4 > 12x$ **50.** $x^2 + 2x \geq 35$

51. $x^2 \geq x$ **52.** $x^2 \geq -3$

53. $x(x - 1) \geq 6$ **54.** $x^2 - 9 < 0$

55. $x^2 - 5 \leq 0$

56. $0.5x^2 - 3x > -1$

57. $7x^2 + 515.2 \geq 179.8x$

58. $-10 < 3x - x^2$

Exercises 59–66: (Refer to Example 5.) Use a table to solve.

59. $x^2 - 9x + 14 \leq 0$ **60.** $x^2 + 10x + 21 > 0$

61. $x^2 \geq 3x + 10$ **62.** $x^2 < 3x + 4$

63. $\frac{1}{8}x^2 + x + 2 \geq 0$ **64.** $x^2 - \frac{1}{2}x - 5 < 0$

65. $x^2 > 3 - 4x$

66. $2x^2 \leq 1 - 4x$

Applications

67. Stopping Distance   The stopping distance D in feet for a car traveling at x miles per hour on *wet* level pavement can be estimated by $D(x) = \frac{1}{9}x^2 + \frac{11}{3}x$. If a driver can see only 300 feet ahead on a curve, find a safe speed limit.

68. Safe Driving Speeds   The stopping distance d in feet for a car traveling at x miles per hour is given by $d(x) = \frac{1}{12}x^2 + \frac{11}{9}x$. Determine the driving speeds that correspond to stopping distances between 300 and 500 feet, inclusive. Round speeds to the nearest mile per hour.

69. Geometry   The volume of a cylinder is given by $V = \pi r^2 h$, where r is the radius and h is the height. If the height of a cylindrical can is 6 inches and the volume must be between 24π and 54π cubic inches, inclusive, find the possible values for the radius of the can.

70. Geometry   A rectangle is 4 feet longer than it is wide. If the area of the rectangle must be less than or equal to 672 square feet, find the possible values for the width x.

71. Heart Rate   Suppose that a person's heart rate, x minutes after vigorous exercise has stopped, can be modeled

by $f(x) = \frac{4}{5}(x - 10)^2 + 80$. The output is in beats per minute, where the domain of f is $0 \leq x \leq 10$.
(a) Evaluate $f(0)$ and $f(2)$. Interpret the result.

(b) Estimate the times when the person's heart rate was between 100 and 120 beats per minute, inclusive.

72. Carbon Monoxide Exposure   When a person breathes carbon monoxide (CO), it enters the bloodstream to form carboxyhemoglobin (COHb), which reduces the transport of oxygen to tissues. The formula given by $T(x) = 0.0079x^2 - 1.53x + 76$ approximates the number of hours T that it takes for a person's bloodstream to reach the 5% COHb level, where x is the concentration of CO in the air in parts per million (ppm) and $50 \leq x \leq 100$. (Smokers routinely have a 5% concentration.) Estimate the CO concentration x necessary for a person to reach the 5% COHb level in 4–5 hours.   (*Source: Indoor Air Quality Environmental Information Handbook.*)

73. AIDS Deaths   Let $f(x) = 2375x^2 + 5134x + 5020$ estimate the number of U.S. AIDS deaths x years after 1984, where $0 \leq x \leq 10$. Estimate when the number of AIDS deaths was from 90,000 to 200,000.

74. Air Density   As the altitude increases, air becomes thinner, or less dense. An approximation of the density of air at an altitude of x meters above sea level is given by

$$d(x) = (3.32 \times 10^{-9})x^2 - (1.14 \times 10^{-4})x + 1.22.$$

The output is the density of air in kilograms per cubic meter. The domain of d is $0 \leq x \leq 10{,}000$.   (*Source:* A. Miller and J. Thompson, *Elements of Meteorology.*)
(a) Denver is sometimes referred to as the mile-high city. Compare the density of air at sea level and in Denver. (*Hint:* 1 ft $\approx$ 0.305 m.)

(b) Determine the altitudes where the density is greater than 1 kilogram per cubic meter.

75. iPod Sales   Sales of iPods in millions x years after 2006 can be modeled by

$$I(x) = -2.277x^2 + 11.71x + 40.4.$$

To the nearest year, estimate when sales were between 50 and 55 million iPods. (*Source:* Apple Corporation.)

76. Heart Rate   The table shows a person's heart rate after exercise has stopped.
(a) Find values for the constants a, h, and k so that the formula $f(x) = a(x - h)^2 + k$ models the data, where x represents time and $0 \leq x \leq 4$.

Time (min)	0	2	4
Heart rate (bpm)	154	106	90

(b) Evaluate $f(1)$ and interpret the result.

(c) Estimate the times when the heart rate was from 115 to 125 beats per minute.

Writing about Mathematics

77. Explain how a table of values can be used to help solve a quadratic inequality, provided that the boundary numbers are listed in the table.

78. Explain how to determine the solution set for the inequality $ax^2 + bx + c < 0$, where $a > 0$. How would the solution set change if $a < 0$?

CHECKING BASIC CONCEPTS FOR SECTIONS 3.3 AND 3.4

1. Simplify by using the imaginary unit i.

 (a) $\sqrt{-25}$ **(b)** $\sqrt{-3} \cdot \sqrt{-18}$

 (c) $\dfrac{7 \pm \sqrt{-98}}{14}$

2. Write each expression in standard form.

 (a) $-3i - (5 - 2i)$ **(b)** $(6 - 7i) + (-1 + i)$

 (c) $i(1 - i)(1 + i)$ **(d)** $\dfrac{1 + 2i}{4 - i}$

3. Use the graph of $y = f(x)$ to solve $f(x) \le 0$ and $f(x) > 0$. Write your answer in set-builder or interval notation.

 (a)   **(b)**

          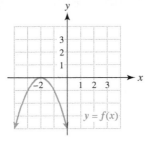

4. Solve each equation and inequality. Write the solution set for each inequality in set-builder or interval notation.

 (a) $2x^2 + 7x - 4 = 0$

 (b) $2x^2 + 7x - 4 < 0$

 (c) $2x^2 + 7x - 4 > 0$

5. Solve each inequality. Use set-builder or interval notation.

 (a) $x^2 - 36 \ge 0$

 (b) $4x^2 + 9 > 9x$

 (c) $2x(x - 1) \le 2$

6. Safe Driving Speeds The stopping distance d in feet for a car traveling x miles per hour on *wet* level pavement can be estimated by $d(x) = \frac{1}{9}x^2 + \frac{11}{3}x$. Determine the driving speeds that correspond to stopping distances between 80 and 180 feet, inclusive.

3.5 Transformations of Graphs

- **Graph functions using vertical and horizontal shifts**
- **Graph functions using stretching and shrinking**
- **Graph functions using reflections**
- **Combine transformations**
- **Model data with transformations (optional)**

Introduction

Graphs are often used to model different types of phenomena. For example, when a cold front moves across the United States, we might use a circular arc on a weather map to describe its shape. (See Exercise 7 in the Extended and Discovery Exercises on page 230.) If the front does not change its shape significantly, we could model the movement of the front on a television weather map by translating the circular arc. Before we can portray a cold front on a weather map, we need to discuss how to transform graphs of functions. (*Sources:* S. Hoggar, *Mathematics for Computer Graphics;* A. Watt, *3D Computer Graphics.*)

Vertical and Horizontal Shifts

Graphs of $f(x) = x^2$ and $g(x) = \sqrt{x}$ will be used to demonstrate shifts, or translations, in the xy-plane. Basic functions such as these are sometimes referred to as **parent functions**. Symbolic, numerical, and graphical representations of f and g are shown in Figures 3.53 and 3.54, respectively. Points listed in the table are plotted on the graph.

Vertical Shifts   If 2 is added to the formula for each parent function, their graphs are shifted upward 2 units. The graphs of $y = x^2 + 2$ and $y = \sqrt{x} + 2$ are shown in Figures 3.55 and 3.56. Notice that the y-values in the graphs and tables increase by 2 units.

If 2 is subtracted from each of the parent formulas, the graphs are shifted downward 2 units. Verify this by graphing $y = x^2 - 2$ and $y = \sqrt{x} - 2$. Translations of this type are called **vertical shifts**, or **vertical translations**. They do not alter the shape of the graph, only its position. The parent and shifted graphs are congruent.

Parent Functions

x	-2	-1	0	1	2
y	4	1	0	1	4

x	0	1	4
y	0	1	2

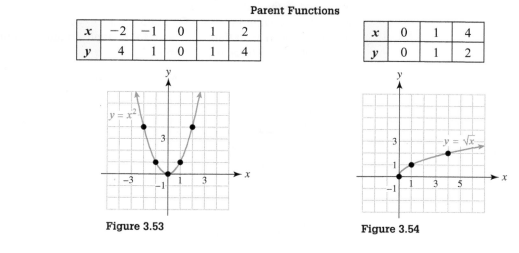

Figure 3.53   Figure 3.54

Shifted Upward 2 Units

x	-2	-1	0	1	2
y	6	3	2	3	6

x	0	1	4
y	2	3	4

Add 2 to each y-value.

Add 2 to each y-value.

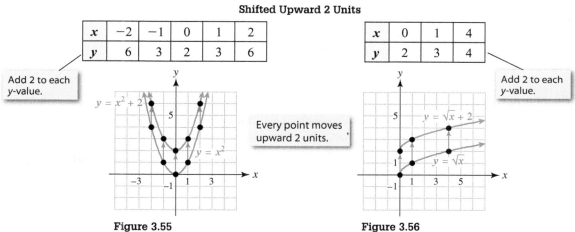

Every point moves upward 2 units.

Figure 3.55   Figure 3.56

Horizontal Shifts   If the variable x is replaced by $(x - 2)$ in the formulas for f and g, a different type of shift results. Figures 3.57 and 3.58 show the graphs and tables of $y = (x - 2)^2$ and $y = \sqrt{(x - 2)}$, together with the graphs of the parent functions.

Shifted Right 2 Units

x	0	1	2	3	4
y	4	1	0	1	4

x	2	3	6
y	0	1	2

Add 2 to each x-value.

Add 2 to each x-value.

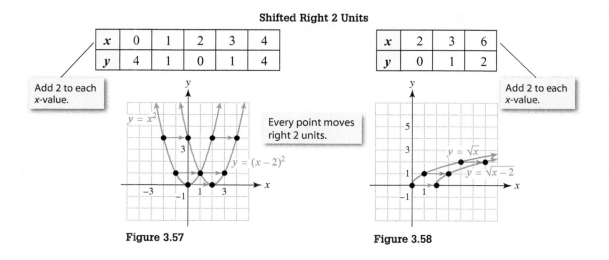

Every point moves right 2 units.

Figure 3.57   Figure 3.58

Each new graph shows a shift of the parent graph to the *right* by 2 units. Notice that a table for a graph shifted *right* 2 units can be obtained from the parent table by *adding* 2 to each *x*-value.

If the variable *x* is replaced by $(x + 3)$ in each equation, the parent graphs are translated to the *left* 3 units. The graphs of $y = (x + 3)^2$ and $y = \sqrt{(x + 3)}$ and their tables are shown in Figures 3.59 and 3.60. This type of translation is a **horizontal shift**, or **horizontal translation**. The table for a graph shifted *left* 3 units is obtained from the parent table by *subtracting* 3 from each *x*-value.

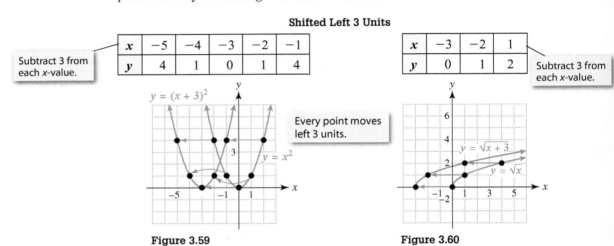

Shifted Left 3 Units

x	−5	−4	−3	−2	−1
y	4	1	0	1	4

Subtract 3 from each *x*-value.

x	−3	−2	1
y	0	1	2

Subtract 3 from each *x*-value.

Every point moves left 3 units.

Figure 3.59   **Figure 3.60**

These ideas are summarized in the following box.

VERTICAL AND HORIZONTAL SHIFTS

Let *f* be a function, and let *c* be a positive number.

To Graph	Shift the Graph of $y = f(x)$ by *c* Units
$y = f(x) + c$	upward
$y = f(x) - c$	downward
$y = f(x - c)$	right
$y = f(x + c)$	left

Shifts can be combined to translate a graph of $y = f(x)$. For example, we can shift the graph of $y = |x|$ to the right 2 units and downward 4 units, as follows.

See the Concept: Shifting $y = |x|$ Graphically

A Start with the graph of $y = |x|$.

B The point (0, 0) moves to (2, 0).

C The point (2, 0) moves to (2, −4).

Shifting y = |x| Symbolically

$$y = |x| \xrightarrow[\text{right 2 units}]{\text{Shift to the}} y = |x - 2| \xrightarrow[\text{4 units}]{\text{Shift down}} y = |x - 2| - 4$$

EXAMPLE 1 Combining vertical and horizontal shifts

Complete the following.
(a) Write an equation that shifts the graph of $f(x) = x^2$ left 2 units. Graph your equation.
(b) Write an equation that shifts the graph of $f(x) = x^2$ left 2 units and downward 3 units. Graph your equation.

SOLUTION
(a) To shift $f(x) = x^2$ left 2 units, replace x with $x + 2$ to obtain $y = f(x + 2)$, or $y = (x + 2)^2$. Its graph is shown in Figure 3.61.
(b) To shift $f(x) = x^2$ left 2 units and downward 3 units, we subtract 3 from the equation found in part (a) to obtain $y = f(x + 2) - 3$, or $y = (x + 2)^2 - 3$. Its graph is shown in Figure 3.62. The graph does not change shape.

Shifting y = x² Left 2 Units

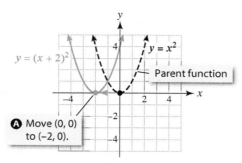

Figure 3.61

Shifting y = x² Left 2 Units and Downward 3 Units

Figure 3.62

Now Try Exercise 9

EXAMPLE 2 Writing formulas

Write a formula for a function g whose graph is similar to that of $f(x) = 4x^2 - 2x + 1$ but is shifted right 1980 units and upward 50 units. Do not simplify the formula.

SOLUTION Replace x with $(x - 1980)$ in the formula for $f(x)$ and then add 50.

$$\begin{aligned} g(x) &= f(x - 1980) + 50 \\ &= 4(x - 1980)^2 - 2(x - 1980) + 1 + 50 \\ &= 4(x - 1980)^2 - 2(x - 1980) + 51 \end{aligned}$$

Now Try Exercise 19

In the next example we translate a circle that is centered at the origin.

EXAMPLE 3 Translating a circle

The equation of a circle having radius 3 and center $(0, 0)$ is $x^2 + y^2 = 9$. Write an equation that shifts this circle to the right 4 units and upward 2 units. What are the center and radius of this circle? (Note that a circle is not a function.)

SOLUTION

Getting Started The standard equation for a circle with center (h, k) and radius r is

$$(x - h)^2 + (y - k)^2 = r^2.$$

If we determine the new center and radius, we can apply the standard equation. ▶

If a circle with center $(0, 0)$ and radius 3 is translated to the right 4 units and upward 2 units, then the center of the new circle is $(0 + 4, 0 + 2)$, or $(4, 2)$; the radius remains the same. The standard equation for a circle with center $(4, 2)$ and radius 3 is

$$(x - 4)^2 + (y - 2)^2 = 9.$$

Figure 3.63 illustrates this translation.

Now Try Exercise 23

Translating a Circle

Figure 3.63

NOTE Example 3 illustrates that to translate a circle horizontally c units, replace x with $(x - c)$, and to translate a circle vertically c units, replace y with $(y - c)$. If c is positive, the translation is either to the right or upward. If c is negative, the translation is either to the left or downward.

Stretching and Shrinking

Vertical Stretching and Shrinking   The graph of a function can be transformed by vertical stretching or shrinking as described next.

VERTICAL STRETCHING AND SHRINKING

If the point (x, y) lies on the graph of $y = f(x)$, then the point (x, cy) lies on the graph of $y = cf(x)$. If $c > 1$, the graph of $y = cf(x)$ is a vertical stretching of the graph of $y = f(x)$, whereas if $0 < c < 1$, the graph of $y = cf(x)$ is a vertical shrinking of the graph of $y = f(x)$.

MAKING CONNECTIONS

Vertical Stretching and Shrinking

Vertical stretching "pulls" the graph away from the x-axis.

Vertical shrinking "pushes" the graph towards the x-axis. In both cases the x-intercepts do not change.

For example, if the point $(4, 2)$ is on the graph of $y = f(x)$, then the point $(4, 4)$ is on the graph of $y = 2f(x)$ and the point $(4, 1)$ is on the graph of $y = \frac{1}{2}f(x)$. The graph of $f(x) = \sqrt{x}$ in Figure 3.64 can be stretched or shrunk *vertically*. In Figure 3.65, the graph of $y = 2f(x)$, or $y = 2\sqrt{x}$, represents a vertical stretching of the graph of $y = \sqrt{x}$. In Figure 3.66, the graph of $y = \frac{1}{2}f(x)$, or $y = \frac{1}{2}\sqrt{x}$, represents a vertical shrinking of the graph of $y = \sqrt{x}$. Compared to the y-values in the table for $y = \sqrt{x}$, the y-values in the tables for $y = 2f(x)$ and $y = \frac{1}{2}f(x)$ have been multiplied by 2 and $\frac{1}{2}$, respectively. The x-values have not changed.

Parent Function

x	0	1	4
$f(x)$	0	1	2

Vertical Stretching

x	0	1	4
$2f(x)$	0	2	4

Vertical Shrinking

x	0	1	4
$\frac{1}{2}f(x)$	0	$\frac{1}{2}$	1

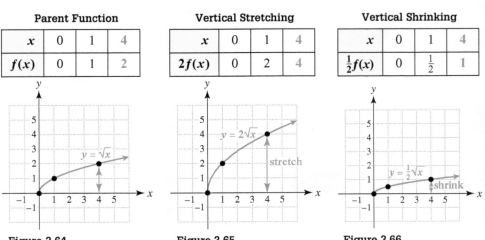

Figure 3.64   Figure 3.65   Figure 3.66

Horizontal Stretching and Shrinking   The line graph in Figure 3.67 can be stretched or shrunk *horizontally*. On one hand, if the line graph represents the graph of a function f, then the graph of $y = f\left(\frac{1}{2}x\right)$ in Figure 3.68 is a horizontal stretching of the graph of $y = f(x)$. On the other hand, the graph of $y = f(2x)$ in Figure 3.69 represents a horizontal shrinking of the graph of $y = f(x)$. Compared to the x-values in the table for $y = f(x)$, the x-values in the table for $y = f\left(\frac{1}{2}x\right)$ have been multiplied by 2 and the x-values in the table for $y = f(2x)$ have been multiplied by $\frac{1}{2}$. The y-values have not changed.

Parent Function

x	-2	-1	1	2
$f(x)$	3	-3	3	-3

Horizontal Stretching

x	-4	-2	2	4
$f\left(\frac{1}{2}x\right)$	3	-3	3	-3

Horizontal Shrinking

x	-1	$-\frac{1}{2}$	$\frac{1}{2}$	1
$f(2x)$	3	-3	3	-3

Figure 3.67

Figure 3.68

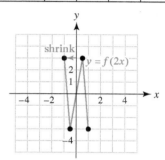

Figure 3.69

> **NOTE**   Horizontal stretching or shrinking does not change the height (maximum or minimum y-values) of the graph, nor does it change the y-intercept. Horizontal stretching and shrinking can be generalized for any function f.

HORIZONTAL STRETCHING AND SHRINKING

If the point (x, y) lies on the graph of $y = f(x)$, then the point $\left(\frac{x}{c}, y\right)$ lies on the graph of $y = f(cx)$. If $c > 1$, the graph of $y = f(cx)$ is a horizontal shrinking of the graph of $y = f(x)$, whereas if $0 < c < 1$, the graph of $y = f(cx)$ is a horizontal stretching of the graph of $y = f(x)$.

For example, if the point $(-2, 3)$ is on the graph of $y = f(x)$, then the point $(-1, 3)$ is on the graph of $y = f(2x)$ and the point $(-4, 3)$ is on the graph of $y = f\left(\frac{1}{2}x\right)$.

MAKING CONNECTIONS

Horizontal Stretching and Shrinking
Horizontal stretching "pulls" the graph away from the y-axis.

Horizontal shrinking "pushes" the graph towards the y-axis. In both cases the y-intercepts do not change.

EXAMPLE 4   Stretching and shrinking of a graph

Use the graph and table of $y = f(x)$ in Figure 3.70 on the next page to sketch a graph of each equation.
(a) $y = 3f(x)$
(b) $y = f\left(\frac{1}{2}x\right)$

SOLUTION

(a) The graph of $y = 3f(x)$, shown in Figure 3.71, is a vertical stretching of the graph of the given function $y = f(x)$, shown in Figure 3.70, and can be obtained by multiplying each y-coordinate on the graph of $y = f(x)$ by 3.

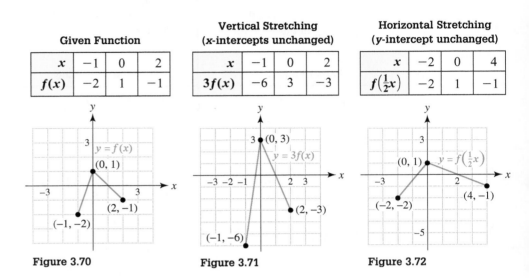

	Given Function		
x	-1	0	2
$f(x)$	-2	1	-1

	Vertical Stretching (x-intercepts unchanged)		
x	-1	0	2
$3f(x)$	-6	3	-3

	Horizontal Stretching (y-intercept unchanged)		
x	-2	0	4
$f\left(\frac{1}{2}x\right)$	-2	1	-1

Figure 3.70 **Figure 3.71** **Figure 3.72**

(b) The graph of $y = f\left(\frac{1}{2}x\right)$, shown in Figure 3.72, is a horizontal stretching of the graph of $y = f(x)$, shown in Figure 3.70, and can be obtained by *dividing* each x-coordinate on the graph of $y = f(x)$ by $\frac{1}{2}$, which is equivalent to multiplying each x-coordinate by 2.

Now Try Exercises 33(a) and (b)

Reflection of Graphs

Another type of translation is called a **reflection**. The reflection of the blue graph of $y = f(x)$ across the x-axis is shown in Figure 3.73 as a red curve. This reflection can be thought of as flipping the graph of $y = f(x)$ across the x-axis.

If (x, y) is a point on the graph of f, then $(x, -y)$ lies on the graph of its reflection across the x-axis, as shown in Figure 3.73. Thus a reflection of $y = f(x)$ is given by the equation $-y = f(x)$, or equivalently, $y = -f(x)$.

If a point (x, y) lies on the graph of a function f, then the point $(-x, y)$ lies on the graph of its reflection across the y-axis, as shown in Figure 3.74. Thus a reflection of $y = f(x)$ across the y-axis is given by $y = f(-x)$. This reflection can be thought of as flipping the graph of $y = f(x)$ across the y-axis. Another example is shown in Figure 3.75.

Reflection Across x-Axis

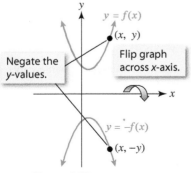

Figure 3.73

Reflections Across y-Axis

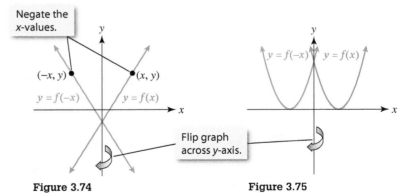

Figure 3.74 **Figure 3.75**

These results are summarized in the following box.

> **REFLECTIONS OF GRAPHS ACROSS THE *x*-AND *y*-AXES**
>
> 1. The graph of $y = -f(x)$ is a reflection of the graph of $y = f(x)$ across the *x*-axis.
> 2. The graph of $y = f(-x)$ is a reflection of the graph of $y = f(x)$ across the *y*-axis.

EXAMPLE 5 Reflecting graphs of functions

Complete the following.
(a) Write an equation that reflects the graph of $f(x) = x^2 + 1$ across the *x*-axis. Graph your equation.
(b) Write an equation that reflects the graph of $f(x) = \sqrt{x}$ across the *y*-axis. Graph your equation.

SOLUTION
(a) To reflect $f(x) = x^2 + 1$ across the *x*-axis, replace $f(x)$ with $-f(x)$ to obtain $y = -f(x)$, or $y = -x^2 - 1$. See Figure 3.76.
(b) To reflect $f(x) = \sqrt{x}$ across the *y*-axis, replace x with $-x$ to obtain $y = f(-x)$, or $y = \sqrt{-x}$. See Figure 3.77.

Reflecting $y = x^2 + 1$ Across x-Axis

$y = -f(x)$ is a reflection of $y = f(x)$ across the x-axis.

Figure 3.76

Reflecting $y = \sqrt{x}$ Across y-Axis

$y = f(-x)$ is a reflection of $y = f(x)$ across the y-axis.

Figure 3.77

> Now Try Exercises 35 and 37

Calculator Help

To access the variable Y_1 as shown in Figure 3.78, see Appendix A (page AP-10).

Graphing Calculators (Optional) On a graphing calculator capable of using function notation, entering equations for reflections of a function f is easy. For example, if $f(x) = (x - 4)^2$, let $Y_1 = (X - 4)^2$, $Y_2 = -Y_1$, and $Y_3 = Y_1(-X)$. See Figures 3.78 and 3.79.

```
Plot1  Plot2  Plot3
\Y1◘(X−4)^2
\Y2◘−Y1
\Y3◘Y1(−X)
\Y4=
\Y5=
\Y6=
\Y7=
```

Figure 3.78

$[-10, 10, 1]$ by $[-10, 10, 1]$

y_3 is a reflection of y_1 across the y-axis.

Figure 3.79

y_2 is a reflection of y_1 across the x-axis.

EXAMPLE 6 Reflecting graphs of functions

For each representation of f, graph the reflection across the *x*-axis and across the *y*-axis.
(a) $f(x) = x^2 + 2x - 3$
(b) The graph of f is a line graph determined by Table 3.10.

x	-2	-1	0	3
$f(x)$	1	-3	-1	2

Table 3.10

SOLUTION

(a) The graph of $f(x) = x^2 + 2x - 3$ is shown in Figure 3.80. To obtain its reflection across the x-axis, graph $y = -f(x)$, or $y = -x^2 - 2x + 3$, as shown in Figure 3.81. The vertex is now $(-1, 4)$.

For the reflection across the y-axis, let $y = f(-x)$, or $y = (-x)^2 + 2(-x) - 3$, and graph, as shown in Figure 3.82. The vertex is now $(1, -4)$.

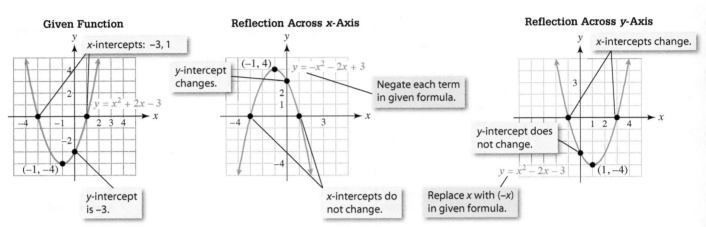

Given Function

Reflection Across x-Axis

Reflection Across y-Axis

Figure 3.80 $y = f(x)$ **Figure 3.81** $y = -f(x)$ **Figure 3.82** $y = f(-x)$

(b) The graph of $y = f(x)$ is a line graph, shown in Figure 3.83. To graph the reflection of f across the x-axis, make a table of values for $y = -f(x)$ by negating each y-value in the table for $f(x)$. Then plot these points and draw a line graph, as in Figure 3.84.

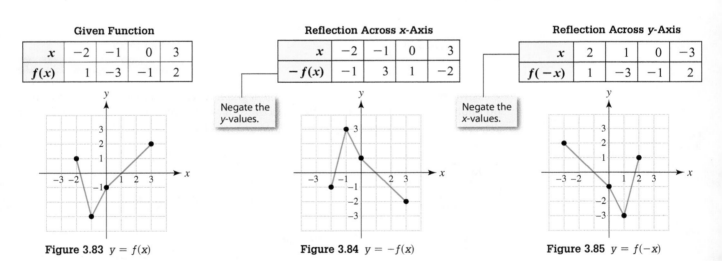

Given Function

x	-2	-1	0	3
$f(x)$	1	-3	-1	2

Reflection Across x-Axis

x	-2	-1	0	3
$-f(x)$	-1	3	1	-2

Reflection Across y-Axis

x	2	1	0	-3
$f(-x)$	1	-3	-1	2

Negate the y-values.

Negate the x-values.

Figure 3.83 $y = f(x)$ **Figure 3.84** $y = -f(x)$ **Figure 3.85** $y = f(-x)$

To graph the reflection of f across the y-axis, make a table of values for $y = f(-x)$ by negating each x-value in the table for $f(x)$. Then plot these points and draw a line graph, as in Figure 3.85.

Now Try Exercises 39 and 43

NOTE Compared to the y-values in a table of values for $y = f(x)$, the y-values in a table of values for $y = -f(x)$ are negated; the x-values do *not* change. Compared to the x-values in a table of values for $y = f(x)$, the x-values in a table of values for $y = f(-x)$ are negated; the y-values do *not* change.

Combining Transformations

CLASS DISCUSSION

Given a table of values for $y = f(x)$, how would you make a table of values for $y = -f(-x)$?

Transformation of graphs can be combined to create new graphs. For example, the graph of $y = -2(x - 1)^2 + 3$ can be obtained by performing four transformations on the graph of $y = x^2$.

1. Shift the graph of $y = x^2$ to the right 1 unit: $y = (x - 1)^2$.
2. Vertically stretch the graph of $y = (x - 1)^2$ by a factor of 2: $y = 2(x - 1)^2$.
3. Reflect the graph of $y = 2(x - 1)^2$ across the x-axis: $y = -2(x - 1)^2$.
4. Shift the graph of $y = -2(x - 1)^2$ upward 3 units: $y = -2(x - 1)^2 + 3$.

These steps are summarized as follows.

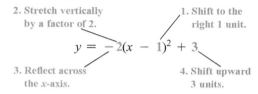

The resulting sequence of graphs is shown in Figures 3.86–3.89.

1. Shift Right

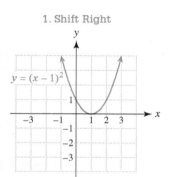

Figure 3.86

2. Vertical Stretch

Figure 3.87

3. Reflect Across x-Axis

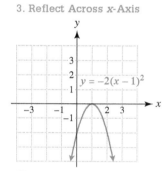

Figure 3.88

4. Shift Upward

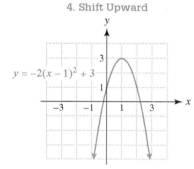

Figure 3.89

NOTE *The order in which transformations are made can be important.* For example, changing the order of a stretch and shift can result in a different equation and graph.

Also be careful when performing reflections and shifts. On the one hand, if we reflect the graph of $y = \sqrt{x}$ across the y-axis to obtain $y = \sqrt{-x}$ and then shift it right 2 units, we obtain $y = \sqrt{-(x - 2)}$. On the other hand, if we shift the graph of $y = \sqrt{x}$ right 2 units to obtain $y = \sqrt{x - 2}$ and then reflect it across the y-axis, we obtain $y = \sqrt{-x - 2}$. The final equations are different and so are their graphs. (Try sketching each graph.)

The following order can be used to graph the functions that we will encounter in this section.

COMBINING TRANSFORMATIONS

To graph a function by applying more than one transformation, use the following order.

1. Horizontal transformations
2. Stretching, shrinking, and reflections
3. Vertical transformations

EXAMPLE 7 Combining transformations of graphs

Describe how the graph of each equation can be obtained by transforming the parent graph of $y = \sqrt{x}$. Then graph the equation.
(a) $y = -\frac{1}{2}\sqrt{x}$ **(b)** $y = \sqrt{-x - 2} - 1$

SOLUTION
(a) Vertically shrink the graph of $y = \sqrt{x}$ by a factor of $\frac{1}{2}$ and then reflect it across the x-axis. See Figure 3.90.
(b) The following transformations can be used to obtain the graph of the equation $y = \sqrt{-x - 2} - 1$ from $y = \sqrt{x}$.

  1. Shift the graph of $y = \sqrt{x}$ right 2 units: $y = \sqrt{x - 2}$.
  2. Reflect the graph of $y = \sqrt{x - 2}$ across the y-axis: $y = \sqrt{-x - 2}$.
  3. Shift the graph of $y = \sqrt{-x - 2}$ down 1 unit: $y = \sqrt{-x - 2} - 1$.

  See Figure 3.91.

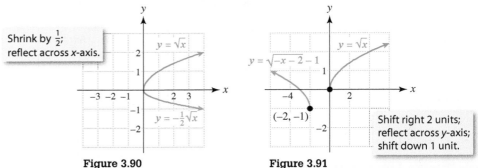

Shrink by $\frac{1}{2}$; reflect across x-axis.

Shift right 2 units; reflect across y-axis; shift down 1 unit.

Figure 3.90   **Figure 3.91**

Now Try Exercises 51 and 65

Modeling with Transformations (Optional)

Transformations of the graph of $y = x^2$ can be used to model some types of nonlinear data. By shifting, stretching, and shrinking this graph, we can transform it into a *portion of a parabola* that has the desired shape and location. In the next example we demonstrate this technique by modeling numbers of Walmart employees.

EXAMPLE 8 Modeling data with a quadratic function

Table 3.11 lists numbers of Walmart employees in millions for selected years.
(a) Make a scatterplot of the data.
(b) Use transformations to determine $f(x) = a(x - h)^2 + k$ so that $f(x)$ models the data. Graph $y = f(x)$ together with the data.
(c) Use $f(x)$ to estimate the number of Walmart employees in 2010. Compare it with the actual value of 2.1 million employees.

SOLUTION
(a) A scatterplot of the data is shown in Figure 3.92. This plot suggests that the data could be modeled by the *right half* of a parabola that opens upward.
(b) Because the parabola opens upward, it follows that $a > 0$ and the vertex is the lowest point on the parabola. The minimum number of employees is 0.20 million in 1987. One possibility for the vertex (h, k) is (1987, 0.20). Translate the graph of $y = x^2$ right 1987 units and upward 0.20 unit. Thus $f(x) = a(x - 1987)^2 + 0.20$.

  To determine a, graph the data and $y = f(x)$ for different values of a. See Figures 3.93 and 3.94. With a little experimentation, a reasonable value for a near 0.005 can be found.

Walmart Employees (in millions)

Year	Employees
1987	0.20
1992	0.37
1997	0.68
2002	1.4
2007	2.2

Source: Walmart.
Table 3.11

A scatterplot of the data and graph of $f(x) = 0.005(x - 1987)^2 + 0.2$ are shown in Figure 3.94. (Answers may vary.) Note that this equation is in *vertex form*.

Testing Values Graphically

[1985, 2010, 5] by [0, 3, 0.5]

Figure 3.92

[1985, 2010, 5] by [0, 3, 0.5]

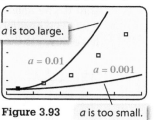

a is too large.

$a = 0.01$

$a = 0.001$

Figure 3.93 *a* is too small.

[1985, 2010, 5] by [0, 3, 0.5]

About right?

$a = 0.005$

Figure 3.94

(c) To estimate the number of employees in 2010, evaluate $f(2010)$.

$$f(2010) = 0.005(2010 - 1987)^2 + 0.2 = 2.845$$

This model provides an estimate of about 2.8 million Walmart employees in 2010. The calculation involves extrapolation and is not accurate.

> **Now Try Exercise 95**

Translations and Computer Graphics In video games, the background is often translated to give the illusion that the player in the game is moving. A simple scene of a mountain and an airplane is shown in Figure 3.95. To make it appear to the player as though the airplane were flying to the right, the image of the mountain could be translated horizontally to the left, as shown in Figure 3.96. Note that the position of the plane does not change. (***Source:*** C. Pokorny and C. Gerald, *Computer Graphics.*)

Shifting the Background to Show Motion

Figure 3.95

Figure 3.96

> **EXAMPLE 9** Using translations to model movement

Suppose that the mountain in Figure 3.95 can be described by $f(x) = -0.4x^2 + 4$ and that the airplane is located at the point $(1, 5)$.

(a) Graph f in $[-4, 4, 1]$ by $[0, 6, 1]$, where the units are in kilometers. Plot a point (a scatterplot with one point) to mark the position of the airplane.

(b) Assume that the airplane is moving horizontally to the right at 0.4 kilometer per second. To give a video player the illusion that the airplane is moving, graph the image of the mountain and the position of the airplane after 5 seconds and then after 10 seconds.

SOLUTION

(a) The graph of $y = f(x) = -0.4x^2 + 4$ and the position of the airplane at $(1, 5)$ are shown in Figure 3.97 on the next page. The "mountain" has been shaded to emphasize its position.

(b) Five seconds later, the airplane has moved $5(0.4) = 2$ kilometers right. In 10 seconds it has moved $10(0.4) = 4$ kilometers right. To graph these new positions, translate the graph of the mountain 2 and 4 kilometers (units) to the left. First, shift the mountain 2 kilometers to the left by replacing x with $(x + 2)$ and graphing

$$y = f(x + 2) = -0.4(x + 2)^2 + 4$$

together with the point $(1, 5)$. Next, graph $y = f(x + 4) = -0.4(x + 4)^2 + 4$ to shift the mountain 4 kilometers to the left. The results are shown in Figures 3.98 and 3.99. The position of the airplane at $(1, 5)$ has not changed. However, it appears to have flown to the right.

Calculator Help

To shade below a parabola, see Appendix A (page AP-10).

[−4, 4, 1] by [0, 6, 1]

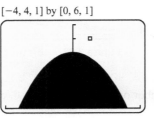

Figure 3.97

[−4, 4, 1] by [0, 6, 1]   [−4, 4, 1] by [0, 6, 1]

Figure 3.98   **Figure 3.99**

Now Try Exercise 101

CLASS DISCUSSION

Discuss how one might create the illusion of the airplane moving to the left and *gaining altitude* as it passes over the mountain.

3.5 Putting It All Together

In this section we discussed several transformations of graphs. The following table summarizes how these transformations affect the graph of $y = f(x)$.

EQUATION	EFFECT ON GRAPH OF $y = f(x)$
Let $c > 0$. $y = f(x) + c$ $y = f(x) - c$ $y = f(x + c)$ $y = f(x - c)$	The graph of $y = f(x)$ is shifted upward c units. The graph of $y = f(x)$ is shifted downward c units. The graph of $y = f(x)$ is shifted to the left c units. The graph of $y = f(x)$ is shifted to the right c units. **Examples:**

EQUATION	EFFECT ON GRAPH OF $y = f(x)$ 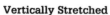
Let $c > 0$. $y = cf(x)$	If (x, y) lies on the graph of $y = f(x)$, then (x, cy) lies on the graph of $y = cf(x)$. The graph is vertically stretched if $c > 1$ and vertically shrunk if $0 < c < 1$. **Examples:** 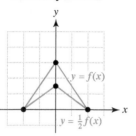
Let $c > 0$. $y = f(cx)$	If (x, y) lies on the graph of $y = f(x)$, then $\left(\frac{x}{c}, y\right)$ lies on the graph of $y = f(cx)$. The graph is horizontally shrunk if $c > 1$ and horizontally stretched if $0 < c < 1$. **Examples:** 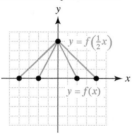
$y = -f(x)$ $y = f(-x)$	The graph of $y = f(x)$ is reflected across the x-axis. The graph of $y = f(x)$ is reflected across the y-axis. **Examples:** 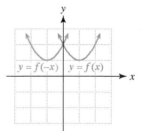

3.5 Exercises

Vertical and Horizontal Translations

Exercises 1–8: Write the equation of the graph. (Note: The given graph is a translation of the graph of one of the following equations: $y = x^2$, $y = \sqrt{x}$, or $y = |x|$.)

1.

2.

3.

4.

5.

6.

7.

8.
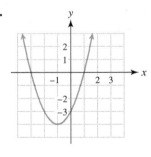

Exercises 9–14: Find an equation that shifts the graph of f by the desired amounts. Do not simplify. Graph f and the shifted graph in the same xy-plane.

9. $f(x) = x^2$; right 2 units, downward 3 units

10. $f(x) = 3x - 4$; left 3 units, upward 1 unit

11. $f(x) = x^2 - 4x + 1$; left 6 units, upward 4 units

12. $f(x) = x^2 - x - 2$; right 2 units, upward 3 units

13. $f(x) = \frac{1}{2}x^2 + 2x - 1$; left 3 units, downward 2 units

14. $f(x) = 5 - 3x - \frac{1}{2}x^2$; right 5 units, downward 8 units

Exercises 15–22: (Refer to Example 2.) Write a formula for a function g whose graph is similar to f(x) but satisfies the given conditions. Do not simplify the formula.

15. $f(x) = 3x^2 + 2x - 5$
  (a) Shifted left 3 units

  (b) Shifted downward 4 units

16. $f(x) = 2x^2 - 3x + 2$
  (a) Shifted right 8 units

  (b) Shifted upward 2 units

17. $f(x) = 2x^2$
  (a) Shifted right 2 units and upward 4 units

  (b) Shifted left 8 units and downward 5 units

18. $f(x) = 5x^2$
  (a) Shifted left 10 units and downward 6 units

  (b) Shifted right 1 unit and upward 10 units

19. $f(x) = 3x^2 - 3x + 2$
  (a) Shifted right 2000 units and upward 70 units

  (b) Shifted left 300 units and downward 30 units

20. $f(x) = |x|$
  (a) Shifted right 4 units and downward 3 units

  (b) Shifted left 5 units and upward 2 units

21. $f(x) = \sqrt{x}$
  (a) Shifted right 4 units, reflected about the x-axis

  (b) Shifted left 2 units, reflected about the y-axis

22. $f(x) = \sqrt{x}$
  (a) Reflected about the x-axis, shifted left 2 units

  (b) Reflected about the y-axis, shifted right 3 units

Exercises 23–26: **Translating Circles** *Write an equation that shifts the given circle in the specified manner. State the center and radius of the translated circle.*

23. $x^2 + y^2 = 4$; right 3 units, downward 4 units

24. $x^2 + y^2 = 9$; right 2 units, downward 6 units

25. $x^2 + y^2 = 5$; left 5 units, upward 3 units

26. $x^2 + y^2 = 7$; left 3 units, downward 7 units

Transforming Graphical Representations

Exercises 27–34: Use the accompanying graph of $y = f(x)$ to sketch a graph of each equation.

27. (a) $y = f(x) + 2$ **28. (a)** $y = f(x + 1)$

(b) $y = f(x - 2) - 1$ **(b)** $y = -f(x)$

(c) $y = -f(x)$ **(c)** $y = 2f(x)$

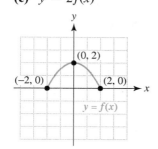

29. (a) $y = f(x + 3) - 2$ **30. (a)** $y = f(x - 1) - 2$

(b) $y = f(-x)$ **(b)** $y = -f(x) + 1$

(c) $y = \frac{1}{2}f(x)$ **(c)** $y = f\left(\frac{1}{2}x\right)$

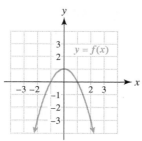

31. (a) $y = f(x + 1) + 1$ **32. (a)** $y = f(x) - 2$

(b) $y = -f(x) - 1$ **(b)** $y = f(x - 1) + 2$

(c) $y = \frac{1}{2}f(2x)$ **(c)** $y = 2f(-x)$

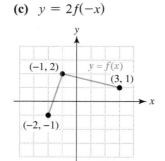

33. (a) $y = f(2x) + 1$ **34. (a)** $y = f(2x)$

(b) $y = 2f\left(\frac{1}{2}x\right) + 1$ **(b)** $y = f\left(\frac{1}{2}x\right) - 1$

(c) $y = \frac{1}{2}f(2 - x)$ **(c)** $y = 2f(1 - x)$

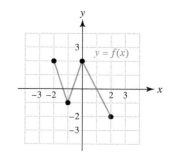

Reflections of Graphs

Exercises 35–38: Write the requested equation. Then graph the given equation and your equation.

35. Reflect $f(x) = \sqrt{x} + 1$ across the x-axis.

36. Reflect $f(x) = |x| - 1$ across the x-axis.

37. Reflect $f(x) = x^2 - x$ across the y-axis.

38. Reflect $f(x) = \sqrt{-x + 1}$ across the y-axis.

Exercises 39–44: (Refer to Example 6.) For the given representation of a function f, graph the reflection across the x-axis and graph the reflection across the y-axis.

39. $f(x) = x^2 - 2x - 3$ **40.** $f(x) = 4 - 7x - 2x^2$

41. $f(x) = |x + 1| - 1$ **42.** $f(x) = \frac{1}{2}|x - 2| + 2$

43. Line graph determined by the table

x	-3	-1	1	2
$f(x)$	2	3	-1	-2

44. Line graph determined by the table

x	-4	-2	0	1
$f(x)$	-1	-4	2	2

Graphing Transformations of Functions

Exercises 45–54. Use transformations to explain how the graph of f can be found by using the graph of $y = x^2$, $y = \sqrt{x}$, or $y = |x|$. You do not need to graph $y = f(x)$.

45. $f(x) = (x - 3)^2 + 1$ **46.** $f(x) = (x + 2)^2 - 3$

47. $f(x) = \frac{1}{4}(x + 1)^2$ **48.** $f(x) = 2(x - 4)^2$

49. $f(x) = -\sqrt{x + 5}$ **50.** $f(x) = -\sqrt{x} - 3$

51. $f(x) = 2\sqrt{-x}$ **52.** $f(x) = \sqrt{-\frac{1}{2}x}$

53. $f(x) = |-(x + 1)|$ **54.** $f(x) = |4 - x|$

Exercises 55–78: Use transformations to sketch a graph of f.

55. $f(x) = x^2 - 3$

56. $f(x) = -x^2$

57. $f(x) = (x - 5)^2 + 3$

58. $f(x) = (x + 4)^2$

59. $f(x) = -\sqrt{x}$

60. $f(x) = 2(x - 1)^2 + 1$

61. $f(x) = -x^2 + 4$

62. $f(x) = \sqrt{-x}$

63. $f(x) = |x| - 4$

64. $f(x) = \sqrt{x} + 1$

65. $f(x) = \sqrt{x - 3} + 2$

66. $f(x) = |x + 2| - 3$

67. $f(x) = |2x|$

68. $f(x) = \frac{1}{2}|x|$

69. $f(x) = 1 - \sqrt{x}$

70. $f(x) = 2\sqrt{x - 2} - 1$

71. $f(x) = -\sqrt{1 - x}$

72. $f(x) = \sqrt{-x} - 1$

73. $f(x) = \sqrt{-(x + 1)}$

74. $f(x) = 2 + \sqrt{-(x - 3)}$

75. $f(x) = (x - 1)^3$

76. $f(x) = (x + 2)^3$

77. $f(x) = -x^3$

78. $f(x) = (-x)^3 + 1$

Transforming Numerical Representations

Exercises 79–86: Two functions, f and g, are related by the given equation. Use the numerical representation of f to make a numerical representation of g.

79. $g(x) = f(x) + 7$

x	1	2	3	4	5	6
$f(x)$	5	1	6	2	7	9

80. $g(x) = f(x) - 10$

x	0	5	10	15	20
$f(x)$	-5	11	21	32	47

81. $g(x) = f(x - 2)$

x	-4	-2	0	2	4
$f(x)$	5	2	-3	-5	-9

82. $g(x) = f(x + 50)$

x	-100	-50	0	50	100
$f(x)$	25	80	120	150	100

83. $g(x) = f(x + 1) - 2$

x	1	2	3	4	5	6
$f(x)$	2	4	3	7	8	10

84. $g(x) = f(x - 3) + 5$

x	-3	0	3	6	9
$f(x)$	3	8	15	27	31

85. $g(x) = f(-x) + 1$

x	-2	-1	0	1	2
$f(x)$	11	8	5	2	-1

86. $g(x) = -f(x + 2)$

x	-4	-2	0	2	4
$f(x)$	5	8	10	8	5

Exercises 87–94: The points $(-12, 6)$, $(0, 8)$, and $(8, -4)$ lie on the graph of $y = f(x)$. Determine three points that lie on the graph of $y = g(x)$.

87. $g(x) = f(x) + 2$

88. $g(x) = f(x) - 3$

89. $g(x) = f(x - 2) + 1$

90. $g(x) = f(x + 1) - 1$

91. $g(x) = -\frac{1}{2}f(x)$

92. $g(x) = -2f(x)$

93. $g(x) = f(-2x)$

94. $g(x) = f\left(-\frac{1}{2}x\right)$

Applications

Exercises 95–98: (Refer to Example 8.) Use transformations of graphs to model the table of data with the formula $f(x) = a(x - h)^2 + k$. (Answers may vary.)

95. Number of iPhones sold (millions)

Year	2008	2009	2010	2011
iPhones	11.6	20.7	40.0	72.3

Source: Apple Corporation.

96. Apple apps downloaded (billions)

Year	2009	2010	2011
Apps	1.1	2.9	6.5

Source: Apple Corporation.

97. Google revenue ($ billions)

Year	2008	2009	2010	2011
Revenue	22	24	29	38

Source: Google.

98. Average price of a home in thousands of dollars

Year	1970	1980	1990	2000	2005
Price	30	80	150	210	300

Source: Bureau of the Census.

99. U.S. Home Ownership The general trend in the percentage P of homes lived in by owners rather than renters between 1990 and 2006 is modeled by

$$P(x) = 0.00075x^2 + 0.17x + 44,$$

where $x = 0$ corresponds to 1990, $x = 1$ to 1991, and so on. Determine a function g that computes P, where x is the actual year. For example, $P(0) = 44$, so $g(1990) = 44$.

100. U.S. AIDS Deaths The function D defined by

$$D(x) = 2375x^2 + 5134x + 5020$$

models AIDS deaths x years after 1984. Write a formula $g(x)$ that computes AIDS deaths during year x, where x is the actual year.

Using Transformations to Model Motion

101. Computer Graphics (Refer to Example 9.) Suppose that the airplane in Figure 3.95 is flying at 0.2 kilometer per second to the left, rather than to the right. If the position of the airplane is fixed at $(-1, 5)$, graph the image of the mountain and the position of the airplane after 15 seconds.

102. Computer Graphics (Refer to Example 9.) Suppose that the airplane in Figure 3.95 is traveling to the right at 0.1 kilometer per second and gaining altitude at 0.05 kilometer per second. If the airplane's position is fixed at $(-1, 5)$, graph the image of the mountain and the position of the airplane after 20 seconds.

103. Modeling a Weather Front Suppose a cold front passing through the United States at noon, has a shape described by the function $y = \frac{1}{20}x^2$. Each unit represents 100 miles. Des Moines, Iowa, is located at $(0, 0)$, and the positive y-axis points north. See the figure at the top of the next column.

(a) If the cold front moves south at 40 miles per hour and retains its present shape, graph its new location at 4 P.M.

(b) Suppose that by midnight the vertex of the front, which is maintaining the same shape, has moved 250 miles south and 210 miles east of Des Moines. Columbus, Ohio, is located approximately 550 miles east and 80 miles south of Des Moines. Plot the locations of Des Moines and Columbus together with the new position of the cold front. Determine whether the cold front has reached Columbus by midnight.

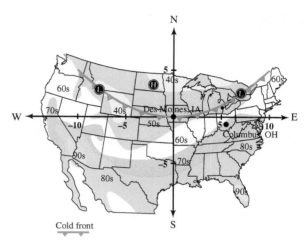

Cold front

104. Modeling Motion The first figure below is a picture composed of lines and curves. In this exercise we will model only the semicircle that outlines the top of the silo. In order to make it appear that the person is walking to the right, the background must be translated horizontally to the left, as shown in the second figure.

The semicircle at the top of the silo in the first figure is described by $f(x) = \sqrt{9 - x^2} + 12$.

(a) Graph f in the window $[-12, 12, 1]$ by $[0, 16, 1]$.

(b) To give the illusion that the person is walking to the right at 2 units per second, graph the top of the silo after 1 second and after 4 seconds.

Writing about Mathematics

105. Explain how to graph the reflection of $y = f(x)$ across the x-axis. Give an example.

106. Let c be a positive number. Explain how to shift the graph of $y = f(x)$ upward, downward, left, or right c units. Give examples.

107. If the graph of $y = f(x)$ undergoes a vertical stretch or shrink to become the graph of $y = g(x)$, do these two graphs have the same x-intercepts? y-intercepts? Explain your answers.

108. If the graph of $y = f(x)$ undergoes a horizontal stretch or shrink to become the graph of $y = g(x)$, do these two graphs have the same x-intercepts? y-intercepts? Explain your answers.

CHECKING BASIC CONCEPTS FOR SECTION 3.5

1. Predict how the graph of each equation will appear compared to the graph of $f(x) = x^2$.
   (a) $y = (x + 4)^2$ **(b)** $y = x^2 - 3$

   (c) $y = (x - 5)^2 + 3$

2. Use the graph shown to sketch a graph of each equation.

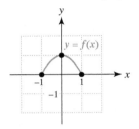

   (a) $y = -2f(x)$ **(b)** $y = f\left(-\frac{1}{2}x\right)$

   (c) $y = f(x - 1) + 1$

3. Write an equation that transforms the graph of $f(x) = x^2$ in the desired ways. Do not simplify.
   (a) Right 3 units, downward 4 units

   (b) Reflected about the x-axis

   (c) Shifted left 6 units, reflected about the y-axis

   (d) Reflected about the y-axis, shifted left 6 units

4. Use transformations to sketch a graph of the equation $y = \sqrt{x + 1} - 2$.

5. Use the table for $f(x)$ to make tables for $g(x)$ and $h(x)$.
   (a) $g(x) = f(x - 2) + 3$ **(b)** $h(x) = -2f(x + 1)$

x	-4	-2	0	2	4
$f(x)$	1	3	6	8	9

3   Summary

CONCEPT	EXPLANATION AND EXAMPLES

Section 3.1 Quadratic Functions and Models

Quadratic Function

General form: $f(x) = ax^2 + bx + c, \quad a \neq 0$

Examples: $f(x) = x^2$ and $f(x) = -3x^2 + x + 5$

Parabola

The graph of a quadratic function is a parabola.

Vertex form: $f(x) = a(x - h)^2 + k$ (standard form for a parabola with a vertical axis)
Leading coefficient: a;   *vertex*: (h, k);   *axis of symmetry*: $x = h$

Example:

Completing the Square to Find the Vertex

The vertex of a parabola can be found by completing the square.

Example:
$$y = x^2 - 4x + 1$$
$$y - 1 = x^2 - 4x \qquad \text{Subtract 1.}$$
$$y - 1 + 4 = x^2 - 4x + 4 \qquad \text{Add } \left(\tfrac{-4}{2}\right)^2 = 4.$$
$$y + 3 = (x - 2)^2 \qquad \text{Perfect square trinomial}$$
$$y = (x - 2)^2 - 3 \qquad \text{Subtract 3.}$$

The vertex is $(2, -3)$.

CONCEPT	EXPLANATION AND EXAMPLES

Section 3.1 Quadratic Functions and Models (CONTINUED)

Vertex Formula

x-coordinate: $x = -\dfrac{b}{2a}$; y-coordinate: $y = f\left(-\dfrac{b}{2a}\right)$

Example: $f(x) = 2x^2 + 4x - 4$

$x = -\dfrac{4}{2(2)} = -1$, $y = 2(-1)^2 + 4(-1) - 4 = -6$

Vertex: $(-1, -6)$

Section 3.2 Quadratic Equations and Problem Solving

Quadratic Equation

Can be written as $ax^2 + bx + c = 0$, $a \neq 0$
A quadratic equation can have zero, one, or two real solutions.

Examples: $x^2 + 1 = 0$, $x^2 + 2x + 1 = 0$,   and $x(x - 1) = 20$
        Zero solutions   One solution   Two solutions

Factoring

Write an equation in the form $ab = 0$ and apply the zero-product property.

Example: $x^2 - 3x = -2$ *Given equation*
        $x^2 - 3x + 2 = 0$ *Set equal to 0.*
        $(x - 1)(x - 2) = 0$ *Factor.*
        $x = 1$ or $x = 2$ *Zero-product property*

Square Root Property

If $x^2 = k$ and $k \geq 0$, then $x = \pm\sqrt{k}$.

Example: $x^2 = 16$ implies $x = \pm 4$.

Completing the Square

If $x^2 + kx = d$, then add $\left(\frac{k}{2}\right)^2$ to each side.

Example: $x^2 - 4x = 2$ *$k = -4$*
        $x^2 - 4x + 4 = 2 + 4$ *Add $\left(\frac{-4}{2}\right)^2 = 4$.*
        $(x - 2)^2 = 6$ *Perfect square trinomial*
        $x - 2 = \pm\sqrt{6}$ *Square root property*
        $x = 2 \pm \sqrt{6}$ *Add 2.*

Quadratic Formula

$x = \dfrac{-b \pm \sqrt{b^2 - 4ac}}{2a}$ *Always works to solve $ax^2 + bx + c = 0$*

Example: $2x^2 - 5x - 3 = 0$

$x = \dfrac{-(-5) \pm \sqrt{(-5)^2 - 4(2)(-3)}}{2(2)} = \dfrac{5 \pm 7}{4} = 3, -\dfrac{1}{2}$

CONCEPT	EXPLANATION AND EXAMPLES

Section 3.2 Quadratic Equations and Problem Solving (CONTINUED)

Discriminant

The number of real solutions to $ax^2 + bx + c = 0$ with $a \neq 0$ can be found by evaluating the discriminant, $b^2 - 4ac$.

1. If $b^2 - 4ac > 0$, there are two real solutions.

2. If $b^2 - 4ac = 0$, there is one real solution.

3. If $b^2 - 4ac < 0$, there are no real solutions (two complex solutions).

Section 3.3 Complex Numbers

Imaginary Unit

$$i = \sqrt{-1}, \qquad i^2 = -1$$

Examples: $\sqrt{-4} = 2i, \ \sqrt{-7} = i\sqrt{7}$

$$\sqrt{-3} \cdot \sqrt{-27} = i\sqrt{3} \cdot i\sqrt{27} = i^2\sqrt{81} = -9$$

Complex Number

$a + bi$, where a and b are real numbers (standard form)

Complex numbers include all real numbers. We can add, subtract, multiply, and divide complex numbers.

Examples:

$(2 - 3i) + (1 + 5i) = (2 + 1) + (-3 + 5)i = 3 + 2i$ (Add)

$3i - (2 + i) = -2 + (3 - 1)i = -2 + 2i$ (Subtract)

$(3 - i)(1 + 2i) = 3(1) + 3(2i) - i(1) - i(2i) = 5 + 5i$ (Multiply)

$\dfrac{1 - i}{2 + i} = \dfrac{(1 - i)(2 - i)}{(2 + i)(2 - i)} = \dfrac{1 - 3i}{5} = \dfrac{1}{5} - \dfrac{3}{5}i$ (Divide)

Complex Conjugate

The conjugate of $a + bi$ is $a - bi$.

Examples:

Number	$5 - 2i$	$5i$	-7	$-1 + 4i$
Conjugate	$5 + 2i$	$-5i$	-7	$-1 - 4i$

Complex Solutions

The quadratic formula can be used to solve quadratic equations with complex solutions.

Example: The solutions to $x^2 - x + 2 = 0$ are

$$x = \frac{1 \pm \sqrt{(-1)^2 - 4(1)(2)}}{2(1)} = \frac{1}{2} \pm i\frac{\sqrt{7}}{2}.$$

Section 3.4 Quadratic Inequalities

Quadratic Inequality

$ax^2 + bx + c < 0$ with $a \neq 0$, where $<$ may be replaced by $\leq$, $>$, or $\geq$.

Example: $3x^2 - x + 1 \leq 0$

CONCEPT	EXPLANATION AND EXAMPLES

Section 3.4 Quadratic Inequalities (CONTINUED)

Graphical Solution

Graph $y = ax^2 + bx + c$ and find the x-intercepts; then determine x-values where the inequality is satisfied.

Example: Solve $-x^2 - x + 2 > 0$.

$y = -x^2 - x + 2$

The x-intercepts are -2 and 1.

Solution set is $\{x \mid -2 < x < 1\}$, or $(-2, 1)$ in interval notation.

Symbolic Solution

First solve $ax^2 + bx + c = 0$ and use a table of values or a number line to determine the x-intervals where the inequality is satisfied.

Example: Solve $x^2 - 4 \geq 0$.

$x^2 - 4 = 0$ implies $x = \pm 2$.

Solution set is $\{x \mid x \leq -2 \text{ or } x \geq 2\}$, or $(-\infty, -2] \cup [2, \infty)$.

Interval	Test Value x	$x^2 - 4$	Positive or Negative?
$(-\infty, -2)$	-3	5	Positive
$(-2, 2)$	0	-4	Negative
$(2, \infty)$	3	5	Positive

Section 3.5 Transformations of Graphs

Vertical Shifts with $c > 0$

$y = f(x) + c$ shifts the graph of $y = f(x)$ upward c units.
$y = f(x) - c$ shifts the graph of $y = f(x)$ downward c units.

Horizontal Shifts with $c > 0$

$y = f(x - c)$ shifts the graph of $y = f(x)$ to the right c units.
$y = f(x + c)$ shifts the graph of $y = f(x)$ to the left c units.

Vertical Stretching and Shrinking

$y = cf(x)$ vertically stretches the graph of $y = f(x)$ when $c > 1$ and shrinks the graph when $0 < c < 1$.

Horizontal Stretching and Shrinking

$y = f(cx)$ horizontally shrinks the graph of $y = f(x)$ when $c > 1$ and stretches the graph when $0 < c < 1$.

Reflections

$y = -f(x)$ is a reflection of $y = f(x)$ across the x-axis.
$y = f(-x)$ is a reflection of $y = f(x)$ across the y-axis.

3 Review Exercises

Exercises 1 and 2: Use the graph to find the following.

(a) *Sign of the leading coefficient*
(b) *Vertex*
(c) *Axis of symmetry*
(d) *Intervals where f is increasing and where f is decreasing*

1.

2.

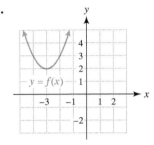

Exercises 3 and 4: Write f(x) in the form $f(x) = ax^2 + bx + c$, and identify the leading coefficient.

3. $f(x) = -2(x - 5)^2 + 1$ **4.** $f(x) = \frac{1}{3}(x + 1)^2 - 2$

Exercises 5 and 6: Use the graph of the quadratic function f to write it as $f(x) = a(x - h)^2 + k$.

5.

6.

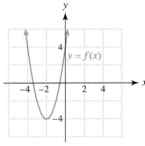

Exercises 7 and 8: Write f(x) in the form $f(x) = a(x - h)^2 + k$, and identify the vertex.

7. $f(x) = x^2 + 6x - 1$ **8.** $f(x) = 2x^2 + 4x - 5$

Exercises 9 and 10: Use the vertex formula to determine the vertex on the graph of f.

9. $f(x) = -3x^2 + 2x - 4$ **10.** $f(x) = x^2 + 8x - 5$

Exercises 11–14: Sketch a graph of the function.

11. $f(x) = -3x^2 + 3$ **12.** $g(x) = 2(x - 1)^2 - 3$

13. $f(x) = -|x + 3|$ **14.** $f(x) = \sqrt{2 - x}$

15. Average Rate of Change   Find the average rate of change of $f(x) = -6x^2 + 7x + 5$ from 2 to 4.

16. Difference Quotient   Find the difference quotient for $f(x) = x^2 - 2x$.

Exercises 17–24: Solve the quadratic equation.

17. $x^2 - x - 20 = 0$ **18.** $-5x^2 - 3x = 0$

19. $4z^2 - 7 = 0$ **20.** $25z^2 = 9$

21. $-2t^2 - 3t + 14 = 0$ **22.** $x(6 - x) = -16$

23. $0.1x^2 - 0.3x = 1$ **24.** $(k + 2)^2 = 7$

Exercises 25–28: Solve by completing the square.

25. $x^2 + 2x = 5$ **26.** $x^2 - 3x = 3$

27. $2z^2 - 6z - 1 = 0$ **28.** $-\frac{1}{4}x^2 - \frac{1}{2}x + 1 = 0$

29. Solve the equation $2x^2 - 3y^2 = 6$ for y. Is y a function of x?

30. Solve $h = -\frac{1}{2}gt^2 + 100$ for t.

31. Use the imaginary unit i to simplify each expression.

(a) $\sqrt{-16}$ (b) $\sqrt{-48}$ (c) $\sqrt{-5} \cdot \sqrt{-15}$

32. Write each expression in standard form.

(a) $(2 - 3i) + (-3 + 3i)$ (c) $(3 + 2i)(-4 - i)$

(b) $(-5 + 3i) - (-3 - 5i)$ (d) $\dfrac{3 + 2i}{2 - i}$

Exercises 33 and 34 Use the graph and the given f(x) to complete the following.

(a) *Find any x-intercepts.*
(b) *Find the complex zeros of f.*

33.

34.

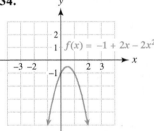

Exercises 35 and 36: Find all complex solutions.

35. $4x^2 + 9 = 0$ **36.** $2x^2 + 3 = 2x$

37. Use the graph of $y = f(x)$ to solve the inequality.

(a) $f(x) > 0$ (b) $f(x) \le 0$

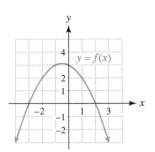

38. Solve the equation or inequality.
(a) $x^2 - 3x + 2 = 0$ (b) $x^2 - 3x + 2 < 0$

(c) $x^2 - 3x + 2 > 0$

Exercises 39–42: Solve the inequality. Use set-builder or interval notation to write a solution set to the inequality.

39. $x^2 - 3x + 2 \le 0$ **40.** $9x^2 - 4 > 0$

41. $n(n - 2) \ge 15$ **42.** $n^2 + 4 \le 6n$

43. If $f(x) = 2x^2 - 3x + 1$, use transformations to graph $y = -f(x)$ and $y = f(-x)$.

44. Use the given graph of $y = f(x)$ to sketch a graph of each expression.
(a) $y = f(x + 1) - 2$

(b) $y = -2f(x)$

(c) $y = f(2x)$

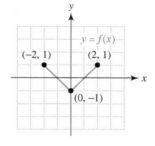

Exercises 45–48: Use transformations to sketch a graph of f.

45. $f(x) = x^2 - 4$ **46.** $f(x) = -4\sqrt{-x}$

47. $f(x) = -2(x - 2)^2 + 3$ **48.** $f(x) = -|x - 3|$

Applications

49. Maximizing Area   A homeowner has 44 feet of fence to enclose a rectangular garden. One side of the garden needs no fencing because it is along the wall of the house. What dimensions will maximize area?

50. Maximizing Revenue   The revenue R in dollars received from selling x radios is $R(x) = x(90 - x)$.
(a) Evaluate $R(20)$ and interpret the result.

(b) What number of radios sold will maximize revenue?

(c) What is the maximum revenue?

(d) What number of radios should be sold for revenue to be $2000 or more?

51. Projectile   A slingshot is used to propel a stone upward so that its height h in feet after t seconds is given by $h(t) = -16t^2 + 88t + 5$.
(a) Evaluate $h(0)$ and interpret the result.

(b) How high was the stone after 2 seconds?

(c) Find the maximum height of the stone.

(d) At what time(s) was the stone 117 feet high?

52. World Population   The function given by the formula $f(x) = 0.000478x^2 - 1.813x + 1720.1$ models world population in billions from 1950 to 2010 during year x.
(a) Evaluate $f(1985)$ and interpret the result.

(b) Estimate world population during the year 2000.

(c) According to this model, when did world population reach 7 billion?

53. Construction   A box is being constructed by cutting 3-inch squares from the corners of a rectangular sheet of metal that is 4 inches longer than it is wide. If the box is to have a volume of 135 cubic inches, find the dimensions of the metal sheet.

54. Room Prices   Room prices are regularly $100, but for each additional room rented by a group, the price is reduced by $3 for each room. For example, 1 room costs $100, 2 rooms cost $2 \times \$97 = \$194$, and so on.
(a) Write a quadratic function C that gives the total cost of renting x rooms.

(b) What is the total cost of renting 6 rooms?

(c) How many rooms are rented if the cost is $730?

(d) What number of rooms rented gives the greatest cost?

55. Minutes Spent on Facebook   The following table gives estimates for the total number of minutes in billions spent on Facebook per year. Find a function in the form $M(x) = a(x - h)^2 + k$ that models this data.

Year	2007	2008	2009
Minutes	60	84	184

Source: Business Insider.

56. Irrigation and Yield   The table shows how irrigation of rice crops affects yield, where x represents the percent of total area that is irrigated and y is the rice yield in tons per hectare. (1 hectare $\approx$ 2.47 acres.)

x	0	20	40	60	80	100
y	1.6	1.8	2.2	3.0	4.5	6.1

Source: D. Grigg, The World Food Problem.

(a) Use least-squares regression to find a quadratic function that models the data.

(b) Solve the equation $f(x) = 3.7$. Interpret the results.

Extended and Discovery Exercises

1. **Shooting a Foul Shot** (Refer to the introduction to this chapter.) When a basketball player shoots a foul shot, the ball follows a parabolic arc. This arc depends on both the angle and velocity with which the basketball is released. If a person shoots the basketball overhand from a position 8 feet above the floor, then the path can sometimes be modeled by the parabola

$$y = \frac{-16x^2}{0.434v^2} + 1.15x + 8,$$

where v is the velocity of the ball in feet per second, as illustrated in the figure. (**Source:** C. Rist, "The Physics of Foul Shots.")

(a) If the basketball hoop is 10 feet high and located 15 feet away, what initial velocity v should the basketball have?

(b) Check your answer from part (a) graphically. Plot the point (0, 8) where the ball is released and the point (15, 10) where the basketball hoop is. Does your graph pass through both points?

(c) What is the maximum height of the basketball?

2. **Shooting a Foul Shot** (Continuation of Exercise 1) If a person releases a basketball underhand from a position 3 feet above the floor, it often has a steeper arc than if it is released overhand and the path sometimes may be modeled by

$$y = \frac{-16x^2}{0.117v^2} + 2.75x + 3.$$

See the figure below. Complete parts (a), (b), and (c) from Exercise 1. Then compare the paths for an overhand shot and an underhand shot.

Exercises 3–6: **Reflecting Functions** *Computer graphics frequently use reflections. Reflections can speed up the generation of a picture or create a figure that appears perfectly symmetrical.* (**Source:** S. Hoggar, *Mathematics for Computer Graphics.*)

(a) For the given $f(x)$, constant k, and viewing rectangle, graph $x = k$, $y = f(x)$, and $y = f(2k - x)$.

(b) Generalize how the graph of $y = f(2k - x)$ compares to the graph of $y = f(x)$.

3. $f(x) = \sqrt{x}$, $k = 2$, $[-1, 8, 1]$ by $[-4, 4, 1]$

4. $f(x) = x^2$, $k = -3$, $[-12, 6, 1]$ by $[-6, 6, 1]$

5. $f(x) = x^4 - 2x^2 + 1$, $k = -6$, $[-15, 3, 1]$ by $[-3, 9, 1]$

6. $f(x) = 4x - x^3$, $k = 5$, $[-6, 18, 1]$ by $[-8, 8, 1]$

7. **Modeling a Cold Front** A weather map of the United States on April 22, 1996, is shown in the figure. There was a cold front roughly in the shape of a circular arc, with a radius of about 750 miles, passing north of Dallas and west of Detroit. The center of the arc was located near Pierre, South Dakota. If Pierre has the coordinates (0, 0) and the positive y-axis points north, then the equation of the front can be modeled by

$$f(x) = -\sqrt{750^2 - x^2},$$

where $0 \le x \le 750$. (**Source:** AccuWeather, Inc.)

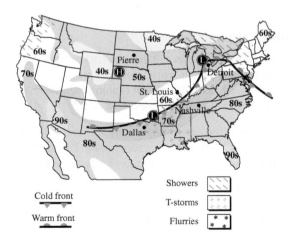

(a) St. Louis is located at $(535, -400)$ and Nashville is at $(730, -570)$, where units are in miles. Plot these points and graph f in the window [0, 1200, 100] by [−800, 0, 100]. Did the cold front reach these cities?

(b) During the next 12 hours, the center of the front moved approximately 110 miles south and 160 miles east. Assuming the cold front did not change shape, use transformations of graphs to determine an equation that models its new location.

(c) Use graphing to determine visually if the cold front reached both cities.

4 More Nonlinear Functions and Equations

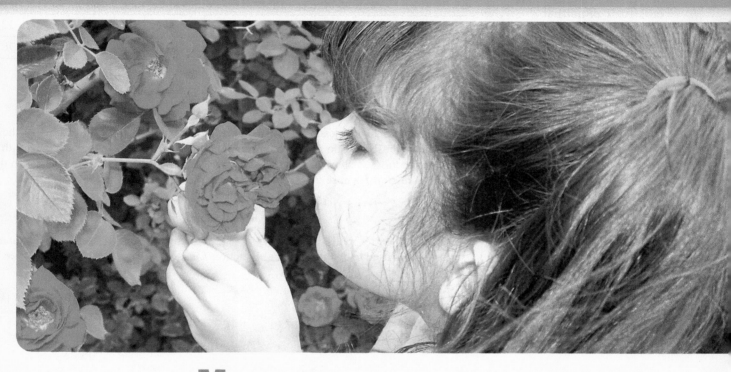

Mathematics can be both abstract and applied. Abstract mathematics is focused on axioms, theorems, and proofs that can be derived independently of empirical evidence. Theorems that were proved centuries ago are still valid today. In this sense, abstract mathematics transcends time. Yet, even though mathematics can be developed in an abstract setting—separate from science and all measured data—it also has countless applications.

There is a common misconception that theoretical mathematics is unimportant, yet many of the ideas that eventually had great practical importance were first born in the abstract. For example, in 1854 George Boole published *Laws of Thought,* which outlined the basis for Boolean algebra. This was 85 years before the invention of the first digital computer. However, Boolean algebra became the basis on which modern computer hardware operates.

Much like Boolean algebra, the topic of complex numbers was at first theoretical. However, today complex numbers are used in the design of electrical circuits, ships, and airplanes.

In this chapter we discuss some important topics in algebra that have had an impact on society. We are privileged to read in a few hours what took people centuries to discover. To ignore either the abstract beauty or the profound applicability of mathematics is like seeing a rose but never smelling one.

4.1 More Nonlinear Functions and Their Graphs

- Learn terminology about polynomial functions
- Find extrema of a function
- Identify symmetry in a graph of a function
- Determine if a function is odd, even, or neither

Introduction

Monthly average high temperatures at Daytona Beach are shown in Table 4.1.

Monthly Average High Temperatures at Daytona Beach

Month	1	2	3	4	5	6	7	8	9	10	11	12
Temperature (°F)	69	70	75	80	85	88	90	89	87	81	76	70

Table 4.1   *Source:* J. Williams, *The USA Weather Almanac.*

Figure 4.1 shows a scatterplot of the data. A linear function would not model these data because these data do not lie on a line. One possibility is to model the data with a quadratic function, as shown in Figure 4.2. However, a better fit can be obtained with the nonlinear function f whose graph is shown in Figure 4.3 and is given by

$$f(x) = 0.0145x^4 - 0.426x^3 + 3.53x^2 - 6.23x + 72,$$

A Polynomial Function

where $x = 1$ corresponds to January, $x = 2$ to February, and so on. (Least-squares regression was used to determine $f(x)$.) Function f is a *polynomial function* with degree 4.

Temperature Data

Figure 4.1

Quadratic Model

Figure 4.2

New Polynomial Model

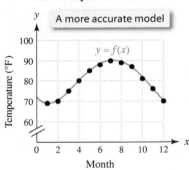

Figure 4.3

Polynomial Functions

The domain of a polynomial function is all real numbers, and its graph is continuous and smooth without breaks or sharp edges.

POLYNOMIAL FUNCTION

A **polynomial function** f of degree n in the variable x can be represented by

$$f(x) = a_n x^n + a_{n-1} x^{n-1} + \cdots + a_2 x^2 + a_1 x + a_0,$$

where each coefficient a_k is a real number, $a_n \neq 0$, and n is a nonnegative integer. The **leading coefficient** is a_n and the **degree** is n.

Algebra Review
To review polynomials, see Chapter R
(page R-12).

Examples of polynomial functions include the following.

Formula	Degree	Leading Coefficient
$f(x) = 10$	0	$a_0 = 10$
$g(x) = 2x - 3.7$	1	$a_1 = 2$
$h(x) = 1 - 1.4x + 3x^2$	2	$a_2 = 3$
$k(x) = -\dfrac{1}{2}x^6 + 4x^4 + x$	6	$a_6 = -\dfrac{1}{2}$

A polynomial function of degree 2 or higher is a *nonlinear* function. Functions f and g are linear, whereas functions h and k are nonlinear.

NOTE Quadratic functions, which were discussed in Chapter 3, are examples of nonlinear functions. This chapter introduces *more* nonlinear functions.

Functions that contain radicals, ratios, or absolute values of variables are not polynomials. For example, $f(x) = 2\sqrt{x}$, $g(x) = \dfrac{1}{x-1}$, and $h(x) = |2x + 5|$ are *not* polynomials. However, they *are* nonlinear functions.

Identifying Extrema

In Figure 4.3 the minimum monthly average temperature of 69°F occurs in January ($x = 1$) and the maximum monthly average temperature of 90°F occurs in July ($x = 7$). Minimum and maximum y-values on the graph of a function often represent important data.

Graphs of two polynomial functions with "hills" and "valleys" are shown in Figures 4.4 and 4.5. These hills and valleys are associated with maximum and minimum y-values on the graphs. The following See the Concept shows how these minimum and maximum y-values are classified.

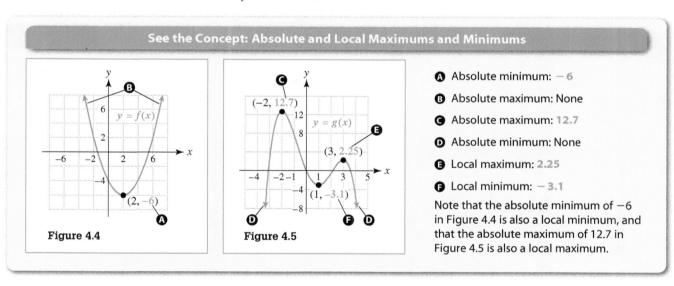

See the Concept: Absolute and Local Maximums and Minimums

Figure 4.4

Figure 4.5

Ⓐ Absolute minimum: -6

Ⓑ Absolute maximum: None

Ⓒ Absolute maximum: 12.7

Ⓓ Absolute minimum: None

Ⓔ Local maximum: 2.25

Ⓕ Local minimum: -3.1

Note that the absolute minimum of -6 in Figure 4.4 is also a local minimum, and that the absolute maximum of 12.7 in Figure 4.5 is also a local maximum.

In Figure 4.4, the minimum y-value on the graph of f is -6. It is called the *absolute minimum* of f. Function f has no *absolute maximum* because there is no largest y-value on a parabola opening upward.

In Figure 4.5 the peak of the highest "hill" on the graph of g is $(-2, 12.7)$. Therefore the absolute maximum of g is 12.7. There is a smaller peak located at the point $(3, 2.25)$. In a small open interval near $x = 3$, the y-value of 2.25 is locally the largest. We say that g has a *local maximum* of 2.25. Similarly, a "valley" occurs on the graph of g, where the lowest point is $(1, -3.1)$. The value -3.1 is not the smallest y-value on the entire graph of g. Therefore it is not an absolute minimum. Rather, -3.1 is a *local minimum*.

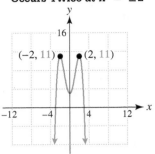

Absolute Maximum: 11
Occurs Twice at $x = \pm 2$

Figure 4.6

Maximum and minimum values that are either absolute or local are called **extrema** (plural of extremum). A function may have several local extrema, but at most one absolute maximum and one absolute minimum. However, it is possible for a function to assume an absolute extremum at two values of x. In Figure 4.6 the absolute maximum is 11. It occurs at $x = \pm 2$.

NOTE In Figure 4.6, the absolute maximum of 11 is *also* a local maximum because it is the largest y-value in a small interval near either $x = -2$ or $x = 2$.

Sometimes an absolute maximum (minimum) is called a *global maximum* (*minimum*). Similarly, sometimes a local maximum (minimum) is called a *relative maximum* (*minimum*).

ABSOLUTE AND LOCAL EXTREMA

Let c be in the domain of f.

$f(c)$ is an **absolute (global) maximum** if $f(c) \geq f(x)$ *for all x in the domain of f.*
$f(c)$ is an **absolute (global) minimum** if $f(c) \leq f(x)$ *for all x in the domain of f.*
$f(c)$ is a **local (relative) maximum** if $f(c) \geq f(x)$ when x is *near c.*
$f(c)$ is a **local (relative) minimum** if $f(c) \leq f(x)$ when x is *near c.*

NOTE The expression "near c" means that there is an open interval in the domain of f containing c where $f(c)$ satisfies the inequality.

EXAMPLE 1 Identifying and interpreting extrema

Figure 4.7 shows the graph of a function f that models the volume of air in a person's lungs, measured in liters, after x seconds. (**Source:** V. Thomas, *Science and Sport.*)
(a) Find the absolute maximum and the absolute minimum of f. Interpret the results.
(b) Identify two local maximums and two local minimums of f. Interpret the results.

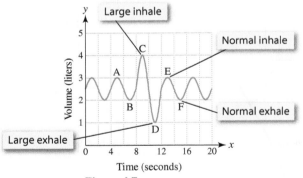

Volume of Air in a Person's Lungs

Figure 4.7

SOLUTION
(a) The absolute maximum is 4 liters and occurs at C. The absolute minimum is 1 liter and occurs at D. At C a deep breath has been taken and the lungs are more inflated. After C, the person exhales until the lungs contain only 1 liter of air at D.
(b) One local maximum is 3 liters. It occurs at A and E and represents the amount of air in a person's lungs after inhaling normally. One local minimum is 2 liters. It occurs at B and F and represents the amount of air after exhaling normally. Another local maximum is 4 liters, which is also the absolute maximum. Similarly, 1 liter is a local minimum and also the absolute minimum.

Now Try Exercise 91

EXAMPLE 2 Identifying extrema

Use the graph of f in Figure 4.8 to estimate any local and absolute extrema.

SOLUTION
Local Extrema The points $(-2, 8)$ and $(1, -19)$ on the graph of f correspond to the low-est point in a "valley." Thus there are local minimums of 8 and -19. The point $(-1, 13)$ corresponds to the highest point on a "hill." Thus there is a local maximum of 13.

Absolute Extrema Because the arrows point upward, there is no maximum y-value on the graph. Thus there is no absolute maximum. However, the minimum y-value on the graph of f occurs at the point $(1, -19)$. The absolute minimum is -19.

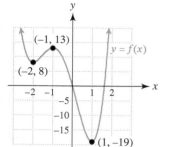

Figure 4.8

Now Try Exercise 15

NOTE Extrema are y-values on the graph of a function, not x-values.

EXAMPLE 3 Modeling ocean temperatures

The monthly average ocean temperature in degrees Fahrenheit at Bermuda can be modeled by $f(x) = 0.0215x^4 - 0.648x^3 + 6.03x^2 - 17.1x + 76.4$, where $x = 1$ corresponds to January and $x = 12$ to December. The domain of f is $D = \{x \mid 1 \le x \le 12\}$.
(a) Graph f in $[1, 12, 1]$ by $[50, 90, 10]$.
(b) Estimate the absolute extrema. Interpret the results.

SOLUTION
(a) The graph of $y_1 = f(x)$ is shown in Figure 4.9.
(b) Many graphing calculators have the capability to find maximum and minimum y-values. The points associated with absolute extrema are shown in Figures 4.9 and 4.10. An absolute minimum of about 61.5 corresponds to the point $(2.01, 61.5)$. This means that the monthly average ocean temperature is coldest during the month of February ($x \approx 2$) when it reaches a minimum of about 61.5°F.

An absolute maximum of approximately 82 corresponds to $(7.61, 82.0)$. Rounding, we might say that the warmest average temperature occurs during August ($x \approx 8$) when it reaches a maximum of 82°F. (Or we might say that this maximum occurs in late July, since $x \approx 7.61$.)

Now Try Exercise 95

[1, 12, 1] by [50, 90, 10]

Figure 4.9

[1, 12, 1] by [50, 90, 10]

Figure 4.10

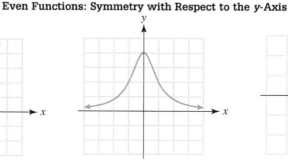

Symmetry

Even Functions Symmetry is used frequently in art, mathematics, science, and computer graphics. Many objects and animals are symmetric along a line so that the left and right sides are mirror images. For example, if a butterfly is viewed from the top, the left wing is typically a mirror image of the right wing. Graphs of functions may also exhibit this type of symmetry, as shown in Figures 4.11–4.13. These graphs are **symmetric with respect to the y-axis.** A function whose graph satisfies this characteristic is called an *even function*.

Even Functions: Symmetry with Respect to the y-Axis

If these graphs are folded on the y-axis, the two halves match.

Figure 4.11

Figure 4.12

Figure 4.13

An Even Function

Figure 4.14

Figure 4.14 shows a graph of an even function f. Since the graph is symmetric with respect to the y-axis, the points (x, y) and $(-x, y)$ both lie on the graph of f. Thus $f(x) = y$ and $f(-x) = y$, and so $f(x) = f(-x)$ for an even function. This means that if we change the sign of the input, the output does not change. For example, if $g(x) = x^2$, then $g(2) = g(-2) = 4$. Since this is true for *every input*, g is an even function.

> **EVEN FUNCTION**
>
> A function f is an **even function** if $f(-x) = f(x)$ for every x in its domain. The graph of an even function is symmetric with respect to the y-axis.

Odd Functions A second type of symmetry is shown in Figures 4.15–4.17. If we could spin or rotate the graph about the origin, the original graph would reappear after half a turn. These graphs are **symmetric with respect to the origin** and represent *odd functions*.

Odd Functions: Symmetry with Respect to the Origin

| Figure 4.15 | Figure 4.16 | Figure 4.17 |

An Odd Function

Figure 4.18

In Figure 4.18 the point (x, y) lies on the graph of an odd function f. If this point spins half a turn, or 180°, around the origin, its new location is $(-x, -y)$. Thus $f(x) = y$ and $f(-x) = -y$. It follows that $f(-x) = -y = -f(x)$ for any odd function f. Changing the sign of the input only changes the sign of the output. For example, if $g(x) = x^3$, then $g(3) = 27$ and $g(-3) = -27$. Since this is true for *every input*, g is an odd function.

> **ODD FUNCTION**
>
> A function f is an **odd function** if $f(-x) = -f(x)$ for every x in its domain. The graph of an odd function is symmetric with respect to the origin.

Identifying Odd and Even Functions The terms *odd* and *even* have special meaning when they are applied to a polynomial function f. If $f(x)$ contains terms that have only odd powers of x, then f is an odd function. Similarly, if $f(x)$ contains terms that have only even powers of x (and possibly a constant term), then f is an even function. For example, $f(x) = x^6 - 4x^4 - 2x^2 + 5$ is an **even** function, whereas $g(x) = x^5 + 4x^3$ is an **odd** function. This fact can be shown *symbolically*.

$$f(-x) = (-x)^6 - 4(-x)^4 - 2(-x)^2 + 5 \qquad \text{Substitute } -x \text{ for } x.$$
$$= x^6 - 4x^4 - 2x^2 + 5 \qquad \text{Simplify.}$$
$$= f(x) \qquad f \text{ is an even function.}$$

$$g(-x) = (-x)^5 + 4(-x)^3 \qquad \text{Substitute } -x \text{ for } x.$$
$$= -x^5 - 4x^3 \qquad \text{Simplify.}$$
$$= -g(x) \qquad g \text{ is an odd function.}$$

> **CLASS DISCUSSION**
>
> If 0 is in the domain of an odd function f, what point must lie on its graph? Explain your reasoning.

NOTE It is important to remember that the graphs of many functions exhibit *no symmetry* with respect to either the *y*-axis or the origin. These functions are *neither* odd *nor* even.

EXAMPLE 4 Identifying odd and even functions

For each representation of a function f, identify whether f is odd, even, or neither.

(a)

x	-3	-2	-1	0	1	2	3
$f(x)$	10.5	2	-0.5	-2	-0.5	2	10.5

(b)

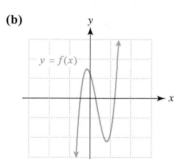

(c) $f(x) = x^3 - 5x$

(d) f is the cube root function.

SOLUTION

Getting Started If either $f(-x) = f(x)$ or its graph is symmetric with respect to the *y*-axis, then f is even. If either $f(-x) = -f(x)$ or its graph is symmetric with respect to the origin, then f is odd. Otherwise, f is neither even nor odd. ▶

(a) The function defined by the table has domain $D = \{-3, -2, -1, 0, 1, 2, 3\}$. Notice that $f(-3) = 10.5 = f(3)$, $f(-2) = 2 = f(2)$, and $f(-1) = -0.5 = f(1)$. The function f satisfies the statement $f(-x) = f(x)$ for every x in D. Thus f is an even function.

(b) If we fold the graph on the *y*-axis, the two halves do not match, so f is *not* an even function. Similarly, f is *not* an odd function since spinning its graph half a turn about the origin does not result in the same graph. The function f is neither odd nor even.

(c) Since f is a polynomial containing only odd powers of x, it is an odd function. This fact can also be shown symbolically.

$$f(-x) = (-x)^3 - 5(-x) \qquad \text{Substitute } -x \text{ for } x.$$
$$= -x^3 + 5x \qquad \text{Simplify.}$$
$$= -(x^3 - 5x) \qquad \text{Distributive property}$$
$$= -f(x) \qquad f \text{ is an odd function.}$$

(d) Note that $\sqrt[3]{-8} = -2$ and that $\sqrt[3]{8} = 2$. In general, $\sqrt[3]{-x} = -\sqrt[3]{x}$, which indicates that $f(-x) = -f(x)$, where $f(x) = \sqrt[3]{x}$. Thus f is an odd function. This fact can also be seen by graphing $f(x) = \sqrt[3]{x}$, as shown in Figure 4.19. Spinning the graph of $f(x) = \sqrt[3]{x}$ a half a turn about the origin results in the same graph.

Now Try Exercises 47, 59, 63, and 71

Algebra Review
To review cube roots, see Chapter R (page R-37).

Cube Root Function

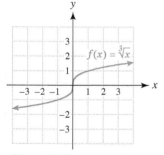

Figure 4.19

CLASS DISCUSSION

Discuss the possibility of the graph of a *function* being symmetric with respect to the *x*-axis.

4.1 Putting It All Together

The following table summarizes some important concepts related to the graphs of nonlinear functions.

CONCEPT	EXPLANATION	GRAPHICAL EXAMPLE
Absolute, or global, maximum (minimum)	The maximum (minimum) y-value on the graph of $y = f(x)$ A graph of a function may or may not have an absolute maximum (minimum).	
Local, or relative, maximum (minimum)	A maximum (minimum) y-value on the graph of $y = f(x)$ in an open interval of the domain of f A graph of a function may or may not have a local maximum (minimum). Note that it is possible for a y-value on the graph of f to be both an absolute maximum (minimum) *and* a local maximum (minimum).	
Even function	$f(-x) = f(x)$ The graph is symmetric with respect to the y-axis. If the graph is folded on the y-axis, the left and right halves match. Changing the sign of the input does not change the output.	
Odd function	$f(-x) = -f(x)$ The graph is symmetric with respect to the origin. If the graph is spun about the origin, the graph reappears after half a turn, or 180°. Changing the sign of the input only changes the sign of the output.	

4.1 Exercises

Note: Many of the answers in this section involve estimations. Your answers may vary slightly, particularly when you are reading a graph.

Polynomials

Exercises 1–10: Determine if the function is a polynomial function. If it is, state its degree and leading coefficient a.

1. $f(x) = 2x^3 - x + 5$ **2.** $f(x) = -x^4 + 1$

3. $f(x) = \sqrt{x}$

4. $f(x) = 2x^3 - \sqrt[3]{x}$

5. $f(x) = 1 - 4x - 5x^4$

6. $f(x) = 5 - 4x$

7. $g(t) = \dfrac{1}{t^2 + 3t - 1}$

8. $g(t) = \dfrac{1}{1 - t}$

9. $g(t) = 22$

10. $g(t) = |2t|$

Finding Extrema of Polynomials

Exercises 11–26: Use the graph of f to estimate the

(a) *local extrema and*

(b) *absolute extrema.*

11.

12.

13.

14.

15.

16.

17.

18.

19.

20.

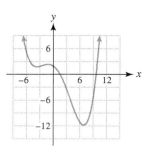

(Hint: *Exercises 21–26: Local extrema cannot occur at end-points because they only occur on open intervals.*)

21.

22.

23.

24.

25.

26.

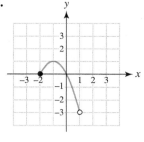

Exercises 27–38: Determine any

(a) *local extrema and*

(b) *absolute extrema.*

(Hint: *Consider the graph* $y = g(x)$.)

27. $g(x) = 1 - 3x$ **28.** $g(x) = \frac{1}{4}x$

29. $g(x) = x^2 + 1$ **30.** $g(x) = 1 - x^2$

31. $g(x) = -2(x + 3)^2 + 4$

32. $g(x) = \frac{1}{3}(x - 1)^2 - 2$

33. $g(x) = 2x^2 - 3x + 1$ **34.** $g(x) = -3x^2 + 4x - 1$

35. $g(x) = |x + 3|$ **36.** $g(x) = -|x| + 2$

37. $g(x) = \sqrt[3]{x}$ **38.** $g(x) = -x^3$

Exercises 39–46: Determine graphically any

(a) *local extrema and*

(b) *absolute extrema.*

39. $g(x) = 3x - x^3$ **40.** $g(x) = \dfrac{1}{1 + |x|}$

41. $f(x) = -3x^4 + 8x^3 + 6x^2 - 24x$

42. $f(x) = -x^4 + 4x^3 - 4x^2$

43. $f(x) = 0.5x^4 - 5x^2 + 4.5$

44. $f(x) = 0.01x^5 + 0.02x^4 - 0.35x^3 - 0.36x^2 + 1.8x$

45. $f(x) = \dfrac{8}{1 + x^2}$ **46.** $f(x) = \dfrac{6}{x^2 + 2x + 2}$

Symmetry

Exercises 47–50: Use the graph to determine if f is odd, even, or neither.

47.

48.

49.

50.

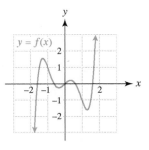

Exercises 51–70: Determine if f is odd, even, or neither.

51. $f(x) = 5x$ **52.** $f(x) = -3x$

53. $f(x) = x + 3$ **54.** $f(x) = 2x - 1$

55. $f(x) = x^2 - 10$ **56.** $f(x) = 8 - 2x^2$

57. $f(x) = x^4 - 6x^2 + 2$ **58.** $f(x) = -x^6 + 5x^2$

59. $f(x) = x^3 - 2x$ **60.** $f(x) = -x^5$

61. $f(x) = x^2 - x^3$ **62.** $f(x) = 3x^3 - 1$

63. $f(x) = \sqrt[3]{x^2}$ **64.** $f(x) = \sqrt{-x}$

65. $f(x) = \sqrt{1 - x^2}$ **66.** $f(x) = \sqrt{x^2}$

67. $f(x) = \dfrac{1}{1 + x^2}$ **68.** $f(x) = \dfrac{1}{x}$

69. $f(x) = |x + 2|$ **70.** $f(x) = \dfrac{1}{x + 1}$

71. The table is a complete representation of f. Decide if f is even, odd, or neither.

x	-100	-10	-1	0	1	10	100
$f(x)$	56	-23	5	0	-5	23	-56

72. The table is a complete representation of f. Decide if f is even, odd, or neither.

x	-5	-3	-1	1	2	3
$f(x)$	-4	-2	1	1	-2	-4

73. Complete the table if f is an even function.

x	-3	-2	-1	0	1	2	3
$f(x)$	21		-25			-12	

74. Complete the table if f is an odd function.

x	-5	-3	-2	0	2	3	5
$f(x)$	13		-5			-1	

75. If the points $(-5, -6)$ and $(-3, 4)$ lie on the graph of an odd function f, then what do $f(5)$ and $f(3)$ equal?

76. If the point $(1 - a, b + 1)$ lies on the graph of an even function f, then what does $f(a - 1)$ equal?

Concepts

77. Sketch a graph of an odd linear function.

78. Sketch a graph of an even linear function.

79. Does there exist a continuous odd function that is always increasing and whose graph passes through the points $(-3, -4)$ and $(2, 5)$? Explain.

80. Is there an even function whose domain is all real numbers and that is always decreasing? Explain.

81. Sketch a graph of a continuous function with an absolute minimum of -3 at $x = -2$ and a local minimum of -1 at $x = 2$.

82. Sketch a graph of a continuous function with no absolute extrema but with a local minimum of -2 at $x = -1$ and a local maximum of 2 at $x = 1$.

83. Sketch a graph of a continuous function that is increasing on $(-\infty, 2)$ and decreasing on $(2, \infty)$. Could this function be quadratic?

84. Sketch a graph of a continuous function with a local maximum of 2 at $x = -1$ and a local maximum of 0 at $x = 1$.

Translations of Graphs

Exercises 85–88: Use the graph of $f(x) = 4x - \frac{1}{3}x^3$ *and translations of graphs to sketch the graph of the equation.*

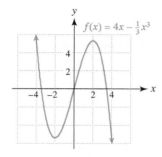

85. $y = f(x + 1)$ **86.** $y = f(x) - 2$

87. $y = 2f(x)$ **88.** $y = f\left(\frac{1}{2}x\right)$

89. If the graph of $y = f(x)$ is increasing on $(1, 4)$, then where is the graph of $y = f(x + 1) - 2$ increasing? Where is the graph of $y = -f(x - 2)$ decreasing?

90. If the graph of f is decreasing on $(0, \infty)$, then what can be said about the graph of $y = f(-x) + 1$? The graph of $y = -f(x) - 1$?

Applications

91. Temperature in Sunlight   The graph shows the temperature readings of a thermometer (on a partly cloudy day) x hours past noon.

(a) Identify the absolute maximum and minimum. Interpret each.

(b) Identify any local maximums and minimums. (Do not consider the endpoints.)

(c) For what x-values was the temperature increasing?

92. Daytona Beach   (Refer to the introduction to this section.) The graph at the top of the next column shows the monthly average high temperatures at Daytona Beach.

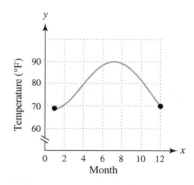

(a) Identify the absolute maximum and minimum.

(b) Identify a local maximum.

(c) For what x-values was the temperature increasing?

93. Facebook Versus Yahoo   During 2009, Facebook surpassed Yahoo for the greatest number of unique monthly users. The formula

$$F(x) = 0.0484x^3 - 1.504x^2 + 17.7x + 53$$

models these numbers in millions of unique monthly users x months after December 2008.

(a) Evaluate $F(1)$ and $F(12)$. Interpret the result.

(b) Graph $y = F(x)$ in $[0, 13, 2]$ by $[0, 150, 25]$. Does F have any local extrema for $1 \le x \le 12$?

(c) Where is F increasing if its domain is $1 \le x \le 12$?

94. Google+ Users   Google+ experienced an increase in the number of users between July 1, 2011 and February 1, 2012. The total number of users in millions can be modeled by the polynomial function

$$G(x) = 0.000014437x^3 - 0.00406x^2 + 0.603x + 3.7,$$

where x represents days after July 1, 2011.

(a) Evaluate $G(31)$ and interpret the result.

(b) Graph $y = G(x)$ in $[0, 215, 20]$ by $[0, 90, 10]$. Does G have any local extrema for $0 \le x \le 215$?

(c) Where is G increasing if its domain is $0 \le x \le 215$?

95. Heating Costs   In colder climates the cost for natural gas to heat homes can vary from one month to the next. The polynomial function given by

$$f(x) = -0.1213x^4 + 3.462x^3 - 29.22x^2 + 64.68x + 97.69$$

models the monthly cost in dollars of heating a typical home. The input x represents the month, where $x = 1$ corresponds to January and $x = 12$ to December.

(a) Where might the absolute extrema occur for $1 \le x \le 12$?

(b) Graph f in $[1, 12, 1]$ by $[0, 150, 10]$. Find the absolute extrema and interpret the results.

96. Natural Gas The U.S. consumption of natural gas from 1965 to 1980 can be modeled by

$$f(x) = 0.0001234x^4 - 0.005689x^3 + 0.08792x^2 - 0.5145x + 1.514,$$

where $x = 6$ corresponds to 1966 and $x = 20$ to 1980. Consumption is measured in trillion cubic feet. (*Source: Department of Energy.*)

(a) Evaluate $f(10)$ and interpret the result.

(b) Graph f in [6, 20, 5] by [0.4, 0.8, 0.1]. Describe the energy usage during this time period.

(c) Determine the local extrema and interpret the results.

97. Average Temperature The graph approximates the monthly *average* temperatures in degrees Fahrenheit in Austin, Texas. In this graph x represents the month, where $x = 0$ corresponds to July.

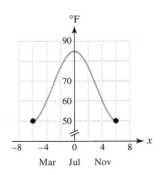

(a) Is this a graph of an odd or even function?

(b) June corresponds to $x = -1$ and August to $x = 1$. The average temperature in June is 83°F. What is the average temperature in August?

(c) March corresponds to $x = -4$ and November to $x = 4$. According to the graph, how do their average temperatures compare?

(d) Interpret what this type of symmetry implies about average temperatures in Austin.

98. Height of a Projectile When a projectile is shot into the air, it attains a maximum height and then falls back to the ground. Suppose that $x = 0$ corresponds to the time when the projectile's height is maximum. If air resistance is ignored, its height h above the ground at any time x may be modeled by $h(x) = -16x^2 + h_{max}$, where h_{max} is the projectile's maximum height above the ground. Height is measured in feet and time in seconds. Let $h_{max} = 400$ feet.

(a) Evaluate $h(-2)$ and $h(2)$. Interpret these results.

(b) Evaluate $h(-5)$ and $h(5)$. Interpret these results.

(c) Graph h for $-5 \le x \le 5$. Is h even or odd?

(d) How do the values of $h(x)$ and $h(-x)$ compare for $-5 \le x \le 5$? What does this result indicate?

Writing About Mathematics

99. Explain the difference between a local and an absolute maximum. Are extrema x-values or y-values?

100. Describe ways to determine if a polynomial function is odd, even, or neither. Give examples.

101. If an odd function f has one local maximum of 5 at $x = 3$, then what else can be said about f? Explain.

102. If an even function f has an absolute minimum of -6 at $x = -2$, then what else can be said about f? Explain.

Extended and Discovery Exercises

1. Maximizing Area Find the dimensions of the rectangle of maximum area that can be inscribed in a semicircle with radius 3. Assume that the rectangle is positioned as shown in the accompanying figure.

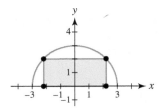

2. Minimizing Area A piece of wire 20 inches long is cut into two pieces. One piece is bent into a square and the other is bent into an equilateral triangle, as illustrated.

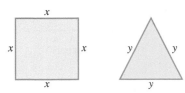

(a) Write a formula that gives the area A of the two shapes in terms of x.

(b) Find the length of wire (to the nearest tenth of an inch) that should be used for the square if the combined area of the two shapes is to be minimized?

3. **Minimizing Time** A person is in a rowboat 3 miles from the closest point on a straight shoreline, as illustrated in the figure. The person would like to reach a cabin that is 8 miles down the shoreline. The person can row at 4 miles per hour and jog at 7 miles per hour.

(a) How long will it take to reach the cabin if the person rows straight toward shore at point A and then jogs to the cabin?

(b) How long will it take to reach the cabin if the person rows straight to the cabin and does no jogging?

(c) Find the minimum time to reach the cabin.

4.2 Polynomial Functions and Models

- **Understand the graphs of polynomial functions**
- **Evaluate and graph piecewise-defined functions**
- **Use polynomial regression to model data (optional)**

Introduction

The consumption of natural gas by the United States has varied in the past. As shown in Table 4.2, energy consumption (in quadrillion Btu) increased, decreased, and then increased again. A scatterplot of the data is shown in Figure 4.20, and one possibility for a polynomial modeling function f is shown in Figure 4.21. Notice that f is neither linear nor quadratic. What degree of polynomial might we use to model these data? This question is answered in Example 4.

Natural Gas Consumption

Year	1960	1970	1980	1990	2000
Consumption	12.4	21.8	20.4	19.3	24.0

Table 4.2 *Source:* Department of Energy.

Figure 4.20

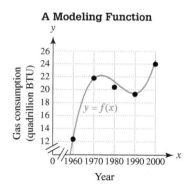

Figure 4.21

Graphs of Polynomial Functions

In Section 4.1 polynomial functions were defined. The following Making Connections helps show the relationship among polynomials, polynomial functions, and polynomial equations with one variable.

MAKING CONNECTIONS

Polynomials, Functions, and Equations

Polynomial of Degree _n_

Degree _n_ (largest exponent)

$$a_n x^n + a_{n-1}x^{n-1} + \cdots + a_2 x^2 + a_1 x + a_0$$

Leading coefficient   Terms   Constant term

Example: $x^3 - 3x^2 + x - 5$ is a polynomial.

Polynomial Function of Degree _n_

$$f(x) = a_n x^n + a_{n-1}x^{n-1} + \cdots + a_2 x^2 + a_1 x + a_0$$

Domain: All real numbers

Graph is continuous and smooth; no breaks or sharp edges.

Example: $f(x) = x^3 - 3x^2 + x - 5$ defines a polynomial function.

Polynomial Equation of Degree _n_

$$a_n x^n + a_{n-1}x^{n-1} + \cdots + a_2 x^2 + a_1 x + a_0 = 0$$

At most _n_ real solutions (See Section 4.4)

Example: $x^3 - 3x^2 + x - 5 = 0$ is a polynomial equation.

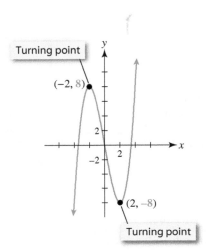

Turning point

$(-2, 8)$

$(2, -8)$

Turning point

Figure 4.22

A **turning point** occurs whenever the graph of a polynomial function changes from increasing to decreasing or from decreasing to increasing. Turning points are associated with "hills" or "valleys" on a graph. The _y_-value at a turning point is either a local maximum or a local minimum of the function. In Figure 4.22 the graph has two turning points, $(-2, 8)$ and $(2, -8)$. A local maximum is 8 and a local minimum is -8.

We discuss the graphs of polynomial functions, starting with degree 0 and continuing to degree 5. Look for patterns in the graphs of these polynomial functions.

Constant Polynomial Functions If $f(x) = a$ and $a \neq 0$, then f is both a constant function and a polynomial function of **degree 0.** (If $a = 0$, then f has an **undefined degree.**) Its graph is a horizontal line that does not coincide with the _x_-axis. Graphs of two constant functions are shown in Figures 4.23 and 4.24. A graph of a polynomial function of degree 0 has no _x_-intercepts or turning points.

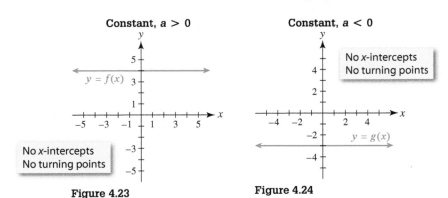

Constant, _a_ > 0

No _x_-intercepts
No turning points

$y = f(x)$

Figure 4.23

Constant, _a_ < 0

No _x_-intercepts
No turning points

$y = g(x)$

Figure 4.24

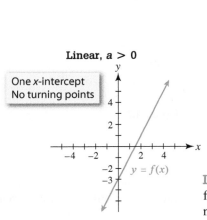

Linear, _a_ > 0

One _x_-intercept
No turning points

$y = f(x)$

Figure 4.25

Linear Polynomial Functions If $f(x) = ax + b$ and $a \neq 0$, then f is both a linear function and a polynomial function of **degree 1.** Its graph is a line that is neither horizontal nor vertical. The graphs of two linear functions are shown in Figures 4.25 and 4.26. A polynomial function of degree 1 has one _x_-intercept and no turning points.

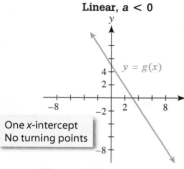

Linear, a < 0

One x-intercept
No turning points

Figure 4.26

The graph of $f(x) = ax + b$ with $a > 0$ is a line sloping upward from left to right. As one traces from left to right, the y-values become larger without a maximum. We say that the **end behavior** of the graph tends to $-\infty$ on the left and ∞ on the right. (Strictly speaking, the graph of a polynomial has infinite length and does not have an end.) More formally, we say that $f(x) \rightarrow -\infty$ as $x \rightarrow -\infty$ and $f(x) \rightarrow \infty$ as $x \rightarrow \infty$.

If $a < 0$, then the end behavior is reversed. The line slopes downward from left to right. The y-values on the left side of the graph become large positive values without a maximum and the y-values on the right side become negative without a minimum. The end behavior tends to ∞ on the left and $-\infty$ on the right, or $f(x) \rightarrow \infty$ as $x \rightarrow -\infty$ and $f(x) \rightarrow -\infty$ as $x \rightarrow \infty$.

Quadratic Polynomial Functions If $f(x) = ax^2 + bx + c$ and $a \neq 0$, then f is both a quadratic function and a polynomial function of **degree 2.** Its graph is a parabola that opens either upward ($a > 0$) or downward ($a < 0$). The graphs of three quadratic functions are shown in Figures 4.27–4.29, respectively. Quadratic functions can have zero, one, or two x-intercepts. A parabola has *exactly one* turning point, which is also the vertex.

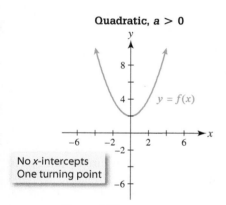

Quadratic, a > 0

No x-intercepts
One turning point

Figure 4.27

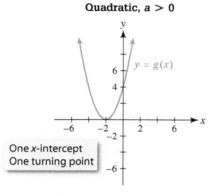

Quadratic, a > 0

One x-intercept
One turning point

Figure 4.28

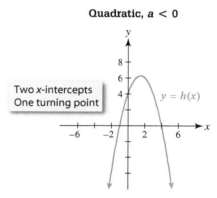

Quadratic, a < 0

Two x-intercepts
One turning point

Figure 4.29

If $a > 0$, as in Figure 4.27, then both sides of the graph go up. The end behavior tends to ∞ on both sides, or $f(x) \rightarrow \infty$ as $x \rightarrow \pm\infty$. If $a < 0$, as in Figure 4.29, then the end behavior is reversed and tends to $-\infty$ on both sides, or $f(x) \rightarrow -\infty$ as $x \rightarrow \pm\infty$.

Cubic Polynomial Functions If $f(x) = ax^3 + bx^2 + cx + d$ and $a \neq 0$, then f is both a **cubic function** and a polynomial function of **degree 3.** The graph of a cubic function can have zero or two turning points. The graph of $y = f(x)$ in Figure 4.30 has two turning points, whereas the graph of $y = g(x)$ in Figure 4.31 has no turning points.

Cubic, a < 0

$y = f(x)$

Three x-intercepts
Two turning points

Figure 4.30

Cubic, a > 0

One x-intercept
No turning points

$y = g(x)$

Figure 4.31

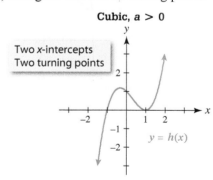

Cubic, a > 0

Two x-intercepts
Two turning points

$y = h(x)$

Figure 4.32

If $a > 0$, the graph of a cubic function falls to the left and rises to the right, as in Figure 4.31. If $a < 0$, its graph rises to the left and falls to the right, as in Figure 4.30. The end behavior of a cubic function is similar to that of a linear function, tending to ∞ on one side and $-\infty$ on the other. Therefore its graph must cross the x-axis at least once. A cubic function can have up to three x-intercepts. The graph of $y = h(x)$ in Figure 4.32 has two x-intercepts.

CLASS DISCUSSION

Can a quartic function have both an absolute maximum and an absolute minimum? Explain.

Quartic Polynomial Functions   If $f(x) = ax^4 + bx^3 + cx^2 + dx + e$ and $a \neq 0$, then f is both a **quartic function** and a polynomial function of **degree 4**. The graph of a quartic function can have up to four x-intercepts and three turning points; the graph of $y = f(x)$ in Figure 4.33 is an example. The graph in Figure 4.34 of $y = g(x)$ has one turning point and two x-intercepts, and the graph in Figure 4.35 of $y = h(x)$ has three turning points and three x-intercepts.

If $a > 0$, then both ends of the graph of a quartic function go up, as in Figure 4.33. If $a < 0$, then both ends of its graph go down, as in Figures 4.34 and 4.35. The end behaviors of quartic and quadratic functions are similar.

Figure 4.33

Figure 4.34

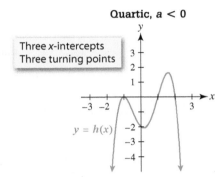

Figure 4.35

CLASS DISCUSSION

Can you sketch the graph of a quadratic function with no turning points, a cubic function with one turning point, or a quartic function with two turning points? Explain.

Quintic Polynomial Functions   If $f(x) = ax^5 + bx^4 + cx^3 + dx^2 + ex + k$ and $a \neq 0$, then f is both a **quintic function** and a polynomial function of **degree 5**. The graph of a quintic function may have up to five x-intercepts and four turning points. An example is shown in Figure 4.36. Other quintic functions are shown in Figures 4.37 and 4.38. The graph of g has one x-intercept and no turning points. The graph of h appears to have two x-intercepts and two turning points. Notice that the end behavior of a quintic function is similar to that of linear and cubic functions.

Figure 4.36

Figure 4.37

Figure 4.38

The maximum numbers of x-intercepts and turning points on the graph of a polynomial function of degree n can be summarized as follows.

DEGREE, x-INTERCEPTS, AND TURNING POINTS

The graph of a polynomial function of degree n, with $n \geq 1$, has at most n x-intercepts and at most $n - 1$ turning points.

The end behavior of a polynomial function depends on whether its degree is even or odd and whether its leading coefficient is positive or negative. The following See the Concept summarizes this discussion. The region inside the oval indicates where the graph might have x-intercepts and turning points.

See the Concept: End Behavior of Polynomial Functions

Even degree

Odd degree

A Up   B Up   F Up   G Up

$a > 0$ $a > 0$

$y = f(x)$ $y = f(x)$

$y = f(x)$ $a < 0$ $y = f(x)$ $a < 0$

C Down   D Down   E Down   H Down

A $f(x) \to \infty$ as $x \to -\infty$ C $f(x) \to -\infty$ as $x \to -\infty$ E $f(x) \to -\infty$ as $x \to -\infty$ G $f(x) \to \infty$ as $x \to -\infty$

B $f(x) \to \infty$ as $x \to \infty$ D $f(x) \to -\infty$ as $x \to \infty$ F $f(x) \to \infty$ as $x \to \infty$ H $f(x) \to -\infty$ as $x \to \infty$

EXAMPLE 1 Analyzing the graph of a polynomial function

Figure 4.39 shows the graph of a polynomial function f.
(a) How many turning points and how many x-intercepts are there?
(b) Is the leading coefficient a positive or negative? Is the degree odd or even?
(c) Determine the minimum possible degree of f.

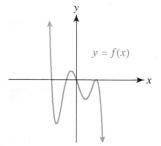

$y = f(x)$

Figure 4.39

SOLUTION
(a) There are four turning points corresponding to the two "hills" and two "valleys." There appear to be four x-intercepts.
(b) The left side of the graph rises and the right side falls. Therefore $a < 0$ and the polynomial function has odd degree.
(c) The graph has four turning points. A polynomial of degree n can have at most $n - 1$ turning points. Therefore f must be *at least* degree 5.

Now Try Exercise 7

NOTE More examples of graphs of polynomials and their characteristics are found in the "Putting It All Together" for this section.

EXAMPLE 2 Analyzing the graph of a polynomial function

Graph $f(x) = x^3 - 2x^2 - 5x + 6$, and then complete the following.
(a) Identify the x-intercepts.
(b) Approximate the coordinates of any turning points to the nearest hundredth.
(c) Use the turning points to approximate any local extrema.

SOLUTION
(a) A calculator graph of f, shown in Figure 4.40 on the next page, *appears* to intersect the x-axis at the points $(-2, 0)$, $(1, 0)$, and $(3, 0)$. Because $f(-2) = 0$, $f(1) = 0$, and $f(3) = 0$, the x-intercepts are $-2, 1$, and 3.

Calculator Help
To find a minimum or maximum point on a graph, see Appendix A (page AP-8).

(b) There are two turning points. From Figures 4.41 and 4.42 their coordinates are approximately $(-0.79, 8.21)$ and $(2.12, -4.06)$.

(c) There is a local maximum of about 8.21 and a local minimum of about -4.06.

Given Function
$[-10, 10, 1]$ by $[-10, 10, 1]$

x-intercepts: $-2, 1, 3$

$y = x^3 - 2x^2 - 5x + 6$

Figure 4.40

Local Maximum ≈ 8.21
$[-10, 10, 1]$ by $[-10, 10, 1]$

Maximum
X=⁻.7862976 Y=8.2088207

Figure 4.41

Local Minimum ≈ -4.06
$[-10, 10, 1]$ by $[-10, 10, 1]$

Minimum
X=2.1196339 Y=⁻4.060673

Figure 4.42

Now Try Exercise 25

EXAMPLE 3 Analyzing the end behavior of a graph

Let $f(x) = 2 + 3x - 3x^2 - 2x^3$.
(a) Give the degree and leading coefficient.
(b) State the end behavior of the graph of f.

SOLUTION
(a) Rewriting gives $f(x) = -2x^3 - 3x^2 + 3x + 2$. The term with highest degree is $-2x^3$, so the degree is 3 and the leading coefficient is -2.
(b) The degree of $f(x)$ is odd, and the leading coefficient is negative. Therefore the graph of f rises to the left and falls to the right. More formally,

$$f(x) \to \infty \text{ as } x \to -\infty \quad \text{and} \quad f(x) \to -\infty \text{ as } x \to \infty.$$

This conclusion is supported by Figure 4.43.

Now Try Exercise 33

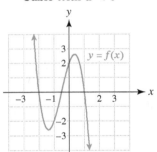

Cubic with $a < 0$

$y = f(x)$

Figure 4.43

An Application In the next example, we analyze the data presented in the introduction to this section.

EXAMPLE 4 Modeling natural gas consumption

Figure 4.20, which shows natural gas consumption from 1960 to 2000, is repeated in the margin.
(a) Could a linear or quadratic function model the data?
(b) What minimum degree polynomial might be appropriate to model the data?
(c) Should the leading coefficient a be positive or negative?

SOLUTION
(a) The data clearly do not lie on a line, so a linear function is not appropriate. Because natural gas consumption increases, decreases, and then increases, a quadratic function would not be a good choice either. The data are not $\cup$-shaped or $\cap$-shaped.
(b) Because the data increase, decrease, and then increase, a polynomial with at least two turning points would be appropriate. A cubic, or degree 3, polynomial is a possibility for a modeling function.
(c) The leading coefficient a should be positive because the data fall to the left and rise to the right.

Now Try Exercises 39(a), (b), and (c)

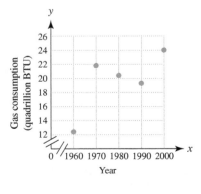

Concavity (Optional)   Graphs of polynomial functions with degree 2 or greater are curves. **Concavity** is a mathematical description of how a curve bends. A line exhibits no, or zero, concavity because it is straight. A parabola that opens upward is said to be **concave upward** everywhere on its domain. See Figure 4.44. A parabola that opens downward is said to be **concave downward** everywhere on its domain. See Figure 4.45. A graph of a higher degree polynomial can be concave upward on one interval of its domain and concave downward on a different interval of its domain. See Figure 4.46, where the graph of $f(x) = 4x - x^3$ is concave upward on the interval $(-\infty, 0)$, shown in blue, and concave downward on $(0, \infty)$, shown in red. Concavity is usually defined for *open* intervals. Determining the exact x-value where a graph switches from concave upward to downward or vice versa can be difficult to do visually and often requires techniques learned in calculus. This point is called the **point of inflection**. (See Extended and Discovery Exercises 2–7 for this section.)

Graphs with Concavity

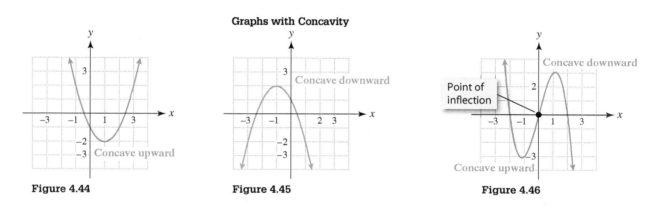

Figure 4.44   Figure 4.45   Figure 4.46

Piecewise-Defined Polynomial Functions

In Section 2.4 piecewise-defined functions were discussed. If each piece is a polynomial, then the function is a **piecewise-defined polynomial function** or **piecewise-polynomial function**. An example is given by $f(x)$.

$$f(x) = \begin{cases} x^3 & \text{if } x < 1 \\ x^2 - 1 & \text{if } x \geq 1 \end{cases}$$

First piece

Second piece

One way to graph f is to first graph $y = x^3$ and $y = x^2 - 1$, as shown in Figures 4.47 and 4.48. Then the graph of f is found by using the blue portion of $y = x^3$ for $x < 1$ and the blue portion of $y = x^2 - 1$ for $x \geq 1$, as illustrated in Figure 4.49. At $x = 1$ there is a break in the graph, where the graph of f is discontinuous.

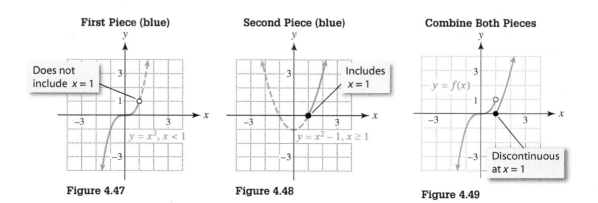

First Piece (blue)   Second Piece (blue)   Combine Both Pieces

Figure 4.47   Figure 4.48   Figure 4.49

EXAMPLE 5 Evaluating a piecewise-defined polynomial function

Evaluate $f(x)$ at $x = -3, -2, 1,$ and 2.

$$f(x) = \begin{cases} x^2 - x & \text{if } -5 \leq x < -2 \\ -x^3 & \text{if } -2 \leq x < 2 \\ 4 - 4x & \text{if } 2 \leq x \leq 5 \end{cases}$$

SOLUTION To evaluate $f(-3)$ we use the formula $f(x) = x^2 - x$, because -3 is in the interval $-5 \leq x < -2$.

$$f(-3) = (-3)^2 - (-3) = 12$$

To evaluate $f(-2)$ we use $f(x) = -x^3$, because -2 is in the interval $-2 \leq x < 2$.

$$f(-2) = -(-2)^3 = -(-8) = 8$$

Similarly, $f(1) = -1^3 = -1$ and $f(2) = 4 - 4(2) = -4$.

Now Try Exercise 73

EXAMPLE 6 Graphing a piecewise-defined function

Complete the following.
(a) Sketch a graph of f.
(b) Determine if f is continuous on its domain.
(c) Solve the equation $f(x) = 1$.

$$f(x) = \begin{cases} \frac{1}{2}x^2 - 2 & \text{if } -4 \leq x \leq 0 \\ 2x - 2 & \text{if } 0 < x < 2 \\ 2 & \text{if } 2 \leq x \leq 4 \end{cases}$$

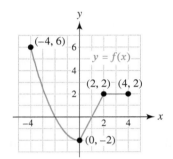

Figure 4.50

SOLUTION
(a) For the first piece, graph the parabola determined by $y = \frac{1}{2}x^2 - 2$ on the interval $-4 \leq x \leq 0$. Place dots at the endpoints, which are $(-4, 6)$ and $(0, -2)$. See Figure 4.50. For the second piece, graph the line determined by $y = 2x - 2$ *between* the points $(0, -2)$ and $(2, 2)$. Note that the left endpoint of the middle piece coincides with the right endpoint of the first piece. Finally, graph the horizontal line $y = 2$ from the points $(2, 2)$ to $(4, 2)$. Note that the left endpoint of the third piece coincides with the right endpoint of the middle piece.
(b) The domain of f is $-4 \leq x \leq 4$. Because there are no breaks in the graph of f on its domain, the graph of f is continuous.
(c) The red horizontal line $y = 1$ intersects the blue graph of $y = f(x)$ at two points, as shown in Figure 4.51. The x-coordinates of these two points of intersection coincide with the green segments and can be found by solving the equations

$$\frac{1}{2}x^2 - 2 = 1 \quad \text{and} \quad 2x - 2 = 1.$$

Solving $f(x) = 1$

Figure 4.51

The solutions are $-\sqrt{6} \approx -2.45$ and $\frac{3}{2}$.

Now Try Exercise 79

An Application When there is a small number of fishing boats in a large area of water, each boat tends to catch its limit each trip. As the number of boats increases dramatically, there comes a point of **diminishing returns**, where the yield for each boat begins to decrease even though the total number of fish caught by all fishing boats continues to increase. This phenomenon can be modeled by a piecewise-polynomial function F defined by

$$F(x) = \begin{cases} x & \text{if } 0 \leq x \leq 5 \\ -0.08x^2 + 1.6x - 1 & \text{if } 5 \leq x \leq 15 \end{cases}$$

where x is the number of fishing boats in hundreds and $F(x)$ outputs thousands of tons of fish harvested. A graph of F is shown in Figure 4.52.

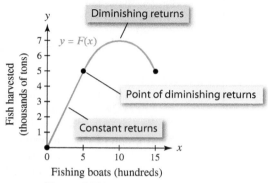

Figure 4.52

EXAMPLE 7 Analyzing diminishing returns

Use the preceding discussion to complete the following.
(a) Evaluate $F(2)$ and interpret the result.
(b) Find the absolute maximum on the graph of F and interpret the result.

SOLUTION
(a) For $0 \leq x \leq 5$, $F(x) = x$, so $F(2) = 2$. When 200 fishing boats are used, 2 thousand tons of fish are harvested.
(b) The second piece is $F(x) = -0.08x^2 + 1.6x - 1$, so its graph is a parabola opening downward. To find the absolute maximum, we first need to find its vertex.

$$x = -\frac{b}{2a} \qquad \text{Vertex formula}$$

$$= -\frac{1.6}{2(-0.08)} \qquad \text{Substitute.}$$

$$= 10 \qquad \text{x-coordinate of vertex}$$

Because $F(10) = -0.08(10)^2 + 1.6(10) - 1 = 7$, the vertex is $(10, 7)$. This result means that 7 thousand tons of fish is the maximum amount of fish that can be caught in these waters and it occurs when 1000 fishing vessels are used. If more boats are used, there is a decrease in the overall catch.

Now Try Exercise 83

Polynomial Regression (Optional)

We now have the mathematical understanding to model the data presented in the introduction to this section. The polynomial modeling function f (shown in Figure 4.21 and repeated in the margin) falls to the left and rises to the right, so it has odd degree and the leading coefficient is positive. Since the graph of f has two turning points, it must be at least degree 3. A cubic polynomial $f(x)$ is a possible choice, where

$$f(x) = ax^3 + bx^2 + cx + d.$$

Trial and error would be a difficult way to find values for a, b, c, and d. Instead, we can use least-squares regression, which was also discussed in Sections 2.1 and 3.1, for linear and quadratic functions. The next example illustrates *cubic regression*.

Natural Gas Usage

Year

EXAMPLE 8 Determining a cubic modeling function

The data in Table 4.2 (repeated in the margin) lists natural gas consumption.
(a) Find a polynomial function of degree 3 that models the data.
(b) Graph f and the data together.
(c) Estimate natural gas consumption in 1974 and in 2010. Compare these estimates to the actual values of 21.2 and 24.9 quadrillion Btu, respectively.
(d) Did your estimates in part (c) involve interpolation or extrapolation? Is there a problem with using higher degree polynomials ($n \geq 3$) for extrapolation? Explain.

Year	Consumption
1960	12.4
1970	21.8
1980	20.4
1990	19.3
2000	24.0

SOLUTION
(a) Enter the five data points (1960, 12.4), (1970, 21.8), (1980, 20.4), (1990, 19.3), and (2000, 24.0) into your calculator. Then select cubic regression, as shown in Figure 4.53. The equation for $f(x)$ is shown in Figure 4.54.
(b) A graph of f and a scatterplot of the data are shown in Figure 4.55.
(c) $f(1974) \approx 21.9$ and $f(2010) \approx 44.5$; the 1974 estimate is reasonably close to 21.2, whereas the 2010 estimate is not close to 24.9.
(d) The 1974 estimate uses interpolation, and the 2010 estimate uses extrapolation. Because the end behavior of a higher degree polynomial rapidly tends to either ∞ or $-\infty$, extrapolation-based estimates are usually inaccurate with higher degree polynomials.

Calculator Help

To find an equation of least-squares fit, see Appendix A (page AP-9). To copy a regression equation into Y_1, see Appendix A (page AP-11.)

Select Cubic Regression

```
EDIT CALC TESTS
1:1-Var Stats
2:2-Var Stats
3:Med-Med
4:LinReg(ax+b)
5:QuadReg
6:CubicReg
7↓QuartReg
```

Figure 4.53

Regression Equation

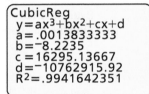

```
CubicReg
y=ax³+bx²+cx+d
a=.0013833333
b=-8.2235
c=16295.13667
d=-10762915.92
R²=.9941642351
```

Figure 4.54

Graph of f and Data
[1955, 2005, 5] by [10, 25, 5]

$y = f(x)$

Figure 4.55

Now Try Exercise 91

4.2 Putting It All Together

Higher degree polynomials generally have more complicated graphs. Each additional degree allows the graph to have one more possible turning point and x-intercept. The graph of a polynomial function is continuous and smooth; it has no breaks or sharp edges. Its domain includes all real numbers. The end behavior of a polynomial always tends to either ∞ or $-\infty$. End behavior describes what happens to the y-values as $|x|$ becomes large.

FUNCTION TYPE	CHARACTERISTICS	EXAMPLE GRAPHS	
Constant (degree 0)	No x-intercepts and no turning points $f(x) = a, a \neq 0$	$a > 0$	$a < 0$

FUNCTION TYPE	CHARACTERISTICS	EXAMPLE GRAPHS
Linear (degree 1)	One x-intercept and no turning points $f(x) = ax + b, a \neq 0$	
Quadratic (degree 2)	At most two x-intercepts and exactly one turning point $f(x) = ax^2 + bx + c, a \neq 0$	
Cubic (degree 3)	At most three x-intercepts and up to two turning points $f(x) = ax^3 + bx^2 + cx + d, a \neq 0$	
Quartic (degree 4)	At most four x-intercepts and up to three turning points $f(x) = ax^4 + bx^3 + cx^2 + dx + e, a \neq 0$	
Quintic (degree 5)	At most five x-intercepts and up to four turning points $f(x) = ax^5 + bx^4 + cx^3 + dx^2 + ex + k, a \neq 0$	

4.2 Exercises

Note: Many of the answers in this section involve estimations. Your answers may vary slightly, particularly when you are reading a graph.

Graphs of Polynomial Functions

1. A runner is working out on a straight track. The graph on the next page shows the runner's distance y in hundreds of feet from the starting line after t minutes.

(a) Estimate the turning points.

(b) Interpret each turning point.

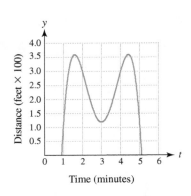

2. A stone is thrown into the air. Its height y in feet after t seconds is shown in the graph. Use the graph to complete the following.

   (a) Estimate the turning point.

   (b) Interpret this point.

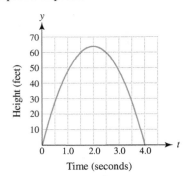

Exercises 3–12: Use the graph of the polynomial function f to complete the following. Let a be the leading coefficient of the polynomial $f(x)$.

(a) Determine the number of turning points and estimate any x-intercepts.

(b) State whether $a > 0$ or $a < 0$.

(c) Determine the minimum degree of f.

3.

4.

5.

6.

7.

8.

9.

10.

11.

12.

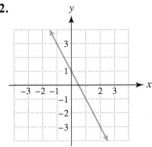

Exercises 13–18: Complete the following without a calculator.

(a) Match the equation with its graph (a–f).
(b) Identify the turning points.
(c) Estimate the x-intercepts.
(d) Estimate any local extrema.
(e) Estimate any absolute extrema.

13. $f(x) = 1 - 2x + x^2$

14. $f(x) = 3x - x^3$

15. $f(x) = x^3 + 3x^2 - 9x$

16. $f(x) = x^4 - 8x^2$

17. $f(x) = 8x^2 - x^4$

18. $f(x) = x^5 + \frac{5}{2}x^4 - \frac{5}{3}x^3 - 5x^2$

a.

b.

c.

d.

e.

f.

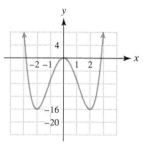

Modeling Data with Polynomials

Exercises 39–44: The data are modeled exactly by a linear, quadratic, cubic, or quartic function f with leading coefficient a. All zeros of f are real numbers located in the interval $[-3, 3]$.

(a) Make a line graph of the data.
(b) State the minimum degree of f.
(c) Is $a > 0$ or is $a < 0$?
(d) Find a formula for $f(x)$.

39.

x	−3	−2	−1	0	1	2	3
$f(x)$	3	−8	−7	0	7	8	−3

40.

x	−3	−2	−1	0	1	2	3
$f(x)$	11	9	7	5	3	1	−1

41.

x	−3	−2	−1	0	1	2	3
$f(x)$	14	7	2	−1	−2	−1	2

42.

x	−3	−2	−1	0	1	2	3
$f(x)$	−13	−6	−1	2	3	2	−1

43.

x	−3	−2	−1	0	1	2	3
$f(x)$	−55	−5	1	−1	1	−5	−55

44.

x	−3	−2	−1	0	1	2	3
$f(x)$	−15	0	3	0	−3	0	15

Sketching Graphs of Polynomials

Exercises 45–56: If possible, sketch a graph of a polynomial that satisfies the conditions. Let a be the leading coefficient.

45. Degree 3 with three real zeros and $a > 0$

46. Degree 4 with four real zeros and $a < 0$

47. Linear with $a < 0$

48. Cubic with one real zero and $a > 0$

49. Degree 4 and an even function with four turning points

50. Degree 5 and symmetric with respect to the y-axis

51. Degree 3 and an odd function with no x-intercepts

52. Degree 6 and an odd function with five turning points

53. Degree 3 with turning points $(-1, 2)$ and $\left(1, \frac{2}{3}\right)$

Exercises 19–26: Complete the following.

(a) Graph $y = f(x)$ in the standard viewing rectangle.
(b) Approximate the coordinates of each turning point.
(c) Estimate any local extrema.

19. $f(x) = \frac{1}{9}x^3 - 3x$

20. $f(x) = x^2 - 4x - 3$

21. $f(x) = 0.025x^4 - 0.45x^2 - 5$

22. $f(x) = -\frac{1}{8}x^4 + \frac{1}{3}x^3 + \frac{5}{4}x^2 - 3x + 3$

23. $f(x) = 1 - 2x + 3x^2$

24. $f(x) = 4x - \frac{1}{3}x^3$

25. $f(x) = \frac{1}{3}x^3 + \frac{1}{2}x^2 - 2x$

26. $f(x) = \frac{1}{4}x^4 + \frac{2}{3}x^3 - \frac{1}{2}x^2 - 2x + 1$

Exercises 27–38: Complete the following.

(a) State the degree and leading coefficient of f.
(b) State the end behavior of the graph of f.

27. $f(x) = -2x + 3$ **28.** $f(x) = \frac{2}{3}x - 2$

29. $f(x) = x^2 + 4x$ **30.** $f(x) = 5 - \frac{1}{2}x^2$

31. $f(x) = -2x^3$ **32.** $f(x) = 4x - \frac{1}{3}x^3$

33. $f(x) = x^2 - x^3 - 4$

34. $f(x) = x^4 - 4x^3 + 3x^2 - 3$

35. $f(x) = 0.1x^5 - 2x^2 - 3x + 4$

36. $f(x) = 3x^3 - 2 - x^4$

37. $f(x) = 4 + 2x - \frac{1}{2}x^2$

38. $f(x) = -0.2x^5 + 4x^2 - 3$

54. Degree 4 with turning points $(-1, -1), (0, 0)$, and $(1, -1)$

55. Degree 2 with turning point $(-1, 2)$, passing through $(-3, 4)$ and $(1, 4)$

56. Degree 5 and an odd function with five x-intercepts and a negative leading coefficient.

Dominant Term of a Polynomial

Exercises 57 and 58: Graph the functions f, g, and h in the same viewing rectangle. What happens to their graphs as the size of the viewing rectangle increases? Explain why the term of highest degree in a polynomial is sometimes called the **dominant term.**

57. $f(x) = 2x^4, g(x) = 2x^4 - 5x^2 + 1$, and $h(x) = 2x^4 + 3x^2 - x - 2$
   (a) $[-4, 4, 1]$ by $[-4, 4, 1]$

   (b) $[-10, 10, 1]$ by $[-100, 100, 10]$

   (c) $[-100, 100, 10]$ by $[-10^6, 10^6, 10^5]$

58. $f(x) = -x^3, g(x) = -x^3 + x^2 + 2$, and $h(x) = -x^3 - 2x^2 + x - 1$
   (a) $[-4, 4, 1]$ by $[-4, 4, 1]$

   (b) $[-10, 10, 1]$ by $[-100, 100, 10]$

   (c) $[-100, 100, 10]$ by $[-10^5, 10^5, 10^4]$

Average Rates of Change

59. Compare the average rates of change from 0 to $\frac{1}{2}$ for $f(x) = x, g(x) = x^2$, and $h(x) = x^3$.

60. Compare the average rates of change from 1 to $\frac{3}{2}$ for $f(x) = x, g(x) = x^2$, and $h(x) = x^3$.

Exercises 61–64: Calculate the average rate of change of f on each interval. What happens to this average rate of change as the interval decreases in length?

(a) $[1.9, 2.1]$
(b) $[1.99, 2.01]$
(c) $[1.999, 2.001]$

61. $f(x) = x^3$ **62.** $f(x) = 4x - \frac{1}{3}x^3$

63. $f(x) = \frac{1}{4}x^4 - \frac{1}{3}x^3$ **64.** $f(x) = 4x^2 - \frac{1}{2}x^4$

Exercises 65–68: Find the difference quotient of g.

65. $g(x) = 3x^3$ **66.** $g(x) = -2x^3$

67. $g(x) = 1 + x - x^3$ **68.** $g(x) = \frac{1}{2}x^3 - 2x$

Piecewise-Defined Functions

Exercises 69–76: Evaluate f(x) at the given values of x.

69. $x = -2$ and 1   **70.** $x = -1, 0$, and 3

 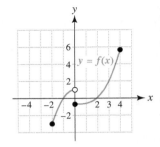

71. $x = -1, 1$, and 2   **72.** $x = -2, 0$, and 2

 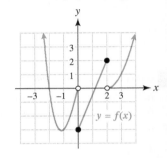

73. $x = -3, 1$, and 4
$$f(x) = \begin{cases} x^3 - 4x^2 & \text{if} & x \le -3 \\ 3x^2 & \text{if} -3 < x < 4 \\ x^3 - 54 & \text{if} & x \ge 4 \end{cases}$$

74. $x = -4, 0$, and 4
$$f(x) = \begin{cases} -4x & \text{if} & x \le -4 \\ x^3 + 2 & \text{if} -4 < x \le 2 \\ 4 - x^2 & \text{if} & x > 2 \end{cases}$$

75. $x = -2, 1$, and 2
$$f(x) = \begin{cases} x^2 + 2x + 6 & \text{if} -5 \le x < 0 \\ x + 6 & \text{if} \ 0 \le x < 2 \\ x^3 + 1 & \text{if} \ 2 \le x \le 5 \end{cases}$$

76. $x = 1975, 1980$, and 1998
$$f(x) = \begin{cases} 0.2(x - 1970)^3 + 60 & \text{if } 1970 \le x < 1980 \\ 190 - (x - 1980)^2 & \text{if } 1980 \le x < 1990 \\ 2(x - 1990) + 100 & \text{if } 1990 \le x \le 2000 \end{cases}$$

Exercises 77–82: Complete the following.

(a) Sketch a graph of f.
(b) Determine if f is continuous on its domain.
(c) Solve f(x) = 0.

77. $f(x) = \begin{cases} 4 - x^2 & \text{if} -3 \le x \le 0 \\ x^2 - 4 & \text{if} \ 0 < x \le 3 \end{cases}$

78. $f(x) = \begin{cases} x^2 & \text{if } -2 \le x < 0 \\ x+1 & \text{if } 0 \le x \le 2 \end{cases}$

79. $f(x) = \begin{cases} 2x & \text{if } -5 \le x < -1 \\ -2 & \text{if } -1 \le x < 0 \\ x^2 - 2 & \text{if } 0 \le x \le 2 \end{cases}$

80. $f(x) = \begin{cases} 0.5x^2 & \text{if } -4 \le x \le -2 \\ x & \text{if } -2 < x < 2 \\ x^2 - 4 & \text{if } 2 \le x \le 4 \end{cases}$

81. $f(x) = \begin{cases} x^3 + 3 & \text{if } -2 \le x \le 0 \\ x+3 & \text{if } 0 < x < 1 \\ 4 + x - x^2 & \text{if } 1 \le x \le 3 \end{cases}$

82. $f(x) = \begin{cases} -2x & \text{if } -3 \le x < -1 \\ x^2 + 1 & \text{if } -1 \le x \le 2 \\ \frac{1}{2}x^3 + 1 & \text{if } 2 < x \le 3 \end{cases}$

Applications

83. Diminishing Returns   (Refer to Example 7.) Let the function F, defined by

$$F(x) = \begin{cases} 2x & \text{if } 0 \le x \le 4 \\ -\frac{1}{4}x^2 + 4x - 4 & \text{if } 4 \le x \le 12, \end{cases}$$

calculate a fish harvest in thousands of tons when x hundred fishing boats are used in a region.
(a) Evaluate $F(3)$ and interpret the result.

(b) Find the absolute maximum on the graph of F and interpret the result.

84. Diminishing Returns   The function F, defined by

$$F(x) = \begin{cases} x & \text{if } 0 \le x \le 5 \\ -0.08x^2 + 1.6x - 1 & \text{if } 5 \le x \le 15, \end{cases}$$

was used in Example 7 to describe a fish harvest in a region.
(a) Evaluate $F(6)$ and interpret your answer.

(b) Solve $F(x) = 6$ and interpret the result.

(c) Use Figure 4.52 to find the point of diminishing returns and interpret its meaning.

85. Electronics   The **Heaviside function** H, used in the study of electrical circuits, is defined by

$$H(t) = \begin{cases} 0 & \text{if } t < 0 \\ 1 & \text{if } t \ge 0. \end{cases}$$

(a) Evaluate $H(-2)$, $H(0)$, and $H(3.5)$.

(b) Graph $y = H(t)$.

86. A Strange Graph   The following definition is discussed in advanced mathematics courses.

$$f(x) = \begin{cases} 0 & \text{if } x \text{ is a rational number} \\ 1 & \text{if } x \text{ is an irrational number} \end{cases}$$

(a) Evaluate $f\left(-\frac{3}{4}\right)$, $f(-\sqrt{2})$, and $f(\pi)$.

(b) Is f a function? Explain.

(c) Discuss the difficulty with graphing $y = f(x)$.

87. Modeling Temperature   In the figure the monthly average temperature in degrees Fahrenheit from January to December in Minneapolis is modeled by a polynomial function f, where $x = 1$ corresponds to January and $x = 12$ to December.   (***Source:*** A. Miller and J. Thompson, *Elements of Meteorology.*)

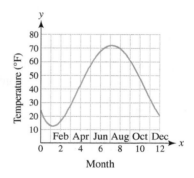

(a) Estimate the turning points.

(b) Interpret each turning point.

88. Natural Gas Consumption   Refer to Example 8 and the introduction to this section.
(a) Solve the equation $f(x) = 20$ graphically. Interpret the solution set.

(b) Calculate the average rate of change in natural gas consumption from 1970 to 1980. Interpret the result.

89. Modeling   An object is lifted rapidly into the air at a constant speed and then dropped. Its height h in feet after x seconds is listed in the table.

x (sec)	0	1	2	3	4	5	6	7
h (ft)	0	36	72	108	144	128	80	0

(a) At what time does it appear that the object was dropped?

(b) Identify the time interval when the height could be modeled by a linear function. When could it be modeled by a nonlinear function?

(*continued*)

(c) Determine values for the constants m, a, and b so that f models the data.

$$f(x) = \begin{cases} mx & \text{if } 0 \le x \le 4 \\ a(x-4)^2 + b & \text{if } 4 < x \le 7 \end{cases}$$

(d) Solve $f(x) = 100$ and interpret your answer.

90. **Modeling** A water tank is filled with a hose and then drained. The table shows the number of gallons y in the tank after t minutes.

t (min)	0	1	2	3	4	5	6	7
y (gal)	0	9	18	27	36	16	4	0

The following function f models the data in the table.

$$f(t) = \begin{cases} 9t & \text{if } 0 \le t \le 4 \\ 4t^2 - 56t + 196 & \text{if } 4 < t \le 7 \end{cases}$$

Solve the equation $f(t) = 12$ and interpret the results.

 91. **Aging in America** The table lists the number N (in thousands) of Americans over 100 years old for selected years x.

x	1960	1970	1980	1990	2000	2010
N	3	5	15	37	50	70

(a) Use regression to find a polynomial of degree 3 that models the data. Let $x = 0$ correspond to 1960.

(b) Graph f and the data.

(c) Estimate N in 1994 and in 2020.

(d) Did your estimates in part (c) involve interpolation or extrapolation?

 92. **Modeling Water Flow** A cylindrical container has a height of 16 centimeters. Water entered the container at a constant rate until it was completely filled. Then water was allowed to leak out through a small hole in the bottom. The height of the water in the container was recorded every half minute over a 5-minute period.

Time (min)	0	0.5	1.0	1.5	2.0	2.5
Height (cm)	0	4	8	12	16	11.6

Time (min)	3.0	3.5	4.0	4.5	5.0
Height (cm)	8.1	5.3	3.1	1.4	0.5

(a) Plot the data.

(b) Find a piecewise-defined function that models the data. (*Hint:* Use regression.)

(c) Approximate the water level after 1.25 minutes and after 3.2 minutes.

(d) Estimate the time when water was flowing out of the tank and the water level was 5 centimeters.

Writing About Mathematics

Exercises 93–96: Discuss possible local extrema and absolute extrema on the graph of f. Assume that a > 0.

93. $f(x) = ax + b$

94. $f(x) = ax^2 + bx + c$

95. $f(x) = ax^3 + bx^2 + cx + d$

96. $f(x) = a|x|$

Extended and Discovery Exercises

1. **Torricelli's Law** A cylindrical tank contains 500 gallons of water. A plug is pulled from the bottom of the tank, and it takes 10 minutes to drain the tank. The amount A of water in gallons remaining in the tank after t minutes is approximated by

$$A(t) = 500\left(1 - \frac{t}{10}\right)^2.$$

(a) What is a reasonable domain for A?

(b) Evaluate $A(1)$ and interpret the result.

(c) What are the degree and leading coefficient of $A(t)$?

(d) Has half the water drained from the tank after 5 minutes? Does this agree with your intuition? Explain.

Exercises 2–7: **Concavity** *Estimate the intervals where the graph of f is concave upward and where the graph is concave downward. Use interval notation.*

2.

3.

4.

5.

6.

7.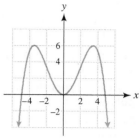

CHECKING BASIC CONCEPTS FOR SECTIONS 4.1 AND 4.2

1. Use the graph of f to complete the following.

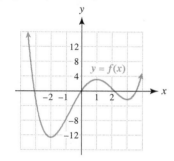

   (a) Determine where f is increasing or decreasing.

   (b) Identify any local extrema.

   (c) Identify any absolute extrema.

   (d) Approximate the x-intercepts and zeros of f. Then solve $f(x) = 0$. How are the x-intercepts, zeros, and solutions to $f(x) = 0$ related?

2. Use the graph to complete the following.

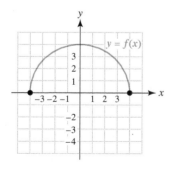

   (a) Evaluate $f(-4)$, $f(0)$, and $f(4)$.

   (b) What type of symmetry does the graph of f exhibit?

   (c) Is f an odd function or an even function? Why?

   (d) Find the domain and range of f.

3. If possible, sketch a graph of a cubic polynomial with a negative leading coefficient that satisfies each of the following conditions.

   (a) Zero x-intercepts

   (b) One x-intercept

   (c) Two x-intercepts

   (d) Four x-intercepts

4. Plot the data in the table.

x	-3.2	-2	0	2	3.2
y	-11	15	-10	15	-11

   (a) What is the minimum degree of the polynomial function f that would be needed to model these data? Explain.

   (b) Should function f be odd, even, or neither? Explain.

   (c) Should the leading coefficient of f be positive or negative? Explain.

5. Use least-squares regression to find a polynomial that models the data in Exercise 4.

4.3 Division of Polynomials

- Divide polynomials by monomials
- Divide polynomials by polynomials
- Apply the division algorithm
- Learn synthetic division
- Understand the remainder theorem

Introduction

The area A of a rectangle with length L and width W is calculated by $A = LW$. If we are given the area and the width of a rectangle, we can find the length L by solving $A = LW$ for L to obtain $L = \frac{A}{W}$. For example, if the area is 48 square feet and the width is 6 feet, then the length of the rectangle equals $L = \frac{48}{6} = 8$ feet. Now consider the more general situation shown in Figure 4.56.

$$x + 3 \quad \boxed{\quad A = x^2 + 8x + 15 \quad}$$
$$L$$

Figure 4.56

The area A is $x^2 + 8x + 15$ and the width W is $x + 3$, so we can find an expression for L in the same way by calculating

$$L = \frac{A}{W} = \frac{x^2 + 8x + 15}{x + 3}.$$

In this case, the calculation of L involves division of polynomials. (See Example 5.) This section discusses basic concepts related to division of polynomials.

Division by Monomials

Adding (or subtracting) fractions having like denominators is straightforward. For example,

$$\frac{3}{17} + \frac{7}{17} = \frac{3 + 7}{17}, \qquad \text{and so} \qquad \frac{3 + 7}{17} = \frac{3}{17} + \frac{7}{17}.$$

Note that when we reverse the process, the denominator of 17 is divided into each term in the numerator. By reversing the process, we can sometimes simplify expressions.

$$\frac{3x^4 + 5x^3}{5x^3} = \frac{3x^4}{5x^3} + \frac{5x^3}{5x^3} = \frac{3}{5}x + 1 \qquad \text{Subtract exponents: } \frac{3x^4}{5x^3} = \frac{3}{5}x.$$

This process is used in the next example.

EXAMPLE 1 Dividing by a monomial

Divide $6x^3 - 3x^2 + 2$ by $2x^2$.

SOLUTION

Getting Started Remember to divide $2x^2$ into *every* term of $6x^3 - 3x^2 + 2$. ▶

Write the problem as $\frac{6x^3 - 3x^2 + 2}{2x^2}$. Then divide $2x^2$ into *every* term in the numerator.

$$\frac{6x^3 - 3x^2 + 2}{2x^2} = \frac{6x^3}{2x^2} - \frac{3x^2}{2x^2} + \frac{2}{2x^2} \qquad \text{Write as three terms.}$$

$$= 3x - \frac{3}{2} + \frac{1}{x^2}$$

Algebra Review
To review simplification of rational expressions, see Chapter R (page R-28).

Now Try Exercise 3

Division by Polynomials

Before dividing a polynomial by a binomial, we review division of natural numbers.

$$\text{quotient} \rightarrow 58$$
$$\text{divisor} \rightarrow 3\overline{)175} \leftarrow \text{dividend}$$
$$\underline{15}$$
$$25$$
$$\underline{24}$$
$$1 \leftarrow \text{remainder}$$

This result is checked as follows: $3 \cdot 58 + 1 = 175$. That is,

$$\text{(Divisor)}\,\text{(Quotient)} + \text{(Remainder)} = \text{(Dividend)}.$$

The quotient and remainder can also be expressed as $58\frac{1}{3}$. Since 3 does not divide into 175 evenly, 3 is *not* a factor of 175. When the remainder is 0, the divisor is a *factor* of the dividend. Division of polynomials is similar to division of natural numbers.

EXAMPLE 2 Dividing polynomials

Divide $2x^3 - 3x^2 - 11x + 7$ by $x - 3$. Check the result.

SOLUTION Begin by dividing x into $2x^3$.

| Start by dividing x into $2x^3$ to get $2x^2$. | $\dfrac{2x^2}{x-3\,)\overline{2x^3 - 3x^2 - 11x + 7}}$ $\underline{2x^3 - 6x^2}$ $3x^2 - 11x$ | $\frac{2x^3}{x} = 2x^2$ $2x^2(x-3) = 2x^3 - 6x^2$ Subtract. Bring down $-11x$. |

In the next step, divide x into $3x^2$.

| Divide x into $3x^2$ to get $3x$. | $\dfrac{2x^2 + 3x}{x-3\,)\overline{2x^3 - 3x^2 - 11x + 7}}$ $\underline{2x^3 - 6x^2}$ $3x^2 - 11x$ $\underline{3x^2 - 9x}$ $-2x + 7$ | $\frac{3x^2}{x} = 3x$ $3x(x-3) = 3x^2 - 9x$ Subtract. Bring down 7. |

Now divide x into $-2x$.

| Divide x into $-2x$ to get -2. | $\dfrac{2x^2 + 3x - 2}{x-3\,)\overline{2x^3 - 3x^2 - 11x + 7}}$ $\underline{2x^3 - 6x^2}$ $3x^2 - 11x$ $\underline{3x^2 - 9x}$ $-2x + 7$ $\underline{-2x + 6}$ 1 | $\frac{-2x}{x} = -2$ $-2(x-3) = -2x + 6$ Subtract. Remainder is 1. |

The quotient is $2x^2 + 3x - 2$ and the remainder is 1. Polynomial division is also checked by multiplying the divisor and quotient and then adding the remainder.

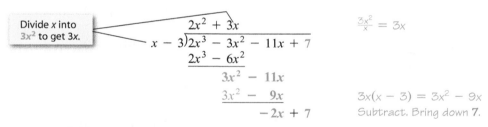

$$(x - 3)(2x^2 + 3x - 2) + 1 = x(2x^2 + 3x - 2) - 3(2x^2 + 3x - 2) + 1$$
$$= 2x^3 + 3x^2 - 2x - 6x^2 - 9x + 6 + 1$$
$$= 2x^3 - 3x^2 - 11x + 7 ✓$$

Algebra Review
To review multiplication of polynomials, see Chapter R (page R-16).

Now Try Exercise 9

A division problem, such as $\frac{175}{3}$, is typically given in the form $\frac{\text{(Dividend)}}{\text{(Divisor)}}$. If we divide each term in the equation

$$\text{(Dividend)} = \text{(Divisor)}\,\text{(Quotient)} + \text{(Remainder)}$$

by **(Divisor)**, we obtain the equation

$$\frac{\text{(Dividend)}}{\text{(Divisor)}} = \text{(Quotient)} + \frac{\text{(Remainder)}}{\text{(Divisor)}}.$$

For example, because 175 divided by 3 equals 58 remainder 1, we can use this equation to justify writing $\frac{175}{3} = 58 + \frac{1}{3}$, or $58\frac{1}{3}$. We can use the results from Example 2 to write

$$\frac{2x^3 - 3x^2 - 11x + 7}{x - 3} = 2x^2 + 3x - 2 + \frac{1}{x - 3}.$$

This process is applied in the next example.

EXAMPLE 3 Dividing polynomials

Divide each expression. Check your answer.

(a) $\dfrac{6x^2 + 5x - 10}{2x + 3}$ (b) $(5x^3 - 4x^2 + 7x - 2) \div (x^2 + 1)$

SOLUTION

(a) Begin by dividing $2x$ into $6x^2$.

$$
\begin{array}{r}
3x \\
2x + 3 \overline{)6x^2 + 5x - 10} \\
6x^2 + 9x \\
\hline
-4x - 10
\end{array}
$$

$\frac{6x^2}{2x} = 3x$

$3x(2x + 3) = 6x^2 + 9x$

Subtract: $5x - 9x = -4x$.
Bring down the -10.

In the next step, divide $2x$ into $-4x$.

$$
\begin{array}{r}
3x - 2 \\
2x + 3 \overline{)6x^2 + 5x - 10} \\
6x^2 + 9x \\
\hline
-4x - 10 \\
-4x - 6 \\
\hline
-4
\end{array}
$$

$\frac{-4x}{2x} = -2$

$-2(2x + 3) = -4x - 6$

Subtract: $-10 - (-6) = -4$.

The quotient is $3x - 2$ with remainder -4. This result can also be written as follows.

$$3x - 2 + \frac{-4}{2x + 3} \qquad \text{(Quotient)} + \frac{\text{(Remainder)}}{\text{(Divisor)}}$$

To check this result use the equation

$$\text{(Divisor)}\text{(Quotient)} + \text{(Remainder)} = \text{(Dividend)}.$$

This result can be checked as follows.

$$(2x + 3)(3x - 2) + (-4) = 6x^2 + 5x - 6 - 4$$
$$= 6x^2 + 5x - 10 \checkmark \qquad \text{The result checks.}$$

(b) Begin by writing $x^2 + 1$ as $x^2 + 0x + 1$.

$$
\begin{array}{r}
5x - 4 \\
x^2 + 0x + 1 \overline{)5x^3 - 4x^2 + 7x - 2} \\
\underline{5x^3 + 0x^2 + 5x} \\
-4x^2 + 2x - 2 \\
\underline{-4x^2 + 0x - 4} \\
2x + 2
\end{array}
$$

Insert the x-term: $0x$ as a "place holder."

Remainder

The quotient is $5x - 4$ with remainder of $2x + 2$. This result can also be written as

$$5x - 4 + \frac{2x + 2}{x^2 + 1}.$$ (Quotient) + $\frac{\text{(Remainder)}}{\text{(Divisor)}}$

This result can be checked as follows.

$$(x^2 + 1)(5x - 4) + 2x + 2 = 5x^3 - 4x^2 + 5x - 4 + 2x + 2$$
$$= 5x^3 - 4x^2 + 7x - 2 \; \checkmark \qquad \text{The result checks.}$$

Now Try Exercises 21 and 25

This process is summarized by the following *division algorithm for polynomials*.

DIVISION ALGORITHM FOR POLYNOMIALS

Let $f(x)$ and $d(x)$ be two polynomials, with the degree of $d(x)$ greater than zero and less than the degree of $f(x)$. Then there exist unique polynomials $q(x)$ and $r(x)$ such that

$$f(x) \quad = \quad d(x) \; \cdot \quad q(x) \quad + \quad r(x),$$

(Dividend) = (Divisor) · (Quotient) + (Remainder)

where either $r(x) = 0$ or the degree of $r(x)$ is less than the degree of $d(x)$. The polynomial $r(x)$ is called the remainder.

The Division Algorithm in Real Life Although the division algorithm may seem unrelated to everyday life, it is actually expressing something that is very common. For example, if there are 5 calculators for 16 students to use, then there should be 3 students to a group leaving 1 extra student, who could join a group of 3. That is, $\frac{16}{5} = 3$ with remainder 1.

Synthetic Division

A shortcut called **synthetic division** can be used to divide $x - k$ into a polynomial. For example, to divide $x - 2$ into $3x^4 - 7x^3 - 4x + 5$, we perform the following steps with $k = 2$. The equivalent steps involving long division are shown to the right.

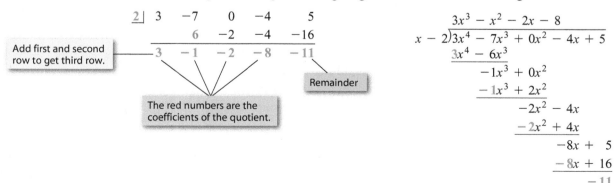

Add first and second row to get third row.

The red numbers are the coefficients of the quotient.

Remainder

$$
\begin{array}{r|rrrrr}
2 & 3 & -7 & 0 & -4 & 5 \\
  &   & 6 & -2 & -4 & -16 \\
\hline
  & 3 & -1 & -2 & -8 & -11
\end{array}
$$

Notice how the red and green numbers in the expression for long division correspond to the third row in synthetic division. The degree of the quotient, $3x^3 - x^2 - 2x - 8$, is one less than the degree of $f(x)$. The steps to divide a polynomial $f(x)$ by $x - k$ using synthetic division can be summarized as follows.

1. Write k to the left and the coefficients of $f(x)$ to the right in the top row. If any power of x does *not* appear in $f(x)$, include a 0 for that term. In this example, an x^2-term did not appear, so a 0 is included in the first row.
2. Copy the leading coefficient of $f(x)$ into the third row and multiply it by k. Write the result below the next coefficient of $f(x)$ in the second row. Add the numbers in the second column and place the result in the third row. Repeat the process. In this example, the leading coefficient is 3 and $k = 2$. Since $3 \cdot 2 = 6$, 6 is placed below the -7. Then add to obtain $-7 + 6 = -1$. Multiply -1 by 2 and repeat.
3. The last number in the third row is the remainder. If the remainder is 0, then the binomial $x - k$ is a factor of $f(x)$. The other red numbers in the third row are the coefficients of the quotient, with terms written in descending powers.

EXAMPLE 4 Performing synthetic division

Use synthetic division to divide $2x^3 + 4x^2 - x + 5$ by $x + 2$.

SOLUTION

Getting Started To find the value of k, write the divisor as $x - k$. Because $x + 2$ equals $x - (-2)$, the value of k is -2 ▶

Let $k = -2$ and perform synthetic division on the problem $\dfrac{2x^3 + 4x^2 - x + 5}{x + 2}$.

Add first and second row to get third row.

$$
\begin{array}{r|rrrr}
-2 & 2 & 4 & -1 & 5 \\
   &   & -4 & 0 & 2 \\
\hline
   & 2 & 0 & -1 & 7
\end{array}
$$

Remainder

The remainder is 7 and the quotient is $2x^2 + 0x - 1 = 2x^2 - 1$. This result is expressed by the equation

$$
\frac{2x^3 + 4x^2 - x + 5}{x + 2} = 2x^2 - 1 + \frac{7}{x + 2}.
$$

Now Try Exercise 41

An Application from Geometry In the final example, we use division to solve the problem presented in the introduction to this section.

EXAMPLE 5 Finding the length of a rectangle

If the area of a rectangle is $x^2 + 8x + 15$ and its width is $x + 3$, use division to find its length.

SOLUTION We use synthetic division to divide $x^2 + 8x + 15$ by $x + 3$. However, long division could also be used.

$$
\begin{array}{r|rrr}
-3 & 1 & 8 & 15 \\
   &   & -3 & -15 \\
\hline
   & 1 & 5 & 0
\end{array}
$$

The remainder is 0, so $x + 3$ divides evenly into $x^2 + 8x + 15$, and the length is $x + 5$.

Now Try Exercise 51

Remainder Theorem If the divisor $d(x)$ is $x - k$, then the *division algorithm for polynomials* simplifies to

$$f(x) = (x - k)q(x) + r,$$

where r is a constant. If we let $x = k$ in this equation, then

$$f(k) = (k - k)q(k) + r = r.$$

Thus $f(k)$ is equal to the remainder obtained in synthetic division. In Example 4, when $f(x) = 2x^3 + 4x^2 - x + 5$ is divided by $x + 2$, the remainder is 7. It follows that $k = -2$ and $f(-2) = 2(-2)^3 + 4(-2)^2 - (-2) + 5 = 7$. This result is summarized by the *remainder theorem*.

REMAINDER THEOREM

If a polynomial $f(x)$ is divided by $x - k$, the remainder is $f(k)$.

4.3 Putting It All Together

$\mathbf{T}$he following table lists some important concepts related to division of polynomials.

CONCEPT	EXPLANATION	EXAMPLE
Division by a monomial	Be sure to divide the denominator into *every term* in the numerator.	$\dfrac{5a^3 - 10a^2}{5a^2} = \dfrac{5a^3}{5a^2} - \dfrac{10a^2}{5a^2} = a - 2$
Division by a polynomial	Division by a polynomial can be done in a manner similar to long division of natural numbers. See Examples 2 and 3.	When $6x^3 + 5x^2 - 8x + 4$ is divided by $2x - 1$, the quotient is $3x^2 + 4x - 2$ with remainder 2 and can be written as $$\dfrac{6x^3 + 5x^2 - 8x + 4}{2x - 1} = 3x^2 + 4x - 2 + \dfrac{2}{2x - 1}.$$
Division algorithm	(Dividend) = (Divisor)(Quotient) + (Remainder) This equation can be written as $\dfrac{\text{(Dividend)}}{\text{(Divisor)}} = \text{(Quotient)} + \dfrac{\text{(Remainder)}}{\text{(Divisor)}}.$	$\dfrac{x^3 - 1}{x + 1} = x^2 - x + 1 + \dfrac{-2}{x + 1}$ Dividend: $x^3 - 1$ Divisor: $x + 1$ Quotient: $x^2 - x + 1$ Remainder: -2
Synthetic division	An efficient method for dividing $x - k$ into a polynomial	Divide $2x^3 - 3x^2 + x + 2$ by $x + 1$. $\begin{array}{r} -1\,\rvert\ \ 2\quad -3\quad\ 1\quad\ \ 2 \\ \underline{\qquad\ \ -2\quad\ 5\quad -6} \\ 2\quad -5\quad\ 6\quad -4 \end{array}$ $k = -1$ The quotient is $2x^2 - 5x + 6$, and the remainder is -4.
Remainder theorem	If a polynomial $f(x)$ is divided by $x - k$, the remainder is $f(k)$.	If $f(x) = 3x^2 - 2x + 6$ is divided by $x - 2$, the remainder is $f(2) = 3(2)^2 - 2(2) + 6 = 14$.

4.3 Exercises

Division by Monomials

Exercises 1–8: Divide the expression.

1. $\dfrac{5x^4 - 15}{10x}$

2. $\dfrac{x^2 - 5x}{5x}$

3. $\dfrac{3x^4 - 2x^2 - 1}{3x^3}$

4. $\dfrac{5x^3 - 10x^2 + 5x}{15x^2}$

5. $\dfrac{x^3 - 4}{4x^3}$

6. $\dfrac{2x^4 - 3x^2 + 4x - 7}{-4x}$

7. $\dfrac{5x(3x^2 - 6x + 1)}{3x^2}$

8. $\dfrac{(1 - 5x^2)(x + 1) + x^2}{2x}$

Division by Polynomials

Exercises 9–14: Divide the first polynomial by the second. State the quotient and remainder.

9. $x^3 - 2x^2 - 5x + 6$ $\qquad x - 3$

10. $3x^3 - 10x^2 - 27x + 10$ $\qquad x + 2$

11. $2x^4 - 7x^3 - 5x^2 - 19x + 17$ $\quad x + 1$

12. $x^4 - x^3 - 4x + 1$ $\qquad x - 2$

13. $3x^3 - 7x + 10$ $\qquad x - 1$

14. $x^4 - 16x^2 + 1$ $\qquad x + 4$

Exercises 15–22: Divide. Check your answer.

15. $\dfrac{x^4 - 3x^3 - x + 3}{x - 3}$

16. $\dfrac{x^3 - 2x^2 - x + 3}{x + 1}$

17. $\dfrac{4x^3 - x^2 - 5x + 6}{x - 1}$

18. $\dfrac{x^4 + 3x^3 - 4x + 1}{x + 2}$

19. $\dfrac{x^3 + 1}{x + 1}$

20. $\dfrac{x^5 + 3x^4 - x - 3}{x + 3}$

21. $\dfrac{6x^3 + 5x^2 - 8x + 4}{2x - 1}$

22. $\dfrac{12x^3 - 14x^2 + 7x - 7}{3x - 2}$

Exercises 23–30: Divide the expression.

23. $\dfrac{3x^4 - 7x^3 + 6x - 16}{3x - 7}$

24. $\dfrac{20x^4 + 6x^3 - 2x^2 + 15x - 2}{5x - 1}$

25. $\dfrac{5x^4 - 2x^2 + 6}{x^2 + 2}$

26. $\dfrac{x^3 - x^2 + 2x - 3}{x^2 + 3}$

27. $\dfrac{8x^3 + 10x^2 - 12x - 15}{2x^2 - 3}$

28. $\dfrac{3x^4 - 2x^2 - 5}{3x^2 - 5}$

29. $\dfrac{2x^4 - x^3 + 4x^2 + 8x + 7}{2x^2 + 3x + 2}$

30. $\dfrac{3x^4 + 2x^3 - x^2 + 4x - 3}{x^2 + x - 1}$

Division Algorithm

Exercises 31 and 32: Use the equation

$$(\text{Dividend}) = (\text{Divisor})(\text{Quotient}) + (\text{Remainder})$$

to complete the following.

31. $\dfrac{x^3 - 8x^2 + 15x - 6}{x - 2} = x^2 - 6x + 3$ implies
$(x - 2)(x^2 - 6x + 3) = \underline{\quad ? \quad}$.

32. $\dfrac{x^4 - 15}{x + 2} = x^3 - 2x^2 + 4x - 8 + \dfrac{1}{x + 2}$
implies $x^4 - 15 = (x + 2) \times \underline{\quad ? \quad} + \underline{\quad ? \quad}$.

Exercises 33–38: Use division to express the (Dividend) *as* (Divisor)(Quotient) + (Remainder).

33. $\dfrac{x^2 - 3x + 1}{x - 2}$

34. $\dfrac{2x^2 - x + 2}{x + 4}$

35. $\dfrac{2x^3 + x^2 - 2x}{2x + 1}$

36. $\dfrac{1 - x^2 + x^3}{x - 1}$

37. $\dfrac{x^3 - x^2 + x + 1}{x^2 + 1}$

38. $\dfrac{2x^3 + x^2 - x + 4}{x^2 + x}$

Synthetic Division

Exercises 39–46: Use synthetic division to divide the first polynomial by the second.

39. $x^3 + 2x^2 - 17x - 10$ $\qquad x + 5$

40. $x^3 - 2x + 1$ $\qquad x + 4$

41. $3x^3 - 11x^2 - 20x + 3$ $\qquad x - 5$

42. $x^4 - 3x^3 - 5x^2 + 2x - 16$ $\qquad x - 3$

43. $x^4 - 3x^3 - 4x^2 + 12x$ $\qquad x - 2$

44. $x^5 + \frac{1}{4}x^4 - x^3 - \frac{1}{4}x^2 + 3x - \frac{5}{4}$ $\quad x + \frac{1}{4}$

45. $2x^5 - x^4 - x^3 + 4x + 3 \quad x + \frac{1}{2}$

46. $x^4 - \frac{1}{2}x^3 + 3x^2 - \frac{5}{2}x + \frac{9}{2} \quad x - \frac{1}{2}$

Remainder Theorem

Exercises 47–50: Use the remainder theorem to find the remainder when $f(x)$ is divided by the given $x - k$.

47. $f(x) = 5x^2 - 3x + 1 \qquad x - 1$

48. $f(x) = -4x^2 + 6x - 7 \qquad x + 4$

49. $f(x) = 4x^3 - x^2 + 4x + 2 \quad x + 2$

50. $f(x) = -x^4 + 4x^3 - x + 3 \quad x - 3$

Applications

51. Area of a Rectangle Use the figure to find the length L of the rectangle from its width and area A. Determine the value of L when $x = 10$ feet.

$3x + 1$ | $A = 12x^2 + 13x + 3$

L

52. Area of a Rectangle Use the figure to find the width W of the rectangle from its length and area A. Determine the value of W when $x = 5$ inches.

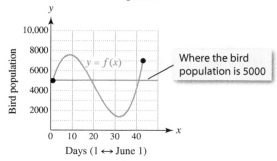

W | $A = 3x^3 - 5x^2 + 3x - 5$

$x^2 + 1$

Writing About Mathematics

53. Compare division of integers to division of polynomials. Give examples.

54. When can you use synthetic division to divide two polynomials? Give one example where synthetic division can be used and one example where it cannot be used.

Real Zeros of Polynomial Functions

- **Understand the factor theorem**
- **Factor higher degree polynomials**
- **Analyze polynomials having multiple zeros**
- **Solve higher degree polynomial equations**
- **Understand the rational zeros test, Descartes' rule of signs, and the intermediate value property**

Introduction

Some species of birds, such as robins, have two nesting periods each summer. Because the survival rate for young birds is low, bird populations can fluctuate greatly during the summer months. (*Source:* S. Kress, *Bird Life.*)

The graph of $f(x) = x^3 - 61x^2 + 839x + 4221$ shown in Figure 4.57 models a population of birds in a small county, x days after May 31.

A Summer Bird Population

Where the bird population is 5000

Figure 4.57

If we want to determine the dates when the population was 5000, we can solve

$$x^3 - 61x^2 + 839x + 4221 = 5000.$$

From the graph of f on the preceding page it appears that there were 5000 birds around June 1 ($x = 1$), June 20 ($x = 20$), and July 10 ($x = 40$). See Example 5.

Factoring Polynomials

The polynomial $f(x) = x^2 - 3x + 2$ can be factored as $f(x) = (x - 1)(x - 2)$. Note that $f(1) = 0$ and $(x - 1)$ is a factor of $f(x)$. Similarly, $f(2) = 0$ and $(x - 2)$ is a factor. This discussion can be generalized. By the remainder theorem we know that

$$f(x) = (x - k)q(x) + r,$$

where r is the remainder. If $r = 0$, then $f(x) = (x - k)q(x)$ and $(x - k)$ is a factor of $f(x)$. Similarly, if $(x - k)$ is a factor of $f(x)$, then $r = 0$. That is,

$$f(x) = (x - k)q(x)$$

and $f(k) = (k - k)q(k) = 0 \cdot q(k) = 0$. This discussion justifies the *factor theorem*.

> **FACTOR THEOREM**
>
> A polynomial $f(x)$ has a factor $x - k$ if and only if $f(k) = 0$.

EXAMPLE 1 Applying the factor theorem

Use the graph in Figure 4.58 and the factor theorem to list the factors of $f(x)$.

SOLUTION
Figure 4.58 shows that the **zeros** (or x-intercepts) of f are -2, 1, and 3. Since $f(-2) = 0$, the factor theorem states that $(x + 2)$ is a factor of $f(x)$. Similarly, $f(1) = 0$ implies that $(x - 1)$ is a factor, and $f(3) = 0$ implies that $(x - 3)$ is a factor. Thus the factors of $f(x)$ are $(x + 2)$, $(x - 1)$, and $(x - 3)$.

NOTE If $f(-2) = 0$, then $(x - (-2))$, or $(x + 2)$, is a factor.

Now Try Exercise 1

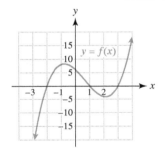

Figure 4.58

See the Concept: x-Intercepts, Zeros, and Factors

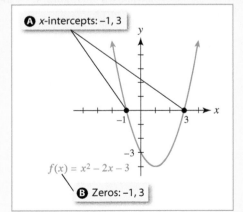

Ⓐ x-intercepts: -1, 3

Ⓑ Zeros: -1, 3

$f(x) = x^2 - 2x - 3$

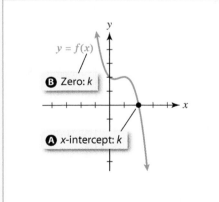

Ⓐ x-intercept: k

Ⓑ Zero: k

$y = f(x)$

Equivalent Concepts:

- The graph of $y = f(x)$ has x-intercept k.

- A real zero of $f(x)$ is k.

- A factor of $f(x)$ is $(x - k)$.

Ⓑ $f(-1) = 0$ and $f(3) = 0$

Ⓒ Factors of $x^2 - 2x - 3$ are $(x + 1)$ and $(x - 3)$.

Ⓑ $f(k) = 0$

Ⓒ Because k is a zero, $(x - k)$ is a factor of $f(x)$.

Zeros with Multiplicity   If $f(x) = (x + 2)^2$, then the factor $(x + 2)$ occurs twice and the zero -2 is called a **zero of multiplicity** 2. See Figure 4.59. The polynomial $g(x) = (x + 1)^3(x - 2)$ has zeros -1 and 2 with *multiplicities* 3 and 1, respectively. See Figure 4.60. *Counting multiplicities,* a polynomial of degree n has at most n real zeros. For $g(x)$, the sum of the multiplicities is $3 + 1 = 4$, which equals its degree.

See the Concept: Zeros, x-Intercepts, and Multiplicities

Figure 4.59

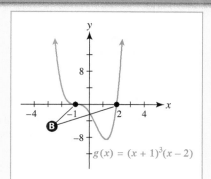

Figure 4.60

Ⓐ The *x*-intercept corresponds to the zero -2, which has multiplicity 2.

Ⓑ The two *x*-intercepts correspond to zeros -1 and 2, which have multiplicities 3 and 1, respectively.

Complete Factored Form   The concepts discussed above, together with the factor theorem, can be used to find the *complete factored form* of a polynomial. The complete factored form of a polynomial is *unique*.

COMPLETE FACTORED FORM

Suppose a polynomial

$$f(x) = a_n x^n + \cdots + a_2 x^2 + a_1 x + a_0$$

has n real zeros $c_1, c_2, c_3, \ldots, c_n$, where a distinct zero is listed as many times as its multiplicity. Then $f(x)$ can be written in **complete factored form** as

$$f(x) = a_n(x - c_1)(x - c_2)(x - c_3) \cdots (x - c_n).$$

EXAMPLE 2   Finding a complete factorization

Write the complete factorization for each polynomial with the given zeros.
(a) $f(x) = 13x^2 - 13x - 26;$ zeros: -1 and 2
(b) $f(x) = 7x^3 - 21x^2 - 7x + 21;$ zeros: -1, 1, and 3

SOLUTION
(a) The leading coefficient is 13 and the zeros are -1 and 2. By the factor theorem, $(x + 1)$ and $(x - 2)$ are factors. The complete factorization is

$$f(x) = 13(x - (-1))(x - 2) = 13(x + 1)(x - 2).$$

f is degree 2 and has two factors.

(b) The leading coefficient is 7 and the zeros are -1, 1, and 3. The complete factorization is

$$f(x) = 7(x + 1)(x - 1)(x - 3).$$

f is degree 3 and has three factors.

Now Try Exercises 5 and 7

> ┌─────────────────────────┐
> │ **MAKING CONNECTIONS** │
> └─────────────────────────┘
> **Types of Factored Forms** If the leading coefficient of a polynomial $f(x)$ is 6 and the only zeros are $\frac{1}{3}$ and $\frac{1}{2}$, then the complete factored form is $f(x) = 6\left(x - \frac{1}{3}\right)\left(x - \frac{1}{2}\right)$ and it is *unique*. Sometimes we factor 6 as $3 \cdot 2$ and distribute the 3 over the first factor and the 2 over the second factor to obtain the slightly different factored form of $f(x) = (3x - 1)(2x - 1)$.

EXAMPLE 3   Factoring a polynomial graphically

Use the graph of f in Figure 4.61 to factor $f(x) = 2x^3 - 4x^2 - 10x + 12$.

SOLUTION

Getting Started To factor $f(x)$ we need to determine the leading coefficient and the zeros of f. The zeros coincide with the x-intercepts of the graph of f. ▶

The leading coefficient is 2, and from the graph the zeros are -2, 1, and 3. The complete factorization is

$$f(x) = 2(x + 2)(x - 1)(x - 3).$$

> f is degree 3 and has three factors.

> **Now Try Exercise 13**

Figure 4.61

When factoring polynomials by hand, it is sometimes helpful to use the techniques of division discussed in Section 4.3.

EXAMPLE 4   Factoring a polynomial symbolically

One of the zeros of the polynomial $f(x) = 2x^3 - 2x^2 - 34x - 30$ is -1. Express $f(x)$ in complete factored form.

SOLUTION

If -1 is a zero, then by the factor theorem $(x + 1)$ is a factor. To factor $f(x)$, divide $x + 1$ into $2x^3 - 2x^2 - 34x - 30$ by using synthetic division.

$$
\begin{array}{r|rrrr}
-1 & 2 & -2 & -34 & -30 \\
   &   & -2 & 4   & 30 \\
\hline
   & 2 & -4 & -30 & 0
\end{array}
$$

> Long division could also be used.

Algebra Review
To review factoring trinomials, see Chapter R (pages R22–R23).

The remainder is 0, so $x + 1$ divides evenly into the dividend. By the division algorithm,

$$2x^3 - 2x^2 - 34x - 30 = (x + 1)(2x^2 - 4x - 30).$$

The quotient $2x^2 - 4x - 30$ can be factored further.

$$2x^2 - 4x - 30 = 2(x^2 - 2x - 15) \qquad \text{Factor out 2.}$$
$$= 2(x + 3)(x - 5) \qquad \text{Factor trinomial.}$$

The complete factored form is $f(x) = 2(x + 1)(x + 3)(x - 5)$.

> **Now Try Exercise 31**

An Application   In the introduction to this section we presented the equation

$$x^3 - 61x^2 + 839x + 4221 = 5000, \qquad \text{Equation to be solved}$$

which can be rewritten as

$$x^3 - 61x^2 + 839x - 779 = 0. \qquad \text{Subtract 5000.}$$

This second equation gives the days when a summer bird population was 5000 and is solved in the next example.

EXAMPLE 5   Factoring a polynomial

Factor $g(x) = x^3 - 61x^2 + 839x - 779$. Use the zeros of $g(x)$ to determine when the bird population was 5000.

A Summer Bird Population

SOLUTION

From Figure 4.57, repeated in the margin, it appears that the bird population was 5000 when $x = 1$. If we substitute $x = 1$ in this polynomial, the result is 0.

$$g(1) = 1^3 - 61(1)^2 + 839(1) - 779 = 0$$

By the factor theorem, $(x - 1)$ is a factor of $g(x)$. We can use synthetic division to divide $x^3 - 61x^2 + 839x - 779$ by $x - 1$.

$$\begin{array}{r|rrrr} 1 & 1 & -61 & 839 & -779 \\ & & 1 & -60 & 779 \\ \hline & 1 & -60 & 779 & 0 \end{array}$$ The remainder is 0.

By the division algorithm,

$$x^3 - 61x^2 + 839x - 779 = (x - 1)(x^2 - 60x + 779).$$

Since it is not obvious how to factor $x^2 - 60x + 779$, we can use the quadratic formula with $a = 1$, $b = -60$, and $c = 779$ to find its zeros.

$$\begin{aligned} x &= \frac{-b \pm \sqrt{b^2 - 4ac}}{2a} \qquad &\text{Quadratic formula} \\ &= \frac{-(-60) \pm \sqrt{(-60)^2 - 4(1)(779)}}{2(1)} \qquad &a = 1, b = -60, c = 779 \\ &= \frac{60 \pm 22}{2} \qquad &\text{Simplify.} \\ &= 41 \text{ or } 19 \qquad &\text{Two zeros} \end{aligned}$$

The zeros of $g(x) = x^3 - 61x^2 + 839x - 779$ are 1, 19, and 41, and its leading coefficient is 1. The complete factorization is $g(x) = (x - 1)(x - 19)(x - 41)$. The bird population equals 5000 on June 1 ($x = 1$), June 19 ($x = 19$), and July 11 ($x = 41$).

Now Try Exercise 113

Graphs and Multiple Zeros

The following See the Concept explains graphs of polynomials with multiple zeros. See Figures 4.62 and 4.63.

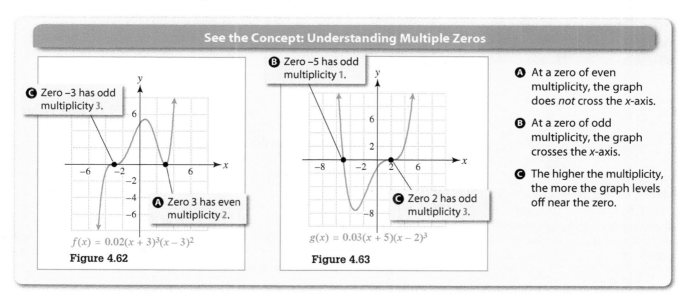

See the Concept: Understanding Multiple Zeros

C Zero −3 has odd multiplicity **3**.

A Zero 3 has even multiplicity **2**.

$f(x) = 0.02(x + 3)^3(x - 3)^2$

Figure 4.62

B Zero −5 has odd multiplicity **1**.

C Zero 2 has odd multiplicity **3**.

$g(x) = 0.03(x + 5)(x - 2)^3$

Figure 4.63

A At a zero of even multiplicity, the graph does *not* cross the x-axis.

B At a zero of odd multiplicity, the graph crosses the x-axis.

C The higher the multiplicity, the more the graph levels off near the zero.

EXAMPLE 6 Finding multiplicities graphically

Figure 4.64 shows the graph of a sixth-degree polynomial $f(x)$ with leading coefficient 1. All zeros are integers. Write $f(x)$ in complete factored form.

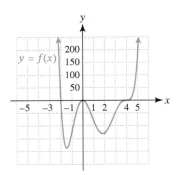

Figure 4.64

SOLUTION
The x-intercepts or zeros of f are -2, 0, and 4. Since the graph crosses the x-axis at -2 and 4, these zeros have odd multiplicity. The graph of f levels off more at $x = 4$ than at $x = -2$, so 4 has a higher multiplicity than -2. At $x = 0$ the graph of f does not cross the x-axis. Thus 0 has even multiplicity. To make $f(x)$ a sixth degree polynomial, -2 has multiplicity 1, 0 has multiplicity 2, and 4 has multiplicity 3. Then the sum of the multiplicities is given by $1 + 2 + 3 = 6$, which equals the degree of $f(x)$. List the zeros as $-2, 0, 0, 4, 4,$ and 4. The leading coefficient is 1, so the complete factorization of $f(x)$ is

$$f(x) = 1(x + 2)(x - 0)(x - 0)(x - 4)(x - 4)(x - 4), \quad \text{or}$$
$$f(x) = x^2(x + 2)(x - 4)^3.$$

Now Try Exercise 47

An Application: "Will It Float?" Multiple zeros can have physical significance. The next example shows how a multiple zero represents the boundary between an object floating and sinking.

EXAMPLE 7 Interpreting a multiple zero

The polynomial $f(x) = \frac{\pi}{3}x^3 - 5\pi x^2 + \frac{500\pi d}{3}$ can be used to find the depth that a ball, 10 centimeters in diameter, sinks in water. The constant d is the density of the ball, where the density of water is 1. The smallest *positive* zero of $f(x)$ equals the depth that the sphere sinks. Approximate this depth for each material and interpret the results.
(a) A wood ball with $d = 0.8$
(b) A solid aluminum sphere with $d = 2.7$
(c) A water balloon with $d = 1$

SOLUTION
(a) Let $d = 0.8$ and graph $Y_1 = (\pi/3)X^3 - 5\pi X^2 + 500\pi(0.8)/3$. In Figure 4.65 the smallest positive zero is near 7.13. This means that the 10-centimeter wood ball sinks about 7.13 centimeters into the water.
(b) Let $d = 2.7$ and graph $Y_2 = (\pi/3)X^3 - 5\pi X^2 + 500\pi(2.7)/3$. In Figure 4.66 there is no positive zero. The aluminum sphere is more dense than water and sinks.
(c) Let $d = 1$ and graph $Y_3 = (\pi/3)X^3 - 5\pi X^2 + 500\pi/3$. In Figure 4.67, y_3 has one positive zero of 10 with multiplicity 2. The water balloon has the same density as water and "floats" even with the surface. The value of $d = 1$ represents the boundary between sinking and floating. If the ball floats, $f(x)$ has two positive zeros; if it sinks, $f(x)$ has no positive zeros. With the water balloon there is one positive zero with multiplicity 2 that represents a transition between floating and sinking.

CLASS DISCUSSION

Make a conjecture about the depth that a ball with a 10-centimeter diameter will sink in water if $d = 0.5$. Test your conjecture graphically.

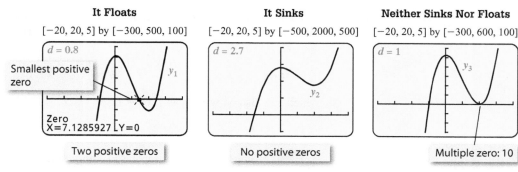

It Floats	It Sinks	Neither Sinks Nor Floats

$[-20, 20, 5]$ by $[-300, 500, 100]$ $[-20, 20, 5]$ by $[-500, 2000, 500]$ $[-20, 20, 5]$ by $[-300, 600, 100]$

Two positive zeros   No positive zeros   Multiple zero: 10

Figure 4.65   **Figure 4.66**   **Figure 4.67**

> Now Try Exercise 111

Rational Zeros

If a polynomial has a rational zero, it can be found by using the **rational zero test**.

RATIONAL ZERO TEST

Let $f(x) = a_n x^n + \cdots + a_2 x^2 + a_1 x + a_0$, where $a_n \neq 0$, represent a polynomial function f with *integer* coefficients. If $\frac{p}{q}$ is a rational number written in lowest terms and if $\frac{p}{q}$ is a zero of f, then p is a factor of the constant term a_0 and q is a factor of the leading coefficient a_n.

The following example illustrates how to find rational zeros by using this test.

EXAMPLE 8 Finding rational zeros of a polynomial

Find all rational zeros of $f(x) = 6x^3 - 5x^2 - 7x + 4$ and factor $f(x)$.

SOLUTION

If $\frac{p}{q}$ is a rational zero in lowest terms, then p is a factor of the constant term 4 and q is a factor of the leading coefficient 6. The possible values for p and q are as follows.

$$p: \quad \pm 1, \quad \pm 2, \quad \pm 4$$
$$q: \quad \pm 1, \quad \pm 2, \quad \pm 3, \quad \pm 6$$

As a result, any rational zero of $f(x)$ in the form $\frac{p}{q}$ must occur in the list

$$\pm\frac{1}{6}, \quad \pm\frac{1}{3}, \quad \pm\frac{1}{2}, \quad \pm\frac{2}{3}, \quad \pm\frac{1}{1}, \quad \pm\frac{4}{3}, \quad \pm\frac{2}{1}, \quad \text{or} \quad \pm\frac{4}{1}.$$

Evaluate $f(x)$ at each value in the list. See Table 4.3.

x	$f(x)$	x	$f(x)$	x	$f(x)$	x	$f(x)$
$\frac{1}{6}$	$\frac{49}{18}$	$\frac{1}{2}$	0	1	-2	2	18
$-\frac{1}{6}$	5	$-\frac{1}{2}$	$\frac{11}{2}$	-1	0	-2	-50
$\frac{1}{3}$	$\frac{4}{3}$	$\frac{2}{3}$	$-\frac{10}{9}$	$\frac{4}{3}$	0	4	280
$-\frac{1}{3}$	$\frac{50}{9}$	$-\frac{2}{3}$	$\frac{14}{3}$	$-\frac{4}{3}$	$-\frac{88}{9}$	-4	-432

Table 4.3

From Table 4.3 there are three rational zeros: -1, $\frac{1}{2}$, and $\frac{4}{3}$. Since a third-degree polynomial has at most three zeros, the complete factored form of $f(x)$ is

$$f(x) = 6(x + 1)\left(x - \frac{1}{2}\right)\left(x - \frac{4}{3}\right),$$

which can also be written as $f(x) = (x + 1)(2x - 1)(3x - 4)$.

Now Try Exercise 57

NOTE Although $f(x)$ in Example 8 had only rational zeros, it is important to realize that many polynomials have irrational zeros. Irrational zeros cannot be found using the rational zero test.

Descartes' Rule of Signs

Descartes' rule of signs helps to determine the numbers of positive and negative real zeros of a polynomial function.

DESCARTES' RULE OF SIGNS

Let $P(x)$ define a polynomial function with real coefficients and a nonzero constant term, with terms in descending powers of x.
(a) The number of positive real zeros either equals the number of variations in sign occurring in the coefficients of $P(x)$ or is less than the number of variations by a positive even integer.
(b) The number of negative real zeros either equals the number of variations in sign occurring in the coefficients of $P(-x)$ or is less than the number of variations by a positive even integer.

A **variation in sign** is a change from positive to negative or negative to positive in successive terms of the polynomial when written in descending powers of the variable. Missing terms (those with 0 coefficients) can be ignored.

EXAMPLE 9 Applying Descartes' rule of signs

Determine the possible numbers of positive real zeros and negative real zeros of $P(x) = x^4 - 6x^3 + 8x^2 + 2x - 1$.

SOLUTION
We first consider the possible number of positive zeros by observing that $P(x)$ has three variations in sign.

$$+x^4 - 6x^3 + 8x^2 + 2x - 1 \qquad \text{Three variations}$$
$$\underset{1}{} \quad \underset{2}{} \qquad \underset{3}{} \qquad \text{in sign.}$$

Thus by Descartes' rule of signs, $P(x)$ has either **3** or $3 - 2 = $ **1** positive real zeros.
For negative zeros, consider the variations in sign for $P(-x)$.

$$P(-x) = (-x)^4 - 6(-x)^3 + 8(-x)^2 + 2(-x) - 1$$
$$= x^4 + 6x^3 + 8x^2 - 2x - 1 \qquad \text{One variation}$$
$$\underset{1}{} \qquad\qquad \text{in sign.}$$

Since there is only one variation in sign, $P(x)$ has only **1** negative real zero.

Now Try Exercise 65

Polynomial Equations

In Section 3.2, factoring was used to solve quadratic equations. Factoring also can be used to solve polynomial equations with degree greater than 2.

EXAMPLE 10 Solving a cubic equation

Solve $x^3 + 3x^2 - 4x = 0$ symbolically. Support your answer graphically and numerically.

SOLUTION

Symbolic Solution

$$x^3 + 3x^2 - 4x = 0 \qquad \text{\textit{Given equation}}$$
$$x(x^2 + 3x - 4) = 0 \qquad \text{\textit{Factor out x.}}$$
$$x(x + 4)(x - 1) = 0 \qquad \text{\textit{Factor the quadratic expression}}$$
$$x = 0, \quad x + 4 = 0, \quad \text{or} \quad x - 1 = 0 \qquad \text{\textit{Zero-product property}}$$
$$x = 0, -4, \text{ or } 1 \qquad \text{\textit{Solve.}}$$

Graphical Solution Graph $y = x^3 + 3x^2 - 4x$ as in Figure 4.68. The x-intercepts are −4, 0, and 1, which correspond to the solutions.

Numerical Solution Table $y = x^3 + 3x^2 - 4x$ as in Figure 4.69. The zeros of y occur at $x = -4$, 0, and 1.

Solving $x^3 + 3x^2 - 4x = 0$

| Figure 4.68 | Figure 4.69 |

Now Try Exercise 71

EXAMPLE 11 Solving a polynomial equation

Find all real solutions to each equation symbolically.
(a) $4x^4 - 5x^2 - 9 = 0$ **(b)** $2x^3 + 12 = 3x^2 + 8x$

SOLUTION
(a) The expression $4x^4 - 5x^2 - 9$ can be factored in a manner similar to the way quadratic expressions are factored.

$$4x^4 - 5x^2 - 9 = 0 \qquad \text{\textit{Given equation}}$$
$$(4x^2 - 9)(x^2 + 1) = 0 \qquad \text{\textit{Factor.}}$$
$$4x^2 - 9 = 0 \quad \text{or} \quad x^2 + 1 = 0 \qquad \text{\textit{Zero-product property}}$$
$$4x^2 = 9 \quad \text{or} \quad x^2 = -1 \qquad \text{\textit{Add 9 or subtract 1.}}$$
$$x^2 = \frac{9}{4} \quad \text{or} \quad x^2 = -1 \qquad \text{\textit{Divide left equation by 4.}}$$
$$x = \pm\frac{3}{2} \quad \text{or} \quad x^2 = -1 \qquad \text{\textit{Square root property}}$$

The equation $x^2 = -1$ has no *real* solutions. The solutions are $-\frac{3}{2}$ and $\frac{3}{2}$.

Algebra Review
To review factoring a cubic polynomial by grouping, see Chapter R (page R-20).

(b) First transpose each term on the right side of the equation to the left side of the equation. Then use *grouping* to factor the polynomial.

$$2x^3 + 12 = 3x^2 + 8x \qquad \text{Given equation}$$

$$2x^3 - 3x^2 - 8x + 12 = 0 \qquad \text{Rewrite the equation.}$$

$$(2x^3 - 3x^2) + (-8x + 12) = 0 \qquad \text{Associative property}$$

$$x^2(2x - 3) - 4(2x - 3) = 0 \qquad \text{Factor.}$$

$$(x^2 - 4)(2x - 3) = 0 \qquad \text{Factor out } 2x - 3.$$

$$x^2 - 4 = 0 \quad \text{or} \quad 2x - 3 = 0 \qquad \text{Zero-product property}$$

$$x = \pm 2 \quad \text{or} \qquad x = \frac{3}{2} \qquad \text{Solve each equation.}$$

The solutions are -2, $\frac{3}{2}$, and 2.

> **Now Try Exercises 79 and 89**

Some types of polynomial equations cannot be solved easily by factoring. The next example illustrates how we can obtain an approximate solution graphically.

EXAMPLE 12 Finding a solution graphically

Solve the equation $\frac{1}{2}x^3 - 2x - 4 = 0$ graphically. Round to the nearest hundredth.

SOLUTION
A graph of $y = \frac{1}{2}x^3 - 2x - 4$ is shown in Figure 4.70. Since there is only one x-intercept, the equation has one *real* solution: $x \approx 2.65$.

Calculator Help
To find a zero of a function, see Appendix A (page AP-7).

Graphical Solution

$[-9, 9, 1]$ by $[-6, 6, 1]$

Figure 4.70

> **Now Try Exercise 97**

Intermediate Value Property

In Example 12, we approximated a solution to $\frac{1}{2}x^3 - 2x - 4 = 0$ to be 2.65. How do we know for sure that there is indeed such a solution? The *intermediate value property* helps answer this question.

> **INTERMEDIATE VALUE PROPERTY**
>
> Let (x_1, y_1) and (x_2, y_2), with $y_1 \neq y_2$ and $x_1 < x_2$, be two points on the graph of a continuous function f. Then, on the interval $x_1 \leq x \leq x_2$, f assumes every value between y_1 and y_2 at least once.

From Example 12, let $f(x) = \frac{1}{2}x^3 - 2x - 4$. Because $f(0) = -4$ and $f(3) = 3.5$, the points $(0, -4)$ and $(3, 3.5)$ lie on the graph of f in Figure 4.70. By the intermediate value property, $f(x) = 0$ for at least one x-value, because 0 is between -4 and 3.5. Although we have not found the exact x-value, we know that a real zero of f does exist. Loosely speaking, the intermediate value property says that if $y_1 < 0$ and $y_2 > 0$, then we cannot draw a continuous graph of f without crossing the x-axis. The only way not to cross the x-axis would be to pick up the pencil, but this would create a discontinuous graph.

Applications There are many examples of the intermediate value property. Physical motion is usually considered to be continuous. Suppose at one time a car is traveling at 20 miles per hour and at another time it is traveling at 40 miles per hour. It is logical to assume that the car traveled 30 miles per hour at least once between these times. In fact, by the intermediate value property, the car must have assumed all speeds between 20 and 40 miles per hour at least once. Similarly, if a jet airliner takes off and flies at an altitude of 30,000 feet, then by the intermediate value property we may conclude that the airliner assumed all altitudes between ground level and 30,000 feet at least once.

4.4 Putting It All Together

$\mathbf{T}$he following table summarizes important topics about real zeros of polynomial functions.

CONCEPT	EXPLANATION	EXAMPLES
Factor theorem	$(x - k)$ is a factor of $f(x)$ if and only if $f(k) = 0$.	$f(x) = x^2 + 3x - 4$, $f(-4) = 0$, and $f(1) = 0$ imply that $(x + 4)$ and $(x - 1)$ are factors of $f(x)$. That is, $f(x) = (x + 4)(x - 1)$.
x-intercepts, zeros, and factors	The following are *equivalent:* **1.** The graph of f has x-intercept k. **2.** A real zero of f is k. That is, $f(k) = 0$. **3.** A factor of f is $(x - k)$.	Let $f(x) = x^2 - 2x - 3$. See the graph below. **1.** The graph of f has x-intercepts -1 and 3. **2.** $f(-1) = 0$ and $f(3) = 0$ **3.** $f(x) = (x + 1)(x - 3)$
Complete factored form	$f(x) = a_n(x - c_1) \cdots (x - c_n)$, where the c_k are zeros of f, with a distinct zero listed as many times as its multiplicity. This form is unique.	$\begin{aligned} f(x) &= 3(x - 5)(x + 3)(x + 3) \\ &= 3(x - 5)(x + 3)^2 \end{aligned}$ $a_n = 3$, $c_1 = 5$, $c_2 = -3$, $c_3 = -3$
Factoring a polynomial graphically (only real zeros)	Graph $y = f(x)$ and locate all the zeros or x-intercepts. If the leading coefficient is a and the zeros are $c_1, c_2,$ and c_3, then $f(x) = a(x - c_1)(x - c_2)(x - c_3)$.	$f(x) = 2x^3 + 4x^2 - 2x - 4$ has zeros $-2, -1,$ and 1 and leading coefficient 2. Thus $$f(x) = 2(x + 2)(x + 1)(x - 1).$$
Solving polynomial equations	Polynomial equations can be solved symbolically, graphically, and numerically. Factoring is a useful symbolic technique.	Solve $x^3 - 4x^2 - 5x = 0$. $$x(x^2 - 4x - 5) = 0$$ $$x(x - 5)(x + 1) = 0$$ $$x = 0, 5, \text{ or } -1$$ See also Examples 10 and 11.

continued on next page

The following explains the concepts of multiple zeros and graphs of polynomials.

CONCEPT	DESCRIPTION
Zeros and multiplicity	If a zero of a polynomial has odd multiplicity, then the graph crosses the x-axis at the zero. If a polynomial has a zero of even multiplicity, then the graph intersects, but does not cross, the x-axis at the zero. The higher the multiplicity of a zero, the more the graph levels off near the zero.

Multiplicity 1 (odd)   **Multiplicity 2 (even)**   **Multiplicity 3 (odd)**   **Multiplicity 4 (even)**

4.4 Exercises

Factoring Polynomials

Exercises 1–4: Use the graph and the factor theorem to list the factors of $f(x)$.

1.

2.

3.

4.
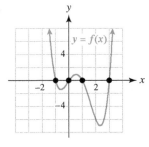

Exercises 5–12: Use the given zeros to write the complete factored form of $f(x)$.

5. $f(x) = 2x^2 - 25x + 77$; zeros: $\frac{11}{2}$ and 7

6. $f(x) = 6x^2 + 21x - 90$; zeros: -6 and $\frac{5}{2}$

7. $f(x) = x^3 - 2x^2 - 5x + 6$; zeros: -2, 1, and 3

8. $f(x) = x^3 + 6x^2 + 11x + 6$; zeros: -3, -2, and -1

9. $f(x) = -2x^3 + 3x^2 + 59x - 30$; zeros: $-5, \frac{1}{2}$, and 6

10. $f(x) = 3x^4 - 8x^3 - 67x^2 + 112x + 240$; zeros: $-4, -\frac{4}{3}, 3$, and 5

11. Let $f(x)$ be a quadratic polynomial with leading coefficient 7. Suppose that $f(-3) = 0$ and $f(2) = 0$. Write the complete factored form of $f(x)$.

12. Let $g(x)$ be a cubic polynomial with leading coefficient -4. Suppose that $g(-2) = 0, g(1) = 0,$ and $g(4) = 0$. Write the complete factored form of $g(x)$.

Exercises 13 and 14: Use the graph to factor f(x).

13. $f(x) = -2x^3 + 2x$

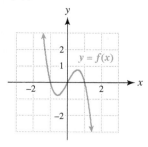

14. $f(x) = \frac{1}{4}x^4 - \frac{3}{2}x^3 + \frac{3}{4}x^2 + \frac{13}{2}x - 6$

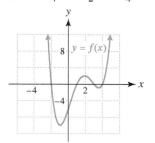

Exercises 15–18: The graph of a polynomial f(x) with leading coefficient ±1 and integer zeros is shown in the figure. Write its complete factored form.

15.

16.

17.

18.

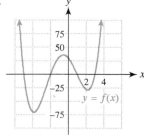

19. Let $f(x)$ be a cubic polynomial with zeros -1, 2, and 3. If the graph of f passes through the point $(0, 3)$, write the complete factored form of $f(x)$.

20. Let $g(x)$ be a quartic polynomial with zeros -2, -1, 1, and 2. If the graph of g passes through the point $(0, 8)$, write the complete factored form of $g(x)$.

Exercises 21–24: The graph of a polynomial f(x) with integer zeros is shown in the figure. Write its complete factored form. Note that the leading coefficient of f(x) is not ±1.

21.

22.

23.

24.

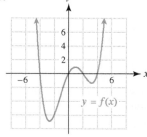

Exercises 25–30: Use graphing to factor f(x).

25. $f(x) = 10x^2 + 17x - 6$

26. $f(x) = 2x^3 + 7x^2 + 2x - 3$

27. $f(x) = -3x^3 - 3x^2 + 18x$

28. $f(x) = \frac{1}{2}x^3 + \frac{5}{2}x^2 + x - 4$

29. $f(x) = x^4 + \frac{5}{2}x^3 - 3x^2 - \frac{9}{2}x$

30. $f(x) = 10x^4 + 7x^3 - 27x^2 + 2x + 8$

Exercises 31–36: (Refer to Example 4.) Write the complete factored form of the polynomial f(x), given that k is a zero.

31. $f(x) = x^3 - 9x^2 + 23x - 15$ $k = 1$

32. $f(x) = 2x^3 + x^2 - 11x - 10$ $k = -2$

33. $f(x) = -4x^3 - x^2 + 51x - 36$ $k = -4$

34. $f(x) = 3x^3 - 11x^2 - 35x + 75$ $k = 5$

35. $f(x) = 2x^4 - x^3 - 13x^2 - 6x$ $k = -2$

36. $f(x) = 35x^4 + 48x^3 - 41x^2 + 6x$ $k = \frac{3}{7}$

Factor Theorem

Exercises 37–40: Use the factor theorem to decide if x − k is a factor of f(x) for the given k.

37. $f(x) = x^3 - 6x^2 + 11x - 6$ $k = 2$

38. $f(x) = x^3 + x^2 - 14x - 24$ $k = -3$

39. $f(x) = x^4 - 2x^3 - 13x^2 - 10x$ $\qquad k = 3$

40. $f(x) = 2x^4 - 11x^3 + 9x^2 + 14x$ $\qquad k = \frac{1}{2}$

Graphs and Multiple Zeros

Exercises 41 and 42: The graph of a polynomial $f(x)$ is shown in the figure. Estimate the zeros and state whether their multiplicities are odd or even. State the minimum degree of $f(x)$.

41.

42.

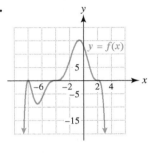

Exercises 43–46: Write a polynomial $f(x)$ in complete factored form that satisfies the conditions. Let the leading coefficient be 1.

43. Degree 3; zeros: -1 with multiplicity 2, and 6 with multiplicity 1

44. Degree 4; zeros: 5 and 7, both with multiplicity 2

45. Degree 4; zeros: 2 with multiplicity 3, and 6 with multiplicity 1

46. Degree 5; zeros: -2 with multiplicity 2, and 4 with multiplicity 3

Exercises 47–52: The graph of either a cubic, quartic, or quintic polynomial $f(x)$ with integer zeros is shown. Write the complete factored form of $f(x)$. (Hint: In Exercises 51 and 52 the leading coefficient is not ± 1.)

47.

48.

49.

50.

51.

52.

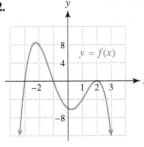

Exercises 53–56: Complete the following.

(a) Find the x- and y-intercepts.

(b) Determine the multiplicity of each zero of f.

(c) Sketch a graph of $y = f(x)$ by hand.

53. $f(x) = 2(x + 2)(x + 1)^2$

54. $f(x) = -(x + 1)(x - 1)(x - 2)$

55. $f(x) = x^2(x + 2)(x - 2)$

56. $f(x) = -\frac{1}{2}(x + 2)^2(x - 1)^3$

Rational Zeros

Exercises 57–64: (Refer to Example 8.)

(a) Use the rational zero test to find any rational zeros of the polynomial $f(x)$.

(b) Write the complete factored form of $f(x)$.

57. $f(x) = 2x^3 + 3x^2 - 8x + 3$

58. $f(x) = x^3 - 7x + 6$

59. $f(x) = 2x^4 + x^3 - 8x^2 - x + 6$

60. $f(x) = 2x^4 + x^3 - 19x^2 - 9x + 9$

61. $f(x) = 3x^3 - 16x^2 + 17x - 4$

62. $f(x) = x^3 + 2x^2 - 3x - 6$

63. $f(x) = x^3 - x^2 - 7x + 7$

64. $f(x) = 2x^3 - 5x^2 - 4x + 10$

Descartes' Rule of Signs

Exercises 65–70: Use Descartes' rule of signs to determine the possible number of positive and negative real zeros for each function. Then, use a graph to determine the actual numbers of positive and negative real zeros.

65. $P(x) = 2x^3 - 4x^2 + 2x + 7$

66. $P(x) = x^3 + 2x^2 + x - 10$

67. $P(x) = 5x^4 + 3x^2 + 2x - 9$

68. $P(x) = 3x^4 + 2x^3 - 8x^2 - 10x - 1$

69. $P(x) = x^5 + 3x^4 - x^3 + 2x + 3$

70. $P(x) = 2x^5 - x^4 + x^3 - x^2 + x + 5$

Polynomial Equations

Exercises 71–76: Solve the equation
(a) symbolically,
(b) graphically, and
(c) numerically.

71. $x^3 + x^2 - 6x = 0$ **72.** $2x^2 - 8x + 6 = 0$

73. $x^4 - 1 = 0$ **74.** $x^4 - 5x^2 + 4 = 0$

75. $-x^3 + 4x = 0$ **76.** $6 - 4x - 2x^2 = 0$

Exercises 77–96: Solve the equation.

77. $x^3 - 25x = 0$ **78.** $x^4 - x^3 - 6x^2 = 0$

79. $x^4 - x^2 = 2x^2 + 4$ **80.** $x^4 + 5 = 6x^2$

81. $x^3 - 3x^2 - 18x = 0$ **82.** $x^4 - x^2 = 0$

83. $2x^3 = 4x^2 - 2x$ **84.** $x^3 = x$

85. $12x^3 = 17x^2 + 5x$ **86.** $3x^3 + 3x = 10x^2$

87. $9x^4 + 4 = 13x^2$ **88.** $4x^4 + 7x^2 - 2 = 0$

89. $4x^3 + 4x^2 - 3x - 3 = 0$

90. $9x^3 + 27x^2 - 2x - 6 = 0$

91. $2x^3 + 4 = x(x + 8)$ **92.** $3x^3 + 18 = x(2x + 27)$

93. $8x^4 = 30x^2 - 27$ **94.** $4x^4 - 21x^2 + 20 = 0$

95. $x^6 - 19x^3 = 216$ **96.** $x^6 = 7x^3 + 8$

Exercises 97–102: (Refer to Example 12.) Solve the equation graphically. Round your answers to the nearest hundredth.

97. $x^3 - 1.1x^2 - 5.9x + 0.7 = 0$

98. $x^3 + x^2 - 18x + 13 = 0$

99. $-0.7x^3 - 2x^2 + 4x + 2.5 = 0$

100. $3x^3 - 46x^2 + 180x - 99 = 0$

101. $2x^4 - 1.5x^3 + 13 = 24x^2 + 10x$

102. $-x^4 + 2x^3 + 20x^2 = 22x + 41$

Intermediate Value Property

Exercises 103–106: Use the intermediate value property to show that $f(x) = 0$ for some x on the given interval.

103. $f(x) = x^2 - 5, 2 \le x \le 3$ (*Hint:* Evaluate $f(2)$ and $f(3)$ and then apply the intermediate value property.)

104. $f(x) = x^3 - x - 1, 1 \le x \le 2$

105. $f(x) = 2x^3 - 1, 0 \le x \le 1$

106. $f(x) = 4x^2 - x - 1, -1 \le x \le 0$

107. Let $f(x) = x^5 - x^2 + 4$. Evaluate $f(1)$ and $f(2)$. Is there a real number k such that $f(k) = 20$? Explain your answer.

108. Sketch a graph of a function f that passes through the points $(-2, 3)$ and $(1, -2)$ but never assumes a value of 0. What must be true about the graph of f?

Applications

109. Winter Temperature The temperature T in degrees Fahrenheit on a cold night x hours past midnight can be approximated by $T(x) = x^3 - 6x^2 + 8x$, where $0 \le x \le 4$. Determine when the temperature was 0°F.

110. Geometry A rectangular box has sides with lengths $x, x + 1$, and $x + 2$. If the volume of the box is 504 cubic inches, find the dimensions of the box.

111. Floating Ball (Refer to Example 7.) If a ball has a 20-centimeter diameter, then

$$f(x) = \frac{\pi}{3}x^3 - 10\pi x^2 + \frac{4000\pi d}{3}$$

determines the depth that it sinks in water. Find the depth that this size ball sinks when $d = 0.6$.

112. Floating Ball (Refer to Example 7.) Determine the depth that a pine ball with a 10-centimeter diameter sinks in water if $d = 0.55$.

113. Bird Populations (Refer to Example 5.) A bird population can be modeled by

$$f(x) = x^3 - 66x^2 + 1052x + 1652,$$

where $x = 1$ corresponds to June 1, $x = 2$ to June 2, and so on. Find the days when f estimates that there were 3500 birds.

114. Insect Population An insect population P in thousands per acre x days past May 31 is approximated by $P(x) = 2x^3 - 18x^2 + 46x$, where $0 \le x \le 6$. Determine the dates when the insect population equaled 30 thousand per acre.

115. Modeling Temperature Complete the following.
(a) Approximate the complete factored form of $f(x) = -0.184x^3 + 1.45x^2 + 10.7x - 27.9$.

(b) The cubic polynomial $f(x)$ models monthly average temperature at Trout Lake, Canada, in degrees Fahrenheit, where $x = 1$ corresponds to January and $x = 12$ represents December. Interpret the zeros of f.

116. Average High Temperatures The monthly average high temperatures in degrees Fahrenheit at Daytona Beach can be modeled by

$$f(x) = 0.0151x^4 - 0.438x^3 + 3.60x^2 - 6.49x + 72.5,$$

where $x = 1$ corresponds to January and $x = 12$ represents December.

(a) Find the average high temperature during March and July.

(b) Graph f in $[0.5, 12.5, 1]$ by $[60, 100, 10]$. Interpret the graph.

(c) Estimate graphically and numerically when the average high temperature is 80°F.

Polynomial Regression

117. Water Pollution In one study, freshwater mussels were used to monitor copper discharge into a river from an electroplating works. Copper in high doses can be lethal to aquatic life. The table lists copper concentrations in mussels after 45 days at various distances downstream from the plant. The concentration C is measured in micrograms of copper per gram of mussel x kilometers downstream.

x	5	21	37	53	59
C	20	13	9	6	5

Source: R. Foster and J. Bates, "Use of mussels to monitor point source industrial discharges."

(a) Describe the relationship between x and C.

(b) Use regression to find a cubic polynomial function $f(x)$ that models the data.

(c) Graph C and the data.

(d) Concentrations above 10 are lethal to mussels. Locate this region in the river.

118. Dog Years There is a saying that every year of a dog's life is equal to 7 years for a human. A more accurate approximation is given by the graph of f. Given a dog's age x, where $x \geq 1$, $f(x)$ models the equivalent age in human years. According to the Bureau of the Census, middle age for people begins at age 45.
(*Source:* J. Brearley and A. Nicholas, *This Is the Bichon Frise.*)

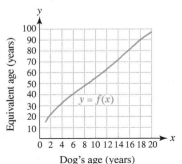

Dog's age (years)

(a) Use the graph of f to estimate the equivalent age for dogs.

(b) Estimate $f(x)$ at $x = 2, 6, 10, 14,$ and 18.

(c) Use regression and the points you estimated to find a quartic polynomial function f that models the data points.

(d) Use $f(x)$ to solve part (a) either graphically or numerically.

Writing About Mathematics

119. Suppose that $f(x)$ is a quintic polynomial with distinct real zeros. Assuming you have access to technology, explain how to factor $f(x)$ approximately. Have you used the factor theorem? Explain.

120. Explain how to determine graphically whether a zero of a polynomial is a multiple zero. Sketch examples.

Extended and Discovery Exercises

Exercises 1–6: **Boundedness Theorem** *The boundedness theorem shows how the bottom row of a synthetic division is used to place upper and lower bounds on possible real zeros of a polynomial function.*

Let $P(x)$ define a polynomial function of degree $n \geq 1$ with real coefficients and with a positive leading coefficient. If $P(x)$ is divided synthetically by $x - c$ and

(a) if $c > 0$ and all numbers in the bottom row of the synthetic division are nonnegative, then $P(x)$ has no zero greater than c;

(b) if $c < 0$ and the numbers in the bottom row of the synthetic division alternate in sign (with 0 considered positive or negative, as needed), then $P(x)$ has no zero less than c.

Use the boundedness theorem to show that the real zeros of each polynomial function satisfy the given conditions.

1. $P(x) = x^4 - x^3 + 3x^2 - 8x + 8$;
no real zero greater than 2

2. $P(x) = 2x^5 - x^4 + 2x^3 - 2x^2 + 4x - 4$;
no real zero greater than 1

3. $P(x) = x^4 + x^3 - x^2 + 3$;
no real zero less than -2

4. $P(x) = x^5 + 2x^3 - 2x^2 + 5x + 5$;
no real zero less than -1

5. $P(x) = 3x^4 + 2x^3 - 4x^2 + x - 1$;
no real zero greater than 1

6. $P(x) = 3x^4 + 2x^3 - 4x^2 + x - 1$;
no real zero less than -2

CHECKING BASIC CONCEPTS FOR SECTIONS 4.3 AND 4.4

1. Simplify the expression $\dfrac{5x^4 - 10x^3 + 5x^2}{5x^2}$.

2. Divide the expression.

   (a) $\dfrac{x^3 - x^2 + 4x - 4}{x - 1}$

   (b) $\dfrac{2x^3 - 3x^2 + 4x + 4}{2x + 1}$

   (c) $\dfrac{x^4 - 3x^3 + 6x^2 - 13x + 9}{x^2 + 4}$

3. Use the graph of the cubic polynomial $f(x)$ in the next column to determine its complete factored form. State the multiplicity of each zero. Assume that all zeros are integers and that the leading coefficient is *not* ± 1.

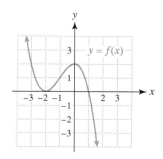

4. Solve $x^3 - 2x^2 - 15x = 0$.

5. Determine graphically the zeros of
$$f(x) = x^4 - x^3 - 18x^2 + 16x + 32.$$
   Write $f(x)$ in complete factored form.

4.5 The Fundamental Theorem of Algebra

- **Apply the fundamental theorem of algebra**
- **Factor polynomials having complex zeros**
- **Solve polynomial equations having complex solutions**

Introduction

In Section 3.2 the quadratic formula was used to solve $ax^2 + bx + c = 0$. Are there similar formulas for higher degree polynomial equations? One of the most spectacular mathematical achievements during the sixteenth century was the discovery of formulas for solving cubic and quartic equations. This was accomplished by the Italian mathematicians Tartaglia, Cardano, Fior, del Ferro, and Ferrari between 1515 and 1545. These formulas are quite complicated and typically used only in computer software. In about 1805, the Italian physician Ruffini proved that finding formulas for quintic or higher degree equations was impossible. Another spectacular result came from Carl Friedrich Gauss. He proved that all polynomials can be completely factored by using complex numbers. This result is called the **fundamental theorem of algebra**. (*Source:* H. Eves, *An Introduction to the History of Mathematics.*)

Fundamental Theorem of Algebra

One of the most brilliant mathematicians of all time, Carl Friedrich Gauss proved the fundamental theorem of algebra as part of his doctoral thesis at age 20. Although his theorem and proof were completed in 1797, they are still valid today.

> **FUNDAMENTAL THEOREM OF ALGEBRA**
>
> A polynomial $f(x)$ of degree n, with $n \geq 1$, has at least one complex zero.

NOTE The fundamental theorem of algebra guarantees that *every polynomial has a complete factorization*, provided we are allowed to use complex numbers.

Justification for Complete Factorization of Polynomials If $f(x)$ is a polynomial of degree 1 or higher, then by the fundamental theorem of algebra there is a zero c_1 such that $f(c_1) = 0$. By the factor theorem, $(x - c_1)$ is a factor of $f(x)$ and $f(x) = (x - c_1)\, q_1(x)$ for some polynomial $q_1(x)$. If $q_1(x)$ has positive degree, then by the fundamental theorem of algebra there exists a zero c_2 of $q_1(x)$. By the factor theorem, $q_1(x)$ can be written as $q_1(x) = (x - c_2)\, q_2(x)$. Then

$$f(x) = (x - c_1)q_1(x) = (x - c_1)(x - c_2)q_2(x).$$

If $f(x)$ has degree n, this process can be continued until $f(x)$ is written in the complete factored form

$$f(x) = a_n(x - c_1)(x - c_2) \cdots (x - c_n),$$

where a_n is the leading coefficient and the c_k are complex zeros of $f(x)$. If each c_k is distinct, then $f(x)$ has n zeros. However, in general the c_k may not be distinct since multiple zeros are possible.

NUMBER OF ZEROS THEOREM

A polynomial of degree n has at most n distinct zeros.

EXAMPLE 1 Classifying zeros

All zeros for the given polynomials are distinct. Use Figures 4.71–4.73 to determine graphically the number of real zeros and the number of imaginary zeros.

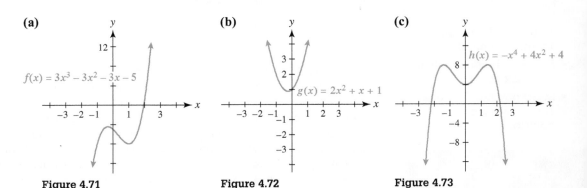

(a) $f(x) = 3x^3 - 3x^2 - 3x - 5$

Figure 4.71

(b) $g(x) = 2x^2 + x + 1$

Figure 4.72

(c) $h(x) = -x^4 + 4x^2 + 4$

Figure 4.73

SOLUTION

Getting Started Each (distinct) real zero corresponds to an x-intercept. Imaginary zeros do *not* correspond to x-intercepts, but their number can be determined after the number of real zeros is known. ▶

(a) The graph of $f(x)$ in Figure 4.71 crosses the x-axis once, so there is one real zero. Since f is degree 3 and all zeros are distinct, there are two imaginary zeros.

(b) The graph of $g(x)$ in Figure 4.72 never crosses the x-axis. Since g is degree 2, there are no real zeros and two imaginary zeros.

(c) The graph of $h(x)$ is shown in Figure 4.73. Since h is degree 4, there are two real zeros and the remaining two zeros are imaginary.

Now Try Exercises 1, 3, and 5

NOTE The sum of the imaginary zeros and the real zeros (counting multiplicities) equals the degree n of the polynomial. A polynomial with real coefficients always has an even number of imaginary zeros.

EXAMPLE 2   Constructing a polynomial with prescribed zeros

Determine a polynomial $f(x)$ of degree 4 with leading coefficient 2 and zeros $-3, 5, i$, and $-i$ in **(a)** complete factored form and **(b)** expanded form.

SOLUTION

(a) Let $a_n = 2, c_1 = -3, c_2 = 5, c_3 = i$, and $c_4 = -i$. Then

$$f(x) = 2(x + 3)(x - 5)(x - i)(x + i).$$

(b) To expand this expression for $f(x)$, perform the following steps.

$$\begin{aligned} 2(x + 3)(x - 5)(x - i)(x + i) &= 2(x + 3)(x - 5)(x^2 + 1) \\ &= 2(x + 3)(x^3 - 5x^2 + x - 5) \\ &= 2(x^4 - 2x^3 - 14x^2 - 2x - 15) \\ &= 2x^4 - 4x^3 - 28x^2 - 4x - 30 \end{aligned}$$

Thus $f(x) = 2x^4 - 4x^3 - 28x^2 - 4x - 30$.

Now Try Exercise 13

EXAMPLE 3   Factoring a cubic polynomial with imaginary zeros

Determine the complete factored form for $f(x) = x^3 + 2x^2 + 4x + 8$.

SOLUTION

We can use factoring by grouping to determine the complete factored form.

$$\begin{aligned} x^3 + 2x^2 + 4x + 8 &= (x^3 + 2x^2) + (4x + 8) &&\text{Associative property} \\ &= x^2(x + 2) + 4(x + 2) &&\text{Distributive property} \\ &= (x^2 + 4)(x + 2) &&\text{Factor out } x + 2. \end{aligned}$$

Algebra Review

To review factoring a cubic polynomial by grouping, see Chapter R (page R-20).

To factor $x^2 + 4$, first find its zeros.

$$\begin{aligned} x^2 + 4 &= 0 \\ x^2 &= -4 \\ x &= \pm\sqrt{-4} \\ x &= \pm 2i \end{aligned}$$

The zeros of $f(x)$ are $-2, 2i$, and $-2i$. Its complete factored form is

$$f(x) = (x + 2)(x - 2i)(x + 2i).$$

Now Try Exercise 29

Conjugate Zeros   Notice that in Example 3 both $2i$ and $-2i$ were zeros of $f(x)$. The numbers $2i$ and $-2i$ are *conjugates*. See Section 3.3. This result can be generalized.

CONJUGATE ZEROS THEOREM

If a polynomial $f(x)$ has only real coefficients and if $a + bi$ is a zero of $f(x)$, then the conjugate $a - bi$ is also a zero of $f(x)$.

EXAMPLE 4   Constructing a polynomial with prescribed zeros

Determine a cubic polynomial $f(x)$ with real coefficients, leading coefficient 2, and zeros 3 and $5i$. Express $f(x)$ in **(a)** complete factored form and **(b)** expanded form.

SOLUTION

(a) Since $f(x)$ has real coefficients, it must also have a third zero of $-5i$, the conjugate of $5i$. Let $c_1 = 3$, $c_2 = 5i$, $c_3 = -5i$, and $a_n = 2$. The complete factored form is

$$f(x) = 2(x - 3)(x - 5i)(x + 5i).$$

(b) To expand $f(x)$, perform the following steps.

$$2(x - 3)(x - 5i)(x + 5i) = 2(x - 3)(x^2 + 25)$$
$$= 2(x^3 - 3x^2 + 25x - 75)$$
$$= 2x^3 - 6x^2 + 50x - 150$$

> **Now Try Exercise 15**

EXAMPLE 5 Finding imaginary zeros of a polynomial

Find the zeros of $f(x) = x^4 + x^3 + 2x^2 + x + 1$, given that one zero is $-i$.

SOLUTION

By the conjugate zeros theorem, it follows that i must also be a zero of $f(x)$. Therefore $(x - i)$ and $(x + i)$ are factors of $f(x)$. Because $(x - i)(x + i) = x^2 + 1$, we can use long division to find another quadratic factor of $f(x)$.

$$
\begin{array}{r}
x^2 + x + 1 \\
x^2 + 0x + 1 \overline{)x^4 + x^3 + 2x^2 + x + 1} \\
\underline{x^4 + 0x^3 + x^2} \\
x^3 + x^2 + x \\
\underline{x^3 + 0x^2 + x} \\
x^2 + 0x + 1 \\
\underline{x^2 + 0x + 1} \\
0
\end{array}
$$

The quotient is $x^2 + x + 1$ with remainder 0. By the division algorithm,

$$x^4 + x^3 + 2x^2 + x + 1 = (x^2 + 1)(x^2 + x + 1).$$

We can use the quadratic formula to find the zeros of $x^2 + x + 1$.

$$x = \frac{-b \pm \sqrt{b^2 - 4ac}}{2a}$$
$$= \frac{-1 \pm \sqrt{1^2 - 4(1)(1)}}{2(1)}$$
$$= -\frac{1}{2} \pm i\frac{\sqrt{3}}{2}$$

The four zeros of $f(x)$ are $\pm i$ and $-\frac{1}{2} \pm i\frac{\sqrt{3}}{2}$.

> **Now Try Exercise 21**

Polynomial Equations with Complex Solutions

Every polynomial equation of degree n can be written in the form

$$a_n x^n + \cdots + a_2 x^2 + a_1 x + a_0 = 0.$$

If we let $f(x) = a_n x^n + \cdots + a_2 x^2 + a_1 x + a_0$ and write $f(x)$ in complete factored form as

$$f(x) = a_n(x - c_1)(x - c_2) \cdots (x - c_n),$$

then the solutions to the polynomial equation are the zeros $c_1, c_2, \ldots, c_n$ of $f(x)$. Solving cubic and quartic polynomial equations with this technique is illustrated in the next two examples.

EXAMPLE 6 Solving a polynomial equation

Solve $x^3 = 3x^2 - 7x + 21$.

SOLUTION

Write the equation as $f(x) = 0$, where $f(x) = x^3 - 3x^2 + 7x - 21$. Although we could use factoring by grouping, as is done in Example 3, we use graphing instead to find one real zero of $f(x)$. Figure 4.74 shows that 3 is a zero of $f(x)$. By the factor theorem, $x - 3$ is a factor of $f(x)$. Using synthetic division, we divide $x - 3$ into $f(x)$.

$[-5, 5, 1]$ by $[-30, 30, 10]$

Figure 4.74

$$
\begin{array}{r|rrrr}
3 & 1 & -3 & 7 & -21 \\
  &   & 3 & 0 & 21 \\
\hline
  & 1 & 0 & 7 & 0
\end{array}
$$

Thus $x^3 - 3x^2 + 7x - 21 = (x - 3)(x^2 + 7)$, and we can solve as follows.

$x^3 - 3x^2 + 7x - 21 = 0$	Solve $f(x) = 0$.
$(x - 3)(x^2 + 7) = 0$	Factor.
$x - 3 = 0$ or $x^2 + 7 = 0$	Zero-product property
$x = 3$ or $x^2 = -7$	Solve.
$x = 3$ or $x = \pm i\sqrt{7}$	Property of i

The solutions are 3 and $\pm i\sqrt{7}$.

Now Try Exercise 33

EXAMPLE 7 Solving a polynomial equation

Solve $x^4 + x^2 = x^3$.

SOLUTION

Write the equation as $f(x) = 0$, where $f(x) = x^4 - x^3 + x^2$.

$[-3, 3, 1]$ by $[-2, 2, 1]$

Figure 4.75

$x^4 - x^3 + x^2 = 0$	$f(x) = 0$
$x^2(x^2 - x + 1) = 0$	Factor out x^2.
$x^2 = 0$ or $x^2 - x + 1 = 0$	Zero-product property

The only solution to $x^2 = 0$ is 0. To solve $x^2 - x + 1 = 0$, use the quadratic formula, as in Example 5. The solutions are 0 and $\frac{1}{2} \pm i\frac{\sqrt{3}}{2}$.

The graphs of $y_1 = x^4 + x^2$ and $y_2 = x^3$ are shown in Figure 4.75. Notice that they appear to intersect only at the origin. This indicates that the only *real* solution is 0.

Now Try Exercise 37

4.5 Putting It All Together

Some of the important topics in this section are summarized in the following table.

CONCEPT	EXPLANATION	COMMENTS AND EXAMPLES
Number of zeros theorem	A polynomial of degree n has at most n distinct zeros. These zeros can be real or imaginary numbers.	The cubic polynomial, $$ax^3 + bx^2 + cx + d,$$ has *at most* three distinct zeros.
Fundamental theorem of algebra	A polynomial of degree n, with $n \geq 1$, has at least one complex zero.	This theorem guarantees that we can always factor a polynomial $f(x)$ into complete factored form: $$f(x) = a_n(x - c_1) \cdots (x - c_n),$$ where the c_k are complex numbers.

continued on next page

CONCEPT	EXPLANATION	COMMENTS AND EXAMPLES
Conjugate zeros theorem	If a polynomial has *real* coefficients and $a + bi$ is a zero, then $a - bi$ is also a zero.	Since $\frac{1}{2} + \frac{1}{2}i$ is a zero of $2x^2 - 2x + 1$, it follows that $\frac{1}{2} - \frac{1}{2}i$ is also a zero.

4.5 Exercises

Zeros of Polynomials

Exercises 1–8: The graph and degree of a polynomial with real coefficients $f(x)$ are given. Determine the number of real zeros and the number of imaginary zeros. Assume that all zeros of $f(x)$ are distinct.

1. Degree 2

2. Degree 2

3. Degree 3

4. Degree 3

5. Degree 4

6. Degree 4

7. Degree 5

8. Degree 5

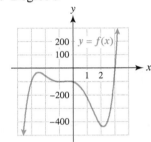

Exercises 9–18: Let a_n be the leading coefficient.

(a) *Find the complete factored form of a polynomial with real coefficients $f(x)$ that satisfy the conditions.*

(b) *Express $f(x)$ in expanded form.*

9. Degree 2; $a_n = 1$;   zeros 6i and $-6i$

10. Degree 3; $a_n = 5$;   zeros 2, i, and $-i$

11. Degree 3; $a_n = -1$;   zeros -1, $2i$, and $-2i$

12. Degree 4; $a_n = 3$;   zeros -2, 4, i, and $-i$

13. Degree 4; $a_n = 10$;   zeros 1, -1, $3i$, and $-3i$

14. Degree 2; $a_n = -5$;   zeros $1 + i$ and $1 - i$

15. Degree 4; $a_n = \frac{1}{2}$;   zeros $-i$ and $2i$

16. Degree 3; $a_n = -\frac{3}{4}$;   zeros $-3i$ and $\frac{2}{5}$

17. Degree 3; $a_n = -2$;   zeros $1 - i$ and 3

18. Degree 4; $a_n = 7$;   zeros $2i$ and $3i$

Exercises 19–22: (Refer to Example 5.) Find the zeros of $f(x)$, given that one zero is k.

19. $f(x) = 3x^3 - 5x^2 + 75x - 125$ $k = \frac{5}{3}$

20. $f(x) = x^4 + 2x^3 + 8x^2 + 8x + 16$ $k = 2i$

21. $f(x) = 2x^4 - x^3 + 19x^2 - 9x + 9$ $k = -3i$

22. $f(x) = 7x^3 + 5x^2 + 12x - 4$ $k = \frac{2}{7}$

Exercises 23–30: Complete the following.
(a) Find all zeros of $f(x)$.
(b) Write the complete factored form of $f(x)$.

23. $f(x) = x^2 + 25$ **24.** $f(x) = x^2 + 11$

25. $f(x) = 3x^3 + 3x$ **26.** $f(x) = 2x^3 + 10x$

27. $f(x) = x^4 + 5x^2 + 4$ **28.** $f(x) = x^4 + 4x^2$

29. $f(x) = x^3 + 2x^2 + 16x + 32$

30. $f(x) = x^4 + 2x^3 + x^2 + 8x - 12$

Exercises 31–42: Solve the polynomial equation.

31. $x^3 + x = 0$ **32.** $2x^3 - x + 1 = 0$

33. $x^3 = 2x^2 - 7x + 14$ **34.** $x^2 + x + 2 = x^3$

35. $x^4 + 5x^2 = 0$ **36.** $x^4 - 2x^3 + x^2 - 2x = 0$

37. $x^4 = x^3 - 4x^2$ **38.** $x^5 + 9x^3 = x^4 + 9x^2$

39. $x^4 + x^3 = 16 - 8x - 6x^2$

40. $x^4 + 2x^2 = x^3$ **41.** $3x^3 + 4x^2 + 6 = x$

42. $2x^3 + 5x^2 + x + 12 = 0$

Writing About Mathematics

43. Could a cubic function with real coefficients have only imaginary zeros? Explain.

44. Give an example of a polynomial function that has only imaginary zeros and a polynomial function that has only real zeros. Explain how to determine graphically if a function has only imaginary zeros.

4.6 Rational Functions and Models

- **Identify a rational function and state its domain**
- **Identify asymptotes**
- **Interpret asymptotes**
- **Graph a rational function by using transformations**
- **Graph a rational function by hand (optional)**

Introduction

Rational functions are (typically) nonlinear functions that frequently occur in applications. For example, rational functions are used to model postings on social networks, design curves for railroad tracks, determine stopping distances on hills, and calculate the average number of people waiting in a line.

Rational Functions

A *rational* number can be expressed as a *ratio* $\frac{p}{q}$, where p and q are integers with $q \neq 0$. A rational function is defined similarly by using the concept of a polynomial.

> **RATIONAL FUNCTION**
>
> A function f represented by $f(x) = \dfrac{p(x)}{q(x)}$, where $p(x)$ and $q(x)$ are polynomials and $q(x) \neq 0$, is a **rational function**.

The domain of a rational function includes all real numbers *except* the zeros of the denominator $q(x)$. The graph of a rational function is continuous except at x-values where $q(x) = 0$.

EXAMPLE 1   Identifying rational functions

Algebra Review
To review rational expressions, see Chapter R (page R-28).

Determine if the function is rational and state its domain.

(a) $f(x) = \dfrac{2x - 1}{x^2 + 1}$ **(b)** $g(x) = \dfrac{1}{\sqrt{x}}$ **(c)** $h(x) = \dfrac{x^3 - 2x^2 + 1}{x^2 - 3x + 2}$

SOLUTION

(a) Both the numerator, $2x - 1$, and the denominator, $x^2 + 1$, are polynomials, so f is a rational function. The domain of f includes all real numbers because its denominator $x^2 + 1 \neq 0$ for any real number x.

(b) The expression $\sqrt{x}$ is not a polynomial, so $g(x) = \frac{1}{\sqrt{x}}$ is not a rational function. The domain is $\{x \mid x > 0\}$.

(c) Both the numerator and the denominator are polynomials, so $h(x) = \frac{x^3 - 2x^2 + 1}{x^2 - 3x + 2}$ is a rational function. Because

$$x^2 - 3x + 2 = (x - 1)(x - 2) = 0$$

when $x = 1$ or $x = 2$, the domain of h is $\{x \mid x \neq 1, x \neq 2\}$.

> **Now Try Exercises 1, 7, and 9**

CLASS DISCUSSION

Is an integer a rational number? Is a polynomial function a rational function?

Vertical Asymptotes

A rational function given by $f(x) = \frac{p(x)}{q(x)}$ is undefined whenever $q(x) = 0$. If $q(k) = 0$ for some k, then a *vertical asymptote* of the graph of f *may* occur at $x = k$. Near a vertical asymptote, the y-values on the graph of f become very large (unbounded) in absolute value.

For example, Figure 4.76 shows the graph of a rational function defined by $f(x) = \frac{1}{x - 2}$. It has a vertical asymptote, which is shown as a dashed red line at $x = 2$. Note that $x = 2$ is *not* in the domain of f.

See the Concept: Rational Functions and Vertical Asymptotes

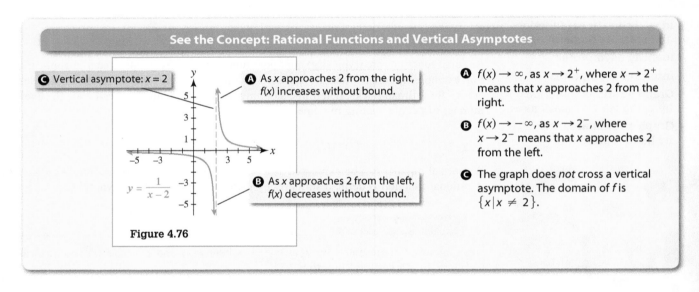

© Vertical asymptote: $x = 2$

$y = \frac{1}{x - 2}$

A As x approaches 2 from the right, $f(x)$ increases without bound.

B As x approaches 2 from the left, $f(x)$ decreases without bound.

A $f(x) \to \infty$, as $x \to 2^+$, where $x \to 2^+$ means that x approaches 2 from the right.

B $f(x) \to -\infty$, as $x \to 2^-$, where $x \to 2^-$ means that x approaches 2 from the left.

© The graph does *not* cross a vertical asymptote. The domain of f is $\{x \mid x \neq 2\}$.

Figure 4.76

NOTE A vertical asymptote is not part of the graph of a rational function; rather, it is an aid that is used to sketch and to better understand the graph of a rational function.

VERTICAL ASYMPTOTE

The line $x = k$ is a **vertical asymptote** of the graph of f if $f(x) \to \infty$ or $f(x) \to -\infty$ as x approaches k from either the left or the right.

An Application If cars leave a parking garage randomly and stop to pay the parking attendant on the way out, then the average length of the line depends on two factors: the average traffic rate at which cars are exiting the ramp and the average rate at which the parking attendant can wait on cars. For instance, if the average traffic rate is **three** cars per minute and the parking attendant can serve **four** cars per minute, then at times a line may form *if* cars arrive in a *random* manner. The **traffic intensity** x is the ratio of the average traffic rate to the average working rate of the attendant. In this example, $x = \frac{3}{4}$. (*Source:* F. Mannering and W. Kilareski, *Principles of Highway Engineering and Traffic Control.*)

EXAMPLE 2 Estimating the length of parking garage lines

If the traffic intensity is x, then the average number of cars waiting in line to exit a parking garage can be estimated by $N(x) = \frac{x^2}{2 - 2x}$, where $0 \le x < 1$.
(a) Evaluate $N(0.5)$ and $N(0.9)$. Interpret the results.
(b) Use the graph of $y = N(x)$ in Figure 4.77 to explain what happens to the length of the line as the traffic intensity x increases to 1 from the left (denoted $x \to 1^-$.)

Parking Garage Lines

Average line length (cars) / Traffic intensity

$N(x) = \dfrac{x^2}{2 - 2x}$

Vertical asymptote: $x = 1$

Figure 4.77

SOLUTION
(a) $N(0.5) = \frac{0.5^2}{2 - 2(0.5)} = 0.25$ and $N(0.9) = \frac{0.9^2}{2 - 2(0.9)} = 4.05$. This means that if the traffic intensity is 0.5, there is little waiting in line. As the traffic intensity increases to 0.9, the average line has more than four cars.
(b) As the traffic intensity x approaches 1 from the left in Figure 4.77 the graph of f increases rapidly without bound. Numerical support is given in Table 4.4. With a traffic intensity slightly less than 1, the attendant has difficulty keeping up. If cars occasionally arrive in groups, long lines will form. At $x = 1$ the denominator, $2 - 2x$, equals 0 and $N(x)$ is undefined.

Traffic Intensity Approaching 1

x	0.94	0.95	0.96	0.97	0.98	0.99	1
$\dfrac{x^2}{2 - 2x}$	7.36	9.03	11.52	15.68	24.01	49.01	—

Table 4.4

Long lines form

Now Try Exercise 97

Horizontal Asymptotes

If the absolute value of x becomes large in the formula $f(x)$ for a rational function, then the graph of f *may* level off and begin to approximate a horizontal line. This horizontal line is called a *horizontal asymptote.*

In See the Concept on the next page, Figure 4.78 shows the graph of the rational function $f(x) = \frac{x^2}{x^2 + 1}$. This rational function does not have a vertical asymptote because the denominator, $x^2 + 1$, has no real zeros. However, the graph does have a horizontal asymptote, which is shown as a dashed red line at $y = 1$.

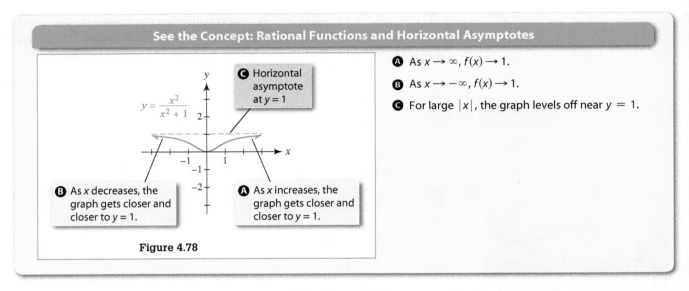

See the Concept: Rational Functions and Horizontal Asymptotes

$y = \dfrac{x^2}{x^2 + 1}$

Ⓒ Horizontal asymptote at $y = 1$

Ⓑ As x decreases, the graph gets closer and closer to $y = 1$.

Ⓐ As x increases, the graph gets closer and closer to $y = 1$.

Ⓐ As $x \to \infty$, $f(x) \to 1$.

Ⓑ As $x \to -\infty$, $f(x) \to 1$.

Ⓒ For large $|x|$, the graph levels off near $y = 1$.

Figure 4.78

Asymptotes and Tables of Values A table of values can be used to illustrate the concept of a horizontal asymptote for $y = \dfrac{x^2}{x^2 + 1}$. See Figures 4.79 and 4.80. Notice that the y-values level off slightly below 1, which agrees with the graph in Figure 4.78.

Tables and Horizontal Asymptotes

Ⓐ As x increases...

Ⓑ the y_1-values approach 1.

X	Y1
0	0
5	.96154
10	.9901
15	.99558
20	.99751
25	.9984
30	.99889

Y1 ▤ X² / (X² + 1)

Figure 4.79

Ⓒ As x decreases...

Ⓓ the y_1-values approach 1.

X	Y1
0	0
−5	.96154
−10	.9901
−15	.99558
−20	.99751
−25	.9984
−30	.99889

Y1 ▤ X² / (X² + 1)

Figure 4.80

HORIZONTAL ASYMPTOTE

The line $y = b$ is a **horizontal asymptote** of the graph of f if $f(x) \to b$ as x approaches either ∞ or $-\infty$.

NOTE Like a vertical asymptote, a horizontal asymptote is *not* part of the graph of a rational function; rather, it is an aid that is used to sketch and to better understand the graph of a rational function. However, unlike in the case of vertical asymptotes, it *is possible* for the graph of a rational function to *cross* a horizontal asymptote. See Examples 4(b) and 11.

An Application The graph of f in Figure 4.81 is an example of a growth curve. It models the length in millimeters of a small fish after x weeks.

Length of a Small Fish

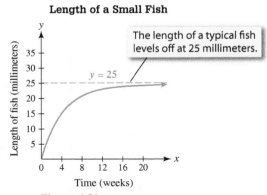

The length of a typical fish levels off at 25 millimeters.

$y = 25$

Length of fish (millimeters)

Time (weeks)

Figure 4.81

After several weeks the length of the fish begins to level off near 25 millimeters. Thus $y = 25$ is a horizontal asymptote of the graph of f. This is denoted by $f(x) \to 25$ as $x \to \infty$.   (*Source:* D. Brown and P. Rothery, *Models in Biology*.)

In real-life applications, time does not actually approach infinity. For example, a fish does not live forever. However, the asymptote $y = 25$ does tend to model the length of the fish as it becomes older.

Identifying Asymptotes

Asymptotes can be found visually from a graph and symbolically from a formula. The next two examples discuss these techniques.

EXAMPLE 3   Determining horizontal and vertical asymptotes visually

Use the graph of each rational function to determine any vertical or horizontal asymptotes.

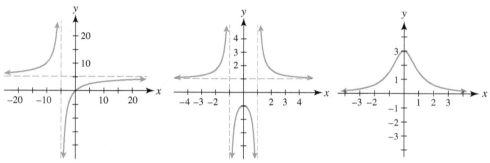

Figure 4.82   Figure 4.83   Figure 4.84

SOLUTION

In Figure 4.82, $x = -5$ is a vertical asymptote and $y = 5$ is a horizontal asymptote. In Figure 4.83, $x = \pm 1$ are vertical asymptotes and $y = 1$ is a horizontal asymptote. In Figure 4.84, there are no vertical asymptotes. The x-axis ($y = 0$) is a horizontal asymptote.

Now Try Exercises **13, 15,** and **17**

The following technique can be used for rational functions to find vertical and horizontal asymptotes symbolically.

FINDING VERTICAL AND HORIZONTAL ASYMPTOTES

Let f be a rational function given by $f(x) = \dfrac{p(x)}{q(x)}$ written in *lowest* terms.

Vertical Asymptote

To find a vertical asymptote, set the denominator, $q(x)$, equal to 0 and solve. If k is a zero of $q(x)$, then $x = k$ is a vertical asymptote. *Caution:* If k is a zero of both $q(x)$ *and* $p(x)$, then $f(x)$ is not written in lowest terms, and $x - k$ is a common factor.

Horizontal Asymptote

(a) If the degree of the numerator is less than the degree of the denominator, then $y = 0$ (the x-axis) is a horizontal asymptote.

(b) If the degree of the numerator equals the degree of the denominator, then $y = \frac{a}{b}$ is a horizontal asymptote, where a is the leading coefficient of the numerator and b is the leading coefficient of the denominator.

(c) If the degree of the numerator is greater than the degree of the denominator, then there are no horizontal asymptotes.

EXAMPLE 4 Finding asymptotes

For each rational function, determine any horizontal or vertical asymptotes.

(a) $f(x) = \dfrac{6x - 1}{3x + 3}$ **(b)** $g(x) = \dfrac{x + 1}{x^2 - 4}$ **(c)** $h(x) = \dfrac{x^2 - 1}{x + 1}$

SOLUTION

(a) The numerator and denominator have no common factors, so the expression is in lowest terms.

Ⓐ Degrees are equal . . .

Ⓑ so $y = \frac{6}{3}$, or $y = 2$, is a horizontal asymptote. See Figure 4.85.

Ⓒ The denominator is equal to 0 when $x = -1$ . . .

Ⓓ so $x = -1$ is a vertical asymptote.

A graph of $f(x) = \frac{6x - 1}{3x + 3}$ is shown in Figure 4.85. In Figures 4.86 and 4.87, the tables support that $y = 2$ is a horizontal asymptote.

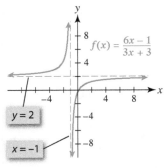

Figure 4.85

Horizontal Asymptote: $y = 2$

Figure 4.86   **Figure 4.87**

(b) In the expression $\frac{x + 1}{x^2 - 4}$, the degree of the numerator is one less than the degree of the denominator, so the x-axis, or $y = 0$, is a horizontal asymptote. When $x = \pm 2$, the denominator, $x^2 - 4$, equals 0 and the numerator, $x + 1$, does not equal 0. Thus $x = \pm 2$ are vertical asymptotes. See Figure 4.88. Note that the graph crosses the horizontal asymptote $y = 0$ but does not cross either vertical asymptote.

Algebra Review

To review simplifying rational expressions, see Chapter R (page R-28).

(c) The degree of the numerator, $x^2 - 1$, is greater than the degree of the denominator, $x + 1$, so there are no horizontal asymptotes. When $x = -1$, both numerator and denominator equal 0, so the expression is *not* in lowest terms. We can simplify $h(x)$ as follows.

$$h(x) = \frac{x^2 - 1}{x + 1} = \frac{(x + 1)(x - 1)}{x + 1} = x - 1, \qquad x \neq -1$$

The graph of $h(x)$ is the line $y = x - 1$ with the point $(-1, -2)$ missing. There are no vertical asymptotes. See Figure 4.89.

Graph with Asymptotes

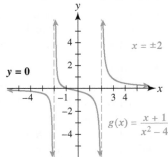

Figure 4.88

Graph with a "Hole"

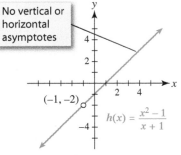

Figure 4.89

Now Try Exercises 21, 23, and 31

Slant Asymptote

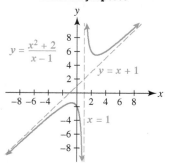

Figure 4.90

Slant, or Oblique, Asymptotes   A third type of asymptote, which is neither vertical nor horizontal, occurs when the numerator of a rational function has degree *one more* than the degree of the denominator. For example, let $f(x) = \frac{x^2 + 2}{x - 1}$. If $x - 1$ is divided into $x^2 + 2$, the quotient is $x + 1$ with remainder 3. Thus

$$f(x) = x + 1 + \frac{3}{x - 1}$$

is an equivalent representation of $f(x)$. For large values of $|x|$, the ratio $\frac{3}{x - 1}$ approaches 0 and the graph of f approaches $y = x + 1$. The line $y = x + 1$ is called a **slant asymptote,** or **oblique asymptote**, of the graph of f. A graph of $f(x) = \frac{x^2 + 2}{x - 1}$ with vertical asymptote $x = 1$ and slant asymptote $y = x + 1$ is shown in Figure 4.90.

MAKING CONNECTIONS

Division Algorithm and Asymptotes   Suppose that the division algorithm is used to write a rational function f in the form

$$f(x) = (\text{Quotient}) + \frac{(\text{Remainder})}{(\text{Divisor})}.$$

1. If the quotient equals a constant k, then $y = k$ is a horizontal asymptote.

   Example: $f(x) = \frac{2x - 1}{x - 1} = 2 + \frac{1}{x - 1}$, so $y = 2$ is a horizontal asymptote.

2. If the quotient equals $ax + b$ with $a \neq 0$ (linear), then $y = ax + b$ is a slant asymptote.

   Example: $f(x) = \frac{x^2 + 2}{x - 1} = x + 1 + \frac{3}{x - 1}$, so $y = x + 1$ is a slant asymptote.

Graphs and Transformations of Rational Functions

Graphs of rational functions can vary greatly in complexity. We begin by graphing $y = \frac{1}{x}$ and then use transformations to graph other rational functions.

EXAMPLE 5   Analyzing the graph of $y = \frac{1}{x}$

Sketch a graph of $y = \frac{1}{x}$ and identify any asymptotes.

SOLUTION

Note that when $x = 0$, the denominator is 0 but the numerator is not. Thus $x = 0$ (the y-axis) is a vertical asymptote. Also, the degree of the numerator is less than the degree of the denominator, so $y = 0$ (the x-axis) is a horizontal asymptote. Table 4.5 lists points that lie on the graph of $y = \frac{1}{x}$. These points and the graph are shown in Figure 4.91.

x	$y = \frac{1}{x}$
-2	$-\frac{1}{2}$
-1	-1
$-\frac{1}{2}$	-2
0	—
$\frac{1}{2}$	2
1	1
2	$\frac{1}{2}$

Table 4.5

Graph of $y = \frac{1}{x}$

Figure 4.91

Now Try Exercise 41

Transformations   Transformations of graphs can be used to graph some types of rational functions by hand, as illustrated in Figures 4.92 and 4.93.

Figure 4.92   **Figure 4.93**

EXAMPLE 6   Graphing with transformations

Graph $y = \dfrac{1}{x - 1} + 2$.

SOLUTION
We can graph $g(x) = \frac{1}{x-1} + 2$ by translating the graph of $f(x) = \frac{1}{x}$ right 1 unit and upward 2 units. That is, $g(x)$ can be written in terms of $f(x)$ using $g(x) = f(x - 1) + 2$. Because the graph of $y = \frac{1}{x}$ in Figure 4.91 has vertical asymptote $x = 0$ and horizontal asymptote $y = 0$, the graph of g in Figure 4.94 has vertical asymptote $x = 1$ and horizontal asymptote $y = 2$.

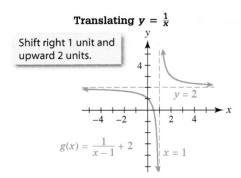

Figure 4.94

Now Try Exercise 49

NOTE   If we are given function g from Example 6 in the form $g(x) = \frac{2x - 1}{x - 1}$, then we can use the division algorithm to divide $x - 1$ into $2x - 1$ and obtain quotient 2 with remainder 1.

$$
\begin{array}{r}
2 \\
x - 1 \overline{)\, 2x - 1} \\
\underline{2x - 2} \\
1
\end{array}
$$

$\frac{2x}{x} = 2$

$2(x - 1) = 2x - 2$

Subtract: $-1 - (-2) = 1.$

Thus $g(x) = 2 + \frac{1}{x - 1}$, and we can graph g as in Figure 4.94.

EXAMPLE 7 Using transformations to graph a rational function

Use the graph of $f(x) = \frac{1}{x^2}$ in Figure 4.95 to sketch a graph of $g(x) = -\frac{1}{(x+2)^2}$. Include all asymptotes in your graph. Write $g(x)$ in terms of $f(x)$.

Graph of $y = \dfrac{1}{x^2}$

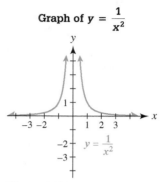

Figure 4.95

SOLUTION
The graph of $y = \frac{1}{x^2}$ has vertical asymptote $x = 0$ and horizontal asymptote $y = 0$. The graph of $g(x) = -\frac{1}{(x+2)^2}$ is a translation of the graph of $f(x) = \frac{1}{x^2}$ left 2 units and then a reflection across the x-axis. The vertical asymptote for $y = g(x)$ is $x = -2$ and the horizontal asymptote is $y = 0$, as shown in Figure 4.96. We can write $g(x)$ in terms of $f(x)$ as $g(x) = -f(x + 2)$.

Translating $y = \dfrac{1}{x^2}$

Shift left 2 units; reflect across x-axis.

Figure 4.96

Now Try Exercise 51

Graphing with Technology Although many graphing calculators have difficulty accurately showing some features of the graph of a rational function, they can be helpful when they are used in conjunction with symbolic techniques.

Calculator Help
To set dot mode, see Appendix A (page AP-8). To set a decimal window, see Appendix A (page AP-11).

NOTE Calculators often graph in connected or dot mode. (See Figure 4.97 on the next page.) If connected mode is used to graph a rational function, it may appear as though the calculator is graphing vertical asymptotes automatically. However, in most instances the calculator is connecting points inappropriately. Sometimes rational functions can be graphed in connected mode using a *decimal* or *friendly* viewing rectangle.

EXAMPLE 8 Analyzing a rational function with technology

Let $f(x) = \frac{2x^2 + 1}{x^2 - 4}$.
(a) Use a calculator to graph f. Find the domain of f.
(b) Identify any vertical or horizontal asymptotes.
(c) Sketch a graph of f that includes the asymptotes.

Graphing in Dot Mode

$[-6, 6, 1]$ by $[-6, 6, 1]$

Figure 4.97

SOLUTION

(a) A calculator graph of $f(x) = \frac{2x^2 + 1}{x^2 - 4}$ using dot mode is shown in Figure 4.97. The function is undefined when $x^2 - 4 = 0$, or when $x = \pm 2$. The domain of function f is given by $D = \{x \mid x \neq 2, x \neq -2\}$.

(b) When $x = \pm 2$, the denominator, $x^2 - 4$, equals 0 and the numerator, $2x^2 + 1$, does not equal 0. Therefore $x = \pm 2$ are vertical asymptotes. The degree of the numerator equals the degree of the denominator, and the ratio of the leading coefficients is $\frac{2}{1} = 2$. A horizontal asymptote of the graph of f is $y = 2$.

(c) A second graph of f and its asymptotes is shown in Figure 4.98.

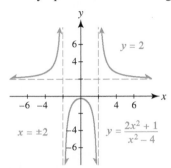

Figure 4.98

Now Try Exercise 57

Graphs with "Holes" If $f(x) = \frac{p(x)}{q(x)}$ is *not* in lowest terms, then it is possible that for some number k both $p(k) = 0$ and $q(k) = 0$. In this case, the graph of f may *not* have a vertical asymptote at $x = k$; rather, it may have a "hole" at $x = k$. See the next example and Figure 4.89.

EXAMPLE 9 Graphing a rational function having a "hole"

Graph $f(x) = \frac{2x^2 - 5x + 2}{x^2 - 3x + 2}$ by hand.

SOLUTION First factor the numerator and the denominator.

$$\frac{2x^2 - 5x + 2}{x^2 - 3x + 2} = \frac{(2x - 1)(x - 2)}{(x - 1)(x - 2)} = \frac{2x - 1}{x - 1}, \qquad x \neq 2$$

After factoring, it is apparent that both the numerator and the denominator equal 0 when $x = 2$. Therefore we simplify the rational expression to lowest terms and restrict the domain to $x \neq 2$.

From our previous work, long division can be used to show that $f(x) = \frac{2x - 1}{x - 1}$ is equivalent to $f(x) = 2 + \frac{1}{x - 1}$. Thus the graph of f is similar to Figure 4.94 except that the point $(2, 3)$ is missing and an open circle appears in its place. See Figure 4.99.

Now Try Exercise 69

Figure 4.99

Graphing Rational Functions by Hand (Optional)

To graph a rational function by hand, we sometimes need to solve a rational equation of the form $\frac{a}{b} = \frac{c}{d}$. One way to solve this equation is to **cross multiply** and obtain $ad = bc$, provided b and d are nonzero. Consider the following example.

$$\frac{2x - 1}{3x + 2} = \frac{5}{4} \qquad \text{Given equation}$$

$$4(2x - 1) = 5(3x + 2) \qquad \text{Cross multiply.}$$

$$8x - 4 = 15x + 10 \qquad \text{Simplify.}$$

$$-7x = 14 \qquad \text{Subtract 15x; add 4.}$$

$$x = -2 \qquad \text{Divide by } -7. \text{ The answer checks.}$$

The following guidelines can be used to graph a rational function by hand.

> **GRAPHING A RATIONAL FUNCTION**
>
> Let $f(x) = \dfrac{p(x)}{q(x)}$ define a rational function in *lowest* terms. To sketch its graph, follow these steps:
>
> **STEP 1:** Find all vertical asymptotes.
>
> **STEP 2:** Find all horizontal or oblique asymptotes.
>
> **STEP 3:** Find the *y*-intercept, if possible, by evaluating $f(0)$.
>
> **STEP 4:** Find the *x*-intercepts, if any, by solving $f(x) = 0$. (These will be the zeros of the numerator $p(x)$.)
>
> **STEP 5:** Determine whether the graph will intersect its nonvertical asymptote $y = b$ by solving $f(x) = b$, where b is the *y*-value of the horizontal asymptote, or by solving $f(x) = mx + b$, where $y = mx + b$ is the equation of the oblique asymptote.
>
> **STEP 6:** Plot selected points as necessary. Choose an *x*-value in each interval of the domain determined by the vertical asymptotes and *x*-intercepts.
>
> **STEP 7:** Complete the sketch.

EXAMPLE 10 Graphing a rational function by hand

Graph $f(x) = \dfrac{2x + 1}{x - 3}$.

SOLUTION

Getting Started As you go through Steps 1 through 7, be sure to sketch all asymptotes first and then plot some key points. Finally, sketch the entire graph. ▶

STEP 1: The vertical asymptote has equation $x = 3$.

STEP 2: The horizontal asymptote has equation $y = 2$.

STEP 3: $f(0) = -\frac{1}{3}$, so the *y*-intercept is $-\frac{1}{3}$.

STEP 4: Solve $f(x) = 0$ to find any *x*-intercepts.

$$\frac{2x + 1}{x - 3} = 0$$

$$2x + 1 = 0 \qquad \text{If a fraction equals 0, its}$$
$$ \qquad \text{numerator must be 0.}$$

$$x = -\frac{1}{2}$$

The *x*-intercept is $-\frac{1}{2}$.

STEP 5: The graph does not intersect its horizontal asymptote, since $f(x) = 2$ has no solutions. (Verify this.)

STEP 6 AND 7: The points $(-4, 1)$, $\left(1, -\frac{3}{2}\right)$, and $\left(6, \frac{13}{3}\right)$ are on the graph and can be used to complete the sketch, shown in Figure 4.100.

Now Try Exercise 87

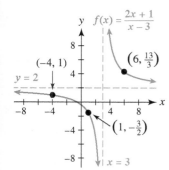

Figure 4.100

EXAMPLE 11 Graphing a function that intersects its horizontal asymptote

Graph $f(x) = \dfrac{3x^2 - 3x - 6}{x^2 + 8x + 16}$.

SOLUTION

Let $f(x) = \dfrac{3x^2 - 3x - 6}{x^2 + 8x + 16}$.

STEP 1: To find the vertical asymptote(s), solve $x^2 + 8x + 16 = 0$.

$$x^2 + 8x + 16 = 0$$
$$(x + 4)^2 = 0$$
$$x = -4$$

Since the numerator is not 0 when $x = -4$, the only vertical asymptote has equation $x = -4$.

STEP 2: Because the degrees of the numerator and denominator both equal 2, the ratio of the leading coefficients gives the horizontal asymptote, which is,

$$y = \frac{3}{1},$$

← Leading coefficient of numerator
← Leading coefficient of denominator

or $y = 3$.

STEP 3: The y-intercept is $f(0) = -\frac{3}{8}$.

STEP 4: To find the x-intercept(s), if any, solve $f(x) = 0$.

$$\frac{3x^2 - 3x - 6}{x^2 + 8x + 16} = 0 \qquad \text{Set } f(x) \text{ equal to 0.}$$
$$3x^2 - 3x - 6 = 0 \qquad \text{Set the numerator equal to 0.}$$
$$x^2 - x - 2 = 0 \qquad \text{Divide by 3.}$$
$$(x - 2)(x + 1) = 0 \qquad \text{Factor.}$$
$$x = 2 \quad \text{or} \quad x = -1 \qquad \text{Zero-product property}$$

The x-intercepts are -1 and 2.

STEP 5: Because the horizontal asymptote is $y = 3$, set $f(x) = 3$ and solve to locate the point where the graph intersects the horizontal asymptote.

$$\frac{3x^2 - 3x - 6}{x^2 + 8x + 16} = 3$$
$$3x^2 - 3x - 6 = 3x^2 + 24x + 48 \qquad \text{Let } 3 = \tfrac{3}{1}; \text{ cross multiply.}$$
$$-3x - 6 = 24x + 48 \qquad \text{Subtract } 3x^2.$$
$$-27x = 54 \qquad \text{Subtract } 24x, \text{ add 6.}$$
$$x = -2 \qquad \text{Divide by } -27.$$

The graph intersects its horizontal asymptote at $(-2, 3)$.

STEP 6 AND 7: Some other points that lie on the graph are $(-10, 9)$, $\left(-8, 13\frac{1}{8}\right)$, and $\left(5, \frac{2}{3}\right)$. These can be used to complete the graph, shown in Figure 4.101.

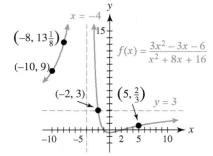

Figure 4.101

Now Try Exercise 91

4.6 Putting It All Together

The following table summarizes some concepts about rational functions (in lowest terms) and rational equations. To determine vertical and horizontal asymptotes see the box on page 293.

CONCEPT	EXPLANATION	EXAMPLES
Rational function	$f(x) = \dfrac{p(x)}{q(x)}$, where $p(x)$ and $q(x)$ are polynomials with $q(x) \neq 0$.	$f(x) = \dfrac{x - 1}{x^2 + 2x + 1}$ $g(x) = 1 + \dfrac{1}{x}$ $\quad \left(Note: 1 + \dfrac{1}{x} = \dfrac{x + 1}{x}. \right)$
Vertical asymptote	If k is a zero of the denominator, but not of the numerator, then $x = k$ is a vertical asymptote.	The graph of $f(x) = \dfrac{2x + 1}{x - 2}$ has a vertical asymptote at $x = 2$ because 2 is a zero of $x - 2$, but not a zero of $2x + 1$.
Horizontal asymptote	A horizontal asymptote occurs when the degree of the numerator is less than or equal to the degree of the denominator.	$$f(x) = \dfrac{1 - 4x^2}{3x^2 - x}$$ Horizontal asymptote: $y = -\dfrac{4}{3}$ $$g(x) = \dfrac{x}{4x^2 + 2x}$$ Horizontal asymptote: $y = 0$
Graph of a rational function	The graph of a rational function is continuous, except at x-values where the denominator equals zero.	The graph of $f(x) = \dfrac{3x^2 + 1}{x^2 - 4}$ is discontinuous at $x = \pm 2$. It has vertical asymptotes of $x = \pm 2$ and a horizontal asymptote of $y = 3$.
Basic rational equation	$\dfrac{a}{b} = \dfrac{c}{d}$ is equivalent to $ad = bc$, provided b and d are nonzero. Check your answer. Can be used to graph a rational function by hand	To solve the rational equation $$\frac{4}{2x - 1} = 8,$$ write 8 as $\frac{8}{1}$ and cross multiply. $$4 = 8(2x - 1)$$ $$12 = 16x$$ $$x = \frac{3}{4}$$

4.6 Exercises

Rational Functions

Exercises 1–12: Determine whether f is a rational function and state its domain.

1. $f(x) = \dfrac{x^3 - 5x + 1}{4x - 5}$

2. $f(x) = \dfrac{6}{x^2}$

3. $f(x) = x^2 - x - 2$

4. $f(x) = \dfrac{x^2 + 1}{\sqrt{x - 8}}$

5. $f(x) = \dfrac{|x - 1|}{x + 1}$

6. $f(x) = \dfrac{4}{x} + 1$

7. $f(x) = \dfrac{3x}{x^2 + 1}$

8. $f(x) = \dfrac{|x + 1|}{x + 1}$

9. $f(x) = \dfrac{3 - \sqrt{x}}{x^2 + x}$

10. $f(x) = \dfrac{x^3 - 3x + 1}{x^2 - 5}$

11. $f(x) = 4 - \dfrac{3}{x + 1}$

12. $f(x) = 5x^3 - 4x$

Asymptotes and Graphs

Exercises 13–18: Identify any horizontal or vertical asymptotes in the graph. State the domain of f.

13.

14.

15.

16.

17.

18.

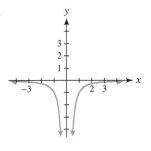

Exercises 19 and 20: In the table, Y_1 is a rational function. Give a possible equation for a horizontal asymptote.

19.

X	Y₁
50	2.8654
100	2.9314
150	2.9539
200	2.9653
250	2.9722
300	2.9768
350	2.9801

X=50

20.

X	Y₁
-10	4.8922
-20	4.9726
-30	4.9878
-40	4.9931
-50	4.9956
-60	4.9969
-70	4.9978

X=-10

Exercises 21–32: Find any horizontal or vertical asymptotes.

21. $f(x) = \dfrac{4x + 1}{2x - 6}$

22. $f(x) = \dfrac{x + 6}{5 - 2x}$

23. $f(x) = \dfrac{3}{x^2 - 5}$

24. $f(x) = \dfrac{3x^2}{x^2 - 9}$

25. $f(x) = \dfrac{x^4 + 1}{x^2 + 3x - 10}$

26. $f(x) = \dfrac{4x^3 - 2}{x + 2}$

27. $f(x) = \dfrac{x^2 + 2x + 1}{2x^2 - 3x - 5}$

28. $f(x) = \dfrac{6x^2 - x - 2}{2x^2 + x - 6}$

29. $f(x) = \dfrac{3x(x + 2)}{(x + 2)(x - 1)}$

30. $f(x) = \dfrac{x}{x^3 - x}$

31. $f(x) = \dfrac{x^2 - 9}{x + 3}$

32. $f(x) = \dfrac{2x^2 - 3x + 1}{2x - 1}$

Exercises 33–36: Let a be a positive constant. Match $f(x)$ with its graph (a–d) without using a calculator.

33. $f(x) = \dfrac{a}{x - 1}$

34. $f(x) = \dfrac{2x + a}{x - 1}$

35. $f(x) = \dfrac{x - a}{x + 2}$

36. $f(x) = \dfrac{-2x}{x^2 - a}$

a.

b.

c.

d.

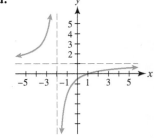

Exercises 37–40: Write a formula f(x) for a rational function so that its graph has the specified asymptotes.

37. Vertical: $x = -3$; horizontal: $y = 1$

38. Vertical: $x = 4$; horizontal: $y = -3$

39. Vertical: $x = \pm 3$; horizontal: $y = 0$

40. Vertical: $x = -2$ and $x = 4$; horizontal: $y = 5$

Graphing Rational Functions

Exercises 41–44: Graph f and identify any asymptotes.

41. $f(x) = \dfrac{1}{x^2}$

42. $f(x) = -\dfrac{1}{x}$

43. $f(x) = -\dfrac{1}{2x}$

44. $f(x) = \dfrac{2}{x^2}$

Exercises 45–54: **Transformations** *Use transformations of the graph of either $f(x) = \frac{1}{x}$ or $h(x) = \frac{1}{x^2}$ to sketch a graph of $y = g(x)$ by hand. Show all asymptotes. Write $g(x)$ in terms of either $f(x)$ or $h(x)$.*

45. $g(x) = \dfrac{1}{x - 3}$

46. $g(x) = \dfrac{1}{x + 2}$

47. $g(x) = \dfrac{1}{x} + 2$

48. $g(x) = 1 - \dfrac{2}{x}$

49. $g(x) = \dfrac{1}{x + 1} - 2$

50. $g(x) = \dfrac{1}{x - 2} + 1$

51. $g(x) = -\dfrac{2}{(x - 1)^2}$

52. $g(x) = \dfrac{1}{x^2} - 1$

53. $g(x) = \dfrac{1}{(x + 1)^2} - 2$

54. $g(x) = 1 - \dfrac{1}{(x - 2)^2}$

Exercises 55–62: Complete the following.

(a) Find the domain of f.

(b) Graph f in an appropriate viewing rectangle.

(c) Find any horizontal or vertical asymptotes.

(d) Sketch a graph of f that includes any asymptotes.

55. $f(x) = \dfrac{x + 3}{x - 2}$

56. $f(x) = \dfrac{6 - 2x}{x + 3}$

57. $f(x) = \dfrac{4x + 1}{x^2 - 4}$

58. $f(x) = \dfrac{0.5x^2 + 1}{x^2 - 9}$

59. $f(x) = \dfrac{4}{1 - 0.25x^2}$

60. $f(x) = \dfrac{x^2}{1 + 0.25x^2}$

61. $f(x) = \dfrac{x^2 - 4}{x - 2}$

62. $f(x) = \dfrac{4(x - 1)}{x^2 - x - 6}$

Exercises 63–72: Graph $y = f(x)$. You may want to use division, factoring, or transformations as an aid. Show all asymptotes and "holes."

63. $f(x) = \dfrac{x^2 - 2x + 1}{x - 1}$

64. $f(x) = \dfrac{4x^2 + 4x + 1}{2x + 1}$

65. $f(x) = \dfrac{x + 2}{x + 1}$

66. $f(x) = \dfrac{2x + 3}{x + 1}$

67. $f(x) = \dfrac{2x^2 - 3x - 2}{x^2 - 4x + 4}$

68. $f(x) = \dfrac{x^2 - x - 2}{x^2 - 2x - 3}$

69. $f(x) = \dfrac{2x^2 + 9x + 9}{2x^2 + 7x + 6}$

70. $f(x) = \dfrac{x^2 - 4}{x^2 - x - 6}$

71. $f(x) = \dfrac{-2x^2 + 11x - 14}{x^2 - 5x + 6}$

72. $f(x) = \dfrac{2x^2 - 3x - 14}{x^2 - 2x - 8}$

Slant Asymptotes

Exercises 73–80: Complete the following.

(a) Find any slant or vertical asymptotes.

(b) Graph $y = f(x)$. Show all asymptotes.

73. $f(x) = \dfrac{x^2 + 1}{x + 1}$

74. $f(x) = \dfrac{2x^2 - 5x - 2}{x - 2}$

75. $f(x) = \dfrac{0.5x^2 - 2x + 2}{x + 2}$

76. $f(x) = \dfrac{0.5x^2 - 5}{x - 3}$

77. $f(x) = \dfrac{x^2 + 2x + 1}{x - 1}$

78. $f(x) = \dfrac{2x^2 + 3x + 1}{x - 2}$

79. $f(x) = \dfrac{4x^2}{2x - 1}$

80. $f(x) = \dfrac{4x^2 + x - 2}{4x - 3}$

Basic Rational Equations

Exercises 81–86: Solve the equation.

81. $\dfrac{4}{x + 2} = -4$

82. $\dfrac{3}{2x + 1} = -1$

83. $\dfrac{x + 1}{x} = 2$

84. $\dfrac{2x}{x - 3} = -4$

85. $\dfrac{1 - x}{3x - 1} = -\dfrac{3}{5}$

86. $\dfrac{3 - 2x}{x + 2} = 12$

Graphing Rational Functions by Hand

Exercises 87–92: (Refer to Examples 10 and 11.) Graph f. Use the steps for graphing a rational function described in this section.

87. $f(x) = \dfrac{2x - 4}{x - 1}$

88. $f(x) = \dfrac{x + 3}{2x - 4}$

89. $f(x) = \dfrac{x^2 - 2x}{x^2 + 6x + 9}$ **90.** $f(x) = \dfrac{2x + 1}{x^2 + 6x + 8}$

91. $f(x) = \dfrac{x^2 + 2x + 1}{x^2 - x - 6}$ **92.** $f(x) = \dfrac{3x^2 + 3x - 6}{x^2 - x - 12}$

Applications

93. Social Network Participation You may have noticed that a relatively small percentage of people do the vast majority of postings on social networks. The rational function defined by

$$f(x) = \frac{100}{101 - x}, \qquad 5 \le x \le 100,$$

models this participation inequality. In this formula, $f(x)$ outputs the percentage of the postings done by the least active (bottom) x percent of the population.
(a) Evaluate $f(98)$. Interpret your answer.

(b) Evaluate $f(100) - f(98)$. Interpret your answer.

94. Probability A container holds x balls numbered 1 through x. Only one ball has the winning number.
(a) Find a function f that computes the probability, or likelihood, of *not* drawing the winning ball.

(b) What is the domain of f?

(c) What happens to the probability of *not* drawing the winning ball as the number of balls increases?

(d) Interpret the horizontal asymptote of the graph of f.

95. Abandoning Websites The first minute is critical to a visitor's decision whether to stay or leave a website. The longer a person visits a website, the less likely it is that he or she will leave the page. If x represents the number of seconds that a visitor has been visiting a website, then the likelihood as a percentage that this visitor is abandoning the website at x seconds is modeled by

$$P(x) = \frac{5}{0.03x + 0.97}, \qquad 1 \le x \le 60.$$

(a) Approximate $P(1)$ and interpret your answer.

(b) Approximate $P(60)$ and interpret your answer.

96. Concentration of a Drug The concentration of a drug in a medical patient's bloodstream is given by the formula $f(t) = \dfrac{5}{t^2 + 1}$, where the input t is in hours, $t \ge 0$, and the output is in milligrams per liter.
(a) Does the concentration of the drug increase or decrease? Explain.

(b) The patient should not take a second dose until the concentration is below 1.5 milligrams per liter. How long should the patient wait before taking a second dose?

97. Time Spent in Line If two parking attendants can wait on 8 vehicles per minute and vehicles are leaving the parking garage randomly at an average rate of x vehicles per minute, then the average time T in minutes spent waiting in line *and* paying the attendant is given by the formula $T(x) = -\dfrac{1}{x - 8}$, where $0 \le x < 8$. A graph of T is shown in the figure.

(a) Evaluate $T(4)$ and $T(7.5)$. Interpret the results.

(b) What happens to the wait as vehicles arrive at an average rate that approaches 8 cars per minute?

98. Time Spent in Line (Refer to Exercise 97.) If the parking attendants can wait on 5 vehicles per minute, the average time T in minutes spent waiting in line *and* paying the attendant becomes $T(x) = -\dfrac{1}{x - 5}$.
(a) What is a reasonable domain for T?

(b) Graph $y = T(x)$. Be sure to include any vertical asymptotes.

(c) Explain what happens to $T(x)$ as $x \to 5^-$.

99. Length of Lines (Refer to Example 2.) Suppose that a parking attendant can wait on 40 cars per hour and that cars arrive randomly at a rate of x cars per hour. Then the average number of cars waiting in line can be estimated by

$$N(x) = \frac{x^2}{1600 - 40x}.$$

(a) Evaluate $N(20)$ and $N(39)$.

(b) Explain what happens to the length of the line as x approaches 40.

(c) Find any vertical asymptotes of the graph of N.

100. Construction Zone Suppose that a construction zone can allow 50 cars per hour to pass through and that cars arrive randomly at a rate of x cars per hour. Then the average number of cars waiting in line to get through the construction zone can be estimated by

$$N(x) = \frac{x^2}{2500 - 50x}.$$

(a) Evaluate $N(20)$, $N(40)$, and $N(49)$.

(b) Explain what happens to the length of the line as x approaches 50.

(c) Find any vertical asymptotes of the graph of N.

101. Interpreting an Asymptote Suppose that an insect population in millions is modeled by $f(x) = \frac{10x + 1}{x + 1}$, where $x \geq 0$ is in months.

(a) Graph f in $[0, 14, 1]$ by $[0, 14, 1]$. Find the equation of the horizontal asymptote.

(b) Determine the initial insect population.

(c) What happens to the population over time?

(d) Interpret the horizontal asymptote.

102. Interpreting an Asymptote Suppose that the population of a species of fish (in thousands) is modeled by $f(x) = \frac{x + 10}{0.5x^2 + 1}$, where $x \geq 0$ is in years.

(a) Graph f in $[0, 12, 1]$ by $[0, 12, 1]$. What is the horizontal asymptote?

(b) Determine the initial population.

(c) What happens to the population of this fish?

(d) Interpret the horizontal asymptote.

103. Train Curves When curves are designed for trains, sometimes the outer rail is elevated or banked, so that a locomotive can safely negotiate the curve at a higher speed. See the figure at the top of the next column. Suppose a circular curve is designed for 60 miles per hour. The formula $f(x) = \frac{2540}{x}$ computes the elevation y in inches of the outer track for a curve having a radius of x feet, where $y = f(x)$. (*Source:* L. Haefner, *Introduction to Transportation Systems.*)

(a) Evaluate $f(400)$ and interpret the result.

(b) Graph f in $[0, 600, 100]$ by $[0, 50, 5]$. How does the elevation change as the radius increases?

(c) Interpret the horizontal asymptote.

(d) Find the radius if the elevation is 12.7 inches.

104. Slippery Roads If a car is moving at 50 miles per hour on a level highway, then its braking distance depends on the road conditions. This distance in feet can be computed by $D(x) = \frac{250}{30x}$, where x is the coefficient of friction between the tires and the road and $0 < x \leq 1$. A smaller value of x indicates that the road is more slippery.

(a) Identify and interpret the vertical asymptote.

(b) Estimate the coefficient of friction associated with a braking distance of 340 feet.

Writing About Mathematics

105. Let $f(x)$ be the formula for a rational function.

(a) Explain how to find any vertical or horizontal asymptotes of the graph of f.

(b) Discuss what a horizontal asymptote represents.

106. Discuss how to find the domain of a rational function symbolically and graphically.

Extended and Discovery Exercises

Exercises 1–4: **Rate of Change/Difference Quotient** *Find the average rate of change of f from $x_1 = 1$ to $x_2 = 3$. Then find the difference quotient of f.*

1. $f(x) = \dfrac{1}{x}$ **2.** $f(x) = \dfrac{1}{x^2}$

3. $f(x) = \dfrac{3}{2x}$ **4.** $f(x) = \dfrac{1}{5 - x}$

CHECKING BASIC CONCEPTS FOR SECTIONS 4.5 AND 4.6

1. Find a quadratic polynomial $f(x)$ with zeros $\pm 4i$ and leading coefficient 3. Write $f(x)$ in complete factored form and expanded form.

2. Sketch a graph of a quartic function (degree 4) with a negative leading coefficient, two real zeros, and two imaginary zeros.

3. Write $x^3 - x^2 + 4x - 4$ in complete factored form.

4. Solve each equation.
 (a) $2x^3 + 45 = 5x^2 - 18x$

 (b) $x^4 + 5x^2 = 36$

5. Let $f(x) = \frac{1}{x-1} + 2$.
 (a) Find the domain of f.

 (b) Identify any vertical or horizontal asymptotes.

 (c) Sketch a graph of f that includes all asymptotes.

6. Find any vertical or horizontal asymptotes for the graph of $f(x) = \frac{4x^2}{x^2 - 4}$. State the domain of f.

7. Sketch a graph of each rational function f. Include all asymptotes and any "holes" in your graph.

 (a) $f(x) = \frac{3x - 1}{2x - 2}$ **(b)** $f(x) = \frac{1}{(x + 1)^2}$

 (c) $f(x) = \frac{x + 2}{x^2 - 4}$ **(d)** $f(x) = \frac{x^2 + 1}{x^2 - 1}$

4.7 More Equations and Inequalities

- **Solve rational equations**
- **Solve variation problems**
- **Solve polynomial inequalities**
- **Solve rational inequalities**

Introduction

Waiting in line is a part of almost everyone's life. When people arrive randomly at a line, rational functions can be used to estimate the average number of people standing in line. For example, if an attendant at a ticket booth can wait on 30 customers per hour and if customers arrive at an average rate of x per hour, then the average number of customers waiting in line is computed by

$$f(x) = \frac{x^2}{900 - 30x},$$ Rational function

where $0 \le x < 30$. Thus $f(28) \approx 13$ indicates that if customers arrive, on average, at 28 per hour, then the average number of people in line is 13. If a line length of 8 customers or fewer is acceptable, then we can use $f(x)$ to estimate customer arrival rates x that one attendant can accommodate by solving the *rational inequality*

$$\frac{x^2}{900 - 30x} \le 8.$$ Rational inequality

(See Example 8.) Rational inequalities are discussed in this section along with other types of inequalities and equations.   (***Source:*** N. Garber and L. Hoel, *Traffic and Highway Engineering*.)

Rational Equations

If $f(x)$ represents a rational function, then an equation that can be written in the form $f(x) = k$ for some constant k is a **rational equation**.

$$\frac{x^2 - 1}{x^2 + x + 3} = 0, \quad \frac{3x}{x^3 + x} = \frac{3}{2}, \quad \text{and} \quad \frac{2}{x - 1} + \frac{1}{x} = -2$$

Rational Equations

Rational equations can be solved symbolically, graphically, and numerically.

EXAMPLE 1 Solving a rational equation

Solve $\frac{4x}{x - 1} = 6$ symbolically, graphically, and numerically.

SOLUTION
Getting Started The equation $\frac{a}{b} = \frac{c}{d}$ with $b \ne 0$ and $d \ne 0$ is equivalent to $ad = bc$. In this example, you can think of 6 as the ratio $\frac{6}{1}$. This technique is sometimes called *cross multiplying*. ▶

Symbolic Solution

$$\frac{4x}{x-1} = 6 \qquad \text{Given equation}$$

$$4x = 6(x-1) \qquad \text{Cross multiply: } \tfrac{a}{b} = \tfrac{c}{d} \text{ implies } ad = bc.$$

$$4x = 6x - 6 \qquad \text{Distributive property}$$

$$-2x = -6 \qquad \text{Subtract } 6x.$$

$$x = 3 \qquad \text{Divide by } -2. \text{ (Check this answer.)}$$

The only solution is 3.

Graphical Solution   Graph $Y_1 = 4X/(X-1)$ and $Y_2 = 6$. Their graphs intersect at $(3, 6)$, so the solution is 3. See Figure 4.102.

Figure 4.102   **Figure 4.103**

Numerical Solution   In Figure 4.103, $y_1 = y_2$ when $x = 3$.

Now Try Exercise 1

Algebra Review
To review clearing fractions, see Chapter R (page R-33).

A common approach to solving rational equations symbolically is to multiply each side of the equation by a common denominator. This technique, which clears fractions from an equation, is used in Examples 2 and 3.

EXAMPLE 2   Solving a rational equation

Solve $\frac{6}{x^2} - \frac{5}{x} = 1$ symbolically.

SOLUTION
The least common denominator for x^2 and x is x^2. Multiply each side of the equation by x^2.

Algebra Review
To review finding a least common denominator, see Chapter R (page R-30).

$$\frac{6}{x^2} - \frac{5}{x} = 1 \qquad \text{Given equation}$$

$$\frac{6}{x^2} \cdot x^2 - \frac{5}{x} \cdot x^2 = 1 \cdot x^2 \qquad \text{Multiply each term by } x^2.$$

$$6 - 5x = x^2 \qquad \text{Simplify.}$$

$$0 = x^2 + 5x - 6 \qquad \text{Add } 5x \text{ and subtract } 6.$$

$$0 = (x + 6)(x - 1) \qquad \text{Factor.}$$

$$x + 6 = 0 \quad \text{or} \quad x - 1 = 0 \qquad \text{Zero-product property}$$

$$x = -6 \quad \text{or} \quad x = 1 \qquad \text{Solve.}$$

Check to verify that each answer is correct.

Now Try Exercise 17

The next example illustrates the importance of checking possible solutions.

EXAMPLE 3 Solving a rational equation

Solve $\dfrac{1}{x+3} + \dfrac{1}{x-3} = \dfrac{6}{x^2-9}$ symbolically. Check the result.

SOLUTION
The least common denominator is $(x+3)(x-3)$, or x^2-9.

NOTE If either -3 or 3 is substituted into the given equation, two of the expressions are undefined. (Their denominators equal 0.) Thus neither of these values can be a solution to the *given* equation.

$$\frac{1}{x+3} + \frac{1}{x-3} = \frac{6}{x^2-9} \qquad \text{Given equation}$$

$$\frac{(x+3)(x-3)}{x+3} + \frac{(x+3)(x-3)}{x-3} = \frac{6(x+3)(x-3)}{x^2-9} \qquad \text{Multiply by } (x+3)(x-3).$$

$$(x-3) + (x+3) = 6 \qquad \text{Simplify.}$$

$$2x = 6 \qquad \text{Combine terms.}$$

$$x = 3 \qquad \text{Divide by 2.}$$

As noted earlier, 3 cannot be a solution to the *given* equation. There are no solutions. (The value 3 is called an **extraneous solution** because it does not satisfy the given equation.)

Now Try Exercise 21

An Application Rational equations are used in real-world applications such as the construction problem in the next example. Steps for solving application problems (see page 95) have been used to structure the solution.

EXAMPLE 4 Designing a box

A box with rectangular sides and a top is being designed to hold 324 cubic inches and to have a surface area of 342 square inches. If the length of the box is four times the height, find possible dimensions of the box.

SOLUTION

STEP 1: We are asked to find the dimensions of a box. If x is the height of the box and y is the width, then the length of the box is $4x$, or four times the height.

x: Height of the box y: Width of the box $4x$: Length of the box

STEP 2: To relate these variables to an equation, sketch a box as shown in Figure 4.104. The volume V of the box is **height** times **width** times **length**.

$$V = xy(4x) = 4x^2y$$

The surface area A of this box is determined by finding the area of the 6 rectangular sides: left and right sides, front and back, and top and bottom.

$$A = 2(4x \cdot x) + 2(x \cdot y) + 2(4x \cdot y)$$

$$= 8x^2 + 10xy$$

If we solve $V = 4x^2y$ for y and let $V = 324$, we obtain

$$y = \frac{V}{4x^2} = \frac{324}{4x^2} = \frac{81}{x^2}.$$

Designing a Box

Figure 4.104

Substituting $y = \frac{81}{x^2}$ in the formula for A eliminates the y variable.

$$A = 8x^2 + 10xy \qquad \text{Area formula}$$

$$= 8x^2 + 10x \cdot \frac{81}{x^2} \qquad \text{Let } y = \frac{81}{x^2}.$$

$$= 8x^2 + \frac{810}{x} \qquad \text{Simplify.}$$

Geometry Review
To review formulas related to box shapes, see Chapter R (page R-3).

Since the surface area is $A = 342$ square inches, the height x can be determined by solving the rational equation

$$8x^2 + \frac{810}{x} = 342. \qquad \text{Area} = 342$$

STEP 3: Figures 4.105 and 4.106 show the graphs of $Y_1 = 8X^2 + 810/X$ and $Y_2 = 342$. There are two *positive* solutions: $x = 3$ and $x = 4.5$.

Locating Solutions Graphically

Figure 4.105   Figure 4.106

NOTE This equation can be written as $8x^3 - 342x + 810 = 0$, and the rational zeros test or factoring could be used to find the solutions, 3 and $\frac{9}{2}$.

For the first solution, the height is $x = 3$ inches, so the length is $4 \cdot 3 = 12$ inches and the width is $y = \frac{81}{3^2} = 9$ inches. (Note that $y = \frac{81}{x^2}$.) For the second solution, the height is 4.5 inches, so the length is $4 \cdot 4.5 = 18$ inches and the width is $y = \frac{81}{4.5^2} = 4$ inches. Thus the dimensions of the box in inches can be either $3 \times 9 \times 12$ or $4.5 \times 4 \times 18$.

STEP 4: We can check our results directly. If the dimensions are $3 \times 9 \times 12$, then

$$V = 3 \cdot 9 \cdot 12 = 324 \checkmark \text{ and}$$
$$S = 2(3 \cdot 9) + 2(3 \cdot 12) + 2(9 \cdot 12) = 342. \checkmark$$

If the dimensions are $4.5 \times 4 \times 18$, then

$$V = 4.5 \cdot 4 \cdot 18 = 324 \checkmark \text{ and}$$
$$S = 2(4.5 \cdot 4) + 2(4.5 \cdot 18) + 2(4 \cdot 18) = 342. \checkmark$$

In both cases our results check.

Now Try Exercise 79

Variation

Direct Variation with the *n*th Power In Section 2.4 direct variation was discussed. Sometimes a quantity y varies directly with a *power* of a variable. For example, the area A of a circle varies directly with the second power (square) of the radius r. That is, $A = \pi r^2$.

DIRECT VARIATION WITH THE *n*TH POWER

Let x and y denote two quantities and n be a positive real number. Then y is **directly proportional to the *n*th power** of x, or y **varies directly with the *n*th power** of x, if there exists a nonzero number k such that

$$y = kx^n.$$

The number k is called the *constant of variation* or the *constant of proportionality*. In the formula $A = \pi r^2$, the constant of variation is π.

Calculator Help
To find a point of intersection, see Appendix A (page AP-7).

Figure 4.107

EXAMPLE 5 Modeling a pendulum

The time T required for a pendulum to swing back and forth once is called its *period*. The length L of a pendulum is directly proportional to the square of T. See Figure 4.107. A 2-foot pendulum has a 1.57-second period.
(a) Find the constant of proportionality k.
(b) Predict T for a pendulum having a length of 5 feet.

SOLUTION
(a) Because L is directly proportional to the square of T, we can write $L = kT^2$. If $L = 2$, then $T = 1.57$. Thus $k = \frac{L}{T^2} = \frac{2}{1.57^2} \approx 0.81$ and $L = 0.81T^2$.
(b) If $L = 5$, then $5 = 0.81T^2$. It follows that $T = \sqrt{5/0.81} \approx 2.48$ seconds.

Now Try Exercise 107

Inverse Variation with the nth Power When two quantities vary inversely, an increase in one quantity results in a decrease in the second quantity. For example, it takes 4 hours to travel 100 miles at 25 miles per hour and 2 hours to travel 100 miles at 50 miles per hour. Greater speed results in less travel time. If s represents the average speed of a car and t is the time to travel 100 miles, then $s \cdot t = 100$, or $t = \frac{100}{s}$. Doubling the speed cuts the time in half; tripling the speed reduces the time by one-third. The quantities t and s are said to *vary inversely*. The constant of variation is 100.

INVERSE VARIATION WITH THE nTH POWER

Let x and y denote two quantities and n be a positive real number. Then y is **inversely proportional to the nth power** of x, or y **varies inversely with the nth power** of x, if there exists a nonzero number k such that

$$y = \frac{k}{x^n}.$$

If $y = \frac{k}{x}$, then y is **inversely proportional** to x or y **varies inversely** with x.

NOTE To review steps for solving variation problems see the box on page 125.

Inverse variation occurs in measuring the intensity of light. If we increase our distance from a lightbulb, the intensity of the light decreases. Intensity I is inversely proportional to the second power of the distance d. The equation $I = \frac{k}{d^2}$ models this phenomenon.

EXAMPLE 6 Modeling the intensity of light

At a distance of 3 meters, a 100-watt bulb produces an intensity of 0.88 watt per square meter. (*Source:* R. Weidner and R. Sells, *Elementary Classical Physics*, Volume 2.)
(a) Find the constant of proportionality k.
(b) Determine the intensity at a distance of 2 meters.

SOLUTION
(a) Substitute $d = 3$ and $I = 0.88$ in the equation $I = \frac{k}{d^2}$. Solve for k.

$$0.88 = \frac{k}{3^2}, \quad \text{or} \quad k = 7.92$$

(b) Let $I = \frac{7.92}{d^2}$ and $d = 2$. Then $I = \frac{7.92}{2^2} = 1.98$. The intensity at 2 meters is 1.98 watts per square meter.

Now Try Exercise 111

Polynomial Inequalities

Algebra Review
To review interval notation, see
Section 1.4.

Graphical Solutions   In Section 3.4 a strategy for solving quadratic inequalities was presented. This strategy involves first finding boundary numbers (*x*-values) where equality holds. Once the boundary numbers are known, a graph or a table of test values can be used to determine the intervals where inequality holds. This strategy can be applied to other types of inequalities.

The following See the Concept illustrates how to solve polynomial inequalities, where $p(x) = -x^4 + 5x^2 - 4$. Note that the solution sets are also shown on the number line above each graph.

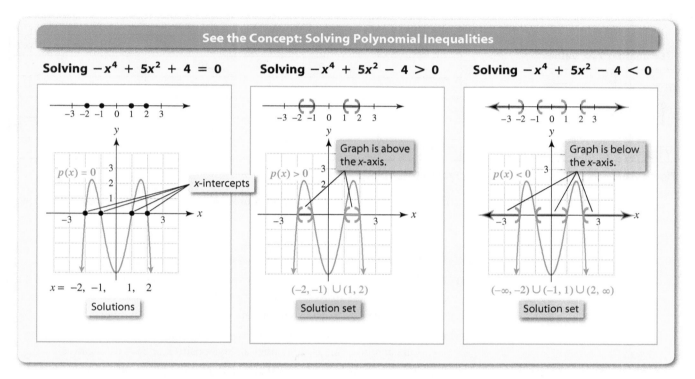

See the Concept: Solving Polynomial Inequalities

Solving $-x^4 + 5x^2 + 4 = 0$

$p(x) = 0$

x-intercepts

$x = -2, -1,$ $1, 2$

Solutions

Solving $-x^4 + 5x^2 - 4 > 0$

Graph is above the *x*-axis.

$p(x) > 0$

$(-2, -1) \cup (1, 2)$

Solution set

Solving $-x^4 + 5x^2 - 4 < 0$

Graph is below the *x*-axis.

$p(x) < 0$

$(-\infty, -2) \cup (-1, 1) \cup (2, \infty)$

Solution set

MAKING CONNECTIONS

Visualization and Inequalities   A *precise* graph of *p* is *not* necessary to solve the polynomial inequality $p(x) > 0$ or $p(x) < 0$. Once the *x*-intercepts have been determined, we can use our knowledge about graphs of quartic polynomials (see Section 4.2) to visualize the graph of *p*. Then we can determine where the graph of *p* is above the *x*-axis and where it is below the *x*-axis.

Symbolic Solutions   Polynomial inequalities can also be solved symbolically. For example, to solve the inequality $-x^4 + 5x^2 - 4 > 0$, begin by finding the boundary numbers.

Boundary numbers

Figure 4.108

$$-x^4 + 5x^2 - 4 = 0 \qquad \text{Replace} > \text{with} =.$$
$$x^4 - 5x^2 + 4 = 0 \qquad \text{Multiply by} -1.$$
$$(x^2 - 4)(x^2 - 1) = 0 \qquad \text{Factor.}$$
$$x^2 - 4 = 0 \quad \text{or} \quad x^2 - 1 = 0 \qquad \text{Zero-product property}$$
$$x = \pm 2 \quad \text{or} \quad x = \pm 1 \qquad \text{Square root property}$$

The boundary numbers $-2, -1, 1,$ and 2 separate the number line into five intervals:

$$(-\infty, -2), (-2, -1), (-1, 1), (1, 2), \text{ and } (2, \infty),$$

as illustrated in Figure 4.108.

The polynomial $p(x) = -x^4 + 5x^2 - 4$ is either always positive or always negative on each of these intervals. To determine which is the case, we can choose one test value (x-value) from each interval and substitute this test value in $p(x)$. From Table 4.6 we see that the test value $x = -1.5$ results in

$$p(-1.5) = -(-1.5)^4 + 5(-1.5)^2 - 4 = 2.1875 > 0.$$

Figure 4.109, which was created by a graphing calculator, is similar to Table 4.6. Since $x = -1.5$ is in the interval $(-2, -1)$, it follows that $p(x)$ is positive on this interval. The sign of $p(x)$ on the other intervals is determined similarly. Thus the solution set to $p(x) = -x^4 + 5x^2 - 4 > 0$ is $(-2, -1) \cup (1, 2)$.

Evaluating Test Values

X	Y1
-3	-40
-1.5	2.1875
0	-4
1.5	2.1875
3	-40

Y1■-X^4+5X²-4

Figure 4.109

Solving $-x^4 + 5x^2 - 4 > 0$

Interval	Test Value x	$-x^4 + 5x^2 - 4$	Positive or Negative?
$(-\infty, -2)$	-3	-40	Negative
$(-2, -1)$	-1.5	2.1875	Positive
$(-1, 1)$	0	-4	Negative
$(1, 2)$	1.5	2.1875	Positive
$(2, \infty)$	3	-40	Negative

Table 4.6

These symbolic and graphical procedures can be summarized verbally as follows.

SOLVING POLYNOMIAL INEQUALITIES

STEP 1: If necessary, write the inequality as $p(x) < 0$, where $p(x)$ is a polynomial and the inequality symbol $<$ may be replaced by $>$, $\leq$, or $\geq$.

STEP 2: Solve $p(x) = 0$. The solutions are called boundary numbers.

STEP 3: Use the boundary numbers to separate the number line into disjoint intervals. On each interval, $p(x)$ is either always positive or always negative.

STEP 4: To solve the inequality, either make a table of test values for $p(x)$ or use a graph of $y = p(x)$. For example, the solution set for $p(x) < 0$ corresponds to intervals where test values result in negative outputs or to intervals where the graph of $y = p(x)$ is below the x-axis.

EXAMPLE 7 Solving a polynomial inequality

Solve $x^3 \geq 2x^2 + 3x$ symbolically and graphically.

SOLUTION

Symbolic Solution

STEP 1: Begin by writing the inequality as $x^3 - 2x^2 - 3x \geq 0$.

STEP 2: Replace the $\geq$ symbol with an equals sign and solve the resulting equation.

$$x^3 - 2x^2 - 3x = 0 \qquad \text{Replace } \geq \text{ with } =.$$
$$x(x^2 - 2x - 3) = 0 \qquad \text{Factor out } x.$$
$$x(x + 1)(x - 3) = 0 \qquad \text{Factor the trinomial.}$$
$$x = 0 \quad \text{or} \quad x = -1 \quad \text{or} \quad x = 3 \qquad \text{Zero-product property}$$

Algebra Review
To review factoring, see Chapter R, (page R-23).

The boundary numbers are -1, 0, and 3.

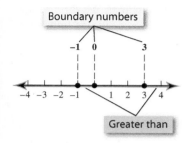

Figure 4.110

Evaluating Test Values

Figure 4.111

$[-5, 5, 1$ by $[-7, 7, 1]$

Figure 4.112

STEP 3: The boundary numbers separate the number line into four disjoint intervals:

$$(-\infty, -1), (-1, 0), (0, 3), \text{ and } (3, \infty),$$

as illustrated in Figure 4.110.

STEP 4: In Table 4.7 the expression $x^3 - 2x^2 - 3x$ is evaluated at a test value from each interval. The solution set is $[-1, 0] \cup [3, \infty)$. In Figure 4.111 a graphing calculator has been used to evaluate the same test values. (*Note:* The boundary numbers are included in the solution set because the inequality involves $\geq$ rather than $>$.)

Interval	Test Value x	$x^3 - 2x^2 - 3x$	Positive or Negative?
$(-\infty, -1)$	-2	-10	Negative
$(-1, 0)$	-0.5	0.875	Positive
$(0, 3)$	1	-4	Negative
$(3, \infty)$	4	20	Positive

Table 4.7

Graphical Solution Graph $y = x^3 - 2x^2 - 3x$, as shown in Figure 4.112. The zeros or x-intercepts are located at -1, 0, and 3. The graph of y is positive (or above the x-axis) for $-1 < x < 0$ or $3 < x < \infty$. If we include the boundary numbers, this result agrees with the symbolic solution.

Now Try Exercise 43

MAKING CONNECTIONS

Functions, Equations, and Inequalities The three concepts are related. For example,

$$f(x) = ax^3 + bx^2 + cx + d \qquad \text{Cubic function}$$
$$ax^3 + bx^2 + cx + d = 0 \qquad \text{Cubic equation}$$
$$ax^3 + bx^2 + cx + d < 0 \qquad \text{Cubic inequality}$$

where $a \neq 0$. These concepts also apply to higher degree polynomials and to rational expressions.

Rational Inequalities

An Application In the introduction we looked at how a rational inequality can be used to estimate the number of people standing in line at a ticket booth. In the next example, this inequality is solved graphically.

$[0, 30, 5]$ by $[0, 10, 2]$

Figure 4.113

EXAMPLE 8 Modeling customers in a line

A ticket booth attendant can wait on 30 customers per hour. To keep the time waiting in line reasonable, the line length should not exceed 8 customers on average. Solve the inequality $\frac{x^2}{900 - 30x} \leq 8$ to determine the rates x at which customers can arrive before a second attendant is needed. Note that the x-values are limited to $0 \leq x < 30$.

SOLUTION Graph $Y_1 = X^2/(900 - 30X)$ and $Y_2 = 8$ for $0 \leq x \leq 30$, as shown in Figure 4.113. The only point of intersection on this interval is near $(26.97, 8)$. The graph of y_1 is below the graph of y_2 for x-values to the left of this point. We conclude that if the arrival rate is about 27 customers per hour *or less*, then the line length does not exceed 8 customers on average. If the arrival rate is more than 27 customers per hour, a second ticket booth attendant is needed.

Now Try Exercise 85

Graphical and Symbolic Solutions To solve rational inequalities, we can use the same basic techniques that we used to solve polynomial inequalities, with one important modification: boundary numbers also occur at x-values where the denominator of any rational expression in the inequality equals 0. The following steps can be used to solve a rational inequality.

> ### SOLVING RATIONAL INEQUALITIES
>
> **STEP 1:** If necessary, write the inequality in the form $\frac{p(x)}{q(x)} > 0$, where $p(x)$ and $q(x)$ are polynomials. Note that $>$ may be replaced by $<$, $\leq$, or $\geq$.
>
> **STEP 2:** Solve $p(x) = 0$ and $q(x) = 0$. The solutions are boundary numbers.
>
> **STEP 3:** Use the boundary numbers to separate the number line into disjoint intervals. On each interval, $\frac{p(x)}{q(x)}$ is either always positive or always negative.
>
> **STEP 4:** Use a table of test values or a graph to solve the inequality in Step 1.

EXAMPLE 9 Solving a rational inequality

Solve $\frac{2 - x}{2x} > 0$ symbolically. Support your answer graphically.

SOLUTION
Symbolic Solution The inequality is written in the form $\frac{p(x)}{q(x)} > 0$, so Step 1 is unnecessary.

STEP 2: Set the numerator and the denominator equal to 0 and solve.

Numerator	**Denominator**
$2 - x = 0$	$2x = 0$
$x = 2$	$x = 0$

STEP 3: The boundary numbers are 0 and 2, which separate the number line into three disjoint intervals: $(-\infty, 0)$, $(0, 2)$, and $(2, \infty)$.

STEP 4: Table 4.8 shows that the expression is positive between the two boundary numbers or when $0 < x < 2$. In interval notation the solution set is $(0, 2)$.

$[-4.7, 4.7, 1]$ by $[-3.1, 3.1, 1]$

$y_1 = \frac{2 - x}{2x}$

X=2   Y=0

Figure 4.114

Solving $\dfrac{2 - x}{2x} > 0$

Interval	Test Value x	$(2 - x)/(2x)$	Positive or Negative?
$(-\infty, 0)$	-1	-1.5	Negative
$(0, 2)$	1	0.5	Positive
$(2, \infty)$	4	-0.25	Negative

Table 4.8

Graphical Solution Graph $Y_1 = (2 - X)/(2X)$, as shown in Figure 4.114. The graph has a vertical asymptote at $x = 0$ and an x-intercept at $x = 2$. Between these boundary numbers the graph of y_1 is positive (or above the x-axis). The solution set is $(0, 2)$. This agrees with our symbolic solution.

Now Try Exercise 59

EXAMPLE 10 Solving a rational inequality symbolically

Solve $\frac{1}{x} \leq \frac{2}{x + 1}$.

SOLUTION

STEP 1: Begin by writing the inequality in the form $\frac{p(x)}{q(x)} \leq 0$.

$$\frac{1}{x} - \frac{2}{x+1} \leq 0 \qquad \text{Subtract } \frac{2}{x+1}.$$

$$\frac{1}{x} \cdot \frac{(x+1)}{(x+1)} - \frac{2}{x+1} \cdot \frac{x}{x} \leq 0 \qquad \text{Common denominator is } x(x+1).$$

$$\frac{x+1}{x(x+1)} - \frac{2x}{x(x+1)} \leq 0 \qquad \text{Multiply.}$$

$$\frac{1-x}{x(x+1)} \leq 0 \qquad \begin{array}{l}\text{Subtract numerators:}\\ x+1-2x = 1-x.\end{array}$$

Algebra Review
To review subtraction of rational expressions, see Chapter R (page R-32).

STEP 2: Find the zeros of the numerator and the denominator.

Numerator	**Denominator**
$1 - x = 0$	$x(x+1) = 0$
$x = 1$	$x = 0 \quad \text{or} \quad x = -1$

STEP 3: The boundary numbers are -1, 0, and 1, which separate the number line into four disjoint intervals: $(-\infty, -1)$, $(-1, 0)$, $(0, 1)$, and $(1, \infty)$.

STEP 4: Table 4.9 can be used to solve the inequality $\frac{1-x}{x(x+1)} \leq 0$. The solution set is $(-1, 0) \cup [1, \infty)$.

> **NOTE**   The boundary numbers -1 and 0 are not included in the solution set because the given inequality is undefined when $x = -1$ or $x = 0$.

Solving $\dfrac{1-x}{x(x+1)} \leq 0$

Interval	Test Value x	$(1-x)/(x(x+1))$	Positive or Negative?
$(-\infty, -1)$	-2	1.5	Positive
$(-1, 0)$	-0.5	-6	Negative
$(0, 1)$	0.5	$0.\overline{6}$	Positive
$(1, \infty)$	2	$-0.1\overline{6}$	Negative

Table 4.9

Now Try Exercise 75

Multiplying an Inequality by a Variable   When solving a rational inequality, it is essential *not* to multiply or divide each side of the inequality by the LCD (least common denominator) if the LCD contains a *variable*. This technique often leads to an incorrect solution set.

For example, if each side of the rational inequality

$$\frac{1}{x} < 2$$

is multiplied by x to clear fractions, the inequality becomes

$$1 < 2x \quad \text{or} \quad x > \frac{1}{2}.$$

However, this solution set is clearly incomplete because $x = -1$ is also a solution to the given inequality. In general, the variable x can be either negative or positive. If $x < 0$, the inequality symbol should be reversed, whereas if $x > 0$, the inequality symbol should not be reversed. Because we have no way of knowing ahead of time which is the case, this technique of multiplying by a variable should be *avoided*.

4.7 Putting It All Together

The following table outlines basic concepts for this section.

CONCEPT	DESCRIPTION
Rational equation	Can be written as $f(x) = k$, where f is a rational function. To solve a rational equation, first clear fractions by multiplying each side by the LCD. *Check your answers.* **Example:** Solve $\frac{1}{x} + \frac{1}{x + 2} = \frac{1}{x(x + 2)}$. Multiply each side of the equation by the LCD: $x(x + 2)$. $$\frac{x(x + 2)}{x} + \frac{x(x + 2)}{x + 2} = \frac{x(x + 2)}{x(x + 2)}$$ $$(x + 2) + x = 1$$ $$x = -\frac{1}{2} \quad \text{It checks.}$$
Variation	*y varies directly with the nth power of x:* $y = kx^n$. **Example:** Let y vary directly with the cube (third power) of x. If the constant of variation is 5, then the variation equation is $y = 5x^3$. *y varies inversely with the nth power of x:* $y = \frac{k}{x^n}$. **Example:** Let y vary inversely with the square (second power) of x. If the constant of variation is 3, then the variation equation is $y = \frac{3}{x^2}$.
Polynomial inequality	Can be written as $p(x) < 0$, where $p(x)$ is a polynomial and $<$ may be replaced by $>$, $\leq$, or $\geq$ **Examples:** $x^3 - x \leq 0, \quad 2x^4 - 3x^2 \geq 5x + 1$
Solving a polynomial inequality	Follow the steps for solving a polynomial inequality presented on page 312. Either graphical or symbolic methods can be used. **Example:** A graph of $y = x^3 - 2x^2 - 5x + 6$ is shown. The boundary numbers are -2, 1, and 3. The solution set to $x^3 - 2x^2 - 5x + 6 > 0$ is $(-2, 1) \cup (3, \infty)$, because the graph is above the x-axis on these intervals.
Rational inequality	Can be written as $\frac{p(x)}{q(x)} < 0$, where $p(x)$ and $q(x) \neq 0$ are polynomials and $<$ may be replaced by $>$, $\leq$, or $\geq$ **Examples:** $\frac{x - 3}{x + 2} \geq 0, \quad 2x - \frac{2}{x^2 - 1} > 5$

CONCEPT	DESCRIPTION
Solving a rational inequality	Follow the steps for solving a rational inequality presented on page 314. Either graphical or symbolic methods can be used. **Example:** A graph of $y = \frac{x-1}{2x+1}$ is shown. Boundary numbers occur where either the numerator or denominator equals zero: $x = 1$ or $x = -\frac{1}{2}$. The solution set to $\frac{x-1}{2x+1} < 0$ is $\left(-\frac{1}{2}, 1\right)$, because the graph is below the x-axis on this interval.

4.7 Exercises

Rational Equations

Exercises 1–6: Solve the rational equation

(a) *symbolically,*

(b) *graphically, and*

(c) *numerically.*

1. $\dfrac{2x}{x+2} = 6$

2. $\dfrac{3x}{2x-1} = 3$

3. $2 - \dfrac{5}{x} + \dfrac{2}{x^2} = 0$

4. $\dfrac{1}{x^2} + \dfrac{1}{x} = 2$

5. $\dfrac{1}{x+1} + \dfrac{1}{x-1} = \dfrac{1}{x^2-1}$

6. $\dfrac{4}{x-2} = \dfrac{3}{x-1}$

Exercises 7–28: Find all real solutions. Check your results.

7. $\dfrac{x+1}{x-5} = 0$

8. $\dfrac{x-2}{x+3} = 1$

9. $\dfrac{6(1-2x)}{x-5} = 4$

10. $\dfrac{2}{5(2x+5)} + 3 = -1$

11. $\dfrac{1}{x+2} + \dfrac{1}{x} = 1$

12. $\dfrac{2x}{x-1} = 5 + \dfrac{2}{x-1}$

13. $\dfrac{1}{x} - \dfrac{2}{x^2} = 5$

14. $\dfrac{1}{x^2-2} = \dfrac{1}{x}$

15. $\dfrac{x^3-4x}{x^2+1} = 0$

16. $\dfrac{1}{x+2} + \dfrac{1}{x+3} = \dfrac{2}{x^2+5x+6}$

17. $\dfrac{35}{x^2} = \dfrac{4}{x} + 15$

18. $6 - \dfrac{35}{x} + \dfrac{36}{x^2} = 0$

19. $\dfrac{x+5}{x+2} = \dfrac{x-4}{x-10}$

20. $\dfrac{x-1}{x+1} = \dfrac{x+3}{x-4}$

21. $\dfrac{1}{x-2} - \dfrac{2}{x-3} = \dfrac{-1}{x^2-5x+6}$

22. $\dfrac{1}{x-1} + \dfrac{3}{x+1} = \dfrac{4}{x^2-1}$

23. $\dfrac{2}{x-1} + 1 = \dfrac{4}{x^2-1}$

24. $\dfrac{1}{x} + 2 = \dfrac{1}{x^2 + x}$

25. $\dfrac{1}{x + 2} = \dfrac{4}{4 - x^2} - 1$

26. $\dfrac{1}{x - 3} + 1 = \dfrac{6}{x^2 - 9}$

27. $\dfrac{1}{x - 1} + \dfrac{1}{x + 1} = \dfrac{2}{x^2 - 1}$

28. $\dfrac{1}{2x + 1} + \dfrac{1}{2x - 1} = \dfrac{2}{4x^2 - 1}$

Graphical Solutions to Inequalities

Exercises 29–34: Solve the equation and inequalities.

(a) $f(x) = 0$ *(b)* $f(x) > 0$ *(c)* $f(x) < 0$

29.

30.

31.

32.

33.

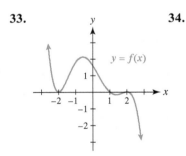

34.

Exercises 35–40: Complete the following.

(a) Identify where $f(x)$ is undefined or $f(x) = 0$.
(b) Solve $f(x) > 0$.
(c) Solve $f(x) < 0$.

35.

36.

37.

38.

39.

40.

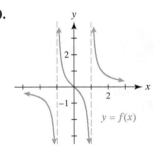

Polynomial Inequalities

Exercises 41–46: Solve the polynomial inequality
(a) symbolically and   (b) graphically.

41. $x^3 - x > 0$ **42.** $8x^3 < 27$

43. $x^3 + x^2 \geq 2x$ **44.** $2x^3 \leq 3x^2 + 5x$

45. $x^4 - 13x^2 + 36 < 0$

46. $4x^4 - 5x^2 - 9 \geq 0$

Exercises 47–52: Solve the polynomial inequality.

47. $7x^4 > 14x^2$

48. $3x^4 - 4x^2 < 7$

49. $(x - 1)(x - 2)(x + 2) \geq 0$

50. $-(x + 1)^2(x - 2) \geq 0$

51. $2x^4 + 2x^3 \leq 12x^2$

52. $x^3 + 6x^2 + 9x > 0$

Exercises 53–56: Solve the polynomial inequality graphically.

53. $x^3 - 7x^2 + 14x \leq 8$

54. $2x^3 + 3x^2 - 3x < 2$

55. $3x^4 - 7x^3 - 2x^2 + 8x > 0$

56. $x^4 - 5x^3 \leq 5x^2 + 45x + 36$

Rational Inequalities

Exercises 57–62: Solve the rational inequality
(a) symbolically and (b) graphically.

57. $\dfrac{1}{x} < 0$

58. $\dfrac{1}{x^2} > 0$

59. $\dfrac{4}{x + 3} \geq 0$

60. $\dfrac{x - 1}{x + 1} < 0$

61. $\dfrac{5}{x^2 - 4} < 0$

62. $\dfrac{x}{x^2 - 1} \geq 0$

Exercises 63–76: Solve the rational inequality.

63. $\dfrac{(x + 1)^2}{x - 2} \leq 0$

64. $\dfrac{2x}{(x - 2)^2} > 0$

65. $\dfrac{3 - 2x}{1 + x} < 0$

66. $\dfrac{x + 1}{4 - 2x} \geq 1$

67. $\dfrac{(x + 1)(x - 2)}{(x + 3)} < 0$

68. $\dfrac{x(x - 3)}{x + 2} \geq 0$

69. $\dfrac{2x - 5}{x^2 - 1} \geq 0$

70. $\dfrac{5 - x}{x^2 - x - 2} < 0$

71. $\dfrac{1}{x - 3} \leq \dfrac{5}{x - 3}$

72. $\dfrac{3}{2 - x} > \dfrac{x}{2 + x}$

73. $2 - \dfrac{5}{x} + \dfrac{2}{x^2} \geq 0$

74. $\dfrac{1}{x - 1} + \dfrac{1}{x + 1} > \dfrac{3}{4}$

75. $\dfrac{1}{x} \leq \dfrac{2}{x + 2}$

76. $\dfrac{1}{x + 1} < \dfrac{1}{x} + 1$

Applications

77. Time Spent in Line Suppose the average number of vehicles arriving at the main gate of an amusement park is equal to 10 per minute, while the average number of vehicles being admitted through the gate per minute is equal to x. Then the average waiting time in minutes for each vehicle at the gate can be computed by $f(x) = \dfrac{x - 5}{x^2 - 10x}$, where $x > 10$. (**Source:** F. Mannering.)

(a) Estimate the admittance rate x that results in an average wait of 15 seconds.

(b) If one attendant can serve 5 vehicles per minute, how many attendants are needed to keep the average wait to 15 seconds or less?

78. Length of Lines (Refer to Example 2 in Section 4.6.) Solve $\dfrac{x^2}{2 - 2x} = 3$ to determine the traffic intensity x when the average number of vehicles in line equals 3.

79. Construction (Refer to Example 4.) Find possible dimensions for a box with a volume of 196 cubic inches, a surface area of 280 square inches, and a length that is twice the width.

80. Minimizing Surface Area An aluminum can is being designed to hold a volume of 100π cubic centimeters.

Geometry Review
To review formulas for cylinders, see Chapter R (page R-4).

(a) Find a formula for the volume V in terms of r and h.

(b) Write a formula for a function S that calculates the outside surface area of the can in terms of only r. Evaluate $S(2)$ and interpret the result.

(c) Find the dimensions that result in the least amount of aluminum being used in its construction.

81. Minimizing Cost A cardboard box with no top and a square base is being constructed and must have a volume of 108 cubic inches. Let x be the length of a side of its base in inches.

(a) Write a formula $A(x)$ that calculates the outside surface area in square feet of the box.

(b) If cardboard costs $0.10 per square foot, write a formula $C(x)$ that gives the cost in dollars of the cardboard in the box.

(c) Find the dimensions of the box that would minimize the cost of the cardboard.

82. Cost-Benefit A cost-benefit function C computes the cost in millions of dollars of implementing a city recycling project when x percent of the citizens participate, where $C(x) = \frac{1.2x}{100 - x}$.

(a) Graph C in $[0, 100, 10]$ by $[0, 10, 1]$. Interpret the graph as x approaches 100.

(b) If 75% participation is expected, determine the cost for the city.

(c) The city plans to spend $5 million on this recycling project. Estimate the percentage of participation that can be expected.

83. Braking Distance The *grade x* of a hill is a measure of its steepness. For example, if a road rises 10 feet for every 100 feet of horizontal distance, then it has an uphill grade of $x = \frac{10}{100}$, or 10%. See the figure. The braking distance D for a car traveling at 50 miles per hour on a wet uphill grade is given by the formula $D(x) = \frac{2500}{30(0.3 + x)}$. (*Source:* L. Haefner.)

(a) Evaluate $D(0.05)$ and interpret the result.

(b) Describe what happens to the braking distance as the hill becomes steeper. Does this agree with your driving experience?

(c) Estimate the grade associated with a braking distance of 220 feet.

84. Braking Distance (Refer to Exercise 83.) If a car is traveling 50 miles per hour downhill, then the car's braking distance on a wet pavement is given by

$$D(x) = \frac{2500}{30(0.3 + x)},$$

where $x < 0$ for a downhill grade.

(a) Evaluate $D(-0.1)$ and interpret the result.

(b) What happens to the braking distance as the downhill grade becomes steeper? Does this agree with your driving experience?

(c) The graph of D has a vertical asymptote at $x = -0.3$. Give the physical significance of this asymptote.

(d) Estimate the grade associated with a braking distance of 350 feet.

85. Waiting in Line (Refer to Example 8.) A parking garage attendant can wait on 40 cars per hour. If cars arrive randomly at a rate of x cars per hour, then the average line length is given by

$$f(x) = \frac{x^2}{1600 - 40x},$$

where the x-values are limited to $0 \le x < 40$.

(a) Solve the inequality $f(x) \le 8$.

(b) Interpret your answer from part (a).

86. Time Spent in Line If a parking garage attendant can wait on 3 vehicles per minute and vehicles are leaving the ramp at x vehicles per minute, then the average wait in minutes for a car trying to exit is given by the formula $f(x) = \frac{1}{3 - x}$.

(a) Solve the three-part inequality $5 \le \frac{1}{3 - x} \le 10$.

(b) Interpret your result from part (a).

87. Slippery Roads The coefficient of friction x measures the friction between the tires of a car and the road, where $0 < x \le 1$. A smaller value of x indicates that the road is more slippery. If a car is traveling at 60 miles per hour, then the braking distance D in feet is given by the formula $D(x) = \frac{120}{x}$.

(a) What happens to the braking distance as the coefficient of friction becomes smaller?

(b) Find values for the coefficient of friction x that correspond to a braking distance of 400 feet or more.

88. Average Temperature The monthly average high temperature in degrees Fahrenheit at Daytona Beach, Florida, can be approximated by

$$f(x) = 0.0145x^4 - 0.426x^3 + 3.53x^2 - 6.22x + 72,$$

where $x = 1$ corresponds to January, $x = 2$ to February, and so on. Estimate graphically when the monthly average high temperature is 75°F or more.

89. Geometry A cubical box is being manufactured to hold 213 cubic inches. If this measurement can vary between 212.8 cubic inches and 213.2 cubic inches inclusive, by how much can the length x of a side of the cube vary?

90. Construction A cylindrical aluminum can is being manufactured so that its height h is 8 centimeters more than its radius r. Estimate values for the radius (to the nearest hundredth) that result in the can having a volume between 1000 and 1500 cubic centimeters inclusive.

Variation

Exercises 91–94: Find the constant of proportionality k.

91. $y = \frac{k}{x}$, and $y = 2$ when $x = 3$

92. $y = \frac{k}{x^2}$, and $y = \frac{1}{4}$ when $x = 8$

93. $y = kx^3$, and $y = 64$ when $x = 2$

94. $y = kx^{3/2}$, and $y = 96$ when $x = 16$

Exercises 95–98: Solve the variation problem.

95. Suppose T varies directly with the $\frac{3}{2}$ power of x. When $x = 4$, $T = 20$. Find T when $x = 16$.

96. Suppose y varies directly with the second power of x. When $x = 3$, $y = 10.8$. Find y when $x = 1.5$.

97. Let y be inversely proportional to x. When $x = 6$, $y = 5$. Find y when $x = 15$.

98. Let z be inversely proportional to the third power of t. When $t = 5$, $z = 0.08$. Find z when $t = 2$.

Exercises 99–102: Assume that the constant of proportionality is positive.

99. Let y be inversely proportional to x. If x doubles, what happens to y?

100. Let y vary inversely with the second power of x. If x doubles, what happens to y?

101. Suppose y varies directly with the third power of x. If x triples, what happens to y?

102. Suppose y is directly proportional to the second power of x. If x is halved, what happens to y?

Exercises 103 and 104: The data satisfy the equation $y = kx^n$, where n is a positive integer. Determine k and n.

103.

x	2	3	4	5
y	2	4.5	8	12.5

104.

x	3	5	7	9
y	32.4	150	411.6	874.8

Exercises 105 and 106: The data in the table satisfy the equation $y = \frac{k}{x^n}$, where n is a positive integer. Determine k and n.

105.

x	2	3	4	5
y	1.5	1	0.75	0.6

106.

x	2	4	6	8
y	9	2.25	1	0.5625

107. Fiddler Crab Growth The weight y of a fiddler crab is directly proportional to the 1.25 power of the weight x of its claws. A crab with a body weight of 1.9 grams has claws weighing 1.1 grams. Estimate the weight of a fiddler crab with claws weighing 0.75 gram. (*Source:* D. Brown.)

108. Gravity The weight of an object varies inversely with the second power of the distance from the *center* of Earth. The radius of Earth is approximately 4000 miles. If a person weighs 160 pounds on Earth's surface, what would this individual weigh 8000 miles above the surface of Earth?

109. Hubble Telescope The brightness, or intensity, of starlight varies inversely with the square of its distance from Earth. The Hubble Telescope can see stars whose intensities are $\frac{1}{50}$ that of the faintest star now seen by ground-based telescopes. Determine how much farther the Hubble Telescope can see into space than ground-based telescopes. (*Source:* National Aeronautics and Space Administration.)

110. Volume The volume V of a cylinder with a fixed height is directly proportional to the square of its radius r. If a cylinder with a radius of 10 inches has a volume of 200 cubic inches, what is the volume of a cylinder with the same height and a radius of 5 inches?

111. Electrical Resistance The electrical resistance R of a wire varies inversely with the square of its diameter d. If a 25-foot wire with a diameter of 2 millimeters has a resistance of 0.5 ohm, find the resistance of a wire having the same length and a diameter of 3 millimeters.

112. Strength of a Beam The strength of a rectangular wood beam varies directly with the square of the depth of its cross section. If a beam with a depth of 3.5 inches can support 1000 pounds, how much weight can the same type of beam hold if its depth is 12 inches?

Exercises 113 and 114: **Violin String** *The frequency F of a vibrating string is directly proportional to the square root of the tension T on the string and inversely proportional to the length L of the string.*

113. If both the tension and the length are doubled, what happens to F?

114. Give two ways to double the frequency F.

Writing About Mathematics

115. Describe the steps to graphically solve a polynomial inequality in the form $p(x) > 0$.

116. Describe the steps to symbolically solve a rational inequality in the form $f(x) > 0$.

4.8 Radical Equations and Power Functions

- **Learn properties of rational exponents**
- **Learn radical notation**
- **Use radical functions and solve radical equations**
- **Understand properties and graphs of power functions**
- **Use power functions to model data**
- **Solve equations involving rational exponents**
- **Use power regression to model data (optional)**

Introduction

Johannes Kepler (1571–1630) was the first to recognize that a power function models the relationship between a planet's distance from the sun and its period of revolution. Table 4.10 lists the average distance x from the sun and the time y in years for several planets to orbit the sun. The distance x has been normalized so that Earth is one unit away from the sun. For example, Jupiter is 5.2 times farther from the sun than Earth and requires 11.9 years to orbit the sun.

Planets and Their Orbits

Planet	Mercury	Venus	Earth	Mars	Jupiter	Saturn
x **(distance)**	0.387	0.723	1.00	1.52	5.20	9.54
y **(period)**	0.241	0.615	1.00	1.88	11.9	29.5

Table 4.10 *Source: C. Ronan, The Natural History of the Universe.*

A scatterplot of the data in Table 4.10 is shown in Figure 4.115. To model these data, we might try a polynomial, such as $f(x) = x$ or $g(x) = x^2$. Figure 4.116 shows that $f(x) = x$ increases too slowly and $g(x) = x^2$ increases too fast. To model these data, a new type of function is required. That is, we need a function in the form $h(x) = x^b$, where $1 < b < 2$. Polynomials allow the exponent b to be only a nonnegative integer, whereas *power functions* allow b to be any real number. See Figure 4.117 and Example 11.

Figure 4.115

Figure 4.116

Figure 4.117

Rational Exponents and Radical Notation

The following properties can be used to simplify expressions with rational exponents.

Algebra Review
To review integer exponents, see Chapter R (page R-7). To review radical notation and rational exponents, see Chapter R (page R-38).

PROPERTIES OF RATIONAL EXPONENTS

Let m and n be positive integers with $\frac{m}{n}$ in *lowest* terms and $n \geq 2$. Let r and p be rational numbers. Assume that b is a nonzero real number and that each expression is a real number.

Property	*Example*
1. $b^{m/n} = (b^m)^{1/n} = (b^{1/n})^m$	$4^{3/2} = (4^3)^{1/2} = (4^{1/2})^3 = 2^3 = 8$
2. $b^{m/n} = \sqrt[n]{b^m} = (\sqrt[n]{b})^m$	$8^{2/3} = \sqrt[3]{8^2} = (\sqrt[3]{8})^2 = 2^2 = 4$
3. $(b^r)^p = b^{rp}$	$(2^{3/2})^4 = 2^{(3/2)4} = 2^6 = 64$
4. $b^{-r} = \dfrac{1}{b^r}$	$4^{-1/2} = \dfrac{1}{4^{1/2}} = \dfrac{1}{2}$
5. $b^r b^p = b^{r+p}$	$3^{5/2} \cdot 3^{3/2} = 3^{(5/2)+(3/2)} = 3^4 = 81$
6. $\dfrac{b^r}{b^p} = b^{r-p}$	$\dfrac{5^{5/4}}{5^{3/4}} = 5^{(5/4)-(3/4)} = 5^{1/2}$

EXAMPLE 1   **Applying properties of exponents**

Simplify each expression by hand.

(a) $16^{3/4}$ **(b)** $\dfrac{4^{1/3}}{4^{5/6}}$ **(c)** $27^{-2/3} \cdot 27^{1/3}$ **(d)** $(5^{3/4})^{2/3}$ **(e)** $(-125)^{-4/3}$

SOLUTION

(a) $16^{3/4} = (\sqrt[4]{16})^3 = (2)^3 = 8$ $b^{m/n} = \sqrt[n]{b^m} = (\sqrt[n]{b})^m$

(b) $\dfrac{4^{1/3}}{4^{5/6}} = 4^{(1/3)-(5/6)} = 4^{-1/2} = \dfrac{1}{\sqrt{4}} = \dfrac{1}{2}$ $\dfrac{b^r}{b^p} = b^{r-p}$

(c) $27^{-2/3} \cdot 27^{1/3} = 27^{(-2/3)+(1/3)} = 27^{-1/3} = \dfrac{1}{\sqrt[3]{27}} = \dfrac{1}{3}$ $b^r b^p = b^{r+p}$

(d) $(5^{3/4})^{2/3} = 5^{(3/4)(2/3)} = 5^{1/2}$ or $\sqrt{5}$ $(b^r)^p = b^{rp}$

(e) $(-125)^{-4/3} = \dfrac{1}{(\sqrt[3]{-125})^4} = \dfrac{1}{(-5)^4} = \dfrac{1}{625}$ $b^{-r} = \frac{1}{b^r}$

> **Now Try Exercises 1, 7, 9, 11, and 13**

EXAMPLE 2   **Writing radicals with rational exponents**

Use positive rational exponents to write each expression.

(a) $\sqrt{x}$ **(b)** $\sqrt[3]{x^2}$ **(c)** $(\sqrt[4]{z})^{-5}$ **(d)** $\sqrt{\sqrt[3]{y} \cdot \sqrt[4]{y}}$

SOLUTION

(a) $\sqrt{x} = x^{1/2}$ **(b)** $\sqrt[3]{x^2} = (x^2)^{1/3} = x^{2/3}$

(c) $(\sqrt[4]{z})^{-5} = (z^{1/4})^{-5} = z^{-5/4} = \dfrac{1}{z^{5/4}}$

(d) $\sqrt{\sqrt[3]{y} \cdot \sqrt[4]{y}} = \left(y^{1/3} \cdot y^{1/4}\right)^{1/2} = \left(y^{(1/3)+(1/4)}\right)^{1/2} = \left(y^{7/12}\right)^{1/2} = y^{7/24}$

> **Now Try Exercises 19, 21, 23, and 27**

Functions Involving Radicals

Expressions involving radicals are sometimes used to define **radical functions**. Two common radical functions are the **square root function** and the **cube root function**. Their graphs and domains are shown in Figure 4.118 and 4.119. The fourth root function is also shown in Figure 4.120.

Square Root Function

$y = \sqrt{x}$

Domain: $[0, \infty)$

Figure 4.118

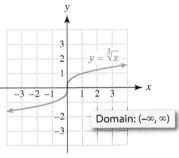

Cube Root Function

$y = \sqrt[3]{x}$

Domain: $(-\infty, \infty)$

Figure 4.119

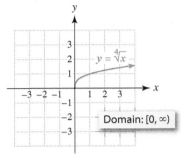

Fourth Root Function

$y = \sqrt[4]{x}$

Domain: $[0, \infty)$

Figure 4.120

EXAMPLE 3 Evaluating radical functions

Evaluate each function for the given value of x.

(a) $f(x) = 2\sqrt[3]{x}$ for $x = 27$
(b) $g(x) = \sqrt{x^3}$ for $x = 4$
(c) $h(x) = \sqrt[4]{2x}$ for $x = 8$

SOLUTION
(a) $f(27) = 2\sqrt[3]{27} = 2(3) = 6$
(b) $g(4) = \sqrt{4^3} = \sqrt{64} = 8$
(c) $h(8) = \sqrt[4]{2(8)} = \sqrt[4]{16} = 2$

> **Now Try Exercises 33, 35, and 37**

In the next example, we use transformations to graph a function.

EXAMPLE 4 Using transformations to graph a function

Graph $g(x) = -\sqrt[3]{x + 1}$.

SOLUTION
To obtain the graph of g we can reflect the graph of $f(x) = \sqrt[3]{x}$ (see Figure 4.119) across the x-axis to obtain $y = -\sqrt[3]{x}$, and then shift this new graph left 1 unit to obtain $y = -\sqrt[3]{(x + 1)}$, as shown in Figures 4.121 and 4.122. (In this example, we could also shift left 1 unit and then reflect across the x-axis.)

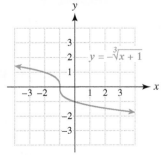

Reflect Across x-Axis

$y = -\sqrt[3]{x}$

Figure 4.121

Shift Left 1 Unit

$y = -\sqrt[3]{x + 1}$

Figure 4.122

> **Now Try Exercise 43**

Functions involving radicals have many applications. In the next example we use the cube root function to model numbers of plant species on different Galápagos islands.

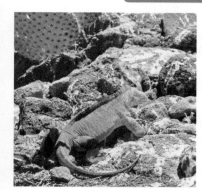

EXAMPLE 5 Estimating numbers of plant species

The number N of different plant species that live on a Galápagos island is sometimes related to the island's area A in square miles by the function

$$N(A) = 28.6\sqrt[3]{A}.$$

(a) Approximate N to the nearest whole number for islands of 100 square miles and 200 square miles. Interpret your answers.

(b) Does N double if A doubles?

SOLUTION

(a) $N(100) = 28.6\sqrt[3]{100} \approx 133$ and $N(200) = 28.6\sqrt[3]{200} \approx 167$. If the island is 100 square miles, there are about 133 different species of plants. This number increases to 167 on an island of 200 square miles.

(b) From part (a), we see that N does not double if A doubles. It increases by a factor of $\sqrt[3]{2} \approx 1.26$, not 2.

> **Now Try Exercise 111**

Equations Involving Radicals

In solving equations that contain square roots, it is common to square each side of an equation and then check the results. This is done in the next example.

EXAMPLE 6 Solving an equation containing a square root

Solve $x = \sqrt{15 - 2x}$. Check your answers.

SOLUTION

Begin by squaring each side of the equation.

$$\begin{aligned}
x &= \sqrt{15 - 2x} && \textit{Given equation} \\
x^2 &= \left(\sqrt{15 - 2x}\right)^2 && \textit{Square each side.} \\
x^2 &= 15 - 2x && \textit{Simplify.} \\
x^2 + 2x - 15 &= 0 && \textit{Add 2x and subtract 15.} \\
(x + 5)(x - 3) &= 0 && \textit{Factor.} \\
x = -5 \quad \text{or} \quad x &= 3 && \textit{Solve.}
\end{aligned}$$

[−9, 9, 1] by [−6, 6, 1]

Figure 4.123

Check: Now substitute these values in the *given* equation $x = \sqrt{15 - 2x}$.

$$-5 \neq \sqrt{15 - 2(-5)} = 5, \qquad 3 = \sqrt{15 - 2(3)} \ \checkmark$$

Thus 3 is the only solution. This result is supported graphically in Figure 4.123. Notice that *no* point of intersection occurs when $x = -5$.

> **Now Try Exercise 57**

The value -5 in Example 6 is called an **extraneous solution** because it does not satisfy the given equation. It is important to check results whenever *squaring* has been used to solve an equation. (Graphical solutions do not have extraneous solutions.)

NOTE If each side of an equation is raised to the same positive integer power, then any solutions to the given equation are *among* the solutions to the new equation. That is, the solutions to the equation $a = b$ are *among* the solutions to $a^n = b^n$. For this reason, we *must* check our answers.

In the next example, we cube each side of an equation that contains a cube root.

EXAMPLE 7 Solving an equation containing a cube root

Solve $\sqrt[3]{2x + 5} - 2 = 1$.

SOLUTION Start by adding 2 to each side. Then cube each side.

$$\sqrt[3]{2x + 5} = 3 \qquad \text{Add 2 to each side.}$$
$$\left(\sqrt[3]{2x + 5}\right)^3 = 3^3 \qquad \text{Cube each side.}$$
$$2x + 5 = 27 \qquad \text{Simplify.}$$
$$2x = 22 \qquad \text{Subtract 5 from each side.}$$
$$x = 11 \qquad \text{Divide each side by 2.}$$

The only solution is 11. The answer checks.

Now Try Exercise 65

Squaring Twice In the next example, we need to square twice to solve a radical equation.

EXAMPLE 8 Squaring twice

Solve $\sqrt{2x + 3} - \sqrt{x + 1} = 1$.

SOLUTION

Getting Started When an equation contains two square root expressions, we frequently need to square twice. Start by isolating the more complicated radical expression and then square each side. ▶

$$\sqrt{2x + 3} - \sqrt{x + 1} = 1 \qquad \text{Given equation}$$
$$\sqrt{2x + 3} = 1 + \sqrt{x + 1} \qquad \text{Isolate } \sqrt{2x + 3}.$$
$$\left(\sqrt{2x + 3}\right)^2 = \left(1 + \sqrt{x + 1}\right)^2 \qquad \text{Square each side.}$$
$$2x + 3 = 1 + 2\sqrt{x + 1} + x + 1 \qquad \text{Simplify.}$$
$$x + 1 = 2\sqrt{x + 1} \qquad \text{Isolate the remaining radical.}$$
$$(x + 1)^2 = \left(2\sqrt{x + 1}\right)^2 \qquad \text{Square each side again.}$$
$$x^2 + 2x + 1 = 4(x + 1) \qquad \text{Simplify.}$$
$$x^2 + 2x + 1 = 4x + 4 \qquad \text{Distributive property}$$
$$x^2 - 2x - 3 = 0 \qquad \text{Subtract } 4x + 4.$$
$$(x - 3)(x + 1) = 0 \qquad \text{Factor.}$$
$$x - 3 = 0 \quad \text{or} \quad x + 1 = 0 \qquad \text{Zero-product property}$$
$$x = 3 \quad \text{or} \qquad x = -1 \qquad \text{Solve each equation.}$$

Checking reveals that both −1 and 3 are solutions to the *given* equation.

Now Try Exercise 63

Power Functions and Models

Functions with rational exponents are often used to model physical characteristics of living organisms. For example, larger animals tend to have slower heart rates and larger birds tend to have bigger wings. There is a relationship between a bird's weight and its wing size. (See Example 10.)

Power functions often have rational exponents, and can be written in radical notation. A special type of power function is a root function.

> ### POWER FUNCTION
>
> A function f given by $f(x) = x^b$, where b is a constant, is a **power function**. If $b = \frac{1}{n}$ for some integer $n \geq 2$, then f is a **root function** given by $f(x) = x^{1/n}$, or equivalently, $f(x) = \sqrt[n]{x}$.

Cube Root Square

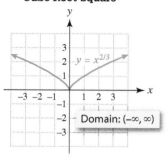

Figure 4.124

Examples of power functions include

$$f_1(x) = x^2, \qquad f_2(x) = x^{3/4}, \qquad f_3(x) = x^{0.4}, \qquad \text{and} \qquad f_4(x) = \sqrt[3]{x^2}.$$
Power Functions

Domains of Power Functions   Suppose a positive rational number $\frac{p}{q}$ is written in lowest terms. Then the domain of $f(x) = x^{p/q}$ is all real numbers whenever q is odd and all *nonnegative* real numbers whenever q is even. A graph of a common power function is shown in Figure 4.124.

EXAMPLE 9   Graphing power functions

Graph $f(x) = x^b$, where $b = 0.3$, 1, and 1.7, for $x \geq 0$. Discuss the effect that b has on the graph of f for $x \geq 1$.

SOLUTION
The graphs of $y = x^{0.3}$, $y = x^1$, and $y = x^{1.7}$ are shown in Figure 4.125. For $x \geq 1$, larger values of b cause the graph of f to increase faster. Note that each graph passes through the point $(1, 1)$. Why?

$$f(x) = x^b, \, x \geq 0$$

Figure 4.125

Now Try Exercises 73 and 74

Modeling   In the next two examples, we use power functions to determine weights of birds based on wing size and to describe planetary motion.

EXAMPLE 10   Modeling wing size of a bird

Heavier birds have larger wings with more surface area than do lighter birds. For some species of birds, this relationship can be modeled by $S(w) = 0.2w^{2/3}$, where w is the weight of the bird in kilograms, with $0.1 \leq w \leq 5$, and S is the surface area of the wings in square meters.   (*Source:* C. Pennycuick, *Newton Rules Biology.*)
(a) Approximate $S(0.5)$ and interpret the result.
(b) What weight corresponds to a surface area of 0.25 square meter?

SOLUTION
(a) $S(0.5) = 0.2(0.5)^{2/3} \approx 0.126$. The wings of a bird that weighs 0.5 kilogram have a surface area of about 0.126 square meter.

(b) To determine the weight that corresponds to a surface area of 0.25 square meter, we must solve the equation $0.2w^{2/3} = 0.25$.

$$0.2w^{2/3} = 0.25 \qquad \text{Equation to solve}$$

$$w^{2/3} = \frac{0.25}{0.2} \qquad \text{Divide by 0.2.}$$

$$(w^{2/3})^3 = \left(\frac{0.25}{0.2}\right)^3 \qquad \text{Cube each side.}$$

$$w^2 = \left(\frac{0.25}{0.2}\right)^3 \qquad \text{Simplify.}$$

$$w = \pm\sqrt{\left(\frac{0.25}{0.2}\right)^3} \qquad \text{Square root property}$$

$$w \approx \pm 1.4 \qquad \text{Approximate.}$$

Since w must be positive, the wings of a 1.4-kilogram bird have a surface area of about 0.25 square meter.

Now Try Exercise 105

EXAMPLE 11 Modeling the period of planetary orbits

Use the data in Table 4.10 on page 322 to complete the following.
(a) Make a scatterplot of the data. Graphically estimate a value for b so that $f(x) = x^b$ models the data.
(b) Check the accuracy of $f(x)$.
(c) The average distances of Uranus, Neptune, and Pluto (no longer a major planet) from the sun are 19.2, 30.1, and 39.5, respectively. Use f to estimate their periods of revolution. Compare these estimates to the actual values of 84.0, 164.8, and 248.5 years.

SOLUTION
(a) Graph the data and $y = x^b$ for different values of b. From the graphs of $y = x^{1.4}$, $y = x^{1.5}$, and $y = x^{1.6}$ in Figures 4.126–4.128, it can be seen that $b \approx 1.5$.

Calculator Help

To make a scatterplot, see Appendix A (page AP-3). To make a table like Figure 4.129, see Appendix A (page AP-9).

Exponent Too Small	Exponent About Right?	Exponent Too Large
[0, 10, 1] by [0, 30, 10]	[0, 10, 1] by [0, 30, 10]	[0, 10, 1] by [0, 30, 10]

| **Figure 4.126** | **Figure 4.127** | **Figure 4.128** |

(b) Let $y_1 = x^{1.5}$. The values shown in Figure 4.129 model the data in Table 4.10 remarkably well.

Comparing Model with True Values

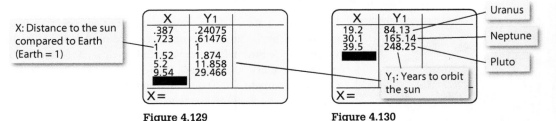

Figure 4.129 **Figure 4.130**

(c) To approximate the number of years required for Uranus, Neptune, and Pluto to orbit the sun, evaluate $y_1 = x^{1.5}$ at $x = 19.2$, 30.1, and 39.5, as shown in Figure 4.130. These values are close to the actual values.

Now Try Exercise 109

Equations Involving Rational Exponents

The next example demonstrates a basic technique that can be used to solve equations with rational exponents.

EXAMPLE 12 Solving an equation with rational exponents

Solve $2x^{5/2} - 7 = 23$. Round to the nearest hundredth and give graphical support.

SOLUTION

Symbolic Solution   Start by adding 7 to each side of the given equation.

$$2x^{5/2} = 30 \qquad \text{Add 7 to each side.}$$
$$x^{5/2} = 15 \qquad \text{Divide each side by 2.}$$
$$(x^{5/2})^2 = 15^2 \qquad \text{Square each side.}$$
$$x^5 = 225 \qquad \text{Properties of exponents}$$
$$x = 225^{1/5} \qquad \text{Take the fifth root of each side.}$$
$$x \approx 2.95 \qquad \text{Approximate.}$$

Graphic Solution   Graphical support is shown in Figure 4.131, where the graphs of $Y_1 = 2X^\wedge(5/2) - 7$ and $Y_2 = 23$ intersect near (2.95, 23).

Now Try Exercise 89

Calculator Help

When entering X^(5/2), be sure to put parentheses around the fraction 5/2.

$[-5, 5, 1]$ by $[-40, 40, 10]$

Figure 4.131

MAKING CONNECTIONS

Solutions to $x^n = k$ (k a constant and $n \geq 2$ an integer)

n odd: The real solution to $x^n = k$ is $x = \sqrt[n]{k}$, or $x = k^{1/n}$, for all k.
See Example 12.

n even: The real solutions to $x^n = k$ are $x = \pm\sqrt[n]{k}$, or $x = \pm k^{1/n}$, for $k \geq 0$.
See Example 10.

Equations that have rational exponents are sometimes reducible to quadratic form.

EXAMPLE 13 Solving an equation having negative exponents

Solve $15n^{-2} - 19n^{-1} + 6 = 0$.

SOLUTION   Two methods for solving this equation are presented.

Method 1:   Use the substitution $u = n^{-1} = \frac{1}{n}$ and $u^2 = n^{-2} = \frac{1}{n^2}$.

$$15n^{-2} - 19n^{-1} + 6 = 0 \qquad \text{Given equation}$$
$$15u^2 - 19u + 6 = 0 \qquad \text{Let } u = n^{-1} \text{ and } u^2 = n^{-2}.$$
$$(3u - 2)(5u - 3) = 0 \qquad \text{Factor.}$$
$$u = \frac{2}{3} \quad \text{or} \quad u = \frac{3}{5} \qquad \text{Zero-product property}$$

Because $u = \frac{1}{n}$, it follows that $n = \frac{1}{u}$. Thus $n = \frac{3}{2}$ or $n = \frac{5}{3}$.

Method 2:   Another way to solve this equation is to multiply each side by n^2 to eliminate negative exponents.

$$15n^{-2} - 19n^{-1} + 6 = 0 \qquad \text{Given equation}$$
$$n^2(15n^{-2} - 19n^{-1} + 6) = n^2(0) \qquad \text{Multiply each side by } n^2.$$
$$15n^2 n^{-2} - 19n^2 n^{-1} + 6n^2 = 0 \qquad \text{Distributive property}$$
$$15 - 19n + 6n^2 = 0 \qquad \text{Properties of exponents}$$

$$6n^2 - 19n + 15 = 0 \qquad \text{Rewrite the equation.}$$

$$(2n - 3)(3n - 5) = 0 \qquad \text{Factor.}$$

$$n = \frac{3}{2} \quad \text{or} \quad n = \frac{5}{3} \qquad \text{Zero-product property}$$

Now Try Exercise 93

In the next example, we solve an equation with fractional exponents that can be written in quadratic form by using substitution.

EXAMPLE 14 Solving an equation having fractions for exponents

Solve $2x^{2/3} + 5x^{1/3} - 3 = 0$.

SOLUTION
To solve this equation, use the substitution $u = x^{1/3}$.

$$2x^{2/3} + 5x^{1/3} - 3 = 0 \qquad \text{Given equation}$$

$$2(x^{1/3})^2 + 5(x^{1/3}) - 3 = 0 \qquad \text{Properties of exponents}$$

$$2u^2 + 5u - 3 = 0 \qquad \text{Let } u = x^{1/3}.$$

$$(2u - 1)(u + 3) = 0 \qquad \text{Factor.}$$

$$u = \frac{1}{2} \quad \text{or} \quad u = -3 \qquad \text{Zero-product property}$$

Because $u = x^{1/3}$, it follows that $x = u^3$. Thus $x = \left(\frac{1}{2}\right)^3 = \frac{1}{8}$ or $x = (-3)^3 = -27$.

Now Try Exercise 97

Power Regression (Optional)

Rather than visually fit a curve to data, as was done in Example 11, we can use least-squares regression to fit the data. Least-squares regression was introduced in Section 2.1. In the next example, we apply this technique to data from biology.

EXAMPLE 15 Modeling the length of a bird's wing

Table 4.11 lists the weight W and the wingspan L for birds of a particular species.

Weights and Wingspans

W (kilograms)	0.5	1.5	2.0	2.5	3.0
L (meters)	0.77	1.10	1.22	1.31	1.40

Table 4.11 *Source:* C. Pennycuick.

(a) Use power regression to model the data with $L = aW^b$. Graph the data and the equation.
(b) Approximate the wingspan for a bird weighing 3.2 kilograms.

SOLUTION
(a) Let x be the weight W and y be the length L. Enter the data, and then select power regression (PwrReg), as shown in Figures 4.132 and 4.133. The results are shown in Figure 4.134. Let

$$y = 0.9674x^{0.3326} \quad \text{or} \quad L = 0.9674W^{0.3326}.$$

The data and equation are graphed in Figure 4.135.
(b) If a bird weighs 3.2 kilograms, this model predicts the wingspan to be

$$L = 0.9674(3.2)^{0.3326} \approx 1.42 \text{ meters.}$$

Calculator Help
To find an equation of least-squares fit, see Appendix A (page AP-9).

Figure 4.132

Figure 4.133

Figure 4.134

$[0, 4, 1]$ by $[0.5, 1.5, 0.5]$

Figure 4.135

$y = 0.9674x^{0.3326}$

Now Try Exercise 115

4.8 Putting It All Together

The following table outlines important concepts in this section.

CONCEPT	EXPLANATION	EXAMPLES
Rational exponents	$x^{m/n} = (x^m)^{1/n}$ $= (x^{1/n})^m$	$9^{3/2} = (9^3)^{1/2} = (729)^{1/2} = 27$ $9^{3/2} = (9^{1/2})^3 = (3)^3 = 27$
Radical notation	$x^{1/2} = \sqrt{x}$ $x^{1/3} = \sqrt[3]{x}$ $x^{m/n} = \sqrt[n]{x^m}$ $= (\sqrt[n]{x})^m$	$25^{1/2} = \sqrt{25} = 5$ $27^{1/3} = \sqrt[3]{27} = 3$ $8^{2/3} = \sqrt[3]{8^2} = \sqrt[3]{64} = 4$ $4^{3/2} = \sqrt{4^3} = (\sqrt{4})^3 = (2)^3 = 8$
Solving radical equations	The solutions to $a = b$ are among the solutions to $a^n = b^n$ when n is a positive integer. *Check your results.*	Solve $\sqrt{2x + 3} = x$. $2x + 3 = x^2$ Square each side. $x^2 - 2x - 3 = 0$ Rewrite equation. $(x + 1)(x - 3) = 0$ Factor. $x = -1$ or $x = 3$ Solve. Checking reveals that 3 is the only solution.
Power function	$f(x) = x^b$, where b is a constant	$f(x) = x^{5/4}$ $g(x) = x^{-3.14}$ $h(x) = x^{1/3}$
Root function	$f(x) = x^{1/n}$, where $n \geq 2$ is an integer	$f(x) = x^{1/2}$ or $f(x) = \sqrt{x}$ $g(x) = x^{1/5}$ or $g(x) = \sqrt[5]{x}$

continued on next page

Several types of functions are listed in the following summary, which may be used as a reference for future work. Unless specified otherwise, each tick mark represents 1 unit.

TYPE OF FUNCTION	EXAMPLES	GRAPHS
Linear function $f(x) = ax + b$	$f(x) = 0.5x - 1$ $g(x) = -3x + 2$ $h(x) = 2$	
Polynomial function $f(x) = a_n x^n + \cdots +$ $\quad a_2 x^2 + a_1 x + a_0$	$f(x) = x^2 - 1$ $g(x) = x^3 - 4x - 1$ $h(x) = -x^4 + 4x^2 - 2$	
Rational function $f(x) = \frac{p(x)}{q(x)}$, where $p(x)$ and $q(x)$ are polynomials with $q(x) \neq 0$	$f(x) = \frac{1}{x}$ $g(x) = \frac{2x - 1}{x + 2}$ $h(x) = \frac{1}{x^2 - 1}$	
Root function $f(x) = x^{1/n}$, where $n \geq 2$ is an integer	$f(x) = x^{1/2} = \sqrt{x}$ $g(x) = x^{1/3} = \sqrt[3]{x}$ $h(x) = x^{1/4} = \sqrt[4]{x}$	
Power function $f(x) = x^b$, where b is a constant	$f(x) = x^{2/3}$ $g(x) = x^{1.41}$ $h(x) = x^3$	

4.8 Exercises

Properties of Exponents

Exercises 1–18: Evaluate the expression by hand.

1. $8^{2/3}$

2. $-16^{3/2}$

3. $16^{-3/4}$

4. $25^{-3/2}$

5. $-81^{0.5}$

6. $32^{1/5}$

7. $(9^{3/4})^2$

8. $(4^{-1/2})^{-4}$

9. $\dfrac{8^{5/6}}{8^{1/2}}$

10. $\dfrac{4^{-1/2}}{4^{3/2}}$

11. $27^{5/6} \cdot 27^{-1/6}$

12. $16^{2/3} \cdot 16^{-1/6}$

13. $(-27)^{-5/3}$

14. $(-32)^{-3/5}$

15. $(0.5^{-2})^2$

16. $(2^{-2})^{-3/2}$

17. $\left(\frac{2}{3}\right)^{-2}$

18. $(8^{-1/3} + 27^{-1/3})^2$

Exercises 19–28: Use positive exponents to rewrite.

19. $\sqrt{2x}$

20. $\sqrt{x+1}$

21. $\sqrt[3]{z^5}$

22. $\sqrt[5]{x^2}$

23. $(\sqrt[4]{y})^{-3}$

24. $(\sqrt[3]{y^2})^{-5}$

25. $\sqrt{x} \cdot \sqrt[3]{x}$

26. $(\sqrt[5]{z})^{-3}$

27. $\sqrt{y} \cdot \sqrt{y}$

28. $\dfrac{\sqrt[3]{x}}{\sqrt{x}}$

Exercises 29–32: Use radical notation to rewrite.

29. $a^{-3/4}b^{1/2}$

30. $a^{-2/3}b^{3/5}$

31. $(a^{1/2} + b^{1/2})^{1/2}$

32. $(a^{3/4} - b^{3/2})^{1/3}$

Functions Involving Radicals

Exercises 33–40: Evaluate the function for the given value of x.

33. $f(x) = \sqrt[3]{2x}$ for $x = 32$

34. $f(x) = 5\sqrt[3]{-x}$ for $x = 8$

35. $f(x) = 2\sqrt{x^5}$ for $x = 4$

36. $f(x) = \sqrt{2x^3}$ for $x = 2$

37. $f(x) = \sqrt[4]{5x}$ for $x = 125$

38. $f(x) = 2\sqrt[4]{-x}$ for $x = -81$

39. $f(x) = \sqrt[5]{32x}$ for $x = -1$

40. $f(x) = 3\sqrt[5]{-x}$ for $x = 32$

Exercises 41–52: Use transformations of $y = \sqrt{x}$, $y = \sqrt[3]{x}$, or $y = \sqrt[4]{x}$ to graph $y = f(x)$.

41. $f(x) = \sqrt[3]{-x}$

42. $f(x) = \sqrt[3]{x+1} - 2$

43. $f(x) = \sqrt[3]{x-1} + 1$

44. $f(x) = -2\sqrt[3]{x}$

45. $f(x) = \sqrt[4]{x+2} - 1$

46. $f(x) = \sqrt[4]{-x-1}$

47. $f(x) = 2\sqrt[4]{x-1}$

48. $f(x) = \sqrt[4]{2x}$

49. $f(x) = \sqrt{x+3} + 2$

50. $f(x) = -\sqrt{-x}$

51. $f(x) = 2\sqrt{x}$

52. $f(x) = \sqrt{-x} + 1$

Equations Involving Radicals

Exercises 53–70: Solve the equation. Check your answers.

53. $\sqrt{x+2} = x - 4$

54. $\sqrt{2x+1} = 13$

55. $\sqrt{3x+7} = 3x + 5$

56. $\sqrt{1-x} = x + 5$

57. $\sqrt{5x-6} = x$

58. $x - 5 = \sqrt{5x-1}$

59. $\sqrt{x+5} + 1 = x$

60. $\sqrt{4-3x} = x + 8$

61. $\sqrt{x+1} + 3 = \sqrt{3x+4}$

62. $\sqrt{x} = \sqrt{x-5} + 1$

63. $\sqrt{2x} - \sqrt{x+1} = 1$

64. $\sqrt{2x-4} + 2 = \sqrt{3x+4}$

65. $\sqrt[3]{z+1} = -3$

66. $\sqrt[3]{z} + 5 = 4$

67. $\sqrt[3]{x+1} = \sqrt[3]{2x-1}$

68. $\sqrt[3]{2x^2+1} = \sqrt[3]{1-x}$

69. $\sqrt[4]{x-2} + 4 = 20$

70. $\sqrt[4]{2x+3} = \sqrt{x+1}$

Power Functions

Exercises 71 and 72: Evaluate each $f(x)$ at the given x. Approximate each result to the nearest hundredth.

71. $f(x) = x^{3/2} - x^{1/2}, \quad x = 50$

72. $f(x) = x^{5/4} - x^{-3/4}, \quad x = 7$

Exercises 73 and 74: Match $f(x)$ with its graph. Assume that a and b are constants with $0 < a < 1 < b$.

73. $f(x) = x^a$

74. $f(x) = x^b$

(a)

(b)

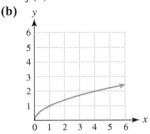

Exercises 75–80: Use translations to graph f.

75. $f(x) = x^{1/2} + 1$

76. $f(x) = (x - 1)^{1/3}$

77. $f(x) = x^{2/3} - 1$

78. $f(x) = (x - 1)^{1/4}$

79. $f(x) = (x + 1)^{2/3} - 2$

80. $f(x) = (x - 1)^{2/3}$

Equations Involving Rational Exponents

Exercises 81–102: Solve the equation. Check your answers.

81. $x^3 = 8$

82. $x^4 = \frac{1}{81}$

83. $x^{1/4} = 3$

84. $x^{1/3} = \frac{1}{5}$

85. $x^{2/5} = 4$

86. $x^{2/3} = 16$

87. $x^{4/3} = 16$

88. $x^{4/5} = 16$

89. $4x^{3/2} + 5 = 21$

90. $2x^{1/3} - 5 = 1$

91. $n^{-2} + 3n^{-1} + 2 = 0$

92. $2n^{-2} - n^{-1} = 3$

93. $5n^{-2} + 13n^{-1} = 28$

94. $3n^{-2} - 19n^{-1} + 20 = 0$

95. $x^{2/3} - x^{1/3} - 6 = 0$

96. $x^{2/3} + 9x^{1/3} + 14 = 0$

97. $6x^{2/3} - 11x^{1/3} + 4 = 0$

98. $10x^{2/3} + 29x^{1/3} + 10 = 0$

99. $x^{3/4} - x^{1/2} - x^{1/4} + 1 = 0$

100. $x^{3/4} - 2x^{1/2} - 4x^{1/4} + 8 = 0$

101. $x^{-2/3} - 2x^{-1/3} - 3 = 0$

102. $6x^{-2/3} - 13x^{-1/3} - 5 = 0$

Exercises 103 and 104: **Average Rate of Change** *Let the distance from home in miles of a person after t hours on a straight path be given by $s(t)$. Approximate the average rate of change of s from $t_1 = \frac{1}{2}$ to $t_2 = \frac{9}{2}$ to the nearest tenth and interpret the result.*

103. $s(t) = \sqrt{96t}$

104. $s(t) = 3t^{3/4}$

Applications and Models

105. **Modeling Wing Size** Suppose that the surface area S of a bird's wings in square feet can be modeled by $S(w) = 1.27w^{2/3}$, where w is the weight of the bird in pounds, with $1 \le w \le 10$. Estimate the weight of a bird with wings having a surface area of 3 square feet.

106. **Modeling Wingspan** The wingspan L in feet of a bird weighing W pounds is given by $L = 2.43W^{0.3326}$. Estimate the wingspan of a bird that weighs 5.2 pounds.

107. **Modeling Planetary Orbits** The formula $f(x) = x^{1.5}$ calculates the number of years it takes for a planet to orbit the sun if its average distance from the sun is x times that of Earth. If there were a planet located 15 times as far from the sun as Earth, how many years would it take for the planet to orbit the sun?

108. **Modeling Planetary Orbits** (Refer to Exercise 107.) If there were a planet that took 200 years to orbit the sun, what would be its average distance x from the sun compared to that of Earth?

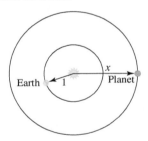

(Not to scale)

109. **Trout and Pollution** Rainbow trout are sensitive to zinc ions in the water. High concentrations are lethal. The average survival times x in minutes for trout in various concentrations of zinc ions y in milligrams per liter (mg/L) are listed in the table.

x (min)	0.5	1	2	3
y (mg/L)	4500	1960	850	525

Source: C. Mason, *Biology of Freshwater Pollution.*

(a) These data can be modeled by $f(x) = ax^b$, where a and b are constants. Determine an appropriate value for a. (*Hint:* Let $f(1) = 1960$.)

(b) Estimate b.

(c) Evaluate $f(4)$ and interpret the result.

110. Lunar Orbits for Jupiter   Use the data in the table to complete the following.

Moons of Jupiter	Distance (10^3 km)	Period (days)
Metis	128	0.29
Almathea	181	0.50
Thebe	222	0.67
Europa	671	3.55
Ganymede	1070	7.16
Callisto	1883	16.69

(a) Make a scatterplot of the data. Estimate a value for b so that $f(x) = 0.0002x^b$ models the data.

(b) Check the accuracy of $f(x)$.

(c) The moon Io is 422 thousand kilometers from Jupiter. Estimate its period and compare the estimate to the actual value of 1.77 days. Did your estimate involve interpolation or extrapolation?

111. Fiddler Crab Size   One study showed that for a male fiddler crab weighing over 0.75 gram, the weight of its claws can be estimated by $f(x) = 0.445x^{5/4}$. The input x is the weight of the crab in grams, and the output $f(x)$ is the weight of the claws in grams.   (*Source:* J. Huxley, *Problems of Relative Growth*.)

(a) Predict the weight of the claws of a 2-gram crab.

(b) Approximate graphically the weight of a crab that has 0.5-gram claws.

(c) Solve part (b) symbolically.

112. Weight and Height   The average weight in pounds for men and women can sometimes be estimated by $f(x) = ax^{1.7}$, where x is a person's height in inches and a is a constant determined by the sex of the individual.

(a) If the average weight of a 68-inch-tall man is 152 pounds, approximate a. Use f to estimate the average weight of a 66-inch-tall man.

(b) If the average weight of a 68-inch-tall woman is 137 pounds, approximate a. Use f to estimate the average weight of a 70-inch-tall woman.

Power Regression

Exercises 113 and 114: The table contains data that can be modeled by a function of the form $f(x) = ax^b$. Use regression to find the constants a and b to the nearest hundredth. Graph f and the data.

113.

x	2	4	6	8
$f(x)$	3.7	4.2	4.6	4.9

114.

x	3	6	9	12
$f(x)$	23.8	58.5	99.2	144

115. Walmart Employees   The table lists numbers N of Walmart employees (in millions) x years after 1980.

x	7	12	17	22	27
N	0.20	0.37	0.68	1.4	2.2

Source: Walmart.

(a) Find a power function f that models the data in the table.

(b) Use f to predict the number of employees in the year 2012. Compare to the true value of 2.1 million employees. Did your answer involve interpolation or extrapolation?

(c) When did the number of employees first reach 1 million?

116. DVD Rentals   The table lists numbers of titles T released for DVD rentals x years after 1995.

x	3	4	5	6	7
T	2049	4787	8723	14,321	21,260

Source: DVD Release Report.

(a) Find a power function f that models the data in the table.

(b) Use f to estimate the number of titles released in 2006. Did your answer involve interpolation or extrapolation?

(c) When did the number of releases first surpass 45,000?

117. Pulse Rate and Weight   According to one model, the rate at which an animal's heart beats varies with its weight. Smaller animals tend to have faster pulses, whereas larger animals tend to have slower pulses. The table lists average pulse rates in beats per minute (bpm) for animals with various weights in pounds (lb). Use regression (or some other method) to find values for a and b so that $f(x) = ax^b$ models these data.

Weight (lb)	40	150	400	1000	2000
Pulse (bpm)	140	72	44	28	20

Source: C. Pennycuick.

118. Pulse Rate and Weight   (Continuation of Exercise 117) Use the results in the previous exercise to calculate the pulse rates for a 60-pound dog and a 2-ton whale.

Writing About Mathematics

119. Can a function be both a polynomial function and a power function? Explain.

120. Explain the basic steps needed to solve equations that contain square roots of variables.

Extended and Discovery Exercises

1. Odd Root Functions Graph $y = \sqrt[n]{x}$ for $n = 3, 5,$ and 7. State some generalizations about a graph of an odd root function.

2. Even Root Functions Graph $y = \sqrt[n]{x}$ for $n = 2, 4,$ and 6. State some generalizations about a graph of an even root function.

Exercises 3 and 4: **Difference Quotient** *Find the difference quotient of f.*

3. $f(x) = \sqrt{x}$ **4.** $f(x) = \frac{1}{x}$

Exercises 5–8: **Negative Rational Exponents** *Write the expression as one ratio without any negative exponents.*

5. $\dfrac{x^{-2/3} + x^{1/3}}{x}$

6. $\dfrac{x^{1/4} - x^{-3/4}}{x}$

7. $\dfrac{\frac{2}{3}(x + 1)x^{-1/3} - x^{2/3}}{(x + 1)^2}$

8. $\dfrac{(x^2 + 1)^{1/2} - \frac{1}{2}x(x^2 + 1)^{-1/2}(2x)}{x^2 + 1}$

9. Wire Between Two Poles Two vertical poles of lengths 12 feet and 16 feet are situated on level ground, 20 feet apart, as shown in the figure. A piece of wire is to be strung from the top of the 12-foot pole to the top of the 16-foot pole, attached to a stake in the ground at a point P on a line connecting the bottoms of the vertical poles. Let x represent the distance from P to D.

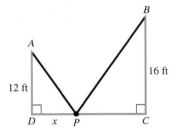

(a) Express the distance from P to C in terms of x.

(b) Express the lengths AP and BP in terms of x.

(c) Give a function f that expresses the total length of the wire used.

(d) Graph f in the window $[0, 20, 5]$ by $[0, 50, 10]$.

(e) Approximate the value of x that will minimize the amount of wire used. What is this minimum?

CHECKING BASIC CONCEPTS FOR SECTIONS 4.7 AND 4.8

1. Solve.

(a) $\dfrac{3x - 1}{1 - x} = 1$

(b) $3 + \dfrac{8}{x} = \dfrac{35}{x^2}$

(c) $\dfrac{1}{x - 1} - \dfrac{1}{3(x + 2)} = \dfrac{1}{x^2 + x - 2}$

2. Solve $2x^3 + x^2 - 6x < 0$.

3. Solve $\dfrac{x^2 - 1}{x + 2} \geq 0$.

4. Let y vary inversely with the cube of x. If $x = \frac{1}{5}$, then $y = 150$. Find y if $x = \frac{1}{2}$.

5. Simplify each expression without a calculator.

(a) $-4^{3/2}$ **(b)** $(8^{-2})^{1/3}$ **(c)** $\sqrt[3]{27^2}$

6. Solve the equation $4x^{3/2} - 3 = 29$.

7. Solve the equation $\sqrt{5x - 4} = x - 2$.

8. Solve each equation.

(a) $n^{-2} + 6n^{-1} = 16$

(b) $2x^{2/3} + 5x^{1/3} - 12 = 0$

9. Find a and b so that $f(x) = ax^b$ models the data.

x	1	2	3	4
$f(x)$	2	2.83	3.46	4

4 | Summary

CONCEPT	EXPLANATION AND EXAMPLES

Section 4.1 More Nonlinear Functions and Their Graphs

Polynomial Function

Can be represented by $f(x) = a_n x^n + a_{n-1}x^{n-1} + \cdots + a_2 x^2 + a_1 x + a_0$
The leading coefficient is $a_n \neq 0$ and the degree is n.

Example: $f(x) = -4x^3 - 2x^2 + 6x + \frac{1}{2}; a_n = -4; n = 3$

Absolute and Local Extrema

The accompanying graph has the following extrema.

Absolute maximum: none

Absolute minimum: -14.8

Local maximum: 1

Local minimums: $-4.3, -14.8$

Symmetry

Even function: $f(-x) = f(x)$; the graph is symmetric with respect to the y-axis.

Odd function: $f(-x) = -f(x)$; the graph is symmetric with respect to the origin.

Examples: $f(x) = x^4 - 3x^2$ $\qquad$ $f(x) = x - x^3$

Even Function $\qquad\qquad$ Odd Function

Section 4.2 Polynomial Functions and Models

Graphs of Polynomial Functions

Their graphs are continuous with no breaks, and their domains include all real numbers. The graph of a polynomial function of degree $n \geq 1$ has at most n x-intercepts and at most $n - 1$ turning points. For a discussion of the end behavior for graphs of polynomial functions, see page 247.

Examples: See "Putting It All Together" for Section 4.2.

Piecewise-Polynomial Functions

Example:

$$f(x) = \begin{cases} x^2 - 2 & \text{if } x < 0 \\ 1 - 2x & \text{if } x \geq 0 \end{cases}$$

$f(-2) = (-2)^2 - 2 = 2$

$f(0) = 1 - 2(0) = 1$

$f(2) = 1 - 2(2) = -3$

f is discontinuous at $x = 0$.

CONCEPT	EXPLANATION AND EXAMPLES

Section 4.3 Division of Polynomials

Division Algorithm

Let $f(x)$ and $d(x)$ be two polynomials with the degree of $d(x)$ greater than zero and less than the degree of $f(x)$. Then there exist unique polynomials $q(x)$ and $r(x)$ such that

$$f(x) = d(x) \cdot q(x) + r(x),$$

where either $r(x) = 0$ or the degree of $r(x)$ is less than the degree of $d(x)$. That is,

$$\text{(Dividend)} = \text{(Divisor)} \cdot \text{(Quotient)} + \text{(Remainder)}.$$

Example: $\dfrac{x^2 - 4x + 5}{x - 1} = x - 3 + \dfrac{2}{x - 1}$. That is,

$$x^2 - 4x + 5 = (x - 1)(x - 3) + 2.$$

Remainder Theorem

If a polynomial $f(x)$ is divided by $x - k$, the remainder is $f(k)$.

Example: If $x^2 - 4x + 5$ is divided by $x - 1$, the remainder is

$$f(1) = 1^2 - 4(1) + 5 = 2.$$

Section 4.4 Real Zeros of Polynomial Functions

Factor Theorem

A polynomial $f(x)$ has a factor $x - k$ if and only if $f(k) = 0$.

Example: $f(x) = x^2 - 3x + 2$;
$f(1) = 0$ implies that $(x - 1)$ is a factor of $x^2 - 3x + 2$.

Complete Factored Form

$f(x) = a_n(x - c_1)(x - c_2) \cdots (x - c_n)$, where a_n is the leading coefficient of the polynomial $f(x)$ and the c_k are its zeros. This form is unique.

Example: $f(x) = -2x^3 + 8x$ has zeros of $-2, 0$, and 2; therefore
$f(x) = -2(x + 2)(x - 0)(x - 2)$.

Multiple Real Zeros

Odd multiplicity: Graph crosses the x-axis.

Even multiplicity: Graph touches but does not cross the x-axis.

Higher multiplicities: Graph levels off more at a zero of higher multiplicity.

Example: Let $f(x) = -2(x + 1)^3(x - 4)^2$; $f(x)$ has a zero of -1 with odd multiplicity 3 and a zero of 4 with even multiplicity 2.

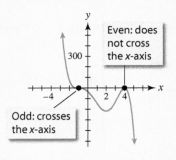

CONCEPT	EXPLANATION AND EXAMPLES

Section 4.4 Real Zeros of Polynomial Functions (CONTINUED)

Polynomial Equations

Polynomial equations can be solved symbolically, graphically, and numerically. A common symbolic technique is factoring.

Example: Solve $x^3 - 4x = 0$ symbolically and graphically.

Symbolic Solution

$$x(x^2 - 4) = 0$$
$$x(x - 2)(x + 2) = 0$$
$$x = 0, \ x = 2, \ \text{ or } \ x = -2$$

Graphical Solution

The x-intercepts are –2, 0, and 2.

Section 4.5 The Fundamental Theorem of Algebra

Fundamental Theorem of Algebra

A polynomial $f(x)$ of degree $n \geq 1$ has at least one complex zero.
Explanation: With complex numbers, any polynomial can be written in complete factored form.

Examples: $x^2 + 1 = (x + i)(x - i)$
$3x^2 - 3x - 6 = 3(x + 1)(x - 2)$

Number of Zeros Theorem

A polynomial of degree n has at most n distinct zeros.

Example: A cubic polynomial has at most three distinct zeros.

Polynomial Equations with Complex Solutions

Polynomial equations can have both real and imaginary solutions.

Example: Solve $x^4 - 1 = 0$.
$$(x^2 - 1)(x^2 + 1) = 0$$
$$(x - 1)(x + 1)(x^2 + 1) = 0$$
$$x = 1, \ x = -1, \ \text{ or } \ x^2 = -1$$
$$x = \pm 1, \pm i$$

The x-intercepts are -1 and 1. The imaginary solutions $\pm i$ cannot be found from a graph.

Section 4.6 Rational Functions and Models

Rational Functions

$$f(x) = \frac{p(x)}{q(x)}, \text{ where } p(x) \text{ and } q(x) \neq 0 \text{ are polynomials}$$

Example: $f(x) = \dfrac{2x - 3}{x - 1}$

Horizontal asymptote: $y = 2$
Vertical asymptote: $x = 1$

To find vertical and horizontal asymptotes, see page 293.
To graph rational functions by hand, see page 299.

CONCEPT	EXPLANATION AND EXAMPLES

Section 4.7 More Equations and Inequalities

Solving Rational Equations

Multiply each side by the LCD. Check your results.

Example: $\dfrac{-24}{x-3} - 4 = x + 3$ LCD is $x - 3$.

$-24 - 4(x - 3) = (x + 3)(x - 3)$ Multiply each term by $x - 3$.

$-24 - 4x + 12 = x^2 - 9$ Multiply.

$0 = x^2 + 4x + 3$ Combine terms.

$0 = (x + 3)(x + 1)$ Factor.

$x = -3 \quad \text{or} \quad x = -1$ Both solutions check.

Direct Variation

Let x and y denote two quantities and n be a positive number. Then y is *directly proportional to the nth power of x*, or *y varies directly with the nth power of x*, if there exists a nonzero number k such that $y = kx^n$.

Example: Because $V = \frac{4}{3}\pi r^3$, the volume of a sphere varies directly with the third power of the radius. The constant of variation is $\frac{4}{3}\pi$.

Inverse Variation

Let x and y denote two quantities and n be a positive number. Then y is *inversely proportional to the nth power of x*, or *y varies inversely with the nth power of x*, if there exists a nonzero number k such that $y = \frac{k}{x^n}$.

Example: Because $I = \frac{k}{d^2}$, the intensity of a light source varies inversely with the square of the distance from the light source.

Polynomial Inequality

Write the inequality as $p(x) > 0$, where $>$ may be replaced by $\geq$, $<$, or $\leq$. Replace the inequality sign with an equals sign, and solve this equation. The solutions are called boundary numbers. Then use a graph or table to find the solution set to the given inequality.

Example: $4x - x^3 > 0$; Boundary numbers: $-2, 0, 2$
The solution set is $(-\infty, -2) \cup (0, 2)$ because the graph is above the x-axis for these intervals of x-values.

Rational Inequality

As with polynomial inequalities, find the boundary numbers, including x-values where any expressions are undefined.

Example: $\dfrac{(x + 2)(x - 3)}{x} \geq 0$
Boundary numbers: $-2, 0, 3$
Solution set: $[-2, 0) \cup [3, \infty)$

CONCEPT	EXPLANATION AND EXAMPLES
Section 4.8 Radical Equations and Power Functions	
Rational Exponents	$x^{m/n} = \sqrt[n]{x^m} = (\sqrt[n]{x})^m$ **Example:** $25^{3/2} = \sqrt{25^3} = (\sqrt{25})^3 = 5^3 = 125$
Functions Involving Radicals	Functions defined by radical expressions **Examples:** $f(x) = \sqrt[3]{x}; \; f(-8) = \sqrt[3]{-8} = -2$ $f(x) = \sqrt[4]{x^3} + 1; \; f(81) = \sqrt[4]{81^3} + 1 = 28$
Solving Radical Equations	When an equation contains a square root, isolate the square root and then square each side. *Be sure to check your results.* **Example:** $x + \sqrt{3x - 3} = 1$ *Given equation* $\sqrt{3x - 3} = 1 - x$ *Subtract x.* $3x - 3 = (1 - x)^2$ *Square each side.* $3x - 3 = 1 - 2x + x^2$ *Square binomial.* $0 = x^2 - 5x + 4$ *Combine terms.* $0 = (x - 1)(x - 4)$ *Factor.* $x = 1 \quad \text{or} \quad x = 4$ *Solve.* *Check:* 1 is a solution, but 4 is not. $1 + \sqrt{3(1) - 3} = 1$ ✓ $4 + \sqrt{3(4) - 3} \neq 1$
Power Function	$f(x) = x^b$, where b is a constant **Example:** $f(x) = x^{4/3}, \quad g(x) = x^{1.72}$

4   Review Exercises

1. State the degree and leading coefficient of the polynomial $f(x) = 4 + x - 2x^2 - 7x^3$.

Exercises 2 and 3: Use the graph of f to estimate any (a) local extrema and   (b) absolute extrema.

2.

3.

4. Graph $f(x) = -0.25x^4 + 0.67x^3 + 9.5x^2 - 20x - 50$.

(a) Approximate any local extrema.

(b) Approximate any absolute extrema.

(c) Determine where f is increasing or decreasing.

Exercises 5–8: Determine if f is even, odd, or neither.

5. $f(x) = 2x^6 - 5x^4 - x^2$ **6.** $f(x) = -5x^3 - 18$

7. $f(x) = 7x^5 + 3x^3 - x$ **8.** $f(x) = \dfrac{1}{1 + x^2}$

Exercises 9 and 10: The table is a complete representation of f. Decide if f is even, odd, or neither.

9.

x	-4	-2	0	2	-4
$f(x)$	13	7	0	-7	-13

10.

x	-5	-3	-1	1	3	5
$f(x)$	-6	2	7	7	2	-6

Exercises 11 and 12: Sketch a graph of a polynomial function that satisfies the given conditions.

11. Cubic polynomial, two x-intercepts, and a positive leading coefficient

12. Degree 4 with a positive leading coefficient, three turning points, and one x-intercept

Exercises 13 and 14: Use the graph of the polynomial function f to complete the following.

(a) Determine the number of turning points and estimate any x-intercepts.

(b) State whether $a > 0$ or $a < 0$.

(c) Determine the minimum degree of f.

13.

14.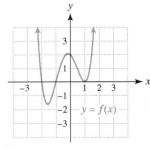

Exercises 15 and 16: State the end behavior of f.

15. $f(x) = -2x^3 + 4x - 2$

16. $f(x) = 1 - 2x - x^4$

17. Find the average rate of change of $f(x) = x^3 + 1$ from $x = -2$ to $x = -1$.

18. Find the difference quotient for $g(x) = 4x^3$.

19. Let $f(x)$ be given by

$$f(x) = \begin{cases} 2x & \text{if } 0 \le x < 2 \\ 8 - x^2 & \text{if } 2 \le x \le 4. \end{cases}$$

   (a) Sketch a graph of f. Is f continuous on its domain?

   (b) Evaluate $f(1)$ and $f(3)$.

   (c) Solve the equation $f(x) = 2$.

20. Determine the type of symmetry that the graph of $g(x) = x^5 - 4x^3$ exhibits.

Exercises 21–24: Divide the expression.

21. $\dfrac{14x^3 - 21x^2 - 7x}{7x}$

22. $\dfrac{2x^3 - x^2 - 4x + 1}{x + 2}$

23. $\dfrac{4x^3 - 7x + 4}{2x + 3}$

24. $\dfrac{3x^3 - 5x^2 + 13x - 18}{x^2 + 4}$

25. The polynomial given by $f(x) = \frac{1}{2}x^3 - 3x^2 + \frac{11}{2}x - 3$ has zeros 1, 2, and 3. Write its complete factored form.

26. Write a complete factored form of a quintic (degree 5) polynomial $f(x)$ that has zeros -2 and 2 with multiplicities 2 and 3, respectively.

27. Use the graph of $y = f(x)$ to write its complete factored form. (Do not assume that the leading coefficient is ± 1.)

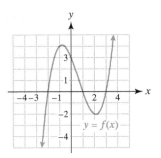

28. What is the maximum number of times that a horizontal line can intersect the graph of each type of polynomial?
   (a) linear (degree 1)   **(b)** quadratic   **(c)** cubic

Exercises 29 and 30: Use the rational zero test to determine any rational zeros of f(x).

29. $f(x) = 2x^3 + x^2 - 13x + 6$

30. $f(x) = x^3 + x^2 - 11x - 11$

Exercises 31–32: Solve the equation.

31. $9x = 3x^3$ 32. $x^4 - 3x^2 + 2 = 0$

Exercises 33 and 34: Solve the equation graphically. Round your answers to the nearest hundredth.

33. $x^3 - 3x + 1 = 0$ 34. $x^4 - 2x = 2$

Exercises 35 and 36: Find all real and imaginary solutions.

35. $x^3 + x = 0$ 36. $x^4 + 3x^2 + 2 = 0$

37. Write a polynomial $f(x)$ in complete factored form that has degree 3, leading coefficient 4, and zeros 1, $3i$, and $-3i$. Then write $f(x)$ in expanded form.

38. Use the graph of $f(x) = 2x^4 - x^2 - 1$ to predict the number of real zeros and the number of imaginary zeros of f. Find these zeros symbolically.

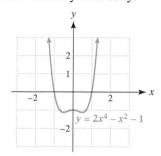

39. If a zero of f is i, find the complete factored form of $f(x) = x^4 + x^3 + 2x^2 + x + 1$.

40. State the domain of $f(x) = \frac{3x - 2}{5x + 4}$. Identify any horizontal or vertical asymptotes in the graph of f.

41. Find any horizontal or vertical asymptotes in the graph of

$$f(x) = \frac{2x^2 + x - 15}{3x^2 + 8x - 3}.$$

42. Let $f(x) = \frac{2x^2}{x^2 - 4}$.

   (a) Find the domain of f.

   (b) Identify any horizontal or vertical asymptotes.

   (c) Graph f with a graphing calculator.

   (d) Sketch a graph of f that includes all asymptotes.

Exercises 43–46: Graph $y = g(x)$ by hand.

43. $g(x) = \frac{1}{x + 1} - 2$ **44.** $g(x) = \frac{x}{x - 1}$

45. $g(x) = \frac{x^2 - 1}{x^2 + 2x + 1}$ **46.** $g(x) = \frac{2x - 3}{2x^2 + x - 6}$

47. Sketch a graph of a function f with vertical asymptote $x = -2$ and horizontal asymptote $y = 2$.

48. Solve the equation $\frac{3x}{x - 2} = 2$ symbolically, graphically, and numerically.

Exercises 49–52: Solve the equation. Check your results.

49. $\frac{5x + 1}{x + 3} = 3$ **50.** $\frac{1}{x} - \frac{1}{x^2} + 2 = 0$

51. $\frac{1}{x + 2} + \frac{1}{x - 2} = \frac{4}{x^2 - 4}$

52. $\frac{x + 5}{x - 2} = \frac{x - 1}{x + 1}$

Exercises 53 and 54: Use the graph of f to solve each inequality.

   (a) $f(x) > 0$ *(b)* $f(x) < 0$

53.   **54.**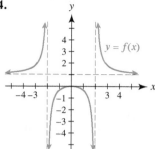

Exercises 55–58: Solve the inequality.

55. $x^3 + x^2 - 6x > 0$ **56.** $x^4 + 4 < 5x^2$

57. $\frac{2x - 1}{x + 2} > 0$ **58.** $\frac{1}{x} + \frac{1}{x + 2} \le \frac{4}{3}$

Exercises 59–62: Evaluate the radical expression by hand.

59. $(36^{3/4})^2$ **60.** $(9^{-3/2})^{-2}$

61. $(2^{-3/2} \cdot 2^{1/2})^{-3}$ **62.** $\left(\frac{4}{9}\right)^{-3/2}$

Exercises 63–66: Write the radical expression using positive exponents.

63. $\sqrt[3]{x^4}$ **64.** $\left(\sqrt[4]{z}\right)^{-1/2}$

65. $\sqrt[3]{y} \cdot \sqrt{y}$ **66.** $\sqrt{x} \cdot \sqrt[3]{x^2} \cdot \sqrt[4]{x^3}$

Exercises 67 and 68: Give the domain of the power function. Approximate $f(3)$ to the nearest hundredth.

67. $f(x) = x^{5/2}$ **68.** $f(x) = x^{-2/3}$

Exercises 69–80: Solve the equation. Check your results.

69. $x^5 = 1024$ **70.** $x^{1/3} = 4$

71. $\sqrt{x - 2} = x - 4$ **72.** $x^{3/2} = 27$

73. $2x^{1/4} + 3 = 6$ **74.** $x^{1/3} + 3x^{1/3} = -2$

75. $\sqrt[3]{2x - 3} + 1 = 4$

76. $m^{-3} + 2m^{-2} + m^{-1} = 0$

77. $2n^{-2} - 5n^{-1} = 3$

78. $x^{3/4} - 16x^{1/4} = 0$

79. $k^{2/3} - 4k^{1/3} - 5 = 0$

80. $\sqrt{x - 2} = 5 - \sqrt{x + 3}$

Applications

81. Pulse Rate and Length During the eighteenth century Bryan Robinson found that the pulse rate of an animal could be approximated by

$$f(x) = \frac{1607}{\sqrt[4]{x^3}}.$$

The input x is the length of the animal in inches, and the output $f(x)$ is the approximate number of heartbeats per minute. (**Source:** H. Lancaster, *Quantitative Methods in Biology and Medical Sciences.*)

(a) Use f to estimate the pulse rates of a 2-foot dog and a 5.5-foot person.

(b) What length corresponds to a pulse rate of 400 beats per minute?

82. Time Spent in Line Suppose a parking garage attendant can wait on 4 vehicles per minute and vehicles are leaving the ramp randomly at an average rate of x vehicles per minute. Then the average time T in minutes spent waiting in line and paying the attendant is given by

$$T(x) = \frac{1}{4 - x},$$

where $0 \le x < 4$. (**Source:** N. Garber and L. Hoel, *Traffic and Highway Engineering.*)

(a) Evaluate $T(2)$ and interpret the result.

(b) Graph T for $0 \le x < 4$.

(c) What happens to the waiting time as x increases from 0 to (nearly) 4?

(d) Find x if the waiting time is 5 minutes.

83. Modeling Ocean Temperatures The formula

$$T(m) = -0.064m^3 + 0.56m^2 + 2.9m + 61$$

approximates the ocean temperature in degrees Fahrenheit at Naples, Florida. In this formula m is the month, with $m = 1$ corresponding to January.

(a) What is the average ocean temperature in May?

(b) Estimate the absolute maximum of T on the closed interval $[1, 12]$ and interpret the result.

84. Minimizing Surface Area Find possible dimensions that minimize the surface area of a box with no top that has a volume of 96 cubic inches and a length that is three times the width.

85. Falling Object If an object is dropped from a height h, then the time t required for the object to strike the ground is directly proportional to the square root of h. If it requires 1 second for an object to fall 16 feet, how long does it take for an object to fall 256 feet?

86. Animals and Trotting Speeds Taller animals tend to take longer, but fewer, steps per second than shorter animals. The relationship between the shoulder height h in meters of an animal and an animal's stepping frequency F in steps per second, while *trotting*, is shown in the table.

h	0.5	1.0	1.5	2.0	2.5
F	2.6	1.8	1.5	1.3	1.2

Source: C. Pennycuick, *Newton Rules Biology.*

(a) Find values for constants a and b so that the formula $f(x) = ax^b$ models the data.

(b) Estimate the stepping frequency for an elephant with a 3-meter shoulder height.

Extended and Discovery Exercises

Exercises 1 and 2: **Velocity** *Suppose that a person is riding a bicycle on a straight road and that $f(t)$ computes the total distance in feet that the rider has traveled after t seconds. To calculate the person's average velocity between time t_1 and time t_2, we can evaluate the difference quotient*

$$\frac{f(t_2) - f(t_1)}{t_2 - t_1}.$$

(a) *For the given $f(t)$ and the indicated values of t_1 and t_2, calculate the average velocity of the bike rider. Make a table to organize your work.*

(b) *Make a conjecture about the velocity of the bike rider precisely at time t_1.*

1. $f(t) = t^2, t_1 = 10$
  (i) $t_2 = 11$
  (ii) $t_2 = 10.1$
  (iii) $t_2 = 10.01$
  (iv) $t_2 = 10.001$

2. $f(t) = \sqrt{t}, t_1 = 4$
  (i) $t_2 = 5$
  (ii) $t_2 = 4.1$
  (iii) $t_2 = 4.01$
  (iv) $t_2 = 4.001$

Exercises 3–6: **Average Rates of Change** *These exercises investigate the relationship between polynomial functions and their average rates of change. For example, the average rate of change of $f(x) = x^2$ from x to $x + 0.001$ for any x can be calculated and graphed as shown in the figures. The graph of f is a parabola, and the graph of its average rate of change is a line. Try to discover what this relationship is by completing the following.*

$[-10, 10, 1]$ by $[-10, 10, 1]$

(a) *Graph each function and its average rate of change from x to x + 0.001.*

(b) *Compare the graphs. How are turning points on the graph of a function related to its average rate of change?*

(c) *Generalize your results. Test your generalization.*

3. Linear Functions

$f_1(x) = 3x + 1$ $f_2(x) = -2x + 6$

$f_3(x) = 1.5x - 5$ $f_4(x) = -4x - 2.5$

4. Quadratic Functions

$f_1(x) = 2x^2 - 3x + 1$ $f_2(x) = -0.5x^2 + 2x + 2$

$f_3(x) = x^2 + x - 2$ $f_4(x) = -1.5x^2 - 4x + 6$

5. Cubic Functions

$f_1(x) = 0.5x^3 - x^2 - 2x + 1$

$f_2(x) = -x^3 + x^2 + 3x - 5$

$f_3(x) = 2x^3 - 5x^2 + x - 3$

$f_4(x) = -x^3 + 3x - 4$

6. Quartic Functions

$f_1(x) = 0.05x^4 + 0.2x^3 - x^2 - 2.4x$

$f_2(x) = -0.1x^4 + 0.1x^3 + 1.3x^2 - 0.1x - 1.2$

$f_3(x) = 0.1x^4 + 0.4x^3 - 0.2x^2 - 2.4x - 2.4$

1–4 Cumulative Review Exercises

1. Let $S = \{(-3, 4), (-1, -2), (0, 4), (1, -2), (-1, 5)\}$.

(a) Find the domain and range of S.

(b) Is S a function?

2. Find the exact distance between $(-1, 4)$ and $(3, -9)$.

3. Use the graph to express the domain and range of f. Then evaluate $f(0)$.

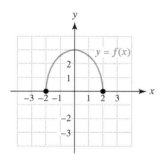

4. Graph $y = g(x)$ by hand.

(a) $g(x) = 2 - 3x$ (b) $g(x) = |2x - 1|$

(c) $g(x) = \frac{1}{2}(x - 2)^2 + 2$ (d) $g(x) = x^3 - 1$

(e) $g(x) = \sqrt{-x}$ (f) $g(x) = \sqrt[3]{x}$

(g) $g(x) = \dfrac{1}{x - 4} + 2$ (h) $g(x) = x^2 - x$

5. The monthly cost of driving a car is $200 for maintenance plus $0.25 a mile. Write a formula for a function C that calculates the monthly cost of driving a car x miles. Evaluate $C(2000)$ and interpret the result.

6. The graph of a linear function f is shown.

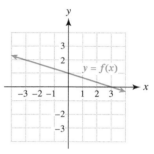

(a) Identify the slope, y-intercept, and x-intercept.

(b) Write a formula for $f(x)$.

(c) Evaluate $f(-3)$ symbolically and graphically.

(d) Find any zeros of f.

7. Find the average rate of change of $f(x) = x^3 - x$ from $x = -3$ to $x = -2$.

8. Find the difference quotient for $f(x) = x^2 + 6x$.

9. Write the slope-intercept form for a line that passes through $(-2, 5)$ and $(3, -4)$.

10. Write the slope-intercept form for a line that passes through $(-1, 4)$ and is perpendicular to the line $3x - 4y = 12$.

11. Write an equation of a line that is parallel to the x-axis and passes through $(4, -5)$.

12. Determine the x- and y-intercepts on the graph of $5x - 4y = 10$. Graph the equation.

13. If $C(x) = 15x + 2000$ calculates the cost in dollars of producing x radios, interpret the numbers 15 and 2000 in the formula for $C(x)$.

14. Solve $-2.4x - 2.1 = \sqrt{3x} + 1.7$ both graphically and numerically. Round your answer to the nearest tenth.

Exercises 15–24: Solve the equation.

15. $-3(2 - 3x) - (-x - 1) = 1$

16. $x^3 + 5 = 5x^2 + x$ 17. $|3x - 4| + 1 = 5$

18. $2x^2 + x + 2 = 0$ 19. $7x^2 + 9x = 10$

20. $x^4 + 9 = 10x^2$ 21. $3x^{2/3} + 5x^{1/3} - 2 = 0$

22. $\sqrt{5 + 2x} + 4 = x + 5$

23. $\dfrac{2x - 3}{5 - x} = \dfrac{4x - 3}{1 - 2x}$ 24. $\sqrt[3]{x - 4} - 1 = 3$

25. Solve $\frac{1}{2}x - (4 - x) + 1 = \frac{3}{2}x - 5$. Is this equation either an identity or a contradiction?

26. Graph f. Is f continuous on its domain? Evaluate $f(1)$.

$$f(x) = \begin{cases} x^2 - 1 & \text{if } -3 \le x \le -1 \\ x + 1 & \text{if } -1 < x < 1 \\ 1 - x^2 & \text{if } \ \ 1 \le x \le 3 \end{cases}$$

Exercises 27–32: Solve the inequality.

27. $-\frac{1}{3}x - (1 + x) > \frac{2}{3}x$ 28. $-4 \le 4x - 6 < \frac{5}{2}$

29. $|5x - 7| \ge 3$ 30. $5x^2 + 13x - 6 < 0$

31. $x^3 - 9x \le 0$ 32. $\dfrac{4x - 3}{x + 2} > 0$

33. The graph of a nonlinear function f is shown. Solve each equation or inequality.
    (a) $f(x) = 0$ (b) $f(x) > 0$ (c) $f(x) \le 0$

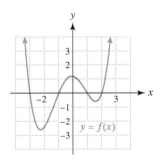

34. Write the quadratic polynomial $f(x) = 2x^2 - 4x + 1$ in the form $f(x) = a(x - h)^2 + k$.

35. Use the given graph of $y = f(x)$ at the top of the next column to sketch a graph of each equation.

(a) $y = f(x + 2) - 1$ (b) $y = -2f(x)$

(c) $y = f(-x) + 1$ (d) $y = f\left(\frac{1}{2}x\right)$

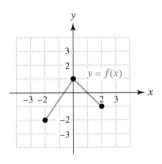

36. Use transformations of graphs to sketch a graph of $y = 2\sqrt{x} + 1$.

37. Use the graph of f to estimate each of the following.
    (a) Where f is increasing or decreasing

    (b) The zeros of f

    (c) The coordinates of any turning points

    (d) Any local extrema

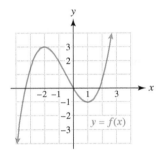

38. Are $f(x) = x^4 - 5x^3 - 7$ and $g(x) = \sqrt{9 - x^2}$ even, odd, or neither?

39. Sketch a graph of a quartic (degree 4) function with a negative leading coefficient, three x-intercepts, and three turning points.

40. State the end behavior of $f(x) = 4 + 3x - x^3$.

41. Divide each expression.
    (a) $\dfrac{4a^3 - 8a^2 + 12}{4a^2}$ (b) $\dfrac{2x^3 - 4x + 1}{x - 1}$

42. A quintic (degree 5) function f with real coefficients has leading coefficient $\frac{1}{2}$ and zeros -2, i, and $-2i$. Write $f(x)$ in complete factored form and expanded form.

43. A degree 6 function f has zeros -3, 1, and 4 with multiplicities 1, 2, and 3, respectively. If the leading coefficient is 4, write the complete factored form of $f(x)$.

44. Use the graph to write the complete factored form of the cubic polynomial $f(x)$.

45. Write $\frac{3 + 4i}{1 - i}$ in standard form.

46. Find all solutions, real or imaginary, to $x^4 - 25 = 0$.

47. State the domain of $f(x) = \frac{2x - 5}{x^2 - 3x - 4}$. Find any vertical or horizontal asymptotes.

48. Write $\sqrt[3]{x^5}$ using rational exponents. Evaluate the expression for $x = 8$.

Applications

49. Water in a Pool The graph shows the amount of water in a swimming pool x hours past noon. Find the slope of each line segment and interpret each slope.

Time (hours)

50. Distance At noon, one runner is heading south at 8 miles per hour and is located 2 miles north of a second runner, who is heading west at 7 miles per hour. Approximate the distance between the runners to the nearest tenth of a mile at 12:30 P.M.

51. Mixing Acid Two liters of a 35% sulfuric acid solution need to be diluted to a 20% solution. How many liters of a 12% sulfuric acid solution should be mixed with the 2-liter solution?

52. Working Together Suppose one person can paint a room in 10 hours and another person can paint the same room in 8 hours. How long will it take to paint the room if they work together?

53. Maximizing Revenue The revenue R in dollars from selling x thousand toy figures is given by the formula $R(x) = x(800 - x)$. How many toy figures should be sold to maximize revenue?

54. Construction A box is being constructed by cutting 2-inch squares from the corners of a rectangular sheet of metal that is 6 inches longer than it is wide. If the box is to have a volume of 270 cubic inches, find the dimensions of the metal sheet.

55. Group Rates Round-trip airline tickets to Hawaii are regularly $800, but for each additional ticket purchased the price is reduced by $5. For example, 1 ticket costs $800, 2 tickets cost $2(795) = \$1590$, and 3 tickets cost $3(790) = \$2370$.

(a) Write a quadratic function C that gives the total cost of purchasing t tickets.

(b) Solve $C(t) = 17,000$ and interpret the result.

(c) Find the absolute maximum for C and interpret your result. Assume that t must be an integer.

56. Modeling Data Find a quadratic function in the form $f(x) = a(x - h)^2 + k$ that models the data in the table. Graph $y = f(x)$ and the data if a graphing calculator is available.

x	4	6	8	10
y	6	15	37	80

57. Minimizing Surface Area A cylindrical can is being constructed to have a volume of 10π cubic inches. Find the dimensions of the can that result in the least amount of aluminum being used in its construction.

5

Exponential and Logarithmic Functions

When a link is posted on a social network, the majority of the engagements with this link occur within the first few hours. For example, within the first 3 hours a link on Facebook will have received half of its "hits." This *half life for* Twitter is even shorter, 2.8 hours, but much longer, 400 hours, for StumbleUpon. (See Section 5.3, Example 12.)

PGA golfers make about 99.2% of their putts that are 3 feet or less. However, every time a putt's distance increases by 6.6 feet, the chances of a pro making it decrease by about half. (See Section 5.3, Exercise 99.)

One reason for the explosive growth in mobile communication is the ability of researchers to increase the electrical efficiency of electronic devices. Since the era of the vacuum tube, the number of calculations that can be made using 1 kilowatt-hour of electricity has doubled every 1.6 years. (See Section 5.6, Example 4.)

Each of the examples above makes use of the mathematical concept of an exponential function. This chapter discusses this important topic.

> The important thing is not to stop questioning.
> —Albert Einstein

Sources: "The Half-Life of a Link", Column Five; "A Deeper Law than Moore's," *The Economist*.

5.1 Combining Functions

- Perform arithmetic operations on functions
- Review function notation
- Perform composition of functions

Introduction

Addition, subtraction, multiplication, and division can be performed on numbers and variables. These arithmetic operations can also be used to combine functions. For example, to model the stopping distance of a car traveling at x miles per hour, we compute two functions. The first function is the *reaction distance, $r(x)$*, which is the distance that a car travels between the time when a driver first recognizes a hazard and the time when the brakes are applied. The second function is *braking distance, $b(x)$*, which is the distance that a car travels after the brakes have been applied. *Stopping distance, $s(x)$*, is equal to the sum of $r(x)$ and $b(x)$. Figure 5.1 illustrates this example of addition of functions.

Stopping Distance Is a Sum of Functions:

$$s(x) = r(x) + b(x)$$

Figure 5.1

Arithmetic Operations on Functions

The concept of finding the sum of two functions can be represented symbolically, graphically, and numerically, as illustrated in the next example.

EXAMPLE 1 Representing stopping distance

For wet, level pavement, highway engineers sometimes let $r(x) = \frac{11}{3}x$ and $b(x) = \frac{1}{9}x^2$.
(*Source:* L. Haefner, *Introduction to Transportation Systems.*)
(a) Evaluate $r(60)$ and $b(60)$ and interpret each result.
(b) Write a formula for $s(x)$ and evaluate $s(60)$. Interpret the result.
(c) Graph r, b, and s. Interpret the graphs.
(d) Illustrate the relationship among r, b, and s numerically.

SOLUTION
(a) Substitute 60 into each formula.

$$r(60) = \frac{11}{3}(60) = 220 \quad \text{and} \quad b(60) = \frac{1}{9}(60)^2 = 400.$$

At 60 miles per hour the reaction distance is 220 feet and the braking distance is 400 feet.
(b) *Symbolic Representation* Let $s(x)$ be the sum of $r(x)$ and $b(x)$.

$$s(x) = r(x) + b(x) = \frac{11}{3}x + \frac{1}{9}x^2$$

Stopping Distance = Reaction Distance + Braking Distance

The stopping distance for a car traveling at 60 miles per hour is

$$s(60) = \frac{11}{3}(60) + \frac{1}{9}(60)^2 = 620 \text{ feet.}$$

(c) *Graphical Representation* Graph $y_1 = \frac{11}{3}x$, $y_2 = \frac{1}{9}x^2$, and $y_3 = \frac{11}{3}x + \frac{1}{9}x^2$, as shown in Figures 5.2–5.4.

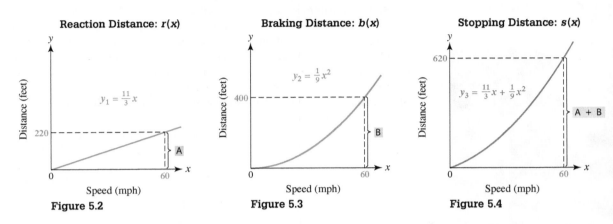

Reaction Distance: r(x)

Figure 5.2

Braking Distance: b(x)

Figure 5.3

Stopping Distance: s(x)

Figure 5.4

For any x-value, the sum of y_1 and y_2 equals y_3. For example, if $x = 60$, then

$$s(60) = r(60) + b(60) = 220 + 400 = 620.$$

(d) *Numerical Representation* Table 5.1 shows $r(x), b(x),$ and $s(x) = r(x) + b(x)$. Values for $s(x)$ can be found by adding $r(x)$ and $b(x)$. For example, $s(60) = 220 + 400 = 620$.

Adding Functions

x	0	12	24	36	48	60	— Speed
$r(x)$	0	44	88	132	176	220	— Reaction distance
$b(x)$	0	16	64	144	256	400	— Braking distance
$s(x)$	0	60	152	276	432	620	— Stopping distance: $s(x) = r(x) + b(x)$

Table 5.1

Now Try Exercise 99

We now formally define arithmetic operations on functions.

OPERATIONS ON FUNCTIONS

If $f(x)$ and $g(x)$ both exist, the sum, difference, product, and quotient of two functions f and g are defined by

$$(f + g)(x) = f(x) + g(x),$$
$$(f - g)(x) = f(x) - g(x),$$
$$(fg)(x) = f(x) \cdot g(x), \quad \text{and}$$
$$\left(\frac{f}{g}\right)(x) = \frac{f(x)}{g(x)}, \quad \text{where } g(x) \neq 0.$$

Operations on Functions and Domains   The domains of the sum, difference, and product of f and g include x-values that are in *both* the domain of f and the domain of g. The domain of the quotient f/g includes all x-values in both the domain of f and the domain of g, where $g(x) \neq 0$.

Graphical, Numerical, and Symbolic Evaluation   In the next example, we evaluate the sum, difference, product, and quotient of two functions in three ways: graphically, numerically, and symbolically.

EXAMPLE 2   Evaluating combinations of functions

If possible, use each representation of f and g to evaluate $(f + g)(4)$, $(f - g)(-2)$, $(fg)(1)$, and $(f/g)(0)$.

(a)

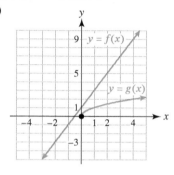

(b)

x	-2	0	1	4
$f(x)$	-3	1	3	9

x	-2	0	1	4
$g(x)$	—	0	1	2

(c) $f(x) = 2x + 1, g(x) = \sqrt{x}$

SOLUTION

(a) *Graphical Evaluation*   From Figure 5.5, $f(4) = 9$ and $g(4) = 2$. Thus
$$(f + g)(4) = f(4) + g(4) = 9 + 2 = 11.$$

Although $f(-2) = -3$, $g(-2)$ is undefined because -2 is not in the domain of g. Thus $(f - g)(-2)$ is undefined. The domains of f and g include 1, and it follows that
$$(fg)(1) = f(1)g(1) = 3(1) = 3.$$

The graph of g intersects the origin, so $g(0) = 0$. Thus $(f/g)(0) = \dfrac{f(0)}{g(0)}$ is undefined.

(b) *Numerical Evaluation*   From the tables, $f(4) = 9$ and $g(4) = 2$. As in part (a),
$$(f + g)(4) = f(4) + g(4) = 9 + 2 = 11.$$

A dash in the table indicates that $g(-2)$ is undefined, so $(f - g)(-2)$ is also undefined. The calculations of $(fg)(1)$ and $(f/g)(0)$ are done in a similar manner.

(c) *Symbolic Evaluation*   Use the formulas $f(x) = 2x + 1$ and $g(x) = \sqrt{x}$.

$$(f + g)(4) = f(4) + g(4) = (2 \cdot 4 + 1) + \sqrt{4} = 9 + 2 = 11$$

$$(f - g)(-2) = f(-2) - g(-2) = (2 \cdot (-2) + 1) - \sqrt{-2} \text{ is undefined.}$$

$$(fg)(1) = f(1)g(1) = (2 \cdot 1 + 1)\sqrt{1} = 3(1) = 3$$

$$\left(\frac{f}{g}\right)(0) = \frac{f(0)}{g(0)} \text{ is undefined, since } g(0) = 0.$$

Now Try Exercises 7, 31, and 35

$f(4) = 9$ and $g(4) = 2$

Figure 5.5

EXAMPLE 3 Performing arithmetic operations on functions symbolically

Let $f(x) = 2 + \sqrt{x - 1}$ and $g(x) = x^2 - 4$.

(a) Find the domains of $f(x)$ and $g(x)$. Then find the domains of $(f + g)(x)$, $(f - g)(x)$, $(fg)(x)$, and $(f/g)(x)$.

(b) If possible, evaluate $(f + g)(5)$, $(f - g)(1)$, $(fg)(0)$, and $(f/g)(3)$.

(c) Write expressions for $(f + g)(x)$, $(f - g)(x)$, $(fg)(x)$, and $(f/g)(x)$.

SOLUTION

(a) Whenever $x \geq 1$, $f(x) = 2 + \sqrt{x - 1}$ is defined. Therefore the domain of $f(x)$ is $\{x \mid x \geq 1\}$. The domain of $g(x) = x^2 - 4$ is all real numbers. The domains of $(f + g)(x)$, $(f - g)(x)$, and $(fg)(x)$ include all x-values in *both* the domain of $f(x)$ and the domain of $g(x)$. Thus their domains are $\{x \mid x \geq 1\}$.

To determine the domain of $(f/g)(x)$, we must also exclude x-values for which $g(x) = x^2 - 4 = 0$. This occurs when $x = \pm 2$. Thus the domain of $(f/g)(x)$ is $\{x \mid x \geq 1, x \neq 2\}$. (Note that $x \neq -2$ is satisfied if $x \geq 1$.)

(b) The expressions can be evaluated as follows.

$$(f + g)(5) = f(5) + g(5) = \left(2 + \sqrt{5 - 1}\right) + (5^2 - 4) = 4 + 21 = 25$$

$$(f - g)(1) = f(1) - g(1) = \left(2 + \sqrt{1 - 1}\right) - (1^2 - 4) = 2 - (-3) = 5$$

$(fg)(0)$ is undefined, since 0 is not in the domain of $f(x)$.

$$(f/g)(3) = \frac{f(3)}{g(3)} = \frac{2 + \sqrt{3 - 1}}{3^2 - 4} = \frac{2 + \sqrt{2}}{5}$$

(c) The sum, difference, product, and quotient of f and g are calculated as follows.

$$(f + g)(x) = f(x) + g(x) = \left(2 + \sqrt{x - 1}\right) + (x^2 - 4) = \sqrt{x - 1} + x^2 - 2$$

$$(f - g)(x) = f(x) - g(x) = \left(2 + \sqrt{x - 1}\right) - (x^2 - 4) = \sqrt{x - 1} - x^2 + 6$$

$$(fg)(x) = f(x) \cdot g(x) = \left(2 + \sqrt{x - 1}\right)(x^2 - 4)$$

$$\left(\frac{f}{g}\right)(x) = \frac{f(x)}{g(x)} = \frac{2 + \sqrt{x - 1}}{x^2 - 4}$$

Now Try Exercises 9 and 15

An Application The next example is an application from business involving the difference between two functions.

EXAMPLE 4 Finding the difference of two functions

The expenses for a band to produce the master sound track for an album include renting a music studio and hiring a music engineer. These *fixed costs* are $12,000, and the cost to produce each album with packaging is $5.

(a) Assuming no other expenses, find a function C that outputs the cost of producing the master sound track plus x albums. Find the cost of making the master track and 3000 albums.

(b) Suppose that each album is sold for $12. Find a function R that computes the revenue from selling x albums. Find the revenue from selling 3000 albums.

(c) Determine a function P that outputs the profit from selling x albums. How much profit is there from selling 3000 albums?

SOLUTION

(a) The cost of producing the master sound track for $12,000 plus x albums at $5 each is given by $C(x) = 5x + 12,000$. The cost of manufacturing the master sound track and 3000 albums is

$$C(3000) = 5(3000) + 12,000 = \$27,000.$$

(b) The revenue from x albums at $12 each is computed by $R(x) = 12x$. The revenue from selling 3000 albums is $R(3000) = 12(3000) = \$36,000$.

(c) Profit P is equal to revenue minus cost. This can be written using function notation.

$$
\begin{aligned}
P(x) &= R(x) - C(x) \\
&= 12x - (5x + 12{,}000) \\
&= 12x - 5x - 12{,}000 \\
&= 7x - 12{,}000
\end{aligned}
$$

If $x = 3000$, $P(3000) = 7(3000) - 12{,}000 = \$9000$.

> **Now Try Exercise 95**

Review of Function Notation

In the next example, we review how to evaluate function notation before we discuss composition of functions.

EXAMPLE 5 Evaluating function notation

Let $g(x) = 3x^2 - 6x + 2$. Evaluate each expression.
(a) $g(2)$ **(b)** $g(k)$ **(c)** $g(x^2)$ **(d)** $g(x + 2)$

SOLUTION
(a) $g(2) = 3(2)^2 - 6(2) + 2 = 12 - 12 + 2 = 2$
(b) $g(k) = 3k^2 - 6k + 2$
(c) $g(x^2) = 3(x^2)^2 - 6(x^2) + 2 = 3x^4 - 6x^2 + 2$
(d) $g(x + 2) = 3(x + 2)^2 - 6(x + 2) + 2$
$$
\begin{aligned}
&= 3(x^2 + 4x + 4) - 6(x + 2) + 2 \\
&= 3x^2 + 12x + 12 - 6x - 12 + 2 \\
&= 3x^2 + 6x + 2
\end{aligned}
$$

Algebra Review
To review squaring a binomial, see Chapter R (page R-17).

> **Now Try Exercise 45**

Composition of Functions

Many tasks in life are performed in sequence. For example, to go to a movie we might get into a car, drive to the movie theater, and get out of the car. A similar situation occurs with functions. For example, to convert miles to inches we might first convert miles to feet and then convert feet to inches in sequence. Since there are 5280 feet in a mile, $f(x) = 5280x$ converts x miles to an equivalent number of feet. Then $g(x) = 12x$ changes feet to inches. To convert x miles to inches, we combine the functions f and g in sequence. Figure 5.6 illustrates how to convert 5 miles to inches. First, $f(5) = 5280(5) = 26{,}400$. Then the output of 26,400 feet from f is used as input for g. The number of inches in 26,400 feet is $g(26{,}400) = 12(26{,}400) = 316{,}800$. This computation is called the *composition* of g and f.

The composition of g and f shown in Figure 5.6 can be expressed symbolically. The symbol $\circ$ is used to denote composition of two functions.

**Composition of Functions
(converting 5 miles to inches)**

Miles   Feet   Inches

Figure 5.6

$$
\begin{aligned}
(g \circ f)(5) &= g(f(5)) && \text{First compute } f(5). \\
&= g(5280 \cdot 5) && f(x) = 5280x \\
&= g(26{,}400) && \text{Simplify.} \\
&= 12(26{,}400) && g(x) = 12x \\
&= 316{,}800 && \text{Simplify.}
\end{aligned}
$$

Composition of g and f

A distance of 5 miles is equivalent to 316,800 inches. The concept of composition of two functions relates to applying functions in sequence and is now defined formally.

COMPOSITION OF FUNCTIONS

If f and g are functions, then the **composite function** $g \circ f$, or **composition** of g and f is defined by

$$(g \circ f)(x) = g(f(x)).$$

We read $g(f(x))$ as "g of f of x."

The domain of $g \circ f$ is all x in the domain of f such that $f(x)$ is in the domain of g.

Symbolic Evaluation of Composite Functions The next three examples discuss how to evaluate composite functions and find their domains symbolically.

EXAMPLE 6 Finding a symbolic representation of a composite function

Find a formula for the composite function $g \circ f$ that converts x miles into inches.

SOLUTION Let $f(x) = 5280x$ and $g(x) = 12x$.

$$\begin{aligned}(g \circ f)(x) &= g(f(x)) && \text{Definition of composition}\\ &= g(5280x) && f(x) = 5280x \text{ is the input for } g.\\ &= 12(5280x) && g \text{ multiplies the input by 12.}\\ &= 63{,}360x && \text{Simplify.}\end{aligned}$$

Thus $(g \circ f)(x) = 63{,}360x$ converts x miles into inches.

Now try Exercises 97

NOTE Converting units is only one application of composition of functions. Another application involves examining how a decrease in the ozone layer causes an increase in ultraviolet sunlight, which in turn causes increases in the number of skin cancer cases. See Example 10.

See the Concept: $(fg)(x)$ and $(f \circ g)(x)$ Are Different

Ⓐ Multiplication: $(fg)(5)$

INPUT 5

$f(x)$ $g(x)$

OUTPUT $f(5)$ OUTPUT $g(5)$

$(fg)(x) = f(x) \cdot g(x)$

OUTPUT $f(5) \cdot g(5)$

Ⓑ Composition: $(f \circ g)(5)$

INPUT 5

$g(x)$

OUTPUT $g(5)$
($g(5)$ becomes the input for f)

$(f \circ g)(x) = f(g(x))$

Ⓒ

OUTPUT $f(g(5))$

Ⓐ With multiplication input 5 is given to both functions and then the outputs are multiplied: $f(5) \cdot g(5)$.

Ⓑ With composition the output of the first function $g(5)$ becomes the input for the second function $f(g(5))$.

Ⓒ Composition is a sequence of functions.

EXAMPLE 7 Evaluating a composite function symbolically

Let $f(x) = x^2 + 3x + 2$ and $g(x) = \frac{1}{x}$.
(a) Evaluate $(f \circ g)(2)$ and $(g \circ f)(2)$. How do they compare?
(b) Find the composite functions defined by $(f \circ g)(x)$ and $(g \circ f)(x)$. Are they equivalent expressions?
(c) Find the domains of $(f \circ g)(x)$ and $(g \circ f)(x)$.

SOLUTION
(a) $(f \circ g)(2) = f(g(2)) = f\left(\frac{1}{2}\right) = \left(\frac{1}{2}\right)^2 + 3\left(\frac{1}{2}\right) + 2 = \frac{15}{4} = 3.75$

$(g \circ f)(2) = g(f(2)) = g(2^2 + 3 \cdot 2 + 2) = g(12) = \frac{1}{12} \approx 0.0833$
The results are *not* equal.

(b) $(f \circ g)(x) = f(g(x)) = f\left(\frac{1}{x}\right) = \left(\frac{1}{x}\right)^2 + 3\left(\frac{1}{x}\right) + 2 = \frac{1}{x^2} + \frac{3}{x} + 2$

$(g \circ f)(x) = g(f(x)) = g(x^2 + 3x + 2) = \dfrac{1}{x^2 + 3x + 2}$

The expressions for $(f \circ g)(x)$ and $(g \circ f)(x)$ are *not* equivalent.

(c) The domain of f is all real numbers, and the domain of g is $\{x \mid x \neq 0\}$. The domain of $(f \circ g)(x) = f(g(x))$ consists of all x in the domain of g such that $g(x)$ is in the domain of f. Thus the domain of $(f \circ g)(x) = \frac{1}{x^2} + \frac{3}{x} + 2$ is $\{x \mid x \neq 0\}$.

The domain of $(g \circ f)(x) = g(f(x))$ consists of all x in the domain of f such that $f(x)$ is in the domain of g. Since $x^2 + 3x + 2 = 0$ when $x = -1$ or $x = -2$, the domain of $(g \circ f)(x) = \frac{1}{x^2 + 3x + 2}$ is $\{x \mid x \neq -1, x \neq -2\}$.

> Now try Exercises 53 and 57

MAKING CONNECTIONS

Composition and Domains To find the domain of a composition of two functions, it is sometimes helpful not to immediately simplify the resulting expression. For example, if $f(x) = x^2$ and $g(x) = \sqrt{x - 1}$, then

$$(f \circ g)(x) = \left(\sqrt{x - 1}\right)^2.$$

From this unsimplified expression, we can see that the domain (input) of $f \circ g$ must be restricted to $x \geq 1$ for the output to be a real number. As a result,

$$(f \circ g)(x) = x - 1, \quad x \geq 1.$$

EXAMPLE 8 Finding symbolic representations for composite functions

Find $(f \circ g)(x)$ and $(g \circ f)(x)$.
(a) $f(x) = x + 2$, $\quad g(x) = x^3 - 2x^2 - 1$
(b) $f(x) = \sqrt{2x}$, $\quad g(x) = \dfrac{1}{x + 1}$
(c) $f(x) = 2x - 3$, $\quad g(x) = x^2 + 5$

SOLUTION

Getting Started When finding a composition of functions, the first step is often to write $(f \circ g)(x) = f(g(x))$ or $(g \circ f)(x) = g(f(x))$. ▶

(a) Begin by writing $(f \circ g)(x) = f(g(x)) = f(x^3 - 2x^2 - 1)$. Function f adds 2 to the input. That is, $f(\text{input}) = (\text{input}) + 2$ because $f(x) = x + 2$. Thus

$$f(x^3 - 2x^2 - 1) = (x^3 - 2x^2 - 1) + 2 = x^3 - 2x^2 + 1.$$

To find the composition $(g \circ f)(x)$, write $(g \circ f)(x) = g(f(x)) = g(x + 2)$. Because $g(x) = x^3 - 2x^2 - 1$, it follows that $g(\text{input}) = (\text{input})^3 - 2(\text{input})^2 - 1$. Thus

$$g(x + 2) = (x + 2)^3 - 2(x + 2)^2 - 1.$$

(b) $(f \circ g)(x) = f(g(x)) = f\left(\dfrac{1}{x + 1}\right) = \sqrt{2 \cdot \dfrac{1}{x + 1}} = \sqrt{\dfrac{2}{x + 1}}$ $\quad f(x) = \sqrt{2x}$

$\qquad (g \circ f)(x) = g(f(x)) = g\left(\sqrt{2x}\right) = \dfrac{1}{\sqrt{2x} + 1}$ $\quad\quad g(x) = \dfrac{1}{x + 1}$

(c) $(f \circ g)(x) = f(g(x)) = f(x^2 + 5) = 2(x^2 + 5) - 3 = 2x^2 + 7$

$\qquad (g \circ f)(x) = g(f(x)) = g(2x - 3) = (2x - 3)^2 + 5 = 4x^2 - 12x + 14$

Now Try Exercises 59, 63, and 65

NOTE A composition of f with itself is denoted $(f \circ f)(x)$. For example, if $f(x) = 3x$, then

$$(f \circ f)(x) = f(3x) = 3(3x) = 9x.$$

That is, f multiplies the input by 3, so $(f \circ f)(x)$ multiplies the input by 3 twice, which is equivalent to multiplying the input by 9.

Graphical Evaluation of Composite Functions The next example shows how to evaluate a composition of functions graphically.

EXAMPLE 9 Evaluating a composite function graphically

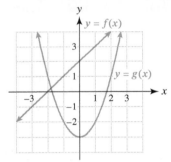

Figure 5.7

Use the graphs of f and g shown in Figure 5.7 to evaluate each expression.
(a) $(f \circ g)(2)$ **(b)** $(g \circ f)(-3)$ **(c)** $(f \circ f)(-3)$

SOLUTION
(a) Because $(f \circ g)(2) = f(g(2))$, first evaluate $g(2)$. From Figure 5.8, $g(2) = 1$ and

$$(f \circ g)(2) = f(g(2)) = f(1).$$

To complete the evaluation of $(f \circ g)(2)$, use Figure 5.9 to determine that $f(1) = 3$. Thus $(f \circ g)(2) = 3$.
(b) Because $(g \circ f)(-3) = g(f(-3))$, first evaluate the expression $f(-3)$. Figure 5.10 shows that $f(-3) = -1$, so

$$(g \circ f)(-3) = g(f(-3)) = g(-1).$$

From Figure 5.11, $g(-1) = -2$. Thus $(g \circ f)(-3) = -2$.
(c) Similarly, $(f \circ f)(-3) = f(f(-3)) = f(-1) = 1$.

Figure 5.8

Figure 5.9

Figure 5.10

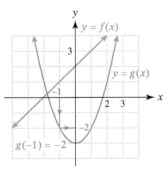

Figure 5.11

Now Try Exercise 75

Numerical Evaluation of Composite Functions Tables 5.2 and 5.3 represent two functions f and g.

x	1	2	3	4
$f(x)$	2	3	4	1

Table 5.2

x	1	2	3	4
$g(x)$	4	3	2	1

Table 5.3

We can use these tables to evaluate expressions, such as $(g \circ f)(3)$ and $(f \circ g)(3)$.

$$(g \circ f)(3) = g(f(3)) \qquad \text{Definition of composition}$$
$$= g(4) \qquad f(3) = 4 \text{ in Table 5.2.}$$
$$= 1 \qquad g(4) = 1 \text{ in Table 5.3.}$$

We see that $(f \circ g)(3) = f(g(3)) = f(2) = 3$ by using Table 5.3 and then Table 5.2.

NOTE Composition of functions is *not* commutative. That is, $(g \circ f)(x) \neq (f \circ g)(x)$ in general. For example, from above, $(g \circ f)(3) \neq (f \circ g)(3)$.

An Application The next example illustrates how composition of functions occurs in the analysis of the ozone layer, ultraviolet (UV) radiation, and cases of skin cancer.

EXAMPLE 10   Evaluating a composite function numerically

Depletion of the ozone layer can cause an increase in the amount of UV radiation reaching the surface of the earth. An increase in UV radiation is associated with skin cancer. In Table 5.4 the function f computes the approximate percent *increase* in UV radiation resulting from an x percent *decrease* in the thickness of the ozone layer. The function g shown in Table 5.5 computes the expected percent increase in cases of skin cancer resulting from an x percent increase in UV radiation. (*Source:* R. Turner, D. Pearce, and I. Bateman, *Environmental Economics.*)

Percent Increase in UV Radiation

x	0	1	2	3	4	5	6
$f(x)$	0	1.5	3.0	4.5	6.0	7.5	9.0

Percent decrease in the ozone layer

Percent increase in UV radiation

Table 5.4

Percent Increase in Skin Cancer

x	0	1.5	3.0	4.5	6.0	7.5	9.0
$g(x)$	0	5.25	10.5	15.75	21.0	26.25	31.5

Percent increase in UV radiation

Percent increase in cases of skin cancer

Table 5.5

(a) Find $(g \circ f)(2)$ and interpret this calculation.
(b) Create a table for $g \circ f$. Describe what $(g \circ f)(x)$ computes.

SOLUTION
(a) $(g \circ f)(2) = g(f(2)) = g(3.0) = 10.5$. This means that a 2% decrease in the thickness of the ozone layer results in a 3% increase in UV radiation, which could cause a 10.5% increase in skin cancer.
(b) The values for $(g \circ f)(x)$ can be found in a similar manner. See Table 5.6.

x	0	1	2	3	4	5	6
$(g \circ f)(x)$	0	5.25	10.5	15.75	21.0	26.25	31.5

Percent decrease in the ozone layer

Percent increase in cases of skin cancer

Table 5.6

The composition $(g \circ f)(x)$ computes the percent increase in cases of skin cancer resulting from an x percent decrease in the ozone layer.

 Now Try Exercise 101

Writing Compositions When you are solving problems, it is sometimes helpful to recognize a function as the composition of two simpler functions. For example, $h(x) = \sqrt[3]{x^2}$ can be thought of as the composition of the cube root function, $g(x) = \sqrt[3]{x}$, and the squaring function, $f(x) = x^2$. Then h can be written as $h(x) = g(f(x)) = \sqrt[3]{x^2}$. This concept is demonstrated in the next example. Note that answers may vary.

EXAMPLE 11 Writing a function as a composition of two functions

Find $f(x)$ and $g(x)$ so that $h(x) = (g \circ f)(x)$.

(a) $h(x) = (x + 3)^2$ **(b)** $h(x) = \sqrt{2x - 7}$ **(c)** $h(x) = \dfrac{1}{x^2 + 2x}$

SOLUTION

(a) Let $f(x) = x + 3$ and $g(x) = x^2$. Then
$$(g \circ f)(x) = g(f(x)) = g(x + 3) = (x + 3)^2.$$

(b) Let $f(x) = 2x - 7$ and $g(x) = \sqrt{x}$. Then
$$(g \circ f)(x) = g(f(x)) = g(2x - 7) = \sqrt{2x - 7}.$$

(c) Let $f(x) = x^2 + 2x$ and $g(x) = \frac{1}{x}$. Then
$$(g \circ f)(x) = g(f(x)) = g(x^2 + 2x) = \frac{1}{x^2 + 2x}.$$

Now try Exercises 81, 85, and 91

5.1 Putting It All Together

The following table summarizes some concepts involved with combining functions.

CONCEPT	NOTATION	EXAMPLES
Sum of two functions	$(f + g)(x) = f(x) + g(x)$	$f(x) = x^2, g(x) = 2x + 1$ $(f + g)(3) = f(3) + g(3) = 9 + 7 = 16$ $(f + g)(x) = f(x) + g(x) = x^2 + 2x + 1$
Difference of two functions	$(f - g)(x) = f(x) - g(x)$	$f(x) = 3x, g(x) = 2x + 1$ $(f - g)(1) = f(1) - g(1) = 3 - 3 = 0$ $(f - g)(x) = f(x) - g(x) = 3x - (2x + 1)$ $\qquad = x - 1$
Product of two functions	$(fg)(x) = f(x) \cdot g(x)$	$f(x) = x^3, g(x) = 1 - 3x$ $(fg)(-2) = f(-2) \cdot g(-2) = (-8)(7) = -56$ $(fg)(x) = f(x) \cdot g(x) = x^3(1 - 3x) = x^3 - 3x^4$
Quotient of two functions	$\left(\dfrac{f}{g}\right)(x) = \dfrac{f(x)}{g(x)}, g(x) \neq 0$	$f(x) = x^2 - 1, g(x) = x + 2$ $\left(\dfrac{f}{g}\right)(2) = \dfrac{f(2)}{g(2)} = \dfrac{3}{4}$ $\left(\dfrac{f}{g}\right)(x) = \dfrac{f(x)}{g(x)} = \dfrac{x^2 - 1}{x + 2}, x \neq -2$
Composition of two functions	$(g \circ f)(x) = g(f(x))$	$f(x) = x^3, g(x) = x^2 - 2x + 1$ $(g \circ f)(2) = g(f(2)) = g(8)$ $\qquad = 64 - 16 + 1 = 49$ $(g \circ f)(x) = g(f(x)) = g(x^3)$ $\qquad = (x^3)^2 - 2(x^3) + 1$ $\qquad = x^6 - 2x^3 + 1$

Concepts

1. If $f(3) = 2$ and $g(3) = 5$, $(f + g)(3) =$ ___.

2. If $f(3) = 2$ and $g(2) = 5$, $(g \circ f)(3) =$ ___.

3. If $f(x) = x^2$ and $g(x) = 4x$, $(fg)(x) =$ ___.

4. If $f(x) = x^2$ and $g(x) = 4x$, $(f \circ g)(x) =$ ___.

5. Cost of Carpet If $f(x)$ calculates the number of square feet in x square yards and $g(x)$ calculates the cost in dollars of x square feet of carpet, what does $(g \circ f)(x)$ calculate?

6. Time Conversion If $f(x)$ calculates the number of days in x hours and $g(x)$ calculates the number of years in x days, what does $(g \circ f)(x)$ calculate?

Arithmetic Operations on Functions

Exercises 7–10: Use $f(x)$ and $g(x)$ to evaluate each expression symbolically.

7. $f(x) = 2x - 3$, $g(x) = 1 - x^2$

  (a) $(f + g)(3)$ **(b)** $(f - g)(-1)$

  (c) $(fg)(0)$ **(d)** $(f/g)(2)$

8. $f(x) = 4x - x^3$, $g(x) = x + 3$

  (a) $(g + g)(-2)$ **(b)** $(f - g)(0)$

  (c) $(gf)(1)$ **(d)** $(g/f)(-3)$

9. $f(x) = 2x + 1$, $g(x) = \dfrac{1}{x}$

  (a) $(f + g)(2)$ **(b)** $(f - g)\left(\frac{1}{2}\right)$

  (c) $(fg)(4)$ **(d)** $(f/g)(0)$

10. $f(x) = \sqrt[3]{x^2}$, $g(x) = |x - 3|$

  (a) $(f + g)(-8)$ **(b)** $(f - g)(-1)$

  (c) $(fg)(0)$ **(d)** $(f/g)(27)$

Exercises 11–30: Use $f(x)$ and $g(x)$ to find a formula for each expression. Identify its domain.

  (a) $(f + g)(x)$ *(b)* $(f - g)(x)$

  (c) $(fg)(x)$ *(d)* $(f/g)(x)$

11. $f(x) = 2x$, $g(x) = x^2$

12. $f(x) = 1 - 4x$, $g(x) = 3x + 1$

13. $f(x) = x^2 - 1$, $g(x) = x^2 + 1$

14. $f(x) = 4x^3 - 8x^2$, $g(x) = 4x^2$

15. $f(x) = x - \sqrt{x - 1}$, $g(x) = x + \sqrt{x - 1}$

16. $f(x) = 3 + \sqrt{2x + 9}$, $g(x) = 3 - \sqrt{2x + 9}$

17. $f(x) = \sqrt{x} - 1$, $g(x) = \sqrt{x} + 1$

18. $f(x) = \sqrt{1 - x}$, $g(x) = x^3$

19. $f(x) = \dfrac{1}{x + 1}$, $g(x) = \dfrac{3}{x + 1}$

20. $f(x) = x^{1/2}$, $g(x) = 3$

21. $f(x) = \dfrac{1}{2x - 4}$, $g(x) = \dfrac{x}{2x - 4}$

22. $f(x) = \dfrac{1}{x}$, $g(x) = x^3$

23. $f(x) = x^2 - 1$, $g(x) = |x + 1|$

24. $f(x) = |2x - 1|$, $g(x) = |2x + 1|$

25. $f(x) = \dfrac{x^2 - 3x + 2}{x + 1}$, $g(x) = \dfrac{x^2 - 1}{x - 2}$

26. $f(x) = \dfrac{4x - 2}{x + 2}$, $g(x) = \dfrac{2x - 1}{3x + 6}$

27. $f(x) = \dfrac{2}{x^2 - 1}$, $g(x) = \dfrac{x + 1}{x^2 - 2x + 1}$

28. $f(x) = \dfrac{1}{x + 2}$, $g(x) = x^2 + x - 2$

29. $f(x) = x^{5/2} - x^{3/2}$, $g(x) = x^{1/2}$

30. $f(x) = x^{2/3} - 2x^{1/3} + 1$, $g(x) = x^{1/3} - 1$

Exercises 31–34: Use the graph to evaluate each expression.

31.

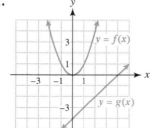

  (a) $(f + g)(2)$

  (b) $(f - g)(1)$

  (c) $(fg)(0)$

  (d) $(f/g)(1)$

32.

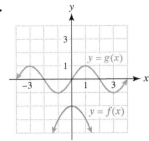

(a) $(f + g)(1)$

(b) $(f - g)(0)$

(c) $(fg)(-1)$

(d) $(f/g)(1)$

33.

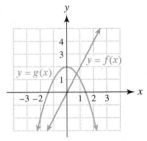

(a) $(f + g)(0)$

(b) $(f - g)(-1)$

(c) $(fg)(1)$

(d) $(f/g)(2)$

34.

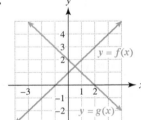

(a) $(f + g)(-1)$

(b) $(f - g)(-2)$

(c) $(fg)(0)$

(d) $(f/g)(2)$

Exercises 35 and 36: Use the tables to evaluate each expression, if possible.

(a) $(f + g)(-1)$ (b) $(g - f)(0)$

(c) $(gf)(2)$ (d) $(f/g)(2)$

35.

x	-1	0	2
$f(x)$	-3	5	1

x	-1	0	2
$g(x)$	-2	3	0

36.

x	-1	0	2
$f(x)$	4	1	3

x	-1	0	2
$g(x)$	2	0	1

Exercises 37 and 38: Use the table to evaluate each expression, if possible.

(a) $(f + g)(2)$ (b) $(f - g)(4)$

(c) $(fg)(-2)$ (d) $(f/g)(0)$

37.

x	-2	0	2	4
$f(x)$	0	5	7	10
$g(x)$	6	0	-2	5

38.

x	-2	0	2	4
$f(x)$	-4	8	5	0
$g(x)$	2	-1	4	0

39. Use the table in Exercise 37 to complete the following table.

x	-2	0	2	4
$(f + g)(x)$				
$(f - g)(x)$				
$(fg)(x)$				
$(f/g)(x)$				

40. Use the table in Exercise 38 to complete the table in Exercise 39.

Review of Function Notation

Exercises 41–52: For the given $g(x)$, evaluate each of the following.

     (a) $g(-3)$ (b) $g(b)$ (c) $g(x^3)$ (d) $g(2x - 3)$

41. $g(x) = 2x + 1$ **42.** $g(x) = 5 - \frac{1}{2}x$

43. $g(x) = 2(x + 3)^2 - 4$ **44.** $g(x) = -(x - 1)^2$

45. $g(x) = \frac{1}{2}x^2 + 3x - 1$ **46.** $g(x) = 2x^2 - x - 9$

47. $g(x) = \sqrt{x + 4}$ **48.** $g(x) = \sqrt{2 - x}$

49. $g(x) = |3x - 1| + 4$ **50.** $g(x) = 2|1 - x| - 7$

51. $g(x) = \dfrac{4x}{x + 3}$ **52.** $g(x) = \dfrac{x + 3}{2}$

Composition of Functions

Exercises 53–56: Use the given $f(x)$ and $g(x)$ to evaluate each expression.

53. $f(x) = \sqrt{x + 5}, \quad g(x) = x^2$

   (a) $(f \circ g)(2)$ (b) $(g \circ f)(-1)$

54. $f(x) = |x^2 - 4|, \quad g(x) = 2x^2 + x + 1$

   (a) $(f \circ g)(1)$ (b) $(g \circ f)(-3)$

55. $f(x) = 5x - 2, \quad g(x) = |x|$

   (a) $(f \circ g)(-4)$ (b) $(g \circ f)(5)$

56. $f(x) = \dfrac{1}{x - 4}, \quad g(x) = 5$

   (a) $(f \circ g)(3)$ (b) $(g \circ f)(8)$

Exercises 57–72: Use the given $f(x)$ and $g(x)$ to find each of the following. Identify its domain.

(a) $(f \circ g)(x)$ (b) $(g \circ f)(x)$ (c) $(f \circ f)(x)$

57. $f(x) = x^3$, $g(x) = x^2 + 3x - 1$

58. $f(x) = 2 - x$, $g(x) = \dfrac{1}{x^2}$

59. $f(x) = x + 2$, $g(x) = x^4 + x^2 - 3x - 4$

60. $f(x) = x^2$, $g(x) = \sqrt{1 - x}$

61. $f(x) = 2 - 3x$, $g(x) = x^3$

62. $f(x) = \sqrt{x}$, $g(x) = 1 - x^2$

63. $f(x) = \dfrac{1}{x + 1}$, $g(x) = 5x$

64. $f(x) = \dfrac{1}{3x}$, $g(x) = \dfrac{2}{x - 1}$

65. $f(x) = x + 4$, $g(x) = \sqrt{4 - x^2}$

66. $f(x) = 2x + 1$, $g(x) = 4x^3 - 5x^2$

67. $f(x) = \sqrt{x - 1}$, $g(x) = 3x$

68. $f(x) = \dfrac{x - 3}{2}$, $g(x) = 2x + 3$

69. $f(x) = 1 - 5x$, $g(x) = \dfrac{1 - x}{5}$

70. $f(x) = \sqrt[3]{x - 1}$, $g(x) = x^3 + 1$

71. $f(x) = \dfrac{1}{kx}, k > 0$, $g(x) = \dfrac{1}{kx}, k > 0$

72. $f(x) = ax^2, a > 0$, $g(x) = \sqrt{ax}, a > 0$

Exercises 73–76: Use the graph to evaluate each expression.

73.

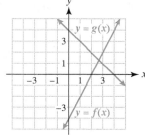

(a) $(f \circ g)(4)$

(b) $(g \circ f)(3)$

(c) $(f \circ f)(2)$

74.

(a) $(f \circ g)(2)$

(b) $(g \circ g)(0)$

(c) $(g \circ f)(4)$

75.

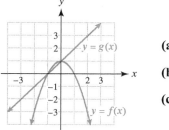

(a) $(f \circ g)(1)$

(b) $(g \circ f)(-2)$

(c) $(g \circ g)(-2)$

76.

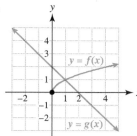

(a) $(f \circ g)(-2)$

(b) $(g \circ f)(1)$

(c) $(f \circ f)(0)$

Exercises 77 and 78: Tables for the functions f and g are given. Evaluate the expression, if possible.

(a) $(g \circ f)(1)$ (b) $(f \circ g)(4)$ (c) $(f \circ f)(3)$

77.

x	1	2	3	4
$f(x)$	4	3	1	2

x	1	2	3	4
$g(x)$	2	3	4	5

78.

x	1	3	4	6
$f(x)$	2	6	5	7

x	2	3	5	7
$g(x)$	4	2	6	0

79. Use the tables for $f(x)$ and $g(x)$ in Exercise 77 to complete the composition shown in the diagram.

80. Use the tables for $f(x)$ and $g(x)$ in Exercise 78 to complete the composition shown in the diagram.

Exercises 81–94: (Refer to Example 11.) Find $f(x)$ and $g(x)$ so that $h(x) = (g \circ f)(x)$. Answers may vary.

81. $h(x) = \sqrt{x - 2}$ **82.** $h(x) = (x + 2)^4$

83. $h(x) = \dfrac{1}{x + 2}$ **84.** $h(x) = 5(x + 2)^2 - 4$

85. $h(x) = 4(2x + 1)^3$

86. $h(x) = \sqrt[3]{x^2 + 1}$

87. $h(x) = (x^3 - 1)^2$

88. $h(x) = 4(x - 5)^{-2}$

89. $h(x) = -4|x + 2| - 3$

90. $h(x) = 5\sqrt{x - 1}$

91. $h(x) = \dfrac{1}{(x - 1)^2}$

92. $h(x) = \dfrac{2}{x^2 - x + 1}$

93. $h(x) = x^{3/4} - x^{1/4}$

94. $h(x) = x^{2/3} - 5x^{1/3} + 4$

Applications

95. Profit (Refer to Example 4.) Determine a profit function P that results if the albums are sold for $15 each. Find the profit from selling 3000 albums.

96. Revenue, Cost, and Profit Suppose that for a major production company it costs $150,000 to produce a master track for a music video and $1.50 to produce each copy.
(a) Write a cost function C that outputs the cost of producing the master track and x copies.

(b) If the music videos are sold for $6.50 each, find a function R that outputs the revenue received from selling x music videos. What is the revenue from selling 8000 videos?

(c) Find a function P that outputs the profit from selling x music videos. What is the profit from selling 40,000 videos?

(d) How many videos must be sold to break even? That is, how many videos must be sold for the revenue to equal the cost?

97. Converting Units There are 36 inches in a yard and 2.54 centimeters in an inch.
(a) Write a function I that converts x yards to inches.

(b) Write a function C that converts x inches to centimeters.

(c) Express a function F that converts x yards to centimeters as a composition of two functions.

(d) Write a formula for F.

98. Converting Units There are 4 quarts in 1 gallon, 4 cups in 1 quart, and 16 tablespoons in 1 cup.
(a) Write a function Q that converts x gallons to quarts.

(b) Write a function C that converts x quarts to cups.

(c) Write a function T that converts x cups to tablespoons.

(d) Express a function F that converts x gallons to tablespoons as a composition of *three* functions.

(e) Write a formula for F.

99. Stopping Distance (Refer to Example 1.) A driver's reaction distance is $r(x) = \frac{11}{6}x$ and braking distance is $b(x) = \frac{1}{9}x^2$.
(a) Find a formula $s(x)$ that computes the stopping distance for this driver traveling at x miles per hour.

(b) Evaluate $s(60)$ and interpret the result.

100. Stopping Distance (Refer to Example 1.) If a driver attempts to stop while traveling at x miles per hour on dry, level pavement, the reaction distance is $r(x) = \frac{11}{5}x$ and the braking distance is $b(x) = \frac{1}{11}x^2$, where both distances are in feet.
(a) Write a formula for a function s in terms of $r(x)$ and $b(x)$ that gives the stopping distance when driving at x miles per hour. Evaluate $s(55)$.

(b) Graph r, b, and s on the same axes. Explain how the graph of s can be found using the graphs of r and b.

(c) Make tables for $r(x)$ and $b(x)$ at $x = 11, 22, 33, 44,$ and 55. Then use these tables to construct a table for $s(x)$.

101. Skin Cancer (Refer to Example 10 and Tables 5.4 and 5.5.) If possible, calculate the composition and interpret the result.
(a) $(g \circ f)(1)$ **(b)** $(f \circ g)(21)$

102. Skin Cancer In Example 10, f and g are both linear.
(a) Find symbolic representations for f and g.

(b) Determine $(g \circ f)(x)$.

(c) Evaluate $(g \circ f)(3.5)$ and interpret the result.

103. Urban Heat Island Urban areas tend to be warmer than the surrounding rural areas. This effect is called the *urban heat island*. In the first figure at the top of the next page, f computes the average increase in nighttime summer temperatures in degrees Celsius at Sky Harbor Airport in Phoenix from 1948 to 1990. In this graph, 1948 is the base year with a zero temperature increase. The rise in urban temperature increased peak demand for electricity. In the second figure at the top of the next page, g computes the percent increase in electrical demand for an average nighttime temperature increase of *x* degrees Celsius. (***Source:*** W. Cotton and R. Pielke, *Human Impacts on Weather and Climate*.)

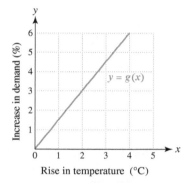

(a) Evaluate $(g \circ f)(1975)$ graphically.

(b) Interpret $(g \circ f)(x)$.

104. Urban Heat Island (Refer to Exercise 103.) If possible, calculate the composition and interpret the result.
(a) $(g \circ f)(1980)$ **(b)** $(f \circ g)(3)$

105. Urban Heat Island (Refer to Exercise 103.) The functions *f* and *g* are given by $f(x) = 0.11(x - 1948)$ and $g(x) = 1.5x$.
(a) Evaluate $(g \circ f)(1960)$.

(b) Find $(g \circ f)(x)$.

(c) What type of functions are, *f*, *g*, and $g \circ f$?

106. Swimming Pools In the figures, *f* computes the cubic feet of water in a pool after *x* days, and *g* converts cubic feet to gallons.

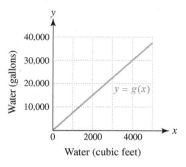

(a) Find the gallons of water in the pool after 2 days.

(b) Interpret $(g \circ f)(x)$.

107. Temperature The function *f* computes the temperature on a summer day after *x* hours, and *g* converts Fahrenheit temperature to Celsius temperature. See the figures.

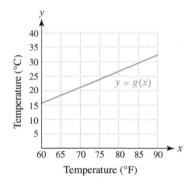

(a) Evaluate $(g \circ f)(2)$.
(b) Interpret $(g \circ f)(x)$.

108. Surface Area of a Balloon The surface area *A* of a balloon with radius *r* is given by $A(r) = 4\pi r^2$. Suppose that the radius of the balloon increases from *r* to $r + h$, where *h* is a small positive number.
(a) Find $A(r + h) - A(r)$. Interpret your answer.

(b) Evaluate your expression in part (a) for $r = 3$ and $h = 0.1$, and then for $r = 6$ and $h = 0.1$.

(c) If the radius of the balloon increases by 0.1, does the surface area always increase by a fixed amount or does the amount depend on the value of *r*?

109. Equilateral Triangle   The area of an equilateral triangle with sides of length s is given by

$$A(s) = \frac{\sqrt{3}}{4}s^2.$$

(a) Find $A(4s)$ and interpret the result.

(b) Find $A(s + 2)$ and interpret the result.

110. Circular Wave   A marble is dropped into a lake, resulting in a circular wave whose radius increases at a rate of 6 inches per second. Write a formula for C that gives the circumference of the circular wave in inches after t seconds.

111. Circular Wave   (Refer to Exercise 110.) Write a function A that gives the area contained inside the circular wave in square inches after t seconds.

112. Geometry   The surface area of a cone (excluding the bottom) is given by $S = \pi r \sqrt{r^2 + h^2}$, where r is its radius and h is its height, as shown in the figure. If the height is twice the radius, write a formula for S in terms of r.

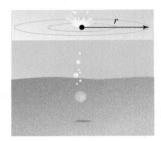

113. Methane Emissions   Methane is a greenhouse gas that lets sunlight into the atmosphere but blocks heat from escaping Earth's atmosphere. In the table, $f(x)$ models the predicted methane emissions in millions of tons produced by *developed* countries. The function $g(x)$ models the same emissions for *developing* countries.

x	1990	2000	2010	2020	2030
$f(x)$	27	28	29	30	31
$g(x)$	5	7.5	10	12.5	15

Source: A. Nilsson, *Greenhouse Earth.*

(a) Make a table for a function h that models the total predicted methane emissions for developed *and* developing countries.

(b) Write an equation that relates $f(x)$, $g(x)$, and $h(x)$.

114. Methane Emissions   (Refer to Exercise 113.) The figure shows graphs of the functions f and g that model methane emissions. Use these graphs to sketch a graph of the function h.

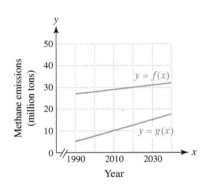

115. Methane Emissions   (Refer to Exercises 113 and 114.) Formulas for f and g are $f(x) = 0.1x - 172$ and $g(x) = 0.25x - 492.5$, where x is the year. Find a symbolic representation for h.

116. Energy of a Falling Object   A ball with mass m is dropped from an initial height of h_0 and lands with a final velocity of v_f. The kinetic energy of the ball is $K(v) = \frac{1}{2}mv^2$, where v is its velocity, and the potential energy of the ball is $P(h) = mgh$, where h is its height and g is a constant.

(a) Show that $P(h_0) = K(v_f)$. (*Hint:* $v_f = \sqrt{2gh_0}$.)

(b) Interpret your result from part (a).

117. Income Differences   From 1990 to 2012, the 50th percentile (median) of U.S. household income in thousands of dollars could be approximated by $M(x) = 0.1x + 48$, where $M(x)$ is in 2012 dollars and x is years after 1990. The 90th percentile could be modeled by $N(x) = -0.15x^2 + 4x + 120$.

(a) Evaluate $M(20)$ and $N(20)$. Interpret the results.

(b) Determine a formula for $D(x) = N(x) - M(x)$. Interpret this formula.

(c) Evaluate $D(20)$. Interpret the results.

118. Sphere   The volume V of a sphere with radius r is given by $V = \frac{4}{3}\pi r^3$, and the surface area S is given by $S = 4\pi r^2$. Show that $V = \frac{4}{3}\pi \left(\frac{S}{4\pi}\right)^{3/2}$.

Applying Concepts

119. Show that the sum of two linear functions is a linear function.

120. Show that if f and g are odd functions, then the composition $g \circ f$ is also an odd function.

121. Let $f(x) = k$ and $g(x) = ax + b$, where k, a, and b are constants.
  (a) Find $(f \circ g)(x)$. What type of function is $f \circ g$?

  (b) Find $(g \circ f)(x)$. What type of function is $g \circ f$?

122. Show that if $f(x) = ax + b$ and $g(x) = cx + d$, then $(g \circ f)(x)$ also represents a linear function. Find the slope of the graph of $(g \circ f)(x)$.

Writing about Mathematics

123. Describe differences between $(fg)(x)$ and $(f \circ g)(x)$. Give examples.

124. Describe differences between $(f \circ g)(x)$ and $(g \circ f)(x)$. Give examples.

5.2 Inverse Functions and Their Representations

- **Calculate inverse operations**
- **Identify one-to-one functions**
- **Find inverse functions symbolically**
- **Use other representations to find inverse functions**

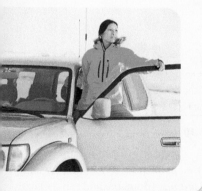

Introduction

Many actions are reversible. A closed door can be opened—an open door can be closed. One hundred dollars can be withdrawn from and deposited into a savings account. These actions undo or cancel each other. But not all actions are reversible. Explosions and weather are two examples. In mathematics the concept of reversing a calculation and arriving at the original value is associated with an *inverse*.

Actions and their inverses occur in everyday life. Suppose a person opens a car door, gets in, and starts the engine. What are the inverse actions? The person turns off the engine, gets out, and closes the car door. Notice that we must reverse the order as well as apply the inverse operation at each step.

Inverse Operations and Inverse Functions

Inverse Operations In mathematics there are basic operations that can be considered inverse operations.

Inverse Operations: Addition and Subtraction

Start with 10. $10 + 5 = 15$ $15 - 5 = 10$ End with 10.

Add 5.   Subtract 5.

Addition and subtraction are inverse operations. The same is true for multiplication and division, as illustrated by the following.

Inverse Operations: Multiplication and Division

Start with 10. $10 \times 2 = 20$ $20 \div 2 = 10$ End with 10.

Multiply by 2.   Divide by 2.

In the next example, we discuss inverse operations further.

EXAMPLE 1 Finding inverse actions and operations

For each of the following, state the inverse actions or operations.
(a) Put on a coat and go outside.
(b) Subtract 5 from x and divide the result by 2.

SOLUTION
(a) To find the inverse actions, reverse the order and apply the inverse action at each step. The inverse actions would be to come inside and take off the coat.
(b) We must reverse the order and apply the inverse operation at each step. The inverse operations would be to multiply x by 2 and add 5. The original operations could be expressed as $\frac{x-5}{2}$, and the inverse operations could be written as $2x + 5$.

> **Now try Exercises 3 and 7**

Inverse Functions   Table 5.7 can be used to convert *gallons* to *pints*. There are 8 pints in a gallon, so $f(x) = 8x$ converts x gallons to an equivalent number of pints. If we want to convert *pints* to *gallons*, we need to divide by 8. This conversion is calculated by $g(x) = \frac{x}{8}$, where x is the number of pints. We say that f and g are *inverse functions* and write this as $g(x) = f^{-1}(x)$. See Table 5.8. We read f^{-1} as "f inverse."

Inverse Functions

Gallons to Pints

x	1	2	3	4
$f(x)$	8	16	24	32

Table 5.7 $\quad$ $f(1) = 8$

Pints to Gallons

x	8	16	24	32
$f^{-1}(x)$	1	2	3	4

Table 5.8 $\quad$ $f^{-1}(8) = 1$

Multiplying by 8 and dividing by 8 are inverse operations. As discussed earlier, adding 5 and subtracting 5 are also inverse operations. If $f(x) = x + 5$, then the *inverse function* of f is given by $f^{-1}(x) = x - 5$. For example, $f(5) = 10$, and $f^{-1}(10) = 5$. If input x produces output y with function f, input y produces output x with function f^{-1}. This can be seen in Tables 5.9 and 5.10.

Inverse Functions

Add 5

x	0	5	10	15
$f(x)$	5	10	15	20

Table 5.9 $\quad$ $f(0) = 5$

Subtract 5

x	5	10	15	20
$f^{-1}(x)$	0	5	10	15

Table 5.10 $\quad$ $f^{-1}(5) = 0$

From Tables 5.9 and 5.10, if $f(a) = b$, then $f^{-1}(b) = a$. That is, if f outputs b with input a, then f^{-1} must output a with input b. *Inputs and outputs* (domains and ranges) *are interchanged for inverse functions.* This statement is illustrated in Figure 5.12.

Inverse Functions

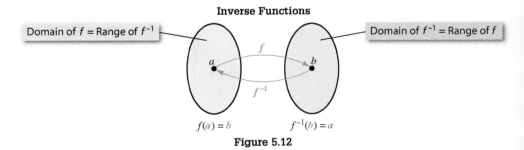

Domain of f = Range of f^{-1} $\qquad$ Domain of f^{-1} = Range of f

$f(a) = b \qquad f^{-1}(b) = a$

Figure 5.12

When $f(x) = x + 5$ and $f^{-1}(x) = x - 5$ are applied in sequence, the output of f is used as input for f^{-1}. This is *composition* of functions.

$$(f^{-1} \circ f)(x) = f^{-1}(f(x)) \qquad \text{Definition of composition}$$
$$= f^{-1}(x + 5) \qquad f(x) = x + 5$$
$$= (x + 5) - 5 \qquad f^{-1} \text{ subtracts 5 from its input.}$$
$$= x \qquad \text{Simplify.}$$

The composition $f^{-1} \circ f$ with input x produces output x. The same action occurs when computing the composition $f \circ f^{-1}$.

$$(f \circ f^{-1})(x) = f(f^{-1}(x)) \qquad \text{Definition of composition}$$
$$= f(x - 5) \qquad f^{-1}(x) = x - 5$$
$$= (x - 5) + 5 \qquad f \text{ adds 5 to its input.}$$
$$= x \qquad \text{Simplify.}$$

Another pair of inverse functions is given by $f(x) = x^3$ and $f^{-1}(x) = \sqrt[3]{x}$. Before a formal definition of inverse functions is given, we must discuss one-to-one functions.

> **MAKING CONNECTIONS**
>
> **The Notation f^{-1} and Negative Exponents** If a represents a real number, then $a^{-1} = \frac{1}{a}$. For example, $4^{-1} = \frac{1}{4}$. On the other hand, if f represents a function, note that $f^{-1}(x) \neq \frac{1}{f(x)}$. Instead, $f^{-1}(x)$ represents the inverse function of f. For instance, if $f(x) = 5x$, then $f^{-1}(x) = \frac{x}{5} \neq \frac{1}{5x}$.

One-to-One Functions

Does every function have an inverse function? The next example answers this question.

EXAMPLE 2   Determining if a function has an inverse function

Table 5.11 represents a function C that computes the percentage of the time that the sky is cloudy in Augusta, Georgia, where x corresponds to the standard numbers for the months. Determine if C has an inverse function.

Cloudy Skies in Augusta

x (month)	1	2	3	4	5	6	7	8	9	10	11	12
$C(x)$(%)	43	40	39	29	28	26	27	25	30	26	31	39

Source: J. Williams, *The Weather Almanac.*
Table 5.11

SOLUTION

For each input (month), C computes exactly one output. For example, $C(3) = 39$ means that during March the sky is cloudy 39% of the time. If C has an inverse function, the inverse must receive 39 as input and produce exactly one output. Both March and December have cloudy skies 39% of the time. Given an input of 39, it is impossible for an inverse *function* to output both 3 and 12. Therefore C does *not* have an inverse function.

Now Try Exercise 19

If *different inputs* of a function f produce the *same output*, then an inverse function of f does *not* exist. However, if different inputs always produce different outputs, f is a *one-to-one function. Every one-to-one function has an inverse function.* For example, $f(x) = x^2$ is *not* one-to-one because

Different Inputs

$f(-2) = 4$ and $f(2) = 4$.   Not one-to-one

Same Output

Therefore $f(x) = x^2$ does not have an inverse function because an inverse *function* cannot receive input 4 and produce both -2 and 2 as outputs. However, $g(x) = 5x$ is one-to-one because different inputs always result in different outputs. Therefore g has an inverse function: $g^{-1}(x) = \frac{x}{5}$.

ONE-TO-ONE FUNCTION

A function f is a **one-to-one function** if, for elements c and d in the domain of f,

$$c \neq d \quad \text{implies} \quad f(c) \neq f(d).$$

That is, different inputs always result in different outputs.

NOTE A function f is one-to-one if equal outputs always have the same input. This statement can be written as $f(c) = f(d)$ implies $c = d$, which is an equivalent definition.

EXAMPLE 3 Determining if a function is one-to-one graphically

Use each graph to determine if f is one-to-one and if f has an inverse function.

(a)

(b)
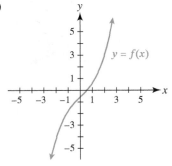

SOLUTION

(a) In Figure 5.13 the horizontal line $y = 2$ intersects the graph of f at $(-1, 2)$, $(1, 2)$, and $(3, 2)$. This means that $f(-1) = f(1) = f(3) = 2$. Three distinct inputs, -1, 1, and 3, produce the same output, 2. Therefore f is *not* one-to-one and does *not* have an inverse function.

(b) See Figure 5.14. Because every horizontal line intersects the graph at most once, different inputs (x-values) always result in different outputs (y-values). Therefore f *is* one-to-one and *has* an inverse function.

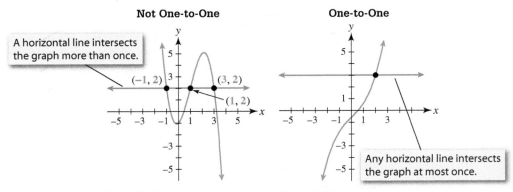

Figure 5.13   **Figure 5.14**

Now Try Exercises 13 and 15

NOTE To show that f is not one-to-one, it is not necessary to find the actual points of intersection—we have to show only that a horizontal line can intersect the graph of f more than once.

The technique of visualizing horizontal lines to determine if a graph represents a one-to-one function is called the *horizontal line test.*

CLASS DISCUSSION

Use the horizontal line test to explain why a nonconstant linear function has an inverse function, whereas a quadratic function does not.

HORIZONTAL LINE TEST

If every horizontal line intersects the graph of a function f at most once, then f is a one-to-one function.

Increasing, Decreasing, and One-to-One Functions If a continuous function f is always increasing on its domain, then every horizontal line will intersect the graph of f at most once. By the horizontal line test, f is a one-to-one function. For example, the function f shown in Example 3(b) is always increasing on its domain and so it is one-to-one. Similarly, if a continuous function g is only decreasing on its domain, then g is a one-to-one function.

Symbolic Representations of Inverse Functions

If a function f is one-to-one, then an inverse function f^{-1} exists. Therefore $f(a) = b$ implies $f^{-1}(b) = a$ for every a in the domain of f. That is,

$$(f^{-1} \circ f)(a) = f^{-1}(f(a)) = f^{-1}(b) = a.$$

Similarly, $f^{-1}(b) = a$ implies $f(a) = b$ for every b in the domain of f^{-1} and so

$$(f \circ f^{-1})(b) = f(f^{-1}(b)) = f(a) = b.$$

These two properties can be used to define an inverse function.

INVERSE FUNCTION

Let f be a one-to-one function. Then f^{-1} is the **inverse function** of f if

$$(f^{-1} \circ f)(x) = f^{-1}(f(x)) = x \quad \text{for every } x \text{ in the domain of } f \text{ and}$$

$$(f \circ f^{-1})(x) = f(f^{-1}(x)) = x \quad \text{for every } x \text{ in the domain of } f^{-1}.$$

In the next two examples, we find an inverse function and verify that it is correct.

EXAMPLE 4   Finding and verifying an inverse function

Let f be the one-to-one function given by $f(x) = x^3 - 2$.
(a) Find a formula for $f^{-1}(x)$.   (b) Identify the domain and range of f^{-1}.
(c) Verify that your result from part (a) is correct.

SOLUTION
(a) Since $f(x) = x^3 - 2$, function f cubes the input x and then subtracts 2. To reverse this calculation, the inverse function must add 2 to the input x and then take the cube root. That is, $f^{-1}(x) = \sqrt[3]{x} + 2$. An important symbolic technique for finding $f^{-1}(x)$ is to solve the equation $y = f(x)$ for x.

$$y = x^3 - 2 \qquad \text{\textit{y = f(x); now solve for x.}}$$

$$y + 2 = x^3 \qquad \text{\textit{Add 2.}}$$

$$\sqrt[3]{y + 2} = x \qquad \text{\textit{Take the cube root.}}$$

Interchange x and y to obtain $y = \sqrt[3]{x} + 2$. This gives us the formula for $f^{-1}(x)$.

(b) Both the domain and the range of the cube root function include all real numbers. The graph of $f^{-1}(x) = \sqrt[3]{x} + 2$ is the graph of the cube root function shifted left 2 units. Therefore the domain and range of f^{-1} also include all real numbers.

(c) To verify that $f^{-1}(x) = \sqrt[3]{x} + 2$ is indeed the inverse of $f(x) = x^3 - 2$, we must show that $f^{-1}(f(x)) = x$ and that $f(f^{-1}(x)) = x$.

$$
\begin{aligned}
f^{-1}(f(x)) &= f^{-1}(x^3 - 2) && f(x) = x^3 - 2 \\
&= \sqrt[3]{(x^3 - 2) + 2} && f^{-1}(x) = \sqrt[3]{x} + 2 \\
&= \sqrt[3]{x^3} && \text{Combine terms.} \\
&= x \checkmark && \text{Simplify.}
\end{aligned}
$$

$$
\begin{aligned}
f(f^{-1}(x)) &= f\left(\sqrt[3]{x} + 2\right) && f^{-1}(x) = \sqrt[3]{x} + 2 \\
&= \left(\sqrt[3]{x} + 2\right)^3 - 2 && f(x) = x^3 - 2 \\
&= (x + 2) - 2 && \text{Cube the expression.} \\
&= x \checkmark && \text{Combine terms.}
\end{aligned}
$$

These calculations verify that our result is correct.

> **Now Try Exercise 73**

The symbolic technique used in Example 4(a) is now summarized.

FINDING A SYMBOLIC REPRESENTATION FOR f^{-1}

To find a formula for f^{-1}, perform the following steps.

STEP 1: Verify that f is a one-to-one function.

STEP 2: Solve the equation $y = f(x)$ for x, obtaining the equation $x = f^{-1}(y)$.

STEP 3: Interchange x and y to obtain $y = f^{-1}(x)$.

To verify $f^{-1}(x)$, show that $(f^{-1} \circ f)(x) = x$ and $(f \circ f^{-1})(x) = x$.

> **NOTE** One reason for interchanging the variables in Step 3 is to make it easier to graph $y = f^{-1}(x)$ in the xy-plane.

EXAMPLE 5 Finding an inverse function

The function $f(x) = \frac{3}{4}x + 39$ gives the percentage of China's population that may live in urban areas x years after 2000, where $0 \leq x \leq 40$.
(a) Explain why f is a one-to-one function.
(b) Find a formula for $f^{-1}(x)$.
(c) Evaluate and interpret the meaning of $f^{-1}(60)$.

SOLUTION
(a) Since f is a linear function, its graph is a line with a nonzero slope of $\frac{3}{4}$. Every horizontal line intersects it at most once. By the horizontal line test, f is one-to-one.
(b) To find $f^{-1}(x)$, solve the equation $y = f(x)$ for x.

$$
\begin{aligned}
y &= \frac{3}{4}x + 39 && y = f(x) \\
y - 39 &= \frac{3}{4}x && \text{Subtract 39.} \\
\frac{4}{3}(y - 39) &= x && \text{Multiply by } \tfrac{4}{3}, \text{ the reciprocal of } \tfrac{3}{4}. \\
\frac{4}{3}y - 52 &= x && \text{Distributive property}
\end{aligned}
$$

Now interchange x and y to obtain $y = \frac{4}{3}x - 52$. The formula for the inverse is, therefore,

$$f^{-1}(x) = \frac{4}{3}x - 52.$$

(c) Substitute 60 for x in $f^{-1}(x) = \frac{4}{3}x - 52$.

$$f^{-1}(60) = \tfrac{4}{3}(60) - 52 = 28$$

The expression $f^{-1}(x)$ predicts the number of years after 2000 when x percent of China's population will live in urban areas. In 2028, it is estimated that 60 percent of China's population will live in urban areas.

> **Now Try Exercise 123**

EXAMPLE 6   Restricting the domain of a function

Let $f(x) = (x - 1)^2$.
(a) Does f have an inverse function? Explain.
(b) Restrict the domain of f so that f^{-1} exists.
(c) Find $f^{-1}(x)$ for the restricted domain.

SOLUTION
(a) The graph of $f(x) = (x - 1)^2$, shown in Figure 5.15, does not pass the horizontal line test. Therefore f is not one-to-one and does not have an inverse function.

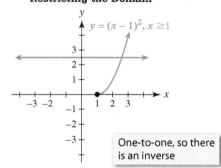

Figure 5.15   Figure 5.16

(b) If we restrict the domain of f to $D = \{x \mid x \geq 1\}$, then f becomes a one-to-one function. To illustrate this, the graph of $y = (x - 1)^2$ for $x \geq 1$ is shown in Figure 5.16. This graph passes the horizontal line test and f^{-1} exists on the restricted domain.
(c) Assume that $x \geq 1$ and solve the equation $y = f(x)$ for x.

$$y = (x - 1)^2 \qquad y = f(x)$$
$$\sqrt{y} = x - 1 \qquad \text{Take the positive square root.}$$
$$\qquad\qquad \text{Note: } x \geq 1 \text{ implies that } x - 1 \geq 0.$$
$$\sqrt{y} + 1 = x \qquad \text{Add 1.}$$
Thus $f^{-1}(x) = \sqrt{x} + 1.$ Write the formula for $f^{-1}(x)$.

> **Now Try Exercise 63**

> **NOTE** In Example 6 we could have restricted the domain to $x \leq 1$, rather than $x \geq 1$. In this case, we would obtain the left half of the parabola, which would also represent a one-to-one function that has an inverse.

College Graduates (%)

x	1940	1970	2010
f(x)	5	11	30

Table 5.12

x	5	11	30
$f^{-1}(x)$	1940	1970	2010

Table 5.13

Other Representations of Inverse Functions

Tables and graphs of a one-to-one function can also be used to find its inverse.

Numerical Representations   In Table 5.12, f has domain $D = \{1940, 1970, 2010\}$ and it computes the percentage of the U.S. population with 4 or more years of college in year x.

Function f is one-to-one because different inputs always produce different outputs. Therefore f^{-1} exists. Since $f(1940) = 5$, it follows that $f^{-1}(5) = 1940$. Similarly, $f^{-1}(11) = 1970$ and $f^{-1}(30) = 2010$. Table 5.13 shows a table for f^{-1}.

The domain of f is $\{1940, 1970, 2010\}$ and the range of f is $\{5, 11, 30\}$. The domain of f^{-1} is $\{5, 11, 30\}$ and the range of f^{-1} is $\{1940, 1970, 2010\}$. The functions f and f^{-1} interchange domains and ranges. Figures 5.17 and 5.18 demonstrate this property.

Interchange Domains and Ranges for f and f^{-1}

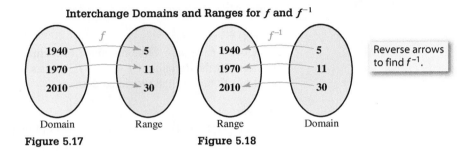

Figure 5.17   **Figure 5.18**

Figure 5.19 shows a function f that is *not* one-to-one. In Figure 5.20 the arrows have been reversed. This relation does *not* represent the inverse *function* because input 4 produces two outputs, 1 and 2.

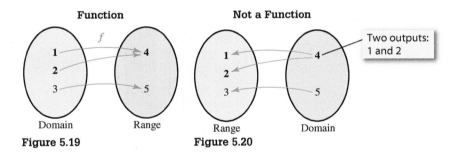

Figure 5.19   **Figure 5.20**

The relationship between domains and ranges is summarized in the following box.

> **DOMAINS AND RANGES OF INVERSE FUNCTIONS**
>
> The domain of f equals the range of f^{-1}.
> The range of f equals the domain of f^{-1}.

Graphical Representations   If the point $(2, 5)$ lies on the graph of f, then $f(2) = 5$ and $f^{-1}(5) = 2$. Therefore the point $(5, 2)$ must lie on the graph of f^{-1}. In general, if the point (a, b) lies on the graph of f, then the point (b, a) lies on the graph of f^{-1}. Refer to Figure 5.21. If a line segment is drawn between the points (a, b) and (b, a), the line $y = x$ is a perpendicular bisector of this line segment. Figure 5.22 shows pairs of points in the form (a, b) and (b, a). Figure 5.23 shows continuous graphs of f and f^{-1} passing through these points. The graph of f^{-1} is a *reflection* of the graph of f across the line $y = x$.

Reflecting to Find f^{-1}

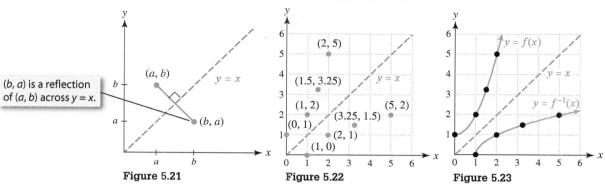

(b, a) is a reflection of (a, b) across y = x.

Figure 5.21

Figure 5.22

Figure 5.23

> **GRAPHS OF FUNCTIONS AND THEIR INVERSES**
>
> The graph of f^{-1} is a reflection of the graph of f across the line $y = x$.

EXAMPLE 7   Representing an inverse function graphically

Let $f(x) = x^3 + 2$. Graph f. Then sketch a graph of f^{-1}.

SOLUTION   Figure 5.24 shows a graph of f. To sketch a graph of f^{-1}, reflect the graph of f across the line $y = x$. The graph of f^{-1} appears as though it were the "reflection" of the graph of f in a mirror located along $y = x$. See Figure 5.25.

Shift $y = x^3$ upward 2 units.

$[-5, 5, 1]$ by $[-5, 5, 1]$

$y = x^3 + 2$

Figure 5.24

f^{-1} is a reflection of f across $y = x$.

Figure 5.25

Calculator Help

To graph an inverse function, see Appendix A (page AP-11).

> **Now Try Exercise 113**

The following See the Concept shows how to represent and find inverse functions.

> **See the Concept: Representing Inverse Functions**

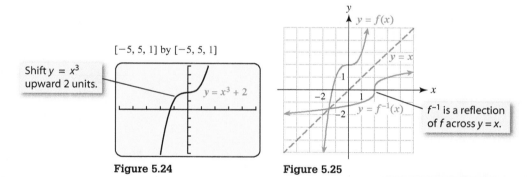

Verbal

f: Multiply x by 2 and add 1.

f^{-1}: Subtract 1 from x and divide by 2.

Use the inverse operations in the reverse order.

Symbolic

$f(x) = 2x + 1$

To find $f^{-1}(x)$:

$y = 2x + 1$

$y - 1 = 2x$

$\dfrac{y - 1}{2} = x$

$f^{-1}(x) = \dfrac{x - 1}{2}$

Solve for x.

Numerical

x	$f(x)$
-2	-3
-1	-1
0	1
1	3
2	5

x	$f^{-1}(x)$
-3	-2
-1	-1
1	0
3	1
5	2

Interchange the x- and y-values.

Graphical

$f(x) = 2x + 1$

$y = x$

$f^{-1}(x) = \dfrac{x - 1}{2}$

Reflect the graph of f across $y = x$.

EXAMPLE 8   Evaluating f and f^{-1} graphically

Use the graph of f in Figure 5.26 to evaluate each expression.
(a) $f(2)$ **(b)** $f^{-1}(3)$ **(c)** $f^{-1}(-3)$

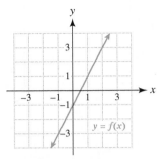

Figure 5.26

SOLUTION

Getting Started   To evaluate $f(a)$ graphically, find a on the x-axis. Move upward or downward to the graph of f and determine the corresponding y-value. To evaluate $f^{-1}(b)$ graphically, find b on the y-axis. Move left or right to the graph of f and determine the corresponding x-value. ▶

(a) To evaluate $f(2)$, find 2 on the x-axis, move upward to the graph of f and then move left to the y-axis to obtain $f(2) = 3$, as shown in Figure 5.27.

$f(2) = 3$

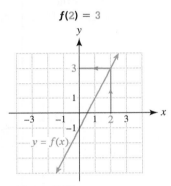

Figure 5.27

(b) Start by finding 3 on the y-axis, move right to the graph of f, and then move downward to the x-axis to obtain $f^{-1}(3) = 2$, as shown in Figure 5.28. Notice that $f(2) = 3$ from part (a) and $f^{-1}(3) = 2$ here.

(c) Find -3 on the y-axis, move left to the graph of f, and then move upward to the x-axis. We can see from Figure 5.29 that $f^{-1}(-3) = -1$.

$f^{-1}(3) = 2$

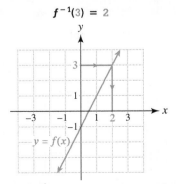

Figure 5.28

$f^{-1}(-3) = -1$

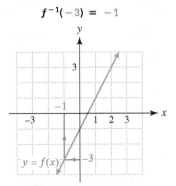

Figure 5.29

CLASS DISCUSSION

Does an inverse function for $f(x) = |2x - 1|$ exist? Explain. What difficulties would you encounter if you tried to evaluate $f^{-1}(3)$ graphically?

Now Try Exercise 101

5.2 Putting It All Together

$\mathbf{T}$he following table summarizes some important concepts about inverse functions.

CONCEPT	COMMENTS	EXAMPLES
One-to-one function	f is one-to-one if different inputs always result in different outputs. That is, $a \neq b$ implies $f(a) \neq f(b)$.	$f(x) = x^2 - 4x$ is not one-to-one because $f(0) = 0$ and $f(4) = 0$. With this function, *different* inputs can result in the *same* output.
Horizontal line test	If every horizontal line intersects the graph of f at most once, then f is one-to-one.	Not one-to-one
Inverse function	If a function f is one-to-one, it has an inverse function f^{-1} that satisfies both $$(f^{-1} \circ f)(x) = f^{-1}(f(x)) = x$$ and $$(f \circ f^{-1})(x) = f(f^{-1}(x)) = x.$$	$f(x) = 3x - 1$ is one-to-one and has inverse function $f^{-1}(x) = \frac{x+1}{3}$. $$f^{-1}(f(x)) = f^{-1}(3x - 1)$$ $$= \frac{(3x - 1) + 1}{3}$$ $$= x$$ Similarly, $$f(f^{-1}(x)) = x.$$
Domains and ranges of inverse functions	The domain of f equals the range of f^{-1}. The range of f equals the domain of f^{-1}.	Let $f(x) = (x + 2)^2$ with restricted domain $x \geq -2$ and range $y \geq 0$. It follows that $f^{-1}(x) = \sqrt{x} - 2$ with domain $x \geq 0$ and range $y \geq -2$.

5.2 Exercises

Inverse Operations

Exercises 1–4: State the inverse action or actions.

1. Opening a window

2. Climbing up a ladder

3. Walking into a classroom, sitting down, and opening a book

4. Opening the door and turning on the lights

Exercises 5–12: Describe verbally the inverse of the statement. Then express both the given statement and its inverse symbolically.

5. Add 2 to x.

6. Multiply x by 5.

7. Subtract 2 from x and multiply the result by 3.

8. Divide x by 20 and then add 10.

9. Take the cube root of x and add 1.

10. Multiply x by -2 and add 3.

11. Take the reciprocal of a nonzero number x.

12. Take the square root of a positive number x.

One-to-One Functions

Exercises 13–18: Use the graph of $y = f(x)$ to determine if f is one-to-one.

13.

14.

15.

16.

17.

18.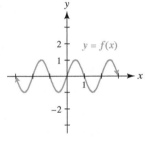

Exercises 19–22: The table is a complete representation of f. Use the table to determine if f is one-to-one and has an inverse.

19.

x	1	2	3	4
$f(x)$	4	3	3	5

20.

x	-2	0	2	4
$f(x)$	4	2	0	-2

21.

x	0	2	4	6	8
$f(x)$	-1	0	4	1	-3

22.

x	-2	-1	0	1	2
$f(x)$	4	1	0	1	4

Exercises 23–36: Determine if f is one-to-one. You may want to graph $y = f(x)$ and apply the horizontal line test.

23. $f(x) = 2x - 7$

24. $f(x) = x^2 - 1$

25. $f(x) = -2x^2 + x$

26. $f(x) = 4 - \frac{3}{4}x$

27. $f(x) = x^4$

28. $f(x) = |2x - 5|$

29. $f(x) = |x - 1|$

30. $f(x) = x^3$

31. $f(x) = \dfrac{1}{1 + x^2}$

32. $f(x) = \dfrac{1}{x}$

33. $f(x) = 3x - x^3$

34. $f(x) = x^{2/3}$

35. $f(x) = x^{1/2}$

36. $f(x) = x^3 - 4x$

Exercises 37–40: **Modeling** *Decide if the situation could be modeled by a one-to-one function.*

37. The distance between the ground and a person who is riding a Ferris wheel after x seconds

38. The cumulative numbers of AIDS cases from 1980 to 2010

39. The population of the United States from 1980 to 2010

40. The height y of a stone thrown upward after x seconds

Symbolic Representations of Inverse Functions

Exercises 41–62: Find a symbolic representation for $f^{-1}(x)$.

41. $f(x) = \sqrt[3]{x}$

42. $f(x) = 2x$

43. $f(x) = -2x + 10$

44. $f(x) = x^3 + 2$

45. $f(x) = 3x - 1$

46. $f(x) = \dfrac{x - 1}{2}$

47. $f(x) = 2x^3 - 5$

48. $f(x) = 1 - \frac{1}{2}x^3$

49. $f(x) = x^2 - 1, x \geq 0$

50. $f(x) = (x + 2)^2, x \leq -2$

51. $f(x) = \dfrac{1}{2x}$

52. $f(x) = \dfrac{2}{\sqrt{x}}$

53. $f(x) = \frac{1}{2}(4 - 5x) + 1$

54. $f(x) = 6 - \frac{3}{4}(2x - 4)$

55. $f(x) = \dfrac{x}{x + 2}$

56. $f(x) = \dfrac{3x}{x - 1}$

57. $f(x) = \dfrac{2x + 1}{x - 1}$

58. $f(x) = \dfrac{1 - x}{3x + 1}$

59. $f(x) = \dfrac{1}{x} - 3$

60. $f(x) = \dfrac{1}{x + 5} + 2$

61. $f(x) = \dfrac{1}{x^3 - 1}$

62. $f(x) = \dfrac{2}{2 - x^3}$

Exercises 63–70: Restrict the domain of f(x) so that f is one-to-one. Then find $f^{-1}(x)$. Answers may vary.

63. $f(x) = 4 - x^2$

64. $f(x) = 2(x + 3)^2$

65. $f(x) = (x - 2)^2 + 4$

66. $f(x) = x^4 - 1$

67. $f(x) = x^{2/3} + 1$

68. $f(x) = 2(x + 3)^{2/3}$

69. $f(x) = \sqrt{9 - 2x^2}$

70. $f(x) = \sqrt{25 - x^2}$

Exercises 71–84: Find a formula for $f^{-1}(x)$. Identify the domain and range of f^{-1}. Verify that f and f^{-1} are inverses.

71. $f(x) = 5x - 15$

72. $f(x) = (x + 3)^2, x \geq -3$

73. $f(x) = \sqrt[3]{x - 5}$

74. $f(x) = 6 - 7x$

75. $f(x) = \dfrac{x - 5}{4}$

76. $f(x) = \dfrac{x + 2}{9}$

77. $f(x) = \sqrt{x - 5}, x \geq 5$

78. $f(x) = \sqrt{5 - 2x}, x \leq \frac{5}{2}$

79. $f(x) = \dfrac{1}{x + 3}$

80. $f(x) = \dfrac{2}{x - 1}$

81. $f(x) = 2x^3$

82. $f(x) = 1 - 4x^3$

83. $f(x) = x^2, x \geq 0$

84. $f(x) = \sqrt[3]{1 - x}$

Numerical Representations of Inverse Functions

Exercises 85–88: Use the table for f(x) to find a table for $f^{-1}(x)$. Identify the domains and ranges of f and f^{-1}.

85.

x	1	2	3
f(x)	5	7	9

86.

x	1	10	100
f(x)	0	1	2

87.

x	0	2	4
f(x)	0	4	16

88.

x	0	1	2
f(x)	1	2	4

Exercises 89 and 90: Use f(x) to complete the table.

89. $f(x) = 4x$

x	0	2	4	6
$f^{-1}(x)$				

90. $f(x) = x^3$

x	-8	-1	8	27
$f^{-1}(x)$				

Exercises 91–98: Use the tables to evaluate the following.

x	0	1	2	3	4
f(x)	1	3	5	4	2

x	-1	1	2	3	4
g(x)	0	2	1	4	5

91. $f^{-1}(3)$

92. $f^{-1}(5)$

93. $g^{-1}(4)$

94. $g^{-1}(0)$

95. $(f \circ g^{-1})(1)$

96. $(g^{-1} \circ g^{-1})(2)$

97. $(g \circ f^{-1})(5)$

98. $(f^{-1} \circ g)(4)$

Graphs and Inverse Functions

99. Interpreting an Inverse The graph of f computes the balance in a savings account after x years. Estimate each expression. Interpret what $f^{-1}(x)$ computes.

(a) $f(1)$ (b) $f^{-1}(110)$ (c) $f^{-1}(160)$

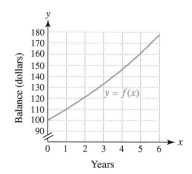

100. Interpreting an Inverse The graph of f computes the Celsius temperature of a pan of water after x minutes. Estimate each expression. Interpret what the expression $f^{-1}(x)$ computes.

(a) $f(4)$ (b) $f^{-1}(90)$ (c) $f^{-1}(80)$

Exercises 101–104: Use the graph to evaluate the expression.

101.

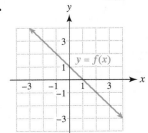

(a) $f(-1)$

(b) $f^{-1}(-2)$

(c) $f^{-1}(0)$

(d) $(f^{-1} \circ f)(3)$

102.

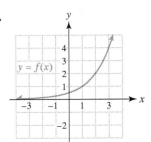

(a) $f(1)$

(b) $f^{-1}(1)$

(c) $f^{-1}(4)$

(d) $(f \circ f^{-1})(2.5)$

103.

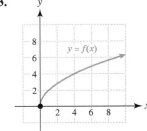

(a) $f(4)$

(b) $f^{-1}(0)$

(c) $f^{-1}(6)$

(d) $(f \circ f^{-1})(4)$

104.

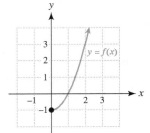

(a) $f(1)$

(b) $f^{-1}(-1)$

(c) $f^{-1}(3)$

(d) $(f \circ f^{-1})(1)$

Exercises 105–110: Use the graph of $y = f(x)$ to sketch a graph of $y = f^{-1}(x)$.

105.

106.

107.

108.

109.

110.

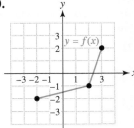

Exercises 111–116: Graph $y = f(x)$ and $y = x$. Then graph $y = f^{-1}(x)$

111. $f(x) = 2x - 1$

112. $f(x) = -\frac{1}{2}x + 1$

113. $f(x) = x^3 - 1$

114. $f(x) = \sqrt[3]{x - 1}$

115. $f(x) = (x + 1)^2, x \geq -1$

116. $f(x) = \sqrt{x + 1}$

Exercises 117–120: Graph $y = f(x)$, $y = f^{-1}(x)$, and $y = x$ in a square viewing rectangle such as $[-4.7, 4.7, 1]$ by $[-3.1, 3.1, 1]$.

117. $f(x) = 3x - 1$

118. $f(x) = \dfrac{3 - x}{2}$

119. $f(x) = \frac{1}{3}x^3 - 1$

120. $f(x) = \sqrt[3]{x - 1}$

Applications

121. Volume The volume V of a sphere with radius r is given by $V = \frac{4}{3}\pi r^3$.

(a) Does V represent a one-to-one function?

(b) What does the inverse of V compute?

(c) Find a formula for the inverse.

(d) Normally we interchange x and y to find the inverse function. Does it make sense to interchange V and r in part (c) of this exercise? Explain.

122. Temperature The formula $F = \frac{9}{5}C + 32$ converts a Celsius temperature to Fahrenheit temperature.

(a) Find a formula for the inverse.

(b) Normally we interchange x and y to find the inverse function. Does it makes sense to interchange F and C in part (a) of this exercise? Explain.

(c) What Celsius temperature is equivalent to 68°F?

123. **Height and Weight** The formula $W = \frac{25}{7}h - \frac{800}{7}$ approximates the recommended minimum weight for a person h inches tall, where $62 \leq h \leq 76$.
    (a) What is the recommended minimum weight for someone 70 inches tall?

    (b) Does W represent a one-to-one function?

    (c) Find a formula for the inverse.

    (d) Evaluate the inverse for 150 pounds and interpret the result.

    (e) What does the inverse compute?

124. **Planetary Orbits** The formula $T(x) = x^{3/2}$ calculates the time in years that it takes a planet to orbit the sun if the planet is x times farther from the sun than Earth is.
    (a) Find the inverse of T.

    (b) What does the inverse of T calculate?

125. **Converting Units** The tables represent a function F that converts yards to feet and a function Y that converts miles to yards. Evaluate each expression and interpret the results.

x (yd)	1760	3520	5280	7040	8800
$F(x)$ (ft)	5280	10,560	15,840	21,120	26,400

x (mi)	1	2	3	4	5
$Y(x)$ (yd)	1760	3520	5280	7040	8800

    (a) $(F \circ Y)(2)$

    (b) $F^{-1}(26,400)$

    (c) $(Y^{-1} \circ F^{-1})(21,120)$

126. **Converting Units** (Refer to Exercise 125.)
    (a) Find formulas for $F(x)$, $Y(x)$, and $(F \circ Y)(x)$.

    (b) Find a formula for $(Y^{-1} \circ F^{-1})(x)$. What does this function compute?

127. **Converting Units** The tables at the top of the next column represent a function C that converts tablespoons to cups and a function Q that converts cups to quarts. Evaluate each expression and interpret the results.

x (tbsp)	32	64	96	128
$C(x)$ (c)	2	4	6	8

x (c)	2	4	6	8
$Q(x)$ (qt)	0.5	1	1.5	2

    (a) $(Q \circ C)(96)$

    (b) $Q^{-1}(2)$

    (c) $(C^{-1} \circ Q^{-1})(1.5)$

128. **Rise in Sea Level** The global sea level could rise due to partial melting of the polar ice caps. The table represents a function R that models this expected rise in sea level in centimeters for the year t. (This model assumes no changes in current trends.)

t (yr)	1990	2000	2030	2070	2100
$R(t)$ (cm)	0	1	18	44	66

Source: A. Nilsson, Greenhouse Earth.

    (a) Is R a one-to-one function? Explain.

    (b) Use $R(t)$ to find a table for $R^{-1}(t)$. Interpret R^{-1}.

Writing about Mathematics

129. Explain how to find verbal, numerical, graphical, and symbolic representations of an inverse function. Give examples.

130. Can a one-to-one function have more than one x-intercept or more than one y-intercept? Explain.

131. If the graphs of $y = f(x)$ and $y = f^{-1}(x)$ intersect at a point (a, b), what can be said about these graphs? Explain.

132. If $f(x) = ax^2 + bx + c$ with $a \neq 0$, does $f^{-1}(x)$ exist? Explain.

Extended and Discovery Exercises

1. **Interpreting an Inverse** Let $f(x)$ compute the height in feet of a rocket after x seconds of upward flight.
    (a) Explain what $f^{-1}(x)$ computes.

    (b) Interpret the solution to the equation $f(x) = 5000$.

    (c) Explain how to solve the equation in part (b) using $f^{-1}(x)$.

2. If the graph of f lies entirely in quadrants I and II, in which quadrant(s) does the graph of f^{-1} lie?

CHECKING BASIC CONCEPTS FOR SECTIONS 5.1 AND 5.2

1. Use the table to evaluate each expression, if possible.

x	-2	-1	0	1	2
$f(x)$	0	1	-2	-1	2
$g(x)$	1	-2	-1	2	0

(a) $(f + g)(1)$
(b) $(f - g)(-1)$
(c) $(fg)(0)$
(d) $(f/g)(2)$
(e) $(f \circ g)(2)$
(f) $(g \circ f)(-2)$

2. Use the graph to evaluate each expression, if possible.

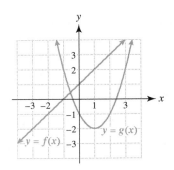

(a) $(f + g)(1)$
(b) $(g - f)(0)$
(c) $(fg)(2)$
(d) $(g/f)(-1)$
(e) $(f \circ g)(2)$
(f) $(g \circ f)(1)$

3. Let $f(x) = x^2 + 3x - 2$ and $g(x) = 3x - 1$. Find each expression.
(a) $(f + g)(x)$
(b) $(f/g)(x)$
(c) $(f \circ g)(x)$

4. If $f(x) = 5 - 2x$, find $f^{-1}(x)$.

5. Use the graph in Exercise 2 to answer the following.
(a) Is f one-to-one? Does f^{-1} exist? If so, find it.

(b) Is g one-to-one? Does g^{-1} exist? If so, find it.

6. Graph $f(x) = \sqrt[3]{x}$ and $y = x$. Then graph $y = f^{-1}(x)$.

7. Use the table in Exercise 1 to evaluate the following. (Assume that f^{-1} exists.)
(a) $f^{-1}(-2)$
(b) $(f^{-1} \circ g)(1)$

8. Use the graph in Exercise 2 to evaluate the following.
(a) $f^{-1}(2)$
(b) $(f^{-1} \circ g)(0)$

5.3 Exponential Functions and Models

- **Distinguish between linear and exponential growth**
- **Recognize exponential growth and decay**
- **Calculate compound interest**
- **Use the natural exponential function in applications**
- **Model data with exponential functions**

Introduction

Suppose that we deposit $500 into a savings account that pays 2% annual interest. If none of the money or interest is withdrawn, then the account increases in value by 2% each year. When an amount A changes by a constant percentage over each fixed time period, such as a year or a month, then the growth (or possibly decay) in A can be described by an exponential model. In this section we use exponential functions to calculate interest and model real data.

Linear and Exponential Functions

A linear function g can be written as $g(x) = mx + b$, where m represents the rate of change. For example, Table 5.14 shows that each time x increases by 1 unit, $g(x)$ increases by 2 units. We can write a formula $g(x) = 2x + 3$ because the rate of change is 2 and $g(0) = 3$.

A Linear Function

x	0	1	2	3	4	5	Each time x increases by 1 unit,
$y = g(x)$	3	5	7	9	11	13	y increases by 2 units.

Table 5.14

An exponential function is different. Rather than *adding* a fixed amount to the previous y-value for each unit increase in x, an exponential function *multiplies* the previous y-value by a fixed amount for each unit increase in x. Table 5.15 shows an exponential function f, where consecutive y-values are found by multiplying the previous y-value by 2. (The y-values increase by 100% for each unit increase in x.)

An Exponential Function

x	0	1	2	3	4	5
$y = f(x)$	3	6	12	24	48	96

Each time x increases by 1 unit, y doubles.

Table 5.15

Compare the following patterns for calculating $g(x)$ and $f(x)$.

Linear Growth

$g(0) = 3$

$g(1) = \underset{g(0)}{\underline{3}} + 2 = 3 + 2 \cdot 1 = 5$ Add 2 each step.

$g(2) = \underset{g(1)}{\underline{3 + 2}} + 2 = 3 + 2 \cdot 2 = 7$

$g(3) = \underset{g(2)}{\underline{3 + 2 + 2}} + 2 = 3 + 2 \cdot 3 = 9$

$g(4) = \underset{g(3)}{\underline{3 + 2 + 2 + 2}} + 2 = 3 + 2 \cdot 4 = 11$

$g(5) = \underset{g(4)}{\underline{3 + 2 + 2 + 2 + 2}} + 2 = 3 + 2 \cdot 5 = 13$

Exponential Growth

$f(0) = 3$

$f(1) = \underset{f(0)}{\underline{3}} \cdot 2 = 3 \cdot 2^1 = 6$ Multiply by 2 each step.

$f(2) = \underset{f(1)}{\underline{3 \cdot 2}} \cdot 2 = 3 \cdot 2^2 = 12$

$f(3) = \underset{f(2)}{\underline{3 \cdot 2 \cdot 2}} \cdot 2 = 3 \cdot 2^3 = 24$

$f(4) = \underset{f(3)}{\underline{3 \cdot 2 \cdot 2 \cdot 2}} \cdot 2 = 3 \cdot 2^4 = 48$

$f(5) = \underset{f(4)}{\underline{3 \cdot 2 \cdot 2 \cdot 2 \cdot 2}} \cdot 2 = 3 \cdot 2^5 = 96$

Notice that if x is a positive integer then

$$g(x) = 3 + \underset{x \text{ terms}}{\underbrace{(2 + 2 + \cdots + 2)}} \quad \text{and} \quad f(x) = 3 \cdot \underset{x \text{ factors}}{\underbrace{(2 \cdot 2 \cdots 2)}}.$$

Using these patterns, we can write formulas for $g(x)$ and $f(x)$ as follows.

$$g(x) = 3 + 2x \quad \text{and} \quad f(x) = 3 \cdot 2^x$$

Linear function   Exponential function

This discussion gives motivation for the following definition.

EXPONENTIAL FUNCTION

A function f represented by

$$f(x) = Ca^x, \quad \text{with} \quad a > 0, \quad a \neq 1, \quad \text{and} \quad C > 0,$$

is an **exponential function with base a and coefficient C.**

Examples of exponential functions include

$$f(x) = 3^x, \qquad g(x) = 5(1.7)^x, \quad \text{and} \quad h(x) = 4\left(\frac{1}{2}\right)^x.$$

$C = 1; a = 3$ $C = 5; a = 1.7$ $C = 4; a = \frac{1}{2}$

NOTE Some definitions for an exponential function require that $C = 1$. In this case, an exponential function is defined as $f(x) = a^x$.

The following Seeing the Concept compares the graph of the exponential function $f(x) = 2^x$ to the graph of the linear function $g(x) = 2x$. See Figures 5.30 and 5.31.

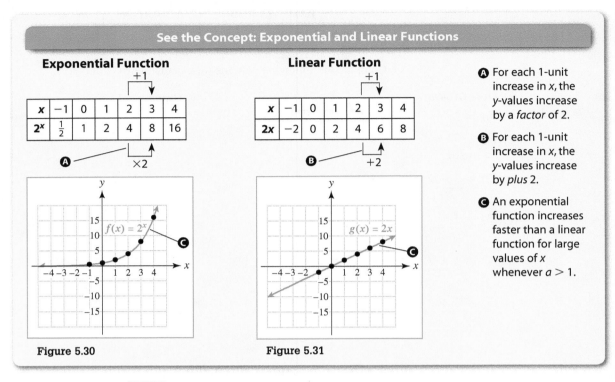

See the Concept: Exponential and Linear Functions

Exponential Function

x	−1	0	1	2	3	4
2^x	$\frac{1}{2}$	1	2	4	8	16

Linear Function

x	−1	0	1	2	3	4
2x	−2	0	2	4	6	8

Ⓐ For each 1-unit increase in x, the y-values increase by a *factor* of 2.

Ⓑ For each 1-unit increase in x, the y-values increase by *plus* 2.

Ⓒ An exponential function increases faster than a linear function for large values of x whenever a > 1.

Figure 5.30

Figure 5.31

NOTE Any *nonzero* number raised to the 0 power equals 1. If $f(x) = Ca^x$, then $f(0) = Ca^0 = C(1) = C$. This means that

- C equals the value of $f(x)$ at $x = 0$,
- C equals the *y*-intercept on the graph of f, and
- C equals the *initial* value of $f(x)$ when x is time.

For example, if $g(x) = 5(1.7)^x$, then $g(0) = 5$, the *y*-intercept is 5, and the *initial* value of $g(x)$ is 5 when x is time.

MAKING CONNECTIONS

Exponential Functions and Polynomial Functions An exponential function has a variable for an exponent, whereas a polynomial function has constants for exponents. For example, $f(x) = 3^x$ represents an exponential function, and $g(x) = x^3$ represents a polynomial function.

EXAMPLE 1 Recognizing linear and exponential data

For each table, find either a linear or an exponential function that models the data.

(a)

x	0	1	2	3
y	−3	−1.5	0	1.5

(b)

x	0	1	2	3	4
y	16	4	1	$\frac{1}{4}$	$\frac{1}{16}$

(c)

x	0	1	2	3
y	3	4.5	6.75	10.125

(d)

x	0	1	2	3	4
y	16	12	8	4	0

SOLUTION

(a) For each unit increase in x, the y-values increase by 1.5, so the data are linear. Because $y = -3$ when $x = 0$, it follows that the data can be modeled by $f(x) = 1.5x - 3$.

(b) For each unit increase in x, the y-values are multiplied by $\frac{1}{4}$. This is an exponential function given by $f(x) = Ca^x$ with $C = f(0) = 16$ and $a = \frac{1}{4}$, so $f(x) = 16\left(\frac{1}{4}\right)^x$.

(c) Since the data do not change by a fixed amount *for each unit increase in x*, the data are not linear. To determine if the data are exponential, calculate ratios of consecutive y-values.

$$\frac{4.5}{3} = 1.5, \quad \frac{6.75}{4.5} = 1.5, \quad \frac{10.125}{6.75} = 1.5$$

For each unit increase in x, the next y-value in the table can be found by multiplying the previous y-value by 1.5, so let $a = 1.5$. Since $y = 3$ when $x = 0$, let $C = 3$. Thus $f(x) = 3(1.5)^x$.

(d) Note that $y = 16$ when $x = 0$. For each unit increase in x, the next y-value is found by adding -4 to the previous y-value, so $f(x) = -4x + 16$.

> **Now Try Exercises 13 and 15**

Determining an Exponential Function   Two points can be used to determine a line. In a similar way, the values of $f(x)$ at two points can be used to determine C and a for an exponential function. This technique is demonstrated in the next example.

EXAMPLE 2   Finding exponential functions

Find values for C and a so that $f(x) = Ca^x$ satisfies the conditions.
(a) $f(0) = 4$ and $f(1) = 8$ **(b)** $f(-1) = 8$ and $f(2) = 1$

SOLUTION
(a) $f(0) = 4$, so $C = 4$. Because $\frac{f(1)}{f(0)} = \frac{8}{4} = 2$, it follows that for each unit increase in x, the output is multiplied by 2. Thus $a = 2$ and $f(x) = 4(2)^x$.

(b) **Getting Started** Because we are not given $f(0)$, we cannot immediately determine C. Instead, first find a by evaluating the following ratios. ▶

$$\frac{f(2)}{f(-1)} = \frac{1}{8} \quad \text{and} \quad \frac{f(2)}{f(-1)} = \frac{Ca^2}{Ca^{-1}} = a^3 \qquad \begin{array}{l} f(x) = Ca^x; \\ \text{subtract exponents.} \end{array}$$

It follows that $a^3 = \frac{1}{8}$, so $a = \frac{1}{2}$. Thus $f(x) = C\left(\frac{1}{2}\right)^x$. Next determine C by using the fact that $f(2) = 1$.

$$f(2) = C\left(\frac{1}{2}\right)^2 = \frac{1}{4}C = 1, \quad \text{or} \quad C = 4$$

Thus $f(x) = 4\left(\frac{1}{2}\right)^x$.

> **Now Try Exercises 29 and 33**

EXAMPLE 3   Finding an exponential model

The number of centenarians (people who are 100 years old or more) in India is projected to increase by a factor of 1.04 each year after 2010 until 2100.
(*Source:* UN Population Prospects, 2010 Revision.)
(a) If there were 50,000 centenarians in India in 2010, write a function f that gives this number x years after 2010.
(b) Estimate the number of centenarians in 2050.

SOLUTION
(a) Because the number of centenarians is expected to increase by a *factor* of 1.04 each year, function f is *exponential* with $a = 1.04$. The variable x represents time and the initial number of centenarians was 50,000, so $C = 50,000$. Thus $f(x) = 50,000(1.04)^x$.
(b) The year 2050 is 40 years after 2010, so let $x = 40$.

$$f(40) = 50,000(1.04)^{40} \approx 240,000$$

This model projects that in 2050 India will have about 240,000 centenarians.

> **Now Try Exercise 85**

Exponential Growth and Decay

Graphs of Exponential Functions If $a > 1$ for the exponential function $f(x) = Ca^x$, then $f(x)$ experiences **exponential growth** with **growth factor** a. If $0 < a < 1$, then $f(x)$ experiences **exponential decay** with **decay factor** a. The following See the Concept illustrates these ideas.

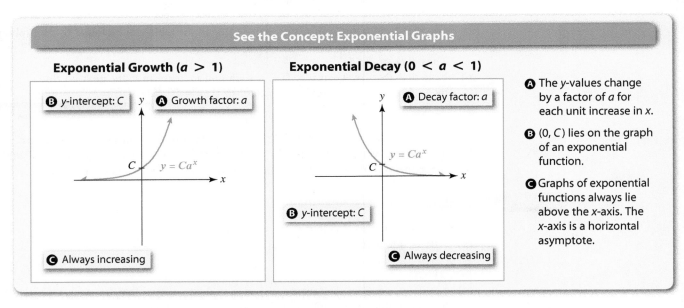

See the Concept: Exponential Graphs

Exponential Growth ($a > 1$)

Ⓑ y-intercept: C ‖ y ‖ Ⓐ Growth factor: a

$y = Ca^x$

Ⓒ Always increasing

Exponential Decay ($0 < a < 1$)

Ⓐ Decay factor: a

$y = Ca^x$

Ⓑ y-intercept: C

Ⓒ Always decreasing

Ⓐ The y-values change by a factor of a for each unit increase in x.

Ⓑ (0, C) lies on the graph of an exponential function.

Ⓒ Graphs of exponential functions always lie above the x-axis. The x-axis is a horizontal asymptote.

Figures 5.32 and 5.33 show graphs having exponential growth or decay. Note that when $a > 1$, the graphs exhibit growth and when $0 < a < 1$, the graphs exhibit decay.

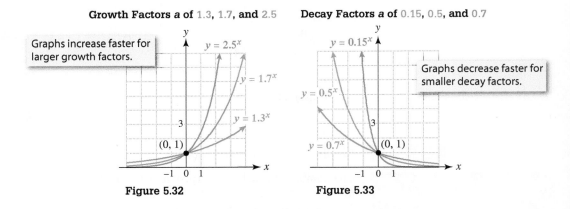

Growth Factors a of 1.3, 1.7, and 2.5   **Decay Factors a of** 0.15, 0.5, and 0.7

Graphs increase faster for larger growth factors.

$y = 2.5^x$

$y = 1.7^x$

$y = 1.3^x$

(0, 1)

Graphs decrease faster for smaller decay factors.

$y = 0.15^x$

$y = 0.5^x$

$y = 0.7^x$

(0, 1)

Figure 5.32   **Figure 5.33**

The following box summarizes some properties of exponential functions and their graphs.

PROPERTIES OF EXPONENTIAL FUNCTIONS

An *exponential function* f, defined by $f(x) = Ca^x$ with $a > 0$, $a \neq 1$, and $C > 0$, has the following properties.

1. The domain of f is $(-\infty, \infty)$ and the range of f is $(0, \infty)$.
2. The graph of f is continuous with no breaks. The x-axis is a horizontal asymptote. There are no x-intercepts and the y-intercept is C.
3. If $a > 1$, f is increasing on its domain; if $0 < a < 1$, f is decreasing on its domain.
4. f is one-to-one and therefore has an inverse. (See Section 5.4.)

Transformations of Exponential Graphs   In Section 3.5 we discussed ways to shift, reflect, stretch, and shrink graphs of functions. These transformations can also be applied to exponential functions as demonstrated in the next example.

EXAMPLE 4   Transformations of exponential graphs

Explain how to obtain the graph of g from the graph of $f(x) = 2^x$. Then graph both f and g in the same xy-plane.

(a) $g(x) = 2^{x-1} - 2$ **(b)** $g(x) = 2^{-x}$

SOLUTION

(a) If we replace x with $x - 1$ and subtract 2 in the formula $f(x) = 2^x$, we obtain $f(x - 1) - 2 = 2^{x-1} - 2$, which is $g(x)$. Thus if we shift the graph of $y = 2^x$ right 1 unit and downward 2 units, we obtain the graph of g. See Figure 5.34.

(b) If we replace x with $-x$ in the formula $f(x) = 2^x$, we obtain $f(-x) = 2^{-x}$, which is $g(x)$. Thus if we reflect the graph of $y = 2^x$ across the y-axis, we obtain the graph of g. See Figure 5.35. Note that by properties of exponents, $2^{-x} = \left(\frac{1}{2}\right)^x$.

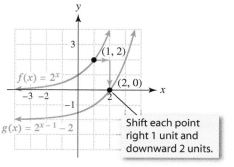

Figure 5.34

Figure 5.35

Now Try Exercises 67 and 69

Compound Interest

We can use exponential functions to calculate interest on money. For example, suppose a **principal** P of $1000 is deposited in an account paying 3% annual interest. At the end of 1 year, the account will contain $1000 plus 3% of $1000, or $30, which totals to $1030. In general, the amount A in an account at the end of 1 year with annual interest rate r (in decimal form) and principal P is

$$A = P + rP \qquad \textit{Amount after 1 year}$$

$$= P(1 + r). \qquad \textit{Factor out P.}$$

That is, the amount A after 1 year equals the principal P times $1 + r$. If no money is withdrawn, the amount in the account after 2 years is found by multiplying P by $1 + r$ a second time.

$$A = P(1 + r)(1 + r) \qquad \textit{Amount after 2 years}$$

$$= P(1 + r)^2 \qquad \textit{Properties of exponents}$$

This pattern continues. After t years, the amount A in the account is found by multiplying the principal P by t factors of $(1 + r)$.

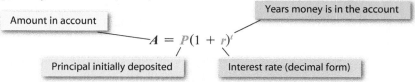

This type of interest is said to be **compounded annually.**

EXAMPLE 5 Calculating an account balance

If the principal is $2000 and the interest rate is 8% compounded annually, calculate the account balance after 4 years.

SOLUTION

The principal is $P = 2000$, the interest rate is $r = 0.08$, and the number of years is $t = 4$.

$$A = P(1 + r)^t = 2000(1 + 0.08)^4 \approx 2720.98$$

After 4 years, the account contains $2720.98.

Now Try Exercise 73

NOTE The value of r can be negative in some applications. For example, if a stock is initially worth $150 and decreases 3% each year for 4 years, then its new value is given by $150(1 - 0.03)^4 \approx \$132.79$.

In most savings accounts, interest is paid more than once a year, where a smaller amount of interest is paid more frequently. For example, if $1000 is deposited at 8% interest *compounded quarterly*, then instead of paying 8% interest once, the account pays $\frac{8\%}{4} = 2\%$ interest four times per year.

$$A = 1000(1 + 0.02)^1 = \$1020.00 \qquad \text{Amount after 3 months}$$
$$A = 1000(1 + 0.02)^2 = \$1040.40 \qquad \text{Amount after 6 months}$$
$$A = 1000(1 + 0.02)^3 \approx \$1061.21 \qquad \text{Amount after 9 months}$$
$$A = 1000(1 + 0.02)^4 \approx \$1082.43 \qquad \text{Amount after 1 year}$$

Paying 8% interest once would give $1000(1 + 0.08)^1 = \$1080$. The extra $2.43 results from compounding quarterly rather than annually.

COMPOUND INTEREST

If a principal of P dollars is deposited in an account paying an annual rate of interest r (expressed in decimal form) compounded (paid) n times per year, then after t years the account will contain A dollars, where

$$A = P\left(1 + \frac{r}{n}\right)^{nt}.$$

EXAMPLE 6 Comparing compound interest

Suppose $1000 is deposited by a 20-year-old worker in an Individual Retirement Account (IRA) that pays an annual interest rate of 12%. Describe the effect on the balance after 45 years at age 65 if interest were compounded quarterly rather than annually.

SOLUTION

Compounded Annually Let $P = 1000$, $r = 0.12$, $n = 1$, and $t = 65 - 20 = 45$.

$$A = P\left(1 + \frac{r}{n}\right)^{nt} = 1000(1 + 0.12)^{45} \approx \$163{,}987.60$$

CLASS DISCUSSION

Make a conjecture about the effect on the IRA balance after 45 years if the interest rate in Example 6 were 6% instead of 12%. Test your conjecture.

Compounded Quarterly Let $P = 1000$, $r = 0.12$, $n = 4$, and $t = 45$.

$$A = 1000\left(1 + \frac{0.12}{4}\right)^{4(45)} = 1000(1 + 0.03)^{180} \approx \$204{,}503.36$$

Because of the very high interest rate and long time period, quarterly compounding results in an increase of $40,515.76!

Now Try Exercise 75

The Natural Exponential Function

In Example 6, compounding interest quarterly rather than annually made a significant difference in the balance. What would happen if interest were compounded daily or even hourly? Would there be a limit to the amount of interest that could be earned? To answer these questions, suppose $1 was deposited in an account at the very high interest rate of 100%. Table 5.16 shows that there *is a limit*. In this example, the interest formula $A = P\left(1 + \frac{r}{n}\right)^{nt}$ simplifies to $A = \left(1 + \frac{1}{n}\right)^n$, because $P = t = r = 1$. The graph of $y = \left(1 + \frac{1}{x}\right)^x$ is shown in Figure 5.36. The graph approaches the horizontal asymptote $y \approx 2.7183$. This means that the y-values never exceed about 2.7183.

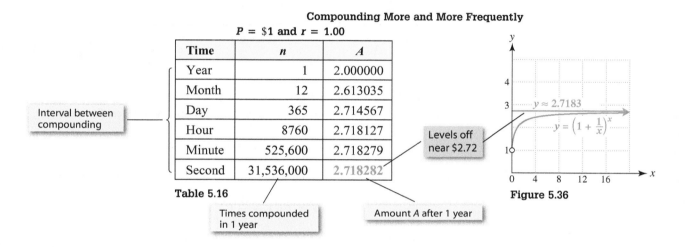

Compounding More and More Frequently

$P = \$1$ and $r = 1.00$

Interval between compounding

Time	n	A
Year	1	2.000000
Month	12	2.613035
Day	365	2.714567
Hour	8760	2.718127
Minute	525,600	2.718279
Second	31,536,000	2.718282

Table 5.16

Times compounded in 1 year

Amount A after 1 year

Levels off near $2.72

$y \approx 2.7183$

$y = \left(1 + \frac{1}{x}\right)^x$

Figure 5.36

Compounding that is done more frequently, by letting n become large without bound, is called **continuous compounding**. The exponential expression $\left(1 + \frac{1}{n}\right)^n$ reaches a limit of approximately 2.718281828 as $n \to \infty$. This value is so important in mathematics that it has been given its own symbol, e, sometimes called **Euler's number**.

As x becomes very large this expression approaches e.

$$\left(1 + \frac{1}{x}\right)^x \to e \quad \text{as} \quad x \to \infty.$$

The number e has many of the same characteristics as π. Its decimal expansion never terminates or repeats in a pattern. It is an irrational number.

CLASS DISCUSSION

Graph $y = 2^x$ and $y = 3^x$ on the same coordinate axes, using the viewing rectangle $[-3, 3, 1]$ by $[0, 4, 1]$. Make a conjecture about how the graph of $y = e^x$ will appear. Test your conjecture.

VALUE OF e

To eleven decimal places, $e \approx 2.71828182846$.

Continuous compounding can be applied to population growth. Compounding annually would mean that all births and deaths occurred on December 31. Similarly, compounding quarterly would mean that births and deaths occurred at the end of March, June, September, and December. In large populations, births and deaths occur *continuously* throughout the year. Compounding continuously is a *natural* way to model large populations.

Calculator Help

When evaluating e^x, be sure to use the built-in key for e^x, rather than using an approximation for e, such as 2.72.

THE NATURAL EXPONENTIAL FUNCTION

The function f, represented by $f(x) = e^x$, is the **natural exponential function**.

EXAMPLE 7 Evaluating the natural exponential function

Approximate to four decimal places $f(x) = e^x$ when $x = 1, 0.5$, and -2.56.

SOLUTION

Figure 5.37 shows that these values are approximated as follows: $f(1) = e^1 \approx 2.7183$, $f(0.5) = e^{0.5} \approx 1.6487$, and $f(-2.56) = e^{-2.56} \approx 0.0773$.

```
e^(1)
          2.718281828
e^(.5)
          1.648721271
e^(-2.56)
           .0773047404
```

Figure 5.37

Now Try Exercise 45

Derivation of Continuous Compounding Formula   To derive the formula for continuous compounding, we begin with the compound interest formula,

$$A = P\left(1 + \frac{r}{n}\right)^{nt}.$$

Let $k = \frac{n}{r}$. Then $n = rk$, and with these substitutions, the formula becomes

$$A = P\left(1 + \frac{1}{k}\right)^{rkt} = P\left[\left(1 + \frac{1}{k}\right)^k\right]^{rt}.$$

If $n \to \infty$, then $k \to \infty$ as well, and the expression $\left(1 + \frac{1}{k}\right)^k \to e$, as discussed earlier. This leads to the formula $A = Pe^{rt}$.

CONTINUOUSLY COMPOUNDED INTEREST

If a principal of P dollars is deposited in an account paying an annual rate of interest r (expressed in decimal form), compounded continuously, then after t years the account will contain A dollars, where

$$A = Pe^{rt}.$$

EXAMPLE 8 Calculating continuously compounded interest

The principal in an IRA is $1000 and the interest rate is 12%, compounded continuously. How much money will there be after 45 years?

SOLUTION

Let $P = 1000, r = 0.12$, and $t = 45$. Then $A = 1000e^{(0.12)45} \approx \$221,406.42$. This is more than the $204,503.36 that resulted from compounding quarterly in Example 6.

Now Try Exercise 77

Natural Exponential Growth and Decay   The natural exponential function is often used to model growth of a quantity. If A_0 is the initial amount of a quantity A at time $t = 0$ and if k is a *positive* constant, then exponential growth of A can be modeled by

$$A(t) = A_0 e^{kt}. \qquad \text{Growth } (k > 0)$$

Figure 5.38 illustrates this type of growth graphically. Similarly,

$$A(t) = A_0 e^{-kt} \qquad \text{Decay } (k > 0)$$

can be used to model exponential decay provided $k > 0$. Figure 5.39 illustrates this type of decay graphically. A larger value of k causes the graph of A to increase or decrease more rapidly. That is, a larger value of k causes the average rate of change in A to be greater in absolute value.

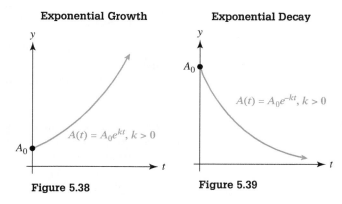

Exponential Growth

$A(t) = A_0 e^{kt},\, k > 0$

A_0

Figure 5.38

Exponential Decay

A_0

$A(t) = A_0 e^{-kt},\, k > 0$

Figure 5.39

> **NOTE** In the compound interest formula $A = Pe^{rt}$, the value of r corresponds to the value of k in the formula $A = A_0 e^{kt}$. If $r > 0$, the principal P grows and if $r < 0$, the principal P decays.

EXAMPLE 9   Modeling the growth of *E. coli* bacteria

E. coli (*Escherichia coli*) is a type of bacteria that inhabits the intestines of animals. These bacteria are capable of rapid growth and can be dangerous to humans—especially children. In one study, *E. coli* bacteria were found to be capable of doubling in number about every 49.5 minutes. Their number N after t minutes could be modeled by $N(t) = N_0 e^{0.014t}$. Suppose that $N_0 = 500{,}000$ is the initial number of bacteria per milliliter. (*Source:* G. S. Stent, *Molecular Biology of Bacterial Viruses.*)

(a) Make a conjecture about the number of bacteria per milliliter after 99 minutes. Verify your conjecture.

(b) Determine graphically the elapsed time when there were 25 million bacteria per milliliter.

SOLUTION

(a) Since the bacteria double every 49.5 minutes, there would be 1,000,000 per milliliter after 49.5 minutes and 2,000,000 after 99 minutes. This is verified by evaluating

$$N(99) = 500{,}000 e^{0.014(99)} \approx 2{,}000{,}000.$$

(b) *Graphical Solution*   Solve $N(t) = 25{,}000{,}000$ by graphing $Y_1 = 500000e^{\wedge}(0.014X)$ and $Y_2 = 25000000$. Their graphs intersect near (279.4, 25000000), as shown in Figure 5.40. Thus in a 1-milliliter sample, half a million *E. coli* bacteria could increase to 25 million in approximately 279 minutes, or 4 hours and 39 minutes.

Now Try Exercise 93

$[0, 400, 100]$ by $[0, 3\times10^7, 1\times10^7]$

y_2

y_1

Intersection
X=279.43021 Y=25000000

Figure 5.40

> **NOTE** You will learn how to solve the equation in Example 9(b) symbolically. See Exercise 88 in Section 5.6.

Exponential Models

The next example analyzes the increase in atmospheric carbon dioxide (CO_2).

EXAMPLE 10   Modeling atmospheric CO_2 concentrations

Predicted concentrations of atmospheric carbon dioxide (CO_2) in parts per million (ppm) are shown in Table 5.17 on the next page. (These concentrations assume that current trends continue.)

Concentrations of Atmospheric CO_2

Year	2000	2050	2100	2150	2200
CO_2 (ppm)	364	467	600	769	987

Source: R. Turner, *Environmental Economics.*

Table 5.17

(a) Let x represent years after 2000. Find values for C and a so that $f(x) = Ca^x$ models these data.

(b) Predict CO_2 concentrations for the year 2025.

SOLUTION

(a) **Getting Started** When modeling data by hand with $f(x) = Ca^x$, one strategy is to let C equal $f(0)$. Then substitute a different data point into this formula to find a. ▶

The concentration is 364 when $x = 0$, so $C = 364$. This gives $f(x) = 364a^x$. One possibility for determining a is to use the last data point and require that the graph of f pass through the point $(200, 987)$. It then follows that $f(200) = 987$.

$$364a^{200} = 987 \qquad \text{\textcolor{gray}{$f(200) = 987$}}$$

$$a^{200} = \frac{987}{364} \qquad \text{\textcolor{gray}{Divide by 364.}}$$

$$\left(a^{200}\right)^{1/200} = \left(\frac{987}{364}\right)^{1/200} \qquad \text{\textcolor{gray}{Take the $\frac{1}{200}$th power.}}$$

$$a = \left(\frac{987}{364}\right)^{1/200} \qquad \text{\textcolor{gray}{Properties of exponents}}$$

$$a \approx 1.005 \qquad \text{\textcolor{gray}{Approximate.}}$$

Thus $f(x) = 364(1.005)^x$. Answers for $f(x)$ may vary slightly.

(b) Since 2025 corresponds to $x = 25$, evaluate $f(25)$.

$$f(25) = 364(1.005)^{25} \approx 412$$

Concentration of CO_2 could reach 412 ppm by 2025.

Now Try Exercise 91

EXAMPLE 11 **Modeling traffic flow**

Cars arrive randomly at an intersection with an average rate of 30 cars per hour. Highway engineers estimate the likelihood, or probability, that at least one car will enter the intersection within a period of x minutes with $f(x) = 1 - e^{-0.5x}$. (*Source:* F. Mannering and W. Kilareski, *Principles of Highway Engineering and Traffic Analysis.*)

(a) Evaluate $f(2)$ and interpret the answer.

(b) Graph f for $0 \le x \le 60$. What is the likelihood that at least one car will enter the intersection during a 60-minute period?

SOLUTION

(a) $f(2) = 1 - e^{-0.5(2)} = 1 - e^{-1} \approx 0.63$. There is a 63% chance that at least one car will enter the intersection during a 2-minute period.

(b) Graph $Y_1 = 1 - e^{\wedge}(-0.5X)$, as shown in Figure 5.41. As time progresses, the probability increases and begins to approach 1. That is, it is almost certain that at least one car will enter the intersection during a 60-minute period. (Note that a horizontal asymptote is $y = 1$.)

Now Try Exercise 95

[0, 60, 10] by [0, 1.2, 0.2]

$y = 1 - e^{-0.5x}$

Graph levels off near $y = 1$.

Figure 5.41

Modeling Half-Life Links on Facebook typically experience half of their engagements ("hits") during the first 3 hours. This pattern can continue over time and is sometimes referred to as a **half-life** of a link on Facebook. Because the number of engagements with a link is decreasing by a factor of $\frac{1}{2}$ over each 3-hour period, we can use an exponential function to model this situation.

EXAMPLE 12 Modeling the half-life of a Facebook link

Initially a link on Facebook has had no hits, so 100% of its hits are yet to occur. Write an exponential function F that gives the percentage of engagements yet to occur on a typical Facebook link if its half-life is 3 hours. Estimate this percentage after 4 hours.

SOLUTION

Let $F(t) = Ca^t$, where t is time in hours. Initially $F(0) = 100$, so $C = 100$ and $F(t) = 100a^t$. Next we must find the value of a. Because the half-life is 3 hours, 50% of the hits remain to occur after 3 hours, so $F(3) = 50$.

$$100a^3 = 50 \qquad \text{F(3) = 50}$$
$$a^3 = \tfrac{1}{2} \qquad \text{Divide each side by 100.}$$
$$(a^3)^{1/3} = \left(\tfrac{1}{2}\right)^{1/3} \qquad \text{Take the cube root of each side.}$$
$$a = \left(\tfrac{1}{2}\right)^{1/3} \qquad \text{Simplify.}$$

Thus we can write $F(t)$ as

$$F(t) = 100\left(\left(\tfrac{1}{2}\right)^{1/3}\right)^t = 100\left(\tfrac{1}{2}\right)^{t/3}.$$

After 4 hours,

$$F(4) = 100\left(\tfrac{1}{2}\right)^{4/3} \approx 40\%.$$

The link has about 40% of its total hits remaining while 60% have already occurred. Note that 4 hours is more than the half-life of 3 hours, so $F(4)$ is less than 50%.

> **Now Try Exercise 97**

These half-life results can be generalized by the following.

> **MODELING HALF-LIFE**
>
> If a quantity initially equals C and has a half-life of k, then the amount A remaining after time t is given by
> $$A(t) = C\left(\tfrac{1}{2}\right)^{t/k}.$$

Radioactive Decay Radioactivity is an application of half-life. For example, the half-life of radium-226 is about 1600 years. After 9600 years, a 2-gram sample decays to

$$A(9600) = 2\left(\tfrac{1}{2}\right)^{9600/1600} = 0.03125 \text{ gram}.$$

EXAMPLE 13 Finding the age of a fossil

Radioactive carbon-14, which is found in all living things, has a half-life of about 5700 years and can be used to date fossils. Suppose a fossil contains 5% of the amount of carbon-14 that the organism contained when it was alive. Graphically estimate its age. The situation is illustrated in Figure 5.42.

SOLUTION

The initial amount of carbon-14 is 100% (or 1), the final amount is 5% (or 0.05), and the half-life is 5700 years, so $A = 0.05$, $C = 1$, and $k = 5700$ in $A(x) = C\left(\tfrac{1}{2}\right)^{x/k}$. To determine the age of the fossil, solve the following equation for x.

Figure 5.42

Figure 5.43

$$0.05 = 1\left(\frac{1}{2}\right)^{x/5700}$$

Graph $Y_1 = 0.05$ and $Y_2 = 0.5^{\wedge}(X/5700)$, as shown in Figure 5.43. Their graphs intersect near (24635, 0.05), so the fossil is about 24,635 years old.

> **Now Try Exercise 101**

5.3 Putting It All Together

The following table summarizes some important concepts about exponential functions and types of growth and decay.

CONCEPT	COMMENTS	EXAMPLES
Exponential function $$f(x) = Ca^x,$$ where $a > 0$, $a \neq 1$, and $C > 0$	Exponential growth occurs when $a > 1$, and exponential decay occurs when $0 < a < 1$. C often represents the initial amount present because $f(0) = C$.	$f(x) = 5(0.8)^x$ Decay $g(x) = 3^x$ Growth Decay: $0 < a < 1$ Growth: $a > 1$
Linear growth $$y = mx + b$$	If data increase by a fixed amount m for each unit increase in x, they can be modeled by a linear function.	The following data can be modeled by $f(x) = 3x + 2$ because the data increase 3 units for each unit increase in x and because $y = 2$ when $x = 0$. { | x | 0 | 1 | 2 | 3 | / | y | 2 | 5 | 8 | 11 | } +3 +3 +3
Exponential growth $$y = Ca^x$$	If data increase by a constant factor a for each unit increase in x, they can be modeled by an exponential function.	The following data can be modeled by $f(x) = 2(3)^x$ because the data increase by a factor of 3 for each unit increase in x and because $y = 2$ when $x = 0$. { | x | 0 | 1 | 2 | 3 | / | y | 2 | 6 | 18 | 54 | } ×3 ×3 ×3
Interest compounded n times per year $$A = P\left(1 + \frac{r}{n}\right)^{nt}$$	P is the principal, r is the interest rate (expressed in decimal form), n is the number of times interest is paid each year, t is the number of years, and A is the amount after t years.	\$500 at 8%, compounded monthly, for 3 years yields $$500\left(1 + \frac{0.08}{12}\right)^{12(3)} \approx \$635.12.$$
The number e	The number e is an irrational number that is important in mathematics, much like π.	$e \approx 2.718282$

CONCEPT	COMMENTS	EXAMPLES
Natural exponential function	This function is an exponential function with base e and $C = 1$.	$f(x) = e^x$
Interest compounded continuously $$A = Pe^{rt}$$	P is the principal, r is the interest rate (expressed in decimal form), t is the number of years, and A is the amount after t years.	\$500 at 8% compounded continuously for 3 years yields $$500e^{0.08(3)} \approx \$635.62.$$
Modeling half-life	If a quantity initially equals C and has a half-life of k, then the amount A remaining after time t is given by $$A(t) = C\left(\tfrac{1}{2}\right)^{t/k}.$$	A 5-gram sample of radioactive material with a half-life of 300 years is modeled by $$A(t) = 5\left(\frac{1}{2}\right)^{t/300}.$$

5.3 Exercises

Review of Exponents

Exercises 1–12: Simplify the expression without a calculator.

1. 2^{-3}

2. $(-3)^{-2}$

3. $3(4)^{1/2}$

4. $5\left(\tfrac{1}{2}\right)^{-3}$

5. $-2(27)^{2/3}$

6. $-4(8)^{-2/3}$

7. $4^{1/6}4^{1/3}$

8. $\dfrac{9^{5/6}}{9^{1/3}}$

9. 3^0

10. $5\left(\tfrac{3}{4}\right)^0$

11. $(5^{101})^{1/101}$

12. $(8^{27})^{1/27}$

Linear and Exponential Growth

Exercises 13–22: (Refer to Example 1.) Find either a linear or an exponential function that models the data in the table.

13.

x	0	1	2	3	4
y	2	0.8	−0.4	−1.6	−2.8

14.

x	0	1	2	3	4
y	2	8	32	128	512

15.

x	−3	−2	−1	0	1
y	64	32	16	8	4

16.

x	−2	−1	0	1	2
y	3	5.5	8	10.5	13

17.

x	−4	−2	0	2	4
y	0.3125	1.25	5	20	80

18.

x	−15	−5	5	15	25
y	22	24	26	28	30

19.

x	−6	−2	2	6
y	−23	−9	5	19

20.

x	−2	3	5	8
y	$\tfrac{3}{4}$	24	96	768

21.

x	−4	−1	2	5
y	6561	243	9	$\tfrac{1}{3}$

22.

x	−20	−4	16	36
y	246	234	219	204

23. Comparing Growth Which function becomes larger for $0 \le x \le 10$: $f(x) = 2^x$ or $g(x) = x^2$?

24. Comparing Growth Which function becomes larger for $0 \le x \le 10$: $f(x) = 4 + 3x$ or $g(x) = 4(3)^x$?

25. Comparing Growth Which function becomes larger for $0 \le x \le 10$: $f(x) = 2x + 1$ or $g(x) = 2^{-x}$?

26. Salaries If you were offered 1¢ for the first week of work, 3¢ for the second week, 5¢ for the third week, 7¢ for the fourth week, and so on for a year, would you accept the offer? Would you accept an offer that pays 1¢ for the first week of work, 2¢ for the second week, 4¢ for the third week, 8¢ for the fourth week, and so on for a year? Explain your answers.

Exponential Functions

Exercises 27–34: Find C and a so that $f(x) = Ca^x$ satisfies the given conditions.

27. $f(0) = 5$ and for each unit increase in x, the output is multiplied by 1.5.

28. $f(1) = 3$ and for each unit increase in x, the output is multiplied by $\frac{3}{4}$.

29. $f(0) = 10$ and $f(1) = 20$

30. $f(0) = 7$ and $f(-1) = 1$

31. $f(1) = 9$ and $f(2) = 27$

32. $f(-1) = \frac{1}{4}$ and $f(1) = 4$

33. $f(-2) = \frac{9}{2}$ and $f(2) = \frac{1}{18}$

34. $f(-2) = \frac{3}{4}$ and $f(2) = 12$

Exercises 35–38: Find a linear function f and an exponential function g whose graphs pass through the two given points.

35. $(0, 4), (1, 8)$ **36.** $\left(0, \frac{3}{2}\right), (1, 2)$

37. $(-2, 12), (1, 1.5)$ **38.** $(1, 3), (5, 48)$

Exercises 39–42: Find C and a so that $f(x) = Ca^x$ models the situation described. State what the variable x represents in your formula. (Answers may vary.)

39. Bacteria There are initially 5000 bacteria, and this sample doubles in size every hour.

40. Savings Fifteen hundred dollars is deposited in an account that triples in value every decade.

41. Home Value In 2008 a house was worth $200,000, and its value *decreases* by 5% each year thereafter.

42. Population A fish population is initially 6000 and decreases by half each year.

43. Tire Pressure The pressure in a tire with a leak is 30 pounds per square inch initially and can be modeled by $f(x) = 30(0.9)^x$ after x minutes. What is the tire's pressure after 9.5 minutes?

44. Population The population of California was about 37 million in 2010 and increasing by 1.0% each year. Estimate the population of California in 2015.

Exercises 45–48: Approximate $f(x)$ to four decimal places.

45. $f(x) = 4e^{-1.2x}$, $x = -2.4$

46. $f(x) = -2.1e^{-0.71x}$, $x = 1.9$

47. $f(x) = \frac{1}{2}(e^x - e^{-x})$, $x = -0.7$

48. $f(x) = 4(e^{-0.3x} - e^{-0.6x})$, $x = 1.6$

Graphs of Exponential Functions

Exercises 49–56: Sketch a graph of $y = f(x)$.

49. $f(x) = 2^x$ **50.** $f(x) = 4^x$

51. $f(x) = 3^{-x}$ **52.** $f(x) = 3(2^{-x})$

53. $f(x) = 2\left(\frac{1}{3}\right)^x$ **54.** $f(x) = 2(3^x)$

55. $f(x) = \left(\frac{1}{2}\right)^x$ **56.** $f(x) = \left(\frac{1}{4}\right)^x$

Exercises 57–60: Use the graph of $y = Ca^x$ to determine values for C and a.

57.

58.

59.

60.

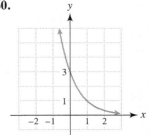

61. Let $f(x) = 7\left(\frac{1}{8}\right)^x$.

  (a) What are the domain and range of f?

  (b) Is f either increasing or decreasing on its domain?

(c) Find any asymptotes on the graph of f.

(d) Find any x- or y-intercepts on the graph of f.

(e) Is f a one-to-one function? Does f have an inverse?

62. Repeat Exercise 61 with $f(x) = e^x$.

63. Match the formula for f with its graph (a–d). Do *not* use a calculator.

(i) $f(x) = e^x$ (ii) $f(x) = 3^{-x}$
(iii) $f(x) = 1.5^x$ (iv) $f(x) = 0.99^x$

a.

b.

c.

d.
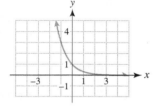

64. Modeling Phenomena   Match the situation with the graph (a–d) that models it best.

(i) Balance in an account after x years earning 10% interest compounded continuously

(ii) Balance in an account after x years earning 5% interest compounded annually

(iii) Air pressure in a car tire with a large hole in it after x minutes

(iv) Air pressure in a car tire with a pinhole in it after x minutes

Transformations of Graphs

Exercises 65 and 66: The graph of $y = f(x)$ is shown in the figure. Sketch a graph of each equation using translations of graphs and reflections. Do not use a graphing calculator

65. $f(x) = 2^x$

(a) $y = 2^x - 2$

(b) $y = 2^{x-1}$

(c) $y = 2^{-x}$

(d) $y = -2^x$

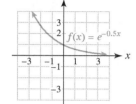

66. $f(x) = e^{-0.5x}$

(a) $y = -e^{-0.5x}$

(b) $y = e^{-0.5x} - 3$

(c) $y = e^{-0.5(x-2)}$

(d) $y = e^{0.5x}$

Exercises 67–72: Graph $y = f(x)$. Then use transformations to graph $y = g(x)$ on the same xy-plane.

67. $f(x) = 2^x, g(x) = 2^{x-1} - 2$

68. $f(x) = 2^x, g(x) = 2^{x+2} + 1$

69. $f(x) = 3^x, g(x) = 3^{-x}$

70. $f(x) = 3^x, g(x) = -3^x$

71. $f(x) = \left(\frac{1}{2}\right)^x, g(x) = 2\left(\frac{1}{2}\right)^x$

72. $f(x) = \left(\frac{1}{2}\right)^x, g(x) = \left(\frac{1}{2}\right)^{x-2} - 1$

Compound Interest

Exercises 73–80: Use the compound interest formula to approximate the final value of each amount.

73. $600 at 7% compounded annually for 5 years

74. $2300 at 2% compounded semiannually for 10 years

75. $950 at 3% compounded daily for 20 years

76. $3300 at 3% compounded quarterly for 2 years

77. $2000 at 10% compounded continuously for 8 years

78. $100 at 1.5% compounded continuously for 50 years

79. $1600 at 1.3% compounded monthly for 2.5 years

80. $2000 at 8.7% compounded annually for 5 years

81. College Tuition   If college tuition is currently $8000 per year, inflating at 6% per year, what will be the cost of tuition in 10 years?

82. Doubling Time How long does it take for an investment to double its value if the interest is 12% compounded annually? 6% compounded annually?

83. Investment Choice Determine the best investment: compounding continuously at 6.0% or compounding annually at 6.3%.

84. Investment Choice Determine the best investment: compounding quarterly at 3.1% or compounding daily at 2.9%.

Applications

85. Bacteria Growth A sample of bacteria taken from a river has an initial concentration of 2.5 million bacteria per milliliter and its concentration triples each week.
(a) Find an exponential model that calculates the concentration after x weeks.

(b) Estimate the concentration after 1.5 weeks.

86. Fish Population A fish population in a small lake is estimated to be 6000. Due to a change in water quality, this population is decreasing by half each year.
(a) Find an exponential model that approximates the number of fish in the lake after x years.

(b) Estimate the fish population to the nearest hundred after 3.5 years.

87. Intensity of Sunlight The intensity I of sunlight at the surface of a lake is 300 watts per square meter. For each 1-foot increase in depth of a lake, the intensity of sunlight decreases by a factor of $\frac{9}{10}$.
(a) Estimate the intensity I of sunlight at a depth of 50 feet.

(b) Graph the intensity of sunlight to a depth of 50 feet. Interpret the y-intercept.

88. Pollution A pollutant in a river has an initial concentration of 3 parts per million and degrades at a rate of 1.5% per year. Approximate its concentration after 20 years.

89. Population Growth The population of Arizona was 6.6 million in 2010 and growing continuously at a 1.44% rate. Assuming this trend continues, estimate the population of Arizona in 2016.

90. Saving for Retirement Suppose $1500 is deposited into an IRA with an interest rate of 6%, compounded continuously. How much money will there be after 30 years?

91. Greenhouse Gases (Refer to Example 10.) Chlorofluorocarbons (CFCs) are gases that might increase the greenhouse effect. The following table lists future concentrations of CFC-12 in parts per billion (ppb) if current trends continue.

Year	2000	2005	2010	2015	2020
CFC-12 (ppb)	0.72	0.88	1.07	1.31	1.60

Source: R. Turner, *Environmental Economics.*

(a) Find values for C and a so that $f(x) = Ca^x$ models these data, where x is years after 2000.

(b) Estimate the CFC-12 concentration in 2013.

92. Bacteria Growth The table lists the concentration of a sample of *E. coli* bacteria B (in billions per liter) after x hours.

x	0	3	5	8
B	0.5	6.2	33.3	414

Source: G. S. Stent, *Molecular Biology of Bacterial Viruses.*

(a) Find values for C and a so that $f(x) = Ca^x$ models these data.

(b) Estimate the bacteria concentration after 6.2 hours.

93. E. Coli Growth (Refer to Example 9.)
(a) Approximate the number of *E. coli* after 3 hours.

(b) Estimate graphically the elapsed time when there are 10 million bacteria per milliliter.

94. Drug Concentrations Sometimes after a patient takes a drug, the amount of medication A in the bloodstream can be modeled by $A = A_0 e^{-rt}$, where A_0 is the initial concentration in milligrams per liter, r is the hourly percentage decrease (in decimal form) of the drug in the bloodstream, and t is the elapsed time in hours. Suppose that a drug's concentration is initially 2 milligrams per liter and that $r = 0.2$.
(a) Find the drug concentration after 3.5 hours.

(b) When did the drug concentration reach 1.5 milligrams per liter?

95. Modeling Traffic Flow Cars arrive randomly at an intersection with an average rate of 50 cars per hour. The likelihood, or probability, that at least one car will enter the intersection within a period of x minutes can be estimated by $P(x) = 1 - e^{-5x/6}$.
(a) Find the likelihood that at least one car enters the intersection during a 3-minute period.

(b) Graphically determine the value of x that gives a 50–50 chance of at least one car entering the intersection during an interval of x minutes.

96. Tree Density Ecologists studied the spacing between individual trees in a forest in British Columbia. The probability, or likelihood, that there is at least one tree located in a circle with a radius of x feet can be estimated by $P(x) = 1 - e^{-0.1144x}$. For example, $P(7) \approx 0.55$ means that if a person picks a point at random in the forest, there is a 55% chance that at least one tree will be located within 7 feet. See the figure. (*Source:* E. Pielou, *Populations and Community Ecology.*)

(a) Evaluate $P(2)$ and $P(20)$, and interpret the results.

(b) Graph P. Explain verbally why it is logical for P to be an increasing function. Does the graph have a horizontal asymptote?

(c) Solve $P(x) = 0.5$ and interpret the result.

97. Half-Life for Twitter (Refer to Example 12.) The half-life for a link on Twitter is 2.8 hours. Write an exponential function T that gives the percentage of engagements remaining on a typical Twitter link after t hours. Estimate this percentage after 5.5 hours.

98. Half-Life for StumbleUpon (Refer to Example 12.) The half-life for a link on StumbleUpon is 400 hours. Write an exponential function S that gives the percentage of engagements remaining on a typical StumbleUpon link after t hours. Estimate this percentage after 250 hours.

99. Putts and Pros At a distance of 3 feet, professional golfers make about 95% of their putts. For each additional foot of distance, this percentage decreases by a factor of 0.9.
(a) Write an exponential function P that gives the percentage of putts pros make at a distance of x feet beyond a 3-foot distance.

(b) Estimate this percentage for 23 feet ($x = 20$).

(c) What additional distance decreases this percentage by half?

100. Filters Impurities in water are frequently removed using filters. Suppose that a 1-inch filter allows 10% of the impurities to pass through it. The other 90% is trapped in the filter.
(a) Find a formula in the form $f(x) = 100a^x$ that calculates the percentage of impurities passing through x inches of this type of filter.

(b) Use $f(x)$ to estimate the percentage of impurities passing through 2.3 inches of the filter.

101. Radioactive Carbon-14 (Refer to Example 13.) A fossil contains 10% of the carbon-14 that the organism contained when it was alive. Graphically estimate its age.

102. Radioactive Carbon-14 A fossil contains 20% of the carbon-14 that the organism contained when it was alive. Estimate its age.

103. Radioactive Radium-226 The half-life of radium-226 is about 1600 years. After 3000 years, what percentage P of a sample of radium remains?

104. Radioactive Strontium-90 Radioactive strontium-90 has a half-life of about 28 years and sometimes contaminates the soil. After 50 years, what percentage of a sample of radioactive strontium would remain?

105. Swimming Pool Maintenance Chlorine is frequently used to disinfect swimming pools. The chlorine concentration should remain between 1.5 and 2.5 parts per million. On warm sunny days with many swimmers agitating the water, 30% of the chlorine can dissipate into the air or combine with other chemicals. (*Source:* D. Thomas, *Swimming Pool Operators Handbook.*)
(a) Find C and a so that $f(x) = Ca^x$ models the amount of chlorine in the pool after x days. Assume that the initial amount is 2.5 parts per million.

(b) What is the chlorine concentration after 2 days if no chlorine is added?

106. Thickness of Runways Heavier aircraft require runways with thicker pavement for landings and takeoffs. A pavement 6 inches thick can accommodate an aircraft weighing 80,000 pounds, whereas a 12-inch-thick pavement is necessary for a 350,000-pound plane. The relation between pavement thickness t in inches and gross weight W in thousands of pounds can be modeled by $W = Ca^t$. (*Source:* FAA.)
(a) Find values for C and a.

(b) What is the weight of the heaviest airplane a 9-inch-thick runway can accommodate?

(c) What is the minimum thickness for a 242,000-pound plane?

107. Trains The faster a locomotive travels, the more horsepower is needed. The formula

$$H(x) = 0.157(1.033)^x$$

calculates this horsepower for a level track. The input x is in miles per hour and the output $H(x)$ is the horsepower required per ton of cargo. (*Source:* L. Haefner, *Introduction to Transportation Systems.*)

(a) Evaluate $H(30)$ and interpret the result.

(b) Determine the horsepower needed to move a 5000-ton train 30 miles per hour.

(c) Some types of locomotives are rated for 1350 horsepower. How many locomotives of this type would be needed in part (b)?

108. Survival of Reindeer For all types of animals, the percentage that survive into the next year decreases. In one study, the survival rate of a sample of reindeer was modeled by $S(t) = 100(0.999993)^{t^5}$. The function S outputs the percentage of reindeer that survive t years. (*Source:* D. Brown.)

(a) Evaluate $S(4)$ and $S(15)$. Interpret the results.

(b) Graph S in $[0, 15, 5]$ by $[0, 110, 10]$. Interpret the graph. Does the graph have a horizontal asymptote?

Writing about Mathematics

109. Explain how linear and exponential functions differ. Give examples.

110. Discuss the domain and range of an exponential function f. Is f one-to-one? Explain.

Extended and Discovery Exercises

Exercises 1–4: **Present Value** *In the compound interest formula* $A = P(1 + r/n)^{nt}$, *we can think of P as the present value of an investment and A as the future value of an investment after t years. For example, if you were saving for college and needed a future value of A dollars, then P would represent the amount needed in an account today to reach your goal in t years at an interest rate of r, compounded n times per year. If we solve the equation for P, it results in*

$$P = A(1 + r/n)^{-nt}.$$

1. Verify that the two formulas are equivalent by transforming the first equation into the second.

2. What should the present value of a savings account be to cover $30,000 of college expenses in 12.5 years, if the account pays 7.5% interest compounded quarterly?

3. Suppose you want to have $15,000 to buy a car in 3 years. What should the present value of a savings account be to reach this goal, if the account pays 5% compounded monthly?

4. A parent expects college costs to reach $40,000 in 6 years. To cover the $40,000 in future expenses, how much should the parent deposit in an account that pays 6% interest compounded *continuously*?

Exercises 5–8: **Average Rate of Change of** e^x *Complete the following. Round your answers to two decimal places.*

(a) *Find the average rate of change of* $f(x) = e^x$ *from x to x + 0.001 for the given x.*

(b) *Approximate* $f(x) = e^x$ *for the given x.*

(c) *Compare your answers in parts (a) and (b).*

5. $x = 0$ 6. $x = -2$

7. $x = -0.5$ 8. $x = 1.5$

9. **Average Rate of Change** What is the pattern in the results from Exercises 5–8? You may want to test your conjecture by trying different values of x.

10. **Average Rate of Change** (Refer to Exercises 5–8.) For any real number k, what is a good approximation for the average rate of change of $f(x) = e^x$ on a small interval near $x = k$? Explain how your answer relates to the graph of $f(x) = e^x$.

5.4 Logarithmic Functions and Models

- **Evaluate the common logarithmic function**
- **Evaluate logarithms with other bases**
- **Solve basic exponential and logarithmic equations**
- **Solve general exponential and logarithmic equations**
- **Convert between exponential and logarithmic forms**

Introduction

Bacteria growth is often exponential. For example, Table 5.18 and Figure 5.44 show the concentration B (in thousands per milliliter) in a bacteria sample after x days, where $B(x) = 10^x$. To determine how long it takes for the concentration to reach 500 thousand per milliliter, we can solve the equation $10^x = 500$. The graphical solution in Figure 5.45 is about 2.7, but finding this value symbolically requires *logarithms*.

Growth of Bacteria (1000/mL)

x	0	1	2	3	
$B(x)$	1	10	100	1000	Elapsed days

Table 5.18

Figure 5.44

Figure 5.45

The Common Logarithmic Function

Notice that the graph of $B(x) = 10^x$ in Figure 5.44 is increasing and one-to-one. Its graph passes the horizontal line test. Therefore B has an inverse function. Because $B(1) = 10$, it follows that $B^{-1}(10) = 1$. Similarly, $B(2) = 100$ implies that $B^{-1}(100) = 2$, and in general, $B(k) = 10^k$ implies that $B^{-1}(10^k) = k$. Table 5.19 lists values for $B^{-1}(x)$. Notice that, unlike B, B^{-1} increases *very slowly* for large values of x.

Inverse Function of B

x	1	10	100	1000
$B^{-1}(x)$	0	1	2	3

Table 5.19

The solution to $10^x = 500$ represents the number of days needed for the bacteria concentration to reach 500 thousand per milliliter. To solve this equation, we must find an exponent k such that $10^k = 500$. Because $B^{-1}(10^k) = k$, this is equivalent to evaluating $B^{-1}(500)$, as shown graphically in Figure 5.45. From Table 5.19, k is between 2 and 3 because $100 \leq 500 \leq 1000$.

The inverse of $y = 10^x$ is defined to be the *common (base-10) logarithm,* denoted $\log x$ or $\log_{10} x$. Thus $10^2 = 100$ implies $\log 100 = 2$, $10^3 = 1000$ implies $\log 1000 = 3$, and in general, $10^a = b$ implies $\log b = a$. Thus $B^{-1}(500) = \log 500$ and $B^{-1}(x) = \log x$.

The common exponential function and the common logarithmic function, represented in Tables 5.20 and 5.21, are inverse functions.

Common Exponential Function

x	-4	-3	-2	-1	0	0.5	1	2	π
10^x	10^{-4}	10^{-3}	10^{-2}	10^{-1}	10^0	$10^{0.5}$	10^1	10^2	10^π

Table 5.20

Inverse Functions

Common Logarithmic Function

x	10^{-4}	10^{-3}	10^{-2}	10^{-1}	10^0	$10^{0.5}$	10^1	10^2	10^π
$\log x$	-4	-3	-2	-1	0	0.5	1	2	π

A common logarithm is an exponent of 10.

Table 5.21

The common logarithm of a positive number x is the exponent k, such that $10^k = x$. This concept can be illustrated visually.

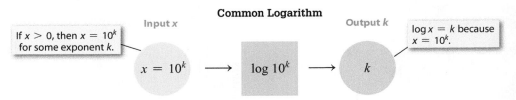

Common Logarithm

Input x

If $x > 0$, then $x = 10^k$ for some exponent k.

Output k

$\log x = k$ because $x = 10^k$.

$$x = 10^k \longrightarrow \log 10^k \longrightarrow k$$

The following See the Concept discusses the graph of $y = \log x$.

See the Concept: The Graph of $y = \log x$

x	y
10^{-1}	-1
10^0	0
$10^{0.5}$	0.5
10^1	1

Range

Vertical asymptote

$y = \log x$

Domain

Domain is $(0, \infty)$.

Range is $(-\infty, \infty)$.

The y-axis is a vertical asymptote.

Graph is continuous and increasing.

Graph passes horizontal line test (one-to-one).

We have shown *verbal*, *numerical*, *graphical*, and *symbolic* descriptions of the common logarithmic function. A formal definition of the common logarithm is now given.

COMMON LOGARITHM

The **common logarithm of a positive number x**, denoted $\log x$, is defined by

$$\log x = k \quad \text{if and only if} \quad x = 10^k,$$

where k is a real number. The function given by

$$f(x) = \log x$$

is called the **common logarithmic function**.

NOTE The common logarithmic function outputs an *exponent k*, which may be positive, negative, or zero. However, a valid input must be positive. Thus its range is $(-\infty, \infty)$ and its domain is $(0, \infty)$.

The equation $\log x = k$ is called **logarithmic form** and the equation $x = 10^k$ is called **exponential form.** These forms are *equivalent*. That is, if one equation is true, the other equation must also be true.

Logarithmic Form	Exponential Form	
$\log 100 = 2$	$10^2 = 100$	Pairs of equivalent equations
$\log 1000 = 3$	$10^3 = 1000$	
$\log \frac{1}{10} = -1$	$10^{-1} = \frac{1}{10}$	
$\log x = k$	$10^k = x$	General forms

MAKING CONNECTIONS

Logarithms and Exponents *A logarithm is an exponent.* For example, to evaluate the logorithm log 1000 ask, "10 to what power equals 1000?" The necessary *exponent* equals log 1000. That is, $\log 1000 = 3$ because $10^3 = 1000$.

EXAMPLE 1 Evaluating common logarithms

Simplify each logarithm by hand.

(a) $\log 100{,}000$ **(b)** $\log 1$ **(c)** $\log \dfrac{1}{1000}$ **(d)** $\log \sqrt{10}$ **(e)** $\log(-2)$

SOLUTION

(a) Ask, "10 to what power equals 100,000?" Because $10^5 = 100{,}000$, it follows that $\log 100{,}000 = 5$. That is,

$$\log 100{,}000 = \log 10^5 = 5.$$

(b) Ask, "10 to what power equals 1?" Because $10^0 = 1$, it follows that $\log 1 = 0$. That is,

$$\log 1 = \log 10^0 = 0.$$

(c) $\log \dfrac{1}{1000} = \log 10^{-3} = -3$

(d) $\log \sqrt{10} = \log(10^{1/2}) = \dfrac{1}{2}$

(e) The domain of $f(x) = \log x$ is $(0, \infty)$, so $\log(-2)$ is undefined because the input is negative.

Now Try Exercise 3

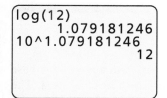

Figure 5.46

Reflection Across $y = x$

Figure 5.47

MAKING CONNECTIONS

Square Roots and Logarithms Much like the square root function, the common logarithmic function does not have an easy-to-evaluate formula. For example, $\sqrt{4} = 2$ and $\sqrt{100} = 10$ can be calculated mentally, but for $\sqrt{2}$ we usually rely on a calculator. Similarly, log 100 = 2 can be found mentally since $100 = 10^2$, whereas log 12 can be approximated using a calculator. See Figure 5.46. To check that $\log 12 \approx 1.079181246$, evaluate $10^{1.079181246} \approx 12$. Another similarity between the square root function and the common logarithmic function is that their domains do not include negative numbers. If outputs are restricted to real numbers, both $\sqrt{-3}$ and $\log(-3)$ are undefined expressions.

Graphs and Inverse Properties Because log x and 10^x are inverses, we can write $f(x) = \log x$ and $f^{-1}(x) = 10^x$. Their graphs are reflections across the line $y = x$, as shown in Figure 5.47. For inverse functions, $f(f^{-1}(x)) = x$ and $f^{-1}(f(x)) = x$, so the following inverse properties hold for all valid inputs x.

> **INVERSE PROPERTIES OF THE COMMON LOGARITHM**
>
> The following inverse properties hold for the common logarithm.
>
> $$\log 10^x = x \quad \text{for any real number } x \text{ and}$$
>
> $$10^{\log x} = x \quad \text{for any positive number } x$$

In Figures 5.48 and 5.49 a graphing calculator has been used to illustrate these properties. (If you have a calculator available, try some other examples.)

```
log(10^5)
              5
log(10^1.6)
            1.6
log(10^(-2.5))
          -2.5
```

Figure 5.48

```
10^log(2)
            2
10^log(3.7)
          3.7
10^log(0.12)
         .12
```

Figure 5.49

An Application Malaria deaths on the continent of Africa have gradually decreased during the past decade largely due to vaccines. These deaths can be modeled by a function that involves the common logarithm. (**Sources:** WHO; Malaria Vaccine Initiative.)

EXAMPLE 2 Modeling malaria deaths in Africa

The number of malaria deaths in millions x years after the year 2000 can be modeled by $D(x) = 0.9 \log \left(10 - \frac{2}{5}x \right)$.
(a) Evaluate $D(0)$ by hand and interpret the result.
(b) Approximate $D(10)$ and interpret the result.

SOLUTION
(a) $D(0) = 0.9 \log \left(10 - \frac{2}{5}(0) \right) = 0.9 \log 10 = 0.9(1) = 0.9$. In 2000 there were about 0.9 million deaths from malaria in Africa.
(b) $D(10) = 0.9 \log \left(10 - \frac{2}{5}(10) \right) = 0.9 \log 6 \approx 0.7$. (Use a calculator.) In 2010 there were about 0.7 million deaths from malaria in Africa.

> **Now Try Exercise 133(a)**

Logarithms with Other Bases

Base-2 Logarithm It is possible to develop base-a logarithms with any positive base $a \neq 1$. For example, in computer science base-2 logarithms are frequently used. The base-2 logarithmic function, denoted $f(x) = \log_2 x$, is shown in Table 5.22. If x can be expressed in the form $x = 2^k$ for some k, then $\log_2 x = k$. Thus $\log_2 x$ is an *exponent*. A graph of $y = \log_2 x$ is shown in Figure 5.50.

Base-2 Logarithm

Figure 5.50

Base-2 Logarithm

x	$2^{-3.1}$	2^{-2}	$2^{-0.5}$	2^0	$2^{0.5}$	2^2	$2^{3.1}$
$\log_2 x$	-3.1	-2	-0.5	0	0.5	2	3.1

Table 5.22

> A logarithm is an exponent.

Natural Logarithm In a similar manner, a table of values for the base-e logarithm is shown in Table 5.23. The base-e logarithm is referred to as the **natural logarithm** and denoted either $\log_e x$ or $\ln x$. Natural logarithms are used in mathematics, science, economics, and technology. A graph of $y = \ln x$ is shown in Figure 5.51.

Natural Logarithm

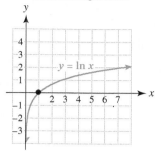

Figure 5.51

Natural Logarithm

x	$e^{-3.1}$	e^{-2}	$e^{-0.5}$	e^0	$e^{0.5}$	e^2	$e^{3.1}$
$\ln x$	-3.1	-2	-0.5	0	0.5	2	3.1

A logarithm is an exponent.

Table 5.23

Base-a Logarithm We can define a logarithm for any positive base a, where $a \neq 1$. As with other logarithms we have discussed, any base-a logarithm has domain $(0, \infty)$ and range $(-\infty, \infty)$.

> **LOGARITHM**
>
> The **logarithm with base a of a positive number x,** denoted by $\log_a x$, is defined by
> $$\log_a x = k \quad \text{if and only if} \quad x = a^k,$$
> where $a > 0$, $a \neq 1$, and k is a real number. The function, given by
> $$f(x) = \log_a x,$$
> is called the **logarithmic function with base a.**

Evaluating Base-a Logarithms *A base-a logarithm is an exponent.* For example, to evaluate $\log_2 16$ ask, "2 to what power equals 16?" The required *exponent* equals $\log_2 16$. That is, $\log_2 16 = 4$ because $2^4 = 16$.

EXAMPLE 3 Evaluating logarithms

Evaluate each logarithm.

(a) $\log_2 8$ **(b)** $\log_5 \frac{1}{25}$ **(c)** $\log_7 49$ **(d)** $\ln e^{-7}$

SOLUTION

(a) Ask, "2 to what power equals 8?" Because $2^3 = 8$, it follows that $\log_2 8 = 3$. That is, $\log_2 8 = \log_2 2^3 = 3$.
(b) Ask, "5 to what power equals $\frac{1}{25}$?" Because $5^{-2} = \frac{1}{25}$, it follows that $\log_5 \frac{1}{25} = -2$. That is, $\log_5 \frac{1}{25} = \log_5 5^{-2} = -2$.
(c) $\log_7 49 = \log_7 7^2 = 2$
(d) $\ln e^{-7} = \log_e e^{-7} = -7$

Now Try Exercises 33, 37, 39, and 49

Although the output from a base-a logarithm can be positive *or* negative, the input for a base-a logarithm must be positive. This fact can be used to determine the domain of logarithmic functions, as demonstrated in the next example.

EXAMPLE 4 Finding the domain of a logarithmic function

State the domain of f.
(a) $f(x) = \log_2(x - 4)$ **(b)** $f(x) = \ln(10^x)$

SOLUTION

(a) *The input for a logarithmic function must be positive.* Any x in the domain of f must satisfy $x - 4 > 0$, or equivalently, $x > 4$. Thus $D = (4, \infty)$.
(b) The expression 10^x is positive for all real numbers x. (See Figure 5.47, where the red graph of $y = 10^x$ is above the x-axis for all values of x.) Thus $D = (-\infty, \infty)$, or all real numbers.

Now Try Exercises 13 and 17

CLASS DISCUSSION

Make a table of values for a base-4 logarithm. Evaluate $\log_4 16$.

Remember that *a logarithm is an exponent.* The expression $\log_a x$ is the exponent k such that $a^k = x$. Logarithms with base a also satisfy inverse properties.

INVERSE PROPERTIES

The following inverse properties hold for logarithms with base a.

$$\log_a a^x = x \quad \text{for any real number } x \text{ and}$$
$$a^{\log_a x} = x \quad \text{for any positive number } x$$

EXAMPLE 5 Applying inverse properties

Use inverse properties to evaluate each expression.
(a) $\log_6 6^{-1.3}$ **(b)** $5^{\log_5 (x+8)}$ **(c)** $\log_{1/2}\left(\frac{1}{2}\right)^{45}$

SOLUTION
(a) $\log_a a^x = x$, so $\log_6 6^{-1.3} = -1.3$.
(b) $a^{\log_a x} = x$, so $5^{\log_5 (x+8)} = x + 8$, provided $x > -8$.
(c) $\log_a a^x = x$, so $\log_{1/2}\left(\frac{1}{2}\right)^{45} = 45$. Note that the base of a logarithmic function can be a positive fraction less than 1.

Now Try Exercises 21, 23, and 25

Graphs and Inverse Functions If $f(x) = a^x$, then its inverse function is given by $f^{-1}(x) = \log_a x$ and their graphs are reflections across the line $y = x$. These and other properties are illustrated for $f(x) = 2^x$ and $g(x) = e^x$ in the following See the Concept.

See the Concept: Inverses and Logarithms

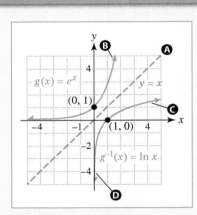

A The graph of the inverse is a reflection across the line $y = x$.

B Rapid exponential growth

C Slow logarithmic growth

D $\log_a x$ is negative (below the x-axis) for x between 0 and 1.

MAKING CONNECTIONS

Exponential and Logarithmic Functions The inverse of an exponential function is a logarithmic function, and the inverse of a logarithmic function is an exponential function. For example,

$$\text{if } f(x) = 10^x \quad \text{then} \quad f^{-1}(x) = \log x,$$
$$\text{if } g(x) = \ln x \quad \text{then} \quad g^{-1}(x) = e^x, \quad \text{and}$$
$$\text{if } h(x) = 2^x \quad \text{then} \quad h^{-1}(x) = \log_2 x.$$

Domains and Ranges of Inverses The domain of $f(x) = \log_a x$ is $(0, \infty)$ and its range is $(-\infty, \infty)$. The domain of its inverse $f^{-1}(x) = a^x$ is $(-\infty, \infty)$ and its range is $(0, \infty)$. Notice how domains and ranges are *interchanged* because they are inverse functions.

Transformations of Logarithmic Graphs

In Section 3.5 we discussed how to shift, reflect, stretch, and shrink graphs of functions. For example, to graph $y = (x - 2)^2$ we can shift the graph of $y = x^2$ right 2 units. In a similar manner, we can graph $y = \log_2(x - 2)$ by shifting the graph of $y = \log_2 x$ right 2 units. The graph of $y = \log_2 x$ has a vertical asymptote at $x = 0$, so the graph of $y = \log_2(x - 2)$ has a vertical asymptote at $x = 2$. See Figure 5.52.

Shifting a Logarithmic Graph

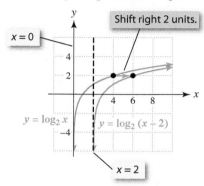

Figure 5.52

EXAMPLE 6   Transformations of a logarithmic graph

Explain how to obtain the graph of $g(x) = \log(-x) + 1$ from the graph of $f(x) = \log x$. Graph both functions in the same xy-plane.

SOLUTION
The graph of $y = \log(-x) + 1$ is similar to the graph of $f(x) = \log x$, except it is reflected about the y-axis and shifted upward 1 unit. Both graphs have a vertical asymptote at $x = 0$. See Figure 5.53.

Transforming $y = \log x$

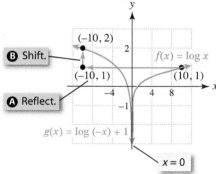

Figure 5.53

Now Try Exercise 113

Basic Equations

Base-10 Exponential Equations   To solve the equation $10 + x = 100$, we **subtract 10 from each side** because addition and subtraction are inverse operations.

$$10 + x - 10 = 100 - 10 \qquad \text{Subtract 10.}$$

$$x = 90$$

To solve the equation $10x = 100$, we **divide each side by 10** because multiplication and division are inverse operations.

$$\frac{10x}{10} = \frac{100}{10} \qquad \textit{Divide by 10.}$$

$$x = 10$$

Now suppose that we want to solve the exponential equation

$$10^x = 100.$$

What is new about this type of equation is that the variable x is an *exponent*. The inverse operation of 10^x is $\log x$. Rather than subtracting 10 from each side or dividing each side by 10, we **take the base-10 logarithm of each side**. Doing so results in

$$\log 10^x = \log 100. \qquad \textit{Take base-10 logarithm.}$$

Because $\log 10^x = x$ for all real numbers x, the equation becomes

$$x = \log 100, \qquad \text{or equivalently,} \qquad x = 2.$$

These concepts are applied in the next example. Note that if $m = n$ (m and n positive), then $\log m = \log n$.

EXAMPLE 7 Solving equations of the form $10^x = k$

Solve each equation, if possible.
(a) $10^x = 0.001$ **(b)** $10^x = 55$ **(c)** $10^x = -1$

SOLUTION
(a) Take the common logarithm of each side of the equation $10^x = 0.001$. Then

$$\log 10^x = \log 0.001, \qquad \text{or} \qquad x = \log 10^{-3} = -3.$$

(b) In a similar manner, $10^x = 55$ is equivalent to $x = \log 55 \approx 1.7404$.
(c) Taking the common logarithm of each side gives

$$\log 10^x = \log(-1).$$

Because $\log(-1)$ is undefined, there are no solutions. Graphical support is given in Figure 5.54, where the graphs of $y_1 = 10^x$ and $y_2 = -1$ do not intersect. The exponential expression 10^x is never negative.

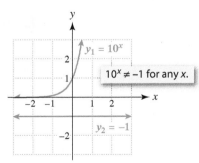

Figure 5.54

Now Try Exercise 57

EXAMPLE 8 Solving a base-10 exponential equation

Solve $4(10^{3x}) = 244$.

SOLUTION Begin by dividing each side by 4.

$$4(10^{3x}) = 244 \qquad \text{Given equation}$$

$$10^{3x} = 61 \qquad \text{Divide by 4.}$$

Changing exponential form to logarithmic form

$$\log 10^{3x} = \log 61 \qquad \text{Take the common logarithm.}$$

$$3x = \log 61 \qquad \text{Inverse property: } \log 10^k = k$$

$$x = \frac{\log 61}{3} \qquad \text{Divide by 3.}$$

$$x \approx 0.595 \qquad \text{Approximate.}$$

Now Try Exercise 69

Converting $10^{3x} = 61$ to $3x = \log 61$ is referred to as changing *exponential form* to *logarithmic form*. We usually include the step of taking the common logarithm of each side to emphasize the fact that *inverse properties* are being used to solve these equations.

Common Logarithmic Equations A **logarithmic equation** contains logarithms. To solve logarithmic equations we *exponentiate* each side of the equation and then apply the inverse property $10^{\log x} = x$. Note that if $m = n$, then $10^m = 10^n$.

Changing logarithmic form to exponential form

$$\log x = 2.5 \qquad \text{Given logarithmic equation}$$

$$10^{\log x} = 10^{2.5} \qquad \text{Exponentiate each side; base 10.}$$

$$x = 10^{2.5} \qquad \text{Inverse property: } 10^{\log k} = k$$

$$x \approx 316.23 \qquad \text{Approximate.}$$

Converting the equation $\log x = 2.5$ to the equivalent equation $x = 10^{2.5}$ is called changing *logarithmic form* to *exponential form*.

EXAMPLE 9 Solving equations of the form **log x = k**

Solve each equation.
(a) $\log x = 3$ **(b)** $\log x = -2$ **(c)** $\log x = 2.7$

SOLUTION

(a)

$$\log x = 3 \qquad \text{Given equation}$$

$$10^{\log x} = 10^3 \qquad \text{Exponentiate each side; base 10.}$$

$$x = 10^3 \qquad \text{Inverse property: } 10^{\log k} = k$$

$$x = 1000 \qquad \text{Simplify.}$$

(b) Similarly, $\log x = -2$ is equivalent to $x = 10^{-2} = 0.01$.
(c) $\log x = 2.7$ is equivalent to $x = 10^{2.7} \approx 501.19$.

Now Try Exercise 81

EXAMPLE 10 Solving a common logarithmic equation

Solve $5 \log 2x = 16$.

SOLUTION Begin by dividing each side by 5.

$$5 \log 2x = 16 \qquad \text{Given equation}$$

$$\log 2x = 3.2 \qquad \text{Divide each side by 5.}$$

Changing logarithmic form to exponential form

$$10^{\log 2x} = 10^{3.2} \qquad \text{Exponentiate each side; base 10.}$$

$$2x = 10^{3.2} \qquad \text{Inverse property: } 10^{\log k} = k$$

$$x = \frac{10^{3.2}}{2} \qquad \text{Divide each side by 2.}$$

$$x \approx 792.45 \qquad \text{Approximate.}$$

Now Try Exercise 91

An Application of Logarithms Some types of data grow slowly and can be modeled by the function given by $f(x) = a + b \log x$. For example, a larger area of land tends to have a wider variety of birds. However, if the land area doubles, the number of species of birds does not double; the land area has to more than double before the number of species doubles.

EXAMPLE 11 Modeling data with logarithms

The number of species of tropical birds on islands of different sizes x near New Guinea can be modeled by $f(x) = 39 + 13 \log x$, where x is in square miles. (***Source:*** B. Freedman, *Environmental Ecology.*)

(a) If the number of square miles x of an island increases tenfold, how many additional species of birds are there?

(b) Determine both symbolically and graphically the size of an island that might have 50 different species of birds.

SOLUTION

(a) Start by evaluating $f(1)$, $f(10)$, and $f(100)$.

$$f(1) = 39 + 13 \log 1 = 39 + 13(0) = 39$$
$$f(10) = 39 + 13 \log 10 = 39 + 13(1) = 52$$
$$f(100) = 39 + 13 \log 100 = 39 + 13(2) = 65$$

x increases tenfold.   Output increases by 13.

Each time x increases tenfold, the number of bird species does not increase by a factor of 10; rather, it only increases by 13 species of birds. This slow growth is an example of *logarithmic growth*.

(b) *Symbolic Solution* We must solve the equation $39 + 13 \log x = 50$.

$39 + 13 \log x = 50$	*Equation to solve*
$13 \log x = 11$	*Subtract 39.*
$\log x = \dfrac{11}{13}$	*Divide by 13.*
$10^{\log x} = 10^{11/13}$	*Exponentiate each side; base 10.*
$x = 10^{11/13}$	*Inverse property:* $10^{\log k} = k$
$x \approx 7$	*Approximate.*

To have 50 species of birds, an island should be about 7 square miles.

Graphical Solution The graphs of $y_1 = 39 + 13 \log x$ and $y_2 = 50$ in Figure 5.55 intersect near the point (7.02, 50). This result agrees with our symbolic solution.

Now Try Exercise 139

[0, 15, 5] by [0, 70, 10]

$y_2 = 50$
$y_1 = 39 + 13 \log x$
Intersection
X=7.0170383_Y=50

Figure 5.55

General Equations

Base-*a* Exponential Equations The exponential function $f(x) = a^x$ is one-to-one and therefore has an inverse function $f^{-1}(x) = \log_a x$. Because $f^{-1}(f(x)) = x$ for all real numbers x, or equivalently $\log_a a^x = x$, it follows that to solve an exponential equation we can take the base-*a* logarithm of each side. Note that if $m = n$ (m and n positive), then $\log_a m = \log_a n$.

EXAMPLE 12 Solving exponential equations

Solve each equation.

(a) $3^x = \dfrac{1}{27}$ (b) $e^x = 5$ (c) $3(2^x) - 7 = 20$

SOLUTION

(a) $\quad \log_3 3^x = \log_3 \frac{1}{27}$ *Take the base-3 logarithm of each side.*

$\qquad\quad \log_3 3^x = \log_3 3^{-3}$ *Properties of exponents*

$\qquad\qquad\quad x = -3$ *Inverse property:* $\log_a a^k = k$

(b) Take the natural logarithm of each side. Then

$$\ln e^x = \ln 5 \quad \text{is equivalent to} \quad x = \ln 5 \approx 1.609.$$

Figure 5.56

Many calculators are able to compute natural logarithms. The evaluation of $\ln 5$ is shown in Figure 5.56. Notice that $e^{1.609437912} \approx 5$.

(c) $\quad 3(2^x) - 7 = 20$ *Given equation*

$\qquad\quad 3(2^x) = 27$ *Add 7 to each side.*

$\qquad\qquad\; 2^x = 9$ *Divide each side by 3.*

Changing exponential form to logarithmic form $\qquad \log_2 2^x = \log_2 9$ *Take the base-2 logarithm of each side.*

$\qquad\qquad\quad x = \log_2 9$ *Inverse property:* $\log_a a^k = k$

> **Now Try Exercises 59 and 71**

Introduction to the Change of Base Formula Figure 5.57 gives a graphical solution of about 3.17 for the equation in Example 12(c). The exact solution of $\log_2 9$ can be approximated as 3.17 by using the following **change of base formula.** (Its derivation is given in Section 5.5.)

[−5, 5, 1] by [−10, 30, 10]

$y_2 = 20$

$y_1 = 3(2^x) - 7$

Intersection
X=3.169925 Y=20

Figure 5.57

$$\log_a x = \frac{\log_b x}{\log_b a} \qquad \text{Change of base formula}$$

Because calculators typically have only $\log x$ and $\ln x$ keys, this formula is often written as

Example of change of base formulas $\qquad \log_a x = \dfrac{\log x}{\log a} \quad \text{or} \quad \log_a x = \dfrac{\ln x}{\ln a}$

For example, $\log_2 9 = \frac{\log 9}{\log 2} \approx 3.17$, which agrees with the graphical solution.

Base-*a* Logarithmic Equations To solve the equation $\log_a x = k$, we exponentiate each side of the equation by using base a. That is, we use the inverse property: $a^{\log_a x} = x$ for all positive x. This is illustrated in the next example. Note that if $m = n$, then $a^m = a^n$.

EXAMPLE 13 Solving logarithmic equations

Solve each equation.
(a) $\log_2 x = 5$ **(b)** $\log_5 x = -2$ **(c)** $\ln x = 4.3$ **(d)** $3\log_2 5x = 9$

SOLUTION

(a) $\qquad \log_2 x = 5$ *Given equation*

$\qquad\quad 2^{\log_2 x} = 2^5$ *Exponentiate each side; base 2.*

$\qquad\qquad\;\; x = 2^5$ *Inverse property:* $a^{\log_a k} = k$

$\qquad\qquad\;\; x = 32$ *Simplify.*

(b) Similarly, $\log_5 x = -2$ is equivalent to $x = 5^{-2} = \frac{1}{25}$.

(c) $\ln x = 4.3$ is equivalent to $x = e^{4.3} \approx 73.7$.

(d) $\qquad 3\log_2 5x = 9$ *Given equation*

Changing logarithmic form to exponential form $\qquad \log_2 5x = 3$ *Divide each side by 3.*

$\qquad\quad 2^{\log_2 5x} = 2^3$ *Exponentiate each side; base 2.*

$\qquad\qquad\;\; 5x = 8$ *Inverse property:* $a^{\log_a k} = k$

$\qquad\qquad\;\;\; x = \dfrac{8}{5}$ *Divide each side by 5.*

> **Now Try Exercises 83 and 87**

5.4 Putting It All Together

The following table summarizes some important concepts about base-a logarithms. Common and natural logarithms satisfy the same properties.

CONCEPT	EXPLANATION	EXAMPLES
Base-a logarithm $a > 0, a \neq 1$	The base-a logarithm of a positive number x is $$\log_a x = k \quad \text{if and only if} \quad x = a^k.$$ That is, a logarithm is an exponent k.	$\log 100 = \log 10^2 = 2$ $\log_2 8 = \log_2 2^3 = 3$ $\log_3 \sqrt[3]{3} = \log_3 3^{1/3} = \frac{1}{3}$ $\ln 5 \approx 1.609$ (using a calculator)
Graph of $y = \log_a x$	The graph of the base-a logarithmic function *always* passes through the point $(1, 0)$ because $\log_a 1 = \log_a a^0 = 0$. The y-axis is a vertical asymptote. The graph passes the horizontal line test, so $f(x) = \log_a x$ is one-to-one and has an inverse given by $f^{-1}(x) = a^x$.	$y = \log_a x, \ a > 1$ $(1, 0)$
Inverse properties	a^x and $\log_a x$ represent inverse operations. That is, $$\log_a a^x = x$$ and $$a^{\log_a x} = x \quad \text{for } x > 0.$$	$\log 10^{-3} = -3$ $\log_4 4^6 = 6$ $10^{\log x} = x, \ x > 0$ $4^{\log_4 2x} = 2x, \ x > 0$ $e^{\ln 5} = 5$
Inverse functions	The inverse function of $f(x) = a^x$ is $$f^{-1}(x) = \log_a x.$$	$f(x) = 10^x \quad \leftrightarrow \quad f^{-1}(x) = \log x$ $g(x) = e^x \quad \leftrightarrow \quad g^{-1}(x) = \ln x$ $h(x) = \log_2 x \quad \leftrightarrow \quad h^{-1}(x) = 2^x$
Exponential and logarithmic forms	$\log_a x = k$ is equivalent to $x = a^k$.	$\log_5 25 = 2$ is equivalent to $25 = 5^2$. $4^3 = 64$ is equivalent to $\log_4 64 = 3$.
Exponential equations	To solve $a^x = k$, take the base-a logarithm of each side.	$10^x = 15$ $\log 10^x = \log 15$ $x = \log 15$ $\bigm\vert$ $e^x = 20$ $\ln e^x = \ln 20$ $x = \ln 20$
Logarithmic equations	To solve $\log_a x = k$, exponentiate each side; use base a.	$\log x = 3$ $10^{\log x} = 10^3$ $x = 1000$ $\bigm\vert$ $\ln x = 5$ $e^{\ln x} = e^5$ $x = e^5$

5.4 Exercises

Common Logarithms

Exercises 1 and 2: Complete the table.

1.

x	10^0	10^4	10^{-8}	$10^{1.26}$
$\log x$		4		

2.

x	10^{-2}	$10^{-\pi}$	10^5	$10^{7.89}$
$\log x$			5	

Exercises 3–8: Evaluate each expression by hand, if possible.

3. (a) $\log(-3)$ (b) $\log \frac{1}{100}$

   (c) $\log \sqrt{0.1}$ (d) $\log 5^0$

4. (a) $\log 10{,}000$ (b) $\log(-\pi)$

   (c) $\log \sqrt{0.001}$ (d) $\log 8^0$

5. (a) $\log 10$ (b) $\log 10,000$

(c) $20 \log 0.1$ (d) $\log 10 + \log 0.001$

6. (a) $\log 100$ (b) $\log 1,000,000$

(c) $5 \log 0.01$ (d) $\log 0.1 - \log 1000$

7. (a) $2 \log 0.1 + 4$ (b) $\log 10^{1/2}$

(c) $3 \log 100 - \log 1000$ (d) $\log (-10)$

8. (a) $\log (-4)$ (b) $\log 1$

(c) $\log 0$ (d) $-6 \log 100$

Exercises 9 and 10: Determine mentally an integer n so that the logarithm is between n and n + 1. Check your result with a calculator.

9. (a) $\log 79$ (b) $\log 500$

(c) $\log 5$ (d) $\log 0.5$

10. (a) $\log 63$ (b) $\log 5000$

(c) $\log 9$ (d) $\log 0.04$

Exercises 11 and 12: Find the exact value of each expression.

11. (a) $\log \sqrt{1000}$ (b) $\log \sqrt[3]{10}$

(c) $\log \sqrt[5]{0.1}$ (d) $\log \sqrt{0.01}$

12. (a) $\log \sqrt{100,000}$ (b) $\log \sqrt[3]{100}$

(c) $2 \log \sqrt{0.1}$ (d) $10 \log \sqrt[3]{10}$

Domains of Logarithmic Functions

Exercises 13–20: Find the domain of f and write it in set-builder or interval notation.

13. $f(x) = \log(x + 3)$ **14.** $f(x) = \ln(2x - 4)$

15. $f(x) = \log_2(x^2 - 1)$ **16.** $f(x) = \log_4(4 - x^2)$

17. $f(x) = \log_3(4^x)$ **18.** $f(x) = \log_5(5^x - 25)$

19. $f(x) = \ln(\sqrt{3 - x} - 1)$ **20.** $f(x) = \log(4 - \sqrt{2 - x})$

General Logarithms

Exercises 21–50: Simplify the expression.

21. $\log_8 8^{-5.7}$ **22.** $\log_4 4^{-1.23}$

23. $7^{\log_7 2x}$ **24.** $6^{\log_6 (x+1)}$

25. $\log_{1/3}\left(\frac{1}{3}\right)^{64}$ **26.** $\log_{0.4}\left(\frac{2}{5}\right)^{-3}$

27. $\ln e^{-4}$ **28.** $2^{\log_2 k}$

29. $\log_5 5^{\pi}$ **30.** $\log_6 6^9$

31. $3^{\log_3 (x-1)}$ **32.** $8^{\log_8 (\pi+1)}$

33. $\log_2 64$ **34.** $\log_2 \frac{1}{4}$

35. $\log_4 2$ **36.** $\log_3 9$

37. $\ln e^{-3}$ **38.** $\ln e$

39. $\log_8 64$ **40.** $\ln \sqrt[3]{e}$

41. $\log_{1/2}\left(\frac{1}{4}\right)$ **42.** $\log_{1/3}\left(\frac{1}{27}\right)$

43. $\log_{1/6} 36$ **44.** $\log_{1/4} 64$

45. $\log_a \frac{1}{a}$ **46.** $\log_a(a^2 \cdot a^3)$

47. $\log_5 5^0$ **48.** $\ln \sqrt{e}$

49. $\log_2 \frac{1}{16}$ **50.** $\log_8 8^k$

Exercises 51 and 52: Complete the table by hand.

51. $f(x) = 2 \log_2(x - 5)$

x	6	7	21
$f(x)$			

52. $f(x) = 2 \log_3(2x)$

x	$\frac{1}{18}$	$\frac{3}{2}$	$\frac{9}{2}$
$f(x)$			

Exponential and Logarithmic Forms

Exercises 53 and 54: Change each equation to its equivalent logarithmic form.

53. (a) $7^{4x} = 4$ (b) $e^x = 7$ (c) $c^x = b$

54. (a) $5^{2x} = 9$ (b) $b^x = a$ (c) $d^{2x} = b$

Exercises 55 and 56: Change each equation to its equivalent exponential form.

55. (a) $\log_8 x = 3$ (b) $\log_9(2 + x) = 5$ (c) $\log_k b = c$

56. (a) $\log x = 4$ (b) $\ln 8x = 7$ (c) $\log_a x = b$

Solving Exponential Equations

Exercises 57–80: Solve each equation. Use the change of base formula to approximate exact answers to the nearest hundredth when appropriate.

57. (a) $10^x = 0.01$ (b) $10^x = 7$ (c) $10^x = -4$

58. (a) $10^x = 1000$ (b) $10^x = 5$ (c) $10^x = -2$

59. (a) $4^x = \frac{1}{16}$ (b) $e^x = 2$ (c) $5^x = 125$

60. (a) $2^x = 9$ (b) $10^x = \frac{1}{1000}$ (c) $e^x = 8$

61. (a) $9^x = 1$ (b) $10^x = \sqrt{10}$ (c) $4^x = \sqrt[3]{4}$

62. (a) $2^x = \sqrt{8}$ (b) $7^x = 1$ (c) $e^x = \sqrt[3]{e}$

63. $e^{-x} = 3$ **64.** $e^{-x} = \frac{1}{2}$

65. $10^x - 5 = 95$ **66.** $2 \cdot 10^x = 66$

67. $10^{3x} = 100$ **68.** $4 \cdot 10^{2x} + 1 = 21$

69. $5(10^{4x}) = 65$ **70.** $3(10^{x-2}) = 72$

71. $4(3^x) - 3 = 13$ **72.** $5(7^x) + 3 = 83$

73. $e^x + 1 = 24$ **74.** $1 - 2e^x = -5$

75. $2^x + 1 = 15$ **76.** $3 \cdot 5^x = 125$

77. $5e^x + 2 = 20$ **78.** $6 - 2e^{3x} = -10$

79. $8 - 3(2)^{0.5x} = -40$ **80.** $2(3)^{-2x} + 5 = 167$

Solving Logarithmic Equations

Exercises 81–102: Solve each equation. Approximate answers to four decimal places when appropriate.

81. (a) $\log x = 2$ (b) $\log x = -3$ (c) $\log x = 1.2$

82. (a) $\log x = 1$ (b) $\log x = -4$ (c) $\log x = 0.3$

83. (a) $\log_2 x = 6$ (b) $\log_3 x = -2$ (c) $\ln x = 2$

84. (a) $\log_4 x = 2$ (b) $\log_8 x = -1$ (c) $\ln x = -2$

85. $\log_2 x = 1.2$ **86.** $\log_4 x = 3.7$

87. $5 \log_7 2x = 10$ **88.** $2 \log_4 x = 3.4$

89. $2 \log x = 6$ **90.** $\log 4x = 2$

91. $2 \log 5x = 4$ **92.** $6 - \log x = 3$

93. $4 \ln x = 3$ **94.** $\ln 5x = 8$

95. $5 \ln x - 1 = 6$ **96.** $2 \ln 3x = 8$

97. $4 \log_2 x = 16$ **98.** $\log_3 5x = 10$

99. $5 \ln (2x) + 6 = 12$ **100.** $16 - 4 \ln 3x = 2$

101. $9 - 3 \log_4 2x = 3$ **102.** $7 \log_6 (4x) + 5 = -2$

Exercises 103 and 104: Find values for a and b so that $f(x)$ models the data exactly.

103. $f(x) = a + b \log x$

x	1	10	100
$f(x)$	5	7	9

104. $f(x) = a + b \log_2 x$

x	1	2	4
$f(x)$	3.1	6	8.9

Graphs of Logarithmic Functions

Exercises 105–108: Use the graph of f to sketch a graph of f^{-1}. Give a symbolic representation of f^{-1}.

105.

106.

107.   **108.**

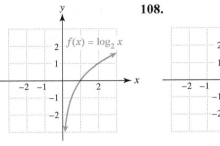

Exercises 109 and 110: Graph $y = f(x)$. Is f increasing or decreasing on its domain?

109. $f(x) = \log_{1/2} x$ **110.** $f(x) = \log_{1/3} x$

Exercises 111 and 112: Complete the following.
   (a) *Graph $y = f(x)$, $y = f^{-1}(x)$, and $y = x$.*
   (b) *Determine the intervals where f and f^{-1} are increasing or decreasing.*

111. $f(x) = \log_3 x$ **112.** $f(x) = \log_{1/2} x$

Transformations of Graphs

Exercises 113–120: Use transformations to graph $y = g(x)$. Give the equation of any asymptotes.

113. $g(x) = \log (x - 2)$ **114.** $g(x) = \log (x + 2)$

115. $g(x) = 3 \log x$ **116.** $g(x) = 2 \log_2 x$

117. $g(x) = \log_2 (-x)$ **118.** $g(x) = -\log_2 x$

119. $g(x) = 2 + \ln (x - 1)$ **120.** $g(x) = \ln (x + 1) - 1$

Exercises 121–124: Graph f and state its domain.

121. $f(x) = \log (x + 1)$ **122.** $f(x) = \log (x - 3)$

123. $f(x) = \ln (-x)$ **124.** $f(x) = \ln (x^2 + 1)$

Applications

125. Decibels Sound levels in decibels (dB) can be calculated by

$$D(x) = 10 \log (10^{16} x),$$

where x is the intensity of the sound in watts per square meter. The human ear begins to hurt when the intensity reaches $x = 10^{-4}$. Find how many decibels this represents.

126. Decibels (Refer to Exercise 125.) If the intensity increases by a *factor* of 10, find the increase in decibels.

127. Runway Length There is a relation between an airplane's weight x and the runway length L required for takeoff. For some airplanes the minimum runway length L in thousands of feet is given by $L(x) = 3 \log x$, where x is measured in thousands of pounds. (*Source:* L. Haefner, *Introduction to Transportation Systems.*)

(a) Evaluate $L(100)$ and interpret the result.

(b) If the weight of an airplane increases tenfold from 10,000 to 100,000 pounds, does the length of the required runway also increase by a factor of 10? Explain.

(c) Generalize your answer from part (b).

128. Runway Length   (Refer to Exercise 127.) Estimate the maximum weight of a plane that can take off from a runway that is 5 thousand feet long.

129. Acid Rain   Air pollutants frequently cause acid rain. A measure of the acidity is pH, which ranges between 1 and 14. Pure water is neutral and has a pH of 7. Acidic solutions have a pH less than 7, whereas alkaline solutions have a pH greater than 7. A pH value can be computed by $\text{pH} = -\log x$, where x represents the hydrogen ion concentration in moles per liter. In rural areas of Europe, rainwater typically has $x = 10^{-4.7}$. (**Source:** G. Howells, *Acid Rain and Acid Water.*)

(a) Find its pH.

(b) Seawater has a pH of 8.2. How many times greater is the hydrogen ion concentration in rainwater from rural Europe than in seawater?

130. Acid Rain   (Refer to Exercise 129.) Find the hydrogen ion concentration for the following pH levels of acid rain. (**Source:** G. Howells.)

(a) 4.92 (pH of rain at Amsterdam Islands)

(b) 3.9 (pH of some rain in the eastern United States)

131. Earthquakes   The Richter scale is used to measure the intensity of earthquakes, where intensity corresponds to the amount of energy released by an earthquake. If an earthquake has an intensity of x, then its *magnitude*, as computed by the Richter scale, is given by the formula $R(x) = \log \frac{x}{I_0}$, where I_0 is the intensity of a small measurable earthquake.

(a) On July 26, 1963, an earthquake in Yugoslavia had a magnitude of 6.0 on the Richter scale, and on August 19, 1977, an earthquake in Indonesia measured 8.0. Find the intensity x for each of these earthquakes if $I_0 = 1$.

(b) How many times more intense was the Indonesian earthquake than the Yugoslavian earthquake?

132. Earthquakes   (Refer to Exercise 131.) If the intensity x of an earthquake increases by a *factor* of 10^3, by how much does the Richter number R increase? Generalize your results.

133. Hurricanes   Hurricanes are some of the largest storms on Earth. They are very low pressure areas with diameters of over 500 miles. The barometric air pressure in inches of mercury at a distance of x miles from the eye of a severe hurricane is modeled by the formula $f(x) = 0.48 \ln (x + 1) + 27$ (**Source:** A. Miller and R. Anthes, *Meteorology.*)

(a) Evaluate $f(0)$ and $f(100)$. Interpret the results.

(b) Graph f in [0, 250, 50] by [25, 30, 1]. Describe how air pressure changes as one moves away from the eye of the hurricane.

(c) At what distance from the eye of the hurricane is the air pressure 28 inches of mercury?

134. Predicting Wind Speed   Wind speed typically varies in the first 20 meters above the ground. For a particular day, let the formula $f(x) = 1.2 \ln x + 2.3$ compute the wind speed in meters per second at a height x meters above the ground for $x \geq 1$. (**Source:** A. Miller.)

(a) Find the wind speed at a height of 5 meters.

(b) Graph f in the window [0, 20, 5] by [0, 7, 1]. Interpret the graph.

(c) Estimate the height where the wind speed is 5 meters per second.

135. Cooling an Object   A pot of boiling water with a temperature of 100°C is set in a room with a temperature of 20°C. The temperature T of the water after x hours is given by $T(x) = 20 + 80e^{-x}$.

(a) Estimate the temperature of the water after 1 hour.

(b) How long did it take the water to cool to 60°C?

136. Warming an Object   A can of soda with a temperature of 5°C is set in a room with a temperature of 20°C. The temperature T of the soda after x minutes is given by $T(x) = 20 - 15(10)^{-0.05x}$.

(a) Estimate the temperature of the soda after 5 minutes.

(b) After how many minutes was the temperature of the soda 15°C?

137. Traffic Flow   (Refer to Example 11, Section 5.3.) Cars arrive randomly at an intersection with an average rate of 20 cars per hour. The likelihood, or probability,

(continued)

that no car enters the intersection within a period of x minutes can be estimated by $f(x) = e^{-x/3}$.
(a) What is the probability that no car enters the intersection during a 5-minute period?

(b) Determine the value of x that gives a 30% chance that no car enters the intersection during an interval of x minutes.

138. Population Growth The population of Nevada in millions is given by $P(x) = 2.7e^{0.014x}$, where $x = 0$ corresponds to 2010. (*Source*: Bureau of the Census.)
(a) Determine symbolically the year when the population of Nevada might be 3 million.

📷 **(b)** Solve part (a) graphically.

139. Diversity of Birds (Refer to Example 11.) The table lists the number of species of birds on islands of various sizes. Find values for a and b so that $f(x) = a + b\log x$ models these data. Estimate the size of an island that might have 16 species of birds.
(*Hint:* Let $f(1) = 7$ and find a. Then let $f(10) = 11$ and find b.)

Area (km²)	0.1	1	10	100	1000
Species of birds	3	7	11	15	19

140. Diversity of Insects The table lists the number of types of insects found in wooded regions with various acreages. Find values for a and b so that $f(x) = a + b\log x$ models these data. Then use f to estimate an acreage that might have 1200 types of insects.

Area (acres)	10	100	1000	10,000
Insect Types	500	800	1100	1400

141. Growth of Bacteria The table lists the number of bacteria y in millions after an elapsed time of x days.

x	0	1	2	3	4
y	3	6	12	24	48

(a) Find values for C and a so that $f(x) = Ca^x$ models the data.

(b) Estimate when there were 16 million bacteria.

142. Growth of an Investment The growth of an investment is shown in the table in the next column.

x (years)	0	5	10	15	20
y (dollars)	100	300	900	2700	8100

(a) Find values for C and a so that $f(x) = Ca^x$ models the data.

(b) Estimate when the account contained $2000.

Writing about Mathematics

143. Describe the relationship among exponential functions and logarithmic functions. Explain why logarithms are needed to solve exponential equations.

144. Give verbal, numerical, graphical, and symbolic representations of a base-5 logarithmic function.

Extended And Discovery Exercises

1. Average Rate of Change of ln x Find the average rate of change of $f(x) = \ln x$ from x to $x + 0.001$ for each value of x. Round your answers to two decimal places.
(a) $x = 1$ **(b)** $x = 2$

(c) $x = 3$ **(d)** $x = 4$

2. Average Rate of Change of ln x (See Exercise 1.) Compare each average rate of change of $\ln x$ to x. What is the pattern? Make a generalization.

3. Climate Change According to one model, the future increases in average global temperatures (due to carbon dioxide levels exceeding 280 parts per million) can be estimated using $T = 6.5 \ln(C/280)$, where C is the concentration of atmospheric carbon dioxide in parts per million (ppm) and T is in degrees Fahrenheit. Let future amounts of carbon dioxide x years after 2000 be modeled by the formula $C(x) = 364(1.005)^x$. (*Source*: W. Clime, *The Economics of Global Warming*.)
(a) Use composition of functions to write T as a function of x. Evaluate T when $x = 100$ and interpret the result.

📷 **(b)** Graph $C(x)$ in [0, 200, 50] by [0, 1000, 100] and $T(x)$ in [0, 200, 50] by [0, 10, 1]. Describe each graph.

(c) How does an exponential growth in carbon dioxide concentrations affect the increase in temperature?

CHECKING BASIC CONCEPTS FOR SECTIONS 5.3 AND 5.4

1. If the principal is $1200 and the interest rate is 9.5% compounded monthly, calculate the account balance after 4 years. Determine the balance if the interest is compounded continuously.

2. Find values for C and a so that $f(x) = Ca^x$ models the data in the table.

x	0	1	2	3
y	4	2	1	0.5

3. Explain verbally what $\log_2 15$ represents. Is it equal to an integer? (Do not use a calculator.)

4. Evaluate each of the following logarithms by hand.

    (a) $\log_6 36$ (b) $\log \sqrt{10} + \log 0.01$ (c) $\ln \dfrac{1}{e^2}$

5. Solve each equation.

    (a) $e^x = 5$ (b) $10^x = 25$ (c) $\log x = 1.5$

6. Solve each equation.

    (a) $2e^x + 1 = 25$ (b) $\log 2x = 2.3$

    (c) $\log x^2 = 1$

7. **Population** The population of California in millions x years after 2010 can be modeled by $P(x) = 37.3e^{0.01x}$. (*Source:* Bureau of the Census.)

    (a) Evaluate $P(2)$. Interpret this result.

    (b) Find the y-intercept on the graph of $y = f(x)$. Interpret this result.

    (c) Estimate the annual percent increase in the population of California.

    (d) Predict when the population might reach 40 million.

8. **Growth in Salary** Suppose that a person's salary is initially \$30,000 and is modeled by $f(x)$, where x represents the number of years of experience. Use $f(x)$ to approximate the years of experience when the salary first *exceeds* \$60,000.

    (a) $f(x) = 30,000(1.1)^x$

    (b) $f(x) = 30,000 \log(10 + x)$

    Would most people prefer that their salaries increase exponentially or logarithmically?

5.5 Properties of Logarithms

- **Apply basic properties of logarithms**
- **Expand and combine logarithmic expressions**
- **Use the change of base formula**

Introduction

The discovery of logarithms by John Napier (1550–1617) played an important role in the history of science. Logarithms were instrumental in allowing Johannes Kepler (1571–1630) to calculate the positions of the planet Mars, which led to his discovery of the laws of planetary motion. Kepler's laws were used by Isaac Newton (1643–1727) to discover the universal laws of gravitation. Although calculators and computers have made tables of logarithms obsolete, applications involving logarithms still play an important role in modern-day computation. One reason is that logarithms possess important properties. For example, the loudness of a sound can be measured in decibels by the formula $f(x) = 10\log(10^{16}x)$, where x is the intensity of the sound. In Example 4, we use properties of logarithms to simplify this formula.

Basic Properties of Logarithms

Logarithms possess several important properties. One property of logarithms states that

> *the sum of the logarithms of two numbers equals the logarithm of their product.*

For example, we see in Figure 5.58 that

$$\log 5 + \log 2 = \log 10 \qquad 5 \cdot 2 = 10$$

and in Figure 5.59 that

$$\log 4 + \log 25 = \log 100. \qquad 4 \cdot 25 = 100$$

These calculations show the product rule of logarithms: $\log_a m + \log_a n = \log_a(mn)$.

Product Rule: $\log m + \log n = \log(m \cdot n)$

Figure 5.58   **Figure 5.59**

Four properties, or rules, of logarithms are as follows.

PROPERTIES OF LOGARITHMS

For positive numbers m, n, and $a \neq 1$ and any real number r:

1. $\log_a 1 = 0$ and $\log_a a = 1$ Logarithms of 1 and a

2. $\log_a m + \log_a n = \log_a(mn)$ Product rule

3. $\log_a m - \log_a n = \log_a\left(\dfrac{m}{n}\right)$ Quotient rule

4. $\log_a(m^r) = r\log_a m$ Power rule

Algebra Review
To review properties of exponents, see Section 4.8 and Chapter R (page R-7).

The properties of logarithms are a direct result of the properties of exponents and the inverse property $\log_a a^k = k$, as shown below.

Logarithms of 1 and a: This property is a direct result of the inverse property: $\log_a a^x = x$.

$$\log_a 1 = \log_a a^0 = 0 \quad \text{and} \quad \log_a a = \log_a a^1 = 1$$

Examples: $\log 1 = 0$ and $\ln e = 1$

Product Rule: If m and n are positive numbers, then we can write $m = a^c$ and $n = a^d$ for some real numbers c and d.

$$\log_a m + \log_a n = \log_a a^c + \log_a a^d = c + d$$
$$\log_a(mn) = \log_a(a^c a^d) = \log_a(a^{c+d}) = c + d$$

> Both expressions equal $c + d$.

Thus $\log_a m + \log_a n = \log_a(mn)$.

Example: Let $m = 100$ and $n = 1000$.

$$\log 100 + \log 1000 = \log 10^2 + \log 10^3 = 2 + 3 = 5$$
$$\log(100 \cdot 1000) = \log 100{,}000 = \log 10^5 = 5$$

Quotient Rule: Let $m = a^c$ and $n = a^d$ for some real numbers c and d.

$$\log_a m - \log_a n = \log_a a^c - \log_a a^d = c - d$$
$$\log_a\left(\frac{m}{n}\right) = \log_a\left(\frac{a^c}{a^d}\right) = \log_a(a^{c-d}) = c - d$$

> Both expressions equal $c - d$.

Thus $\log_a m - \log_a n = \log_a\left(\frac{m}{n}\right)$.

Example: Let $m = 100$ and $n = 1000$.

$$\log 100 - \log 1000 = \log 10^2 - \log 10^3 = 2 - 3 = -1$$
$$\log\left(\frac{100}{1000}\right) = \log\left(\frac{1}{10}\right) = \log(10^{-1}) = -1$$

Power Rule: Let $m = a^c$ and r be any real number.

$$\log_a m^r = \log_a(a^c)^r = \log_a(a^{cr}) = cr$$
$$r\log_a m = r\log_a a^c = rc = cr$$

> Both expressions equal cr.

Thus $\log_a(m^r) = r\log_a m$.

Example: Let $m = 100$ and $r = 3$.

$$\log 100^3 = \log 1{,}000{,}000 = \log 10^6 = 6$$
$$3\log 100 = 3\log 10^2 = 3 \cdot 2 = 6$$

Caution: $\log_a(m + n) \neq \log_a m + \log_a n; \quad \log_a(m - n) \neq \log_a m - \log_a n$

EXAMPLE 1   Recognizing properties of logarithms

Use a calculator to evaluate each pair of expressions. Then state which rule of logarithms this calculation illustrates.

(a) $\ln 5 + \ln 4$, $\ln 20$ **(b)** $\log 10 - \log 5$, $\log 2$ **(c)** $\log 5^2$, $2 \log 5$

SOLUTION

(a) From Figure 5.60, we see that the two expressions are equal. These calculations illustrate the product rule because $\ln 5 + \ln 4 = \ln(5 \cdot 4) = \ln 20$.

(b) The two expressions are equal in Figure 5.61, and these calculations illustrate the quotient rule because $\log 10 - \log 5 = \log \frac{10}{5} = \log 2$.

(c) The two expressions are equal in Figure 5.62, and these calculations illustrate the power rule because $\log 5^2 = 2 \log 5$.

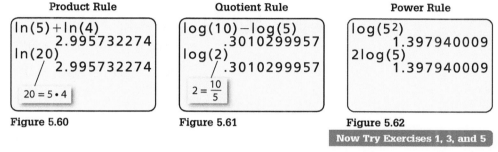

Product Rule	Quotient Rule	Power Rule

Figure 5.60   Figure 5.61   Figure 5.62

Now Try Exercises 1, 3, and 5

Expanding and Combining Logarithmic Expressions

We can use the properties of logarithms to expand and combine logarithmic expressions, as illustrated by the following.

Expanding: Moving Left to Right →

$$\log 5b = \log 5 + \log b \qquad \text{Product rule}$$

$$\log \frac{x}{2} = \log x - \log 2 \qquad \text{Quotient rule}$$

$$\log x^2 = 2 \log x \qquad \text{Power rule}$$

← Combining: Moving Right to Left

The next two examples demonstrate how to expand logarithmic expressions.

EXAMPLE 2   Expanding logarithmic expressions

Use properties of logarithms to expand each expression. Write your answers without exponents.

(a) $\log xy$ **(b)** $\ln \frac{5}{z}$ **(c)** $\log_4 \frac{\sqrt[3]{x}}{\sqrt{k}}$

SOLUTION

(a) By the product rule, $\log xy = \log x + \log y$.

(b) By the quotient rule, $\ln \frac{5}{z} = \ln 5 - \ln z$.

(c) Begin by using the quotient rule.

$$\log_4 \frac{\sqrt[3]{x}}{\sqrt{k}} = \log_4 \sqrt[3]{x} - \log_4 \sqrt{k} \qquad \text{Quotient rule}$$

$$= \log_4 x^{1/3} - \log_4 k^{1/2} \qquad \text{Properties of exponents}$$

$$= \tfrac{1}{3} \log_4 x - \tfrac{1}{2} \log_4 k \qquad \text{Power rule}$$

Now Try Exercises 7, 11, and 21

EXAMPLE 3 Expanding logarithmic expressions

Expand each expression. Write your answers without exponents.

(a) $\log_2 2x^4$ (b) $\ln \frac{7x^3}{k^2}$ (c) $\log \frac{\sqrt{x+1}}{(x-2)^3}$

SOLUTION

(a) $\log_2 2x^4 = \log_2 2 + \log_2 x^4$ *Product rule*

$\qquad\qquad = 1 + 4\log_2 x$ *Power rule; logarithm of a*

(b) $\ln \frac{7x^3}{k^2} = \ln 7x^3 - \ln k^2$ *Quotient rule*

$\qquad\qquad = \ln 7 + \ln x^3 - \ln k^2$ *Product rule*

$\qquad\qquad = \ln 7 + 3\ln x - 2\ln k$ *Power rule*

(c) $\log \frac{\sqrt{x+1}}{(x-2)^3} = \log \sqrt{x+1} - \log(x-2)^3$ *Quotient rule*

$\qquad\qquad = \log(x+1)^{1/2} - \log(x-2)^3$ *Property of exponents*

$\qquad\qquad = \frac{1}{2}\log(x+1) - 3\log(x-2)$ *Power rule*

Now Try Exercises 9, 15, and 27

An Application Sometimes properties of logarithms are used in applications to simplify a formula. This is illustrated in the next example.

EXAMPLE 4 Analyzing sound with decibels

Sound levels in decibels (dB) can be computed by $D(x) = 10\log(10^{16}x)$.
(a) Use properties of logarithms to simplify the formula for D.
(b) Ordinary conversation has an intensity of $x = 10^{-10}$ w/cm^2. Find the decibel level.

SOLUTION
(a) To simplify the formula, use the product rule.

$\qquad D(x) = 10\log(10^{16}x)$ *Given formula*

$\qquad\qquad = 10(\log 10^{16} + \log x)$ *Product rule*

$\qquad\qquad = 10(16 + \log x)$ *Inverse property*

$\qquad\qquad = 160 + 10\log x$ *Distributive property*

(b) $D(10^{-10}) = 160 + 10\log(10^{-10}) = 160 + 10(-10) = 160 - 100 = 60$

Ordinary conversation occurs at about 60 decibels.

Now Try Exercise 83

The next two examples demonstrate how properties of logarithms can be used to combine logarithmic expressions.

EXAMPLE 5 Combining terms in logarithmic expressions

Write each expression as the logarithm of a single expression.

(a) $\ln 2e + \ln \frac{1}{e}$ (b) $\log_2 27 + \log_2 x^3$ (c) $\log x^3 - \log x^2$

SOLUTION
(a) By the product rule, $\ln 2e + \ln \frac{1}{e} = \ln\left(2e \cdot \frac{1}{e}\right) = \ln 2$.
(b) By the product rule, $\log_2 27 + \log_2 x^3 = \log_2(27x^3)$.
(c) By the quotient rule, $\log x^3 - \log x^2 = \log \frac{x^3}{x^2} = \log x$.

Now Try Exercises 41, 43, and 49

EXAMPLE 6 Combining terms in logarithmic expressions

Write each expression as the logarithm of a single expression.

(a) $\log 5 + \log 15 - \log 3$ (b) $2\ln x - \frac{1}{2}\ln y - 3\ln z$

(c) $5\log_3 x + \log_3 2x - \log_3 y$

SOLUTION

(a)
$$\log 5 + \log 15 - \log 3 = \log(5 \cdot 15) - \log 3 \qquad \text{Product rule}$$

$$= \log\left(\frac{5 \cdot 15}{3}\right) \qquad \text{Quotient rule}$$

$$= \log 25 \qquad \text{Simplify.}$$

Algebra Review

To review rational exponents and radical notation, see Chapter R (page R-38).

(b)
$$2\ln x - \frac{1}{2}\ln y - 3\ln z = \ln x^2 - \ln y^{1/2} - \ln z^3 \qquad \text{Power rule}$$

$$= \ln\left(\frac{x^2}{y^{1/2}}\right) - \ln z^3 \qquad \text{Quotient rule}$$

$$= \ln\frac{x^2}{y^{1/2}z^3} \qquad \text{Quotient rule}$$

$$= \ln\frac{x^2}{z^3\sqrt{y}} \qquad \text{Properties of exponents}$$

(c)
$$5\log_3 x + \log_3 2x - \log_3 y = \log_3 x^5 + \log_3 2x - \log_3 y \qquad \text{Power rule}$$

$$= \log_3(x^5 \cdot 2x) - \log_3 y \qquad \text{Product rule}$$

$$= \log_3 \frac{2x^6}{y} \qquad \text{Quotient rule}$$

Now Try Exercises 39, 47, and 51

Change of Base Formula

Calculators usually have keys to approximate common and natural logarithms. Occasionally it is necessary to evaluate a logarithm with a base other than 10 or e. This computation can be accomplished by using a change of base formula.

CHANGE OF BASE FORMULA

Let x, $a \neq 1$, and $b \neq 1$ be positive real numbers. Then

$$\log_a x = \frac{\log_b x}{\log_b a}.$$

The change of base formula can be derived as follows.

$$y = \log_a x$$

$$a^y = a^{\log_a x} \qquad \text{Exponentiate each side; base } a.$$

$$a^y = x \qquad \text{Inverse property}$$

$$\log_b a^y = \log_b x \qquad \text{Take base-}b\text{ logarithm of each side.}$$

$$y\log_b a = \log_b x \qquad \text{Power rule}$$

$$y = \frac{\log_b x}{\log_b a} \qquad \text{Divide by } \log_b a.$$

$$\log_a x = \frac{\log_b x}{\log_b a} \qquad \text{Substitute } \log_a x \text{ for } y. \text{ (First equation)}$$

To calculate $\log_2 5$, evaluate $\frac{\log 5}{\log 2} \approx 2.322$. The change of base formula was used with $x = 5$, $a = 2$, and $b = 10$. We could also have evaluated $\frac{\ln 5}{\ln 2} \approx 2.322$.

EXAMPLE 7 Applying the change of base formula

Use a calculator to approximate each expression to the nearest thousandth.
(a) $\log_4 20$ **(b)** $\log_2 125 + \log_7 39$

SOLUTION
(a) Using the change of base formula, we have $\log_4 20 = \frac{\log 20}{\log 4} \approx 2.161$. We could also evaluate $\frac{\ln 20}{\ln 4}$, as shown in Figure 5.63.

(b) $\log_2 125 + \log_7 39 = \frac{\log 125}{\log 2} + \frac{\log 39}{\log 7} \approx 8.848$. See Figure 5.64.

Finding log₄20

```
log(20)/log(4)
          2.160964047
ln(20)/ln(4)
          2.160964047
```

Figure 5.63

Finding log₂125 + log₇39

```
log(125)/log(2)+
log(39)/log(7)
          8.848482542
```

Figure 5.64

Now Try Exercises 67 and 71

The change of base formula can be used to graph base-*a* logarithmic functions.

EXAMPLE 8 Using the change of base formula for graphing

$[-10, 10, 1]$ by $[-10, 10, 1]$

Solve the equation $\log_2(x^3 + x - 1) = 5$ graphically.

SOLUTION
Graph $y_1 = \log(x^3 + x - 1)/\log 2$ and $y_2 = 5$. See Figure 5.65. Their graphs intersect near the point $(3.104, 5)$. The solution is given by $x \approx 3.104$.

Now Try Exercise 77

Intersection
X=3.1036499 Y=5

Figure 5.65

5.5 Putting It All Together

The following table summarizes some properties of logarithms.

CONCEPT	EXPLANATION	EXAMPLES
Properties of logarithms	1. $\log_a 1 = 0$ and $\log_a a = 1$ 2. $\log_a m + \log_a n = \log_a(mn)$ 3. $\log_a m - \log_a n = \log_a(\frac{m}{n})$ 4. $\log_a(m^r) = r\log_a m$	1. $\ln 1 = 0$ and $\log_2 2 = 1$ 2. $\log 3 + \log 6 = \log(3 \cdot 6) = \log 18$ 3. $\log_3 8 - \log_3 2 = \log_3 \frac{8}{2} = \log_3 4$ 4. $\log 6^7 = 7 \log 6$
Change of base formula	Let $x, a \neq 1$, and $b \neq 1$ be positive real numbers. Then $$\log_a x = \frac{\log_b x}{\log_b a}.$$	$\log_3 6 = \frac{\log 6}{\log 3} = \frac{\ln 6}{\ln 3} \approx 1.631$
Graphing logarithmic functions	Use the change of base formula to graph $y = \log_a x$ whenever $a \neq 10$ and $a \neq e$.	To graph $y = \log_2 x$, let $Y_1 = \log(X)/\log(2)$ or $Y_1 = \ln(X)/\ln(2)$.

5.5 Exercises

Note: When applying properties of logarithms, assume that all variables are positive.

Properties of Logarithms

Exercises 1–6: (Refer to Example 1.) Use a calculator to approximate each pair of expressions. Then state which property of logarithms this calculation illustrates.

1. $\log 4 + \log 7$, $\log 28$
2. $\ln 12 + \ln 5$, $\ln 60$
3. $\ln 72 - \ln 8$, $\ln 9$
4. $3 \log 4$, $\log 4^3$
5. $10 \log 2$, $\log 1024$
6. $\log 100 - \log 20$, $\log 5$

Exercises 7–32: (Refer to Examples 2 and 3.) Expand the expression. If possible, write your answer without exponents.

7. $\log_2 ab$
8. $\ln 3x$
9. $\ln 7a^4$
10. $\log \dfrac{a^3}{3}$
11. $\log \dfrac{6}{z}$
12. $\ln \dfrac{xy}{z}$
13. $\log \dfrac{x^2}{3}$
14. $\log 3x^6$
15. $\ln \dfrac{2x^7}{3k}$
16. $\ln \dfrac{kx^3}{5}$
17. $\log_2 4k^2 x^3$
18. $\log \dfrac{5kx^2}{11}$
19. $\log_5 \dfrac{25x^3}{y^4}$
20. $\log_2 \dfrac{32}{xy^2}$
21. $\ln \dfrac{x^4}{y^2 \sqrt{z^3}}$
22. $\ln \dfrac{x\sqrt[3]{y^2}}{z^6}$
23. $\log_4 (0.25(x + 2)^3)$
24. $\log (0.001(a - b)^{-3})$
25. $\log_5 \dfrac{x^3}{(x - 4)^4}$
26. $\log_8 \dfrac{(3x - 2)^2}{x^2 + 1}$
27. $\log_2 \dfrac{\sqrt{x}}{z^2}$
28. $\log \sqrt{\dfrac{xy^2}{z}}$
29. $\ln \sqrt[3]{\dfrac{2x + 6}{(x + 1)^5}}$
30. $\log \dfrac{\sqrt{x^2 + 4}}{\sqrt[3]{x - 1}}$
31. $\log_2 \dfrac{\sqrt[3]{x^2 - 1}}{\sqrt{1 + x^2}}$
32. $\log_8 \sqrt[3]{\dfrac{x + y^2}{2z + 1}}$

Exercises 33–56: (Refer to Examples 5 and 6.) Combine the expressions by writing them as a logarithm of a single expression.

33. $\log 2 + \log 3$
34. $\log \sqrt{2} + \log \sqrt[3]{2}$
35. $\ln \sqrt{5} - \ln 25$
36. $\ln 33 - \ln 11$
37. $\log 20 + \log \frac{1}{10}$
38. $\log_2 24 + \log_2 \frac{1}{48}$
39. $\log 4 + \log 3 - \log 2$
40. $\log_3 5 - \log_3 10 - \log_3 \frac{1}{2}$
41. $\log_7 5 + \log_7 k^2$
42. $\log_6 45 + \log_6 b^3$
43. $\ln x^6 - \ln x^3$
44. $\log 10x^5 - \log 5x$
45. $\log \sqrt{x} + \log x^2 - \log x$
46. $\log \sqrt[4]{x} + \log x^4 - \log x^2$
47. $3 \ln x - \frac{3}{2} \ln y + 4 \ln z$
48. $\frac{2}{3} \ln y - 4 \ln x - \frac{1}{2} \ln z$
49. $\ln \dfrac{1}{e^2} + \ln 2e$
50. $\ln 4e^3 - \ln 2e^2$
51. $2 \ln x - 4 \ln y + \frac{1}{2} \ln z$
52. $\frac{1}{3} \log_5 (x + 1) + \frac{1}{3} \log_5 (x - 1)$
53. $\log 4 - \log x + 7 \log \sqrt{x}$
54. $\ln 3e - \ln \dfrac{1}{4e}$
55. $2 \log (x^2 - 1) + 4 \log (x - 2) - \frac{1}{2} \log y$
56. $\log_3 x + \log_3 \sqrt{x + 3} - \frac{1}{3} \log_3 (x - 4)$

Exercises 57–62: Complete the following.

(a) Make a table of $f(x)$ and $g(x)$ to determine whether $f(x) = g(x)$.

(b) If possible, use properties of logarithms to show that $f(x) = g(x)$.

57. $f(x) = \log 3x + \log 2x$, $g(x) = \log 6x^2$
58. $f(x) = \ln 3x - \ln 2x$, $g(x) = \ln x$
59. $f(x) = \ln 2x^2 - \ln x$, $g(x) = \ln 2x$
60. $f(x) = \log x^2 + \log x^3$, $g(x) = 5 \log x$

61. $f(x) = \ln x^4 - \ln x^2,$ $g(x) = 2\ln x$

62. $f(x) = (\ln x)^2,$ $g(x) = 2\ln x$

Exercises 63–66: Sketch a graph of f.

63. $f(x) = \log_2 x$

64. $f(x) = \log_2 x^2$

65. $f(x) = \log_3|x|$

66. $f(x) = \log_4 2x$

Change of Base Formula

Exercises 67–76: Use the change of base formula to approximate the logarithm to the nearest thousandth.

67. $\log_2 25$

68. $\log_3 67$

69. $\log_5 130$

70. $\log_6 0.77$

71. $\log_2 5 + \log_2 7$

72. $\log_9 85 + \log_7 17$

73. $\sqrt{\log_4 46}$

74. $2\log_5 15 + \sqrt[3]{\log_3 67}$

75. $\dfrac{\log_2 12}{\log_2 3}$

76. $\dfrac{\log_7 125}{\log_7 25}$

Exercises 77–80: Solve the equation graphically. Express any solutions to the nearest thousandth.

77. $\log_2(x^3 + x^2 + 1) = 7$

78. $\log_3(1 + x^2 + 2x^4) = 4$

79. $\log_2(x^2 + 1) = 5 - \log_3(x^4 + 1)$

80. $\ln(x^2 + 2) = \log_2(10 - x^2)$

Applications

81. Runway Length   (Refer to Exercise 127, Section 5.4.) Use a natural logarithm (instead of a common logarithm) to write the formula $L(x) = 3\log x$. Evaluate $L(50)$ for each formula. Do your answers agree?

82. Biology   The equation $y = bx^a$ is used in applications involving biology. Another form of this equation is $\log y = \log b + a\log x$. Use properties of logarithms to obtain this second equation from the first. (**Source:** H. Lancaster, *Quantitative Methods in Biological and Medical Sciences.*)

83. Decibels   (Refer to Example 4.) If the intensity x of a sound increases by a factor of 10, by how much does the decibel level increase?

84. Decibels   (Refer to Example 4.) Use a natural logarithm to write the formula $f(x) = 160 + 10\log x$. Evaluate $f(5 \times 10^{-8})$ for each formula. Do your answers agree?

85. Light Absorption   When sunlight passes through lake water, its initial intensity I_0 decreases to a weaker intensity I at a depth of x feet according to the formula

$$\ln I - \ln I_0 = -kx,$$

where k is a positive constant and I_0 is the sun's intensity at the surface. Solve this equation for I.

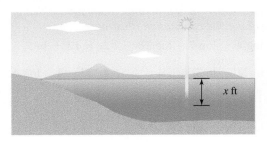

86. Dissolving Salt   If C grams of salt are added to a sample of water, the amount A of undissolved salt is modeled by $A = Ca^x$, where x is time. Solve the equation for x.

87. Population Growth   The population P (in millions) of California x years after 2010 can be modeled by $P = 37.3e^{0.01x}$.
   (a) Use properties of logarithms to solve this equation for x.

   (b) Use your equation to find x when $P = 40$. Interpret your answer.

88. Population Growth   The population P (in millions) of Georgia x years after 2010 can be modeled by the equation $P = 9.7e^{0.017x}$.
   (a) Use properties of logarithms to solve this equation for x.

   (b) Use your equation to find x when $P = 12$. Interpret your answer.

89. Solve $A = Pe^{rt}$ for t.

90. Solve $P = P_0 e^{r(t-t_0)} + 5$ for t.

91. Write the sum

$$\log 1 + 2\log 2 + 3\log 3 + 4\log 4 + 5\log 5$$

as a logarithm of a single expression.

92. Show that

$$\log_2\left(x + \sqrt{x^2 - 4}\right) + \log_2\left(x - \sqrt{x^2 - 4}\right)$$

equals 2. What is the domain of the given expression?

Writing about Mathematics

93. A student insists that $\log(x + y)$ and $\log x + \log y$ are equal. How could you convince the student otherwise?

94. A student insists that $\log\left(\frac{x}{y}\right)$ and $\frac{\log x}{\log y}$ are equal. How could you convince the student otherwise?

5.6 Exponential and Logarithmic Equations

- **Solve exponential equations**
- **Solve logarithmic equations**

Introduction

The population of the world has grown rapidly during the past century. Near the end of 2011, world population was estimated to be 7 billion. Exponential functions and equations are often used to model this type of rapid growth, whereas logarithms are used to model slower growth.

Exponential Equations

The population P of the world was 7 billion in 2011 and can be modeled by the function $P(x) = 7(1.01)^{x-2011}$, where x is the year. We can use P to predict the year when world population might reach 8 billion by solving the *exponential equation*

$$7(1.01)^{x-2011} = 8. \qquad \text{Exponential equation}$$

An equation in which the variable occurs in the *exponent* of an expression is called an **exponential equation**. In the next example, we use the power rule of logarithms, $\log_a(m^r) = r\log_a m$, to solve this equation.

EXAMPLE 1   Modeling world population

World population in billions during year x can be modeled by $P(x) = 7(1.01)^{x-2011}$, shown in Figure 5.66. Solve the equation $7(1.01)^{x-2011} = 8$ symbolically to predict the year when world population might reach 8 billion.

SOLUTION   First divide each side by 7, and then take the common logarithm of each side. (The natural logarithm could also be used.)

$$7(1.01)^{x-2011} = 8 \qquad \text{Given equation}$$

$$(1.01)^{x-2011} = \frac{8}{7} \qquad \text{Divide by 7.}$$

$$\log(1.01)^{x-2011} = \log\frac{8}{7} \qquad \text{Take the common logarithm.}$$

$$(x - 2011)\log(1.01) = \log\frac{8}{7} \qquad \log(m^r) = r\log m$$

$$x - 2011 = \frac{\log(8/7)}{\log(1.01)} \qquad \text{Divide by } \log(1.01).$$

$$x = 2011 + \frac{\log(8/7)}{\log(1.01)} \qquad \text{Add 2011.}$$

$$x \approx 2024 \qquad \text{Approximate.}$$

This model predicts that world population might reach 8 billion during 2024.

Now Try Exercise 79

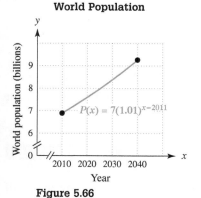

World Population

$P(x) = 7(1.01)^{x-2011}$

Figure 5.66

CLASS DISCUSSION

What is the growth factor for $P(x) = 7(1.01)^{x-2011}$? By what percentage is it predicted that world population will grow, on average, each year after 2011?

> **SOLVING EXPONENTIAL EQUATIONS SYMBOLICALLY**
>
> The following steps can be used to solve several types of exponential equations.
>
> **STEP 1:** Isolate the exponential expression on one side of the equation.
>
> **STEP 2:** Take a logarithm of each side of the equation.
>
> **STEP 3:** Apply either the inverse property or the power rule.
>
> **STEP 4:** Solve for the variable.

The steps above are applied in Example 2 to solve the equation symbolically.

EXAMPLE 2 Calculating the thickness of a runway

Heavier aircraft require runways with thicker pavement for landings and takeoffs. The relation between the thickness of the pavement t in inches and gross weight W in thousands of pounds can be approximated by

$$W(t) = 18.29e^{0.246t}.$$

(a) Determine the required thickness of the runway for a 130,000-pound plane.
(b) Solve part (a) graphically and numerically.

SOLUTION
(a) *Symbolic Solution* Because the unit for W is thousands of pounds, we can solve the equation $W(t) = 130$ for t.

$$18.29e^{0.246t} = 130 \qquad \text{\textit{W(t) = 130}}$$

$$e^{0.246t} = \frac{130}{18.29} \qquad \text{\textit{STEP 1: Divide by 18.29.}}$$

$$\ln e^{0.246t} = \ln \frac{130}{18.29} \qquad \text{\textit{STEP 2: Take the natural logarithm of each side.}}$$

$$0.246t = \ln \frac{130}{18.29} \qquad \text{\textit{STEP 3: Inverse property: }} \ln e^k = k$$

$$t = \frac{\ln(130/18.29)}{0.246} \qquad \text{\textit{STEP 4: Divide by 0.246.}}$$

$$t \approx 7.97 \qquad \text{\textit{Approximate.}}$$

The runway should be about 8 inches thick.

(b) *Graphical Solution* Let $Y_1 = 18.29e^{\wedge}(.246X)$ and $Y_2 = 130$. In Figure 5.67, their graphs intersect near (7.97, 130).

Numerical Solution Numerical support of this result is shown in Figure 5.68, where $y_1 \approx y_2$ when $x = 8$.

Now Try Exercise 81

Graphical Solution
[0, 10, 1] by [0, 200, 50]

Figure 5.67

Numerical Solution

Figure 5.68

To solve an exponential equation with a base other than 10 or e, the power rule of logarithms can be used. This technique is used in Examples 1 and 3.

EXAMPLE 3 Modeling the decline of bluefin tuna

Bluefin tuna are large fish that can weigh 1500 pounds and swim at speeds of 55 miles per hour. Because they are used for sushi, a prime fish can be worth over $50,000. As a result, the western Atlantic bluefin tuna have had their numbers decline exponentially. Their numbers in thousands from 1974 to 1991 can be modeled by the formula $f(x) = 230(0.881)^x$, where x is years after 1974. (In more recent years, controls have helped slow this decline.) (*Source:* B. Freedman, *Environmental Ecology.*)

(a) Estimate the number of bluefin tuna in 1974 and 1991.
(b) Determine symbolically the year when they numbered 50 thousand.

SOLUTION

(a) To determine their numbers in 1974 and 1991, evaluate $f(0)$ and $f(17)$.

$$f(0) = 230(0.881)^0 = 230(1) = 230$$

$$f(17) = 230(0.881)^{17} \approx 26.7$$

Bluefin tuna decreased from 230 thousand in 1974 to fewer than 27 thousand in 1991.

(b) Solve the equation $f(x) = 50$ for x.

$$230(0.881)^x = 50 \qquad \text{\small $f(x) = 50$}$$

$$0.881^x = \frac{5}{23} \qquad \text{\small STEP 1: Divide by 230; simplify.}$$

The common logarithm could also be used.

$$\ln 0.881^x = \ln \frac{5}{23} \qquad \text{\small STEP 2: Take the natural logarithm of each side.}$$

$$x \ln 0.881 = \ln \frac{5}{23} \qquad \text{\small STEP 3: $\ln m^r = r \ln m$}$$

$$x = \frac{\ln(5/23)}{\ln 0.881} \qquad \text{\small STEP 4: Divide by $\ln 0.881$.}$$

$$x \approx 12.04 \qquad \text{\small Approximate.}$$

They numbered about 50 thousand in $1974 + 12.04 \approx 1986$.

Now Try Exercise 87

Moore's law states that the processing speed and memory capacity of computers doubles every 2 years. Researchers have recently found an even more profound law relating energy efficiency and computing power. This law says that the number of computations that a computer can perform on a fixed amount of electricity (such as a kilowatt-hour) has doubled every 1.6 years since the mid-1940s, when vacuum tubes were used in computers. In the next example we use an exponential function to model this new law and make a prediction. (***Source:*** *The Economist.*)

EXAMPLE 4 Modeling the electrical efficiency of computers

In 1945 computers could perform about 1000 computations with 1 kilowatt-hour of electricity. This number has doubled every 1.6 years.

(a) Find an exponential function $E(x) = Ca^x$ that gives the number of computations a computer can perform on 1 kilowatt-hour, where x is years after 1945.

(b) Evaluate $E(65)$ and interpret your result.

(c) In what year did computers first perform 1,000,000 calculations per kilowatt-hour?

SOLUTION

(a) The initial value is 1000 when $x = 0$, so $C = 1000$ and $E(x) = 1000a^x$. When $x = 1.6$ the number of computations doubles to 2000 per kilowatt-hour, so let $E(1.6) = 2000$ and solve for a.

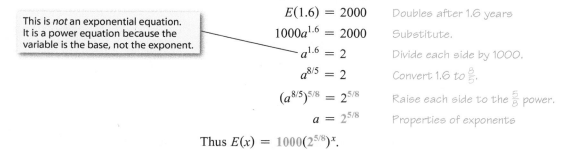

This is *not* an exponential equation. It is a power equation because the variable is the base, not the exponent.

$$E(1.6) = 2000 \qquad \text{\small Doubles after 1.6 years}$$

$$1000a^{1.6} = 2000 \qquad \text{\small Substitute.}$$

$$a^{1.6} = 2 \qquad \text{\small Divide each side by 1000.}$$

$$a^{8/5} = 2 \qquad \text{\small Convert 1.6 to $\frac{8}{5}$.}$$

$$(a^{8/5})^{5/8} = 2^{5/8} \qquad \text{\small Raise each side to the $\frac{5}{8}$ power.}$$

$$a = 2^{5/8} \qquad \text{\small Properties of exponents}$$

Thus $E(x) = 1000(2^{5/8})^x$.

(b) $E(65) = 1000(2^{5/8})^{65} \approx 1.7 \times 10^{15}$. In $1945 + 65 = 2010$, computers could perform about 1.7 *quadrillion* computations on 1 kilowatt-hour.

(c) We must determine a value for x, so that $E(x) = 1,000,000$.

$$1000(2^{5/8})^x = 1,000,000 \qquad \textit{E(x) = 1,000,000.}$$
$$(2^{5/8})^x = 1000 \qquad \textit{STEP 1: Divide by 1000.}$$
$$\log(2^{5/8})^x = \log 1000 \qquad \textit{STEP 2: Take common logarithm.}$$
$$x \log 2^{5/8} = 3 \qquad \textit{STEP 3: Power rule}$$
$$x = \frac{3}{\log 2^{5/8}} \qquad \textit{STEP 4: Divide by log } 2^{5/8}.$$
$$x \approx 16 \qquad \textit{Approximate.}$$

Thus in $1945 + 16 = 1961$ computers first performed 1 million computations on 1 kilowatt-hour.

> **Now Try Exercise 83**

Exponential equations can occur in many forms. Although some types of exponential equations cannot be solved symbolically, Example 5 shows four equations that can.

EXAMPLE 5 Solving exponential equations symbolically

Solve each equation.

(a) $10^{x+2} = 10^{3x}$ **(b)** $5(1.2)^x + 1 = 26$ **(c)** $\left(\frac{1}{4}\right)^{x-1} = \frac{1}{9}$ **(d)** $5^{x-3} = e^{2x}$

SOLUTION

(a) Start by taking the common logarithm of each side.

$$10^{x+2} = 10^{3x} \qquad \textit{Given equation}$$
$$\log 10^{x+2} = \log 10^{3x} \qquad \textit{Take the common logarithm.}$$
$$x + 2 = 3x \qquad \textit{Inverse property: log } 10^k = k$$
$$2 = 2x \qquad \textit{Subtract x.}$$
$$x = 1 \qquad \textit{Divide by 2; rewrite.}$$

(b) Start by isolating the exponential term on one side of the equation.

$$5(1.2)^x = 25 \qquad \textit{Subtract 1.}$$
$$(1.2)^x = 5 \qquad \textit{Divide by 5.}$$
$$\log(1.2)^x = \log 5 \qquad \textit{Take the common logarithm.}$$
$$x \log 1.2 = \log 5 \qquad \textit{log } m^r = r \log m$$
$$x = \frac{\log 5}{\log 1.2} \qquad \textit{Divide by log 1.2.}$$
$$x \approx 8.827 \qquad \textit{Approximate.}$$

(c) Begin by taking the common logarithm of each side.

$$\left(\frac{1}{4}\right)^{x-1} = \frac{1}{9} \qquad \textit{Given equation}$$
$$\log\left(\frac{1}{4}\right)^{x-1} = \log\frac{1}{9} \qquad \textit{Take the common logarithm.}$$
$$(x - 1)\log\left(\frac{1}{4}\right) = \log\frac{1}{9} \qquad \textit{log } m^r = r \log m$$
$$x - 1 = \frac{\log(1/9)}{\log(1/4)} \qquad \textit{Divide by log } \tfrac{1}{4}.$$
$$x = 1 + \frac{\log(1/9)}{\log(1/4)} \approx 2.585 \quad \textit{Add 1 and approximate.}$$

This equation could also be solved by taking the natural logarithm of each side.

(d) Begin by taking the natural (or common) logarithm of each side.

$$5^{x-3} = e^{2x} \qquad \text{Given equation}$$
$$\ln 5^{x-3} = \ln e^{2x} \qquad \text{Take the natural logarithm.}$$
$$(x-3)\ln 5 = 2x \qquad \ln m^r = r \ln m$$
$$x \ln 5 - 3\ln 5 = 2x \qquad \text{Distributive property}$$
$$x \ln 5 - 2x = 3\ln 5 \qquad \text{Subtract 2x; add 3 ln 5.}$$
$$x(\ln 5 - 2) = 3\ln 5 \qquad \text{Factor out x.}$$
$$x = \frac{3\ln 5}{\ln 5 - 2} \qquad \text{Divide by ln 5} - 2.$$
$$x \approx -12.36 \qquad \text{Approximate.}$$

> **Now Try Exercises 13, 17, 23, and 25**

Solving Equations Involving Like Bases If a function is one-to-one, then $f(a) = f(b)$ implies that $a = b$. In Example 5(a) we were given the equation $10^{x+2} = 10^{3x}$. Because $f(x) = 10^x$ is one-to-one, it follows that $x + 2 = 3x$, or $x = 1$. We can use this technique to solve some exponential equations if we can write the expressions on each side of the equation in terms of the same base a. Then $a^x = a^y$ implies that $x = y$.

EXAMPLE 6 Solving an exponential equation using like bases

Solve the equation $4^{x+1} = 8^{2-x}$.

SOLUTION
Because $4 = 2^2$ and $8 = 2^3$, we can write this equation using only base 2.

$$4^{x+1} = 8^{2-x} \qquad \text{Given equation}$$
$$(2^2)^{x+1} = (2^3)^{2-x} \qquad \text{Substitute.}$$
$$2^{2x+2} = 2^{6-3x} \qquad \text{Properties of exponents}$$
$$2x + 2 = 6 - 3x \qquad 2^x \text{ is one-to-one.}$$
$$5x = 4 \qquad \text{Add 3x and subtract 2.}$$
$$x = \frac{4}{5} \qquad \text{Divide by 5.}$$

> **Now Try Exercise 37**

NOTE The technique used in Example 6 does not work for some exponential equations. For example, $5^{x-3} = e^{2x}$ cannot easily be written in terms of equal bases. However, this equation can be solved by taking a logarithm of each side as in Example 5(d).

An Application If a hot object is put in a room with temperature T_0, then according to **Newton's law of cooling**, the temperature T of the object after time t is modeled by

$$T(t) = T_0 + Da^t, \qquad 0 < a < 1,$$

where D is the initial temperature *difference* between the object and the room.

EXAMPLE 7 Modeling coffee cooling

A pot of coffee with a temperature of 100°C is set down in a room with a temperature of 20°C. The coffee cools to 60°C after 1 hour.
(a) Find values for T_0, D, and a so that $T(t) = T_0 + Da^t$ models the data.
(b) Find the temperature of the coffee after half an hour.
(c) How long did it take for the coffee to reach 50°C? Support your result graphically.

SOLUTION
(a) The room has temperature $T_0 = 20°C$, and the initial temperature difference between the coffee and the room is $D = 100 - 20 = 80°C$. Thus $T(t) = 20 + 80a^t$. To find a, use the fact that the temperature of the coffee after 1 hour was 60°C.

Let $t = 1$ and $T = 60$ in $T(t) = 20 + 80a^t$ and solve for a.

$$T(1) = 60 \qquad \text{Temperature is 60° after 1 hour.}$$
$$20 + 80a^1 = 60 \qquad \text{Let } t = 1 \text{ in } T(t) = 20 + 80a^t.$$
$$80a = 40 \qquad \text{Subtract 20.}$$
$$a = \frac{1}{2} \qquad \text{Divide by 80.}$$

Thus $T(t) = 20 + 80\left(\frac{1}{2}\right)^t$.

(b) After half an hour, the temperature is

$$T\left(\frac{1}{2}\right) = 20 + 80\left(\frac{1}{2}\right)^{1/2} \approx 76.6°\text{C}.$$

(c) *Symbolic Solution* To determine when the coffee reached 50°C, solve $T(t) = 50$.

$$20 + 80\left(\frac{1}{2}\right)^t = 50 \qquad T(t) = 50$$

$$80\left(\frac{1}{2}\right)^t = 30 \qquad \text{Subtract 20.}$$

$$\left(\frac{1}{2}\right)^t = \frac{3}{8} \qquad \text{Divide by 80; simplify.}$$

$$\log\left(\frac{1}{2}\right)^t = \log\frac{3}{8} \qquad \text{Take the common logarithm.}$$

$$t\log\left(\frac{1}{2}\right) = \log\frac{3}{8} \qquad \text{Power rule}$$

$$t = \frac{\log(3/8)}{\log(1/2)} \qquad \text{Divide by } \log\frac{1}{2}.$$

$$t \approx 1.415 \qquad \text{Approximate.}$$

The temperature reaches 50°C after about 1.415 hours, or 1 hour and 25 minutes.

Graphical Solution The graphs of $Y_1 = 20 + 80(1/2)\wedge X$ and $Y_2 = 50$ intersect near $(1.415, 50)$, as shown in Figure 5.69. This result agrees with the symbolic solution.

Graphical Solution

$[0, 3, 1]$ by $[0, 100, 10]$

Figure 5.69

Now Try Exercise 91

NOTE Newton's law of cooling can also model the temperature of a cold object that is brought into a warm room. In this case, the temperature difference D is *negative*.

Some exponential equations *cannot* be solved symbolically but can be solved graphically. This is demonstrated in the next example.

EXAMPLE 8 Solving an exponential equation graphically

Solve $e^{-x} + 2x = 3$ graphically. Approximate all solutions to the nearest hundredth.

SOLUTION The graphs of $Y_1 = e\wedge(-X) + 2X$ and $Y_2 = 3$ intersect near the points $(-1.92, 3)$ and $(1.37, 3)$, as shown in Figures 5.70 and 5.71. Thus the solutions are approximately -1.92 and 1.37.

Graphical Solutions

$[-6, 6, 1]$ by $[-4, 4, 1]$ $\qquad$ $[-6, 6, 1]$ by $[-4, 4, 1]$

Figure 5.70 $\qquad\qquad$ **Figure 5.71**

Now Try Exercise 73

Logarithmic Equations

Logarithmic equations contain logarithms. To solve a logarithmic equation, we use the inverse property $a^{\log_a x} = x$. This technique is illustrated in the next example.

EXAMPLE 9 Solving a logarithmic equation

Solve $3\log_3 x = 12$.

SOLUTION Begin by dividing each side by 3.

$$\log_3 x = 4 \qquad \text{Divide by 3.}$$
$$3^{\log_3 x} = 3^4 \qquad \text{Exponentiate each side; base 3.}$$
$$x = 81 \qquad \text{Inverse property: } a^{\log_a k} = k$$

Now Try Exercise 57

We can solve logarithmic equations by using the following steps.

SOLVING LOGARITHMIC EQUATIONS SYMBOLICALLY

The following steps can be used to solve several types of logarithmic equations.

STEP 1: Isolate the logarithmic expression on one side of the equation. (You may need to apply properties of logarithms.)

STEP 2: Exponentiate each side of the equation with the same base as the logarithm.

STEP 3: Apply the inverse property $a^{\log_a k} = k$.

STEP 4: Solve for the variable. *Check your answer.*

EXAMPLE 10 Solving a logarithmic equation symbolically

In developing countries, there is a relationship between the amount of land a person owns and the average daily calories consumed. This relationship is modeled by the formula $C(x) = 280\ln(x + 1) + 1925$, where x is the amount of land owned in acres and $0 \le x \le 4$. (***Source:*** D. Grigg, *The World Food Problem.*)
(a) Find the average caloric intake for a person who owns no land.
(b) A graph of C is shown in Figure 5.72. Interpret the graph.
(c) Determine symbolically the number of acres owned by someone whose average intake is 2000 calories per day.

SOLUTION
(a) Since $C(0) = 280\ln(0 + 1) + 1925 = 1925$, a person without land consumes an average of 1925 calories per day.
(b) The y-intercept of 1925 represents the caloric intake for a person who owns no land. As the amount of land x increases, the caloric intake y also increases. However, the rate of increase slows. This would be expected because there is a limit to the number of calories an average person would eat, regardless of his or her economic status.
(c) Solve the equation $C(x) = 2000$ for x.

$$280\ln(x + 1) + 1925 = 2000 \qquad C(x) = 2000$$
$$280\ln(x + 1) = 75 \qquad \text{STEP 1: Subtract 1925.}$$
$$\ln(x + 1) = \frac{75}{280} \qquad \text{STEP 1: Divide by 280.}$$
$$e^{\ln(x+1)} = e^{75/280} \qquad \text{STEP 2: Exponentiate each side; base } e.$$
$$x + 1 = e^{75/280} \qquad \text{STEP 3: Inverse property: } e^{\ln k} = k$$
$$x = e^{75/280} - 1 \qquad \text{STEP 4: Subtract 1.}$$
$$x \approx 0.307 \qquad \text{Approximate.}$$

A person who owns about 0.3 acre has an average intake of 2000 calories per day.

Now Try Exercise 95

Land and Calories

$C(x) = 280\ln(x + 1) + 1925$

Calories

Land owned (acres)

Figure 5.72

Like exponential equations, logarithmic equations can occur in many forms. The next example illustrates three equations that can be solved symbolically.

> **EXAMPLE 11** Solving logarithmic equations symbolically
>
> Solve each equation.
> **(a)** $\log(2x + 1) = 2$ **(b)** $\log_2 4x = 2 - \log_2 x$
> **(c)** $2\ln(x + 1) = \ln(1 - 2x)$
>
> **SOLUTION**
> **(a)** To solve the equation, exponentiate each side of the equation using base 10.
>
> | | |
> |---|---|
> | $\log(2x + 1) = 2$ | Given equation (Step 1 not needed) |
> | $10^{\log(2x+1)} = 10^2$ | STEP 2: Exponentiate each side; base 10. |
> | $2x + 1 = 100$ | STEP 3: Inverse property: $10^{\log k} = k$ |
> | $x = 49.5$ | STEP 4: Solve for x. |
>
> **(b)** To solve this equation, apply properties of logarithms.
>
> | | |
> |---|---|
> | $\log_2 4x = 2 - \log_2 x$ | Given equation |
> | $\log_2 4x + \log_2 x = 2$ | STEP 1: Add $\log_2 x$. |
> | $\log_2 4x^2 = 2$ | STEP 1: $\log_a m + \log_a n = \log_a(mn)$ |
> | $2^{\log_2 4x^2} = 2^2$ | STEP 2: Exponentiate each side; base 2. |
> | $4x^2 = 4$ | STEP 3: Inverse property: $a^{\log_a k} = k$ |
> | $x = \pm 1$ | STEP 4: Solve for x. |
>
> However, -1 is not a solution since $\log_2 x$ in the given equation is undefined for negative values of x. Thus the only solution is 1.
> **(c)** For this equation we isolate a logarithmic expression on each side of the equation and then exponentiate.
>
> | | |
> |---|---|
> | $2\ln(x + 1) = \ln(1 - 2x)$ | Given equation (Step 1 not needed) |
> | $\ln(x + 1)^2 = \ln(1 - 2x)$ | Power rule |
> | $e^{\ln(x+1)^2} = e^{\ln(1-2x)}$ | STEP 2: Exponentiate; base e. |
> | $(x + 1)^2 = 1 - 2x$ | STEP 3: Inverse property: $a^{\log_a k} = k$ |
> | $x^2 + 2x + 1 = 1 - 2x$ | STEP 4: Expand the binomial. |
> | $x^2 + 4x = 0$ | Combine terms. |
> | $x(x + 4) = 0$ | Factor. |
> | $x = 0$ or $x = -4$ | Zero-product property |
>
> Substituting $x = 0$ and $x = -4$ in the given equation shows that 0 is a solution but -4 is not a solution.
>
> **Now Try Exercises 61, 65, and 69**

MAKING CONNECTIONS

Solving Exponential and Logarithmic Equations
At some point in the process of solving an exponential equation, we often take a logarithm of each side of the equation. Similarly, when solving a logarithmic equation, we often exponentiate each side of the equation.

5.6 Putting It All Together

The following table summarizes techniques that can be used to solve some types of exponential and logarithmic equations symbolically.

CONCEPT	EXPLANATION	EXAMPLES
Exponential equations	Typical form: $Ca^x = k$ Solve for a^x. Then take a base-a logarithm of each side. Use the inverse property: $\qquad\log_a a^x = x.$	$4e^x = 24$ $e^x = 6$ $\ln e^x = \ln 6$ $x = \ln 6 \approx 1.79$

CONCEPT	EXPLANATION	EXAMPLES
Logarithmic equations	**Equation 1:** $C\log_a x = k$ Solve for $\log_a x$. Then exponentiate each side with base a. Use the inverse property: $$a^{\log_a x} = x.$$	**1.** $4\log x = 10$ $\log x = 2.5$ $10^{\log x} = 10^{2.5}$ $x = 10^{2.5} \approx 316$
	Equation 2: $\log_a bx \pm \log_a cx = k$ When more than one logarithm with the same base occurs, use properties of logarithms to combine logarithms. *Be sure to check any solutions.*	**2.** $\log x + \log 4x = 2$ $\log 4x^2 = 2$ $4x^2 = 10^2$ $x^2 = 25$ $x = \pm 5$ The only solution is 5.

5.6 Exercises

Solving Exponential Equations

Exercises 1–4: The graphical and symbolic representations of f and g are shown.

   (a) *Use the graph to solve $f(x) = g(x)$.*
   (b) *Solve $f(x) = g(x)$ symbolically.*

1.

2.

3.

4.

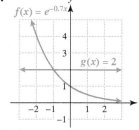

Exercises 5–32: Solve the exponential equation.

5. $4e^x = 5$

6. $2e^{-x} = 8$

7. $2(10)^x + 5 = 45$

8. $100 - 5(10)^x = 7$

9. $2.5e^{-1.2x} = 1$

10. $9.5e^{0.005x} = 19$

11. $1.2(0.9)^x = 0.6$

12. $0.05(1.15)^x = 5$

13. $4(1.1)^{x-1} = 16$

14. $3(2)^{x-2} = 99$

15. $5(1.2)^{3x-2} + 94 = 100$

16. $1.4(2)^{x+3} = 2.8$

17. $5^{3x} = 5^{1-2x}$

18. $7^{x^2} = 7^{4x-3}$

19. $10^{(x^2)} = 10^{3x-2}$

20. $e^{2x} = e^{5x-3}$

21. $\left(\frac{1}{5}\right)^x = -5$

22. $2^x = -4$

23. $\left(\frac{2}{5}\right)^{x-2} = \frac{1}{3}$

24. $\left(\frac{3}{2}\right)^{x+1} = \frac{7}{3}$

25. $4^{x-1} = 3^{2x}$

26. $3^{1-2x} = e^{0.5x}$

27. $e^{x-3} = 2^{3x}$

28. $6^{x+1} = 4^{2x-1}$

29. $3(1.4)^x - 4 = 60$

30. $2(1.05)^x + 3 = 10$

31. $5(1.015)^{x-1980} = 8$

32. $30 - 3(0.75)^{x-1} = 29$

Exercises 33–42: (Refer to Example 6.) Use the fact that $a^x = a^y$ implies $x = y$, to solve each equation.

33. $5^{2x} = 5^{x-3}$

34. $7^{-x} = 7^{2x+1}$

35. $e^{-x} = e^{x^2}$ **36.** $e^{x^2} = e^{2x+1}$

37. $2^{3x} = 8^{-x+2}$ **38.** $9^{2x} = 27^{1-x}$

39. $25^{2x} = 125^{2-x}$ **40.** $16^x = 4^{2-x}$

41. $32^{3x} = 16^{5x+3}$ **42.** $16^{x-5} = 64^{1-2x}$

Solving Logarithmic Equations

Exercises 43–72: Solve the logarithmic equation.

43. $3\log x = 2$ **44.** $5\ln x = 10$

45. $\ln 2x = 5$ **46.** $\ln 4x = 1.5$

47. $\log 2x^2 = 2$ **48.** $\log(2 - x) = 0.5$

49. $\log_2(3x - 2) = 4$ **50.** $\log_3(1 - x) = 1$

51. $\log_5(8 - 3x) = 3$ **52.** $\log_6(2x + 4) = 2$

53. $160 + 10\log x = 50$ **54.** $160 + 10\log x = 120$

55. $\ln x + \ln x^2 = 3$ **56.** $\log x^5 = 4 + 3\log x$

57. $2\log_2 x = 4.2$ **58.** $3\log_2 3x = 1$

59. $\log x + \log 2x = 2$ **60.** $\ln 2x + \ln 3x = \ln 6$

61. $\log(2 - 3x) = 3$ **62.** $\log(x^2 + 1) = 2$

63. $\ln x + \ln(3x - 1) = \ln 10$

64. $\log x + \log(2x + 5) = \log 7$

65. $2\ln x = \ln(2x + 1)$

66. $\log(x^2 + 3) = 2\log(x + 1)$

67. $\log(x + 1) + \log(x - 1) = \log 3$

68. $\ln(x^2 - 4) - \ln(x + 2) = \ln(3 - x)$

69. $\log_2 2x = 4 - \log_2(x + 2)$

70. $\log_3 x + \log_3(x + 2) = \log_3 24$

71. $\log_5(x + 1) + \log_5(x - 1) = \log_5 15$

72. $\log_7 4x - \log_7(x + 3) = \log_7 x$

Solving Equations Graphically

Exercises 73–78: The following equations cannot be solved symbolically. Solve these equations graphically and round your answers to the nearest hundredth.

73. $2x + e^x = 2$ **74.** $xe^x - 1 = 0$

75. $x^2 - x\ln x = 2$ **76.** $x\ln|x| = -2$

77. $xe^{-x} + \ln x = 1$ **78.** $2^{x-2} = \log x^4$

Applications

79. Population Growth World population P in billions during year x can be modeled by $P(x) = 7(1.01)^{x-2011}$. Predict the year when world population might reach 7.5 billion.

80. Population of Arizona The population P of Arizona has been increasing at an annual rate of 2.3%. In 2010 the population of Arizona was 6.4 million.
(a) Write a formula for $P(x)$, where x is the years after 2010 and P is in millions.

(b) Estimate the population of Arizona in 2014.

81. Light Absorption When light passes through water, its intensity I decreases according to the formula $I(x) = I_0 e^{-kx}$, where I_0 is the initial intensity of the light and x is the depth in feet. If $I_0 = 1000$ lumens per square meter and $k = 0.12$, determine the depth at which the intensity is 25% of I_0.

82. Light Absorption (Refer to Exercise 81.) Let $I(x) = 500e^{-0.2x}$ and determine the depth x at which the intensity I is 1% of $I_0 = 500$.

83. Moore's Law According to Moore's law the number of transistors that can be placed on an integrated circuit has doubled every 2 years. In 1971 there were only 2300 transistors on an integrated circuit.
(a) Find an exponential function $T(x) = Ca^x$ that gives the number of transistors on an integrated circuit x years after 1971.

(b) Evaluate $T(40)$ and interpret your result.

(c) Determine the year when integrated circuits first had 10 million transistors.

84. Electrical Efficiency (Refer to Example 4.) Use the formula $E(x) = 1000(2^{5/8})^x$ to determine when 1 billion computations could first be performed with 1 kilowatt-hour.

85. **Corruption and Human Development** There is a relationship between perceived corruption and human development in a country that can be modeled by $H(x) = 0.3 + 0.28 \ln x$. In this formula x represents the Corruption Perception Index, where 1 is very corrupt and 10 is least corrupt. The output gives the Human Development Index, which is between 0.1 and 1 with 1 being the best for human development. (*Sources:* Transparency International; UN Human Development Report.)
    (a) For Britain $x = 8$. Evaluate $H(8)$ and interpret the result.

    (b) The Human Development Index is 0.68 for China. Find the Corruption Perception Index for China.

86. **Urbanization of Brazil** The percentage of Brazil's population that lives in urban areas can be modeled by $U(x) = 72 + 4.33 \ln x$, where $x \geq 1$ is the number of years after 1990.
    (a) Evaluate $U(24)$ and interpret the result.

    (b) Predict when urbanization will first reach 88%.

87. **Bluefin Tuna** The number of Atlantic bluefin tuna in thousands x years after 1974 can be modeled by $f(x) = 230(0.881)^x$. Estimate the year when the number of bluefin tuna reached 95 thousand.

88. **Modeling Bacteria** (Refer to Section 5.3, Example 9.) The number N of *E. coli* bacteria in millions per milliliter after t minutes can be modeled by $N(t) = 0.5e^{0.014t}$. Determine symbolically the elapsed time required for the concentration of bacteria to reach 25 million per milliliter.

89. **Population Growth** In 2000 the population of India reached 1 billion, and in 2025 it is projected to be 1.4 billion. (*Source:* Bureau of the Census.)
    (a) Find values for C and a so that $P(x) = Ca^{x-2000}$ models the population of India in year x.

    (b) Estimate India's population in 2010.

    (c) Use P to determine the year when India's population might reach 1.5 billion.

90. **Population of Pakistan** In 2007 the population of Pakistan was 164 million, and it is expected to be 250 million in 2025. (*Source:* United Nations.)
    (a) Approximate C and a so that $P(x) = Ca^{x-2007}$ models these data, where P is in millions and x is the year.

    (b) Estimate the population of Pakistan in 2015, and compare your estimate to the predicted value of 204 million.

    (c) Estimate when this population could reach 212 million.

91. **Newton's Law of Cooling** A pan of boiling water with a temperature of 212°F is set in a bin of ice with a temperature of 32°F. The pan cools to 70°F in 30 minutes.
    (a) Find T_0, D, and a so that $T(t) = T_0 + Da^t$ models the data, where t is in hours.

    (b) Find the temperature of the pan after 10 minutes.

    (c) How long did it take the pan to reach 40°F? Support your result graphically.

92. **Warming an Object** A pan of cold water with a temperature of 35°F is brought into a room with a temperature of 75°F. After 1 hour, the temperature of the pan of water is 45°F.
    (a) Find T_0, D, and a so that $T(t) = T_0 + Da^t$ models the data, where t is in hours.

    (b) Find the temperature of the water after 3 hours.

    (c) How long would it take the water to reach 60°F?

93. **Warming a Soda Can** Suppose that a can of soda, initially at 5°C, warms to 18°C after 2 hours in a room that has a temperature of 20°C.
    (a) Find the temperature of the soda can after 1.5 hours.

    (b) How long did it take for the soda to warm to 15°C?

94. **Cooling a Soda Can** A soda can at 80°F is put into a cooler containing ice at 32°F. The temperature of the soda after t minutes is given by $T(t) = 32 + 48(0.9)^t$.
    (a) Evaluate $T(30)$ and interpret your results.

    (b) How long did it take for the soda to cool to 50°F?

95. **Caloric Intake** (Refer to Example 10.) The formula

    $$C(x) = 280 \ln(x + 1) + 1925$$

    models the number of calories consumed daily by a person owning x acres of land in a developing country. Estimate the number of acres owned for which average intake is 2300 calories per day.

96. **Salinity** The salinity of the oceans changes with latitude and with depth. In the tropics, the salinity increases on the surface of the ocean due to rapid evaporation. In the higher latitudes, there is less evaporation and rainfall causes the salinity to be less on the surface than at lower depths. The function given by

    $$S(x) = 31.5 + 1.1 \log(x + 1)$$

    models salinity to depths of 1000 meters at a latitude of 57.5°N. The input x is the depth in meters and the output $S(x)$ is in grams of salt per kilogram of seawater. (*Source:* D. Hartman, *Global Physical Climatology.*)
    (a) Evaluate $S(500)$. Interpret your result.

(b) Graph S. Discuss any trends.

(c) Find the depth where the salinity equals 33.

97. Life Span In one study, the life spans of 129 robins were monitored over a 4-year period. The equation $y = \dfrac{2 - \log(100 - x)}{0.42}$ can be used to calculate the number of years y required for x percent of the robin population to die. For example, to find the time when 40% of the robins had died, substitute $x = 40$ into the equation. The result is $y \approx 0.53$, or about half a year. Find the percentage of the robins that had died after 2 years. (**Source:** D. Lack, *The Life of a Robin.*)

98. Life Span of Sparrows (Refer to Exercise 97.) The life span of a sample of sparrows was studied. The equation $y = \dfrac{2 - \log(100 - x)}{0.37}$ calculates the number of years y required for x percent of the sparrows to die, where $0 \le x \le 95$.
(a) Find y when $x = 40$. Interpret your answer.

(b) Find x when $y = 1.5$. Interpret your answer.

99. Bacteria Growth The concentration of bacteria in a sample can be modeled by $B(t) = B_0 e^{kt}$, where t is in hours and B is the concentration in billions of bacteria per liter.
(a) If the concentration increases by 15% in 6 hours, find k.

(b) If $B_0 = 1.2$, find B after 8.2 hours.

(c) By what percentage does the concentration increase each hour?

100. Voltage The voltage in a circuit can be modeled by $V(t) = V_0 e^{kt}$, where t is in milliseconds.
(a) If the voltage decreases by 85% in 5 milliseconds, find k.

(b) If $V_0 = 4.5$ volts, find V after 2.3 milliseconds.

(c) By what percentage does the voltage decrease each millisecond?

Exercises 101 and 102: For the given annual interest rate r, estimate the time for P dollars to double.
101. $P = \$1000$, $r = 8.5\%$ compounded quarterly

102. $P = \$750$, $r = 2\%$ compounded continuously

Exercises 103 and 104: **Continuous Compounding** *Suppose that P dollars is deposited in a savings account paying 3% interest compounded continuously. After t years, the account will contain $A(t) = Pe^{0.03t}$ dollars.*
(a) Solve $A(t) = b$ for the given values of P and b.
(b) Interpret your results.

103. $P = 500$ and $b = 750$

104. $P = 1000$ and $b = 2000$

105. Radioactive Carbon-14 The percentage P of radioactive carbon-14 remaining in a fossil after t years is given by $P = 100\left(\frac{1}{2}\right)^{t/5700}$. Suppose a fossil contains 35% of the carbon-14 that the organism contained when it was alive. Estimate the age of the fossil.

106. Radioactive Radium-226 The amount A of radium in milligrams remaining in a sample after t years is given by $A(t) = 0.02\left(\frac{1}{2}\right)^{t/1600}$. How many years will it take for the radium to decay to 0.004 milligram?

107. Traffic Flow (Refer to Section 5.3, Example 11.) The probability that a car will enter an intersection within a period of x minutes is given by $P(x) = 1 - e^{-0.5x}$. Determine symbolically the elapsed time x when there is a 50–50 chance that a car has entered the intersection. (*Hint:* Solve $P(x) = 0.5$.)

108. Modeling Traffic Flow Cars arrive randomly at an intersection with an average traffic volume of one car per minute. The likelihood, or probability, that at least one car enters the intersection during a period of x minutes can be estimated by $f(x) = 1 - e^{-x}$.
(a) What is the probability that at least one car enters the intersection during a 5-minute period?

(b) Determine the value of x that gives a 40% chance that at least one car enters the intersection during an interval of x minutes.

109. Modeling Bacteria Growth Suppose that the concentration of a bacteria sample is 100,000 bacteria per milliliter. If the concentration doubles every 2 hours, how long will it take for the concentration to reach 350,000 bacteria per milliliter?

110. Modeling Bacteria Growth Suppose that the concentration of a bacteria sample is 50,000 bacteria per milliliter. If the concentration triples in 4 days, how long will it take for the concentration to reach 85,000 bacteria per milliliter?

111. Continuous Compounding Suppose that $2000 is deposited in an account and the balance increases to $2300 after 4 years. How long will it take for the account to grow to $3200? Assume continuous compounding.

112. Modeling Radioactive Decay Suppose that a 0.05-gram sample of a radioactive substance decays to 0.04 gram in 20 days. How long will it take for the sample to decay to 0.025 gram?

113. Drug Concentrations The concentration of a drug in a patient's bloodstream after t hours is modeled by the formula $C(t) = 11(0.72)^t$, where C is measured in milligrams per liter.

(a) What is the initial concentration of the drug?

(b) How long does it take for the concentration to decrease to 50% of its initial level?

114. **Reducing Carbon Emissions**   When fossil fuels are burned, carbon is released into the atmosphere. Governments could reduce carbon emissions by placing a tax on fossil fuels. The **cost-benefit** equation

$$\ln(1 - P) = -0.0034 - 0.0053x$$

estimates the relationship between a tax of x dollars per ton of carbon and the percent P reduction in emissions of carbon, where P is in decimal form. Determine P when $x = 60$. Interpret the result (**Source:** W. Clime, *The Economics of Global Warming*.)

115. **Investments**   The formula $A = P\left(1 + \frac{r}{n}\right)^{nt}$ can be used to calculate the future value of an investment. Solve the equation for t.

116. **Decibels**   The formula $D = 160 + 10\log x$ can be used to calculate loudness of a sound in decibels. Solve the equation for x.

Writing about Mathematics

117. Explain how to solve the equation $Ca^x = k$ symbolically for x. Demonstrate your method.

118. Explain how to solve the equation $b\log_a x = k$ symbolically for x. Demonstrate your method.

Extended and Discovery Exercise

1. **Exponential Functions**   Show that any exponential function in the form $f(x) = Ca^x$ can be written as $f(x) = Ce^{kx}$. That is, write k in terms of a. Use your method to write $g(x) = 2^x$ in the form e^{kx} for some k.

CHECKING BASIC CONCEPTS FOR SECTIONS 5.5 AND 5.6

1. Use properties of logarithms to expand $\log \dfrac{x^2 y^3}{\sqrt[3]{z}}$. Write your answer without exponents.

2. Combine the expression $\frac{1}{2}\ln x - 3\ln y + \ln z$ as a logarithm of a single expression.

3. Solve each equation.
   (a) $5(1.4)^x - 4 = 25$ **(b)** $4^{2-x} = 4^{2x+1}$

4. Solve each equation.
   (a) $5\log_2 2x = 25$

   (b) $\ln(x + 1) + \ln(x - 1) = \ln 3$

5. The temperature T of a cooling object in degrees Fahrenheit after x minutes is given by

$$T = 80 + 120(0.9)^x.$$

   (a) What happens to T after a long time?

   (b) After how long is the object's temperature 100°F?

5.7 Constructing Nonlinear Models

- **Find an exponential model**
- **Find a logarithmic model**
- **Find a logistic model**
- **Select a model**

Introduction

If data change at a constant rate, then they can be modeled with a linear function. However, real-life data often change at a nonconstant rate. For example, a tree grows slowly when it is small and then gradually grows faster as it becomes larger. Finally, when the tree is mature, its height begins to level off. This type of growth is nonlinear.

Three types of nonlinear data are shown in Figures 5.73–5.75 on the next page, where t represents time. In Figure 5.73 the data increase rapidly, and an *exponential function* might be an appropriate modeling function. In Figure 5.74 the data are growing, but at a slower rate than in Figure 5.73. These data could be modeled by a *logarithmic function*. Finally, in Figure 5.75 the data increase slowly, then increase faster, and finally level off. These data might represent the height of a tree over a 50-year period. To model these data, we need a new type of function called a *logistic function*.

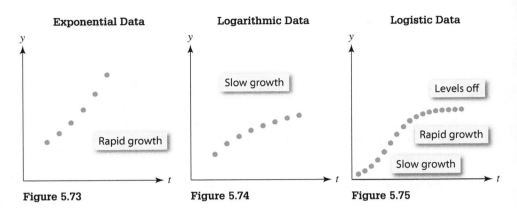

| Figure 5.73 | Figure 5.74 | Figure 5.75 |

Exponential Model

Both world population and bacteria growth can sometimes be modeled by an exponential function that *increases*. Exponential functions can also be used to model data that *decrease*. In the next example, an exponential function is used to model atmospheric pressure.

EXAMPLE 1 Modeling atmospheric pressure

As altitude increases, air pressure decreases. The atmospheric pressure P in millibars (mb) at a given altitude x in meters is listed in Table 5.24.

Altitude and Air Pressure

x (m)	0	5000	10,000	15,000	20,000	25,000	30,000
P (mb)	1013	541	265	121	55	26	12

Source: A. Miller and J. Thompson, *Elements of Meteorology.*
Table 5.24

(a) Make a scatterplot of the data. What type of function might model the data?
(b) Use regression to find an exponential function given by $f(x) = ab^x$. Graph the data and f in the same viewing rectangle.
(c) Use f to estimate the air pressure at an altitude of 23,000 feet.

Calculator Help

To find an equation of least-squares fit, see Appendix A (page AP-9). To copy a regression equation directly into Y_1, see Appendix A (page AP-11).

SOLUTION

(a) The data are shown in Figure 5.76. A *decreasing* exponential function might model the data.

NOTE It is possible for a different function, such as a portion of a polynomial graph, to model the data. Answers may vary.

(b) Figures 5.77 and 5.78 show that values of $a \approx 1104.9$ and $b \approx 0.99985$ are obtained from exponential regression, where $f(x) = ab^x$. Figure 5.79 illustrates that f models the data quite accurately.

(c) $f(23,000) = 1104.9(0.99985)^{23,000} \approx 35.1$ millibars

Plot the Data

[−5000, 35000, 5000] by
[−100, 1200, 100]

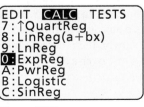

Figure 5.76

Select Exponential Regression

```
EDIT  CALC  TESTS
7:↑QuartReg
8:LinReg(a+bx)
9:LnReg
0:ExpReg
A:PwrReg
B:Logistic
C:SinReg
```

Figure 5.77

Exponential Function

```
ExpReg
y=a*b^x
a=1104.920403
b=.9998503659
```

Figure 5.78

Graph Function with Data

[−5000, 35000, 5000] by
[−100, 1200, 100]

$y_1 = 1104.9(0.99985)^x$

Figure 5.79

Now Try Exercise 15

Logarithmic Model

An investor buying a certificate of deposit (CD) usually gets a higher interest rate if the money is deposited for a longer period of time. However, the interest rate for a 9-month CD is not usually triple the rate for a 3-month CD. Instead, the rate of interest slowly increases with a longer-term CD. In the next example, we model interest rates with a logarithmic function.

> **EXAMPLE 2** Modeling interest rates

Table 5.25 lists the interest rates for certificates of deposit. Use the data to complete the following.

Yield on Certificates of Deposit

Time (months)	1	3	6	9	24	36	60
Yield (%)	0.25	0.39	0.74	0.80	1.25	1.40	1.50

Source: USA Today.
Table 5.25

(a) Make a scatterplot of the data. What type of function might model these data?
(b) Use least-squares regression to find a formula $f(x) = a + b \ln x$ that models the data.
(c) Graph f and the data in the same viewing rectangle.

SOLUTION
(a) Enter the data in Table 5.25 into your calculator. A scatterplot of the data is shown in Figure 5.80. The data increase but gradually level off. A logarithmic modeling function may be appropriate.
(b) In Figures 5.81 and 5.82 least-squares regression has been used to find a logarithmic function f given (approximately) by $f(x) = 0.143 + 0.334 \ln x$.
(c) A graph of f and the data are shown in Figure 5.83.

Plot the Data
[0, 70, 10] by [0, 2, 0.5]

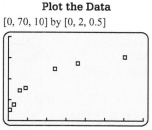

Figure 5.80

Select Logarithm Regression

Figure 5.81

Regression Function

Figure 5.82

Graph Function with Data
[0, 70, 10] by [0, 2, 0.5]

Figure 5.83

> Now Try Exercise 13

Sigmoidal Curve

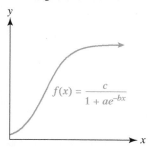

Figure 5.84

Logistic Model

In real life, populations of bacteria, insects, and animals do not continue to grow indefinitely. Initially, population growth may be slow. Then, as their numbers increase, so does the rate of growth. After a region has become heavily populated or saturated, the population usually levels off because of limited resources.

This type of growth may be modeled by a **logistic function** represented by $f(x) = \dfrac{c}{1 + ae^{-bx}}$, where a, b, and c are positive constants. A typical graph of a logistic function f is shown in Figure 5.84. The graph of f is referred to as a **sigmoidal curve**. The next example demonstrates how a logistic function can be used to describe the growth of a yeast culture.

EXAMPLE 3 Modeling logistic growth

One of the earliest studies about population growth was done in 1913 using yeast plants. A small amount of yeast was placed in a container with a fixed amount of nourishment. The units of yeast were recorded every 2 hours. The data are listed in Table 5.26.

Growth of Yeast Plants

Time	0	2	4	6	8	10	12	14	16	18
Yeast	9.6	29.0	71.1	174.6	350.7	513.3	594.8	640.8	655.9	661.8

Source: T. Carlson, *Biochem.;* D. Brown, *Models in Biology.*

Table 5.26

(a) Make a scatterplot of the data in Table 5.26. Describe the growth.
(b) Use least-squares regression to find a logistic function *f* that models the data.
(c) Graph *f* and the data in the same viewing rectangle.
(d) Approximate graphically the time when the amount of yeast was 200 units.

Plot the Data

$[-2, 20, 1]$ by $[-100, 800, 100]$

Figure 5.85

SOLUTION

(a) A scatterplot of the data is shown in Figure 5.85. The yeast increase slowly at first. Then they grow more rapidly until the amount of yeast gradually levels off. The limited amount of nourishment causes this leveling off.

(b) In Figure 5.86 and 5.87 we see least-squares regression being used to find a logistic function *f* given (approximately) by

$$f(x) = \frac{661.8}{1 + 74.46e^{-0.552x}}.$$

(c) In Figure 5.88 the data and *f* are graphed in the same viewing rectangle. The fit for the *real* data is remarkably good.

Select Logistic Regression

```
EDIT  CALC  TESTS
7:↑QuartReg
8:LinReg(a+bx)
9:LnReg
0:ExpReg
A:PwrReg
B:Logistic
C:SinReg
```

Figure 5.86

Regression Function

```
Logistic
y=c/(1+ae^(-bx))
a=74.46113243
b=.551931828
c=661.8044322
```

Figure 5.87

Graph Function with Data

$[-2, 20, 1]$ by $[-100, 800, 100]$

Figure 5.88

Graphical Solution

$[-2, 20, 1]$ by $[-100, 800, 100]$

```
Intersection
X=6.2932648   Y=200
```

Figure 5.89

(d) The graphs of $Y_1 = f(x)$ and $Y_2 = 200$ intersect near (6.29, 200), as shown in Figure 5.89. The amount of yeast reached 200 units after about 6.29 hours.

Now Try Exercise 19

CLASS DISCUSSION

In Example 3, suppose that after 18 hours the experiment had been extended and more nourishment had been provided for the yeast plants. Sketch a possible graph of the amount of yeast.

MAKING CONNECTIONS

Logistic Functions and Horizontal Asymptotes If a logistic function is given by $f(x) = \frac{c}{1 + ae^{-bx}}$, where *a*, *b*, and *c* are positive constants, then the graph of *f* has a horizontal asymptote of $y = c$. (Try to explain why this is true.) In Example 3, the value of *c* was 661.8. This means that the amount of yeast leveled off at about 661.8 units.

Selecting a Model

In real-data applications, a modeling function is seldom given. Many times we must choose the type of modeling function and then find it using least-squares regression. Thus far in this section, we have used exponential, logarithmic, and logistic functions to model data. In the next two examples, we select a modeling function.

EXAMPLE 4 Modeling highway design

To allow enough distance for cars to pass on two-lane highways, engineers often calculate minimum sight distances between curves and hills. See the figure. Table 5.27 shows the minimum sight distance y in feet for a car traveling at x miles per hour.

Passing Distance

x (mph)	20	30	40	50	60	65	70
y (ft)	810	1090	1480	1840	2140	2310	2490

Source: L. Haefner, *Introduction to Transportation Systems.*
Table 5.27

(a) Find a modeling function for the data.
(b) Graph the data and your modeling function.
(c) Estimate the minimum sight distance for a car traveling at 43 miles per hour.

SOLUTION

Getting Started One strategy is to plot the data and then decide if the data are linear or nonlinear. If the data are approximately linear, use linear regression to find the modeling function. If the data are nonlinear, think about how the data increase or decrease. You may want to try several types of modeling functions, such as quadratic, cubic, power, exponential, or logarithmic, before making a final decision. ▶

(a) A scatterplot is shown in Figure 5.90. The data appear to be (nearly) linear, so linear regression has been used to obtain $f(x) = 33.93x + 113.4$. See Figure 5.91.
(b) The data and f are graphed in Figure 5.92. Function f gives a good fit.

Plot the Data
[0, 80, 10] by [0, 3000, 1000]

Figure 5.90

Linear Regression Function

```
LinReg
 y=ax+b
 a=33.92832765
 b=113.4300341
 r²=.9986779453
 r =.999338754
```

Figure 5.91

Graph Function with Data
[0, 80, 10] by [0, 3000, 1000]

$y = 33.93x + 113.4$

Figure 5.92

(c) $f(43) = 33.93(43) + 113.4 \approx 1572$ feet

Now Try Exercise 11

You may have seen or heard of asbestos being removed from buildings. Before 1960 people were generally unaware of its health hazards. As a result, insulation workers who worked with asbestos experienced higher rates of lung cancer. The following example models data from this era.

EXAMPLE 5 Modeling asbestos and cancer

Table 5.28 lists the number N of lung cancer cases occurring within a group of asbestos insulation workers with a cumulative total of 100,000 years of work experience, with their first date of employment x years ago.

Lung Cancer and Asbestos

x (years)	10	15	20	25	30
N (cases)	6.9	25.4	63.6	130	233

Years since employment began

Cases in a group with 100,000 years of work experience

Source: A. Walker, *Observation and Inference.*
Table 5.28

(a) Find a modeling function for the data.
(b) Graph the data and your modeling function.
(c) Estimate the number of lung cancer cases for $x = 23$ years. Interpret your answer.

SOLUTION

Getting Started The data are nonlinear and increasing, so there are a number of functions you can try. Three possibilities are quadratic, power, and exponential. ▶

(a) A scatterplot is shown in Figure 5.93. To model the data we have used a power function given by $f(x) = 0.004334x^{3.2}$. See Figure 5.94. (Answers may vary.)
(b) The data and f are graphed in Figure 5.95. Function f gives a good fit.

Plot the Data	Power Regression Function	Graph Function with Data
[0, 40, 10] by [−50, 250, 50]		[0, 40, 10] by [−50, 250, 50]
Figure 5.93	**Figure 5.94**	**Figure 5.95**

(c) $f(23) = 0.004334(23)^{3.2} \approx 99$ cases. If a group of asbestos workers began their employment 23 years earlier and had a cumulative work experience of 100,000 years, then the group experienced 99 cases of lung cancer.

> **Now Try Exercise 21**

5.7 Putting It All Together

The following table summarizes the basics of exponential, logarithmic, and logistic models. Least-squares regression can be used to determine the constants a, b, c, and C.

CONCEPT	EXPLANATION	EXAMPLES
Exponential model	$f(x) = Ca^x$, $f(x) = ab^x$, or $A(t) = A_0 e^{kt}$	Exponential functions can be used to model data that increase or decrease rapidly over time.
Logarithmic model	$f(x) = a + b\log x$ or $f(x) = a + b\ln x$	Logarithmic functions can be used to model data that increase gradually over time.
Logistic model	$f(x) = \dfrac{c}{1 + ae^{-bx}}$	Logistic functions can be used to model data that at first increase slowly, then increase rapidly, and finally level off.

5.7 Exercises

Note: *Because different functions can be used to model the same data, your answers may vary from the given answers. You can check the validity of your answer by graphing the data and your modeling function in the same viewing rectangle.*

Selecting a Model

Exercises 1–4: Select an appropriate type of modeling function for the data shown in the graph. Choose from the following.

    i. Exponential   ii. Logarithmic   iii. Logistic

1.

2.

3.

4.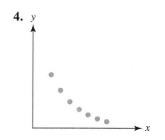

Exercises 5–10: Make a scatterplot of the data. Then find an exponential, logarithmic, or logistic function f that best models the data.

5.

x	1	2	3	4
y	2.04	3.47	5.90	10.02

6.

x	1	2	3	4	5
y	1.98	2.35	2.55	2.69	2.80

7.

x	1	2	3	4	5
y	1.1	3.1	4.3	5.2	5.8

8.

x	1	2	3	4	5	6
y	1	2	4	7	9	10

9.

x	0	1	2	3	4	5
y	0.3	1.3	4.0	7.5	9.3	9.8

10.

x	1	2	3	4	5
y	2.0	1.6	1.3	1.0	0.82

Applications

11. SlideShare Growth   The following table shows the number of visitors in millions who visited the website SlideShare.

Year	2007	2008	2009	2010	2011
Visitors	1.5	6.3	17.0	33.2	60.1

Source: SlideShare.

  (a) Choose a linear, quadratic, or logarithmic function $V(x)$ that best models the data, where x is years after 2007.

  (b) Estimate the number of visitors in 2012.

12. Heart Disease Death Rates   The following table contains heart disease death rates per 100,000 people for selected ages.

Age	30	40	50	60	70
Death rate	30.5	108.2	315	776	2010

Source: Department of Health and Human Services.

  (a) Make a scatterplot of the data in the viewing rectangle $[25, 75, 5]$ by $[-100, 2100, 200]$.

  (b) Find a function f that models the data.

  (c) Estimate the heart disease death rate for people who are 80 years old.

13. Telecommuting   In the past some workers used technology such as e-mail, computers, and multiple phone lines to work at home, rather than in the office. However, because of the need for teamwork and collaboration in the workplace, fewer employees telecommuted than expected. The table lists telecommuters T in millions during year x.

x	1997	1998	1999	2000	2001
T	9.2	9.6	10.0	10.4	10.6

x	2002	2003	2004	2005	2006
T	11.0	11.1	11.2	11.3	11.4

Source: USA Today.

Find a function f that models the data, where $x = 1$ corresponds to 1997, $x = 2$ to 1998, and so on.

14. Hurricanes The table shows the air pressure y in inches of mercury x miles from the eye of a hurricane.

x	2	4	8	15	30	100
y	27.3	27.7	28.04	28.3	28.7	29.3

Source: A. Miller and R. Anthes, *Meteorology.*

(a) Make a scatterplot of the data.

(b) Find a function f that models the data.

(c) Estimate the air pressure at 50 miles.

15. Atmospheric Density The table lists the atmospheric density y in kilograms per cubic meter (kg/m^3) at an altitude of x meters.

x (m)	0	5000	10,000	15,000
y (kg/m³)	1.2250	0.7364	0.4140	0.1948

x (m)	20,000	25,000	30,000
y (kg/m³)	0.0889	0.0401	0.0184

Source: A. Miller.

(a) Find a function f that models the data.

(b) Predict the density at 7000 meters. (The actual value is 0.59 kg/m³.)

16. Modeling Data Use the table to complete the following.

x	1	2	5	10
y	2.5	2.1	1.6	1.2

(a) Find a function f that models the data.

(b) Solve the equation $f(x) = 1.8$.

17. Insect Population The table shows the density y of a species of insect measured in thousands per acre after x days.

x	2	4	6	8	10	12	14
y	0.38	1.24	2.86	4.22	4.78	4.94	4.98

(a) Find a function f that models the data.

(b) Use f to estimate the insect density after a long time.

18. Heart Disease As age increases, so does the likelihood of coronary heart disease (CHD). The percentage P of people x years old with signs of CHD is shown in the table.

x	15	25	35	45	55	65	75
P(%)	2	7	19	43	68	82	87

Source: D. Hosmer and S. Lemeshow, *Applied Logistics Regression.*

(a) Evaluate $P(25)$ and interpret the answer.

(b) Find a function that models the data.

(c) Graph P and the data.

(d) At what age does a person have a 50% chance of having signs of CHD?

19. Mobile Phones in India The following table shows the number of cell phone subscriptions in India in billions for selected years.

Year	2005	2006	2007	2008
Cell Phones	0.05	0.12	0.21	0.40

Year	2009	2010	2011
Cell Phones	0.60	0.75	0.85

Source: Chetan Sharma Consulting.

(a) Find a function $C(x)$ that models the data, where x is years after 2005.

(b) Predict the number of cell phone subscriptions in 2014.

20. U.S. Radio Stations The numbers N of radio stations on the air for selected years x are listed in the table.

x	1970	1980	1990	2000	2010
$N(x)$	6760	8566	10,788	12,808	14,420

Source: M. Street Corporation.

(a) Find a function that models the data.

(b) Graph N and the data.

(c) Predict when the number of radio stations on the air might reach 16,000.

21. Wing Size Heavier birds tend to have larger wings than smaller birds. For one species of bird, the table lists the area A of the bird's wing in square inches if the bird weighs w pounds.

w (lb)	2	6	10	14	18
$A(w)$ (in²)	160	330	465	580	685

Source: C. Pennycuick, *Newton Rules Biology.*

(a) Find a function that models the data.

(b) Graph A and the data.

(c) What weight corresponds to a wing area of 500 square inches?

22. Wing Span Heavier birds tend to have a longer wing span than smaller birds. For one species of bird, the table lists the length L of the bird's wing span in feet if the bird weighs w pounds.

w (lb)	0.22	0.88	1.76	2.42
$L(w)$ (ft)	1.38	2.19	2.76	3.07

Source: C. Pennycuick, *Newton Rules Biology.*

(a) Find a function that models the data.

(b) Graph L and the data.

(c) What weight corresponds to a wing span of 2 feet?

23. Tree Growth (Refer to the introduction to this section.) The height H of a tree in feet after x years is listed in the table.

x (yr)	1	5	10	20	30	40
H(x) (ft)	1.3	3	8	32	47	50

(a) Evaluate $H(5)$ and interpret the answer.

(b) Find a function that models the data.

(c) Graph H and the data.

(d) What is the age of the tree when its height is 25 feet?

(e) Did your answer involve interpolation or extrapolation?

24. Bird Populations Near New Guinea there is a relationship between the number of bird species found on an island and the size of the island. The table lists the number of species of birds y found on an island with an area of x square kilometers.

x (km²)	0.1	1	10	100	1000
y (species)	10	15	20	25	30

Source: B. Freedman, *Environmental Ecology.*

(a) Find a function f that models the data.

(b) Predict the number of bird species on an island of 5000 square kilometers.

(c) Did your answer involve interpolation or extrapolation?

25. Fertilizer Usage Between 1950 and 1980 the use of chemical fertilizers increased. The table lists worldwide average usage y in kilograms per hectare of cropland x years after 1950. (*Note:* 1 hectare $\approx$ 2.47 acres.)

x	0	13	22	29
y	12.4	27.9	54.3	77.1

Source: D. Grigg, *The World Food Problem.*

(a) Graph the data. Are the data linear?

(b) Find a function f that models the data.

(c) Predict fertilizer usage in 1989. The actual value was 98.7 kilograms per hectare. What does this indicate about usage of fertilizer during the 1980s?

26. Social Security If major reform occurs in the Social Security system, individuals might be able to invest some of their contributions into individual accounts. These accounts would be managed by financial firms, which often charge fees. The table lists the amount in billions of dollars that might be collected if fees are 0.93% of the assets each year.

Year	2005	2010	2015	2020
Fees ($ billions)	20	41	80	136

Source: Social Security Advisory Council.

(a) Use exponential regression to find a and b so that $f(x) = ab^x$ models the data x years after 2000.

(b) Graph f and the data.

(c) Estimate the fees in 2013.

(d) Did your answer involve interpolation or extrapolation?

Writing about Mathematics

27. How can you distinguish data that illustrate exponential growth from data that illustrate logarithmic growth?

28. Give an example of data that could be modeled by a logistic function and explain why.

Extended And Discovery Exercise

1. For medical reasons, dyes may be injected into the bloodstream to determine the health of internal organs. In one study involving animals, the dye BSP was injected to assess the blood flow in the liver. The results are listed in the table, where x represents the elapsed time in minutes and y is the concentration of the dye in the bloodstream in milligrams per milliliter.

x	1	2	3	4	5	7
y	0.102	0.077	0.057	0.045	0.036	0.023

x	9	13	16	19	22
y	0.015	0.008	0.005	0.004	0.003

Source: F. Harrison, "The measurement of liver blood flow in conscious calves."

(a) Find a function that models the data.

(b) Estimate the elapsed time when the concentration of the dye reaches 30% of its initial concentration of 0.133 mg/ml.

(c) Let $g(x) = 0.133(0.878(0.73^x) + 0.122(0.92^x))$. This formula was used by the researchers to model the data. Compare the accuracy of your formula to that of $g(x)$.

CHECKING BASIC CONCEPTS FOR SECTION 5.7

Exercises 1–4: Find a function that models the data. Choose from exponential, logarithmic, or logistic functions.

1.

x	2	3	4	5	6	7
y	0.72	0.86	1.04	1.24	1.49	1.79

2.

x	2	3	4	5	6	7
y	0.08	1.30	2.16	2.83	3.38	3.84

3.

x	2	3	4	5	6	7
y	0.25	0.86	2.19	3.57	4.23	4.43

4. World Population The table lists the actual or projected world population y (in billions) for selected years x.

x	1950	1960	2000	2050	2075
y	2.5	3.0	6.1	8.9	9.2

Source: U.N. Dept. of Economic and Social Affairs.

5 Summary

CONCEPT	EXPLANATION AND EXAMPLES

Section 5.1 Combining Functions

Arithmetic Operations on Functions

Addition: $(f + g)(x) = f(x) + g(x)$

Subtraction: $(f - g)(x) = f(x) - g(x)$

Multiplication: $(fg)(x) = f(x) \cdot g(x)$

Division: $(f/g)(x) = \dfrac{f(x)}{g(x)}, g(x) \neq 0$

Examples: Let $f(x) = x^2 - 5, g(x) = x^2 - 4$.

$(f + g)(x) = (x^2 - 5) + (x^2 - 4) = 2x^2 - 9$

$(f - g)(x) = (x^2 - 5) - (x^2 - 4) = -1$

$(fg)(x) = (x^2 - 5)(x^2 - 4) = x^4 - 9x^2 + 20$

$(f/g)(x) = \dfrac{x^2 - 5}{x^2 - 4}, x \neq 2, x \neq -2$

Composition of Functions

Composition: $(g \circ f)(x) = g(f(x))$

$(f \circ g)(x) = f(g(x))$

Examples: Let $f(x) = 3x + 2, g(x) = 2x^2 - 4x + 1$.

$g(f(x)) = g(3x + 2)$

$\qquad = 2(3x + 2)^2 - 4(3x + 2) + 1$

$f(g(x)) = f(2x^2 - 4x + 1)$

$\qquad = 3(2x^2 - 4x + 1) + 2$

Section 5.2 Inverse Functions and Their Representations

Inverse Function

The inverse function of f is f^{-1} if

$f^{-1}(f(x)) = x$ for every x in the domain of f and

$f(f^{-1}(x)) = x$ for every x in the domain of f^{-1}.

Note: If $f(a) = b$, then $f^{-1}(b) = a$.

CONCEPT	EXPLANATION AND EXAMPLES

Section 5.2 Inverse Functions and Their Representations (CONTINUED)

	Example: Find the inverse function of $f(x) = 4x - 5$. $y = 4x - 5$ is equivalent to $\frac{y + 5}{4} = x$. (Solve for x.) Thus $f^{-1}(x) = \frac{x + 5}{4}$.
One-to-One Function	If different inputs always result in different outputs, then f is one-to-one. That is, $a \neq b$ implies $f(a) \neq f(b)$. (A function is also one-to-one if $f(a) = f(b)$ implies $a = b$.) *Note*: If f is one-to-one, then f has an inverse denoted f^{-1}. **Example:** $f(x) = x^2 + 1$ is not one-to-one because $f(2) = f(-2) = 5$.
Horizontal Line Test	If every horizontal line intersects the graph of a function f at most once, then f is a one-to-one function.

Section 5.3 Exponential Functions and Models

Exponential Function	$f(x) = Ca^x$, $a > 0$, $a \neq 1$, and $C > 0$ Exponential growth: $a > 1$; exponential decay: $0 < a < 1$ **Examples:** $f(x) = 3(2)^x$ (growth); $f(x) = 1.2(0.5)^x$ (decay)
Exponential Data	For each unit increase in x, the y-values increase (or decrease) by a constant factor a. **Example:** The data in the table are modeled by $y = 5(2)^x$. | x	0	1	2	3
---	---	---	---	---
y	5	10	20	40	
Natural Exponential Function	$f(x) = e^x$, where $e \approx 2.718282$
Compound Interest	$A = P\left(1 + \frac{r}{n}\right)^{nt}$, where P is the principal, r is the interest expressed as a decimal, n is the number of times interest is paid each year, and t is the number of years. **Example:** $A = 2000\left(1 + \frac{0.10}{12}\right)^{12(4)} \approx \$2978.71$ calculates the future value of \$2000 invested at 10% compounded monthly for 4 years.
Continuously Compounded Interest	$A = Pe^{rt}$, where P is the principal, r is the interest expressed as a decimal, and t is the number of years **Example:** $A = 2000e^{0.10(4)} \approx \$2983.65$ calculates the future value of \$2000 invested at 10% compounded continuously for 4 years.

CONCEPT	EXPLANATION AND EXAMPLES

Section 5.4 Logarithmic Functions and Models

Common Logarithm

$\log x = k$ if and only if $x = 10^k$

Natural Logarithm

$\ln x = k$ if and only if $x = e^k$

General Logarithm

$\log_a x = k$ if and only if $x = a^k$

Examples: $\log 100 = 2$ because $100 = 10^2$.

$\ln \sqrt{e} = \dfrac{1}{2}$ because $\sqrt{e} = e^{1/2}$.

$\log_2 \frac{1}{8} = -3$ because $\frac{1}{8} = 2^{-3}$.

Inverse Properties

$\log 10^k = k$, $\quad 10^{\log k} = k$, $\quad k > 0$
$\ln e^k = k$, $\quad e^{\ln k} = k$, $\quad k > 0$
$\log_a a^k = k$, $\quad a^{\log_a k} = k$, $\quad k > 0$

Examples: $10^{\log 100} = 100$; $e^{\ln 23} = 23$; $\log_4 64 = \log_4 4^3 = 3$

Inverse Functions

The inverse function of $f(x) = a^x$ is $f^{-1}(x) = \log_a x$.

Examples: If $f(x) = 10^x$, then $f^{-1}(x) = \log x$.
If $f(x) = \ln x$, then $f^{-1}(x) = e^x$.
If $f(x) = \log_5 x$, then $f^{-1}(x) = 5^x$.

Exponential and Logarithmic Forms

$\log_a x = k$ is equivalent to $x = a^k$.

Examples: $\log_2 16 = 4$ is equivalent to $16 = 2^4$.
$81 = 3^4$ is equivalent to $\log_3 81 = 4$.

Section 5.5 Properties of Logarithms

Properties of Logarithms

1. $\log_a 1 = 0$ and $\log_a a = 1$ Logarithms of 1 and of a
2. $\log_a m + \log_a n = \log_a (mn)$ Product rule

3. $\log_a m - \log_a n = \log_a \left(\dfrac{m}{n}\right)$ Quotient rule

4. $\log_a (m^r) = r \log_a m$ Power rule

Examples: 1. $\log_4 1 = 0$ and $\log_4 4 = 1$
2. $\log 2 + \log 5 = \log (2 \cdot 5) = \log 10 = 1$
3. $\log 500 - \log 5 = \log (500/5) = \log 100 = 2$
4. $\log_2 2^3 = 3 \log_2 2 = 3(1) = 3$

Change of Base Formula

$\log_a x = \dfrac{\log_b x}{\log_b a}$

Example: $\log_3 23 = \dfrac{\log 23}{\log 3} \approx 2.854$

CONCEPT	EXPLANATION AND EXAMPLES

Section 5.6 Exponential and Logarithmic Equations

Solving Exponential Equations

To solve an exponential equation we typically take the logarithm of each side.

Example:

$4e^x = 48$	*Given equation*
$e^x = 12$	*Divide by 4.*
$\ln e^x = \ln 12$	*Take the natural logarithm.*
$x = \ln 12$	*Inverse property*
$x \approx 2.485$	*Approximate.*

Solving Logarithmic Equations

To solve a logarithmic equation we typically need to exponentiate each side.

Example:

$5\log_3 x = 10$	*Given equation*
$\log_3 x = 2$	*Divide by 5.*
$3^{\log_3 x} = 3^2$	*Exponentiate; base 3.*
$x = 9$	*Inverse property*

Section 5.7 Constructing Nonlinear Models

Exponential Model

$f(x) = Ca^x$, $f(x) = ab^x$, or $A(t) = A_0 e^{kt}$
Models data that increase or decrease rapidly

Logarithmic Model

$f(x) = a + b\ln x$ or $f(x) = a + b\log x$.
Models data that increase slowly

Logistic Model

$f(x) = \dfrac{c}{1 + ae^{-bx}}$, where a, b, and c are positive constants.

Models data that increase slowly at first, then increase more rapidly, and finally level off near the value of c. Its graph is a sigmoidal curve. See Figure 5.84.

5 Review Exercises

1. Use the tables to evaluate, if possible.

x	-1	0	1	3
$f(x)$	3	5	7	9

x	-1	0	1	3
$g(x)$	-2	0	1	9

  (a) $(f + g)(1)$ (b) $(f - g)(3)$

  (c) $(fg)(-1)$ (d) $(f/g)(0)$

2. Use the graph to evaluate each expression.
  (a) $(f - g)(2)$ (b) $(fg)(0)$

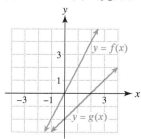

3. Let $f(x) = x^2$ and $g(x) = 1 - x$ and evaluate.
  (a) $(f + g)(3)$ (b) $(f - g)(-2)$

  (c) $(fg)(1)$ (d) $(f/g)(3)$

4. Use $f(x) = x^2 + 3x$ and $g(x) = x^2 - 1$ to find each expression. Identify its domain.
  (a) $(f + g)(x)$ (b) $(f - g)(x)$

  (c) $(fg)(x)$ (d) $(f/g)(x)$

5. Tables for f and g are given. Evaluate each expression.

x	-2	0	2	4
$f(x)$	1	4	3	2

x	1	2	3	4
$g(x)$	2	4	-2	0

  (a) $(g \circ f)(-2)$ (b) $(f \circ g)(3)$ (c) $f^{-1}(3)$

6. Use the graph to evaluate each expression.
  (a) $(f \circ g)(2)$ **(b)** $(g \circ f)(0)$ **(c)** $f^{-1}(1)$

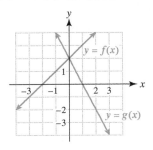

7. Let $f(x) = \sqrt{x}$ and $g(x) = x^2 + x$ and evaluate.
  (a) $(f \circ g)(2)$ **(b)** $(g \circ f)(9)$

8. Use $f(x) = x^2 + 1$ and $g(x) = x^3 - x^2 + 2x + 1$ to find each expression.
  (a) $(f \circ g)(x)$ **(b)** $(g \circ f)(x)$

Exercises 9–12: Find $(f \circ g)(x)$ and identify its domain.

  9. $f(x) = x^3 - x^2 + 3x - 2$ $g(x) = x^{-1}$

10. $f(x) = \sqrt{x + 3}$ $g(x) = 1 - x^2$

11. $f(x) = \sqrt[3]{2x - 1}$ $g(x) = \frac{1}{2}x^3 + \frac{1}{2}$

12. $f(x) = \dfrac{2}{x - 5}$ $g(x) = \dfrac{1}{x + 1}$

Exercises 13 and 14: Find f and g so that $h(x) = (g \circ f)(x)$.

13. $h(x) = \sqrt{x^2 + 3}$ **14.** $h(x) = \dfrac{1}{(2x + 1)^2}$

Exercises 15 and 16: Describe the inverse operations of the given statement. Then express both the statement and its inverse symbolically.

15. Divide x by 10 and add 6.

16. Subtract 5 from x and take the cube root.

Exercises 17 and 18: Determine if f is one-to-one.

17. $f(x) = 3x - 1$ **18.** $f(x) = 3x^2 - 2x + 1$

Exercises 19 and 20: Determine if f is one-to-one.

19.   **20.**

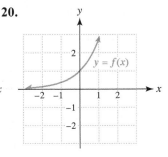

21. The table is a complete representation of f. Use the table of f to determine a table for f^{-1}. Identify the domains and ranges of f and f^{-1}.

x	-1	0	4	6
$f(x)$	6	4	3	1

22. Use the graph of f to sketch a graph of f^{-1}.

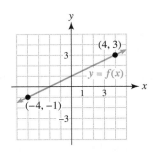

Exercises 23 and 24: Find $f^{-1}(x)$.

23. $f(x) = 3x - 5$ **24.** $f(x) = \dfrac{3x}{x + 7}$

25. Verify that $f(x) = 2x - 1$ and $f^{-1}(x) = \dfrac{x + 1}{2}$ are inverses.

26. Restrict the domain of $f(x) = 2(x - 4)^2 + 3$ so that f is one-to-one. Then find $f^{-1}(x)$.

Exercises 27 and 28: Use the tables to evaluate the given expression.

x	0	1	2	3
$f(x)$	4	3	2	1

x	0	1	2	3
$g(x)$	0	2	3	4

27. $(f \circ g^{-1})(4)$ **28.** $(g^{-1} \circ f^{-1})(1)$

29. Find $f^{-1}(x)$ if $f(x) = \sqrt{x + 1}, x \geq -1$. Identify the domain and range of f and of f^{-1}.

30. Simplify $e^x e^{-2x}$.

Exercises 31 and 32: Find C and a so that $f(x) = Ca^x$ satisfies the given conditions.

31. $f(0) = 3$ and $f(3) = 24$

32. $f(-1) = 8$ and $f(1) = 2$

Exercises 33–36: Sketch a graph of $y = f(x)$. Identify the domain of f.

33. $f(x) = 4(2)^{-x}$ **34.** $f(x) = 3^{x-1}$

35. $f(x) = \log(-x)$ **36.** $f(x) = \log(x + 1)$

Exercises 37 and 38: Use the graph of $f(x) = Ca^x$ to determine values for C and a.

37.

38.

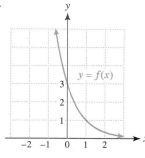

39. Determine the final value of $1200 invested at 9% compounded semiannually for 3 years.

40. Determine the final value of $500 invested at 6.5% compounded continuously for 8 years.

41. Solve $e^x = 19$ symbolically.

42. Solve $2^x - x^2 = x$ graphically. Round each solution to the nearest thousandth.

Exercises 43–46: Evaluate the expression without a calculator.

43. $\log 1000$

44. $\log 0.001$

45. $10 \log 0.01 + \log \frac{1}{10}$

46. $\log 100 + \log \sqrt[3]{10}$

Exercises 47–50: Evaluate the logarithm without a calculator.

47. $\log_3 9$

48. $\log_5 \frac{1}{25}$

49. $\ln e$

50. $\log_2 32$

Exercises 51 and 52: Approximate to the nearest thousandth.

51. $\log_3 18$

52. $\log_2 173$

Exercises 53–60: Solve the equation.

53. $10^x = 125$

54. $1.5^x = 55$

55. $e^{0.1x} = 5.2$

56. $4e^{2x} - 5 = 3$

57. $5^{-x} = 10$

58. $3(10)^{-x} = 6$

59. $50 - 3(0.78)^{x-10} = 21$

60. $5(1.3)^x + 4 = 104$

Exercises 61 and 62: Find either a linear or an exponential function that models the data in the table.

61.

x	0	1	2
y	1.5	3	6

62.

x	0	1	2
y	3	4.5	6

Exercises 63–66: Solve the equation.

63. $\log x = 1.5$

64. $\log_3 x = 4$

65. $\ln x = 3.4$

66. $4 - \ln(5 - x) = \frac{5}{2}$

Exercises 67 and 68: Use properties of logarithms to combine the expression as a logarithm of a single expression.

67. $\log 6 + \log 5x$

68. $\log \sqrt{3} - \log \sqrt[3]{3}$

69. Expand $\ln \frac{y}{x^2}$.

70. Expand $\log \frac{4x^3}{k}$.

Exercises 71–76: Solve the logarithmic equation.

71. $8 \log x = 2$

72. $\ln 2x = 2$

73. $2 \log 3x + 5 = 15$

74. $5 \log_2 x = 25$

75. $2 \log_5 (x + 2) = \log_5 (x + 8)$

76. $\ln(5 - x) - \ln(5 + x) = -\ln 9$

77. Suppose that b is the y-intercept on the graph of a one-to-one function f. What is the x-intercept on the graph of f^{-1}? Explain your reasoning.

78. Let $f(x) = ax + b$ with $a \neq 0$.
 (a) Show that f^{-1} is also linear by finding $f^{-1}(x)$.

 (b) How is the slope of the graph of f related to the slope of the graph of f^{-1}?

Applications

79. Bacteria Growth There are initially 4000 bacteria per milliliter in a sample, and after 1 hour their concentration increases to 6000 bacteria per milliliter. Assume exponential growth.
 (a) How many bacteria are there after 2.5 hours?

 (b) After how long are there 8500 bacteria per milliliter?

80. Newton's Law of Cooling A pan of boiling water with a temperature of 100°C is set in a room with a temperature of 20°C. The water cools to 50°C in 40 minutes.
 (a) Find values for T_0, D, and a so that the formula $T(t) = T_0 + Da^t$ models the data, where t is in hours.

 (b) Find the temperature of the water after 90 minutes.

 (c) How long does it take the water to reach 30°C?

81. Combining Functions The total number of gallons of water passing through a pipe after x seconds is computed by $f(x) = 10x$. Another pipe delivers $g(x) = 5x$ gallons after x seconds. Find a function h that gives the volume of water passing through both pipes in x seconds.

82. Test Scores Let scores on a standardized test be modeled by $f(x) = 36e^{-(x-20)^2/49}$. The function f computes the number in thousands of people that received score x. Solve the equation $f(x) = 30$. Interpret your result.

83. Modeling Growth The function given by

$$W(x) = 175.6(1 - 0.66e^{-0.24x})^3$$

models the weight in milligrams of a small fish called the *Lebistes reticulatus* after x weeks, where $0 \leq x \leq 14$. Solve the equation $W(x) = 50$. Interpret the result. (*Source:* D. Brown and P. Rothery, *Models in Biology*.)

84. Radioactive Decay After 23 days, a 10-milligram sample of a radioactive material decays to 5 milligrams. After how many days will there be 1 milligram of the material?

85. Tire Pressure A car tire has a small leak, and the tire pressure in pounds per square inch after t minutes is given by $P(t) = 32e^{-0.2t}$. After how many minutes is the pressure 15 pounds per square inch?

86. Converting Units The figures show graphs of a function f that converts fluid ounces to pints and a function g that converts pints to quarts. Evaluate each expression. Interpret the results.

(a) $(g \circ f)(32)$

(b) $f^{-1}(1)$

(c) $(f^{-1} \circ g^{-1})(1)$

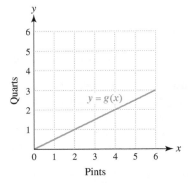

87. Modeling Epidemics In 1666 the village of Eyam, located in England, experienced an outbreak of the Great Plague. Out of 261 people in the community, only 83 people survived. The tables at the top of the next column show a function f that computes the number of people who were infected after x days.

x	0	15	30	45
$f(x)$	7	21	57	111

x	60	75	90	125
$f(x)$	136	158	164	178

Source: G. Raggett, "Modeling the Eyam plague."

Find a function f that models the given data. (Answers may vary.)

88. Greenhouse Gases Methane is a greenhouse gas that is produced when fossil fuels are burned. In 1600 methane had an atmospheric concentration of 700 parts per billion (ppb), whereas in 2000 its concentration was about 1700 ppb. (*Source:* D. Wuebbles and J. Edmonds, *Primer on Greenhouse Gases*.)

(a) Find values for C and a so that $f(x) = Ca^x$ models the data, where x is the year.

(b) Solve $f(x) = 1000$ and interpret the answer.

89. Exponential Regression The data in the table can be modeled by $f(x) = ab^x$. Use regression to estimate the constants a and b. Graph f and the data.

x	1	2	3	4
y	2.59	1.92	1.42	1.05

90. Logarithmic Regression The data in the table can be modeled by $f(x) = a + b \ln x$. Use regression to estimate the constants a and b. Graph f and the data.

x	2	3	4	5
y	2.93	3.42	3.76	4.03

Extended and Discovery Exercises

1. Modeling Data with Power Functions There is a procedure to determine whether data can be modeled by $y = ax^b$, where a and b are constants. Start by taking the natural logarithm of each side of this equation.

$\ln y = \ln(ax^b)$

$\ln y = \ln a + \ln x^b$ $\ln(mn) = \ln m + \ln n$

$\ln y = \ln a + b \ln x$ $\ln(m^r) = r \ln m$

If we let $z = \ln y$, $d = \ln a$, and $w = \ln x$, then the equation $\ln y = \ln a + b \ln x$ becomes $z = d + bw$. Thus the data points $(w, z) = (\ln x, \ln y)$ lie on the line having a slope of b and y-intercept $d = \ln a$. The following steps provide a procedure for finding the constants a and b.

Modeling Data with the Equation $y = ax^b$

If a data set (x, y) can be modeled by the (power) equation $y = ax^b$, then the following procedure can be applied to determine the constants a and b.

STEP 1: Let $w = \ln x$ and $z = \ln y$ for each data point. Graph the points (w, z). If these data are not linear, then do *not* use this procedure.

STEP 2: Find an equation of a line in the form $z = bw + d$ that models the data points (w, z). (Linear regression may be used.)

STEP 3: The slope of the line equals the constant b. The value of a is given by $a = e^d$.

Apply this procedure to the table of data for the orbital distances and periods of the moons of Jupiter. Let the distance be x and the period be y.

Moons of Jupiter	Distance (10^3 km)	Period (days)
Metis	128	0.29
Almathea	181	0.50
Thebe	222	0.67
Io	422	1.77
Europa	671	3.55
Ganymede	1070	7.16
Callisto	1883	16.69

2. **Climate Change** Greenhouse gases such as carbon dioxide trap heat from the sun. Presently, the net incoming solar radiation reaching Earth's surface is approximately 240 watts per square meter (w/m^2). Any portion of this amount that is due to greenhouse gases is called *radiative forcing*. The table lists the estimated increase in radiative forcing R above the levels in 1750.

x (year)	1800	1850	1900	1950	2000
$R(x)$ (w/m^2)	0.2	0.4	0.6	1.2	2.4

Source: A. Nilsson, *Greenhouse Earth.*

(a) Estimate constants C and k so that $R(x) = Ce^{kx}$ models the data. Let $x = 0$ correspond to 1800.

(b) Estimate the year when the additional radiative forcing could reach 3 w/m^2.

Exercises 3 and 4: Try to decide if the expression is precisely an integer. (Hint: *Use computer software capable of calculating a large number of decimal places.*)

3. $\left(\dfrac{1}{\pi} \ln(640{,}320^3 + 744) \right)^2$

(*Source:* I. J. Good, "What is the most amazing approximate integer in the universe?")

4. $e^{\pi\sqrt{163}}$ (*Source:* W. Cheney and D. Kincaid, *Numerical Mathematics and Computing.*)

9 Systems of Equations and Inequalities

In 2000, less than 6% of the world's population had Internet access. Today, the majority of people on Earth are able to get online. It would be impossible for billions of people to download, post, tweet, and stream data, without the mathematics used to create and manage Internet networks. Systems of equations and matrices are vitally important to the success of social networks such as Facebook, Twitter, Spotify, and Pinterest.

Special types of graphs can be used to represent simple networks, and matrices can be used to summarize these graphs. With matrices it is possible to identify the connections between friends in a social network or to analyze web page links. (See Examples 2 and 9 in Section 9.5.)

In this chapter, we will see that mathematics can be used to solve systems of equations, compute movement in computer graphics, analyze web page links, and even represent social networks. Throughout history, many important discoveries have been based on the insights of a few people. The mathematicians who first worked with matrices and systems of equations could not have imagined the profound impact their work would have in the 21st century.

> Go deep enough into anything and you will find mathematics.
> —Dean Schlicter

Source: Internet World Stats; R. Hanneman and M. Riddle, *Introduction to Social Network Methods.*

Functions and Systems of Equations in Two Variables

- **Evaluate functions of two variables**
- **Understand basic concepts about systems of equations**
- **Recognize types of linear systems**
- **Apply the method of substitution**
- **Apply the elimination method**
- **Apply graphical and numerical methods**
- **Solve problems involving joint variation**

Figure 9.1

Introduction

Many quantities in everyday life depend on more than one variable.

- Finding the area of a rectangular room requires both its *length* and *width*.
- The heat index is a function of *temperature* and *humidity*.
- Grade point average is computed using *grades* and *credit hours*.

Quantities determined by more than one variable often are computed by a *function* of more than one variable. The mathematical concepts that we have already studied concerning functions of one input also apply to functions of more than one input. One unifying concept about every function is that it produces *at most one output* each time it is evaluated.

Functions of Two Variables

In order to perform addition, two numbers must be provided. The addition of x and y results in one output, z. The addition function f can be represented symbolically by

$$f(x, y) = x + y, \text{ where } z = f(x, y).$$

For example, the addition of 3 and 4 can be written as

$$z = f(3, 4) = 3 + 4 = 7.$$

In this case, $f(x, y)$ is a **function of two inputs** or a **function of two variables**. The **independent variables** are x and y, and z is the **dependent variable**. The output z depends on the inputs x and y. Other arithmetic operations can be defined similarly. For example, a division function can be defined by $g(x, y) = \frac{x}{y}$, where $z = g(x, y)$.

EXAMPLE 1   Evaluating functions of more than one input

For each function, evaluate the expression and interpret the result.
- **(a)** $f(3, -4)$, where $f(x, y) = xy$ represents the multiplication function
- **(b)** $M(120, 5)$, where $M(m, g) = \frac{m}{g}$ computes the gas mileage when traveling m miles on g gallons of gasoline
- **(c)** $V(0.5, 2)$, where $V(r, h) = \pi r^2 h$ calculates the volume of a cylindrical barrel with radius r feet and height h feet. (See Figure 9.1.)

SOLUTION
- **(a)** $f(3, -4) = (3)(-4) = -12$. The product of 3 and -4 is -12.
- **(b)** $M(120, 5) = \frac{120}{5} = 24$. If a car travels 120 miles on 5 gallons of gasoline, its gas mileage is 24 miles per gallon.
- **(c)** $V(0.5, 2) = \pi(0.5)^2(2) = 0.5\pi \approx 1.57$. If a barrel has a radius of 0.5 foot and a height of 2 feet, it holds about 1.57 cubic feet of liquid.

> **Now Try Exercises 1, 3, and 5**

Systems of Equations in Two Variables

A **linear equation in two variables** can be written in the form

$$ax + by = k,$$

where a, b, and k are constants and a and b are not equal to 0. Examples of linear equations in two variables include

$$2x - 3y = 4, \quad -x - 5y = 0, \quad \text{and} \quad 5x - y = 10.$$

Many situations involving two variables result in the need to determine values for x and y that satisfy *two* equations. For example, suppose that we would like to find a pair of numbers whose average is 10 and whose difference is 2. The function $f(x, y) = \frac{x + y}{2}$ calculates the average of two numbers, and $g(x, y) = x - y$ computes their difference. The solution can be found by solving two linear equations $f(x, y) = 10$ and $g(x, y) = 2$.

$$\frac{x + y}{2} = 10$$
$$x - y = 2$$

System of linear equations

This pair of equations is called a **system of linear equations** because we are solving more than one linear equation at once. A **solution** to a system of equations in two variables consists of an x-value *and* a y-value that satisfy *both* equations simultaneously. The set of all solutions is called the **solution set**. Using trial and error, we see that $x = 11$ and $y = 9$ satisfy both equations. This is the only solution and it can be expressed as the *ordered pair* (**11**, **9**).

Systems of equations that have at least one nonlinear equation are called **nonlinear systems of equations**.

Nonlinear Systems of Equations

One nonlinear equation

$$x^2 - 5y = 8$$
$$2x + 3y = 3$$

and

$$x^2 + y^2 = 5$$
$$\sqrt{x} - y = -2$$

Two nonlinear equations

Types of Linear Systems in Two Variables

Any system of linear equations in two variables can be written in the form

$$a_1 x + b_1 y = c_1$$
$$a_2 x + b_2 y = c_2,$$

CLASS DISCUSSION

Explain why a system of linear equations in two variables cannot have two or three solutions.

where a_1, b_1, c_1, a_2, b_2, and c_2 are constants. The graph of this system consists of *two* lines in the xy-plane. The following See the Concept summarizes the three possible types of linear systems. Note that **coincident lines** are identical lines and indicate that the two equations are equivalent and have the same graph. (See ❸ below.)

See the Concept: Three Types of Linear Systems

One Solution	**Infinitely Many Solutions**	**No Solutions**

One Solution

Ⓐ Intersecting lines

Consistent System
Independent Equations

Ⓐ The solution is given by the coordinates of the point of intersection.

Infinitely Many Solutions

Ⓑ Coincident lines

Consistent System
Dependent Equations

Ⓑ Every point on the coincident lines represents a solution.

No Solutions

Ⓒ Parallel lines

Inconsistent System

Ⓒ The distinct parallel lines have no points in common.

A **consistent system** of linear equations has either one solution, meaning the equations are **independent**, or infinitely many solutions, meaning the equations are **dependent**. An **inconsistent system** has no solutions.

EXAMPLE 2 Recognizing types of linear systems

Graph each system of equations and find any solutions. Identify the system as consistent or inconsistent. If the system is consistent, state whether the equations are dependent or independent.

(a) $\begin{aligned} x - y &= 2 \\ -x + y &= 1 \end{aligned}$ (b) $\begin{aligned} 4x - y &= 2 \\ x - 2y &= -3 \end{aligned}$ (c) $\begin{aligned} 2x - y &= 1 \\ -4x + 2y &= -2 \end{aligned}$

SOLUTION

Getting Started Start by solving each equation for y. Use the resulting slope-intercept form to graph each line. Determine any points of intersection. ▶

(a) Graph $y = x - 2$ and $y = x + 1$, as shown in Figure 9.2. Their graphs (parallel lines) do not intersect, so there are no solutions. The system is inconsistent.

(b) Graph $y = 4x - 2$ and $y = \frac{1}{2}x + \frac{3}{2}$, as shown in Figure 9.3. Their graphs intersect at $(1, 2)$. There is one solution, so the system is consistent and the equations are independent. Because graphical solutions can be approximate, we check this solution by substituting 1 for x and 2 for y in the given system.

$$4(1) - \quad 2 = \quad 2 \checkmark \quad \text{True}$$
$$(1) - 2(2) = -3 \checkmark \quad \text{True}$$

Because $(1, 2)$ satisfies *both* equations, it is the solution.

(c) Solving the equations $2x - y = 1$ and $-4x + 2y = -2$ for y results in the same equation: $y = 2x - 1$. Therefore their graphs coincide, as shown in Figure 9.4. (Note that the second equation results when the first equation is multiplied by -2, so the equations are equivalent.) Any point on this line is a solution to both equations. Thus the system has infinitely many solutions of the form $\{(x, y) \mid 2x - y = 1\}$ and is consistent. The equations are dependent.

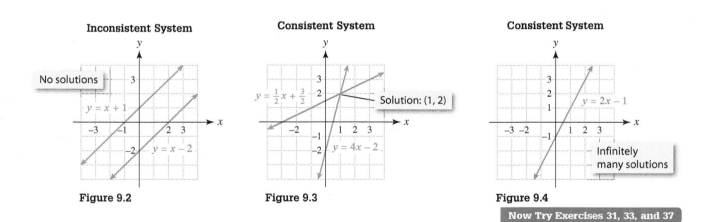

Figure 9.2   Figure 9.3   Figure 9.4

Now Try Exercises 31, 33, and 37

The Method of Substitution

The **method of substitution** is often used to solve systems of equations symbolically. It is summarized by the following steps.

THE METHOD OF SUBSTITUTION

To use the method of substitution to solve a system of two equations in two variables, perform the following steps.

STEP 1: Choose a variable in one of the two equations. Solve the equation for that variable.

STEP 2: Substitute the result from Step 1 into the other equation and solve for the remaining variable.

STEP 3: Use the value of the variable from Step 2 to determine the value of the other variable. To do this, you may want to use the equation you found in Step 1.

To check your answer, substitute the value of each variable into the *given* equations. These values should satisfy *both* equations.

An Application   In the next example, we use the method of substitution to solve an example involving real data.

EXAMPLE 3   Applying the method of substitution

In the first quarter of 2011, Apple Corporation sold a combined total of 35.7 million iPods and iPhones. There were 3.3 million more iPods sold than iPhones.   (*Source:* Apple Corporation.)

(a) Write a system of equations whose solution gives the individual sales of iPods and of iPhones.

(b) Solve the system of equations. Interpret the results.

(c) Is your system consistent or inconsistent? If it is consistent, state whether the equations are dependent or independent.

SOLUTION

Getting Started   When setting up a system of equations, it is important to identify what each variable represents. Then express the situation with equations. Finally, apply the method of substitution. ▶

(a) Let x be the number of iPods sold in millions and y be the number of iPhones sold in millions. The combined total is 35.7 million, so let $x + y = 35.7$. Because iPod sales exceeded iPhone sales by 3.3 million, let $x - y = 3.3$. Thus the system of equations is as follows.

$$x + y = 35.7 \quad \text{Total sales are 35.7 million.}$$
$$x - y = 3.3 \quad \text{iPod sales exceeded iPhone sales by 3.3 million.}$$

(b) **STEP 1:** With this system, we can solve for either variable in either equation. If we solve for x in the second equation, we obtain the equation $x = y + 3.3$.

STEP 2: Substitute $(y + 3.3)$ for x in the first equation, $x + y = 35.7$, and solve.

$$(y + 3.3) + y = 35.7 \quad \text{Substitute } (y + 3.3) \text{ for } x.$$
$$2y = 32.4 \quad \text{Subtract 3.3; combine terms.}$$
$$y = 16.2 \quad \text{Divide each side by 2.}$$

STEP 3: To find x, substitute 16.2 for y in the equation $x = y + 3.3$ from Step 1 to obtain $x = 16.2 + 3.3 = 19.5$. The solution is $(19.5, 16.2)$.

Thus, there were 19.5 million iPods and 16.2 million iPhones sold.

(c) There is one solution, so the system is consistent and the equations are independent.

Now Try Exercise 113

In the next example, we solve a system and check our result.

EXAMPLE 4   **Using the method of substitution**

Solve the system symbolically. Check your answer.

$$5x - 2y = -16$$
$$x + 4y = -1$$

SOLUTION

STEP 1: Begin by solving one of the equations for one of the variables. One possibility is to solve the second equation for x.

$$x + 4y = -1 \qquad \textit{Second equation}$$
$$x = -4y - 1 \qquad \textit{Subtract 4y from each side.}$$

STEP 2: Next, substitute $(-4y - 1)$ for x in the first equation and solve the resulting equation for y.

$$5x - 2y = -16 \qquad \textit{First equation}$$
$$5(-4y - 1) - 2y = -16 \qquad \textit{Let } x = -4y - 1.$$
$$-20y - 5 - 2y = -16 \qquad \textit{Distributive property}$$
$$-5 - 22y = -16 \qquad \textit{Combine like terms.}$$
$$-22y = -11 \qquad \textit{Add 5 to each side.}$$
$$y = \frac{1}{2} \qquad \textit{Divide each side by } -22; \text{ Simplify.}$$

STEP 3: Now find the value of x by using the equation $x = -4y - 1$ from Step 1. Since $y = \frac{1}{2}$, it follows that $x = -4\left(\frac{1}{2}\right) - 1 = -3$. The solution can be written as an ordered pair: $\left(-3, \frac{1}{2}\right)$.

Check: Substitute $x = -3$ and $y = \frac{1}{2}$ in both given equations.

$$5(-3) - 2\left(\frac{1}{2}\right) \overset{?}{=} -16 \ \checkmark \qquad \text{True}$$

$$-3 + 4\left(\frac{1}{2}\right) \overset{?}{=} -1 \ \checkmark \qquad \text{True}$$

Both equations are satisfied, so the solution is $\left(-3, \frac{1}{2}\right)$.

Now Try Exercise 39

Nonlinear Systems of Equations   The method of substitution can also be used to solve nonlinear systems of equations. In the next example, we solve a nonlinear system of equations having two solutions. In general, a nonlinear system of equations can have *any number of solutions*.

EXAMPLE 5   **Solving a nonlinear system of equations**

Solve the system symbolically.

$$6x + 2y = 10$$
$$2x^2 - 3y = 11$$

SOLUTION

STEP 1: Begin by solving one of the equations for one of the variables. One possibility is to solve the first equation for y.

$$6x + 2y = 10 \qquad \textit{First equation}$$
$$2y = 10 - 6x \qquad \textit{Subtract 6x from each side.}$$
$$y = 5 - 3x \qquad \textit{Divide each side by 2.}$$

STEP 2: Next, substitute $(5 - 3x)$ for y in the second equation and solve the resulting quadratic equation for x.

$$2x^2 - 3y = 11 \qquad \text{Second equation}$$
$$2x^2 - 3(5 - 3x) = 11 \qquad \text{Let } y = 5 - 3x.$$
$$2x^2 - 15 + 9x = 11 \qquad \text{Distributive property}$$
$$2x^2 + 9x - 26 = 0 \qquad \text{Subtract 11 from each side; rewrite.}$$
$$(2x + 13)(x - 2) = 0 \qquad \text{Factor.}$$
$$x = -\frac{13}{2} \quad \text{or} \quad x = 2 \qquad \text{Zero-product property}$$

Algebra Review
To review factoring, see Chapter R (pages R-22–R-23).

STEP 3: Now find the corresponding y-values for each x-value. From Step 1 we know that $y = 5 - 3x$, so it follows that $y = 5 - 3\left(-\frac{13}{2}\right) = \frac{49}{2}$ or $y = 5 - 3(2) = -1$. Thus the solutions are $\left(-\frac{13}{2}, \frac{49}{2}\right)$ and $(2, -1)$.

> **Now Try Exercise 51**

> **EXAMPLE 6** Solving a nonlinear system of equations

Use the method of substitution to determine the points where the line $y = 2x$ intersects the circle $x^2 + y^2 = 5$. Sketch a graph that illustrates the solutions.

SOLUTION Substitute $(2x)$ for y in the equation $x^2 + y^2 = 5$.

$$x^2 + y^2 = 5 \qquad \text{Second equation}$$
$$x^2 + (2x)^2 = 5 \qquad y = 2x$$
$$x^2 + 4x^2 = 5 \qquad \text{Square the expression.}$$
$$5x^2 = 5 \qquad \text{Add like terms.}$$
$$x^2 = 1 \qquad \text{Divide each side by 5.}$$
$$x = \pm 1 \qquad \text{Square root property}$$

Two Solutions

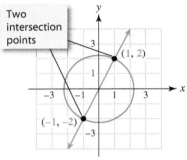

Two intersection points

Figure 9.5

Since $y = 2x$ we see that when $x = 1$, $y = 2$ and when $x = -1$, $y = -2$. The graphs of $x^2 + y^2 = 5$ and $y = 2x$ intersect at the points $(1, 2)$ and $(-1, -2)$. This nonlinear system has two solutions, which are shown in Figure 9.5.

> **Now Try Exercise 99**

> **EXAMPLE 7** Identifying a system with zero or infinitely many solutions

If possible, solve each system of equations.

(a) $\begin{aligned} x^2 + y &= 1 \\ x^2 - y &= -2 \end{aligned}$
(b) $\begin{aligned} 2x - 4y &= 5 \\ -x + 2y &= -\frac{5}{2} \end{aligned}$

SOLUTION

(a) **STEP 1:** Solve the second equation for y, which gives $y = x^2 + 2$.

STEP 2: Substitute $(x^2 + 2)$ for y in the first equation and then solve for x, if possible.

$$x^2 + y = 1 \qquad \text{First equation}$$
$$x^2 + (x^2 + 2) = 1 \qquad \text{Let } y = x^2 + 2.$$
$$2x^2 + 2 = 1 \qquad \text{Combine like terms.}$$
$$2x^2 = -1 \qquad \text{Subtract 2 from each side.}$$

Because $2x^2 \geq 0$, it follows that there are no real solutions and the system is inconsistent.

No Solutions

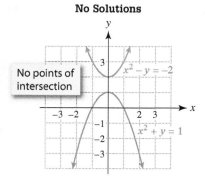

Figure 9.6

Infinitely Many Solutions

Figure 9.7

STEP 3: This step is not necessary because there are no real solutions for x. Figure 9.6 shows that the graphs, which are parabolas, do not intersect.

(b) STEP 1: First solve the second equation for x to obtain $x = 2y + \frac{5}{2}$.

STEP 2: Substitute $\left(2y + \frac{5}{2}\right)$ for x in the first equation and then solve for y.

$$2x - 4y = 5 \qquad \text{First equation}$$

$$2\left(2y + \frac{5}{2}\right) - 4y = 5 \qquad \text{Let } x = 2y + \tfrac{5}{2}.$$

$$4y + 5 - 4y = 5 \qquad \text{Distributive property}$$

$$5 = 5 \qquad \text{Combine like terms.}$$

The equation $5 = 5$ is an identity and indicates that there are infinitely many solutions. The system is consistent and the equations are dependent. Note that we can multiply each side of the second equation by -2 to obtain the first equation.

$$-2(-x + 2y) = -2\left(-\frac{5}{2}\right) \qquad \text{Multiply second equation by } -2.$$

$$2x - 4y = 5 \qquad \text{Distributive property}$$

STEP 3: In Figure 9.7 the graphs of the equations are identical lines. The solution set is $\{(x, y) \mid 2x - 4y = 5\}$ and includes all points on this line; $\left(0, -\frac{5}{4}\right)$ and $\left(2, -\frac{1}{4}\right)$ are examples of solutions to this system.

Now Try Exercises 45 and 57

The Elimination Method

The **elimination method** is another way to solve systems of equations symbolically. This method is based on the property that *equals added to equals are equal*. That is, if

$$a = b \quad \text{and} \quad c = d, \qquad \text{then} \qquad a + c = b + d.$$

The goal of this method is to obtain an equation where one of the two variables has been eliminated. This task is sometimes accomplished by adding two equations. The elimination method is demonstrated in the next example for three types of linear systems.

EXAMPLE 8   Using elimination to solve a system

Use elimination to solve each system of equations, if possible. Identify the system as consistent or inconsistent. If the system is consistent, state whether the equations are dependent or independent. Support your results graphically.

(a) $2x - y = -4$　　**(b)**　$4x - y = 10$　　**(c)**　$x - y = 6$
　　$3x + y = -1$　　　　　$-4x + y = -10$　　　　$x - y = 3$

SOLUTION

(a) *Symbolic Solution*   We can eliminate the y-variable by adding the equations.

$$2x - y = -4 \qquad \text{First equation}$$

$$\underline{3x + y = -1} \qquad \text{Second equation}$$

$$5x \quad\;\; = -5 \quad \text{or} \quad x = -1 \qquad \text{Add equations.}$$

Now the y-variable can be determined by substituting $x = -1$ in either equation.

$$2x - y = -4 \qquad \text{First equation}$$

$$2(-1) - y = -4 \qquad \text{Let } x = -1.$$

$$-y = -2 \qquad \text{Add 2.}$$

$$y = 2 \qquad \text{Multiply by } -1.$$

One Solution

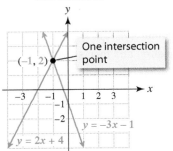

Figure 9.8

Infinitely Many Solutions

Coincident lines

Figure 9.9

No Solutions

Figure 9.10   No points of intersection

The solution is $(-1, 2)$. There is a unique solution so the system is consistent and the equations are independent.

Graphical Solution   Start by solving each given equation for y.

$$2x - y = -4 \quad \text{is equivalent to} \quad y = 2x + 4.$$
$$3x + y = -1 \quad \text{is equivalent to} \quad y = -3x - 1.$$

The graphs of $y = 2x + 4$ and $y = -3x - 1$ intersect at the point $(-1, 2)$, as shown in Figure 9.8.

(b) *Symbolic Solution*   If we add the equations, we obtain the following result.

$$
\begin{array}{ll}
4x - y = 10 & \text{First equation} \\
\underline{-4x + y = -10} & \text{Second equation} \\
0 = 0 & \text{Add equations.}
\end{array}
$$

The equation $0 = 0$ is an identity. The two given equations are equivalent: if we multiply the first equation by -1, we obtain the second equation. Thus there are infinitely many solutions, and we can write the solution set in set-builder notation.

$$\{(x, y) \,|\, 4x - y = 10\}$$

Some examples of solutions are $(3, 2)$, $(4, 6)$, and $(1, -6)$. The system is consistent and the equations are dependent.

Graphical Solution   For a graphical solution, start by solving each equation for y. Both equations are equivalent to $y = 4x - 10$. Their graphs are identical and coincide. The graph of $y = 4x - 10$ is shown in Figure 9.9. Any point on the line represents a solution to the system. For example, $(3, 2)$ is a solution.

(c) *Symbolic Solution*   If we subtract the second equation from the first, we obtain the following result. (Note that subtracting the second equation from the first is equivalent to multiplying the second equation by -1 and then adding it to the first.)

$$
\begin{array}{ll}
x - y = 6 & \\
\underline{x - y = 3} & \\
0 = 3 & \text{Subtract.}
\end{array}
$$

The equation $0 = 3$ is a contradiction. Therefore there are no solutions, and the system is inconsistent.

Graphical Solution   For a graphical solution, start by solving each equation for y to obtain $y = x - 6$ and $y = x - 3$. The graphs of $y = x - 6$ and $y = x - 3$, shown in Figure 9.10, are parallel lines that never intersect, so there are no solutions.

Now Try Exercises 71, 75, and 77

Sometimes multiplication is performed before elimination is used, as illustrated in the next example.

EXAMPLE 9   Multiplying before using elimination

Solve each system of equations by using elimination.
(a) $2x - 3y = 18$ **(b)** $5x + 10y = 10$
   $5x + 2y = 7$ $x + 2y = 2$

SOLUTION
(a) If we multiply the first equation by 2 and the second equation by 3, then the y-coefficients become -6 and 6. Addition eliminates the y-variable.

$$
\begin{array}{ll}
4x - 6y = 36 & \text{Multiply first equation by 2.} \\
\underline{15x + 6y = 21} & \text{Multiply second equation by 3.} \\
19x = 57, \quad \text{or} \quad x = 3 & \text{Add equations.}
\end{array}
$$

Substituting $x = 3$ in $2x - 3y = 18$ (first equation) results in

$$2(3) - 3y = 18, \text{ or } y = -4.$$

The solution is $(3, -4)$.

(b) If the second equation is multiplied by -5, addition eliminates both variables.

$$
\begin{array}{ll}
5x + 10y = 10 & \text{First equation} \\
-5x - 10y = -10 & \text{Multiply second equation by } -5. \\
\hline
0 = 0 & \text{Add equations.}
\end{array}
$$

The statement $0 = 0$ is an identity. The equations are dependent and there are infinitely many solutions. The solution set is $\{(x, y) \mid x + 2y = 2\}$.

> **Now Try Exercises 81 and 83**

Elimination and Nonlinear Systems   Elimination can also be used to solve some nonlinear systems of equations, as illustrated in the next example.

EXAMPLE 10   **Using elimination to solve a nonlinear system**

Solve the system of equations.

$$
\begin{aligned}
x^2 + y^2 &= 4 \\
2x^2 - y &= 7
\end{aligned}
$$

SOLUTION   If we multiply each side of the first equation by 2, multiply each side of the second equation by -1, and then add the equations, the x variable is eliminated.

$$
\begin{array}{ll}
2x^2 + 2y^2 = 8 & \text{Multiply first equation by 2.} \\
-2x^2 + y = -7 & \text{Multiply second equation by } -1. \\
\hline
2y^2 + y = 1 & \text{Add equations.}
\end{array}
$$

Next we solve $2y^2 + y - 1 = 0$ for y.

$$
\begin{array}{ll}
(2y - 1)(y + 1) = 0 & \text{Factor.} \\
y = \dfrac{1}{2} \quad \text{or} \quad y = -1 & \text{Solve.}
\end{array}
$$

Solving $x^2 + y^2 = 4$ for x results in $x = \pm\sqrt{4 - y^2}$. If $y = \frac{1}{2}$, then $x = \pm\sqrt{\frac{15}{4}}$, which can be written as $\pm\frac{\sqrt{15}}{2}$. If $y = -1$, then $x = \pm\sqrt{3}$. Thus there are four solutions: $\left(\pm\frac{\sqrt{15}}{2}, \frac{1}{2}\right)$ and $(\pm\sqrt{3}, -1)$.

A graph of the system of equations is shown in Figure 9.11. The four points of intersection correspond to the four solutions. In Figure 9.12 the four points of intersection are labeled.

Four Solutions to a Nonliner System

Figure 9.11

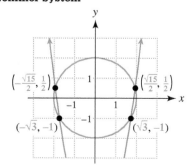

Figure 9.12

> **Now Try Exercise 93**

Graphical and Numerical Methods

An Application The next example illustrates how a system with two variables can be solved symbolically, graphically, and numerically.

EXAMPLE 11 Modeling roof trusses

Linear systems occur in the design of roof trusses for homes and buildings. See Figure 9.13. One of the simplest types of roof trusses is an equilateral triangle. If a 200-pound force is applied to the peak of a truss, as shown in Figure 9.14, then the weights W_1 and W_2 exerted on each rafter of the truss are determined by the following system of linear equations. (***Source:*** R. Hibbeler, *Structural Analysis*.)

$$W_1 - W_2 = 0$$
$$\frac{\sqrt{3}}{2}(W_1 + W_2) = 200$$

Estimate the solution symbolically, graphically, and numerically.

Equilateral Triangle Roof Trusses

Figure 9.13

Figure 9.14

SOLUTION

Symbolic Solution The system of equations can be written as follows.

$$W_1 - W_2 = 0 \qquad \text{First equation}$$
$$\frac{\sqrt{3}}{2}W_1 + \frac{\sqrt{3}}{2}W_2 = 200 \qquad \text{Distributive property}$$

We can apply elimination by multiplying the first equation by $\frac{\sqrt{3}}{2}$ and then adding.

$$\frac{\sqrt{3}}{2}W_1 - \frac{\sqrt{3}}{2}W_2 = 0 \qquad \text{Multiply by } \frac{\sqrt{3}}{2}.$$
$$\frac{\sqrt{3}}{2}W_1 + \frac{\sqrt{3}}{2}W_2 = 200$$
$$\overline{\qquad\qquad\qquad\qquad}$$
$$\sqrt{3}\,W_1 = 200 \qquad \text{Add equations.}$$

Dividing by $\sqrt{3}$ gives $W_1 = \frac{200}{\sqrt{3}} \approx 115.47$ pounds. From the first equation, it follows that $W_1 = W_2$, and so $W_2 \approx 115.47$ pounds.

Graphical Solution Begin by solving each equation for the variable W_2.

$$W_2 = W_1$$
$$W_2 = \frac{400}{\sqrt{3}} - W_1$$

Solve each equation for W_2.

Graph the equations $y_1 = x$ and $y_2 = \frac{400}{\sqrt{3}} - x$. Their graphs intersect near the point (115.47, 115.47), as shown in Figure 9.15. This means that each rafter supports a weight of approximately 115 pounds.

Graphical Solution

Numerical Solution

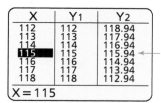

Figure 9.15　　　　Figure 9.16

Numerical Solution　In Figure 9.16, $y_1 \approx y_2$ for $x = 115$.

Now Try Exercise 115

EXAMPLE 12　Determining the dimensions of a cylinder

The volume V of a cylindrical container with a radius r and height h is computed by $V(r, h) = \pi r^2 h$. See Figure 9.17. The lateral surface area S of the container, *excluding* the circular top and bottom, is computed by $S(r, h) = 2\pi r h$.

Volume and Lateral Surface Area of a Cylinder

Geometry Review
To review formulas related to cylinders, see Chapter R (page R-4).

Figure 9.17

(a) Write a system of equations whose solution is the dimensions for a cylinder with a volume of 38 cubic inches and a lateral surface area of 63 square inches.
(b) Solve the system of equations graphically and symbolically.

SOLUTION
(a) The equations $V(r, h) = 38$ and $S(r, h) = 63$ must be satisfied. This results in the following system of nonlinear equations.

$$\pi r^2 h = 38 \qquad \textit{Volume}$$

$$2\pi r h = 63 \qquad \textit{Lateral surface area}$$

(b) *Graphical Solution*　To find the solution graphically, we can solve each equation for h and then apply the intersection-of-graphs method.

Graphical Solution
[0, 4, 1] by [0, 20, 5]

Figure 9.18

$$h = \frac{38}{\pi r^2}$$
$$h = \frac{63}{2\pi r}$$

 Solve each equation for h.

Let r correspond to x and h to y. Graph $y_1 = \frac{38}{\pi x^2}$ and $y_2 = \frac{63}{2\pi x}$. Their graphs intersect near the point (1.206, 8.312), as shown in Figure 9.18. Therefore a cylinder with a radius of $r \approx 1.206$ inches and height of $h \approx 8.312$ inches has a volume of 38 cubic inches and lateral surface area of 63 square inches.

Symbolic Solution Because $h = \frac{38}{\pi r^2}$ and $h = \frac{63}{2\pi r}$, we can determine r by solving the following equation.

$$\frac{38}{\pi r^2} = \frac{63}{2\pi r} \qquad \text{Equation to be solved}$$

$$2\pi r^2\left(\frac{38}{\pi r^2}\right) = 2\pi r^2\left(\frac{63}{2\pi r}\right) \qquad \text{Multiply each side by the LCD, } 2\pi r^2.$$

$$76 = 63r \qquad \text{Simplify.}$$

$$\frac{76}{63} = r \qquad \text{Divide each side by 63.}$$

Because $r = \frac{76}{63} \approx 1.206$, $h = \frac{63}{2\pi r} = \frac{63}{2\pi(76/63)} \approx 8.312$; the symbolic result verifies our graphical result.

> **Now Try Exercise 117**

An Example That Requires a Graphical Solution Sometimes it is either difficult or impossible to solve a nonlinear system of equations symbolically. However, it might be possible to solve such a system graphically.

EXAMPLE 13 Solving a nonlinear system of equations graphically

Solve the system graphically to the nearest thousandth.

$$2x^3 - y = 2$$
$$\ln x^2 - 3y = -1$$

SOLUTION Begin by solving both equations for y. The first equation becomes $y = 2x^3 - 2$. Solving the second equation for y gives the following results.

Graphical Solution

$[-6, 6, 1]$ by $[-4, 4, 1]$

Intersection
X=1.0583853 Y=.37116297

Figure 9.19

$$\ln x^2 - 3y = -1 \qquad \text{Second equation}$$

$$\ln x^2 + 1 = 3y \qquad \text{Add } 3y \text{ and 1 to each side.}$$

$$\frac{\ln x^2 + 1}{3} = y \qquad \text{Divide each side by 3.}$$

The graphs of $y_1 = 2x^3 - 2$ and $y_2 = \frac{\ln x^2 + 1}{3}$ in Figure 9.19 intersect at one point. To the nearest thousandth, the solution is $(1.058, 0.371)$.

> **Now Try Exercise 107**

Joint Variation

A quantity may depend on more than one variable. For example, the volume V of a cylinder is given by $V = \pi r^2 h$. We say that V *varies jointly* with h and the square of r. The *constant of variation* is π.

JOINT VARIATION

Let m and n be real numbers. Then z **varies jointly** with the mth power of x and the nth power of y if a nonzero real number k exists such that

$$z = kx^m y^n.$$

In the following example we use joint variation to determine the amount of timber in a tree with a specified diameter and height.

EXAMPLE 14   Modeling the amount of wood in a tree

Figure 9.20

To estimate the volume of timber in a given area of forest, formulas have been developed to find the amount of wood contained in a tree with height h in feet and diameter d in inches. See Figure 9.20. One study concluded that the volume V of wood in a tree varies jointly with the 1.12 power of h and the 1.98 power of d. (The diameter is measured 4.5 feet above the ground.) (***Source:*** B. Ryan, B. Joiner, and T. Ryan, *Minitab Handbook.*)

(a) Write an equation that relates V, h, and d.

(b) A tree with a 13.8-inch diameter and a 64-foot height has a volume of 25.14 cubic feet. Estimate the constant of variation k.

(c) Estimate the volume of wood in a tree with $d = 11$ inches and $h = 47$ feet.

SOLUTION

(a) $V = kh^{1.12}d^{1.98}$, where k is the constant of variation.

(b) Substitute $d = 13.8$, $h = 64$, and $V = 25.14$ into the equation and solve for k.

$$25.14 = k(64)^{1.12}(13.8)^{1.98}$$

$$k = \frac{25.14}{(64)^{1.12}(13.8)^{1.98}} \approx 0.00132$$

Thus let $V = 0.00132\,h^{1.12}d^{1.98}$.

(c) $V = 0.00132(47)^{1.12}(11)^{1.98} \approx 11.4$ cubic feet

Now Try Exercise 143

9.1 Putting It All Together

The following table summarizes some mathematical concepts involved with functions and equations in two variables.

CONCEPT	COMMENTS	EXAMPLE
Function of two inputs or variables	$z = f(x, y)$ where x and y are inputs and z is the output.	$f(x, y) = x^2 + 5y$ $f(2, 3) = 2^2 + 5(3) = 19$
System of two linear equations	The equations can be written as $ax + by = k$. A solution is an ordered pair (x, y) that satisfies both equations.	$2x - 3y = 6$ $5x + 4y = -8$ Solution: $(0, -2)$
Nonlinear system of two equations	A system of equations that has at least one nonlinear equation is a nonlinear system. A solution is an ordered pair (x, y) that satisfies both equations. A nonlinear system of equations can have any number of solutions.	$5x^2 - 4xy = -3$ $\dfrac{5}{x} - 2y = 1$ Solutions: $(1, 2)$, $\left(-\frac{7}{5}, -\frac{16}{7}\right)$
Consistent system of linear equations in two variables	A consistent linear system has either one or infinitely many solutions. Its graph is either distinct, intersecting lines or identical lines.	$\begin{aligned} x + y &= 10 \\ x - y &= 4 \\ \hline 2x \phantom{{}+y} &= 14 \end{aligned}$ Solution is given by $x = 7$ and $y = 3$. The equations are independent.
System of dependent linear equations in two variables	A system of dependent linear equations has infinitely many solutions. The graph consists of two identical lines.	$2x + 2y = 2$ and $x + y = 1$ are equivalent (dependent) equations. The solution set is $\{(x, y) \mid x + y = 1\}$.

continued on next page

CONCEPT	COMMENTS	EXAMPLE
Inconsistent system of linear equations in two variables	An inconsistent linear system has no solutions. The graph is two parallel lines.	$\begin{aligned} x + y &= 1 \\ x + y &= 2 \quad \text{Subtract.} \\ \hline 0 &= -1 \quad \text{Always false} \end{aligned}$
Method of substitution	Solve one equation for a variable. Then substitute the result in the second equation and solve.	$\begin{aligned} x - y &= 1 \\ x + y &= 5 \end{aligned}$ If $x - y = 1$, then $x = 1 + y$. Substitute in the second equation: $(1 + y) + y = 5$. This results in $y = 2$ and $x = 3$. The solution is $(3, 2)$.
Elimination method	By performing arithmetic operations on a system, a variable is eliminated.	$\begin{aligned} 2x + y &= 5 \\ x - y &= 1 \quad \text{Add.} \\ \hline 3x &= 6 \end{aligned}$ so $x = 2$ and $y = 1$.
Graphical method for two equations	Solve both equations for the same variable. Then apply the intersection-of-graphs method.	If $x + y = 3$, then $y = 3 - x$. If $4x - y = 2$, then $y = 4x - 2$. Graph and locate the point of intersection at $(1, 2)$.

9.1 # Exercises

Functions of More Than One Input

Exercises 1 and 2: Evaluate the function for the indicated inputs and interpret the result.

1. $A(5, 8)$, where $A(b, h) = \frac{1}{2}bh$ (A computes the area of a triangle with base b and height h.)

2. $A(20, 35)$, where $A(w, l) = wl$ (A computes the area of a rectangle with width w and length l.)

Exercises 3–8: Evaluate the expression for the given $f(x, y)$.

3. $f(2, -3)$ if $f(x, y) = x^2 + y^2$

4. $f(-1, 3)$ if $f(x, y) = 2x^2 - y^2$

5. $f(-2, 3)$ if $f(x, y) = 3x - 4y$

6. $f(5, -2)$ if $f(x, y) = 6y - \frac{1}{2}x$

7. $f\left(\frac{1}{2}, -\frac{7}{4}\right)$ if $f(x, y) = \frac{2x}{y + 3}$

8. $f(0.2, 0.5)$ if $f(x, y) = \frac{5x}{2y + 1}$

Exercises 9–12: Write a symbolic representation for $f(x, y)$ if the function f computes the following quantity.

9. The sum of y and twice x

10. The product of x^2 and y^2

11. The product of x and y divided by $1 + x$

12. The square root of the sum of x and y

Exercises 13–18: Solve the equation for x and then solve it for y.

13. $3x - 4y = 7$

14. $-x - 5y = 4$

15. $x - y^2 = 5$

16. $2x^2 + y = 4$

17. $\dfrac{2x - y}{3y} = 1$

18. $\dfrac{x + y}{x - y} = 2$

Solutions to Systems of Equations

Exercises 19–22: Determine which ordered pairs are solutions to the given system of equations. State whether the system is linear or nonlinear.

19. $(2, 1), (-2, 1), (1, 0)$
$2x + y = 5$
$x + y = 3$

20. $(3, 2), (3, -4), (5, 0)$
$x - y = 5$
$2x + y = 10$

21. $(4, -3), (0, 5), (4, 3)$
$x^2 + y^2 = 25$
$2x + 3y = -1$

22. $(4, 8), (8, 4), (-4, -8)$
$xy = 32$
$x + y = 12$

Exercises 23–26: The figure shows the graph of a system of two linear equations. Use the graph to estimate the solution to this system of equations. Then solve the system symbolically.

23.

24.

25.

26.
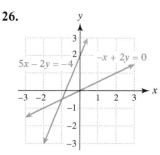

Consistent and Inconsistent Linear Systems

Exercises 27–30: The figure represents a system of linear equations. Classify the system as consistent or inconsistent. Solve the system graphically and symbolically, if possible.

27.

28.

29.

30.

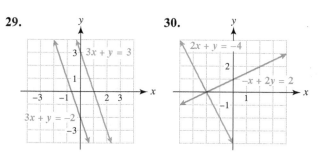

Exercises 31–38: Graph each system of equations and find any solutions. Check your answers. Identify the system as consistent or inconsistent. If the system is consistent, state whether the equations are dependent or independent.

31. $2x + y = 3$
$-2x - y = 4$

32. $x - 4y = 4$
$2x - 8y = 4$

33. $3x - y = 7$
$-2x + y = -5$

34. $-x + 2y = 3$
$3x - y = 1$

35. $x - 2y = -6$
$-2x + y = 6$

36. $2x - 3y = 1$
$x + y = -2$

37. $2x - y = -4$
$-4x + 2y = 8$

38. $3x - y = -2$
$-3x + y = 2$

The Method of Substitution

Exercises 39–50: If possible, solve the system of linear equations and check your answer.

39. $x + 2y = 0$
$3x + 7y = 1$

40. $-2x - y = -2$
$3x + 4y = -7$

41. $2x - 9y = -17$
$8x + 5y = 14$

42. $3x + 6y = 0$
$4x - 2y = -5$

43. $\frac{1}{2}x - y = -5$
$x + \frac{1}{2}y = 10$

44. $-x - \frac{1}{3}y = -4$
$\frac{1}{3}x + 2y = 7$

45. $3x - 2y = 5$
$-6x + 4y = -10$

46. $\frac{1}{2}x - \frac{3}{4}y = \frac{1}{2}$
$\frac{1}{5}x - \frac{3}{10}y = \frac{1}{5}$

47. $2x - 7y = 8$
$-3x + \frac{21}{2}y = 5$

48. $0.6x - 0.2y = 2$
$-1.2x + 0.4y = 3$

49. $0.2x - 0.1y = 0.5$
$0.4x + 0.3y = 2.5$

50. $100x + 200y = 300$
$200x + 100y = 0$

Exercises 51–64: If possible, solve the nonlinear system of equations.

51. $x^2 - y = 0$
$2x + y = 0$

52. $x^2 - y = 3$
$x + y = 3$

53. $xy = 8$
$x + y = 6$

54. $2x - y = 0$
$2xy = 4$

55. $x^2 + y^2 = 20$
$y = 2x$

56. $x^2 + y^2 = 9$
$x + y = 3$

57. $\sqrt{x} - 2y = 0$
$x - y = -2$

58. $x^2 + y^2 = 4$
$2x^2 + y = -3$

59. $2x^2 - y = 5$
$-4x^2 + 2y = -10$

60. $-6\sqrt{x} + 2y = -3$
$2\sqrt{x} - \frac{2}{3}y = 1$

61. $x^2 - y = 4$
$x^2 + y = 4$

62. $x^2 + x = y$
$2x^2 - y = 2$

63. $x^3 - x = 3y$
$x - y = 0$

64. $x^4 + y = 4$
$3x^2 - y = 0$

Exercises 65–68: Write a system of linear equations with two variables whose solution satisfies the problem. State what each variable represents. Then solve the system.

65. Screen Dimensions The screen of a rectangular television set is 2 inches wider than it is high. If the perimeter of the screen is 38 inches, find its dimensions.

66. Numbers The sum of two numbers is 300 and their difference is 8. Find the two numbers.

67. Tickets Admission prices to a movie are $4 for children and $7 for adults. If 75 tickets were sold for $456, how many of each type of ticket were sold?

68. Coins A sample of 16 dimes and quarters has a value of $2.65. How many of each type of coin are there?

Exercises 69 and 70: **Area and Perimeter** *The area of a rectangle with length l and width w is computed by $A(l, w) = lw$, and its perimeter is calculated by $P(l, w) = 2l + 2w$. Assume that $l > w$ and use the method of substitution to solve the system of equations for l and w.*

69. $A(l, w) = 35$
$P(l, w) = 24$

70. $A(l, w) = 300$
$P(l, w) = 70$

The Elimination Method

Exercises 71–80: Use elimination to solve the system of equations, if possible. Identify the system as consistent or inconsistent. If the system is consistent, state whether the equations are dependent or independent. Support your results graphically or numerically.

71. $x + y = 20$
$x - y = 8$

72. $2x + y = 15$
$x - y = 0$

73. $x + 3y = 10$
$x - 2y = -5$

74. $4x + 2y = 10$
$-2x - y = 10$

75. $x + y = 500$
$-x - y = -500$

76. $2x + 3y = 5$
$5x - 2y = 3$

77. $2x + 4y = 7$
$-x - 2y = 5$

78. $4x - 3y = 5$
$3x + 4y = 2$

79. $2x + 3y = 2$
$x - 2y = -5$

80. $x - 3y = 1$
$2x - 6y = 2$

Exercises 81–92: Solve the system, if possible.

81. $\frac{1}{2}x - y = 5$
$x - \frac{1}{2}y = 4$

82. $\frac{1}{2}x - \frac{1}{3}y = 1$
$\frac{1}{3}x - \frac{1}{2}y = 1$

83. $7x - 3y = -17$
$-21x + 9y = 51$

84. $-\frac{1}{3}x + \frac{1}{6}y = -1$
$2x - y = 6$

85. $\frac{2}{3}x + \frac{4}{3}y = \frac{1}{3}$
$-2x - 4y = 5$

86. $5x - 2y = 7$
$10x - 4y = 6$

87. $0.2x + 0.3y = 8$
$-0.4x + 0.2y = 0$

88. $2x - 3y = 1$
$3x - 2y = 2$

89. $2x + 3y = 7$
$-3x + 2y = -4$

90. $5x + 4y = -3$
$3x - 6y = -6$

91. $7x - 5y = -15$
$-2x + 3y = -2$

92. $-5x + 3y = -36$
$4x - 5y = 34$

Exercises 93–98: Use elimination to solve the nonlinear system of equations.

93. $x^2 + y = 12$
$x^2 - y = 6$

94. $x^2 + 2y = 15$
$2x^2 - y = 10$

95. $x^2 + y^2 = 25$
$x^2 + 7y = 37$

96. $x^2 + y^2 = 36$
$x^2 - 6y = 36$

97. $x^2 + y^2 = 4$
$2x^2 + y^2 = 8$

98. $x^2 + y^2 = 4$
$x^2 - y^2 = 4$

Using More Than One Method

Exercises 99–102: Solve the nonlinear system of equations (a) symbolically and (b) graphically.

99. $x^2 + y^2 = 16$
$x - y = 0$

100. $x^2 - y = 1$
$3x + y = -1$

101. $xy = 12$
$x - y = 4$

102. $x^2 + y^2 = 2$
$x^2 - y = 0$

Exercises 103–106: Solve the system of linear equations (a) graphically, (b) numerically, and (c) symbolically.

103. $2x + y = 1$
$x - 2y = 3$

104. $3x + 2y = -2$
$2x - y = -6$

105. $-2x + y = 0$
$7x - 2y = 3$

106. $x - 4y = 15$
$3x - 2y = 15$

Finding Approximate Solutions

Exercises 107–112: Approximate, to the nearest thousandth, any solutions to the nonlinear system of equations graphically.

107. $x^3 - 3x + y = 1$
$x^2 + 2y = 3$

108. $x^2 + y = 5$
$x + y^2 = 6$

109. $2x^3 - x^2 = 5y$
$2^{-x} - y = 0$

110. $x^4 - 3x^3 = y$
$\log x^2 - y = 0$

111. $e^{2x} + y = 4$
　　$\ln x - 2y = 0$

112. $3x^2 + y = 3$
　　$(0.3)^x + 4y = 1$

Applications

113. Population In 2010, the combined population of Minneapolis/St. Paul, Minnesota, was 670,000. The population of Minneapolis was 98,000 greater than the population of St. Paul. (*Source:* Census Bureau.)

　(a) Write a system of equations whose solution gives the population of each city in thousands.

　(b) Solve the system of equations.

　(c) Is your system consistent or inconsistent? If it is consistent, state whether the equations are dependent or independent.

114. U.S. Energy Consumption In 2010, the United States consumed 94.58 quadrillion (10^{15}) Btu of energy from renewable and nonrenewable sources. It used 79.44 quadrillion Btu more from nonrenewable sources than from renewable sources. (*Source:* Department of Energy.)

　(a) Write a system of equations whose solution gives the consumption of energy from renewable and nonrenewable sources (in quadrillion Btu).

　(b) Solve the system of equations.

　(c) Is your system consistent or inconsistent? If it is consistent, state whether the equations are dependent or independent.

115. Roof Truss (Refer to Example 11.) The weights W_1 and W_2 exerted on each rafter for the roof truss shown in the figure are determined by the system of linear equations. Solve the system.

$$W_1 + \sqrt{2}W_2 = 300$$
$$\sqrt{3}W_1 - \sqrt{2}W_2 = 0$$

150 pounds

W_1　　W_2

30°　45°

116. Time on the Internet From 2001 to 2010 the average number of hours that a user spent on the Internet each week increased by 180%. This percent increase amounted to 8 hours. Find the average number of hours that a user spent on the Internet each week in 2001 and 2010. (*Source:* eMarketer.)

117. Geometry (Refer to Example 12.) Find the radius and height of a cylindrical container with a volume of 50 cubic inches and a lateral surface area of 65 square inches.

118. Geometry (Refer to Example 12.) Determine if it is possible to construct a cylindrical container, *including* the top and bottom, with a volume of 38 cubic inches and a surface area of 38 square inches.

119. Dimensions of a Box A box has an *open* top, rectangular sides, and a square base. Its volume is 576 cubic inches, and its outside surface area is 336 square inches. Find the dimensions of the box.

120. Dimensions of a Box A box has rectangular sides, and its rectangular top and base are twice as long as they are wide. Its volume is 588 cubic inches, and its outside surface area is 448 square inches. Find its dimensions.

121. Bank Theft The total incidences of bank theft in 2009 and 2010 was 11,693. There were 437 fewer incidences in 2009 than in 2010. (*Source:* FBI.)

　(a) Write a system of equations whose solution represents the incidences of bank theft in each of these years.

　(b) Solve the system symbolically.

　(c) Solve the system graphically.

122. e-Waste The United States and China together produce 5.9 million tons of e-waste each year. About 0.7 million more tons are produced in the United States than in China.

　(a) Write a system of equations whose solution represents the amount of e-waste produced in each country.

　(b) Solve the system symbolically.

　(c) Solve the system graphically.

123. Student Loans A student takes out two loans totaling $3000 to help pay for college expenses. One loan is at 8% interest, and the other is at 10%. Interest for both loans is compounded annually.

　(a) If the first-year interest is $264, write a system of equations whose solution is the amount of each loan.

　(b) Find the amount of each loan.

124. Student Loans (Refer to Exercise 123.) Suppose that both loans have an interest rate of 10% and the total first-year interest is $300. If possible, determine the amount of each loan. Interpret your results.

125. Student Loans (Refer to Exercises 123 and 124.) Suppose that both loans are at 10% and the total annual interest is $264. If possible, determine the amount of each loan. Interpret your results.

126. Investments A student invests $5000 at two annual interest rates, 5% and 7%. After 1 year the student receives a total of $325 in interest. How much did the student invest at each interest rate?

127. Air Speed A jet airliner travels 1680 miles in 3 hours with a tail wind. The return trip, into the wind, takes 3.5 hours. Find both the speed of the jet with no wind and the wind speed. (*Hint*: First find the ground speed of the airplane in each direction.)

128. River Current A tugboat can pull a barge 60 miles upstream in 15 hours. The same tugboat and barge can make the return trip downstream in 6 hours. Determine the speed of the current in the river.

129. Maximizing Area Suppose a rectangular pen for a pet is to be made using 40 feet of fence. Let l represent its length and w its width, with $l \geq w$.
(a) Find l and w if the area is 91 square feet.

(b) Write a formula for the area A in terms of w.

(c) What is the maximum area possible for the pen? Interpret this result.

130. The Toll of War American battlefield deaths in World Wars I and II totaled about 345,000. There were about 5.5 times as many deaths in World War II as World War I. Find the number of American battlefield deaths in each war. Round your answers to the nearest whole number. (*Source:* Defense Department.)

131. Height and Weight The relationship between a professional basketball player's height h in inches and weight w in pounds was modeled using two samples of players. The resulting modeling equations for the two samples were $w = 7.46h - 374$ and $w = 7.93h - 405$. Assume that $65 \leq h \leq 85$.
(a) Use each equation to predict the weight of a professional basketball player who is $6'11''$.

(b) Determine graphically the height where the two models give the same weight.

(c) For each model, what change in weight is associated with a 1-inch increase in height?

132. Heart Rate In one study a group of athletes were exercised to exhaustion. Let x and y represent an athlete's heart rate 5 seconds and 10 seconds after stopping exercise, respectively. It was found that the maximum heart rate H for these athletes satisfied the following two equations.

$$H = \quad 0.491x + 0.468y + 11.2$$
$$H = -0.981x + 1.872y + 26.4$$

If an athlete had a maximum heart rate of $H = 180$, determine x and y graphically. Interpret your answer. (*Source:* V. Thomas, *Science and Sport*.)

133. Surface Area and the Human Body The surface area of the skin covering the human body is a function of more than one variable. A taller person tends to have a larger surface area, as does a heavier person. Both height and weight influence the surface area of a person's body. A formula used to determine the surface area of a person's body in square meters is given by

$$S(w, h) = 0.007184w^{0.425}h^{0.725},$$

where w is weight in kilograms and h is height in centimeters. Use S to estimate the surface area of a person who is 65 inches (165.1 centimeters) tall and weighs 154 pounds (70 kilograms). (*Source:* H. Lancaster, *Quantitative Methods in Biological and Medical Sciences*.)

Exercises 134–136: **Skin and the Human Body** *(Refer to Exercise 133.) Estimate, to the nearest tenth, the surface area of a person with weight w and height h.*

134. $w = 86$ kilograms, $h = 185$ centimeters

135. $w = 132$ pounds, $h = 62$ inches

136. $w = 220$ pounds, $h = 75$ inches

Joint Variation

Exercises 137 and 138: Approximate the constant of variation to the nearest hundredth.

137. The variable z varies jointly with the second power of x and the third power of y. When $x = 2$ and $y = 2.5$, $z = 31.9$.

138. The variable z varies jointly with the 1.5 power of x and the 2.1 power of y. When $x = 4$ and $y = 3.5$, $z = 397$.

139. The variable z varies jointly with the square root of x and the cube root of y. If $z = 10.8$ when $x = 4$ and $y = 8$, find z when $x = 16$ and $y = 27$.

140. The variable z varies jointly with the third powers of x and y. If $z = 2160$ when $x = 3$ and $y = 4$, find z when $x = 2$ and $y = 5$.

141. **Wind Power**   The electrical power generated by a windmill varies jointly with the square of the diameter of the area swept out by the blades and the cube of the wind velocity. If a windmill with an 8-foot diameter and a 10-mile-per-hour wind generates 2405 watts, how much power would be generated if the blades swept out an area 6 feet in diameter and the wind was 20 miles per hour?

142. **Strength of a Beam**   The strength of a rectangular beam varies jointly with its width and the square of its thickness. If a beam 5.5 inches wide and 2.5 inches thick supports 600 pounds, how much can a similar beam that is 4 inches wide and 1.5 inches thick support?

143. **Volume of Wood**   (Refer to Example 14.) One cord of wood contains 128 cubic feet. Estimate the number of cords in a tree that is 105 feet tall and has a diameter of 38 inches.

144. **Carpeting**   The cost of carpet for a rectangular room varies jointly with its width and length. If a room 10 feet wide and 12 feet long costs $1560 to carpet, find the cost to carpet a room that is 11 feet by 23 feet. Interpret the constant of variation.

145. **Surface Area**   Use the results of Exercise 133 to find a formula for $S(w, h)$ that calculates the surface area of a person if w is given in *pounds* and h is given in *inches*.

146. **Surface Area**   Use the results of Exercise 145 to solve Exercises 135 and 136.

Writing about Mathematics

147. Give an example of a quantity occurring in everyday life that can be computed by a function of more than one input. Identify the inputs and the output.

148. Give an example of a system of linear equations with two variables. Explain how to solve the system graphically and symbolically

R Reference: Basic Concepts from Algebra and Geometry

Throughout the text there are algebra and geometry review notes that direct students to "see Chapter R." This reference chapter contains seven sections, which provide a review of important topics from algebra and geometry. Students can refer to these sections for more explanation or extra practice. Instructors can use these sections to emphasize a variety of mathematical skills.

R.1 Formulas from Geometry

- Use formulas for shapes in a plane
- Find sides of right triangles by applying the Pythagorean theorem
- Apply formulas to three-dimensional objects
- Use similar triangles to solve problems

Geometric Shapes in a Plane

This subsection discusses formulas related to rectangles, triangles, and circles.

Rectangles   The distance around the boundary of a geometric shape in a plane is called its **perimeter**. The perimeter of a rectangle equals the sum of the lengths of its four sides. For example, the perimeter of the rectangle shown in Figure R.1 is $5 + 4 + 5 + 4 = 18$ feet. The perimeter P of a rectangle with length L and width W is $P = 2L + 2W$.

Rectangle

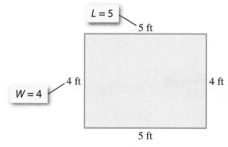

Figure R.1

The area A of a rectangle equals the product of its length and width: $A = LW$. So the rectangle in Figure R.1 has an area of $5 \cdot 4 = 20$ square feet.

Many times the perimeter or area of a rectangle is written in terms of variables, as demonstrated in the next example.

EXAMPLE 1   Finding the perimeter and area of a rectangle

The length of a rectangle is three times greater than its width. If the width is x inches, write expressions that give the perimeter and area.

Figure R.2

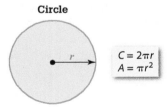
Triangle

Figure R.3

SOLUTION The width of the rectangle is x inches, so its length is $3x$ inches. A sketch is shown in Figure R.2. The perimeter is

$$P = 2L + 2W$$
$$= 2(3x) + 2(x)$$
$$= 8x \text{ inches.}$$

Write the length in terms of the width.

The area is $A = LW = 3x \cdot x = 3x^2$ square inches.

Now Try Exercise 7

Triangles If the base of a triangle is b and its height is h, as illustrated in Figure R.3, then the area A of the triangle is given by

$$A = \frac{1}{2}bh.$$

EXAMPLE 2 Finding the area of a triangle

Calculate the area of the triangle.

5 ft

8 ft

SOLUTION The triangle has a base of 8 feet and a height of 5 feet. Therefore its area is

$$A = \frac{1}{2}bh = \frac{1}{2} \cdot 8 \cdot 5 = 20 \text{ square feet.}$$

Now Try Exercise 11

Circle

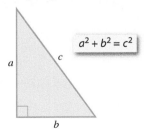

$C = 2\pi r$
$A = \pi r^2$

Figure R.4

Circles The perimeter of a circle is called its **circumference** C and is given by $C = 2\pi r$, where r is the radius of the circle. The area A of a circle is $A = \pi r^2$. See Figure R.4.

EXAMPLE 3 Finding the circumference and area of a circle

A circle has a radius of 12.5 inches. Approximate its circumference and area.

SOLUTION
Circumference: $C = 2\pi r = 2\pi(12.5) = 25\pi \approx 78.5$ inches
Area: $A = \pi r^2 = \pi(12.5)^2 = 156.25\pi \approx 490.9$ square inches

Now Try Exercise 21

Pythagorean Theorem

$a^2 + b^2 = c^2$

a c

b

Figure R.5

The Pythagorean Theorem

One of the most famous theorems in mathematics is the Pythagorean theorem. It states that a triangle with legs a and b and hypotenuse c is a right triangle if and only if

$$a^2 + b^2 = c^2,$$

as illustrated in Figure R.5.

EXAMPLE 4   Finding the perimeter of a right triangle

Find the perimeter of the triangle shown in Figure R.6.

One Side Unknown

Figure R.6

SOLUTION   Given one leg and the hypotenuse of a right triangle, we can use the Pythagorean theorem to find the other leg. Let $a = 7$, $c = 25$, and find b.

$$a^2 + b^2 = c^2 \qquad \textit{Pythagorean theorem}$$
$$b^2 = c^2 - a^2 \qquad \textit{Subtract } a^2.$$
$$b^2 = 25^2 - 7^2 \qquad \textit{Let } a = 7 \textit{ and } c = 25.$$
$$b^2 = 576 \qquad \textit{Simplify.}$$
$$b = 24 \qquad \textit{Solve for } b > 0.$$

The perimeter of the triangle is
$$a + b + c = 7 + 24 + 25 = 56 \text{ inches.}$$

Now Try Exercise 29

Three-Dimensional Objects

Rectangular Box

Figure R.7

Objects that occupy space have both volume and surface area. This subsection discusses rectangular boxes, spheres, cylinders, and cones.

Rectangular Boxes   The volume V of a rectangular box with length L, width W, and height H equals $V = LWH$. See Figure R.7. The surface area S of the box equals the sum of the areas of the six sides: $S = 2LW + 2WH + 2LH$.

EXAMPLE 5   Finding the volume and surface area of a box

The box in Figure R.8 has dimensions x by $2x$ by y. Find its volume and surface area.

Figure R.8

SOLUTION

Volume: $LWH = 2x \cdot x \cdot y = 2x^2 y$ cubic units

Surface Area: Base and top: $2x \cdot x + 2x \cdot x = 4x^2$
Front and back: $xy + xy = 2xy$
Left and right sides: $2xy + 2xy = 4xy$
Total surface area: $4x^2 + 2xy + 4xy = 4x^2 + 6xy$ square units

> Find the area of each side and add.

Now Try Exercise 41

Sphere

Figure R.9

Spheres   The volume V of a sphere with radius r is $V = \frac{4}{3}\pi r^3$, and its surface area S is $S = 4\pi r^2$. See Figure R.9.

EXAMPLE 6 Finding the volume and surface area of a sphere

Estimate, to the nearest tenth, the volume and surface area of a sphere with a radius of 5.1 feet.

SOLUTION

Volume: $V = \frac{4}{3}\pi r^3 = \frac{4}{3}\pi(5.1)^3 \approx 555.6$ cubic feet

Surface Area: $S = 4\pi r^2 = 4\pi(5.1)^2 \approx 326.9$ square feet

Now Try Exercise 47

Cylinders The volume of a cylinder with radius r and height h is $V = \pi r^2 h$. See Figure R.10. To find the total surface area of a cylinder, we add the area of the top and bottom to the area of the side. Figure R.11 illustrates a cylinder cut open to determine its surface area. The top and bottom are circular with areas of πr^2 each, and the side has a surface area of $2\pi rh$. The total surface area is $S = 2\pi r^2 + 2\pi rh$. The side surface area is called the **lateral surface area**.

Cylinder

A Cylinder Cut Open

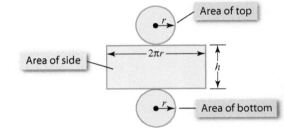

Figure R.10   **Figure R.11**

EXAMPLE 7 Finding the volume and surface area of a cylinder

A cylinder has radius $r = 3$ inches and height $h = 2.5$ feet. Find its volume and total surface area to the nearest tenth.

SOLUTION
Begin by changing 2.5 feet to 30 inches so that all units are in inches.

Volume: $V = \pi r^2 h = \pi(3)^2(30) = 270\pi \approx 848.2$ cubic inches

Total Surface Area: $S = 2\pi r^2 + 2\pi rh = 2\pi(3)^2 + 2\pi(3)(30) = 198\pi \approx 622.0$ square inches

Now Try Exercise 51

Cone

Figure R.12

Cones The volume of a cone with radius r and height h is $V = \frac{1}{3}\pi r^2 h$, as shown in Figure R.12. (Compare this formula with the formula for the volume of a cylinder.) Excluding the bottom of the cone, the side (or lateral) surface area is $S = \pi r\sqrt{r^2 + h^2}$. The bottom of the cone is circular and has a surface area of πr^2.

EXAMPLE 8 Finding the volume and surface area of a cone

Approximate, to the nearest tenth, the volume and surface area (side only) of a cone with a radius of 1.45 inches and a height of 5.12 inches.

SOLUTION

Volume: $V = \frac{1}{3}\pi r^2 h = \frac{1}{3}\pi(1.45)^2(5.12) \approx 11.3$ cubic inches

Surface Area (side only): $S = \pi r\sqrt{r^2 + h^2} = \pi(1.45)\sqrt{(1.45)^2 + (5.12)^2} \approx 24.2$ square inches

Now Try Exercise 55

Similar Triangles

The corresponding angles of **similar triangles** have equal measure, but similar triangles are not necessarily the same size. Two similar triangles are shown in Figure R.13. Notice that both triangles have angles of 30°, 60°, and 90°. Corresponding sides are not equal in length; however, corresponding ratios are equal. For example, in triangle ABC the ratio of the shortest leg to the hypotenuse equals $\frac{2}{4} = \frac{1}{2}$, and in triangle DEF this ratio is $\frac{3}{6} = \frac{1}{2}$.

Similar Triangles

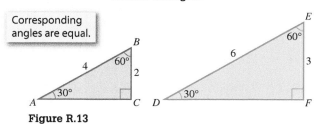

Corresponding angles are equal.

Figure R.13

EXAMPLE 9 Using similar triangles

Find the length of BC in Figure R.14.

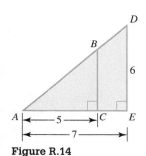

Figure R.14

SOLUTION Notice that triangle ABC and triangle ADE are both right triangles. These triangles share an angle at vertex A. Therefore triangles ABC and ADE have two corresponding angles that are congruent. Because the sum of the angles in a triangle equals 180°, all three corresponding angles in these two triangles are congruent. Thus triangles ABC and ADE are similar.

Since corresponding ratios are equal, we can find BC as follows.

$$\frac{BC}{AC} = \frac{DE}{AE}$$

Corresponding ratios are equal.

$$\frac{BC}{5} = \frac{6}{7}$$

Solving this equation for BC gives $BC = \frac{30}{7} \approx 4.3$.

Now Try Exercise 61

NOTE For a summary of these formulas, see the back endpapers of this text.

R.1 Exercises

Rectangles

Exercises 1–6: Find the area and perimeter of the rectangle with length L and width W.

1. $L = 15$ feet, $W = 7$ feet

2. $L = 16$ inches, $W = 10$ inches

3. $L = 100$ meters, $W = 35$ meters

4. $L = 80$ yards, $W = 13$ yards

5. $L = 3x$, $W = y$ **6.** $L = a + 5$, $W = a$

Exercises 7–10: Find the area and perimeter of the rectangle in terms of the width W.

7. The width W is half the length.

8. Triple the width W minus 3 equals the length.

9. The length equals the width W plus 5.

10. The length is 2 less than twice the width W.

Triangles

Exercises 11 and 12: Find the area of the triangle shown in the figure.

11.

12.

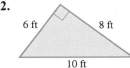

Exercises 13–20: Find the area of the triangle with base b and height h.

13. $b = 5$ inches, $h = 8$ inches

14. $b = 24$ inches, $h = 9$ feet

15. $b = 10.1$ meters, $h = 730$ meters

16. $b = 52$ yards, $h = 102$ feet

17. $b = 2x, h = 6x$ **18.** $b = x, h = x + 4$

19. $b = z, h = 5z$ **20.** $b = y + 1, h = 2y$

Circles

Exercises 21–26: Find the circumference and area of the circle. Approximate each value to the nearest tenth when appropriate.

21. $r = 4$ meters   **22.** $r = 1.5$ feet

23. $r = 19$ inches   **24.** $r = 22$ miles

25. $r = 2x$ **26.** $r = 5z$

Pythagorean Theorem

Exercises 27–32: Use the Pythagorean theorem to find the missing side of the right triangle with legs a and b and hypotenuse c. Then calculate the perimeter. Approximate values to the nearest tenth when appropriate.

27. $a = 60$ feet, $b = 11$ feet

28. $a = 21$ feet, $b = 11$ yards

29. $a = 5$ centimeters, $c = 13$ centimeters

30. $a = 6$ meters, $c = 15$ meters

31. $b = 7$ millimeters, $c = 10$ millimeters

32. $b = 1.2$ miles, $c = 2$ miles

Exercises 33–36: Find the area of the right triangle that satisfies the conditions. Approximate values to the nearest tenth when appropriate.

33. Legs with lengths 3 feet and 6 feet

34. Hypotenuse 10 inches and leg 6 inches

35. Hypotenuse 15 inches and leg 11 inches

36. Shorter leg 40 centimeters and hypotenuse twice the shorter leg

Rectangular Boxes

Exercises 37–44: Find the volume and surface area of a rectangular box with length L, width W, and height H.

37. $L = 4$ feet, $W = 3$ feet, $H = 2$ feet

38. $L = 6$ meters, $W = 4$ meters, $H = 1.5$ meters

39. $L = 4.5$ inches, $W = 4$ inches, $H = 1$ foot

40. $L = 9.1$ yards, $W = 8$ yards, $H = 6$ feet

41. $L = 3x, W = 2x, H = x$

42. $L = 6z, W = 5z, H = 7z$

43. $L = x, W = 2y, H = 3z$

44. $L = 8x, W = y, H = z$

Exercises 45 and 46: Find the volume of the rectangular box in terms of the width W.

45. The length is twice the width W, and the height is half the width.

46. The width W is three times the height and one-third of the length.

Spheres

Exercises 47–50: Find the volume and surface area of the sphere satisfying the given condition, where r is the radius and d is the diameter. Approximate values to the nearest tenth.

47. $r = 3$ feet   **48.** $r = 4.1$ inches

49. $d = 6.4$ meters   **50.** $d = 16$ feet

Cylinders

Exercises 51–54: Find the volume, the surface area of the side, and the total surface area of the cylinder that satisfies the given conditions, where r is the radius and h is the height. Approximate values to the nearest tenth.

51. $r = 0.5$ foot, $h = 2$ feet

52. $r = \frac{1}{3}$ yard, $h = 2$ feet

53. $r = 12$ millimeters, and h is twice r

54. r is one-fourth of h, and $h = 2.1$ feet

Cones

Exercises 55–60: Approximate, to the nearest tenth, the volume and surface area (side only) of the cone satisfying the given conditions, where r is the radius and h is the height.

55. $r = 5$ centimeters, $h = 6$ centimeters

56. $r = 8$ inches, $h = 30$ inches

57. $r = 24$ inches, $h = 3$ feet

58. $r = 100$ centimeters, $h = 1.3$ meters

59. Three times r equals h, and $r = 2.4$ feet

60. Twice h equals r, and $h = 3$ centimeters

Similar Triangles

Exercises 61–64: Use the fact that triangles ABC and DEF are similar to find the value of x.

61.

62.

63.

64.

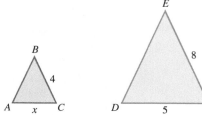

Integer Exponents

- Use bases and exponents
- Use zero and negative exponents
- Apply the product, quotient, and power rules

Bases and Positive Exponents

The expression 8^2 is an exponential expression with base 8 and exponent 2. Table R.1 contains examples of other exponential expressions.

Exponential Expressions

Equal Expressions	Base	Exponent
$2 \cdot 2 \cdot 2 = 2^3$	2	3
$6 \cdot 6 \cdot 6 \cdot 6 = 6^4$	6	4
$7 = 7^1$	7	1
$0.5 \cdot 0.5 = 0.5^2$	0.5	2
$x \cdot x \cdot x = x^3$	x	3

Table R.1

We read 0.5^2 as "0.5 squared," 2^3 as "2 cubed," and 6^4 as "6 to the fourth power."

EXAMPLE 1 Writing numbers in exponential notation

Use the given base to write each number as an exponential expression. Check your results with a calculator.

(a) 10,000 (base 10)   **(b)** 27 (base 3)   **(c)** 32 (base 2)

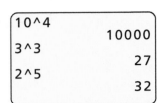

Figure R.15

SOLUTION

(a) $10{,}000 = 10 \cdot 10 \cdot 10 \cdot 10 = 10^4$ **(b)** $27 = 3 \cdot 3 \cdot 3 = 3^3$

(c) $32 = 2 \cdot 2 \cdot 2 \cdot 2 \cdot 2 = 2^5$

These values are supported in Figure R.15, where exponential expressions are evaluated with a calculator, using the $\boxed{\wedge}$ key.

Now Try Exercises 11 and 13

Zero and Negative Exponents

Exponents can be defined for any integer. The following box lists some properties for integer exponents.

INTEGER EXPONENTS

Let a and b be nonzero real numbers and m and n be positive integers. Then

1. $a^n = a \cdot a \cdot a \cdot \cdots \cdot a$ (n factors of a)
2. $a^0 = 1$ (*Note:* 0^0 is undefined.)
3. $a^{-n} = \dfrac{1}{a^n}$ and $\dfrac{1}{a^{-n}} = a^n$
4. $\dfrac{a^{-n}}{b^{-m}} = \dfrac{b^m}{a^n}$
5. $\left(\dfrac{a}{b}\right)^{-n} = \left(\dfrac{b}{a}\right)^n$

EXAMPLE 2 Evaluating expressions

Evaluate each expression.

(a) 3^{-4} **(b)** $\dfrac{1}{2^{-3}}$ **(c)** $\left(\dfrac{5}{7}\right)^{-2}$ **(d)** $\dfrac{1}{(xy)^{-1}}$ **(e)** $\dfrac{2^{-2}}{3t^{-3}}$

SOLUTION

(a) $3^{-4} = \dfrac{1}{3^4} = \dfrac{1}{3 \cdot 3 \cdot 3 \cdot 3} = \dfrac{1}{81}$ **(b)** $\dfrac{1}{2^{-3}} = 2^3 = 2 \cdot 2 \cdot 2 = 8$

(c) $\left(\dfrac{5}{7}\right)^{-2} = \left(\dfrac{7}{5}\right)^2 = \dfrac{7}{5} \cdot \dfrac{7}{5} = \dfrac{49}{25}$ **(d)** $\dfrac{1}{(xy)^{-1}} = (xy)^1 = xy$

Base is xy.

(e) Note that only t, not $3t$, is raised to the power of -3.

$$\frac{2^{-2}}{3t^{-3}} = \frac{t^3}{3(2^2)} = \frac{t^3}{3 \cdot 4} = \frac{t^3}{12}$$

Base is t.

Now Try Exercises 27, 29, 31, 65, and 67

Product, Quotient, and Power Rules

We can calculate products and quotients of exponential expressions *provided their bases are the same*. For example,

$$3^2 \cdot 3^3 = \overbrace{(3 \cdot 3) \cdot (3 \cdot 3 \cdot 3)}^{\text{5 factors of 3}} = 3^5.$$

This expression has a total of $2 + 3 = 5$ factors of 3, so the result is 3^5. To multiply exponential expressions with *like bases*, add exponents.

THE PRODUCT RULE

For any nonzero number a and integers m and n,

$$a^m \cdot a^n = a^{m+n}.$$

The product rule holds for negative exponents. For example,

$$10^5 \cdot 10^{-2} = 10^{5+(-2)} = 10^3.$$

> Product rule: add exponents.

EXAMPLE 3   Using the product rule

Multiply and simplify.

(a) $7^3 \cdot 7^{-4}$ **(b)** $x^3 x^{-2} x^4$ **(c)** $(3y^2)(2y^{-4})$

SOLUTION

(a) $7^3 \cdot 7^{-4} = 7^{3+(-4)} = 7^{-1} = \dfrac{1}{7}$ **(b)** $x^3 x^{-2} x^4 = x^{3+(-2)+4} = x^5$

(c) $(3y^2)(2y^{-4}) = 3 \cdot 2 \cdot y^2 \cdot y^{-4} = 6y^{2+(-4)} = 6y^{-2} = \dfrac{6}{y^2}$

Note that 6 is not raised to the power of -2 in the expression $6y^{-2}$.

> **Now Try Exercises 35, 37, and 39**

Consider division of exponential expressions using the following example.

$$\frac{6^5}{6^3} = \frac{6 \cdot 6 \cdot \cancel{6} \cdot \cancel{6} \cdot \cancel{6}}{\cancel{6} \cdot \cancel{6} \cdot \cancel{6}} = 6 \cdot 6 = 6^2$$

After simplifying, there are two 6s left in the numerator. The result is $6^{5-3} = 6^2 = 36$. To divide exponential expressions with *like bases*, subtract exponents.

> **THE QUOTIENT RULE**
>
> For any nonzero number a and integers m and n,
>
> $$\frac{a^m}{a^n} = a^{m-n}.$$

The quotient rule holds true for negative exponents. For example,

$$\frac{2^{-6}}{2^{-4}} = 2^{-6-(-4)} = 2^{-2} = \frac{1}{2^2} = \frac{1}{4}.$$

> Quotient rule: subtract exponents.

```
2^(−6)/2^(−4)
              .25
.25▶Frac
              1/4
```

Figure R.16

This result is supported by Figure R.16.

EXAMPLE 4   Using the quotient rule

Simplify the expression. Use positive exponents.

(a) $\dfrac{10^4}{10^6}$ **(b)** $\dfrac{x^5}{x^2}$ **(c)** $\dfrac{15x^2 y^3}{5x^4 y}$

SOLUTION

(a) $\dfrac{10^4}{10^6} = 10^{4-6} = 10^{-2} = \dfrac{1}{10^2} = \dfrac{1}{100}$ **(b)** $\dfrac{x^5}{x^2} = x^{5-2} = x^3$

(c) $\dfrac{15x^2 y^3}{5x^4 y} = \dfrac{15}{5} \cdot \dfrac{x^2}{x^4} \cdot \dfrac{y^3}{y^1} = 3 \cdot x^{(2-4)} y^{(3-1)} = 3x^{-2} y^2 = \dfrac{3y^2}{x^2}$

> **Now Try Exercises 45, 49, and 51**

How should we evaluate $(4^3)^2$? To answer this question, consider

$$(4^3)^2 = \underbrace{4^3 \cdot 4^3}_{\text{2 factors of } 4^3} = 4^{3+3} = 4^6.$$

Similarly,

$$(x^4)^3 = \underbrace{x^4 \cdot x^4 \cdot x^4}_{\text{3 factors of } x^4} = x^{4+4+4} = x^{12}.$$

These results suggest that to raise a power to a power, we must multiply the exponents.

> **RAISING POWERS TO POWERS**
>
> For any nonzero real number a and integers m and n,
> $$(a^m)^n = a^{mn}.$$

EXAMPLE 5 Raising powers to powers

Simplify each expression. Use positive exponents.
(a) $(5^2)^3$ **(b)** $(2^4)^{-2}$ **(c)** $(b^{-7})^5$

SOLUTION

(a) $(5^2)^3 = 5^{2 \cdot 3} = 5^6 = 15{,}625$ **(b)** $(2^4)^{-2} = 2^{4(-2)} = 2^{-8} = \dfrac{1}{2^8} = \dfrac{1}{256}$

Multiply exponents.

(c) $(b^{-7})^5 = b^{-7 \cdot 5} = b^{-35} = \dfrac{1}{b^{35}}$

> **Now Try Exercises 55 and 57**

How can we simplify the expression $(2x)^3$? Consider the following.

$$(2x)^3 = 2x \cdot 2x \cdot 2x = \underbrace{(2 \cdot 2 \cdot 2)}_{3 \text{ factors}} \cdot \underbrace{(x \cdot x \cdot x)}_{3 \text{ factors}} = 2^3 x^3$$

This result suggests that to cube a product, we can cube each factor.

> **RAISING PRODUCTS TO POWERS**
>
> For any nonzero real numbers a and b and integer n,
> $$(ab)^n = a^n b^n.$$

EXAMPLE 6 Raising products to powers

Simplify each expression. Use positive exponents.
(a) $(6y)^2$ **(b)** $(x^2 y)^{-2}$ **(c)** $(2xy^3)^4$

SOLUTION

(a) $(6y)^2 = 6^2 y^2 = 36y^2$ **(b)** $(x^2 y)^{-2} = (x^2)^{-2} y^{-2} = x^{-4} y^{-2} = \dfrac{1}{x^4 y^2}$

(c) $(2xy^3)^4 = 2^4 x^4 (y^3)^4 = 16x^4 y^{12}$

> **Now Try Exercises 59 and 73**

To simplify a power of a quotient, use the following rule.

> **RAISING QUOTIENTS TO POWERS**
>
> For nonzero numbers a and b and any integer n,
> $$\left(\frac{a}{b}\right)^n = \frac{a^n}{b^n}.$$

EXAMPLE 7 Raising quotients to powers

Simplify each expression. Use positive exponents.

(a) $\left(\dfrac{3}{x}\right)^3$ **(b)** $\left(\dfrac{1}{2^3}\right)^{-2}$ **(c)** $\left(\dfrac{3x^{-3}}{y^2}\right)^4$

SOLUTION

(a) $\left(\dfrac{3}{x}\right)^3 = \dfrac{3^3}{x^3} = \dfrac{27}{x^3}$ **(b)** $\left(\dfrac{1}{2^3}\right)^{-2} = \dfrac{1^{-2}}{(2^3)^{-2}} = \dfrac{1}{2^{-6}} = 2^6 = 64$

(c) $\left(\dfrac{3x^{-3}}{y^2}\right)^4 = \dfrac{3^4(x^{-3})^4}{(y^2)^4} = \dfrac{81x^{-12}}{y^8} = \dfrac{81}{x^{12}y^8}$

Now Try Exercises 61, 63, and 81

In the next example, we use several properties of exponents to simplify expressions.

EXAMPLE 8   Simplifying expressions

Write each expression using positive exponents. Simplify the result completely.

(a) $\left(\dfrac{x^2 y^{-3}}{3z^{-4}}\right)^{-2}$ **(b)** $\dfrac{(rt^3)^{-3}}{(r^2 t^3)^{-2}}$

SOLUTION

(a) $\left(\dfrac{x^2 y^{-3}}{3z^{-4}}\right)^{-2} = \left(\dfrac{3z^{-4}}{x^2 y^{-3}}\right)^2$ **(b)** $\dfrac{(rt^3)^{-3}}{(r^2 t^3)^{-2}} = \dfrac{(r^2 t^3)^2}{(rt^3)^3}$

$= \left(\dfrac{3y^3}{x^2 z^4}\right)^2$ $= \dfrac{r^4 t^6}{r^3 t^9}$

$= \dfrac{9y^6}{x^4 z^8}$ $= \dfrac{r}{t^3}$

Now Try Exercises 77 and 79

R.2   Exercises

Concepts

1. Are the expressions 2^3 and 3^2 equal? Explain your answer.

2. Are the expressions -4^2 and $(-4)^2$ equal? Explain your answer.

3. $7^{-n} = $ _____

4. $6^m \cdot 6^n = $ _____

5. $\dfrac{5^m}{5^n} = $ _____

6. $(3x)^k = $ _____

7. $(2^m)^k = $ _____

8. $\left(\dfrac{x}{y}\right)^m = $ _____

9. $5 \times 10^3 = $ _____

10. $5 \times 10^{-3} = $ _____

Properties of Exponents

Exercises 11–16: (Refer to Example 1.) Write the number as an exponential expression, using the base shown. Check your result with a calculator.

11. 8 (base 2)

12. 1000 (base 10)

13. 256 (base 4)

14. $\frac{1}{64}$ (base 4)

15. 1 (base 3)

16. $\frac{1}{49}$ (base 7)

Exercises 17–34: Evaluate the expression by hand. Check your result with a calculator.

17. 5^3

18. 5^{-3}

19. -2^4

20. $(-2)^4$

21. 5^0

22. $\left(-\frac{2}{3}\right)^{-3}$

23. $\left(\frac{2}{3}\right)^3$

24. $\frac{1}{4^{-2}}$

25. $\left(-\frac{1}{2}\right)^4$

26. $\left(-\frac{3}{4}\right)^3$

27. 4^{-3}

28. 10^{-4}

29. $\frac{1}{2^{-4}}$

30. $\frac{1}{3^{-2}}$

31. $\left(\frac{3}{4}\right)^{-3}$

32. $\left(\frac{1}{2}\right)^0$

33. $\frac{3^{-2}}{2^{-3}}$

34. $\frac{10^{-4}}{4^{-3}}$

Exercises 35–44: Use the product rule to simplify.

35. $6^3 \cdot 6^{-4}$

36. $10^2 \cdot 10^5 \cdot 10^{-3}$

37. $2x^2 \cdot 3x^{-3} \cdot x^4$

38. $3y^4 \cdot 6y^{-4} \cdot y$

39. $10^0 \cdot 10^6 \cdot 10^2$

40. $y^3 \cdot y^{-5} \cdot y^4$

41. $5^{-2} \cdot 5^3 \cdot 2^{-4} \cdot 2^3$ **42.** $2^{-3} \cdot 3^4 \cdot 3^{-2} \cdot 2^5$

43. $(2a^3)(b^2)(a^{-4})(4b^{-5})$ **44.** $(3x^{-4})(2x^2)(5y^4)(y^{-3})$

Exercises 45–54: Use the quotient rule to simplify the expression. Use positive exponents to write your answer.

45. $\dfrac{5^4}{5^2}$ **46.** $\dfrac{6^2}{6^{-7}}$

47. $\dfrac{a^{-3}}{a^2 \cdot a}$ **48.** $\dfrac{y^0 \cdot y \cdot y^5}{y^{-2} \cdot y^{-3}}$

49. $\dfrac{24x^3}{6x}$ **50.** $\dfrac{10x^5}{5x^{-3}}$

51. $\dfrac{12a^2b^3}{18a^4b^2}$ **52.** $\dfrac{-6x^7y^3}{3x^2y^{-5}}$

53. $\dfrac{21x^{-3}y^4}{7x^4y^{-2}}$ **54.** $\dfrac{32x^3y}{-24x^5y^{-3}}$

Exercises 55–64: Use the power rules to simplify the expression. Use positive exponents to write your answer.

55. $(5^{-1})^3$ **56.** $(-4^2)^3$

57. $(y^4)^{-2}$ **58.** $(x^2)^4$

59. $(4y^2)^3$ **60.** $(-2xy^3)^{-4}$

61. $\left(\dfrac{4}{x}\right)^3$ **62.** $\left(\dfrac{-3}{x^3}\right)^2$

63. $\left(\dfrac{2x}{z^4}\right)^{-5}$ **64.** $\left(\dfrac{2xy}{3z^5}\right)^{-1}$

Exercises 65–90: Use rules of exponents to simplify the expression. Use positive exponents to write your answer.

65. $\dfrac{2}{(ab)^{-1}}$ **66.** $\dfrac{5a^2}{(xy)^{-1}}$

67. $\dfrac{2^{-3}}{2t^{-2}}$ **68.** $\dfrac{t^{-3}}{2t^{-1}}$

69. $\dfrac{6a^2b^{-3}}{4ab^{-2}}$ **70.** $\dfrac{20a^{-2}b}{4a^{-2}b^{-1}}$

71. $\dfrac{5r^2st^{-3}}{25rs^{-2}t^2}$ **72.** $\dfrac{36r^{-1}(st)^2}{9(rs)^2t^{-1}}$

73. $(3x^2y^{-3})^{-2}$ **74.** $(-2x^{-3}y^{-2})^3$

75. $\dfrac{(d^3)^{-2}}{(d^{-2})^3}$ **76.** $\dfrac{(b^2)^{-1}}{(b^{-4})^3}$

77. $\left(\dfrac{3t^2}{2t^{-1}}\right)^3$ **78.** $\left(\dfrac{-2t}{4t^{-2}}\right)^{-1}$

79. $\dfrac{(-m^2n^{-1})^{-2}}{(mn)^{-1}}$ **80.** $\dfrac{(-mn^4)^{-1}}{(m^2n)^{-3}}$

81. $\left(\dfrac{2a^3}{6b}\right)^4$ **82.** $\left(\dfrac{-3a^2}{9b^3}\right)^4$

83. $\dfrac{8x^{-3}y^{-2}}{4x^{-2}y^{-4}}$ **84.** $\dfrac{6x^{-1}y^{-1}}{9x^{-2}y^3}$

85. $\dfrac{(r^2t^2)^{-2}}{(r^3t)^{-1}}$ **86.** $\dfrac{(2rt)^2}{(rt^4)^{-2}}$

87. $\dfrac{4x^{-2}y^3}{(2x^{-1}y)^2}$ **88.** $\dfrac{(ab)^3}{a^4b^{-4}}$

89. $\left(\dfrac{15r^2t}{3r^{-3}t^4}\right)^3$ **90.** $\left(\dfrac{4(xy)^2}{(2xy^{-2})^3}\right)^{-2}$

R.3 Polynomial Expressions

- **Perform addition and subtraction on monomials**
- **Perform addition and subtraction on polynomials**
- **Apply the distributive property**
- **Perform multiplication on polynomials**
- **Find the product of a sum and difference**
- **Square a binomial**

Addition and Subtraction of Monomials

A **term** is a number, a variable, or a *product* of numbers and variables raised to powers. Examples of terms include

$$-15, \quad y, \quad x^4, \quad 3x^3z, \quad x^{-1/2}y^{-2}, \quad \text{and} \quad 6x^{-1}y^3.$$
Terms

If the variables in a term have only *nonnegative integer* exponents, the term is called a *monomial*. Examples of monomials include

$$-4, \quad 5y, \quad x^2, \quad 5x^2z^6, \quad -xy^7, \quad \text{and} \quad 6xy^3.$$
Monomials

If two terms contain the same variables raised to the same powers, we call them **like terms**. We can add or subtract *like* terms, but not *unlike* terms. For example, the terms

$$x^3 + y^3$$ Unlike terms cannot be combined.

cannot be combined because they are *unlike terms.* However,

$$x^3 + 3x^3 = (1 + 3)x^3 = 4x^3 \quad \boxed{\text{Like terms can be combined.}}$$

because x^3 and $3x^3$ are *like terms.* To add or subtract monomials, we simply combine like terms, as illustrated in the next example.

EXAMPLE 1 Adding and subtracting monomials

Simplify each of the following expressions by combining like terms.
(a) $8x^2 - 4x^2 + x^3$ **(b)** $9x - 6xy^2 + 2xy^2 + 4x$

SOLUTION
(a) The terms $8x^2$ and $-4x^2$ are like terms, so they may be combined.

$$8x^2 - 4x^2 + x^3 = (8 - 4)x^2 + x^3 \quad \text{Combine like terms.}$$
$$= 4x^2 + x^3 \quad \text{Subtract.}$$

$\boxed{\text{Unlike terms cannot be combined.}}$

(b) The terms $9x$ and $4x$ may be combined, as may $-6xy^2$ and $2xy^2$.

$$9x - 6xy^2 + 2xy^2 + 4x = 9x + 4x - 6xy^2 + 2xy^2 \quad \text{Commutative property}$$
$$= (9 + 4)x + (-6 + 2)xy^2 \quad \text{Combine like terms.}$$
$$= 13x - 4xy^2 \quad \text{Add.}$$

$\boxed{\textbf{Now Try Exercises 5 and 11}}$

Addition and Subtraction of Polynomials

A polynomial is either a monomial or a sum (or difference) of monomials. Examples of polynomials include

$$5x^4z^2, \qquad 9x^4 - 5, \qquad 4x^2 + 5xy - y^2, \qquad \text{and} \qquad 4 - y^2 + 5y^4 + y^5.$$
$$\text{1 term} \qquad \text{2 terms} \qquad \text{3 terms} \qquad\qquad\qquad \text{4 terms}$$

Polynomials containing one variable are called polynomials of one variable. The second and fourth polynomials shown above are examples of polynomials of one variable. The leading coefficient of a polynomial of one variable is the coefficient of the monomial with highest degree. The degree of a polynomial with one variable equals the exponent of the monomial with the highest power. Table R.2 shows several polynomials of one variable along with their degrees and leading coefficients. A polynomial of degree 1 is a *linear* polynomial, a polynomial of degree 2 is a *quadratic* polynomial, and a polynomial of degree 3 is a *cubic* polynomial.

Characterizing Polynomials

Polynomial	Degree	Leading Coefficient	Type
-98	0	-98	Constant
$2x - 7$	1	2	Linear
$-5z + 9z^2 + 7$	2	9	Quadratic
$-2x^3 + 4x^2 + x - 1$	3	-2	Cubic
$7 - x + 4x^2 + x^5$	5	1	Fifth Degree

Table R.2

To add two polynomials, we combine like terms.

EXAMPLE 2   Adding polynomials

Simplify.
(a) $(2x^2 - 3x + 7) + (3x^2 + 4x - 2)$ **(b)** $(z^3 + 4z + 8) + (4z^2 - z + 6)$

SOLUTION
(a) $(2x^2 - 3x + 7) + (3x^2 + 4x - 2) = 2x^2 + 3x^2 - 3x + 4x + 7 - 2$
$$= (2 + 3)x^2 + (-3 + 4)x + (7 - 2)$$
$$= 5x^2 + x + 5$$
(b) $(z^3 + 4z + 8) + (4z^2 - z + 6) = z^3 + 4z^2 + 4z - z + 8 + 6$
$$= z^3 + 4z^2 + (4 - 1)z + (8 + 6)$$
$$= z^3 + 4z^2 + 3z + 14$$

Now Try Exercises 21 and 27

To subtract integers, we add the first integer and the **opposite, or additive inverse,** of the second integer. For example, to evaluate $3 - 5$, we perform the following operations.

Subtracting integers ——— $3 - 5 = 3 + (-5)$ *Add the opposite.*
$$= -2$$ *Simplify.*

Similarly, to subtract two polynomials, we add the first polynomial and the opposite, or additive inverse, of the second polynomial. To find the opposite of a polynomial, we simply negate each term. Table R.3 shows three polynomials and their opposites.

Finding the Additive Inverse

Polynomial	Opposite
$9 - x$	$-9 + x$
$5x^2 + 4x - 1$	$-5x^2 - 4x + 1$
$-x^4 + 5x^3 - x^2 + 5x - 1$	$x^4 - 5x^3 + x^2 - 5x + 1$

Table R.3

EXAMPLE 3   Subtracting polynomials

Simplify.
(a) $(y^5 + 3y^3) - (-y^4 + 2y^3)$ **(b)** $(5x^3 + 9x^2 - 6) - (5x^3 - 4x^2 - 7)$

SOLUTION
(a) The opposite of $(-y^4 + 2y^3)$ is $(y^4 - 2y^3)$.

Add the opposite.

$$(y^5 + 3y^3) - (-y^4 + 2y^3) = (y^5 + 3y^3) + (y^4 - 2y^3)$$
$$= y^5 + y^4 + (3 - 2)y^3$$
$$= y^5 + y^4 + y^3$$

(b) The opposite of $(5x^3 - 4x^2 - 7)$ is $(-5x^3 + 4x^2 + 7)$.
$$(5x^3 + 9x^2 - 6) - (5x^3 - 4x^2 - 7) = (5x^3 + 9x^2 - 6) + (-5x^3 + 4x^2 + 7)$$
$$= (5 - 5)x^3 + (9 + 4)x^2 + (-6 + 7)$$
$$= 0x^3 + 13x^2 + 1$$
$$= 13x^2 + 1$$

Now Try Exercises 39 and 41

Distributive Properties

Distributive properties are used frequently in the multiplication of polynomials. For all real numbers a, b, and c,

$$a(b + c) = ab + ac \qquad \text{and}$$

$$a(b - c) = ab - ac.$$

In the next example, we use these distributive properties to multiply expressions.

EXAMPLE 4 Using distributive properties

Multiply.
(a) $4(5 + x)$ **(b)** $-3(x - 4y)$ **(c)** $(2x - 5)(6)$

SOLUTION

(a) $4(5 + x) = 4 \cdot 5 + 4 \cdot x = 20 + 4x$

(b) $-3(x - 4y) = -3 \cdot x - (-3) \cdot (4y) = -3x + 12y$

(c) $(2x - 5)(6) = 2x \cdot 6 - 5 \cdot 6 = 12x - 30$ Now Try Exercises 47, 51, and 53

You can visualize the product in part (a) of Example 4 by using areas of rectangles. If a rectangle has width 4 and length $5 + x$, its area is $20 + 4x$, as shown in Figure R.17.

$4(5 + x) = 20 + 4x$

Visualize the solution by using areas.

Figure R.17

Multiplying Polynomials

A polynomial with two terms is a **binomial**, and a polynomial with three terms is a **trinomial**. Examples are shown in Table R.4.

Types of Polynomials

One term — **Monomials**	$2x^2$	$-3x^4$	9
Two terms — **Binomials**	$3x - 1$	$2x^3 - x$	$x^2 + 5$
Three terms — **Trinomials**	$x^2 - 3x + 5$	$5x^2 - 2x + 10$	$2x^3 - x^2 - 2$

Table R.4

In the next example, we multiply two binomials.

EXAMPLE 5 Multiplying binomials

Multiply $(x + 1)(x + 3)$.

SOLUTION To multiply $(x + 1)(x + 3)$, we apply the distributive property.

$$(x + 1)(x + 3) = (x + 1)(x) + (x + 1)(3)$$
$$= x \cdot x + 1 \cdot x + x \cdot 3 + 1 \cdot 3$$
$$= x^2 + x + 3x + 3$$
$$= x^2 + 4x + 3$$

Now Try Exercise 55

To multiply the bionomials $(x + 1)$ and $(x + 3)$, we multiplied every term in $x + 1$ by every term in $x + 3$. That is,

$$(x + 1)(x + 3) = x^2 + 3x + x + 3$$
$$= x^2 + 4x + 3.$$

NOTE This process of multiplying binomials is called *FOIL*. You may use the name to remind yourself to multiply the first terms (F), outside terms (O), inside terms (I), and last terms (L).

Multiply the *First terms* to obtain x^2. $(x + 1)(x + 3)$ F

Multiply the *Outside terms* to obtain $3x$. $(x + 1)(x + 3)$ O

Multiply the *Inside terms* to obtain x. $(x + 1)(x + 3)$ I

Multiply the *Last terms* to obtain 3. $(x + 1)(x + 3)$ L

The following box summarizes how to multiply two polynomials in general.

> **MULTIPLYING POLYNOMIALS**
>
> The product of two polynomials may be found by multiplying every term in the first polynomial by every term in the second polynomial and then combining like terms.

EXAMPLE 6 Multiplying binomials

Multiply each binomial.
(a) $(2x - 1)(x + 2)$ **(b)** $(1 - 3x)(2 - 4x)$ **(c)** $(x^2 + 1)(5x - 3)$

SOLUTION

(a) $(2x - 1)(x + 2) = 2x \cdot x + 2x \cdot 2 - 1 \cdot x - 1 \cdot 2$
$$= 2x^2 + 4x - x - 2$$
$$= 2x^2 + 3x - 2$$

(b) $(1 - 3x)(2 - 4x) = 1 \cdot 2 - 1 \cdot 4x - 3x \cdot 2 + 3x \cdot 4x$
$$= 2 - 4x - 6x + 12x^2$$
$$= 2 - 10x + 12x^2$$

(c) $(x^2 + 1)(5x - 3) = x^2 \cdot 5x - x^2 \cdot 3 + 1 \cdot 5x - 1 \cdot 3$
$$= 5x^3 - 3x^2 + 5x - 3$$

Now Try Exercises 57, 59, and 77

EXAMPLE 7 Multiplying polynomials

Multiply each expression.
(a) $3x(x^2 + 5x - 4)$ **(b)** $-x^2(x^4 - 2x + 5)$ **(c)** $(x + 2)(x^2 + 4x - 3)$

SOLUTION

(a) $3x(x^2 + 5x - 4) = 3x \cdot x^2 + 3x \cdot 5x - 3x \cdot 4$
$$= 3x^3 + 15x^2 - 12x$$

(b) $-x^2(x^4 - 2x + 5) = -x^2 \cdot x^4 + x^2 \cdot 2x - x^2 \cdot 5$
$$= -x^6 + 2x^3 - 5x^2$$

(c) $(x + 2)(x^2 + 4x - 3) = x \cdot x^2 + x \cdot 4x - x \cdot 3 + 2 \cdot x^2 + 2 \cdot 4x - 2 \cdot 3$
$$= x^3 + 4x^2 - 3x + 2x^2 + 8x - 6$$
$$= x^3 + 6x^2 + 5x - 6$$

Now Try Exercises 67, 69, and 73

Some Special Products

Sum and Difference   The following special product often occurs in mathematics.

| Product of a sum of two numbers and their difference | $(a + b)(a - b) = a \cdot a - a \cdot b + b \cdot a - b \cdot b$ |

$$= a^2 - ab + ba - b^2$$

$$= a^2 - b^2$$

That is, the product of a sum of two numbers and their difference equals the difference of their squares: $(a + b)(a - b) = a^2 - b^2$.

EXAMPLE 8   Finding the product of a sum and difference

Multiply.
(a) $(x - 3)(x + 3)$ **(b)** $(5 + 4x^2)(5 - 4x^2)$

SOLUTION
(a) If we let $a = x$ and $b = 3$, we can apply $(a - b)(a + b) = a^2 - b^2$. Thus

$$(x - 3)(x + 3) = (x)^2 - (3)^2$$

$$= x^2 - 9.$$

Product is the difference of the squares of x and 3.

(b) Similarly,

$$(5 + 4x^2)(5 - 4x^2) = (5)^2 - (4x^2)^2$$

$$= 25 - 16x^4.$$

Now Try Exercises 79 and 95

Squaring a Binomial   Two other special products involve *squaring a binomial*:

$$(a + b)^2 = (a + b)(a + b)$$

$$= a^2 + ab + ba + b^2$$

$$= a^2 + 2ab + b^2$$

and

$$(a - b)^2 = (a - b)(a - b)$$

$$= a^2 - ab - ba + b^2$$

$$= a^2 - 2ab + b^2.$$

Note that to obtain the middle term, we multiply the two terms in the binomial and double the result.

EXAMPLE 9   Squaring a binomial

Multiply.
(a) $(x + 5)^2$ **(b)** $(3 - 2x)^2$

SOLUTION
(a) If we let $a = x$ and $b = 5$, we can apply $(a + b)^2 = a^2 + 2ab + b^2$. Thus

$$(x + 5)^2 = (x)^2 + 2(x)(5) + (5)^2$$

$$= x^2 + 10x + 25.$$

(b) Applying the formula $(a - b)^2 = a^2 - 2ab + b^2$, we find

$$(3 - 2x)^2 = (3)^2 - 2(3)(2x) + (2x)^2$$

$$= 9 - 12x + 4x^2.$$

Now Try Exercises 85 and 91

R.3 Exercises

Monomials and Polynomials

Exercises 1–12: Combine like terms whenever possible.

1. $3x^3 + 5x^3$

2. $-9z + 6z$

3. $5y^7 - 8y^7$

4. $9x - 7x$

5. $5x^2 + 8x + x^2$

6. $5x + 2x + 10x$

7. $9x^2 - x + 4x - 6x^2$

8. $-y^2 - \frac{1}{2}y^2$

9. $x^2 + 9x - 2 + 4x^2 + 4x$

10. $6y + 4y^2 - 6y + y^2$

11. $7y + 9x^2y - 5y + x^2y$

12. $5ab - b^2 + 7ab + 6b^2$

Exercises 13–18: Identify the degree and leading coefficient of the polynomial.

13. $5x^2 - 4x + \frac{3}{4}$

14. $-9y^4 + y^2 + 5$

15. $5 - x + 3x^2 - \frac{2}{5}x^3$

16. $7x + 4x^4 - \frac{4}{3}x^3$

17. $8x^4 + 3x^3 - 4x + x^5$

18. $5x^2 - x^3 + 7x^4 + 10$

Exercises 19–28: Add the polynomials.

19. $(5x + 6) + (-2x + 6)$

20. $(5y^2 + y^3) + (12y^2 - 5y^3)$

21. $(2x^2 - x + 7) + (-2x^2 + 4x - 9)$

22. $(x^3 - 5x^2 + 6) + (5x^2 + 3x + 1)$

23. $(4x) + (1 - 4.5x)$

24. $(y^5 + y) + \left(5 - y + \frac{1}{3}y^2\right)$

25. $(x^4 - 3x^2 - 4) + \left(-8x^4 + x^2 - \frac{1}{2}\right)$

26. $(3z + z^4 + 2) + (-3z^4 - 5 + z^2)$

27. $(2z^3 + 5z - 6) + (z^2 - 3z + 2)$

28. $(z^4 - 6z^2 + 3) + (5z^3 + 3z^2 - 3)$

Exercises 29–34: Find the opposite of the polynomial.

29. $7x^3$

30. $-3z^8$

31. $19z^5 - 5z^2 + 3z$

32. $-x^2 - x + 6$

33. $z^4 - z^2 - 9$

34. $1 - 8x + 6x^2 - \frac{1}{6}x^3$

Exercises 35–42: Subtract the polynomials.

35. $(5x - 3) - (2x + 4)$

36. $(10x + 5) - (-6x - 4)$

37. $(x^2 - 3x + 1) - (-5x^2 + 2x - 4)$

38. $(-x^2 + x - 5) - (x^2 - x + 5)$

39. $(4x^4 + 2x^2 - 9) - (x^4 - 2x^2 - 5)$

40. $(8x^3 + 5x^2 - 3x + 1) - (-5x^3 + 6x - 11)$

41. $(x^4 - 1) - (4x^4 + 3x + 7)$

42. $(5x^4 - 6x^3 + x^2 + 5) - (x^3 + 11x^2 + 9x - 3)$

Exercises 43–54: Apply the distributive property.

43. $5x(x - 5)$

44. $3x^2(-2x + 2)$

45. $-5(3x + 1)$

46. $-(-3x + 1)$

47. $5(y + 2)$

48. $4(x - 7)$

49. $-2(5x + 9)$

50. $-3x(5 + x)$

51. $(y - 3)6y$

52. $(2x - 5)8x^3$

53. $-4(5x - y)$

54. $-6(3y - 2x)$

Exercises 55–66: Multiply the binomials.

55. $(y + 5)(y - 7)$

56. $(3x + 1)(2x + 1)$

57. $(3 - 2x)(3 + x)$

58. $(7x - 3)(4 - 7x)$

59. $(-2x + 3)(x - 2)$

60. $(z - 2)(4z + 3)$

61. $(x - \frac{1}{2})(x + \frac{1}{4})$

62. $\left(z - \frac{1}{3}\right)\left(z - \frac{1}{6}\right)$

63. $(x^2 + 1)(2x^2 - 1)$

64. $(x^2 - 2)(x^2 + 4)$

65. $(x + y)(x - 2y)$

66. $(x^2 + y^2)(x - y)$

Exercises 67–78: Multiply the polynomials.

67. $3x(2x^2 - x - 1)$

68. $-2x(3 - 2x + 5x^2)$

69. $-x(2x^4 - x^2 + 10)$

70. $-2x^2(5x^3 + x^2 - 2)$

71. $(2x^2 - 4x + 1)(3x^2)$

72. $(x - y + 5)(xy)$

73. $(x + 1)(x^2 + 2x - 3)$

74. $(2x - 1)(3x^2 - x + 6)$

75. $(2 - 3x)(5 - 2x)(x^2 - 1)$

76. $(3 + z)(6 - 4z)(4 + 2z^2)$

77. $(x^2 + 2)(3x - 2)$

78. $(4 + x)(2x^2 - 3)$

Exercises 79–96: Multiply the expressions.

79. $(x - 7)(x + 7)$

80. $(x + 9)(x - 9)$

81. $(3x + 4)(3x - 4)$

82. $(9x - 4)(9x + 4)$

83. $(2x - 3y)(2x + 3y)$

84. $(x + 2y)(x - 2y)$

85. $(x + 4)^2$

86. $(z + 9)^2$

87. $(2x + 1)^2$

88. $(3x + 5)^2$

89. $(x - 1)^2$

90. $(x - 7)^2$

91. $(2 - 3x)^2$

92. $(5 - 6x)^2$

93. $3x(x + 1)(x - 1)$

94. $-4x(3x - 5)^2$

95. $(2 - 5x^2)(2 + 5x^2)$

96. $(6y - x^2)(6y + x^2)$

R.4 Factoring Polynomials

- **Use common factors**
- **Factor by grouping**
- **Factor $x^2 + bx + c$**
- **Factor trinomials by grouping**
- **Factor trinomials with FOIL**
- **Factor the difference of two squares**
- **Factor perfect square trinomials**
- **Factor the sum and difference of two cubes**

Common Factors

When factoring a polynomial, we first look for factors that are common to each term in an expression. By applying a distributive property, we can write a polynomial as two factors. For example, each term in $2x^2 + 4x$ contains a factor of $2x$.

$$2x^2 = 2x \cdot x$$
$$4x = 2x \cdot 2$$

Factor $2x$ out of each term.

Thus the polynomial $2x^2 + 4x$ can be factored as follows.

$$2x^2 + 4x = 2x(x + 2)$$

Apply a distributive property to factor.

EXAMPLE 1 Finding common factors

Factor.
(a) $6z^3 - 2z^2 + 4z$ **(b)** $4x^3y^2 + x^2y^3$

SOLUTION
(a) Each of the terms $6z^3$, $2z^2$, and $4z$ contains a common factor of $2z$. That is,

$$6z^3 = 2z \cdot 3z^2, \quad 2z^2 = 2z \cdot z, \quad \text{and} \quad 4z = 2z \cdot 2.$$

Thus $6z^3 - 2z^2 + 4z = 2z(3z^2 - z + 2)$.
(b) Both $4x^3y^2$ and x^2y^3 contain a common factor of x^2y^2. That is,

$$4x^3y^2 = x^2y^2 \cdot 4x \quad \text{and} \quad x^2y^3 = x^2y^2 \cdot y.$$

Thus $4x^3y^2 + x^2y^3 = x^2y^2(4x + y)$.

Now Try Exercises 5 and 15

Many times we factor out the *greatest common factor*. For example, the polynomial $15x^4 - 5x^2$ has a common factor of $5x$. We could write this polynomial as

$$15x^4 - 5x^2 = 5x(3x^3 - x).$$

However, we can also factor out $5x^2$ to obtain

$$15x^4 - 5x^2 = 5x^2(3x^2 - 1).$$

Because $5x^2$ is the common factor with the highest degree and largest coefficient, we say that $5x^2$ is the **greatest common factor** (GCF) of $15x^4 - 5x^2$.

EXAMPLE 2 Factoring greatest common factors

Factor.

(a) $6m^3n^2 - 3mn^2 + 9m$ **(b)** $-9x^4 + 6x^3 - 3x^2$

SOLUTION

(a) The GCF of $6m^3n^2$, $3mn^2$, and $9m$ is $3m$.

$$6m^3n^2 = 3m \cdot 2m^2n^2, \quad 3mn^2 = 3m \cdot n^2, \quad \text{and} \quad 9m = 3m \cdot 3$$

Thus $6m^3n^2 - 3mn^2 + 9m = 3m(2m^2n^2 - n^2 + 3)$.

(b) Rather than factoring out $3x^2$, we can factor out $-3x^2$ and make the leading coefficient of the remaining expression positive.

$$-9x^4 = -3x^2 \cdot 3x^2, \quad 6x^3 = -3x^2 \cdot -2x, \quad \text{and} \quad -3x^2 = -3x^2 \cdot 1$$

Thus $-9x^4 + 6x^3 - 3x^2 = -3x^2(3x^2 - 2x + 1)$.

Now Try Exercises 11 and 17

Factoring by Grouping

Factoring by grouping is a technique that makes use of the associative and distributive properties. The next example illustrates the first step in this factoring technique.

Consider the cubic polynomial

$$3t^3 + 6t^2 + 2t + 4.$$

We can factor this polynomial by first grouping it into two binomials.

$$(3t^3 + 6t^2) + (2t + 4) \qquad \text{Associative property}$$
$$3t^2(t + 2) + 2(t + 2) \qquad \text{Factor out common factors.}$$
$$(3t^2 + 2)(t + 2). \qquad \text{Factor out } (t + 2).$$

The following steps summarize factoring four terms by grouping.

FACTORING BY GROUPING

STEP 1: Use parentheses to group the terms into binomials with common factors. Begin by writing the expression with a plus sign between the binomials.

STEP 2: Factor out the common factor in each binomial.

STEP 3: Factor out the common binomial. If there is no common binomial, try a different grouping or a different method of factoring.

EXAMPLE 3 Factoring by grouping

Factor each polynomial.

(a) $12x^3 - 9x^2 - 8x + 6$ **(b)** $2x - 2y + ax - ay$

SOLUTION

(a) $12x^3 - 9x^2 - 8x + 6 = (12x^3 - 9x^2) + (-8x + 6)$ Write with a plus sign between binomials.

$$= 3x^2(4x - 3) - 2(4x - 3) \qquad \text{Factor out } 3x^2 \text{ and } -2.$$
$$= (3x^2 - 2)(4x - 3) \qquad \text{Factor out } 4x - 3.$$

(b) $2x - 2y + ax - ay = (2x - 2y) + (ax - ay)$ Group terms.

$$= 2(x - y) + a(x - y) \qquad \text{Factor out 2 and } a.$$
$$= (2 + a)(x - y) \qquad \text{Factor out } x - y.$$

Now Try Exercises 21 and 31

Factoring $x^2 + bx + c$

The product $(x + 3)(x + 4)$ can be found as follows.

Multiply using FOIL.

$$(x + 3)(x + 4) = x^2 + 4x + 3x + 12$$
$$= x^2 + \quad 7x \quad + 12$$

The middle term $7x$ is found by calculating the sum $4x + 3x$, and the last term is found by calculating the product $3 \cdot 4 = 12$.

When we factor polynomials, we are *reversing* the process of multiplication. To factor $x^2 + 7x + 12$, we must find m and n that satisfy

$$x^2 + 7x + 12 = (x + m)(x + n).$$

Because

$$(x + m)(x + n) = x^2 + (m + n)x + mn,$$

it follows that $mn = 12$ and $m + n = 7$. To determine m and n, we list factors of 12 and their sum, as shown in Table R.5.

Because $3 \cdot 4 = 12$ and $3 + 4 = 7$, we can write the factored form as

$$x^2 + 7x + 12 = (x + 3)(x + 4).$$

This result can always be checked by multiplying the two binomials.

$$(x + 3) \ (x + 4) = x^2 + 7x + 12$$

$3x$
$+4x$
$7x$ ⟵ The middle term checks.

Factor Pairs for 12

Factors	1, 12	2, 6	3, 4
Sum	13	8	7

Table R.5

> **FACTORING $x^2 + bx + c$**
>
> To factor the trinomial $x^2 + bx + c$, find integers m and n that satisfy
>
> $$m \cdot n = c \qquad \text{and} \qquad m + n = b.$$
>
> Then $x^2 + bx + c = (x + m)(x + n)$.

EXAMPLE 4   Factoring the form $x^2 + bx + c$

Factor each trinomial.
(a) $x^2 + 10x + 16$ **(b)** $x^2 + 7x - 30$

SOLUTION
(a) We need to find a factor pair for 16 whose sum is 10. From Table R.6 the required factor pair is $m = 2$ and $n = 8$. Thus

$$x^2 + 10x + 16 = (x + 2)(x + 8).$$

(b) Factors of -30 whose sum equals 7 are -3 and 10. Thus

$$x^2 + 7x - 30 = (x - 3)(x + 10).$$

Factor Pairs for 16

Factors	1, 16	2, 8	4, 4
Sum	17	10	8

Table R.6

Now Try Exercises 33 and 37

EXAMPLE 5   Removing common factors first

Factor completely.
(a) $3x^2 + 15x + 18$ **(b)** $5x^3 + 5x^2 - 60x$

SOLUTION
(a) If we first factor out the common factor of 3, the resulting trinomial is easier to factor.

$$3x^2 + 15x + 18 = 3(x^2 + 5x + 6)$$

Now we find m and n such that $mn = 6$ and $m + n = 5$. These numbers are 2 and 3.

$$3x^2 + 15x + 18 = 3(x^2 + 5x + 6)$$
$$= 3(x + 2)(x + 3)$$

(b) First, we factor out the common factor of $5x$. Then we factor the resulting trinomial.

$$5x^3 + 5x^2 - 60x = 5x(x^2 + x - 12)$$
$$= 5x(x - 3)(x + 4)$$

Now Try Exercises 51 and 53

Factoring Trinomials by Grouping

In this subsection we use grouping to factor trinomials in the form $ax^2 + bx + c$ with $a \neq 1$. For example, one way to factor $3x^2 + 14x + 8$ is to find two numbers m and n such that $mn = 3 \cdot 8 = 24$ and $m + n = 14$. Because $2 \cdot 12 = 24$ and $2 + 12 = 14$, we let $m = 2$ and $n = 12$. Using grouping, we can now factor this trinomial.

$$
\begin{array}{ll}
3x^2 + 14x + 8 = 3x^2 + 2x + 12x + 8 & \text{Write 14x as 2x + 12x.} \\
\quad = (3x^2 + 2x) + (12x + 8) & \text{Associative property} \\
\quad = x(3x + 2) + 4(3x + 2) & \text{Factor out x and 4.} \\
\quad = (x + 4)(3x + 2) & \text{Distributive property}
\end{array}
$$

Writing the polynomial as $3x^2 + 12x + 2x + 8$ would also work.

FACTORING $ax^2 + bx + c$ BY GROUPING

To factor $ax^2 + bx + c$, perform the following steps. (Assume that a, b, and c have no factor in common.)

1. Find numbers m and n such that $mn = ac$ and $m + n = b$. This step may require trial and error.
2. Write the trinomial as $ax^2 + mx + nx + c$.
3. Use grouping to factor this expression as two binomials.

EXAMPLE 6 Factoring $ax^2 + bx + c$ by grouping

Factor each trinomial.
(a) $12y^2 + 5y - 3$ **(b)** $6r^2 - 19r + 10$

SOLUTION
(a) In this trinomial $a = 12$, $b = 5$, and $c = -3$. Because $mn = ac$ and $m + n = b$, the numbers m and n satisfy $mn = -36$ and $m + n = 5$. Thus $m = 9$ and $n = -4$.

$$
\begin{array}{ll}
12y^2 + 5y - 3 = 12y^2 + 9y - 4y - 3 & \text{Write 5y as 9y - 4y.} \\
\quad = (12y^2 + 9y) + (-4y - 3) & \text{Associative property} \\
\quad = 3y(4y + 3) - 1(4y + 3) & \text{Factor out 3y and -1.} \\
\quad = (3y - 1)(4y + 3) & \text{Distributive property}
\end{array}
$$

(b) In this trinomial $a = 6$, $b = -19$, and $c = 10$. Because $mn = ac$ and $m + n = b$, the numbers m and n satisfy $mn = 60$ and $m + n = -19$. Thus $m = -4$ and $n = -15$.

$$
\begin{array}{ll}
6r^2 - 19r + 10 = 6r^2 - 4r - 15r + 10 & \text{Write -19r as -4r - 15r.} \\
\quad = (6r^2 - 4r) + (-15r + 10) & \text{Associative property} \\
\quad = 2r(3r - 2) - 5(3r - 2) & \text{Factor out 2r and -5.} \\
\quad = (2r - 5)(3r - 2) & \text{Distributive property}
\end{array}
$$

Now Try Exercises 41 and 43

Factoring Trinomials with FOIL

An alternative to factoring trinomials by grouping is to use FOIL in *reverse*. For example, the factors of $3x^2 + 7x + 2$ are two binomials.

$$3x^2 + 7x + 2 \overset{?}{=} (\underline{\quad} + \underline{\quad})(\underline{\quad} + \underline{\quad})$$

The expressions to be placed in the four blanks are yet to be found. By the FOIL method, we know that the product of the first terms is $3x^2$. Because $3x^2 = 3x \cdot x$, we can write

$$3x^2 + 7x + 2 \overset{?}{=} (\underline{\ 3x\ } + \underline{\quad})(\underline{\ x\ } + \underline{\quad}).$$

The product of the last terms in each binomial must equal 2. Because $2 = 1 \cdot 2$, we can put the 1 and 2 in the blanks, but we must be sure to place them correctly so that the product of the *outside terms* plus the product of the *inside terms* equals $7x$.

Determine where to place the 1 and 2 and then check the middle term.

$$(3x + 1)\ (x + 2) = 3x^2 + 7x + 2$$

$1x$

$+ 6x$

$7x$ ⟵ Middle term checks. ⟶ Correct

If we had interchanged the 1 and 2, we would have obtained an incorrect result.

$$(3x + 2)\ (x + 1) = 3x^2 + 5x + 2$$

$2x$

$+ 3x$

$5x$ ⟵ Middle term is *not* $7x$. ⟶ Incorrect

In the next example, we factor expressions of the form $ax^2 + bx + c$, where $a \ne 1$. In this situation, we may need to *guess and check* or use *trial and error* a few times to find the correct factors.

EXAMPLE 7   **Factoring the form $ax^2 + bx + c$**

Factor each trinomial.
(a) $6x^2 - x - 2$ **(b)** $4x^3 - 14x^2 + 6x$

SOLUTION
(a) The factors of $6x^2$ are either $2x$ and $3x$ or $6x$ and x. The factors of -2 are either -1 and 2 or 1 and -2. To obtain a middle term of $-x$, we use the following factors.

$$(3x - 2)\ (2x + 1) = 6x^2 - x - 2$$

$- 4x$

$+ 3x$

$- x$ ⟵ It checks.

To find the correct factorization, we may need to guess and check a few times.
(b) Each term contains a common factor of $2x$, so we do the following step first.

$$4x^3 - 14x^2 + 6x = 2x(2x^2 - 7x + 3)$$

Next we factor $2x^2 - 7x + 3$. The factors of $2x^2$ are $2x$ and x. Because the middle term is negative, we use -1 and -3 for factors of 3.

$$4x^3 - 14x^2 + 6x = 2x(2x^2 - 7x + 3)$$
$$= 2x(2x - 1)(x - 3)$$

Now Try Exercises 55 and 57

Difference of Two Squares

When we factor polynomials, we are *reversing* the process of multiplying polynomials. In Section R.3 we discussed the equation

$$(a - b)(a + b) = a^2 - b^2.$$

We can use this equation to factor a difference of two squares.

DIFFERENCE OF TWO SQUARES

For any real numbers a and b,

$$a^2 - b^2 = (a - b)(a + b).$$

NOTE The sum of two squares *cannot* be factored (using real numbers). For example, $x^2 + y^2$ cannot be factored, whereas $x^2 - y^2$ can be factored. It is important to remember that $x^2 + y^2 \neq (x + y)^2$.

EXAMPLE 8 Factoring the difference of two squares

Factor each polynomial, if possible.
(a) $9x^2 - 64$ **(b)** $4x^2 + 9y^2$ **(c)** $4a^3 - 4a$

SOLUTION
(a) Note that $9x^2 = (3x)^2$ and $64 = 8^2$.

$$9x^2 - 64 = (3x)^2 - (8)^2 \qquad \text{Factor difference of two squares.}$$
$$= (3x - 8)(3x + 8)$$

(b) Because $4x^2 + 9y^2$ is the *sum* of two squares, it *cannot* be factored.
(c) Start by factoring out the common factor of $4a$.

$$4a^3 - 4a = 4a(a^2 - 1)$$
$$= 4a(a - 1)(a + 1)$$

Now Try Exercises 61, 65, and 69

EXAMPLE 9 Applying the difference of two squares

Factor each expression.
(a) $x^4 - y^4$ **(b)** $6r^2 - 24t^4$

SOLUTION
(a) Use $a^2 - b^2 = (a - b)(a + b)$, with $a = x^2$ and $b = y^2$.

$$x^4 - y^4 = (x^2)^2 - (y^2)^2 \qquad \text{Write as difference of squares.}$$
$$= (x^2 - y^2)(x^2 + y^2) \qquad \text{Difference of squares}$$
$$= (x - y)(x + y)(x^2 + y^2) \qquad \text{Difference of squares}$$

(b) Start by factoring out the common factor of 6.

$$6r^2 - 24t^4 = 6(r^2 - 4t^4) \qquad \text{Factor out 6.}$$
$$= 6\left(r^2 - (2t^2)^2\right) \qquad \text{Write as difference of squares.}$$
$$= 6(r - 2t^2)(r + 2t^2) \qquad \text{Difference of squares}$$

Now Try Exercises 66 and 67

Perfect Square Trinomials

In Section R.3 we expanded $(a + b)^2$ and $(a - b)^2$ as follows.

$$(a + b)^2 = a^2 + 2ab + b^2 \quad \text{and} \quad (a - b)^2 = a^2 - 2ab + b^2$$

The expressions $a^2 + 2ab + b^2$ and $a^2 - 2ab + b^2$ are called **perfect square trinomials**. We can use the following formulas to factor them.

PERFECT SQUARE TRINOMIALS

For any real numbers a and b,

$$a^2 + 2ab + b^2 = (a + b)^2 \quad \text{and}$$

$$a^2 - 2ab + b^2 = (a - b)^2.$$

EXAMPLE 10 Factoring perfect square trinomials

Factor each expression.
(a) $x^2 + 6x + 9$ **(b)** $81x^2 - 72x + 16$

SOLUTION
(a) Let $a^2 = x^2$ and $b^2 = 3^2$. In a perfect square trinomial, the middle term is $2ab$.

$$2ab = 2(x)(3) = 6x,$$

which equals the given middle term. Thus $a^2 + 2ab + b^2 = (a + b)^2$ implies

Perfect square trinomial

$$x^2 + 6x + 9 = (x + 3)^2.$$

(b) Let $a^2 = (9x)^2$ and $b^2 = 4^2$. In a perfect square trinomial, the middle term is $2ab$.

$$2ab = 2(9x)(4) = 72x,$$

which equals the given middle term. Thus $a^2 - 2ab + b^2 = (a - b)^2$ implies

$$81x^2 - 72x + 16 = (9x - 4)^2.$$

Now Try Exercises 77 and 81

EXAMPLE 11 Factoring perfect square trinomials

Factor $25a^3 + 10a^2b + ab^2$.

SOLUTION Start by factoring out the common factor of a. Then factor the resulting perfect square trinomial.

$$25a^3 + 10a^2b + ab^2 = a(25a^2 + 10ab + b^2)$$

Perfect square trinomial

$$= a(5a + b)^2$$

Now Try Exercise 89

Sum and Difference of Two Cubes

The sum or difference of two cubes may be factored. This fact is justified by the following two equations.

$$(a + b)(a^2 - ab + b^2) = a^3 + b^3 \quad \text{and}$$

$$(a - b)(a^2 + ab + b^2) = a^3 - b^3$$

These equations can be verified by multiplying the left side to obtain the right side. For example,

$$(a + b)(a^2 - ab + b^2) = a \cdot a^2 - a \cdot ab + a \cdot b^2 + b \cdot a^2 - b \cdot ab + b \cdot b^2$$

$$= a^3 - a^2b + ab^2 + a^2b - ab^2 + b^3$$

$$= a^3 + b^3.$$

SUM AND DIFFERENCE OF TWO CUBES

For any real numbers a and b,

$$a^3 + b^3 = (a + b)(a^2 - ab + b^2) \quad \text{and}$$

$$a^3 - b^3 = (a - b)(a^2 + ab + b^2).$$

EXAMPLE 12 Factoring the sum and difference of two cubes

Factor each polynomial.
(a) $x^3 + 8$ **(b)** $27x^3 - 64y^3$ **(c)** $27p^9 - 8q^6$

SOLUTION
(a) Because $x^3 = (x)^3$ and $8 = 2^3$, we let $a = x$, $b = 2$ and factor. Substituting in

$$a^3 + b^3 = (a + b)(a^2 - ab + b^2)$$

gives $\qquad x^3 + 2^3 = (x + 2)(x^2 - x \cdot 2 + 2^2)$

$$= (x + 2)(x^2 - 2x + 4).$$

Note that the quadratic expression does not factor further.
(b) Here, $27x^3 = (3x)^3$ and $64y^3 = (4y)^3$, so

$$27x^3 - 64y^3 = (3x)^3 - (4y)^3.$$

Substituting $a = 3x$ and $b = 4y$ in

$$a^3 - b^3 = (a - b)(a^2 + ab + b^2)$$

gives $\qquad (3x)^3 - (4y)^3 = (3x - 4y)((3x)^2 + 3x \cdot 4y + (4y)^2)$

$$= (3x - 4y)(9x^2 + 12xy + 16y^2).$$

(c) Let $a^3 = (3p^3)^3$ and $b^3 = (2q^2)^3$. Then $a^3 - b^3 = (a - b)(a^2 + ab + b^2)$ implies

$$27p^9 - 8q^6 = (3p^3 - 2q^2)(9p^6 + 6p^3q^2 + 4q^4).$$

Now Try Exercises 93, 95, and 99

R.4 Exercises

Greatest Common Factor
Exercises 1–18: Factor out the greatest common factor.

1. $10x - 15$

2. $32 - 16x$

3. $2x^3 - 5x$

4. $3y - 9y^2$

5. $8x^3 - 4x^2 + 16x$

6. $-5x^3 + x^2 - 4x$

7. $5x^4 - 15x^3 + 15x^2$

8. $28y + 14y^3 - 7y^5$

9. $15x^3 + 10x^2 - 30x$

10. $14a^4 - 21a^2 + 35a$

11. $6r^5 - 8r^4 + 12r^3$

12. $15r^6 + 20r^4 - 10r^3$

13. $8x^2y^2 - 24x^2y^3$

14. $36xy - 24x^3y^3$

15. $18mn^2 - 12m^2n^3$

16. $24m^2n^3 + 12m^3n^2$

17. $-4a^2 - 2ab + 6ab^2$

18. $-5a^2 + 10a^2b^2 - 15ab$

Factoring by Grouping
Exercises 19–32: Use grouping to factor the polynomial.

19. $x^3 + 3x^2 + 2x + 6$ **20.** $4x^3 + 3x^2 + 8x + 6$

21. $6x^3 - 4x^2 + 9x - 6$ **22.** $x^3 - 3x^2 - 5x + 15$

23. $z^3 - 5z^2 + z - 5$ **24.** $y^3 - 7y^2 + 8y - 56$

25. $y^4 + 2y^3 - 5y^2 - 10y$ **26.** $4z^4 + 4z^3 + z^2 + z$

27. $2x^3 - 3x^2 + 2x - 3$ **28.** $8x^3 - 2x^2 + 12x - 3$

29. $2x^4 - x^3 + 4x - 2$ **30.** $2x^4 - 5x^3 + 10x - 25$

31. $ab - 3a + 2b - 6$ **32.** $2ax - 6bx - ay + 3by$

Factoring Trinomials

Exercises 33–58: Factor the expression completely.

33. $x^2 + 7x + 10$ **34.** $x^2 + 3x - 10$

35. $x^2 + 8x + 12$ **36.** $x^2 - 8x + 12$

37. $z^2 + z - 42$ **38.** $z^2 - 9z + 20$

39. $z^2 + 11z + 24$ **40.** $z^2 + 15z + 54$

41. $24x^2 + 14x - 3$ **42.** $25x^2 - 5x - 6$

43. $6x^2 - x - 2$ **44.** $10x^2 + 3x - 1$

45. $1 + x - 2x^2$ **46.** $3 - 5x - 2x^2$

47. $20 + 7x - 6x^2$ **48.** $4 + 13x - 12x^2$

49. $5x^3 + x^2 - 6x$ **50.** $2x^3 + 8x^2 - 24x$

51. $3x^3 + 12x^2 + 9x$ **52.** $12x^3 - 8x^2 - 20x$

53. $2x^2 - 14x + 20$ **54.** $7x^2 + 35x + 42$

55. $60t^4 + 230t^3 - 40t^2$ **56.** $24r^4 + 8r^3 - 80r^2$

57. $4m^3 + 10m^2 - 6m$ **58.** $30m^4 + 3m^3 - 9m^2$

Difference of Two Squares

Exercises 59–76: Factor the expression completely, if possible.

59. $x^2 - 25$ **60.** $z^2 - 169$

61. $4x^2 - 25$ **62.** $36 - y^2$

63. $36x^2 - 100$ **64.** $9x^2 - 4y^2$

65. $64z^2 - 25z^4$ **66.** $100x^3 - x$

67. $16x^4 - y^4$ **68.** $x^4 - 9y^2$

69. $a^2 + 4b^2$ **70.** $9r^4 + 25t^4$

71. $4 - r^2t^2$ **72.** $25 - x^4y^2$

73. $(x - 1)^2 - 16$ **74.** $(y + 2)^2 - 1$

75. $4 - (z + 3)^2$ **76.** $64 - (t - 3)^2$

Perfect Square Trinomials

Exercises 77–90: Factor the expression.

77. $x^2 + 2x + 1$ **78.** $x^2 - 6x + 9$

79. $4x^2 + 20x + 25$ **80.** $x^2 + 10x + 25$

81. $x^2 - 12x + 36$ **82.** $16z^4 - 24z^3 + 9z^2$

83. $9z^3 - 6z^2 + z$ **84.** $49y^2 + 42y + 9$

85. $9y^3 + 30y^2 + 25y$ **86.** $25y^3 - 20y^2 + 4y$

87. $4x^2 - 12xy + 9y^2$ **88.** $25a^2 + 60ab + 36b^2$

89. $9a^3b - 12a^2b + 4ab$ **90.** $16a^3 + 8a^2b + ab^2$

Sum and Difference of Two Cubes

Exercises 91–102: Factor the expression.

91. $x^3 - 1$ **92.** $x^3 + 1$

93. $y^3 + z^3$ **94.** $y^3 - z^3$

95. $8x^3 - 27$ **96.** $8 - z^3$

97. $x^4 + 125x$ **98.** $3x^4 - 81x$

99. $8r^6 - t^3$ **100.** $125r^6 + 64t^3$

101. $10m^9 - 270n^6$ **102.** $5t^6 + 40r^3$

General Factoring

Exercises 103–158: Factor the expression completely.

103. $16x^2 - 25$ **104.** $25x^2 - 30x + 9$

105. $x^3 - 64$ **106.** $1 + 8y^3$

107. $x^2 + 16x + 64$ **108.** $12x^2 + x - 6$

109. $5x^2 - 38x - 16$ **110.** $125x^3 - 1$

111. $x^4 + 8x$ **112.** $2x^3 - 12x^2 + 18x$

113. $64x^3 + 8y^3$ **114.** $54 - 16x^3$

115. $3x^2 - 5x - 8$ **116.** $15x^2 - 11x + 2$

117. $7a^3 + 20a^2 - 3a$ **118.** $b^3 - b^2 - 2b$

119. $2x^3 - x^2 + 6x - 3$ **120.** $3x^3 - 5x^2 + 3x - 5$

121. $2x^4 - 5x^3 - 25x^2$ **122.** $10x^3 + 28x^2 - 6x$

123. $2x^4 + 5x^2 + 3$ **124.** $2x^4 + 2x^2 - 4$

125. $x^3 + 3x^2 + x + 3$ **126.** $x^3 + 5x^2 + 4x + 20$

127. $5x^3 - 5x^2 + 10x - 10$

128. $5x^4 - 20x^3 + 10x - 40$

129. $ax + bx - ay - by$ **130.** $ax - bx - ay + by$

131. $18x^2 + 12x + 2$ **132.** $-3x^2 + 30x - 75$

133. $-4x^3 + 24x^2 - 36x$ **134.** $18x^3 - 60x^2 + 50x$

135. $27x^3 - 8$ **136.** $27x^3 + 8$

137. $-x^4 - 8x$ **138.** $x^5 - 27x^2$

139. $x^4 - 2x^3 - x + 2$ **140.** $x^4 + 3x^3 + x + 3$

141. $r^4 - 16$ **142.** $r^4 - 81$

143. $25x^2 - 4a^2$ **144.** $9y^2 - 16z^2$

145. $2x^4 - 2y^4$ **146.** $a^4 - b^4$

147. $9x^3 + 6x^2 - 3x$ **148.** $8x^3 + 28x^2 - 16x$

149. $(z - 2)^2 - 9$ **150.** $(y + 2)^2 - 4$

151. $3x^5 - 27x^3 + 3x^2 - 27$

152. $2x^5 - 8x^3 - 16x^2 + 64$

153. $(x + 2)^2(x + 4)^4 + (x + 2)^3(x + 4)^3$

154. $(x - 3)(2x + 1)^3 + (x - 3)^2(2x + 1)^2$

155. $(6x + 1)(8x - 3)^4 - (6x + 1)^2(8x - 3)^3$

156. $(2x + 3)^4(x + 1)^4 - (2x + 3)^3(x + 1)^5$

157. $4x^2(5x - 1)^5 + 2x(5x - 1)^6$

158. $x^4(7x + 3)^3 + x^5(7x + 3)^2$

R.5 Rational Expressions

- Simplify rational expressions
- Multiply and divide fractions
- Perform multiplication and division on rational expressions
- Find least common multiples and denominators
- Add and subtract fractions
- Perform addition and subtraction on rational expressions
- Clear fractions from equations
- Simplify complex fractions

Simplifying Rational Expressions

When simplifying fractions, we sometimes use the **basic principle of fractions**, which states that

$$\frac{a \cdot c}{b \cdot c} = \frac{a}{b}.$$

This principle holds because $\frac{c}{c} = 1$ and $\frac{a}{b} \cdot 1 = \frac{a}{b}$. It can be used to simplify a fraction.

$$\frac{6}{44} = \frac{3 \cdot 2}{22 \cdot 2} = \frac{3}{22} \qquad \boxed{\text{Factor out 2 in the numerator and denominator and simplify.}}$$

This same principle can also be used to simplify rational expressions.

> **SIMPLIFYING RATIONAL EXPRESSIONS**
>
> The following principle can be used to simplify rational expressions, where A, B, and C are polynomials.
>
> $$\frac{A \cdot C}{B \cdot C} = \frac{A}{B}, \quad B \text{ and } C \text{ are nonzero.}$$

EXAMPLE 1 Simplifying rational expressions

Simplify each expression.

(a) $\dfrac{9x}{3x^2}$ **(b)** $\dfrac{2z^2 - 3z - 9}{z^2 + 2z - 15}$ **(c)** $\dfrac{a^2 - b^2}{a + b}$

SOLUTION

(a) First factor out the greatest common factor, $3x$, in the numerator and denominator.

$$\frac{9x}{3x^2} = \frac{3 \cdot 3x}{x \cdot 3x} = \frac{3}{x} \cdot 1 = \frac{3}{x}$$

(b) Start by factoring the numerator and denominator.

$$\frac{2z^2 - 3z - 9}{z^2 + 2z - 15} = \frac{(2z + 3)(z - 3)}{(z + 5)(z - 3)} = \frac{2z + 3}{z + 5}$$

(c) Start by factoring the numerator as the difference of squares.

$$\frac{a^2 - b^2}{a + b} = \frac{(a - b)(a + b)}{a + b} = a - b$$

> **Now Try Exercises 1, 5, and 11**

Review of Multiplication and Division of Fractions

Recall that to multiply two fractions we use the property

$$\frac{a}{b} \cdot \frac{c}{d} = \frac{ac}{bd}.$$

For example, $\frac{2}{5} \cdot \frac{3}{7} = \frac{2 \cdot 3}{5 \cdot 7} = \frac{6}{35}$.

EXAMPLE 2 Multiplying fractions

Multiply and simplify the product.

(a) $\dfrac{4}{9} \cdot \dfrac{3}{8}$ **(b)** $\dfrac{2}{3} \cdot \dfrac{3}{4} \cdot \dfrac{5}{6}$

SOLUTION

(a) $\dfrac{4}{9} \cdot \dfrac{3}{8} = \dfrac{4 \cdot 3}{9 \cdot 8} = \dfrac{12}{72} = \dfrac{1 \cdot 12}{6 \cdot 12} = \dfrac{1}{6}$ **(b)** $\dfrac{2}{3} \cdot \dfrac{3}{4} \cdot \dfrac{5}{6} = \dfrac{6 \cdot 5}{12 \cdot 6} = \dfrac{5}{12}$

> **Now Try Exercises 15 and 17**

Recall that to divide two fractions we "invert and multiply." That is, we change a division problem to a multiplication problem. For example,

$$\frac{3}{4} \div \frac{5}{4} = \frac{3}{4} \cdot \frac{4}{5} = \frac{3 \cdot 4}{5 \cdot 4} = \frac{3}{5}.$$

Multiplication and Division of Rational Expressions

Multiplying and dividing rational expressions is similar to multiplying and dividing fractions.

PRODUCTS AND QUOTIENTS OF RATIONAL EXPRESSIONS

To multiply two rational expressions, multiply numerators and multiply denominators.

$$\frac{A}{B} \cdot \frac{C}{D} = \frac{AC}{BD}, \qquad B \text{ and } D \text{ are nonzero.}$$

To divide two rational expressions, multiply by the reciprocal of the divisor.

$$\frac{A}{B} \div \frac{C}{D} = \frac{A}{B} \cdot \frac{D}{C}, \qquad B, C, \text{ and } D \text{ are nonzero.}$$

EXAMPLE 3 Multiplying rational expressions

Multiply.

(a) $\dfrac{1}{x} \cdot \dfrac{2x}{x + 1}$ **(b)** $\dfrac{x - 1}{x} \cdot \dfrac{x - 1}{x + 2}$

SOLUTION

(a) $\dfrac{1}{x} \cdot \dfrac{2x}{x + 1} = \dfrac{1 \cdot 2x}{x(x + 1)} = \dfrac{2}{x + 1}$ **(b)** $\dfrac{x - 1}{x} \cdot \dfrac{x - 1}{x + 2} = \dfrac{(x - 1)(x - 1)}{x(x + 2)}$

> **Now Try Exercises 33 and 37**

EXAMPLE 4 Dividing two rational expressions

Divide and simplify.

(a) $\dfrac{2}{x} \div \dfrac{2x - 1}{4x}$ **(b)** $\dfrac{x^2 - 1}{x^2 + x - 6} \div \dfrac{x - 1}{x + 3}$

SOLUTION

(a)
$$\dfrac{2}{x} \div \dfrac{2x - 1}{4x} = \dfrac{2}{x} \cdot \dfrac{4x}{2x - 1}$$ *"Invert and multiply."*

$$= \dfrac{8x}{x(2x - 1)}$$ *Multiply.*

$$= \dfrac{8}{2x - 1}$$ *Simplify.*

(b)
$$\dfrac{x^2 - 1}{x^2 + x - 6} \div \dfrac{x - 1}{x + 3} = \dfrac{x^2 - 1}{x^2 + x - 6} \cdot \dfrac{x + 3}{x - 1}$$ *"Invert and multiply."*

$$= \dfrac{(x + 1)(x - 1)}{(x - 2)(x + 3)} \cdot \dfrac{x + 3}{x - 1}$$ *Factor.*

$$= \dfrac{(x + 1)(x - 1)(x + 3)}{(x - 2)(x - 1)(x + 3)}$$ *Commutative property*

$$= \dfrac{x + 1}{x - 2}$$ *Simplify.*

Now Try Exercises 45 and 53

Least Common Multiples and Denominators

To add or subtract fractions and rational expressions, we need to find a common denominator. The **least common denominator** (LCD) is equivalent to the **least common multiple** (LCM) of the denominators. The following procedure can be used to find the least common multiple.

FINDING THE LEAST COMMON MULTIPLE

The least common multiple (LCM) of two polynomials can be found as follows.

STEP 1: Factor each polynomial completely.

STEP 2: List each factor the greatest number of times that it occurs in either factorization.

STEP 3: Find the product of this list of factors. The result is the LCM.

The next example illustrates how to use this procedure.

EXAMPLE 5 Finding least common multiples

Find the least common multiple for each pair of expressions.
(a) $4x, 5x^3$ **(b)** $x^2 + 4x + 4, x^2 + 3x + 2$

SOLUTION

(a) STEP 1: Factor each polynomial completely.

$$4x = 2 \cdot 2 \cdot x \quad \text{and} \quad 5x^3 = 5 \cdot x \cdot x \cdot x$$

STEP 2: The factor 2 occurs twice, the factor 5 occurs once, and the factor x occurs at most three times. The list then is 2, 2, 5, x, x, and x.

STEP 3: The LCM is the product $2 \cdot 2 \cdot 5 \cdot x \cdot x \cdot x$, or $20x^3$.

(b) STEP 1: Factor each polynomial as follows.

$$x^2 + 4x + 4 = (x + 2)(x + 2) \quad \text{and} \quad x^2 + 3x + 2 = (x + 1)(x + 2)$$

STEP 2: The factor $(x + 1)$ occurs once, and $(x + 2)$ occurs at most twice.

STEP 3: The LCM is the product $(x + 1)(x + 2)^2$, which is left in factored form.

> Now Try Exercises 61 and 65

EXAMPLE 6 Finding a least common denominator

Find the LCD for the expressions $\dfrac{1}{x^2 + 4x + 4}$ and $\dfrac{5}{x^2 + 3x + 2}$.

SOLUTION From Example 5(b), the LCM for $x^2 + 4x + 4$ and $x^2 + 3x + 2$ is

$$(x + 1)(x + 2)^2.$$

> The LCD is the same as the LCM of the denominators.

Therefore the LCD is *also* $(x + 1)(x + 2)^2$.

> Now Try Exercise 69

Review of Addition and Subtraction of Fractions

Recall that to add two fractions we use the property $\frac{a}{c} + \frac{b}{c} = \frac{a + b}{c}$. This property requires *like* denominators. For example, $\frac{1}{5} + \frac{3}{5} = \frac{1 + 3}{5} = \frac{4}{5}$. When the denominators are not alike, we must find a common denominator. Before adding two fractions, such as $\frac{2}{3}$ and $\frac{1}{4}$, we write them with 12 as their common denominator. That is, we multiply each fraction by 1 written in an appropriate form. For example, to write $\frac{2}{3}$ with a denominator of 12, we multiply $\frac{2}{3}$ by 1, written as $\frac{4}{4}$.

$$\frac{2}{3} = \frac{2}{3} \cdot \frac{4}{4} = \frac{8}{12} \quad \text{and} \quad \frac{1}{4} = \frac{1}{4} \cdot \frac{3}{3} = \frac{3}{12}$$

> 1. Write each fraction with a common denominator.

Once the fractions have a common denominator, we can add them, as in

$$\frac{2}{3} + \frac{1}{4} = \frac{8}{12} + \frac{3}{12} = \frac{11}{12}.$$

> 2. Add numerators. Keep the common denominator.

The *least common denominator* (LCD) for $\frac{2}{3}$ and $\frac{1}{4}$ is equal to the *least common multiple* (LCM) of 3 and 4. Thus the least common denominator is 12.

EXAMPLE 7 Adding fractions

Simplify $\dfrac{3}{5} + \dfrac{2}{7}$.

SOLUTION The LCD is 35.

$$\frac{3}{5} + \frac{2}{7} = \frac{3}{5} \cdot \frac{7}{7} + \frac{2}{7} \cdot \frac{5}{5} = \frac{21}{35} + \frac{10}{35} = \frac{31}{35}$$

> Now Try Exercise 27

Recall that subtraction is similar to addition. To subtract two fractions with *like* denominators, we use the property $\frac{a}{c} - \frac{b}{c} = \frac{a - b}{c}$. For example, $\frac{3}{11} - \frac{7}{11} = \frac{3 - 7}{11} = -\frac{4}{11}$.

EXAMPLE 8 Subtracting fractions

Simplify $\dfrac{3}{8} - \dfrac{5}{6}$.

> Multiply each fraction by 1 in the appropriate form.

SOLUTION The LCD is 24.

$$\frac{3}{8} - \frac{5}{6} = \frac{3}{8} \cdot \frac{3}{3} - \frac{5}{6} \cdot \frac{4}{4} = \frac{9}{24} - \frac{20}{24} = -\frac{11}{24}$$

> Now Try Exercise 29

Addition and Subtraction of Rational Expressions

Addition and subtraction of rational expressions with like denominators are performed in the following manner.

SUMS AND DIFFERENCES OF RATIONAL EXPRESSIONS

To add (or subtract) two rational expressions with like denominators, add (or subtract) their numerators. The denominator does not change.

$$\frac{A}{C} + \frac{B}{C} = \frac{A + B}{C}$$

$$\frac{A}{C} - \frac{B}{C} = \frac{A - B}{C}, \quad C \neq 0$$

NOTE If the denominators are not alike, begin by writing each rational expression, using a common denominator. The LCD equals the LCM of the denominators.

EXAMPLE 9 Adding rational expressions

Add the expressions.

(a) $\dfrac{x}{x + 2} + \dfrac{3x + 1}{x + 2}$ **(b)** $\dfrac{1}{x - 1} + \dfrac{2x}{x + 1}$

SOLUTION

(a) The denominators are alike, so we add the numerators and keep the same denominator.

$$\frac{x}{x + 2} + \frac{3x + 1}{x + 2} = \frac{x + 3x + 1}{x + 2} \qquad \text{Add numerators.}$$

$$= \frac{4x + 1}{x + 2} \qquad \text{Combine like terms.}$$

(b) The LCM for $x - 1$ and $x + 1$ is their product, $(x - 1)(x + 1)$.

$$\frac{1}{x - 1} + \frac{2x}{x + 1} = \frac{1}{x - 1} \cdot \frac{x + 1}{x + 1} + \frac{2x}{x + 1} \cdot \frac{x - 1}{x - 1} \qquad \begin{array}{l}\text{Change to a common}\\\text{denominator.}\end{array}$$

$$= \frac{x + 1}{(x - 1)(x + 1)} + \frac{2x(x - 1)}{(x + 1)(x - 1)} \qquad \text{Multiply.}$$

$$= \frac{x + 1 + 2x^2 - 2x}{(x - 1)(x + 1)} \qquad \begin{array}{l}\text{Add numerators;}\\\text{distributive property}\end{array}$$

$$= \frac{2x^2 - x + 1}{(x - 1)(x + 1)} \qquad \text{Combine like terms.}$$

Now Try Exercises 73 and 81

Subtraction of rational expressions is similar.

EXAMPLE 10 Subtracting rational expressions

Subtract the expressions: $\dfrac{x - 1}{x} - \dfrac{5}{x + 5}$.

SOLUTION The LCD is $x(x + 5)$.

$$\frac{x - 1}{x} - \frac{5}{x + 5} = \frac{x - 1}{x} \cdot \frac{x + 5}{x + 5} - \frac{5}{x + 5} \cdot \frac{x}{x} \qquad \begin{array}{l}\text{Change to a common}\\\text{denominator.}\end{array}$$

$$= \frac{(x - 1)(x + 5)}{x(x + 5)} - \frac{5x}{x(x + 5)} \qquad \text{Multiply.}$$

$$= \frac{(x - 1)(x + 5) - 5x}{x(x + 5)} \qquad \text{Subtract numerators.}$$

$$= \frac{x^2 + 4x - 5 - 5x}{x(x + 5)} \qquad \text{Multiply binomials.}$$

$$= \frac{x^2 - x - 5}{x(x + 5)} \qquad \text{Combine like terms.}$$

Now Try Exercise 79

Clearing Fractions

To solve rational equations, it is sometimes advantageous to multiply each side by the LCD to clear fractions. For example, the LCD for the equation $\frac{1}{x+2} + \frac{1}{x-2} = 0$ is $(x+2)(x-2)$. Multiplying each side by the LCD results in the following.

$$(x+2)(x-2)\left(\frac{1}{x+2} + \frac{1}{x-2}\right) = 0 \qquad \text{Multiply each side by LCD.}$$

$$\frac{(x+2)(x-2)}{x+2} + \frac{(x+2)(x-2)}{x-2} = 0 \qquad \text{Distributive property}$$

$$(x-2) + (x+2) = 0 \qquad \text{Simplify.}$$

$$x = 0 \qquad \text{Combine like terms and solve.}$$

This technique is applied in the next example.

EXAMPLE 11 Clearing fractions

Clear fractions from the equation and solve.

$$\frac{3}{x} + \frac{x}{x^2-1} - \frac{4}{x+1} = 0$$

SOLUTION The LCD is $x(x^2 - 1) = x(x-1)(x+1)$.

$$x(x^2-1)\left(\frac{3}{x} + \frac{x}{x^2-1} - \frac{4}{x+1}\right) = x(x^2-1) \cdot 0$$

$$\frac{3x(x^2-1)}{x} + \frac{x(x)(x^2-1)}{x^2-1} - \frac{4x(x^2-1)}{x+1} = 0$$

$$\frac{3x(x^2-1)}{x} + \frac{x^2(x^2-1)}{x^2-1} - \frac{4x(x-1)(x+1)}{x+1} = 0$$

$$3(x^2-1) + x^2 - 4x(x-1) = 0$$

$$3x^2 - 3 + x^2 - 4x^2 + 4x = 0$$

$$4x - 3 = 0$$

$$x = \frac{3}{4}$$

The solution is $\frac{3}{4}$. Check this answer.

Now Try Exercise 111

Complex Fractions

A complex fraction is a rational expression that contains fractions in its numerator, denominator, or both. One strategy for simplifying a complex fraction is to multiply the numerator and denominator by the LCD of the fractions in the numerator and denominator. For example, the LCD for the complex fraction

$$\frac{1 - \dfrac{1}{x}}{1 + \dfrac{1}{2x}}$$

is $2x$. To simplify, multiply the complex fraction by 1, expressed in the form $\frac{2x}{2x}$.

$$\frac{\left(1 - \dfrac{1}{x}\right) \cdot 2x}{\left(1 + \dfrac{1}{2x}\right) \cdot 2x} = \frac{2x - \dfrac{2x}{x}}{2x + \dfrac{2x}{2x}} \qquad \text{Distributive property}$$

$$= \frac{2x - 2}{2x + 1} \qquad \text{Simplify.}$$

In the next example, we simplify a complex fraction.

EXAMPLE 12 Simplifying a complex fraction

Simplify the complex fraction.

$$\frac{\dfrac{3}{x-1} - \dfrac{2}{x}}{\dfrac{1}{x-1} + \dfrac{3}{x}}$$

SOLUTION The LCD is the product, $x(x-1)$. Multiply the expression by $\dfrac{x(x-1)}{x(x-1)}$.

$$\frac{\left(\dfrac{3}{x-1} - \dfrac{2}{x}\right)}{\left(\dfrac{1}{x-1} + \dfrac{3}{x}\right)} \cdot \frac{x(x-1)}{x(x-1)} = \frac{\dfrac{3x(x-1)}{x-1} - \dfrac{2x(x-1)}{x}}{\dfrac{x(x-1)}{x-1} + \dfrac{3x(x-1)}{x}} \qquad \text{Distributive property}$$

$$= \frac{3x - 2(x-1)}{x + 3(x-1)} \qquad \text{Simplify.}$$

$$= \frac{3x - 2x + 2}{x + 3x - 3} \qquad \text{Distributive property}$$

$$= \frac{x+2}{4x-3} \qquad \text{Combine like terms.}$$

Now Try Exercise 115

R.5 Exercises

Simplifying Rational Expressions

Exercises 1–14: Simplify the expression.

1. $\dfrac{10x^3}{5x^2}$

2. $\dfrac{24t^3}{6t^2}$

3. $\dfrac{(x-5)(x+5)}{x-5}$

4. $-\dfrac{5-a}{a-5}$

5. $\dfrac{x^2-16}{x-4}$

6. $\dfrac{(x+5)(x-4)}{(x+7)(x+5)}$

7. $\dfrac{x+3}{2x^2+5x-3}$

8. $\dfrac{2x^2-9x+4}{6x^2+7x-5}$

9. $-\dfrac{z+2}{4z+8}$

10. $\dfrac{x^2-25}{x^2+10x+25}$

11. $\dfrac{x^2+2x}{x^2+3x+2}$

12. $\dfrac{x^2-3x-10}{x^2-6x+5}$

13. $\dfrac{a^3+b^3}{a+b}$

14. $\dfrac{a^3-b^3}{a-b}$

Review of Fractions

Exercises 15–32: Simplify.

15. $\dfrac{5}{8} \cdot \dfrac{4}{15}$

16. $\dfrac{7}{2} \cdot \dfrac{4}{21}$

17. $\dfrac{5}{6} \cdot \dfrac{3}{10} \cdot \dfrac{8}{3}$

18. $\dfrac{9}{5} \cdot \dfrac{10}{3} \cdot \dfrac{1}{27}$

19. $\dfrac{4}{7} \div \dfrac{8}{7}$

20. $\dfrac{5}{12} \div \dfrac{10}{9}$

21. $\dfrac{1}{2} \div \dfrac{3}{4} \div \dfrac{5}{6}$

22. $\dfrac{3}{4} \div \dfrac{7}{8} \div \dfrac{5}{14}$

23. $\dfrac{3}{8} + \dfrac{5}{8}$

24. $\dfrac{5}{9} + \dfrac{2}{9}$

25. $\dfrac{3}{7} - \dfrac{4}{7}$

26. $\dfrac{8}{11} - \dfrac{9}{11}$

27. $\dfrac{2}{3} + \dfrac{5}{11}$

28. $\dfrac{9}{13} + \dfrac{3}{2}$

29. $\dfrac{4}{5} - \dfrac{1}{10}$

30. $\dfrac{3}{4} - \dfrac{7}{12}$

31. $\dfrac{1}{3} + \dfrac{3}{4} - \dfrac{3}{7}$

32. $\dfrac{6}{11} - \dfrac{1}{2} + \dfrac{3}{8}$

Multiplication and Division of Rational Expressions

Exercises 33–58: Simplify. Leave numerators and denominators in factored form when appropriate.

33. $\dfrac{1}{x^2} \cdot \dfrac{3x}{2}$

34. $\dfrac{6a}{5} \cdot \dfrac{5}{12a^2}$

35. $\dfrac{5x}{3} \div \dfrac{10x}{6}$

36. $\dfrac{2x^2 + x}{3x + 9} \div \dfrac{x}{x + 3}$

37. $\dfrac{x + 1}{2x - 5} \cdot \dfrac{x}{x + 1}$

38. $\dfrac{4x + 8}{2x} \cdot \dfrac{x^2}{x + 2}$

39. $\dfrac{(x - 5)(x + 3)}{3x - 1} \cdot \dfrac{x(3x - 1)}{(x - 5)}$

40. $\dfrac{b^2 + 1}{b^2 - 1} \cdot \dfrac{b - 1}{b + 1}$

41. $\dfrac{x^2 - 2x - 35}{2x^3 - 3x^2} \cdot \dfrac{x^3 - x^2}{2x - 14}$

42. $\dfrac{2x + 4}{x + 1} \cdot \dfrac{x^2 + 3x + 2}{4x + 2}$

43. $\dfrac{6b}{b + 2} \div \dfrac{3b^4}{2b + 4}$

44. $\dfrac{5x^5}{x - 2} \div \dfrac{10x^3}{5x - 10}$

45. $\dfrac{3a + 1}{a^7} \div \dfrac{a + 1}{3a^8}$

46. $\dfrac{x^2 - 16}{x + 3} \div \dfrac{x + 4}{x^2 - 9}$

47. $\dfrac{x + 5}{x^3 - x} \div \dfrac{x^2 - 25}{x^3}$

48. $\dfrac{x^2 + x - 12}{2x^2 - 9x - 5} \div \dfrac{x^2 + 7x + 12}{2x^2 - 7x - 4}$

49. $\dfrac{x - 2}{x^3 - x} \div \dfrac{x^2 - 2x}{x^2 - 1}$

50. $\dfrac{x^2 + 3x + 2}{2x^2 + 7x + 3} \div \dfrac{x^2 - 4}{2x^2 - x - 1}$

51. $\dfrac{x^2 - 3x + 2}{x^2 + 5x + 6} \div \dfrac{x^2 + x - 2}{x^2 + 2x - 3}$

52. $\dfrac{2x^2 + x - 1}{6x^2 + x - 2} \div \dfrac{2x^2 + 5x + 3}{6x^2 + 13x + 6}$

53. $\dfrac{x^2 - 4}{x^2 + x - 2} \div \dfrac{x - 2}{x - 1}$

54. $\dfrac{x^2 + 2x + 1}{x - 2} \div \dfrac{x + 1}{2x - 4}$

55. $\dfrac{3y}{x^2} \div \dfrac{y^2}{x} \div \dfrac{y}{5x}$

56. $\dfrac{x + 1}{y - 2} \div \dfrac{2x + 2}{y - 2} \div \dfrac{x}{y}$

57. $\dfrac{x - 3}{x - 1} \div \dfrac{x^2}{x - 1} \div \dfrac{x - 3}{x}$

58. $\dfrac{2x}{x - 2} \div \dfrac{x + 2}{x} \div \dfrac{7x}{x^2 - 4}$

Least Common Multiples

Exercises 59–66: Find the least common multiple.

59. 12, 18

60. 9, 15

61. $5a^3, 10a$

62. $6a^2, 9a^5$

63. $z^2 - 4z, (z - 4)^2$

64. $z^2 - 1, z^2 + 2z + 1$

65. $x^2 - 6x + 9, x^2 - 5x + 6$

66. $x^2 - 4, x^2 - 4x + 4$

Common Denominators

Exercises 67–72: Find the LCD for the rational expressions.

67. $\dfrac{1}{x + 1}, \dfrac{1}{7}$

68. $\dfrac{1}{2x - 1}, \dfrac{1}{x + 1}$

69. $\dfrac{1}{x + 4}, \dfrac{1}{x^2 - 16}$

70. $\dfrac{4}{2x^2}, \dfrac{1}{2x + 2}$

71. $\dfrac{3}{2}, \dfrac{x}{2x + 1}, \dfrac{x}{2x - 4}$

72. $\dfrac{1}{x}, \dfrac{1}{x^2 - 4x}, \dfrac{1}{2x}$

Addition and Subtraction of Rational Expressions

Exercises 73–102: Simplify. Leave numerators and denominators in factored form when appropriate.

73. $\dfrac{4}{x + 1} + \dfrac{3}{x + 1}$

74. $\dfrac{2}{x^2} + \dfrac{5}{x^2}$

75. $\dfrac{2}{x^2 - 1} - \dfrac{x + 1}{x^2 - 1}$

76. $\dfrac{2x}{x^2 + x} - \dfrac{2x}{x + 1}$

77. $\dfrac{x}{x + 4} - \dfrac{x + 1}{x(x + 4)}$

78. $\dfrac{4x}{x + 2} + \dfrac{x - 5}{x - 2}$

79. $\dfrac{2}{x^2} - \dfrac{4x - 1}{x}$

80. $\dfrac{2x}{x - 5} - \dfrac{x}{x + 5}$

81. $\dfrac{x + 3}{x - 5} + \dfrac{5}{x - 3}$

82. $\dfrac{x}{2x - 1} + \dfrac{1 - x}{3x}$

83. $\dfrac{3}{x-5} - \dfrac{1}{x-3} - \dfrac{2x}{x-5}$

84. $\dfrac{2x+1}{x-1} - \dfrac{3}{x+1} + \dfrac{x}{x-1}$

85. $\dfrac{x}{x^2-9} + \dfrac{5x}{x-3}$ **86.** $\dfrac{a^2+1}{a^2-1} + \dfrac{a}{1-a^2}$

87. $\dfrac{b}{2b-4} - \dfrac{b-1}{b-2}$ **88.** $\dfrac{y^2}{2-y} - \dfrac{y}{y^2-4}$

89. $\dfrac{2x}{x-5} + \dfrac{2x-1}{3x^2-16x+5}$

90. $\dfrac{x+3}{2x-1} + \dfrac{3}{10x^2-5x}$

91. $\dfrac{x}{(x-1)^2} - \dfrac{1}{(x-1)(x+3)}$

92. $\dfrac{3}{x^2-x-6} - \dfrac{2}{x^2+5x+6}$

93. $\dfrac{x}{x^2-5x+4} + \dfrac{2}{x^2-2x-8}$

94. $\dfrac{3}{x^2-2x+1} + \dfrac{1}{x^2-3x+2}$

95. $\dfrac{x}{x^2-4} - \dfrac{1}{x^2+4x+4}$

96. $\dfrac{3x}{x^2+2x-3} + \dfrac{1}{x^2-2x+1}$

97. $\dfrac{3x}{x-y} - \dfrac{3y}{x^2-2xy+y^2}$

98. $\dfrac{4c}{ab} + \dfrac{3b}{ac} - \dfrac{2a}{bc}$ **99.** $x + \dfrac{1}{x-1} - \dfrac{1}{x+1}$

100. $5 - \dfrac{6}{n^2-36} + \dfrac{3}{n-6}$

101. $\dfrac{6}{t-1} + \dfrac{2}{t-2} + \dfrac{1}{t}$

102. $\dfrac{3}{x-5} - \dfrac{1}{x-3} - \dfrac{2x}{x-5}$

Clearing Fractions

Exercises 103–112: (Refer to Example 11.) Clear fractions and solve. Check your answers.

103. $\dfrac{1}{x} + \dfrac{3}{x^2} = 0$ **104.** $\dfrac{1}{x-2} + \dfrac{3}{x+1} = 0$

105. $\dfrac{1}{x} + \dfrac{3x}{2x-1} = 0$ **106.** $\dfrac{x}{2x-5} + \dfrac{4}{x} = 0$

107. $\dfrac{2x}{9-x^2} + \dfrac{1}{3-x} = 0$

108. $\dfrac{1}{1-x^2} + \dfrac{1}{1+x} = 0$

109. $\dfrac{1}{2x} + \dfrac{1}{2x^2} - \dfrac{1}{x^3} = 0$

110. $\dfrac{1}{x^2-16} + \dfrac{4}{x+4} - \dfrac{5}{x-4} = 0$

111. $\dfrac{1}{x} - \dfrac{2}{x+5} + \dfrac{1}{x-5} = 0$

112. $\dfrac{1}{x-2} + \dfrac{1}{x-3} - \dfrac{2}{x} = 0$

Complex Fractions

Exercises 113–124: Simplify. Leave numerators and denominators in factored form when appropriate.

113. $\dfrac{1+\dfrac{1}{x}}{1-\dfrac{1}{x}}$ **114.** $\dfrac{\dfrac{1}{2}-x}{\dfrac{1}{x}-2}$

115. $\dfrac{\dfrac{1}{x-5}}{\dfrac{4}{x}-\dfrac{1}{x-5}}$ **116.** $\dfrac{1+\dfrac{1}{x-3}}{\dfrac{1}{x-3}-1}$

117. $\dfrac{\dfrac{1}{x}+\dfrac{2-x}{x^2}}{\dfrac{3}{x^2}-\dfrac{1}{x}}$ **118.** $\dfrac{\dfrac{1}{x-1}+\dfrac{2}{x}}{2-\dfrac{1}{x}}$

119. $\dfrac{\dfrac{1}{x+3}+\dfrac{2}{x-3}}{2-\dfrac{1}{x-3}}$ **120.** $\dfrac{\dfrac{1}{x}+\dfrac{2}{x}}{\dfrac{1}{x-1}+\dfrac{x}{2}}$

121. $\dfrac{\dfrac{4}{x-5}}{\dfrac{1}{x+5}+\dfrac{1}{x}}$ **122.** $\dfrac{\dfrac{2}{x-4}}{1-\dfrac{1}{x+4}}$

123. $\dfrac{\dfrac{1}{2a}-\dfrac{1}{2b}}{\dfrac{1}{a^2}-\dfrac{1}{b^2}}$ **124.** $\dfrac{\dfrac{1}{2x^2}-\dfrac{1}{2y^2}}{\dfrac{1}{3y^2}+\dfrac{1}{3x^2}}$

R.6 Radical Notation and Rational Exponents

- Use radical notation
- Apply rational exponents
- Use properties of rational exponents

Radical Notation

Square Root Recall the definition of the **square root** of a number a.

> **SQUARE ROOT**
>
> The number b is a *square root* of a if $b^2 = a$.

Every positive number a has two square roots, one positive and one negative. For example, the square roots of 100 are 10 and -10. Recall that the *positive square root* is called the **principal square root** and is denoted $\sqrt{a}$. The *negative square root* is denoted $-\sqrt{a}$. To identify both square roots, we write $\pm\sqrt{a}$. The symbol $\pm$ is read "plus or minus." The symbol $\sqrt{}$ is called the **radical sign**. The expression under the radical sign is called the **radicand**, and an expression containing a radical sign is called a **radical expression**. Examples of radical expressions include

$$\sqrt{6}, \quad 5 + \sqrt{x+1}, \quad \text{and} \quad \sqrt{\frac{3x}{2x-1}}.$$

Radical sign — Radicand

Radical Expressions

EXAMPLE 1 Finding principal square roots

Find the principal square root of each expression.

(a) 25 **(b)** 17 **(c)** $\dfrac{4}{9}$ **(d)** $c^2, c > 0$

SOLUTION

(a) Because $5 \cdot 5 = 25$, the principal, or positive, square root of 25 is $\sqrt{25} = 5$.

(b) The principal square root of 17 is $\sqrt{17}$. This value is not an integer, but we can approximate it. Figure R.18 shows that $\sqrt{17} \approx 4.12$, rounded to the nearest hundredth. Note that calculators do not give *exact* answers when approximating many radical expressions; they give decimal *approximations*.

(c) Because $\frac{2}{3} \cdot \frac{2}{3} = \frac{4}{9}$, the principal square root of $\frac{4}{9}$ is $\sqrt{\frac{4}{9}} = \frac{2}{3}$.

(d) The principal square root of c^2 is $\sqrt{c^2} = c$, as it is given that c is positive.

Now Try Exercises 7, 9, 11 and 13

```
√(17)
        4.123105626
```

Figure R.18

Cube Root Another common radical expression is the **cube root** of a number a, denoted $\sqrt[3]{a}$.

> **CUBE ROOT**
>
> The number b is a *cube root* of a if $b^3 = a$.

Although the square root of a negative number is not a real number, the cube root of a negative number is a negative real number. *Every real number has one real cube root.*

EXAMPLE 2 Finding cube roots

Find the cube root of each expression.

(a) 8 **(b)** -27 **(c)** 16 **(d)** $\dfrac{1}{64}$ **(e)** d^6

$3\sqrt{(16)}$

$\qquad$ 2.5198421

Figure R.19

SOLUTION

(a) $\sqrt[3]{8} = 2$ because $2^3 = 2 \cdot 2 \cdot 2 = 8$.

(b) $\sqrt[3]{-27} = -3$ because $(-3)^3 = (-3)(-3)(-3) = -27$.

(c) $\sqrt[3]{16}$ is not an integer. Figure R.19 shows that $\sqrt[3]{16} \approx 2.52$.

(d) $\sqrt[3]{\frac{1}{64}} = \frac{1}{4}$ because $\left(\frac{1}{4}\right)^3 = \frac{1}{4} \cdot \frac{1}{4} \cdot \frac{1}{4} = \frac{1}{64}$.

(e) $\sqrt[3]{d^6} = d^2$ because $(d^2)^3 = d^2 \cdot d^2 \cdot d^2 = d^{2+2+2} = d^6$.

> **Now Try Exercises 15, 17, 19, 21, and 31**

nth Root We can generalize square roots and cube roots to include the nth root of a number a. The number b is an **nth root** of a if $b^n = a$, where n is a positive integer, and the **principal nth root** is denoted $\sqrt[n]{a}$. The number n is called the **index**. For the square root, the index is 2, although we usually write $\sqrt{a}$ rather than $\sqrt[2]{a}$. When n is odd, we are finding an **odd root**, and when n is even, we are finding an **even root**. The square root $\sqrt{a}$ is an example of an even root, and the cube root $\sqrt[3]{a}$ is an example of an odd root.

> **NOTE** An odd root of a negative number is a negative number, but the even root of a negative number is *not* a real number. For example, $\sqrt[3]{-8} = -2$, whereas $\sqrt[4]{-81}$ is *not* a real number.

EXAMPLE 3 Finding nth roots

Find each root.

(a) $\sqrt[4]{16}$ (b) $\sqrt[5]{-32}$

SOLUTION

(a) $\sqrt[4]{16} = 2$ because $2^4 = 2 \cdot 2 \cdot 2 \cdot 2 = 16$. Note that when n is even the principal nth root is positive.

(b) $\sqrt[5]{-32} = -2$ because $(-2)^5 = (-2)(-2)(-2)(-2)(-2) = -32$.

> **Now Try Exercises 37 and 38**

Rational Exponents

When m and n are integers, the product rule states that $a^m a^n = a^{m+n}$. This rule can be extended to include exponents that are fractions. For example,

$$4^{1/2} \cdot 4^{1/2} = 4^{1/2+1/2} = 4^1 = 4.$$

That is, if we multiply $4^{1/2}$ by itself, the result is 4. Because we also know that $\sqrt{4} \cdot \sqrt{4} = 4$, this discussion suggests that $4^{1/2} = \sqrt{4}$ and motivates the following definition.

> **THE EXPRESSION $a^{1/n}$**
>
> If n is an integer greater than 1, then
>
> $$a^{1/n} = \sqrt[n]{a}.$$
>
> If $a < 0$ and n is an even positive integer, then $a^{1/n}$ is not a real number.

The next two examples show how to interpret rational exponents.

EXAMPLE 4 Interpreting rational exponents

Write each expression in radical notation. Then evaluate the expression (to the nearest hundredth when appropriate).

(a) $36^{1/2}$ (b) $23^{1/5}$ (c) $(5x)^{1/2}$

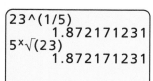

Figure R.20

SOLUTION

(a) The exponent $\frac{1}{2}$ indicates a square root. Thus $36^{1/2} = \sqrt{36}$, which evaluates to 6.

(b) The exponent $\frac{1}{5}$ indicates a fifth root. Thus $23^{1/5} = \sqrt[5]{23}$, which is not an integer. Figure R.20 shows this expression approximated in both exponential and radical notation. In either case $23^{1/5} \approx 1.87$.

(c) The exponent $\frac{1}{2}$ indicates a square root, so $(5x)^{1/2} = \sqrt{5x}$.

Now Try Exercises 39, 43, and 55

Suppose that we want to define the expression $8^{2/3}$. On the one hand, using properties of exponents we have

$$8^{1/3} \cdot 8^{1/3} = 8^{1/3+1/3} = 8^{2/3}.$$

On the other hand, we have

$$8^{1/3} \cdot 8^{1/3} = \sqrt[3]{8} \cdot \sqrt[3]{8} = 2 \cdot 2 = 4.$$

Thus $8^{2/3} = 4$, and that value is obtained whether we interpret $8^{2/3}$ as either

$$8^{2/3} = (8^2)^{1/3} = \sqrt[3]{8^2} = \sqrt[3]{64} = 4$$

or

$$8^{2/3} = (8^{1/3})^2 = (\sqrt[3]{8})^2 = 2^2 = 4.$$

This result illustrates that $8^{2/3} = \sqrt[3]{8^2} = (\sqrt[3]{8})^2 = 4$ and suggests the following definition.

THE EXPRESSION $a^{m/n}$

If m and n are positive integers with $\frac{m}{n}$ in lowest terms, then

$$a^{m/n} = \sqrt[n]{a^m} = (\sqrt[n]{a})^m.$$

If $a < 0$ and n is an even integer, then $a^{m/n}$ is not a real number.

EXAMPLE 5 Interpreting rational exponents

Write each expression in radical notation. Then evaluate the expression when the result is an integer.

(a) $(-27)^{2/3}$ (b) $12^{3/5}$

SOLUTION

(a) The exponent $\frac{2}{3}$ indicates either that we take the cube root of -27 and then square it or that we square -27 and then take the cube root. In either case the result will be the same. Thus

$$(-27)^{2/3} = (\sqrt[3]{-27})^2 = (-3)^2 = 9$$

or

$$(-27)^{2/3} = \sqrt[3]{(-27)^2} = \sqrt[3]{729} = 9.$$

(b) The exponent $\frac{3}{5}$ indicates either that we take the fifth root of 12 and then cube it or that we cube 12 and then take the fifth root. Thus

$$12^{3/5} = (\sqrt[5]{12})^3 \quad \text{or} \quad 12^{3/5} = \sqrt[5]{12^3}.$$

This result is not an integer.

Now Try Exercises 47 and 61

From properties of exponents we know that $a^{-n} = \frac{1}{a^n}$, where n is a positive integer. We now define this property for negative rational exponents.

THE EXPRESSION $a^{-m/n}$

If m and n are positive integers with $\frac{m}{n}$ in lowest terms, then

$$a^{-m/n} = \frac{1}{a^{m/n}}, \qquad a \neq 0.$$

EXAMPLE 6 Interpreting negative rational exponents

Write each expression in radical notation and then evaluate.
(a) $(64)^{-1/3}$ **(b)** $(81)^{-3/4}$

SOLUTION

(a) $(64)^{-1/3} = \dfrac{1}{64^{1/3}} = \dfrac{1}{\sqrt[3]{64}} = \dfrac{1}{4}$

(b) $(81)^{-3/4} = \dfrac{1}{81^{3/4}} = \dfrac{1}{\left(\sqrt[4]{81}\right)^3} = \dfrac{1}{3^3} = \dfrac{1}{27}$

> **Now Try Exercises 51 and 53**

Properties of Rational Exponents

Any rational number can be written as a ratio of two integers. That is, if p is a rational number, then $p = \frac{m}{n}$, where m and n are integers. Properties for integer exponents also apply to rational exponents—with one exception. If n is even in the expression $a^{m/n}$ and $\frac{m}{n}$ is written in lowest terms, then a must be nonnegative (not negative) for the result to be a real number.

PROPERTIES OF EXPONENTS

Let p and q be rational numbers written in lowest terms. For all real numbers a and b for which the expressions are real numbers, the following properties hold.

1. $a^p \cdot a^q = a^{p+q}$ Product rule for exponents

2. $a^{-p} = \dfrac{1}{a^p}, \quad \dfrac{1}{a^{-p}} = a^p$ Negative exponents

3. $\left(\dfrac{a}{b}\right)^{-p} = \left(\dfrac{b}{a}\right)^{p}$ Negative exponents for quotients

4. $\dfrac{a^p}{a^q} = a^{p-q}$ Quotient rule for exponents

5. $(a^p)^q = a^{pq}$ Power rule for exponents

6. $(ab)^p = a^p b^p$ Power rule for products

7. $\left(\dfrac{a}{b}\right)^{p} = \dfrac{a^p}{b^p}$ Power rule for quotients

---

In the next example, we apply these properties.

EXAMPLE 7 Applying properties of exponents

Write each expression using rational exponents and simplify. Write the answer with a positive exponent. Assume that all variables are positive numbers.

(a) $\sqrt{x} \cdot \sqrt[3]{x}$ **(b)** $\sqrt[3]{27x^2}$ **(c)** $\left(\dfrac{x^2}{81}\right)^{-1/2}$

SOLUTION

(a) $\sqrt{x} \cdot \sqrt[3]{x} = x^{1/2} \cdot x^{1/3}$ Use rational exponents.

$\qquad\qquad = x^{1/2+1/3}$ Product rule for exponents

$\qquad\qquad = x^{5/6}$ Simplify.

(b) $\sqrt[3]{27x^2} = (27x^2)^{1/3}$ Use rational exponents.

$\qquad\qquad = 27^{1/3}(x^2)^{1/3}$ Power rule for products

$\qquad\qquad = 3x^{2/3}$ Power rule for exponents

(c) $\left(\dfrac{x^2}{81}\right)^{-1/2} = \left(\dfrac{81}{x^2}\right)^{1/2}$ Negative exponents for quotients

$\qquad\qquad = \dfrac{(81)^{1/2}}{(x^2)^{1/2}}$ Power rule for quotients

$\qquad\qquad = \dfrac{9}{x}$ Power rule for exponents; simplify.

Now Try Exercises 81, 89, and 99

R.6 Exercises

Square Roots and Cube Roots

Exercises 1–6: Find the square roots of the number. Approximate your answers to the nearest hundredth whenever appropriate.

1. 25

2. 49

3. $\dfrac{16}{25}$

4. $\dfrac{64}{81}$

5. 11

6. 17

Exercises 7–14: Find the principal square root of the number. Approximate your answer to the nearest hundredth whenever appropriate.

7. 144

8. 100

9. 23

10. 45

11. $\dfrac{4}{49}$

12. $\dfrac{16}{121}$

13. $b^2, b < 0$

14. $(xy)^2, xy > 0$

Exercises 15–22: Find the cube root of the number.

15. 27

16. 64

17. -8

18. -125

19. $\dfrac{1}{27}$

20. $-\dfrac{1}{64}$

21. b^9

22. $8x^6$

Radical Notation

Exercises 23–40: If possible, simplify the expression by hand. If you cannot, approximate the answer to the nearest hundredth. Variables represent any real number.

23. $\sqrt{9}$

24. $\sqrt{121}$

25. $-\sqrt{5}$

26. $\sqrt{11}$

27. $\sqrt[3]{27}$

28. $\sqrt[3]{64}$

29. $\sqrt[3]{-64}$

30. $-\sqrt[3]{-1}$

31. $\sqrt[3]{5}$

32. $\sqrt[3]{-13}$

33. $-\sqrt[3]{x^9}$

34. $\sqrt[3]{(x+1)^6}$

35. $\sqrt[3]{(2x)^6}$

36. $\sqrt[3]{9x^3}$

37. $\sqrt[4]{81}$

38. $\sqrt[5]{-1}$

39. $\sqrt[5]{-7}$

40. $\sqrt[4]{6}$

Rational Exponents

Exercises 41–46: Write the expression in radical notation.

41. $6^{1/2}$

42. $7^{1/3}$

43. $(xy)^{1/2}$

44. $x^{2/3}y^{1/5}$

45. $y^{-1/5}$

46. $\left(\dfrac{x}{y}\right)^{-2/7}$

Exercises 47–54: Write the expression in radical notation. Then evaluate the expression when the result is an integer.

47. $27^{2/3}$

48. $8^{4/3}$

49. $(-1)^{4/3}$

50. $81^{3/4}$

51. $8^{-1/3}$

52. $16^{-3/4}$

53. $13^{-3/5}$

54. $23^{-1/2}$

Exercises 55–76: Evaluate the expression by hand. Approximate the answer to the nearest hundredth when appropriate.

55. $16^{1/2}$

56. $8^{1/3}$

57. $256^{1/4}$

58. $4^{3/2}$

59. $32^{1/5}$

60. $(-32)^{1/5}$

61. $(-8)^{4/3}$

62. $(-1)^{3/5}$

63. $2^{1/2} \cdot 2^{2/3}$

64. $5^{3/5} \cdot 5^{1/10}$

65. $\left(\dfrac{4}{9}\right)^{1/2}$

66. $\left(\dfrac{27}{64}\right)^{1/3}$

67. $\dfrac{4^{2/3}}{4^{1/2}}$

68. $\dfrac{6^{1/5} \cdot 6^{3/5}}{6^{2/5}}$

69. $4^{-1/2}$

70. $9^{-3/2}$

71. $(-8)^{-1/3}$

72. $49^{-1/2}$

73. $\left(\frac{1}{16}\right)^{-1/4}$

74. $\left(\frac{16}{25}\right)^{-3/2}$

75. $(2^{1/2})^3$

76. $(5^{6/5})^{-1/2}$

Exercises 77–106: Simplify the expression and write it with rational exponents. Assume that all variables are positive.

77. $(x^2)^{3/2}$

78. $(y^4)^{1/2}$

79. $(x^2y^8)^{1/2}$

80. $(y^{10}z^4)^{1/4}$

81. $\sqrt[3]{x^3y^6}$

82. $\sqrt{16x^4}$

83. $\sqrt{\dfrac{y^4}{x^2}}$

84. $\sqrt[3]{\dfrac{x^{12}}{z^6}}$

85. $\sqrt{y^3} \cdot \sqrt[3]{y^2}$

86. $\left(\dfrac{x^6}{81}\right)^{1/4}$

87. $\left(\dfrac{x^6}{27}\right)^{2/3}$

88. $\left(\dfrac{1}{x^8}\right)^{-1/4}$

89. $\left(\dfrac{x^2}{y^6}\right)^{-1/2}$

90. $\dfrac{\sqrt{x}}{\sqrt[3]{27x^6}}$

91. $\sqrt{\sqrt{y}}$

92. $\sqrt{\sqrt[3]{(3x)^2}}$

93. $(a^{-1/2})^{4/3}$

94. $(x^{-3/2})^{2/3}$

95. $(a^3b^6)^{1/3}$

96. $(64x^3y^{18})^{1/6}$

97. $\dfrac{(k^{1/2})^{-3}}{(k^2)^{1/4}}$

98. $\dfrac{(b^{3/4})^4}{(b^{4/5})^{-5}}$

99. $\sqrt{b} \cdot \sqrt[4]{b}$

100. $\sqrt[3]{t} \cdot \sqrt[5]{t}$

101. $\sqrt{z} \cdot \sqrt[3]{z^2} \cdot \sqrt[4]{z^3}$

102. $\sqrt{b} \cdot \sqrt[3]{b} \cdot \sqrt[5]{b}$

103. $p^{1/2}\big(p^{3/2} + p^{1/2}\big)$

104. $d^{3/4}(d^{1/4} - d^{-1/4})$

105. $\sqrt[3]{x}\big(\sqrt{x} - \sqrt[3]{x^2}\,\big)$

106. $\frac{1}{2}\sqrt{x}\big(\sqrt{x} + \sqrt[4]{x^2}\,\big)$

R.7 Radical Expressions

- **Apply the product rule**
- **Simplify radical expressions**
- **Apply the quotient rule**
- **Perform addition, subtraction, and multiplication on radical expressions**
- **Rationalize the denominator**

Product Rule for Radical Expressions

The product of two (like) roots is equal to the root of their product.

> **PRODUCT RULE FOR RADICAL EXPRESSIONS**
>
> Let a and b be real numbers, where $\sqrt[n]{a}$ and $\sqrt[n]{b}$ are both defined. Then
> $$\sqrt[n]{a} \cdot \sqrt[n]{b} = \sqrt[n]{a \cdot b}.$$

NOTE The product rule works only when the radicals have the *same* index.

We apply the product rule in the next two examples.

EXAMPLE 1 Multiplying radical expressions

Multiply each pair of radical expressions.

(a) $\sqrt{5} \cdot \sqrt{20}$ **(b)** $\sqrt[3]{-3} \cdot \sqrt[3]{9}$

SOLUTION

(a) $\sqrt{5} \cdot \sqrt{20} = \sqrt{5 \cdot 20} = \sqrt{100} = 10$

(b) $\sqrt[3]{-3} \cdot \sqrt[3]{9} = \sqrt[3]{-3 \cdot 9} = \sqrt[3]{-27} = -3$

Now Try Exercises 3 and 5

EXAMPLE 2 Multiplying radical expressions containing variables

Multiply each pair of radical expressions. Assume that all variables are positive.

(a) $\sqrt{x} \cdot \sqrt{x^3}$ **(b)** $\sqrt[3]{2a} \cdot \sqrt[3]{5a}$ **(c)** $\sqrt[5]{\dfrac{2x}{y}} \cdot \sqrt[5]{\dfrac{16y}{x}}$

SOLUTION

(a) $\sqrt{x} \cdot \sqrt{x^3} = \sqrt{x \cdot x^3} = \sqrt{x^4} = x^2$

(b) $\sqrt[3]{2a} \cdot \sqrt[3]{5a} = \sqrt[3]{2a \cdot 5a} = \sqrt[3]{10a^2}$

(c) $\sqrt[5]{\dfrac{2x}{y}} \cdot \sqrt[5]{\dfrac{16y}{x}} = \sqrt[5]{\dfrac{2x}{y} \cdot \dfrac{16y}{x}}$ Product rule

$= \sqrt[5]{\dfrac{32xy}{xy}}$ Multiply fractions.

$= \sqrt[5]{32}$ Simplify.

$= 2$ $2^5 = 32$

Now Try Exercises 27, 33, and 35

Simplifying Radicals An integer a is a **perfect nth power** if there exists an integer b such that $b^n = a$. Thus 36 is a **perfect square** because $6^2 = 36$, 8 is a **perfect cube** because $2^3 = 8$, and 81 is a *perfect fourth power* because $3^4 = 81$.

The product rule for radicals can be used to simplify radical expressions. For example, because the largest perfect square factor of 50 is 25, the expression $\sqrt{50}$ can be simplified as

25 is a perfect square.

$$\sqrt{50} = \sqrt{25 \cdot 2} = \sqrt{25} \cdot \sqrt{2} = 5\sqrt{2}.$$

This procedure is generalized as follows.

SIMPLIFYING RADICALS (nth ROOTS)

STEP 1: Determine the largest perfect nth power factor of the radicand.

STEP 2: Use the product rule to factor out and simplify this perfect nth power.

EXAMPLE 3 Simplifying radical expressions

Simplify each expression.

(a) $\sqrt{300}$ (b) $\sqrt[3]{16}$ (c) $\sqrt[4]{512}$

SOLUTION

(a) First note that $300 = 100 \cdot 3$ and that 100 is the largest perfect square factor of 300.
$$\sqrt{300} = \sqrt{100} \cdot \sqrt{3} = 10\sqrt{3}$$

(b) The largest perfect cube factor of 16 is 8. Thus $\sqrt[3]{16} = \sqrt[3]{8} \cdot \sqrt[3]{2} = 2\sqrt[3]{2}$.

(c) $\sqrt[4]{512} = \sqrt[4]{256} \cdot \sqrt[4]{2} = 4\sqrt[4]{2}$ because $4^4 = 256$.

Now Try Exercises 37, 39, and 41

NOTE To simplify a cube root of a negative number, we usually factor out the negative of the largest perfect cube factor. For example, because $-16 = -8 \cdot 2$, it follows that $\sqrt[3]{-16} = \sqrt[3]{-8} \cdot \sqrt[3]{2} = -2\sqrt[3]{2}$. This procedure can be used with any odd root of a negative number.

EXAMPLE 4 Simplifying radical expressions

Simplify each expression. Assume that all variables are positive.

(a) $\sqrt{25x^4}$ (b) $\sqrt{32n^3}$ (c) $\sqrt[3]{-16x^3y^5}$ (d) $\sqrt[3]{2a} \cdot \sqrt[3]{4a^2b}$

SOLUTION

(a) $\sqrt{25x^4} = 5x^2$ $\qquad$ $(5x^2)^2 = 25x^4$

(b) $\sqrt{32n^3} = \sqrt{(16n^2)2n}$ $\qquad$ $16n^2$ is the largest perfect square factor.

$\qquad\qquad = \sqrt{16n^2} \cdot \sqrt{2n}$ $\qquad$ Product rule

$\qquad\qquad = 4n\sqrt{2n}$ $\qquad$ $(4n)^2 = 16n^2$

(c) $\sqrt[3]{-16x^3y^5} = \sqrt[3]{(-8x^3y^3)2y^2}$ $\qquad$ $8x^3y^3$ is the largest perfect cube factor.

$\qquad\qquad = \sqrt[3]{-8x^3y^3} \cdot \sqrt[3]{2y^2}$ $\qquad$ Product rule

$\qquad\qquad = -2xy\sqrt[3]{2y^2}$ $\qquad$ $(-2xy)^3 = -8x^3y^3$

(d) $\sqrt[3]{2a} \cdot \sqrt[3]{4a^2b} = \sqrt[3]{(2a)(4a^2b)}$ $\qquad$ Product rule

$\qquad\qquad = \sqrt[3]{(8a^3)b}$ $\qquad$ $8a^3$ is the largest perfect cube factor.

$\qquad\qquad = \sqrt[3]{8a^3} \cdot \sqrt[3]{b}$ $\qquad$ Product rule

$\qquad\qquad = 2a\sqrt[3]{b}$ $\qquad$ $(2a)^3 = 8a^3$

> **Now Try Exercises 45, 47, 49, and 51**

The product rule for radical expressions cannot be used if the radicals do not have the same indexes. In this case we use rational exponents, as illustrated in the next example.

EXAMPLE 5 Multiplying radicals with different indexes

Simplify each expression. Write your answer in radical notation.

(a) $\sqrt{2} \cdot \sqrt[3]{4}$ $\qquad$ (b) $\sqrt[3]{x} \cdot \sqrt[4]{x}$

SOLUTION

(a) First note that $\sqrt[3]{4} = \sqrt[3]{2^2} = 2^{2/3}$. Thus

$$\sqrt{2} \cdot \sqrt[3]{4} = 2^{1/2} \cdot 2^{2/3} = 2^{1/2+2/3} = 2^{7/6}.$$

In radical notation, $2^{7/6} = \sqrt[6]{2^7} = \sqrt[6]{2^6 \cdot 2^1} = \sqrt[6]{2^6} \cdot \sqrt[6]{2} = 2\sqrt[6]{2}$.

(b) $\sqrt[3]{x} \cdot \sqrt[4]{x} = x^{1/3} \cdot x^{1/4} = x^{7/12} = \sqrt[12]{x^7}$

> **Now Try Exercises 57 and 59**

Quotient Rule for Radical Expressions

The root of a quotient is equal to the quotient of the roots.

> **QUOTIENT RULE FOR RADICAL EXPRESSIONS**
>
> Let a and b be real numbers, where $\sqrt[n]{a}$ and $\sqrt[n]{b}$ are both defined and $b \neq 0$. Then
>
> $$\sqrt[n]{\frac{a}{b}} = \frac{\sqrt[n]{a}}{\sqrt[n]{b}}.$$

EXAMPLE 6 Simplifying quotients

Simplify each radical expression. Assume that all variables are positive.

(a) $\sqrt[3]{\dfrac{5}{8}}$ $\qquad$ (b) $\sqrt{\dfrac{16}{y^2}}$

SOLUTION

(a) $\sqrt[3]{\dfrac{5}{8}} = \dfrac{\sqrt[3]{5}}{\sqrt[3]{8}} = \dfrac{\sqrt[3]{5}}{2}$ $\qquad$ Quotient rule

(b) $\sqrt{\dfrac{16}{y^2}} = \dfrac{\sqrt{16}}{\sqrt{y^2}} = \dfrac{4}{y}$ $\qquad$ because $y > 0$.

> **Now Try Exercises 7 and 21**

EXAMPLE 7 Simplifying radical expressions

Simplify each radical expression. Assume that all variables are positive.

(a) $\dfrac{\sqrt{40}}{\sqrt{10}}$ (b) $\sqrt[4]{\dfrac{16x^3}{y^4}}$ (c) $\sqrt{\dfrac{5a^2}{8}} \cdot \sqrt{\dfrac{5a^3}{2}}$

SOLUTION

(a) $\dfrac{\sqrt{40}}{\sqrt{10}} = \sqrt{\dfrac{40}{10}} = \sqrt{4} = 2$

(b) $\sqrt[4]{\dfrac{16x^3}{y^4}} = \dfrac{\sqrt[4]{16x^3}}{\sqrt[4]{y^4}} = \dfrac{\sqrt[4]{16} \cdot \sqrt[4]{x^3}}{\sqrt[4]{y^4}} = \dfrac{2\sqrt[4]{x^3}}{y}$

(c) To simplify this expression, we use both the product and quotient rules.

$$\sqrt{\dfrac{5a^2}{8}} \cdot \sqrt{\dfrac{5a^3}{2}} = \sqrt{\dfrac{25a^5}{16}} \qquad \textit{Product rule}$$

$$= \dfrac{\sqrt{25a^5}}{\sqrt{16}} \qquad \textit{Quotient rule}$$

$$= \dfrac{\sqrt{25a^4} \cdot \sqrt{a}}{\sqrt{16}} \qquad \textit{Factor out largest perfect square.}$$

$$= \dfrac{5a^2\sqrt{a}}{4} \qquad (5a^2)^2 = 25a^4$$

> **Now Try Exercises 13, 19, and 53**

Addition and Subtraction

We can add $2x^2$ and $5x^2$ to obtain $7x^2$ because they are *like* terms. That is,

$$2x^2 + 5x^2 = (2 + 5)x^2 = 7x^2.$$

We can add and subtract **like radicals**, which have the same index and the same radicand. For example, we can add $3\sqrt{2}$ and $5\sqrt{2}$ because they are like radicals.

$$3\sqrt{2} + 5\sqrt{2} = (3 + 5)\sqrt{2} = 8\sqrt{2}$$

Sometimes two radical expressions that are not alike can be added by changing them to like radicals. For example, $\sqrt{20}$ and $\sqrt{5}$ are unlike radicals. However,

$$\sqrt{20} = \sqrt{4 \cdot 5} = \sqrt{4} \cdot \sqrt{5} = 2\sqrt{5},$$

so it follows that

$$\sqrt{20} + \sqrt{5} = 2\sqrt{5} + \sqrt{5} = 3\sqrt{5}.$$

> Write $\sqrt{20}$ as a multiple of $\sqrt{5}$.

We cannot combine $x + x^2$ because they are unlike terms. Similarly, we cannot combine $\sqrt{2} + \sqrt{5}$ because they are unlike radicals.

EXAMPLE 8 Adding radical expressions

Add the expressions and simplify.

(a) $10\sqrt{11} + 4\sqrt{11}$ (b) $5\sqrt[3]{6} + \sqrt[3]{6}$ (c) $\sqrt{12} + 7\sqrt{3}$

SOLUTION

(a) $10\sqrt{11} + 4\sqrt{11} = (10 + 4)\sqrt{11} = 14\sqrt{11}$

(b) $5\sqrt[3]{6} + \sqrt[3]{6} = (5 + 1)\sqrt[3]{6} = 6\sqrt[3]{6}$

(c) $\sqrt{12} + 7\sqrt{3} = \sqrt{4 \cdot 3} + 7\sqrt{3}$

$\qquad = \sqrt{4} \cdot \sqrt{3} + 7\sqrt{3}$

$\qquad = 2\sqrt{3} + 7\sqrt{3}$

$\qquad = 9\sqrt{3}$

> **Now Try Exercises 63, 67, and 69**

EXAMPLE 9 Adding radical expressions

Add the expressions and simplify. Assume that all variables are positive.
(a) $-2\sqrt{4x} + \sqrt{x}$ **(b)** $3\sqrt{3k} + 5\sqrt{12k} + 9\sqrt{48k}$

SOLUTION
(a) Note that $\sqrt{4x} = \sqrt{4} \cdot \sqrt{x} = 2\sqrt{x}$.
$$-2\sqrt{4x} + \sqrt{x} = -2(2\sqrt{x}) + \sqrt{x} = -4\sqrt{x} + \sqrt{x} = -3\sqrt{x}$$
(b) Note that $\sqrt{12k} = \sqrt{4} \cdot \sqrt{3k} = 2\sqrt{3k}$ and that $\sqrt{48k} = \sqrt{16} \cdot \sqrt{3k} = 4\sqrt{3k}$.
$$3\sqrt{3k} + 5\sqrt{12k} + 9\sqrt{48k} = 3\sqrt{3k} + 5(2\sqrt{3k}) + 9(4\sqrt{3k})$$
$$= (3 + 10 + 36)\sqrt{3k}$$
$$= 49\sqrt{3k}$$
Now Try Exercises 77 and 83

Subtraction of radical expressions is similar to addition of radical expressions, as illustrated in the next example.

EXAMPLE 10 Subtracting radical expressions

Subtract and simplify. Assume that all variables are positive.
(a) $3\sqrt[3]{xy^2} - 2\sqrt[3]{xy^2}$ **(b)** $\sqrt{16x^3} - \sqrt{x^3}$

SOLUTION
(a) $3\sqrt[3]{xy^2} - 2\sqrt[3]{xy^2} = (3 - 2)\sqrt[3]{xy^2} = \sqrt[3]{xy^2}$
(b) $\sqrt{16x^3} - \sqrt{x^3} = \sqrt{16} \cdot \sqrt{x^3} - \sqrt{x^3}$
$$= 4\sqrt{x^3} - \sqrt{x^3}$$
$$= 3\sqrt{x^3}$$
$$= 3x\sqrt{x}$$
Now Try Exercises 75 and 81

Multiplication

Some types of radical expressions can be multiplied like binomials. The next example demonstrates this technique.

EXAMPLE 11 Multiplying radical expressions

Multiply and simplify.
(a) $(\sqrt{b} - 4)(\sqrt{b} + 5)$ **(b)** $(4 + \sqrt{3})(4 - \sqrt{3})$

SOLUTION
(a) This expression can be multiplied and then simplified.
$$(\sqrt{b} - 4)(\sqrt{b} + 5) = \sqrt{b} \cdot \sqrt{b} + 5\sqrt{b} - 4\sqrt{b} - 4 \cdot 5$$
$$= b + \sqrt{b} - 20$$
(Compare this product to $(b - 4)(b + 5) = b^2 + b - 20$.)
(b) This expression is in the form $(a + b)(a - b)$, which equals $a^2 - b^2$.
$$(4 + \sqrt{3})(4 - \sqrt{3}) = (4)^2 - (\sqrt{3})^2$$
$$= 16 - 3$$
$$= 13$$
Now Try Exercises 89 and 95

Rationalizing the Denominator

Quotients containing radical expressions can appear to be different but actually be equal. For example, $\frac{1}{\sqrt{3}}$ and $\frac{\sqrt{3}}{3}$ represent the same real number even though they do not look equal. To show this fact, we multiply the first quotient by 1 in the form $\frac{\sqrt{3}}{\sqrt{3}}$.

$$\frac{1}{\sqrt{3}} \cdot \frac{\sqrt{3}}{\sqrt{3}} = \frac{1 \cdot \sqrt{3}}{\sqrt{3} \cdot \sqrt{3}} = \frac{\sqrt{3}}{3}$$

NOTE $\sqrt{b} \cdot \sqrt{b} = \sqrt{b^2} = b$ for any *positive* number b.

One way to standardize radical expressions is to remove any radical expressions from the denominator. This process is called **rationalizing the denominator**. The next example demonstrates how to rationalize the denominator of two quotients.

EXAMPLE 12   Rationalizing the denominator

Rationalize each denominator. Assume that all variables are positive.

(a) $\dfrac{3}{5\sqrt{3}}$ **(b)** $\sqrt{\dfrac{x}{24}}$

SOLUTION

(a) We multiply this expression by 1 in the form $\frac{\sqrt{3}}{\sqrt{3}}$.

$$\frac{3}{5\sqrt{3}} \cdot \frac{\sqrt{3}}{\sqrt{3}} = \frac{3\sqrt{3}}{5\sqrt{9}} = \frac{3\sqrt{3}}{5 \cdot 3} = \frac{\sqrt{3}}{5}$$

(b) Because $\sqrt{24} = \sqrt{4} \cdot \sqrt{6} = 2\sqrt{6}$, we start by simplifying the expression.

$$\sqrt{\frac{x}{24}} = \frac{\sqrt{x}}{\sqrt{24}} = \frac{\sqrt{x}}{2\sqrt{6}}$$

To rationalize the denominator, we multiply this expression by 1 in the form $\frac{\sqrt{6}}{\sqrt{6}}$.

$$\frac{\sqrt{x}}{2\sqrt{6}} = \frac{\sqrt{x}}{2\sqrt{6}} \cdot \frac{\sqrt{6}}{\sqrt{6}} = \frac{\sqrt{6x}}{12}$$

Now Try Exercises 99 and 101

If the denominator consists of two terms, at least one of which contains a radical expression, then the **conjugate** of the denominator is found by changing a $+$ sign to a $-$ sign or vice versa. For example, the conjugate of $\sqrt{2} + \sqrt{3}$ is $\sqrt{2} - \sqrt{3}$, and the conjugate of $\sqrt{3} - 1$ is $\sqrt{3} + 1$. In the next example, we multiply the numerator and denominator by the conjugate of the *denominator* to rationalize the denominator of fractions that contain radicals.

EXAMPLE 13   Rationalizing the denominator

Rationalize the denominator. Assume that all variables are positive.

(a) $\dfrac{3 + \sqrt{5}}{2 - \sqrt{5}}$ **(b)** $\dfrac{\sqrt{x}}{\sqrt{x} - 2}$

SOLUTION

(a) The conjugate of the denominator $2 - \sqrt{5}$ is $2 + \sqrt{5}$.

$$\frac{3 + \sqrt{5}}{2 - \sqrt{5}} = \frac{(3 + \sqrt{5})}{(2 - \sqrt{5})} \cdot \frac{(2 + \sqrt{5})}{(2 + \sqrt{5})} \qquad \text{Multiply by } \frac{conjugate}{conjugate}.$$

$$= \frac{6 + 3\sqrt{5} + 2\sqrt{5} + (\sqrt{5})^2}{(2)^2 - (\sqrt{5})^2} \qquad \text{Multiply.}$$

$$= \frac{11 + 5\sqrt{5}}{4 - 5} \qquad \text{Combine terms.}$$

$$= -11 - 5\sqrt{5} \qquad \text{Simplify.}$$

(b) The conjugate of the denominator $\sqrt{x} - 2$ is $\sqrt{x} + 2$.

$$\frac{\sqrt{x}}{\sqrt{x} - 2} = \frac{\sqrt{x}}{(\sqrt{x} - 2)} \cdot \frac{(\sqrt{x} + 2)}{(\sqrt{x} + 2)} \qquad \text{Multiply by } \frac{conjugate}{conjugate}.$$

$$= \frac{x + 2\sqrt{x}}{x - 4} \qquad \text{Multiply.}$$

Now Try Exercises 103 and 109

R.7 Exercises

Multiplying and Dividing

Exercises 1–36: Simplify the expression. Assume that all variables are positive.

1. $\sqrt{3} \cdot \sqrt{3}$

2. $\sqrt{2} \cdot \sqrt{18}$

3. $\sqrt{2} \cdot \sqrt{50}$

4. $\sqrt[3]{-2} \cdot \sqrt[3]{-4}$

5. $\sqrt[3]{4} \cdot \sqrt[3]{16}$

6. $\sqrt[3]{x} \cdot \sqrt[3]{x^2}$

7. $\sqrt{\dfrac{9}{25}}$

8. $\sqrt[3]{\dfrac{x}{8}}$

9. $\sqrt{\dfrac{1}{2}} \cdot \sqrt{\dfrac{1}{8}}$

10. $\sqrt{\dfrac{5}{3}} \cdot \sqrt{\dfrac{1}{3}}$

11. $\sqrt{\dfrac{x}{2}} \cdot \sqrt{\dfrac{x}{8}}$

12. $\sqrt{\dfrac{4}{y}} \cdot \sqrt{\dfrac{y}{5}}$

13. $\dfrac{\sqrt{45}}{\sqrt{5}}$

14. $\dfrac{\sqrt{7}}{\sqrt{28}}$

15. $\sqrt[4]{9} \cdot \sqrt[4]{9}$

16. $\sqrt[5]{16} \cdot \sqrt[5]{-2}$

17. $\dfrac{\sqrt[5]{64}}{\sqrt[5]{-2}}$

18. $\dfrac{\sqrt[4]{324}}{\sqrt[4]{4}}$

19. $\sqrt{\dfrac{36}{z^4}}$

20. $\dfrac{\sqrt{4xy^2}}{\sqrt{x}}$

21. $\sqrt[3]{\dfrac{x^3}{8}}$

22. $\dfrac{\sqrt{a^2b}}{\sqrt{b}}$

23. $\sqrt{4x^4}$

24. $\sqrt[3]{-8y^3}$

25. $\sqrt[4]{16x^4y}$

26. $\sqrt[3]{8xy^3}$

27. $\sqrt{3x} \cdot \sqrt{12x}$

28. $\sqrt{6x^5} \cdot \sqrt{6x}$

29. $\sqrt[3]{8x^6y^3z^9}$

30. $\sqrt{16x^4y^6}$

31. $\sqrt[4]{\dfrac{3}{4}} \cdot \sqrt[4]{\dfrac{27}{4}}$

32. $\sqrt[5]{\dfrac{4}{-9}} \cdot \sqrt[5]{\dfrac{8}{-27}}$

33. $\sqrt[4]{25z} \cdot \sqrt[4]{25z}$

34. $\sqrt[5]{3z^2} \cdot \sqrt[5]{7z}$

35. $\sqrt[5]{\dfrac{7a}{b^2}} \cdot \sqrt[5]{\dfrac{b^2}{7a^6}}$

36. $\sqrt[3]{\dfrac{8m}{n}} \cdot \sqrt[3]{\dfrac{n^4}{m^2}}$

Exercises 37–54: Simplify the radical expression by factoring out the largest perfect nth power. Assume that all variables are positive.

37. $\sqrt{200}$

38. $\sqrt{72}$

39. $\sqrt[3]{81}$

40. $\sqrt[3]{256}$

41. $\sqrt[4]{64}$

42. $\sqrt[5]{27 \cdot 81}$

43. $\sqrt[5]{-64}$

44. $\sqrt[3]{-81}$

45. $\sqrt{8n^3}$

46. $\sqrt{32a^2}$

47. $\sqrt{12a^2b^5}$

48. $\sqrt{20a^3b^2}$

49. $\sqrt[3]{-125x^4y^5}$

50. $\sqrt[3]{-81a^5b^2}$

51. $\sqrt[3]{5t} \cdot \sqrt[3]{125t}$

52. $\sqrt[4]{4bc^3} \cdot \sqrt[4]{64ab^3c^2}$

53. $\sqrt[4]{\dfrac{9t^5}{r^8}} \cdot \sqrt[4]{\dfrac{9r}{5t}}$

54. $\sqrt[5]{\dfrac{4t^6}{r}} \cdot \sqrt[5]{\dfrac{8t}{r^6}}$

Exercises 55–62: Simplify the expression. Assume that all variables are positive and write your answer in radical notation.

55. $\sqrt{3} \cdot \sqrt[3]{3}$

56. $\sqrt{5} \cdot \sqrt[3]{5}$

57. $\sqrt[4]{8} \cdot \sqrt[3]{4}$

58. $\sqrt[5]{16} \cdot \sqrt{2}$

59. $\sqrt[4]{x^3} \cdot \sqrt[3]{x}$

60. $\sqrt[4]{x^3} \cdot \sqrt{x}$

61. $\sqrt[4]{rt} \cdot \sqrt[3]{r^2t}$

62. $\sqrt[3]{a^3b^2} \cdot \sqrt{a^2b}$

Exercises 63–88: Simplify the expression. Assume that all variables are positive.

63. $2\sqrt{3} + 7\sqrt{3}$

64. $8\sqrt{7} + 2\sqrt{7}$

65. $\sqrt{x} + \sqrt{x} - \sqrt{y}$

66. $\sqrt{xy^2} - \sqrt{x}$

67. $2\sqrt[3]{6} + 7\sqrt[3]{6}$

68. $18\sqrt[3]{3} + 3\sqrt[3]{3}$

69. $3\sqrt{28} + 3\sqrt{7}$

70. $9\sqrt{18} - 2\sqrt{8}$

71. $\sqrt{44} - 4\sqrt{11}$

72. $\sqrt[4]{5} + 2\sqrt[4]{5}$

73. $2\sqrt[3]{16} + \sqrt[3]{2} - \sqrt{2}$

74. $5\sqrt[3]{x} - 3\sqrt[3]{x}$

75. $\sqrt[3]{xy} - 2\sqrt[3]{xy}$

76. $3\sqrt{x^3} - \sqrt{x}$

77. $\sqrt{4x + 8} + \sqrt{x + 2}$

78. $\sqrt{2a + 1} + \sqrt{8a + 4}$

79. $\dfrac{15\sqrt{8}}{4} - \dfrac{2\sqrt{2}}{5}$

80. $\dfrac{23\sqrt{11}}{2} - \dfrac{\sqrt{44}}{8}$

81. $20\sqrt[3]{b^4} - 4\sqrt[3]{b}$

82. $2\sqrt[4]{64} - \sqrt[4]{324} + \sqrt[4]{4}$

83. $2\sqrt{3z} + 3\sqrt{12z} + 3\sqrt{48z}$

84. $\sqrt{64x^3} - \sqrt{x} + 3\sqrt{x}$

85. $\sqrt[4]{81a^5b^5} - \sqrt[4]{ab}$

86. $\sqrt[4]{xy^5} + \sqrt[4]{x^5y}$

87. $5\sqrt[3]{\dfrac{n^4}{125}} - 2\sqrt[3]{n}$

88. $\sqrt[3]{\dfrac{8x}{27}} - \dfrac{2\sqrt[3]{x}}{3}$

Exercises 89–96: Multiply and simplify.

89. $(3 + \sqrt{7})(3 - \sqrt{7})$

90. $(5 - \sqrt{5})(5 + \sqrt{5})$

91. $(\sqrt{x} + 8)(\sqrt{x} - 8)$

92. $(\sqrt{ab} - 3)(\sqrt{ab} + 3)$

93. $(\sqrt{ab} - \sqrt{c})(\sqrt{ab} + \sqrt{c})$

94. $(\sqrt{2x} + \sqrt{3y})(\sqrt{2x} - \sqrt{3y})$

95. $(\sqrt{x} - 7)(\sqrt{x} + 8)$

96. $(\sqrt{ab} - 1)(\sqrt{ab} - 2)$

Exercises 97–112: Rationalize the denominator.

97. $\dfrac{4}{\sqrt{3}}$

98. $\dfrac{8}{\sqrt{2}}$

99. $\dfrac{5}{3\sqrt{5}}$

100. $\dfrac{6}{11\sqrt{3}}$

101. $\sqrt{\dfrac{b}{12}}$

102. $\sqrt{\dfrac{5b}{72}}$

103. $\dfrac{1}{3 - \sqrt{2}}$

104. $\dfrac{1}{\sqrt{3} - 2}$

105. $\dfrac{\sqrt{2}}{\sqrt{5} + 2}$

106. $\dfrac{\sqrt{3} - 1}{\sqrt{3} + 1}$

107. $\dfrac{1}{\sqrt{7} - \sqrt{6}}$

108. $\dfrac{1}{\sqrt{8} - \sqrt{7}}$

109. $\dfrac{\sqrt{z}}{\sqrt{z} - 3}$

110. $\dfrac{2\sqrt{z}}{2 - \sqrt{z}}$

111. $\dfrac{\sqrt{a} + \sqrt{b}}{\sqrt{a} - \sqrt{b}}$

112. $\dfrac{1}{\sqrt{a + 1} + \sqrt{a}}$

Appendix A: Using the Graphing Calculator

Overview of the Appendix

The intent of this appendix is to provide instruction in the TI-83, TI-83 Plus, and TI-84 Plus graphing calculators that may be used in conjunction with this textbook. It includes specific keystrokes needed to work several examples from the text. Students are also advised to consult the *Graphing Calculator Guidebook* provided by the manufacturer.

The following is a listing of the topics covered in this appendix.

Figure A.1

Figure A.2

Figure A.3 Normal Mode

Displaying Numbers in Scientific Notation

To display numbers in scientific notation when the calculator is in normal mode, set the graphing calculator in scientific mode (SCI) by using the following keystrokes. See Figure A.1.

(MODE) (▷) (ENTER) (2nd) (MODE [QUIT])

Figure A.2 shows the numbers 5432 and 0.00001234 displayed in scientific notation.

> **SUMMARY: SETTING SCIENTIFIC MODE**
>
> If your calculator is in normal mode, it can be set in scientific mode by pressing
>
> (MODE) (▷) (ENTER) (2nd) (MODE [QUIT]).
>
> These keystrokes return the graphing calculator to the home screen.

Entering Numbers in Scientific Notation

Numbers can be entered in scientific notation. For example, to enter 4.2×10^{-3} in scientific notation, use the following keystrokes. (Be sure to use the negation key $(-)$ rather than the subtraction key.)

Use the negation key not the subtraction key.

(4) (.) (2) (2nd) (,[EE]) ((-)) (3)

This number can also be entered using the following keystrokes. See Figure A.3.

(4) (.) (2) (×) (1) (0) (^) (() ((-)) (3) ())

> **SUMMARY: ENTERING NUMBERS IN SCIENTIFIC NOTATION**
>
> One way to enter a number in scientific notation is to use the keystrokes
>
> (2nd) (,[EE])
>
> to access an exponent (EE) of 10.

Entering Mathematical Expressions

Several expressions are evaluated in Example 7, Section 1.1. To evaluate $\sqrt[3]{131}$, use the following keystrokes from the home screen.

(MATH) (4) (1) (3) (1) ()) (ENTER)

To calculate $\pi^3 + 1.2^2$, use the following keystrokes. (Do *not* use 3.14 for π.)

(2nd) (^[π]) (^) (3) (+) (1) (.) (2) (x^2) (ENTER)

To calculate $|\sqrt{3} - 6|$, use the following keystrokes.

(MATH) (▷) (1) (2nd) ($x^2[\sqrt{\ }]$) (3) ()) (−) (6) ()) (ENTER)

> **SUMMARY: ENTERING COMMON MATHEMATICAL EXPRESSIONS**
>
> To calculate a cube root, use the keystrokes (MATH) (4).
>
> To access the number π, use the keystrokes (2nd) (^[π]).
>
> To access the absolute value, use the keystrokes (MATH) (▷) (1).
>
> To access the square root, use the keystrokes (2nd) ($x^2[\sqrt{\ }]$).

```
 ZOOM MEMORY
1:ZBox
2:Zoom In
3:Zoom Out
4:ZDecimal
5:ZSquare
6:ZStandard
7↓ZTrig
```
Figure A.4

```
WINDOW
 Xmin = ⁻10
 Xmax = 10
 Xscl = 1
 Ymin = ⁻10
 Ymax = 10
 Yscl = 1
 Xres = 1
```
Figure A.5

```
WINDOW
 Xmin = ⁻30
 Xmax = 40
 Xscl = 10
 Ymin = ⁻400
 Ymax = 800
 Yscl = 100
 Xres = 1
```
Figure A.6

```
 L1   L2   L3   1
 1    4    ------
 2    5
 3    6
 ------
 L1={1,2,3}
```
Figure A.7

```
 L1    L2    L3   1
 ⁻5    ⁻5    ------
 ⁻2    3
 1     ⁻7
 4     8
 ████  ------
 L1(5) =
```
Figure A.8

```
STAT PLOTS
1: Plot1...Off
   ⸬  L1   L2    □
2: Plot2...Off
   ⸬  L1   L2    □
3: Plot3...Off
   ⸬  L1   L2    □
4↓PlotsOff
```
Figure A.9

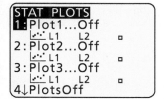

Figure A.10

Setting the Viewing Rectangle

In Example 12, Section 1.2, there are at least two ways to set the standard viewing rectangle to $[-10, 10, 1]$ by $[-10, 10, 1]$. The first method involves pressing (ZOOM) followed by (6). (See Figure A.4.) The second method is to press (WINDOW) and enter the following keystrokes. (See Figure A.5.)

(Be sure to use the negation key $(-)$ rather than the subtraction key.) The viewing rectangle $[-30, 40, 10]$ by $[-400, 800, 100]$ can be set in a similar manner, as shown in Figure A.6. To see the viewing rectangle, press (GRAPH).

> **SUMMARY: SETTING THE VIEWING RECTANGLE**
>
> To set the standard viewing rectangle, press (ZOOM) (6). To set any viewing rectangle, press (WINDOW) and enter the necessary values. To see the viewing rectangle, press (GRAPH).
>
> *Note:* You do not need to change "Xres".

Making a Scatterplot or a Line Graph

In Example 13, Section 1.2, we are asked to make a scatterplot with $(-5, -5)$, $(-2, 3)$, $(1, -7)$, and $(4, 8)$. Begin this task by following these steps.

1. Press (STAT) followed by (1).
2. If list L1 is not empty, use the arrow keys to place the cursor on L1, as shown in Figure A.7. Then press (CLEAR) followed by (ENTER). This deletes all elements in the list. Similarly, if L2 is not empty, clear the list.
3. Input each *x*-value into list L1, followed by (ENTER). Input each *y*-value into list L2, followed by (ENTER). See Figure A.8.

It is essential that both lists have the same number of values—otherwise an error message will appear when a scatterplot is attempted. Before these four points can be plotted, STATPLOT must be turned on. It is accessed by pressing

(2nd) (Y=[STAT PLOT])

as shown in Figure A.9.

There are three possible STATPLOTS, numbered 1, 2, and 3. Any one of the three can be selected. The first plot is selected by pressing (1). Next, place the cursor over "On" and press (ENTER) to turn Plot1 on. There are six types of plots that can be selected. The first type is a *scatterplot* and the second type is a *line graph*, so place the cursor over the first type of plot and press (ENTER) to select a scatterplot. (To make the line graph in Example 14, Section 1.2, be sure to select the line graph.) The *x*-values are stored in list L1, so select L1 for "Xlist" by pressing (2nd) (1). Similarly, press (2nd) (2) for "Ylist," since the *y*-values are stored in list L2. Finally, there are three styles of marks that can be used to show data points in the graph. We usually use the first, because it is largest and shows up the best. Make the screen appear as in Figure A.10. Before plotting the four data points, be sure to set an appropriate viewing rectangle. Then press (GRAPH). The data points will appear as in Figure A.11 on the next page.

NOTE 1 A fast way to set the viewing rectangle for any scatterplot is to select the ZOOMSTAT feature by pressing (ZOOM) (9). This feature automatically scales the viewing rectangle so that all data points are shown.

[−10, 10, 1] by [−10, 10, 1]

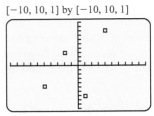

Figure A.11

If an equation has been entered into the $(Y =)$ menu and selected, it will be graphed with the data. Throughout this textbook, this feature is used frequently in modeling data.

NOTE 3 When the error message "ERR: DIM MISMATCH" appears, it usually means that there are not equal numbers of x-values and y-values in lists L1 and L2.

SUMMARY: MAKING A SCATTERPLOT OR A LINE GRAPH

The following are basic steps necessary to make either a scatterplot or a line graph.

STEP 1: Use $(STAT)$ (1) to access lists L1 and L2.

STEP 2: If list L1 is not empty, place the cursor on L1 and press $(CLEAR)$ $(ENTER)$. Repeat for list L2 if it is not empty.

STEP 3: Enter the x-values into list L1 and the y-values into list L2.

STEP 4: Use $(2nd)$ $(Y = [STAT PLOT])$ to set the appropriate parameters for the scatterplot or line graph.

STEP 5: Either set an appropriate viewing rectangle or press $(ZOOM)$ (9). This feature automatically sets the viewing rectangle and plots the data.

Note: $(ZOOM)$ (9) *cannot* be used to set a viewing rectangle for the graph of a function.

Deleting and Inserting a List A list, such as L2, can be deleted. Press $(STAT)$ (1) and then place the cursor on L2 and press (DEL). If you want to insert a deleted list, press $(STAT)$ (1) and then place the cursor where you want to insert the list. For example, to insert L2, place the cursor on L3. Press $(2nd)$ $(DEL [INS])$ $(2nd)$ $(2[L2])$ $(ENTER)$.

Entering a Formula for a Function

To enter the formula for a function f, press $(Y =)$. For example, use the following keystrokes after "$Y_1 = $" to enter $f(x) = 2x^2 - 3x + 7$. See Figure A.12.

$$(Y =)\ (CLEAR)\ (2)\ (X,T,\theta,n)\ (\wedge)\ (2)\ (-)\ (3)\ (X,T,\theta,n)\ (+)\ (7)$$

Note that there is a built-in key for entering the variable X. If "$Y_1 = $" does not appear after you press $(Y =)$, press $(MODE)$ and make sure the calculator is set in function mode, denoted "Func". See Figure A.13.

SUMMARY: ENTERING A FORMULA FOR A FUNCTION

To enter the formula for a function, press $(Y =)$. To delete an existing formula, press $(CLEAR)$. Then enter the symbolic representation for the function.

Figure A.12

Figure A.13

Figure A.14

[−10, 10, 1] by [−10, 10, 1]

Figure A.15

Graphing a Function

To graph a function such as $f(x) = x^2 - 4$, start by pressing $(Y =)$ and then enter $Y_1 = X^2 - 4$. If there is an equation already entered, remove it by pressing $(CLEAR)$. The equals sign in "$Y_1 = $" should be in reverse video (a dark rectangle surrounding a white equals sign), which indicates that the equation will be graphed. If the equals sign is not in reverse video, place the cursor over it and press $(ENTER)$. Set an appropriate viewing rectangle and then press $(GRAPH)$. The graph of f will appear in the specified viewing rectangle. See Figures A.14 and A.15.

NOTE If the error message "ERR: DIM MISMATCH" appears when you try to graph a function, check to see if one of the STATPLOTS is turned on. If it is, turn it off and then try graphing the function.

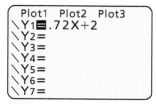

Figure A.16

```
TABLE SETUP
 TblStart=60
 ΔTbl=1
Indpnt: Auto Ask
Depend: Auto Ask
```

Figure A.17

```
   X      Y1
  60     45.2
  61     45.92
  62     46.64
  63     47.36
  64     48.08
  65     48.8
  66     49.52
Y1■.72X+2
```

Figure A.18

```
ZOOM MEMORY
1:ZBox
2:Zoom In
3:Zoom Out
4:ZDecimal
5:ZSquare
6:ZStandard
7↓ZTrig
```

Figure A.19

Use the $\boxed{Y=}$ menu to enter the formula for the function and the $\boxed{WINDOW}$ menu to set an appropriate viewing rectangle. Then press $\boxed{GRAPH}$.

ZoomFit The ZoomFit feature can be used to find an appropriate window when graphing a function. ZoomFit leaves the current Xmin and Xmax settings unchanged and adjusts the current Ymin and Ymax values so that they are equal to the smallest and largest y-values on the graph of the function between Xmin and Xmax. To use ZoomFit, press $\boxed{ZOOM}$ $\boxed{0}$.

Making a Table

To make a table of values for a function, such as $f(x) = 0.72x + 2$, start by pressing $\boxed{Y=}$ and then entering the formula $Y_1 = .72X + 2$, as shown in Figure A.16. To set the table parameters, use the following keystrokes. (See Figure A.17.)

$$\boxed{2nd} \boxed{WINDOW\,[TBLSET]} \boxed{6} \boxed{0} \boxed{ENTER} \boxed{1}$$

These keystrokes specify a table that starts at $x = 60$ and increments the x-values by 1. Therefore the values of Y_1 at $x = 60, 61, 62, \ldots$ appear in the table. To create this table, press the following keys.

$$\boxed{2nd} \boxed{GRAPH\,[TABLE]}$$

One can scroll through x- and y-values by using the arrow keys. See Figure A.18. Note that there is no first or last x-value in the table.

SUMMARY: MAKING A TABLE OF A FUNCTION

Enter the formula for the function using $\boxed{Y=}$. Then press

$$\boxed{2nd} \boxed{WINDOW\,[TBLSET]}$$

to set the starting x-value and the increment between x-values appearing in the table. Create the table by pressing

$$\boxed{2nd} \boxed{GRAPH\,[TABLE]}.$$

Squaring a Viewing Rectangle

In a square viewing rectangle, the graph of $y = x$ is a line that makes a 45° angle with the positive x-axis, a circle appears circular, and all sides of a square have the same length. An approximately square viewing rectangle can be set if the distance along the x-axis is 1.5 times the distance along the y-axis. Examples of viewing rectangles that are (approximately) square include

$$[-6, 6, 1] \text{ by } [-4, 4, 1] \quad \text{and} \quad [-9, 9, 1] \text{ by } [-6, 6, 1].$$

Square viewing rectangles can be set automatically by pressing either

$$\boxed{ZOOM} \boxed{4} \quad \text{or} \quad \boxed{ZOOM} \boxed{5}.$$

ZOOM 4 provides a decimal window, which is discussed later. See Figure A.19.

SUMMARY: SQUARING A VIEWING RECTANGLE

Either $\boxed{ZOOM} \boxed{4}$ or $\boxed{ZOOM} \boxed{5}$ may be used to produce a square viewing rectangle. An (approximately) square viewing rectangle has the form

$$[-1.5k, 1.5k, 1] \text{ by } [-k, k, 1],$$

where k is a positive number.

Figure A.20

Plotting Data and an Equation

In Example 3, Section 2.4, we are asked to plot data and graph a modeling function in the same xy-plane. (You may want to refer to the subsection on making a scatterplot and line graph in this appendix.) Start by entering the x-values into list L1 and the y-values into list L2, as shown in Figure A.20. Then press $(Y=)$ and enter the formula $Y_1 = .65X$ for $f(x)$. Make sure that STATPLOT is on, and set an appropriate viewing rectangle. See Figures A.21 and A.22, and note that Figure A.21 shows "Plot1" in reverse video, which indicates that the scatterplot is on. Now press $(GRAPH)$ to have both the scatterplot and the graph of Y_1 appear in the same viewing rectangle, as shown in Figure A.23.

Figure A.21

Figure A.22

[0, 900, 100] by [0, 800, 100]

Figure A.23

> **SUMMARY: PLOTTING DATA AND AN EQUATION**
>
> **STEP 1:** Enter the x-values into list L1 and the y-values into list L2 using the STAT EDIT menu. Turn on Plot1 so that the scatterplot appears.
>
> **STEP 2:** Use the $(Y=)$ menu to enter the equation to be graphed.
>
> **STEP 3:** Use $(WINDOW)$ or $(ZOOM)$ to set an appropriate viewing rectangle.
>
> **STEP 4:** Press $(GRAPH)$ to graph both the scatterplot and the equation in the same viewing rectangle.

Accessing the Greatest Integer Function

To access the greatest integer function, enter the following keystrokes from the home screen.

$$(MATH)\ (\triangleright)\ (5)$$

Figure A.24

See Figure A.24.

> **SUMMARY: ACCESSING THE GREATEST INTEGER FUNCTION**
>
> **STEP 1:** Press $(MATH)$.
>
> **STEP 2:** Position the cursor over "NUM".
>
> **STEP 3:** Press (5) to select the greatest integer function, which is denoted "int(".

Finding the Line of Least-Squares Fit

In Example 11, Section 2.1, the line of least-squares fit for the points $(1, 1)$, $(2, 3)$, and $(3, 4)$ is found. Begin by entering the points in the same way as for a scatterplot. See Figure 2.14, where the x-values are in list L1 and the y-values are in list L2.

After the data have been entered, perform the following keystrokes from the home screen.

$$(CLEAR)\ (STAT)\ (\triangleright)\ (4)$$

Figure A.25

(See Figure 2.15.) This causes "LinReg(ax+b)" to appear on the home screen, as shown in Figure A.25. The graphing calculator assumes that the x-values are in list L1 and the y-values are in list L2. Now press $(ENTER)$. The result is shown in Figure 2.16.

Figure A.26

Figure A.27

Figure A.28

Figure A.29

Figure A.30

Figure A.31

Figure A.32

If the correlation coefficient r does not appear, enter the keystrokes

(2nd) (0 [CATALOG])

and scroll down until you find "DiagnosticsOn". Press (ENTER) twice. See Figures A.26 and A.27. The graphs of the data and the least-squares regression line are shown in Figure 2.17.

SUMMARY: LINEAR LEAST-SQUARES FIT

STEP 1: Enter the data using (STAT) (1), as is done for a scatterplot. Input the x-values into list L1 and the y-values into list L2.

STEP 2: Press (STAT) (▷) (4) from the home screen to access the least-squares regression line. Press (ENTER) to start the computation. See page AP-11 to learn how to copy a regression equation into Y_1.

Locating a Point of Intersection

In Example 8, Section 2.2, we are asked to find the point of intersection for two lines. To find the point of intersection for the graphs of

$$f(x) = 5.91x + 13.7 \quad \text{and} \quad g(x) = -4.71x + 64.7,$$

start by entering Y_1 and Y_2, as shown in Figure A.28. Set the viewing rectangle to [0, 12, 2] by [0, 100, 10], and graph both equations in the same viewing rectangle, as shown in Figure 2.24. Then press the following keys to find the intersection point.

(2nd) (TRACE [CALC]) (5)

See Figure A.29, where the intersect utility is being selected. The calculator prompts for the first curve, as shown in Figure A.30. Use the arrow keys to locate the cursor near the point of intersection and press (ENTER). Repeat these steps for the second curve, as shown in Figure A.31. Finally the calculator prompts for a guess. For each of the three prompts, place the free-moving cursor near the point of intersection and press (ENTER). The approximate coordinates of the point of intersection are shown in Figure 2.25.

SUMMARY: FINDING A POINT OF INTERSECTION

STEP 1: Graph the two functions in an appropriate viewing rectangle.

STEP 2: Press (2nd) (TRACE [CALC]) (5).

STEP 3: Use the arrow keys to select an approximate location for the point of intersection. Press (ENTER) to make the three selections for "First curve?", "Second curve?", and "Guess?". (If the cursor is near the point of intersection, you usually do not need to move the cursor for each selection. Just press (ENTER) three times.)

Locating a Zero of a Function

In Example 4, Section 2.3, we are asked to locate an x-intercept, or *zero*, of the function f given by $f(x) = 1 - x - \frac{1}{2}x + 2$. Start by entering $Y_1 = 1 - X - .5X + 2$ into the (Y =) menu. Set the viewing rectangle to $[-6, 6, 1]$ by $[-4, 4, 1]$ and graph Y_1. Afterwards, press the following keys to invoke the zero finder. (See Figure A.32.)

(2nd) (TRACE [CALC]) (2)

The calculator prompts for a left bound. Use the arrow keys to set the cursor to the left of the x-intercept and press (ENTER). The calculator then prompts for a right bound. Set the cursor to the right of the x-intercept and press (ENTER). Finally the calculator prompts for a guess. Set the cursor roughly at the x-intercept and press (ENTER). See Figures A.33–A.35 on the next page. The calculator then approximates the x-intercept, or zero, automatically, as shown in Figure 2.35(b).

Figure A.33

Figure A.34

Figure A.35

SUMMARY: LOCATING A ZERO OF A FUNCTION

STEP 1: Graph the function in an appropriate viewing rectangle.

STEP 2: Press (2nd) (TRACE [CALC]) (2).

STEP 3: Select the left and right bounds, followed by a guess. Press (ENTER) after each selection. The calculator then approximates the zero.

Setting Connected and Dot Mode

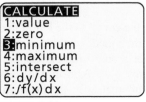
Figure A.36

In Figure 2.48 of Section 2.4 a form of the greatest integer function is graphed in dot mode, and in Figure 2.49 it is graphed in connected mode. To set your graphing calculator in dot mode, press (MODE), position the cursor over "Dot", and press (ENTER). See Figure A.36. Graphs will now appear in dot mode rather than connected mode.

SUMMARY: SETTING CONNECTED OR DOT MODE

STEP 1: Press (MODE).

STEP 2: Position the cursor over "Connected" or "Dot". Press (ENTER).

Accessing the Absolute Value

In Example 1, Section 2.5, the absolute value is used to graph $f(x) = |x + 2|$. To graph f, begin by entering $Y_1 = abs(X + 2)$. The absolute value (abs) is accessed by pressing

$$(MATH) (\triangleright) (1).$$

See Figure A.37.

SUMMARY: ACCESSING THE ABSOLUTE VALUE

STEP 1: Press (MATH).

STEP 2: Position the cursor over "NUM".

STEP 3: Press (1) to select the absolute value.

Finding Extrema (Minima and Maxima)

To find a minimum point (or vertex) on a graph, such as $f(x) = 1.5x^2 - 6x + 4$, start by entering $Y_1 = 1.5X^2 - 6X + 4$ into the (Y =) menu. Set the viewing rectangle to $[-4.7, 4.7, 1]$ by $[-3.1, 3.1, 1]$ by entering (ZOOM) (4). Then perform the following keystrokes to find the minimum y-value.

$$(2nd) (TRACE [CALC]) (3)$$

See Figure A.38.

Figure A.37

Figure A.38

[−4.7, 4.7, 1] by [−3.1, 3.1, 1]

Figure A.39

[−4.7, 4.7, 1] by [−3.1, 3.1, 1]

Figure A.40

[−4.7, 4.7, 1] by [−3.1, 3.1, 1]

Figure A.41

[−4.7, 4.7, 1] by [−3.1, 3.1, 1]

Figure A.42

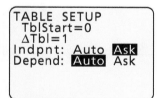

Figure A.43

Figure A.44

The calculator prompts for a left bound. Use the arrow keys to position the cursor to the left of the vertex and press (ENTER). Similarly, position the cursor to the right of the vertex for the right bound and press (ENTER). Finally the calculator asks for a guess between the left and right bounds. Place the cursor near the minimum point and press (ENTER). See Figures A.39–A.41. The minimum point (or vertex) is shown in Figure A.42.

To find a maximum of the function f on an interval, use a similar approach, except enter

$$\boxed{\text{2nd}}\ \boxed{\text{TRACE [CALC]}}\ \boxed{4}\ .$$

The calculator prompts for left and right bounds, followed by a guess. Press (ENTER) after the cursor has been located appropriately for each prompt. An example of a maximum point is displayed in Figure 3.17 in Section 3.1.

SUMMARY: FINDING EXTREMA (MAXIMA AND MINIMA)

STEP 1: Graph the function in an appropriate viewing rectangle.

STEP 2: Press (2nd) (TRACE [CALC]) (3) to find a minimum point or (2nd) (TRACE [CALC]) (4) to find a maximum point.

STEP 3: Use the arrow keys to locate the left and right x-bounds, followed by a guess. Press (ENTER) to select each position of the cursor.

Using the Ask Table Feature

In Example 10, Section 3.1, a table with x-values of 0, 2, 4, 6, and 8 is created. Start by entering $Y_1 = 1.875(X - 8)^2 + 80$. To obtain the table shown in Figure 3.20, use the Ask feature rather than the Auto feature for the independent variable (Indpnt:). Press (2nd) (GRAPH [TABLE]). Whenever an x-value is entered, the corresponding y-value is calculated automatically. See Figures A.43 and A.44.

SUMMARY: USING THE ASK FEATURE FOR A TABLE

STEP 1: Enter the formula for $f(x)$ into Y_1 by using the (Y =) menu.

STEP 2: Press (2nd) (WINDOW [TBLSET]) to access "TABLE SETUP" and then select "Ask" for the independent variable (Indpnt:). "TblStart" and "ΔTbl" do not need to be set.

STEP 3: Enter x-values of your choice. The corresponding y-values will be calculated automatically.

Finding a Nonlinear Function of Least-Squares Fit

In Example 11, Section 3.1, a quadratic function of least-squares fit is found in a manner similar to the way a linear function of least-squares fit is found. To solve Example 11, start by pressing (STAT) (1) and then enter the data points from Table 3.4, as shown in Figure 3.22. Input the x-values into list L1 and the y-values into list L2. To find the equation for a quadratic polynomial of least-squares fit, perform the following keystrokes from the home screen.

$$\boxed{\text{CLEAR}}\ \boxed{\text{STAT}}\ \boxed{\triangleright}\ \boxed{5}$$

This causes "Quadreg" to appear on the home screen. The calculator assumes that the x-values are in list L1 and the y-values are in list L2, unless otherwise designated. Press (ENTER) to obtain the quadratic regression equation, as shown in Figure 3.24. Graphs of the data and the regression equation are shown in Figure 3.25.

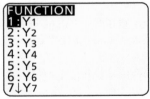

Figure A.45

Other types of regression equations, such as cubic, quartic, power, and exponential, can be selected from the STAT CALC menu. See Figure A.45.

> **SUMMARY: NONLINEAR LEAST-SQUARES FIT**
>
> **STEP 1:** Enter the data using (STAT)(1). Input the x-values into list L1 and the y-values into list L2, as is done for a scatterplot.
>
> **STEP 2:** From the home screen, press (STAT)(▷) and select a type of least-squares modeling function from the menu. Press (ENTER) to initiate the computation.

Evaluating Complex Arithmetic

Complex arithmetic can be performed in much the same way as other arithmetic expressions are evaluated. The imaginary unit i is obtained by entering

(2nd)(. [i])

from the home screen. For example, to add the numbers $(-2 + 3i) + (4 - 6i)$, perform the following keystrokes on the home screen.

(1 (-) 2 + 3 (2nd) (. [i])) + (4 - 6 (2nd) (. [i])) (ENTER)

The result is shown in the first two lines of Figure 3.37 in Section 3.3. Other complex arithmetic operations are done similarly.

> **SUMMARY: EVALUATING COMPLEX ARITHMETIC**
>
> Enter a complex expression in the same way as any other arithmetic expression. To obtain the complex number i, use (2nd)(. [i]).

Figure A.46

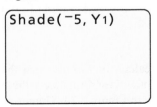

Figure A.47

Accessing the Variable Y_1

In Figure 3.78, Section 3.5, the expressions $-Y_1$ and $Y_1(-X)$ in the (Y =) menu are used to graph reflections. The Y_1 variable can be found by pressing the following keys. (See Figures A.46 and A.47.)

(VARS)(▷)(1)(1)

> **SUMMARY: ACCESSING THE VARIABLE Y_1**
>
> **STEP 1:** Press (VARS).
>
> **STEP 2:** Position the cursor over "Y-VARS".
>
> **STEP 3:** Press (1) twice.
>
> These keystrokes will make Y_1 appear on the screen.

Shading between Two Graphs

In Example 9, Section 3.5, the region below the graph of $f(x) = -0.4x^2 + 4$ is shaded to make it look like a mountain, as illustrated in Figure 3.97. One way to shade below the graph of f is to begin by entering $Y_1 = -.4X^2 + 4$ after pressing (Y =). Then use the following keystrokes from the home screen.

(2nd)(PRGM [DRAW])(7)((-))(5)(,)(VARS)(▷)(1)(1)( ))

Figure A.48

Shade(−5, Y₁)

Figure A.49

The expression Shade(-5, Y_1) should appear on your home screen. See Figures A.48 and A.49. The shading utility, accessed from the DRAW menu, requires a lower function and then an upper function, separated by a comma. When (ENTER) is pressed, the graphing calculator shades between the graph of the lower function and the graph of the upper function.

For the lower function we have arbitrarily selected $y = -5$ because its graph lies below the graph of f and does not appear in the viewing rectangle in Figure 3.97. Instead of entering the variable Y_1, we could enter the formula $-.4X^2 + 4$ for the upper function.

SUMMARY: SHADING A GRAPH

STEP 1: Press (2nd) (PRGM [DRAW]) (7) from the home screen.

STEP 2: Enter a formula or a variable such as Y_1 for the lower function, followed by a comma.

STEP 3: Enter a formula or a variable such as Y_2 for the upper function, followed by a right parenthesis.

STEP 4: Set an appropriate viewing rectangle.

STEP 5: Press (ENTER). The region between the two graphs will be shaded.

Copying a Regression Equation into $Y_1 =$

Figure A.50

Figure A.51

In Example 8, Section 4.2, we are asked to use cubic regression to model real data. The resulting formula for the cubic function, shown in Figure 4.54, is quite complicated and tedious to enter into $Y_1 =$ by hand. A graphing calculator has the capability to copy this equation into Y_1 automatically. To do this, clear the equation for $Y_1 =$. Then enter Y_1 after "CubicReg", as shown in Figure A.50. When (ENTER) is pressed, the regression equation will be calculated and then copied into $Y_1 =$, as shown in Figure A.51. The following keystrokes may be used from the home screen. (Be sure to enter the data into lists L1 and L2.)

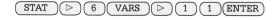

SUMMARY: COPYING A REGRESSION EQUATION INTO $Y_1 =$

STEP 1: Clear Y_1 in the (Y =) menu if an equation is present. Return to the home screen.

STEP 2: Select a type of regression from the STAT CALC menu.

STEP 3: Press (VARS) (▷) (1) (1) (ENTER).

Setting a Decimal Window

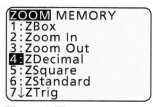

Figure A.52

In Example 1, Section 4.7, a decimal (or friendly) window is used to trace the graph of f. With a decimal window, the cursor stops on convenient x-values. In the decimal window $[-9.4, 9.4, 1]$ by $[-6.2, 6.2, 1]$, the cursor stops on x-values that are multiples of 0.2. If we reduce the viewing rectangle to $[-4.7, 4.7, 1]$ by $[-3.1, 3.1, 1]$, the cursor stops on x-values that are multiples of 0.1. To set this smaller window automatically, press (ZOOM) (4). See Figure A.52. Decimal windows are useful when graphing rational functions with asymptotes in connected mode.

SUMMARY: SETTING A DECIMAL WINDOW

Press (ZOOM) (4) to set the viewing rectangle $[-4.7, 4.7, 1]$ by $[-3.1, 3.1, 1]$. A convenient larger decimal window is $[-9.4, 9.4, 1]$ by $[-6.2, 6.2, 1]$.

Graphing an Inverse Function

In Example 7, Section 5.2, the inverse function of $f(x) = x^3 + 2$ is graphed. A graphing calculator can graph the inverse of a function without a formula for $f^{-1}(x)$. Begin by entering $Y_1 = X^3 + 2$ into the (Y =) menu. Then return to the home screen by pressing

Figure A.53

Figure A.54

Figure A.55

Figure A.56

The DrawInv utility may be accessed by pressing

$$\boxed{\text{2nd}}\ \boxed{\text{PRGM [DRAW]}}\ \boxed{8},$$

followed by

$$\boxed{\text{VARS}}\ \boxed{\triangleright}\ \boxed{1}\ \boxed{1}$$

to obtain the variable Y_1. See A.53. Pressing $\boxed{\text{ENTER}}$ causes both Y_1 and its inverse to be graphed, as shown in A.54.

SUMMARY: GRAPHING AN INVERSE FUNCTION

STEP 1: Enter the formula for $f(x)$ into Y_1 using the $\boxed{\text{Y =}}$ menu.

STEP 2: Set an appropriate viewing rectangle by pressing $\boxed{\text{WINDOW}}$.

STEP 3: Return to the home screen by pressing $\boxed{\text{2nd}}\ \boxed{\text{MODE [QUIT]}}$.

STEP 4: Press $\boxed{\text{2nd}}\ \boxed{\text{PRGM [DRAW]}}\ \boxed{8}\ \boxed{\text{VARS}}\ \boxed{\triangleright}\ \boxed{1}\ \boxed{1}\ \boxed{\text{ENTER}}$ to create the graphs of f and f^{-1}.

Shading a System of Inequalities

In Example 2(b), Section 9.2, we are asked to shade the solution set for the system of linear inequalities $x + 3y \le 9, 2x - y \le -1$. Begin by solving each system for y to obtain $y \le -\frac{1}{3}x + 3$ and $y \ge 2x + 1$. Then let $Y_1 = -X/3 + 3$ and $Y_2 = 2X + 1$, as shown in Figure 9.30. Position the cursor to left of Y_1 and press $\boxed{\text{ENTER}}$ three times. The triangle that appears indicates that the calculator will shade the region below the graph of Y_1. Next locate the cursor to the left of Y_2 and press $\boxed{\text{ENTER}}$ twice. This triangle indicates that the calculator will shade the region above the graph of Y_2. After setting the viewing rectangle to $[-6, 6, 1]$ by $[-6, 6, 1]$, press $\boxed{\text{GRAPH}}$. The result is shown in Figure 9.31. The solution set could also be shaded using Shade(Y_2, Y_1) from the home screen. See Figures A.55 and A.56.

SUMMARY: SHADING A SYSTEM OF INEQUALITIES

STEP 1: Solve each inequality for y.

STEP 2: Enter the formulas as Y_1 and Y_2 in the $\boxed{\text{Y =}}$ menu.

STEP 3: Locate the cursor to the left of Y_1 and press $\boxed{\text{ENTER}}$ two or three times, to shade either above or below the graph of Y_1. Repeat for Y_2.

STEP 4: Set an appropriate viewing rectangle.

STEP 5: Press $\boxed{\text{GRAPH}}$.

Note: The Shade utility under the DRAW menu can also be used to shade the region *between* two graphs.

Entering the Elements of a Matrix

In Example 9, Section 9.4, the augmented matrix A is given by

$$A = \begin{bmatrix} 2 & 1 & 2 & | & 10 \\ 1 & 0 & 2 & | & 5 \\ 1 & -2 & 2 & | & 1 \end{bmatrix}.$$

On the TI-83 Plus and TI-84 Plus, use the following keystrokes to define a matrix A with dimension 3×4. (On the TI-83 graphing calculator, the matrix menu is found by pressing $\boxed{\text{MATRIX}}$.)

$$\boxed{\text{2nd}}\ \boxed{x^{-1}\ \text{[MATRIX]}}\ \boxed{\triangleright}\ \boxed{\triangleright}\ \boxed{1}\ \boxed{3}\ \boxed{\text{ENTER}}\ \boxed{4}\ \boxed{\text{ENTER}}$$

See Figures 9.41 and 9.42. Then input the 12 elements of the matrix A, row by row, as shown in Figure 9.42. Finish each entry by pressing (ENTER). After these elements have been entered, press

(2nd)(MODE [QUIT])

to return to the home screen. To display the matrix A, press

(2nd)(x^{-1} [MATRIX])(1)(ENTER).

See Figure 9.43.

SUMMARY: ENTERING THE ELEMENTS OF A MATRIX A

STEP 1: Begin by accessing the matrix A by pressing (2nd)(x^{-1} [MATRIX])(▷)(▷)(1).

STEP 2: Enter the dimension of A by pressing (m)(ENTER)(n)(ENTER), where the dimension of the matrix is $m \times n$.

STEP 3: Input each element of the matrix, row by row. Finish each entry by pressing (ENTER). Use (2nd)(MODE [QUIT]) to return to the home screen.

Note: On the TI-83, replace the keystrokes (2nd)(x^{-1} [MATRIX]) with (MATRIX).

Reduced Row-Echelon Form

In Example 9, Section 9.4, the reduced row-echelon form of a matrix is found. To find this reduced row-echelon form on the TI-83 Plus and TI-84 Plus, use the following keystrokes from the home screen. (See Figure 9.44.)

(2nd)(x^{-1} [MATRIX])(▷)(ALPHA)(APPS [B])(2nd)(x^{-1} [MATRIX])(1)( ))(ENTER)

The resulting matrix is shown in Figure 9.45. On the TI-83 graphing calculator, use the following keystrokes to find the reduced row-echelon form.

(MATRIX)(▷)(ALPHA)(MATRIX [B])(MATRIX)(1)( ))(ENTER)

SUMMARY: FINDING THE REDUCED ROW-ECHELON FORM OF A MATRIX

STEP 1: To make rref([A]) appear on the home screen, use the following keystrokes.

(2nd)(x^{-1} [MATRIX])(▷)(ALPHA)(APPS [B])(2nd)(x^{-1} [MATRIX])(1)( ))(ENTER)

STEP 2: Press (ENTER) to calculate the reduced row-echelon form. Use arrow keys to access elements that do not appear on the screen.

Note: On the TI-83, replace the keystrokes (2nd)(x^{-1} [MATRIX]) with (MATRIX) and (APPS [B]) with (MATRIX [B]).

Performing Arithmetic Operations on Matrices

In Example 10, Section 9.5, the matrices A and B are multiplied. Begin by entering the elements for the matrices A and B. The following keystrokes can be used to define a matrix A with dimension 3×3.

(2nd)(x^{-1} [MATRIX])(▷)(▷)(1)(3)(ENTER)(3)(ENTER)

Next input the 9 elements in the matrix A, row by row. Finish each entry by pressing (ENTER). See Figure 9.59. Repeat this process to define a matrix B with dimension 3×3.

(2nd)(x^{-1} [MATRIX])(▷)(▷)(2)(3)(ENTER)(3)(ENTER)

Enter the 9 elements in B. See Figure 9.60. After the elements of A and B have been entered, press

$$\boxed{\text{2nd}}\ \boxed{\text{MODE [QUIT]}}$$

to return to the home screen. To multiply the expression AB, use the following keystrokes from the home screen.

$$\boxed{\text{2nd}}\ \boxed{x^{-1}\ \text{[MATRIX]}}\ \boxed{1}\ \boxed{\times}\ \boxed{\text{2nd}}\ \boxed{x^{-1}\ \text{[MATRIX]}}\ \boxed{2}\ \boxed{\text{ENTER}}$$

The result is shown in Figure 9.61.

SUMMARY: PERFORMING ARITHMETIC OPERATIONS ON MATRICES

STEP 1: Enter the elements of each matrix, beginning with the keystrokes

$$\boxed{\text{2nd}}\ \boxed{x^{-1}\ \text{[MATRIX]}}\ \boxed{\triangleright}\ \boxed{\triangleright}\ \boxed{k}\ \boxed{m}\ \boxed{\text{ENTER}}\ \boxed{n}\ \boxed{\text{ENTER}},$$

where k is the menu number of the matrix and the dimension of the matrix is $m \times n$.

STEP 2: Return to the home screen by pressing $\boxed{\text{2nd}}\ \boxed{\text{MODE [QUIT]}}$.

STEP 3: Enter the matrix expression, followed by $\boxed{\text{ENTER}}$. Use the keystrokes

$$\boxed{\text{2nd}}\ \boxed{x^{-1}\ \text{[MATRIX]}}\ \boxed{k}$$

to access the matrix with menu number k.

Note: On the TI-83, replace the keystrokes $\boxed{\text{2nd}}\ \boxed{x^{-1}\ \text{[MATRIX]}}$ with $\boxed{\text{MATRIX}}$.

Finding the Inverse of a Matrix

In Example 8, Section 9.6, the inverse of A, denoted A^{-1}, is displayed in Figure 9.65. To calculate A^{-1}, start by entering the elements of the matrix A, as shown in Figure A.57. To compute A^{-1}, perform the following keystrokes from the home screen.

$$\boxed{\text{2nd}}\ \boxed{x^{-1}\ \text{[MATRIX]}}\ \boxed{1}\ \boxed{x^{-1}}\ \boxed{\text{ENTER}}$$

The results are shown in Figure 9.65.

SUMMARY: FINDING THE INVERSE OF A SQUARE MATRIX

STEP 1: Enter the elements of the square matrix A.

STEP 2: Return to the home screen by pressing

$$\boxed{\text{2nd}}\ \boxed{\text{MODE [QUIT]}}.$$

STEP 3: Perform the following keystrokes from the home screen to display A^{-1}.

$$\boxed{\text{2nd}}\ \boxed{x^{-1}\ \text{[MATRIX]}}\ \boxed{1}\ \boxed{x^{-1}}\ \boxed{\text{ENTER}}$$

Note: On the TI-83, replace the keystrokes $\boxed{\text{2nd}}\ \boxed{x^{-1}\ \text{[MATRIX]}}$ with $\boxed{\text{MATRIX}}$.

Solving a Linear System with a Matrix Inverse

In Example 8, Section 9.6, the solution to a system of equations is found. The matrix equation $AX = B$ has the solution $X = A^{-1}B$, provided A^{-1} exists, and is given by

$$AX = \begin{bmatrix} 1 & 3 & -1 \\ 0 & -2 & 1 \\ -1 & 1 & -3 \end{bmatrix} \begin{bmatrix} x \\ y \\ z \end{bmatrix} = \begin{bmatrix} 6 \\ -2 \\ 4 \end{bmatrix} = B.$$

```
MATRIX[A]  3 ×3
[ 1      3     -1    ]
[ 0     -2      1    ]
[ -1     1     -3    ]
```

Figure A.57

To solve this equation, start by entering the elements of the matrices A and B. To compute the solution $A^{-1}B$, perform the following keystrokes from the home screen.

(2nd) (x^{-1} [MATRIX]) (1) (x^{-1}) ($\times$) (2nd) (x^{-1} [MATRIX]) (2) (ENTER)

The results are shown in Figure 9.66.

> ### SUMMARY: SOLVING A LINEAR SYSTEM WITH A MATRIX INVERSE
>
> **STEP 1:** Write the system of equations as $AX = B$.
>
> **STEP 2:** Enter the elements of the matrices A and B.
>
> **STEP 3:** Return to the home screen by pressing
>
> (2nd) (MODE [QUIT]).
>
> **STEP 4:** Perform the following keystrokes.
>
> (2nd) (x^{-1} [MATRIX]) (1) (x^{-1}) ($\times$) (2nd) (x^{-1} [MATRIX]) (2) (ENTER)
>
> *Note:* On the TI-83, replace the keystrokes with (2nd) (x^{-1} [MATRIX]) with (MATRIX).

Evaluating a Determinant

In Example 4(a), Section 9.7, a graphing calculator is used to evaluate a determinant of a matrix. Start by entering the 9 elements of the 3×3 matrix A, as shown in Figure A.58. To compute det A, perform the following keystrokes from the home screen.

(2nd) (x^{-1} [MATRIX]) ($\triangleright$) (1) (2nd) (x^{-1} [MATRIX]) (1) ( )) (ENTER)

The results are shown in Figure 9.68.

> ### SUMMARY: EVALUATING A DETERMINANT OF A SQUARE MATRIX
>
> **STEP 1:** Enter the elements of the matrix A.
>
> **STEP 2:** Return to the home screen by pressing
>
> (2nd) (MODE [QUIT]).
>
> **STEP 3:** Perform the following keystrokes.
>
> (2nd) (x^{-1} [MATRIX]) ($\triangleright$) (1) (2nd) (x^{-1} [MATRIX]) (1) ( )) (ENTER)
>
> *Note:* On the TI-83, replace the keystrokes (2nd) (x^{-1} [MATRIX]) with (MATRIX).

Creating a Sequence

A graphing calculator can be used to calculate the terms of the sequence given by $f(n) = 2n - 5$ for $n = 1, 2, 3, 4$. See Example 1(a), Section 11.1. Start by setting the mode of the calculator to sequence ("Seq") using the following keystrokes. (See Figure A.59.)

(MODE) ($\triangledown$) ($\triangledown$) ($\triangledown$) ($\triangleright$) ($\triangleright$) ($\triangleright$) (ENTER) (2nd) (MODE [QUIT])

Then enter the following from the home screen.

(2nd) (STAT [LIST]) ($\triangleright$) (5)

On the home screen, "seq(" will appear, as shown in Figure A.60. This sequence utility requires that four things be entered—all separated by commas. They are the formula, the variable, the subscript of the first term, and the subscript of the last term. Use the following keystrokes to

Figure A.58

Figure A.59

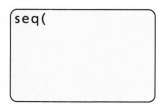

Figure A.60

obtain the first four terms (a_1, a_2, a_3, a_4) of the sequence $a_n = 2n - 5$, as shown in Figure 11.1.

$$\boxed{2}\;\boxed{X, T, \theta, n}\;\boxed{-}\;\boxed{5}\;\boxed{,}\;\boxed{X, T, \theta, n}\;\boxed{,}\;\boxed{1}\;\boxed{,}\;\boxed{4}\;\boxed{)}\;\boxed{\text{ENTER}}$$

SUMMARY: CREATING A SEQUENCE

STEP 1: To create a sequence, use the keystrokes

$$\boxed{\text{2nd}}\;\boxed{\text{STAT [LIST]}}\;\boxed{\triangleright}\;\boxed{5}.$$

STEP 2: Enter the formula, the variable, the subscript of the first term, and the subscript of the last term—all separated by commas. For example, if you want the first 10 terms (a_1, a_2, a_3, ..., a_{10}) of $a_n = n^2$, enter seq(n^2, n, 1, 10). Be sure to set your calculator in sequence mode.

STEP 3: Press $\boxed{\text{ENTER}}$ to get the terms of the sequence to appear.

Entering, Tabling, and Graphing a Sequence

In Example 5, Section 11.1, a table and a graph of a sequence are created with a graphing calculator. The calculator should be set to sequence mode by entering the following keystrokes.

$$\boxed{\text{MODE}}\;\boxed{\triangledown}\;\boxed{\triangledown}\;\boxed{\triangledown}\;\boxed{\triangleright}\;\boxed{\triangleright}\;\boxed{\triangleright}\;\boxed{\text{ENTER}}$$

To enter the formula for a sequence, press $\boxed{\text{Y =}}$. See Figure A.61. Let $n\text{Min} = 1$, since the initial value of n is equal to 1. To enter $a_n = 2.85a_{n-1} - .19a_{n-1}^2$, use the following keystrokes, after clearing out any old formula. (Notice that the graphing calculator uses u instead of a to denote a term of the sequence.)

$$\boxed{2}\;\boxed{.}\;\boxed{8}\;\boxed{5}\;\boxed{\text{2nd}}\;\boxed{7[u]}\;\boxed{(}\;\boxed{X, T, \theta, n}\;\boxed{-}\;\boxed{1}\;\boxed{)}\;\boxed{-}\;\boxed{.}\;\boxed{1}\;\boxed{9}$$

$$\boxed{\text{2nd}}\;\boxed{7[u]}\;\boxed{(}\;\boxed{X, T, \theta, n}\;\boxed{-}\;\boxed{1}\;\boxed{)}\;\boxed{\wedge}\;\boxed{2}\;\boxed{\text{ENTER}}$$

Since $a_1 = 1$, let $u(n\text{Min}) = \{1\}$. This can be done as follows. See Figure A.61.

$$\boxed{\text{CLEAR}}\;\boxed{\text{2nd}}\;\boxed{(}\;\boxed{1}\;\boxed{\text{2nd}}\;\boxed{)}$$

To create a table for this sequence, starting with a_1 and incrementing n by 1, perform the following keystrokes. See Figure A.62 and Figure 11.7.

$$\boxed{\text{2nd}}\;\boxed{\text{WINDOW [TBLSET]}}\;\boxed{1}\;\boxed{\text{ENTER}}\;\boxed{1}\;\boxed{\text{2nd}}\;\boxed{\text{GRAPH [TABLE]}}$$

To graph the first 20 terms of this sequence, start by selecting $\boxed{\text{WINDOW}}$. Since we want the first 20 terms plotted, let $n\text{Min} = 1$, $n\text{Max} = 20$, PlotStart = 1, and PlotStep = 1. The window can be set as [0, 21, 1] by [0, 14, 1]. See Figure A.63. To graph the sequence, press $\boxed{\text{GRAPH}}$. The resulting graph uses dot mode and is shown in Figure 11.9.

SUMMARY: ENTERING, TABLING, AND GRAPHING A SEQUENCE

STEP 1: Set the mode to "Seq" by using the $\boxed{\text{MODE}}$ menu.

STEP 2: Enter the formula for the sequence by pressing $\boxed{\text{Y =}}$.

STEP 3: To create a table of a sequence, set the start and increment values with

$$\boxed{\text{2nd}}\;\boxed{\text{WINDOW [TBLSET]}}$$

and then press

$$\boxed{\text{2nd}}\;\boxed{\text{GRAPH [TABLE]}}.$$

STEP 4: To graph a sequence, set the viewing rectangle by using $\boxed{\text{WINDOW}}$ and then press $\boxed{\text{GRAPH}}$. Be sure to use dot mode.

```
 Plot1  Plot2  Plot3
 nMin=1
\.u(n)▪2.85u(n−1)
−.19u(n−1)^2
 u(nMin)▪{1}
\v(n)=
 v(nMin)=
\w(n)=
```

Figure A.61

```
TABLE SETUP
 TblStart=1
 ΔTbl=1
Indpnt: Auto  Ask
Depend: Auto  Ask
```

Figure A.62

```
WINDOW
 nMin=1
 nMax=20
 PlotStart=1
 PlotStep=1
 Xmin=0
 Xmax=21
↓Xscl=1
```

Figure A.63

Summing a Series

In Example 3, Section 11.2, the sum of the series $\sum_{n=1}^{50} \left(\frac{1}{n^4}\right)$ is found by using a graphing calculator. Use the following keystrokes from the home screen.

[2nd] [STAT [LIST]] [▷] [▷] [5] [2nd] [STAT [LIST]] [▷] [5]

[1] [÷] [X, T, θ, n] [^] [4] [,] [X, T, θ, n] [,] [1] [,] [5] [0] [)] [)] [ENTER]

The results are shown in the first three lines of Figure 11.12.

SUMMARY: SUMMING A SERIES

STEP 1: Use [2nd] [STAT [LIST]] [▷] [▷] [5] to access the sum utility.

STEP 2: Use [2nd] [STAT [LIST]] [▷] [5] to access the sequence utility. (To use the sequence utility, see "Creating a Sequence" in this appendix.)

Calculating Factorial Notation

In Example 4, Section 11.3, factorial notation is evaluated with a graphing calculator. The factorial utility is found under the MATH PRB menus. To calculate 8!, use the following keystrokes from the home screen.

[8] [MATH] [▷] [▷] [▷] [4] [ENTER]

The results are shown in the first two lines of Figure 11.15.

SUMMARY: CALCULATING FACTORIAL NOTATION

To calculate n factorial, use the following keystrokes.

[n] [MATH] [▷] [▷] [▷] [4] [ENTER]

The value of n should be entered as a number, not a variable.

Calculating Permutations and Combinations

In Example 5(a), Section 11.3, the permutation $P(7, 3)$ is evaluated. To perform this calculation, use the following keystrokes from the home screen.

[7] [MATH] [▷] [▷] [▷] [2] [3] [ENTER]

The results are shown in the first two lines of Figure 11.17.

In Example 8(a), Section 11.3, the combination $C(7, 3)$ can be calculated by using the following keystrokes.

[7] [MATH] [▷] [▷] [▷] [3] [3] [ENTER]

The results are shown in the first two lines of Figure 11.18.

SUMMARY: CALCULATING PERMUTATIONS AND COMBINATIONS

STEP 1: To calculate $P(n, r)$, use [MATH] and select "PRB" followed by [2].

STEP 2: To calculate $C(n, r)$, use [MATH] and select "PRB" followed by [3].

Graphing Parametric Equations

In Figure 8.72, Section 8.4, the parametric equations $x = t + 3$, $y = t^2$ for $-3 \leq t \leq 3$ are graphed. To set your graphing calculator in parametric mode, press (MODE), position the cursor over "Par", and press (ENTER). See Figure A.64. Next Press (Y =) and enter the equations for x and y, as shown in Figure A.65.

Figure A.64

Figure A.65

To set a viewing rectangle, press (WINDOW). In addition to setting Xmin, Xmax, Xscl, Ymin, Ymax, and Yscl, you must set values for Tmin, Tmax, and Tstep. Tmin refers to the minimum value of t in the graph, and Tmax refers to the maximum value of t. It is given that $-3 \leq t \leq 3$, so it follows that Tmin $= -3$ and Tmax $= 3$. However, when an interval for t is not given, it may take a little experimentation to determine an appropriate interval for t. Tstep represents the increment between consecutive t-values on the graph. If Tstep is too large, the graph appears more like a line graph than a smooth curve. If Tstep is too small, the graphing calculator will take a long time to create the graph. Many times a reasonable value is Tstep $= 0.1$. See Figure 8.70. A parametric graph can be created by pressing (GRAPH).

Tables for parametric equations can be created. Press

(2nd) (WINDOW [TBLSET])

and proceed in the usual manner. Note that the variables TblStart and ΔTbl refer to t and not x. See Figure 8.71.

SUMMARY: GRAPHING PARAMETRIC EQUATIONS

1. Press (MODE), move the cursor to "Par", and press (ENTER).
2. Press (Y =) and enter the equations for x and y.
3. Press (WINDOW) and set the viewing rectangle. Be sure to set Tmin, Tmax, and Tstep. When in doubt, let Tstep $= 0.1$.
4. To make the graph appear, press (GRAPH).

Graphing in Polar Coordinates

In Figure 8.102, Section 8.5, the polar equation $r = 2 + 2 \cos \theta$ for $0° \leq \theta \leq 360°$ is graphed. To set your graphing calculator in polar coordinate mode, press (MODE), position the cursor over "Pol", and press (ENTER). See Figure A.66. Polar equations can be graphed in either degree or radian mode. To set your calculator in degree mode, position the cursor over "Degree" and press (ENTER). See Figure A.67. Next press (Y =) and enter the equation for "$r_1 = $", as shown in Figure A.68. Note that the polar equation must be solved for the variable r.

Figure A.66

Figure A.67

Figure A.68

```
WINDOW
 θmin = 0
 θmax = 360
 θstep = 7.5
 Xmin = ⁻6
 Xmax = 6
 Xscl = 1
↓Ymin = ⁻4
```

Figure A.69 Degree Mode

To set a viewing rectangle, press (WINDOW). In addition to setting Xmin, Xmax, Xscl, Ymin, Ymax, and Yscl, you must set values for θmin, θmax, and θstep. The variable θmin refers to the minimum value of θ, and θmax refers to the maximum value of θ. Since cos θ is periodic with 360°, the entire graph will appear if we let $0° \leq \theta \leq 360°$. Let θmin = 0 and θmax = 360. The variable θstep represents the increment between consecutive θ-values on the polar graph. If θstep is too large, the graph appears more like a line graph than a smooth curve. If θstep is too small, the graphing calculator will take a long time to create the graph. In degree mode a reasonable value for θstep is 7.5°, and in radian mode a reasonable value for θstep is 0.1 radian. See Figure A.69. A polar graph can be created by pressing (GRAPH).

Tables for polar coordinates can be created. Press

(2nd) (WINDOW [TBLSET])

and proceed in the usual manner. Note that the variables TblStart and ΔTbl refer to θ and not x. See Figure 8.101.

SUMMARY: GRAPHING IN POLAR COORDINATES

1. Press (MODE), move the cursor to "Pol", and press (ENTER). Set the calculator to either degree or radian mode.
2. Press (Y =) and enter the polar equation.
3. Press (WINDOW) and set the viewing rectangle. Be sure to set θmin, θmax, and θstep. When in doubt, let θstep = 7.5 in degree mode and θstep = 0.1 in radian mode.
4. To make the graph appear, press (GRAPH).

Appendix B: A Library of Functions

Basic Functions

The following are symbolic, numerical, and graphical representations of several functions used in algebra and trigonometry. Their domains D and ranges R are given.

Identity Function: $f(x) = x$

x	-2	-1	0	1	2
$y = x$	-2	-1	0	1	2

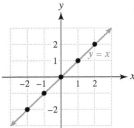

$D = (-\infty, \infty)$
$R = (-\infty, \infty)$

Absolute Value Function: $f(x) = |x|$

x	-2	-1	0	1	2
$y = |x|$	2	1	0	1	2

$D = (-\infty, \infty)$
$R = [0, \infty)$

Square Function: $f(x) = x^2$

x	-2	-1	0	1	2
$y = x^2$	4	1	0	1	4

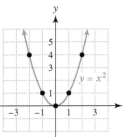

$D = (-\infty, \infty)$
$R = [0, \infty)$

Cube Function: $f(x) = x^3$

x	-2	-1	0	1	2
$y = x^3$	-8	-1	0	1	8

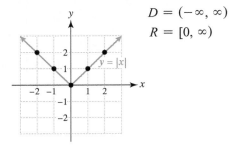

$D = (-\infty, \infty)$
$R = (-\infty, \infty)$

Square Root Function: $f(x) = \sqrt{x}$

x	0	1	4	9
$y = \sqrt{x}$	0	1	2	3

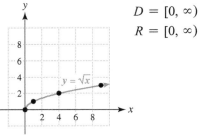

$D = [0, \infty)$
$R = [0, \infty)$

Cube Root Function: $f(x) = \sqrt[3]{x}$

x	-8	-1	0	1	8
$y = \sqrt[3]{x}$	-2	-1	0	1	2

$D = (-\infty, \infty)$
$R = (-\infty, \infty)$

Greatest Integer Function: $f(x) = [\![x]\!]$

x	-2.5	-1.5	0	1.5	2.5
$y = [\![x]\!]$	-3	-2	0	1	2

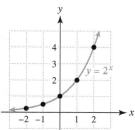

$D = (-\infty, \infty)$
$R = \text{Integers}$

Reciprocal Function: $f(x) = \frac{1}{x}$

x	-2	-1	0	1	2
$y = \frac{1}{x}$	$-\frac{1}{2}$	-1	—	1	$\frac{1}{2}$

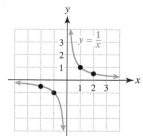

$D = (-\infty, 0) \cup (0, \infty)$
$R = (-\infty, 0) \cup (0, \infty)$

Base-2 Exponential Function: $f(x) = 2^x$

x	-2	-1	0	1	2
$y = 2^x$	$\frac{1}{4}$	$\frac{1}{2}$	1	2	4

$D = (-\infty, \infty)$
$R = (0, \infty)$

Natural Exponential Function: $f(x) = e^x$

x	-2	-1	0	1	2
$y = e^x$	e^{-2}	e^{-1}	1	e^1	e^2

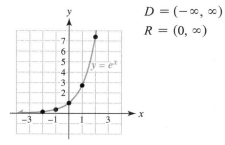

$D = (-\infty, \infty)$
$R = (0, \infty)$

Common Logarithmic Function: $f(x) = \log x$

x	0.1	1	4	7	10
$y = \log x$	-1	0	$\log 4$	$\log 7$	1

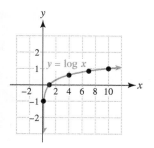

$D = (0, \infty)$
$R = (-\infty, \infty)$

Natural Logarithmic Function: $f(x) = \ln x$

x	$\frac{1}{2}$	1	2	e	e^2
$y = \ln x$	$\ln \frac{1}{2}$	0	$\ln 2$	1	2

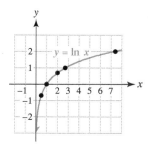

$D = (0, \infty)$
$R = (-\infty, \infty)$

Sine Function: $f(x) = \sin x$

x	0	$\frac{\pi}{2}$	π	$\frac{3\pi}{2}$	2π
$y = \sin x$	0	1	0	-1	0

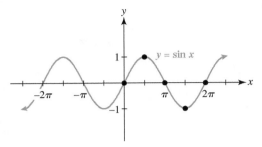

$D = (-\infty, \infty), R = [-1, 1]$

Cosine Function: $f(x) = \cos x$

x	0	$\frac{\pi}{2}$	π	$\frac{3\pi}{2}$	2π
$y = \cos x$	1	0	-1	0	1

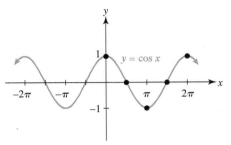

$D = (-\infty, \infty), R = [-1, 1]$

Tangent Function: $f(x) = \tan x$

x	$-\frac{\pi}{3}$	$-\frac{\pi}{4}$	0	$\frac{\pi}{4}$	$\frac{\pi}{3}$
$y = \tan x$	$-\sqrt{3}$	-1	0	1	$\sqrt{3}$

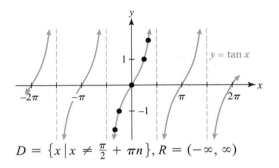

$D = \left\{x \,|\, x \neq \frac{\pi}{2} + \pi n\right\}, R = (-\infty, \infty)$

Cotangent Function: $f(x) = \cot x$

x	$\frac{\pi}{6}$	$\frac{\pi}{4}$	$\frac{\pi}{2}$	$\frac{3\pi}{4}$	$\frac{5\pi}{6}$
$y = \cot x$	$\sqrt{3}$	1	0	-1	$-\sqrt{3}$

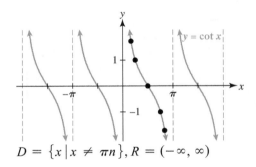

$D = \left\{x \,|\, x \neq \pi n\right\}, R = (-\infty, \infty)$

Cosecant Function: $f(x) = \csc x$

x	$\frac{\pi}{6}$	$\frac{\pi}{4}$	$\frac{\pi}{2}$	$\frac{3\pi}{4}$	$\frac{5\pi}{6}$
$y = \csc x$	2	$\sqrt{2}$	1	$\sqrt{2}$	2

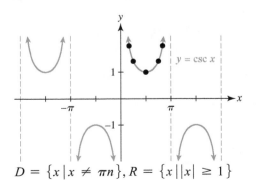

$D = \left\{x \,|\, x \neq \pi n\right\}, R = \left\{x \,|\, |x| \geq 1\right\}$

Secant Function: $f(x) = \sec x$

x	$-\frac{\pi}{3}$	$-\frac{\pi}{4}$	0	$\frac{\pi}{4}$	$\frac{\pi}{3}$
$y = \sec x$	2	$\sqrt{2}$	1	$\sqrt{2}$	2

$D = \left\{x \,|\, x \neq \frac{\pi}{2} + \pi n\right\}, R = \left\{x \,|\, |x| \geq 1\right\}$

Families of Functions

This subsection shows the formulas and graphs of some families of functions, such as linear, quadratic, and exponential. Notice that the appearance of the graphs of these functions depends on the value of k, m, or a.

Constant Functions: $f(x) = k$

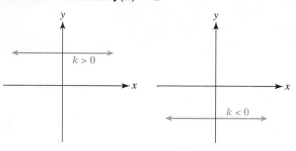

Linear Functions: $f(x) = mx + b$

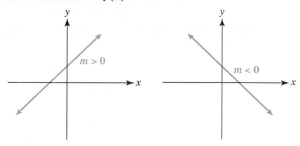

Quadratic Functions: $f(x) = ax^2 + bx + c$

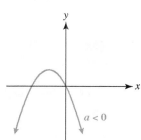

Cubic Functions: $f(x) = ax^3 + bx^2 + cx + d$

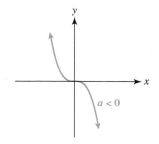

Power Functions: $f(x) = x^a, x > 0$

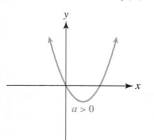

Sinusoidal Functions: $f(x) = a \sin (b(x - c)) + d$ or $f(x) = a \cos (b(x - c)) + d$

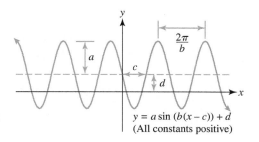

$y = a \sin (b(x - c)) + d$
(All constants positive)

Exponential Functions: $f(x) = Ca^x, C > 0$

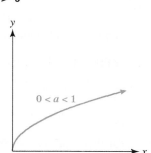

Logarithmic Functions: $f(x) = \log_a x$

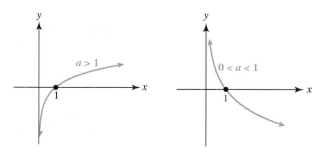

Appendix C: Partial Fractions

Decomposition of Rational Expressions

The sums of rational expressions are found by combining two or more rational expressions into one rational expression. Here, the reverse process is considered: given one rational expression, express it as the sum of two or more rational expressions. A special type of sum of rational expressions is called the **partial fraction decomposition**; each term in the sum is a **partial fraction**. The technique of finding partial fraction decompositions can be accomplished by using the following steps.

PARTIAL FRACTION DECOMPOSITION OF $\frac{f(x)}{g(x)}$

STEP 1: If $\frac{f(x)}{g(x)}$ is not a proper fraction (a fraction with the numerator of lower degree than the denominator), divide $f(x)$ by $g(x)$. For example,

$$\frac{x^4 - 3x^3 + x^2 + 5x}{x^2 + 3} = x^2 - 3x - 2 + \frac{14x + 6}{x^2 + 3}.$$

Then apply the following steps to the remainder, which is a proper fraction.

STEP 2: Factor $g(x)$ completely into factors of the form $(ax + b)^m$ or $(cx^2 + dx + e)^n$, where $cx^2 + dx + e$ is *irreducible* and m and n are positive integers.

STEP 3: **(a)** For each distinct linear factor $(ax + b)$, include in the decomposition the term

$$\frac{A}{ax + b}.$$

(b) For each repeated linear factor $(ax + b)^m$, include in the decomposition the terms

$$\frac{A_1}{ax + b} + \frac{A_2}{(ax + b)^2} + \cdots + \frac{A_m}{(ax + b)^m}.$$

STEP 4: **(a)** For each distinct quadratic factor $(cx^2 + dx + e)$, include in the decomposition the term

$$\frac{Bx + C}{cx^2 + dx + e}.$$

(b) For each repeated quadratic factor $(cx^2 + dx + e)^n$, include in the decomposition the terms

$$\frac{B_1x + C_1}{cx^2 + dx + e} + \frac{B_2x + C_2}{(cx^2 + dx + e)^2} + \cdots + \frac{B_nx + C_n}{(cx^2 + dx + e)^n}.$$

STEP 5: Use algebraic techniques to solve for the constants in the numerators.

To find the constants in Step 5, the goal is to get a system of equations with as many equations as there are unknowns in the numerators. One method for finding these equations is to substitute values for x on each side of the rational equation formed in Steps 3 and 4.

Distinct Linear Factors

EXAMPLE 1 Finding a partial fraction decomposition

Find the partial fraction decomposition of

$$\frac{2x^4 - 8x^2 + 5x - 2}{x^3 - 4x}.$$

SOLUTION The given fraction is not a proper fraction; the numerator has higher degree than the denominator. Perform the following division.

$$\begin{array}{r} 2x \\ x^3 - 4x \overline{\smash{\big)}\, 2x^4 - 8x^2 + 5x - 2} \\ \underline{2x^4 - 8x^2} \\ 5x - 2 \end{array}$$

Algebra Review
To review clearing fractions from rational equations, see chapter R (page R-33).

The result is $2x + \frac{5x - 2}{x^3 - 4x}$. Now work with the remainder fraction. Factor the denominator as $x^3 - 4x = x(x + 2)(x - 2)$. Since the factors are distinct linear factors, use Step 3(a) to write the decomposition as

$$\frac{5x - 2}{x^3 - 4x} = \frac{A}{x} + \frac{B}{x + 2} + \frac{C}{x - 2}, \qquad \text{Equation 1}$$

where A, B, and C are constants that need to be found. Multiply each side of equation 1 by $x(x + 2)(x - 2)$ to clear fractions and get

$$5x - 2 = A(x + 2)(x - 2) + Bx(x - 2) + Cx(x + 2). \qquad \text{Equation 2}$$

Equation 1 is an identity, since both sides represent the same rational expression. Thus equation 2 is also an identity. Equation 1 holds for all values of x except 0, -2, and 2. However, equation 2 holds for all values of x. In particular, substituting 0 for x in equation 2 gives $-2 = -4A$, so $A = \frac{1}{2}$. Similarly, choosing $x = -2$ gives $-12 = 8B$, so $B = -\frac{3}{2}$. Finally, choosing $x = 2$ gives $8 = 8C$, so $C = 1$. The remainder rational expression can be written as the sum of partial fractions

$$\frac{5x - 2}{x^3 - 4x} = \frac{1}{2x} + \frac{-3}{2(x + 2)} + \frac{1}{x - 2},$$

and the given rational expression can be written as

Partial fractions

$$\frac{2x^4 - 8x^2 + 5x - 2}{x^3 - 4x} = 2x + \frac{1}{2x} + \frac{-3}{2(x + 2)} + \frac{1}{x - 2}.$$

Partial fraction decomposition

Check the work by combining the terms on the right.

Now Try Exercise 11

Repeated Linear Factors

EXAMPLE 2 Finding a partial fraction decomposition

Find the partial fraction decomposition of

$$\frac{2x}{(x-1)^3}.$$

SOLUTION This is a proper fraction. The denominator is already factored with repeated linear factors. We write the decomposition as shown, using Step 3(b).

$$\frac{2x}{(x-1)^3} = \frac{A}{x-1} + \frac{B}{(x-1)^2} + \frac{C}{(x-1)^3}$$

We clear denominators by multiplying each side of this equation by $(x-1)^3$.

$$2x = A(x-1)^2 + B(x-1) + C$$

Substituting 1 for x leads to $C = 2$, so

$$2x = A(x-1)^2 + B(x-1) + 2. \qquad \text{Equation 1}$$

We found C and we still need to find values for A and B. *Any* number can be substituted for x. For example, when we choose $x = -1$ (because it is easy to substitute), equation 1 becomes

$$-2 = 4A - 2B + 2$$
$$-4 = 4A - 2B$$
$$-2 = 2A - B. \qquad \text{Equation 2}$$

Substituting 0 for x in equation 1 gives

$$0 = A - B + 2$$
$$2 = -A + B. \qquad \text{Equation 3}$$

Now we solve the system of equations 2 and 3 to get $A = 0$ and $B = 2$. Since $A = 0$, the term $\frac{A}{x-1}$ is not used. The partial fraction decomposition is

$$\frac{2x}{(x-1)^3} = \frac{2}{(x-1)^2} + \frac{2}{(x-1)^3}.$$

We needed three substitutions because there were three constants to find: A, B, and C. To check this result, we could combine the terms on the right.

Now Try Exercise 13

Distinct Linear and Quadratic Factors

EXAMPLE 3 Finding a partial fraction decomposition

Find the partial fraction decomposition of

$$\frac{x^2 + 3x - 1}{(x+1)(x^2+2)}.$$

SOLUTION This denominator has distinct linear and quadratic factors, neither of which is repeated. Since $x^2 + 2$ cannot be factored, it is *irreducible*. The partial fraction decomposition is

$$\frac{x^2 + 3x - 1}{(x+1)(x^2+2)} = \frac{A}{x+1} + \frac{Bx+C}{x^2+2}.$$

Multiply each side by $(x + 1)(x^2 + 2)$ to get

$$x^2 + 3x - 1 = A(x^2 + 2) + (Bx + C)(x + 1). \qquad \text{Equation 1}$$

First substitute -1 for x to get

$$(-1)^2 + 3(-1) - 1 = A((-1)^2 + 2) + 0$$

$$-3 = 3A$$

$$A = -1.$$

Replace A with -1 in equation 1 and substitute any value for x. If $x = 0$, then

$$0^2 + 3(0) - 1 = -1(0^2 + 2) + (B \cdot 0 + C)(0 + 1)$$

$$-1 = -2 + C$$

$$C = 1.$$

Now, letting $A = -1$ and $C = 1$, substitute again in equation 1, using another number for x. For $x = 1$,

$$3 = -3 + (B + 1)(2)$$

$$6 = 2B + 2$$

$$B = 2.$$

With $A = -1, B = 2$, and $C = 1$, the partial fraction decomposition is

$$\frac{x^2 + 3x - 1}{(x + 1)(x^2 + 2)} = \frac{-1}{x + 1} + \frac{2x + 1}{x^2 + 2}.$$

This work can be checked by combining terms on the right. **Now Try Exercise 21**

For fractions with denominators that have quadratic factors, another method is often more convenient. The system of equations is formed by equating coefficients of like terms on each side of the partial fraction decomposition. For instance, in Example 3, after each side was multiplied by the common denominator, equation 1 was

$$x^2 + 3x - 1 = A(x^2 + 2) + (Bx + C)(x + 1). \qquad \text{Equation 1}$$

Multiplying on the right and collecting like terms, we have

$$x^2 + 3x - 1 = Ax^2 + 2A + Bx^2 + Bx + Cx + C$$

$$x^2 + 3x - 1 = (A + B)x^2 + (B + C)x + (C + 2A).$$

Now equating the coefficients of like powers of x gives three equations:

$$1 = A + B$$

$$3 = B + C$$

$$-1 = C + 2A.$$

Solving this system of equations for A, B, and C would give the partial fraction decomposition. The next example uses a combination of the two methods.

Repeated Quadratic Factors

EXAMPLE 4 Finding a partial fraction decomposition

Find the partial fraction decomposition of

$$\frac{2x}{(x^2 + 1)^2 (x - 1)}.$$

SOLUTION This expression has both a linear factor and a repeated quadratic factor. By Steps 3(a) and 4(b),

$$\frac{2x}{(x^2 + 1)^2(x - 1)} = \frac{Ax + B}{x^2 + 1} + \frac{Cx + D}{(x^2 + 1)^2} + \frac{E}{x - 1}.$$

Multiplying each side by $(x^2 + 1)^2(x - 1)$ leads to

$$2x = (Ax + B)(x^2 + 1)(x - 1) + (Cx + D)(x - 1) + E(x^2 + 1)^2. \qquad \text{Equation 1}$$

If $x = 1$, equation 1 reduces to $2 = 4E$, or $E = \frac{1}{2}$. Substituting $\frac{1}{2}$ for E in equation 1 and combining terms on the right gives

$$2x = \left(A + \frac{1}{2}\right)x^4 + (-A + B)x^3 + (A - B + C + 1)x^2$$

$$+ (-A + B + D - C)x + \left(-B - D + \frac{1}{2}\right). \qquad \text{Equation 2}$$

To get additional equations involving the unknowns, equate the coefficients of like powers of x on each side of equation 2. Setting corresponding coefficients of x^4 equal gives $0 = A + \frac{1}{2}$, or $A = -\frac{1}{2}$. From the corresponding coefficients of x^3, $0 = -A + B$, which means that since $A = -\frac{1}{2}$, $B = -\frac{1}{2}$. From the coefficients of x^2, $0 = A - B + C + 1$. Since $A = -\frac{1}{2}$ and $B = -\frac{1}{2}$, it follows that $C = -1$. Finally, from the coefficients of x, $2 = -A + B + D - C$. Substituting for A, B, and C gives $D = 1$. With

$$A = -\frac{1}{2}, \quad B = -\frac{1}{2}, \quad C = -1, \quad D = 1, \quad \text{and} \quad E = \frac{1}{2},$$

the given fraction has the partial fraction decomposition

$$\frac{2x}{(x^2 + 1)^2(x - 1)} = \frac{-\frac{1}{2}x - \frac{1}{2}}{x^2 + 1} + \frac{-x + 1}{(x^2 + 1)^2} + \frac{\frac{1}{2}}{x - 1},$$

or

$$\frac{2x}{(x^2 + 1)^2(x - 1)} = \frac{-(x + 1)}{2(x^2 + 1)} + \frac{-x + 1}{(x^2 + 1)^2} + \frac{1}{2(x - 1)}.$$

Now Try Exercise 25

In summary, to solve for the constants in the numerators of a partial fraction decomposition, use either of the following methods or a combination of the two.

TECHNIQUES FOR DECOMPOSITION INTO PARTIAL FRACTIONS

Method 1 for Linear Factors

STEP 1: Multiply each side of the rational expression by the common denominator.

STEP 2: Substitute the zero of each factor in the resulting equation. For repeated linear factors, substitute as many other numbers as necessary to find all the constants in the numerators. The number of substitutions required will equal the number of constants.

Method 2 for Quadratic Factors

STEP 1: Multiply each side of the rational expression by the common denominator.

STEP 2: Collect terms on the right side of the resulting equation.

STEP 3: Equate the coefficients of like terms to get a system of equations.

STEP 4: Solve the system to find the constants in the numerators.

Exercises 1–30: Find the partial fraction decomposition for the rational expression.

1. $\dfrac{5}{3x(2x+1)}$

2. $\dfrac{3x-1}{x(x+1)}$

3. $\dfrac{4x+2}{(x+2)(2x-1)}$

4. $\dfrac{x+2}{(x+1)(x-1)}$

5. $\dfrac{x}{x^2+4x-5}$

6. $\dfrac{5x-3}{(x+1)(x-3)}$

7. $\dfrac{2x}{(x+1)(x+2)^2}$

8. $\dfrac{2}{x^2(x+3)}$

9. $\dfrac{4}{x(1-x)}$

10. $\dfrac{4x^2-4x^3}{x^2(1-x)}$

11. $\dfrac{4x^2-x-15}{x(x+1)(x-1)}$

12. $\dfrac{2x+1}{(x+2)^3}$

13. $\dfrac{x^2}{x^2+2x+1}$

14. $\dfrac{3}{x^2+4x+3}$

15. $\dfrac{2x^5+3x^4-3x^3-2x^2+x}{2x^2+5x+2}$

16. $\dfrac{6x^5+7x^4-x^2+2x}{3x^2+2x-1}$

17. $\dfrac{x^3+4}{9x^3-4x}$

18. $\dfrac{x^3+2}{x^3-3x^2+2x}$

19. $\dfrac{-3}{x^2(x^2+5)}$

20. $\dfrac{2x+1}{(x+1)(x^2+2)}$

21. $\dfrac{3x-2}{(x+4)(3x^2+1)}$

22. $\dfrac{3}{x(x+1)(x^2+1)}$

23. $\dfrac{1}{x(2x+1)(3x^2+4)}$

24. $\dfrac{x^4+1}{x(x^2+1)^2}$

25. $\dfrac{3x-1}{x(2x^2+1)^2}$

26. $\dfrac{3x^4+x^3+5x^2-x+4}{(x-1)(x^2+1)^2}$

27. $\dfrac{-x^4-8x^2+3x-10}{(x+2)(x^2+4)^2}$

28. $\dfrac{x^2}{x^4-1}$

29. $\dfrac{5x^5+10x^4-15x^3+4x^2+13x-9}{x^3+2x^2-3x}$

30. $\dfrac{3x^6+3x^4+3x}{x^4+x^2}$

D

Percent Change and Exponential Functions

Percentages and Percent Change

Percentages A percentage can be written either in **percent form** or in **decimal form**. For example, the percent form of 15% can also be written in decimal form as 0.15. To change a percent form $R\%$ to a decimal form r we divide R by 100. That is, $r = \frac{R}{100}$.

EXAMPLE 1 Writing percentages as decimals

Write each percentage as a decimal.
(a) 45% **(b)** 0.03% **(c)** 420% **(d)** -1.45% **(e)** $\frac{2}{5}\%$

SOLUTION
(a) Let $R = 45$. Then $r = \frac{45}{100} = 0.45$.

(b) Let $R = 0.03$. Then $r = \frac{0.03}{100} = 0.0003$.

(c) Let $R = 420$. Then $r = \frac{420}{100} = 4.2$.

(d) Let $R = -1.45$. Then $r = \frac{-1.45}{100} = -0.0145$. A negative percentage generally corresponds to a quantity decreasing rather than increasing.

(e) Let $R = \frac{2}{5}$. Then $r = \frac{\frac{2}{5}}{100} = \frac{2}{500} = 0.004$.

Now Try Exercise 1

NOTE Dividing a number by 100 is equivalent to moving the decimal point two places to the *left*.

In a similar manner a decimal form r can be changed to a percent form R by using the formula $R = 100r$. For example, the decimal form 0.047 has the percent form

$$R = 100r = 100(0.047) = 4.7\%.$$

In this calculation the decimal point is moved 2 places to the *right*.

Percent Change When an amount A_1 changes to a new amount A_2, then the **percent change** is

$$\frac{A_2 - A_1}{A_1} \times 100. \qquad \textit{Percent change}$$

We multiply by 100 to change decimal form to percent form.

EXAMPLE 2 Finding percent change

Complete the following.
(a) Find the percent change if an account increases from \$1200 to \$1500.
(b) Find the percent change if an account decreases from \$1500 to \$1200.
(c) Comment on your results from parts (a) and (b).

SOLUTION

(a) Let $A_1 = 1200$ and $A_2 = 1500$.

$$\frac{1500 - 1200}{1200} \times 100 = \frac{300}{1200} \times 100$$

$$= \frac{1}{4} \times 100$$

$$= 25\%$$

The percent change (increase) is 25%.

(b) Let $A_1 = 1500$ and $A_2 = 1200$.

$$\frac{1200 - 1500}{1500} \times 100 = -\frac{300}{1500} \times 100$$

$$= -\frac{1}{5} \times 100$$

$$= -20\%$$

The percent change (decrease) is −20%.

(c) Notice that the account increased by 25% and then decreased by 20% to return to its initial value. Because the initial amount of $A_1 = \$1500$ in part (b) is larger than the initial amount $A_1 = \$1200$ in part (a), the amount of $1500 only needs to decrease by 20% or $300, to return to the original $1200.

> **Now Try Exercise 9**

Suppose a child's weight increases from 20 pounds to 60 pounds over a period of years. The percent increase is

$$\frac{60 - 20}{20} \times 100 = 2 \times 100 = 200\%.$$

Notice that the child's weight *tripled* and the percent change is 200%, *not* 300%. The actual *increase* in weight is 40 pounds and can be found by taking 200% of 20 pounds.

$$200\% \text{ of } 20 = 2.00 \times 20 = 40 \text{ pounds} \qquad \textit{Change 200\% to decimal form.}$$

If we want to find the percent change, expressed in *decimal form*, of an amount A_1 changing to an amount A_2, then we do not need to multiply by 100. Thus

$$r = \frac{A_2 - A_1}{A_1}.$$

We can solve this equation for A_2.

$$r = \frac{A_2 - A_1}{A_1} \qquad \textit{Percent change in decimal form}$$

$$rA_1 = A_2 - A_1 \qquad \textit{Multiply each side by } A_1.$$

$$A_1 + rA_1 = A_2 \qquad \textit{Add } A_1 \textit{ to each side.}$$

$$A_2 = A_1 + rA_1 \qquad \textit{Rewrite the equation.}$$

Thus, if the percent increase in an amount A_1 is given by r in *decimal form*, then the *increase* (or *decrease*) in A_1 is given by rA_1 and the *final amount* is given by $A_1 + rA_1$, or $A_1(1 + r)$. The initial amount A_1 changes by the *factor* $1 + r$.

For example, if a $100,000 budget decreases by 12%, then

$$rA_1 = -0.12(100,000) = -\$12,000$$

and the budget decrease is $12,000. Also,

$$A_1 + rA_1 = 100,000 + (-0.12)(100,000) = \$88,000$$

and the new budget decreased to $88,000. The budget changed by a factor of

$$1 + r = 1 + (-0.12) = 0.88,$$

or the budget is now 88% of the original budget.

EXAMPLE 3 Analyzing the increase in an account

An account that contains $5000 increases in value by 150%.
(a) Find the increase in value of the account.
(b) Find the final value of the account.
(c) By what factor did the account increase?

SOLUTION
(a) Let $A_1 = 5000$ and $r = 1.50$ (150% in decimal form). The increase is

$$rA_1 = 1.50(5000) = 7500.$$

The account increased in value by $7500.
(b) The final value of the account is $A_1 + rA_1 = 5000 + 7500 = \$12{,}500$.
(c) The account increased in value by a factor of $1 + r = 1 + 1.50 = 2.5$. Note that $5000(2.5) = 12{,}500$.

> Now Try Exercise 15

More Exponential Functions and Models

Section 5.3 discussed how an exponential function results when the *initial value C* is multiplied by a *constant factor a* for each unit increase in x. For example, if an initial value of $C = 3$ is multiplied by a *constant growth factor* of $a = 2$ for each unit increase in x, then the exponential function

$$f(x) = 3(2)^x \qquad \text{Initial value} = 3, \text{growth factor} = 2$$

models this growth. This concept can be used to describe exponential functions and models in terms of *constant percent change*.

Suppose that an initial population of a country is $P_0 = 10$ million and the population increases by 1.2% in 1 year. Then the increase is

$$rP_0 = 0.012(10) = 0.12 \text{ million}, \qquad \text{1.2\% equals 0.012 in decimal form.}$$

and after 1 year the new population is

$$P_0(1 + r)^1 = 10(1.012)^1 = 10.12 \text{ million.}$$

After 1 year the population has increased by a *growth factor* of $1 + r$, or 1.012. If the rate of growth were to remain constant in future years, then after x years the population would be

$$P_0(1 + r)^x = 10(1.012)^x$$

with initial value $C = 10$ and *growth* factor $a = 1.012$.

EXAMPLE 4 Finding exponential models

A sample of 10,000 insects is decreasing in number by 8% per week. Find an exponential model $f(x)$ that describes this population after x weeks.

SOLUTION The initial value is $C = 10{,}000$, the rate of decrease is $r = -0.08$, and the *decay* factor is

$$a = 1 + r = 1 + (-0.08) = 0.92.$$

Thus the sample of insects contains

$$f(x) = 10,000(0.92)^x$$

insects after x weeks.

Now Try Exercise 21

These concepts are summarized in the following box.

PERCENT CHANGE AND EXPONENTIAL FUNCTIONS

Suppose that an amount A changes by R percent (or r expressed in decimal form) for each unit increase in x. Then the following hold.

1. $r = \dfrac{R}{100}$ and $R = 100r$.
2. If $r > 0$, the **constant growth factor** is $a = 1 + r$ and $a > 1$.
3. If $r < 0$, the **constant decay factor** is $a = 1 + r$ and $0 < a < 1$.
4. If the initial amount is C, then the amount A after an x-unit increase in time is given by the exponential model

$$A(x) = C(1 + r)^x, \quad \text{or} \quad A(x) = Ca^x.$$

EXAMPLE 5 Analyzing constant percent change

For each $f(x)$, give the initial value, the growth or decay factor, and percent change for each unit increase in x.

(a) $f(x) = 5(1.034)^x$ **(b)** $f(x) = 10(0.45)^x$ **(c)** $f(x) = 3^x$

SOLUTION

(a) For $f(x) = 5(1.034)^x$ the initial value is $C = 5$ and the growth factor is $a = 1.034$. Because $a = 1 + r$, it follows that

$$r = a - 1 = 1.034 - 1 = 0.034.$$

The percent change for each unit increase in x is 3.4%.

(b) For $f(x) = 10(0.45)^x$ the initial value is $C = 10$ and the decay factor is $a = 0.45$. The percent change for each unit increase in x is

$$r = a - 1 = 0.45 - 1 = -0.55, \text{ or } -55\%.$$

(c) For $f(x) = 3^x$ the initial value is $C = 1$ and the growth factor is $a = 3$. The percent change for each unit increase in x is $r = a - 1 = 3 - 1 = 2$, or 200%.

Now Try Exercises 27, 29, and 31

Growth and Decay Models If an initial quantity A_0 either grows or decays by a factor of b each k units of time, then the amount A after t units of time is given by the exponential model

$$A(t) = Ab^{t/k}.$$

For example, if 700 bacteria triple every 5 days, the formula

$$A(t) = 700(3)^{t/5}$$

gives the number of bacteria after t days.

EXAMPLE 6 Applying an exponential model

The population of a city is currently 239,000 and is increasing at a constant rate of 8.5% every 4 years. Find the population of this city after 7 years.

SOLUTION The population of the city is 239,000 and increasing by a factor of 1.085 every 4 years. Thus $A_0 = 239,000$, $b = 1.085$, $k = 4$, and

$$A(t) = 239,000(1.085)^{t/4}.$$

After 7 years the population is

$$A(7) = 239,000(1.085)^{7/4} \approx 275,677.$$

Now Try Exercise 37

Rule of 70 The **rule of 70** can be used to quickly estimate the number of years it takes for an investment to double. If R is the interest rate (in percent form) and T is the number of years for a quantity to double, then

$$RT = 70. \qquad \text{Rule of 70}$$

Interest rate (%)   Years to double

This formula is most accurate for continuous compounding, but it can also be applied to other types of compound interest. For example, if we deposit an amount of money at 5% interest compounded continuously, then it will require about

$$T = \frac{70}{R} = \frac{70}{5} = 14 \text{ years}$$

to double. Similarly, if a city's population doubles in 35 years, then its annual growth rate is about

$$R = \frac{70}{T} = \frac{70}{35} = 2\%.$$

See Exercises 45–50.

D   Exercises

Percentages

Exercises 1–4: Write each percentage in decimal form.

1. (a) 35%   **(b)** −0.07%   **(c)** 721%   **(d)** $\frac{3}{10}$%

2. (a) 95%   **(b)** 0.321%   **(c)** −175%   **(d)** $\frac{4}{5}$%

3. (a) −5.5%   **(b)** −1.54%   **(c)** 120%   **(d)** $\frac{3}{20}$%

4. (a) −4.7%   **(b)** −0.01%   **(c)** 500%   **(d)** $\frac{1}{40}$%

Exercises 5–8: Write each decimal form in percent form.

5. (a) 0.37   **(b)** −0.095   **(c)** 1.9   **(d)** $\frac{7}{20}$

6. (a) 0.97   **(b)** −0.04   **(c)** 10   **(d)** $\frac{9}{10}$

7. (a) −0.121   **(b)** 1.4   **(c)** 3.2   **(d)** $-\frac{1}{4}$

8. (a) 0.001   **(b)** 12   **(c)** 1.01   **(d)** $-\frac{1}{8}$

Percent Change

Exercises 9–14: For the given amounts A and B, find each of the following. Round values to the nearest hundredth when appropriate.

(a) The percent change if A changes to B
(b) The percent change if B changes to A

   9. $A = \$500, B = \$1000$ 10. $A = \$500, B = \$200$

11. $A = \$1.27, B = \$1.30$ 12. $A = 15, B = 5$

13. $A = 45, B = 65$ 14. $A = 75, B = 50$

Exercises 15–20: An account that initially contains A dollars increases/decreases by R percent. For each A and R, complete the following.

(a) Find the increase/decrease in value of the account.
(b) Find the final value of the account.
(c) By what factor did the account value increase/decrease?

15. $A = \$1500, R = 120\%$

16. $A = \$3500, R = 210\%$

17. $A = \$4000, R = -55\%$

18. $A = \$6000, R = -75\%$

19. $A = \$7500, R = -60\%$

20. $A = \$9000, R = 85\%$

Exponential Models

Exercises 21–26: Find an exponential model f(x) that describes each situation.

21. A sample of 9500 insects decreases in number by 35% per week

22. A sample of 5000 insects increases in number by 120% per day

23. A sample of 2500 fish increases in number by 5% per month

24. A sample of 152 birds decreases in number by 3.4% per week

25. A mutual fund account contains $1000 and decreases by 6.5% per year

26. A mutual fund account contains $2500 and increases by 2.1% per year

Exercises 27–36: For the given f(x), state the initial value, the growth or decay factor, and percent change for each unit increase in x.

27. $f(x) = 8(1.12)^x$ 28. $f(x) = 9(1.005)^x$

29. $f(x) = 1.5(0.35)^x$

30. $f(x) = 100(1.23)^x$

31. $f(x) = 0.55^x$

32. $f(x) = 0.4^x$

33. $f(x) = 7e^x$

34. $f(x) = 91e^{x/2}$

35. $f(x) = 6(3^{-x})$

36. $f(x) = 9(4^{-x})$

Exercises 37–44: (Refer to Example 6.) Write a formula for f(t) that models the situation and then answer the question.

37. The population of a city is currently 35,000 and is increasing at a constant rate of 9.8% every 2 years. What is the population after 5 years?

38. A savings account contains $2500 and increases by 10% in 3 years. How much is in the account after 8 years?

39. A sample of 1000 bacteria triples in number every 7 hours. How many bacteria are there after 11 hours?

40. A sample of 5 million insects decreases in number by $\frac{2}{3}$ every 10 days. In millions, how many insects are there after 65 days?

41. The intensity I_0 of a light passing through colored glass decreases by $\frac{1}{3}$ for each 2 millimeters in thickness of the glass. What is the intensity of the light in terms of I_0 after passing through 4.3 millimeters of colored glass?

42. The intensity I_0 of a sound passing through the atmosphere decreases 20% for each 100 feet of distance. What is the intensity of the sound in terms of I_0 after traveling a distance of 450 feet?

43. An investment of $5000 will quadruple every 35 years. How much is the investment worth after 8 years?

44. An investment of $2500 increases by a factor of 1.2 every 4 years. How much is the investment worth after 9 years?

Exercises 45–50: **Rule of 70** *Use the rule of 70 to estimate the time required for the given principal P to double at the annual percent interest rate R. Check your answer by using the continuously compounded interest formula.*

45. $P = \$2000, R = 7\%$ 46. $P = \$1200, R = 14\%$

47. $P = \$500, R = 20\%$ 48. $P = \$9000, R = 10\%$

49. $P = \$1500, R = 25\%$ 50. $P = \$5000, R = 8\%$

Exercises 51–56: **Rule of 70** *Use the rule of 70 to estimate the annual percent rate of growth for a city whose population P doubles in time T.*

51. $P = 150,000, T = 40$ years

52. $P = 400,000, T = 25$ years

53. $P = 1,500,000$, $T = 35$ years

54. $P = 20,000$, $T = 10$ years

55. $P = 750,000$, $T = 70$ years

56. $P = 80,000$, $T = 50$ years

Applications

57. Bacteria Growth A population of bacteria increases by 6% every 8 hours. By what percentage does the sample increase in 3 hours?

58. Bacteria Growth A population of bacteria decreases by 40% every 4 hours. By what percentage does the sample decrease in 7 hours?

59. Percent Change The number of cell phone subscribers to a company increases by 25% during the first year and then decreases by 20% the second year. Compare the number of subscribers at the beginning of the first year with the number of subscribers at the end of the second year.

60. Wage Increase If your wages are $8 per hour and you receive a 300% raise for excellent work, determine your new wages.

61. Wages If a wage of $9.81 decreases by 9% each year, what is the new wage after 3 years?

62. Pollution A pollutant in a river has an initial concentration of 3 parts per million and degrades at a rate of 3% every 2 years. Approximate its concentration after 20 years.

63. Radioactive Half-Life A radioactive element decays to 40% of its original amount every 2 years. Approximate the percentage that remains after 8 years.

64. Radioactive Half-Life A radioactive element decays to 80% of its original amount every 3 years. Approximate the percentage that remains after 8 years.

Appendix E: Rotation of Axes

Rotation of xy-Plane

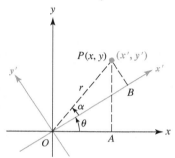

Figure E.1

Derivation of Rotation Equations

If we begin with an xy-coordinate system having origin O and rotate the axes about O through an angle θ, the new coordinate system is called a **rotation** of the xy-system. Trigonometric identities can be used to obtain equations for converting the coordinates of a point from the xy-system to the rotated $x'y'$-system. Let P be any point other than the origin, with coordinates (x, y) in the xy-system and (x', y') in the $x'y'$-system. See Figure E.1. Let $OP = r$, and let α represent the angle made by OP and the x'-axis. As shown in Figure E.1,

$$\cos(\theta + \alpha) = \frac{OA}{r} = \frac{x}{r}, \quad \sin(\theta + \alpha) = \frac{AP}{r} = \frac{y}{r},$$

$$\cos\alpha = \frac{OB}{r} = \frac{x'}{r}, \quad \sin\alpha = \frac{BP}{r} = \frac{y'}{r}.$$

These four statements can be rewritten as

$$x = r\cos(\theta + \alpha), \quad y = r\sin(\theta + \alpha), \quad x' = r\cos\alpha, \quad y' = r\sin\alpha.$$

Using the trigonometric identity for the cosine of the sum of two angles gives

$$x = r\cos(\theta + \alpha)$$

$$= r(\cos\theta\cos\alpha - \sin\theta\sin\alpha)$$

$$= (r\cos\alpha)\cos\theta - (r\sin\alpha)\sin\theta$$

$$= x'\cos\theta - y'\sin\theta.$$

Using the identity for the sine of the sum of two angles in the same way gives $y = x'\sin\theta + y'\cos\theta$. This proves the following result.

> **ROTATION EQUATIONS**
>
> If the rectangular coordinate axes are rotated about the origin through an angle θ and if the coordinates of a point P are (x, y) and (x', y') with respect to the xy-system and the $x'y'$-system, respectively, then the rotation equations are
>
> $$x = x'\cos\theta - y'\sin\theta \quad \text{and} \quad y = x'\sin\theta + y'\cos\theta.$$

Applying a Rotation Equation

EXAMPLE 1 Finding an equation after a rotation

The equation of a curve is $x^2 + y^2 + 2xy + 2\sqrt{2}x - 2\sqrt{2}y = 0$. Find the resulting equation if the axes are rotated $45°$. Graph the equation.

SOLUTION If $\theta = 45°$, then $\sin \theta = \frac{\sqrt{2}}{2}$ and $\cos \theta = \frac{\sqrt{2}}{2}$, and the rotation equations become

$$x = \frac{\sqrt{2}}{2}x' - \frac{\sqrt{2}}{2}y' \quad \text{and} \quad y = \frac{\sqrt{2}}{2}x' + \frac{\sqrt{2}}{2}y'.$$

Substituting these values into the given equation yields

$$x^2 + y^2 + 2xy + 2\sqrt{2}x - 2\sqrt{2}y = 0$$

$$\left(\frac{\sqrt{2}}{2}x' - \frac{\sqrt{2}}{2}y'\right)^2 + \left(\frac{\sqrt{2}}{2}x' + \frac{\sqrt{2}}{2}y'\right)^2$$

$$+ 2\left(\frac{\sqrt{2}}{2}x' - \frac{\sqrt{2}}{2}y'\right)\left(\frac{\sqrt{2}}{2}x' + \frac{\sqrt{2}}{2}y'\right)$$

$$+ 2\sqrt{2}\left(\frac{\sqrt{2}}{2}x' - \frac{\sqrt{2}}{2}y'\right) - 2\sqrt{2}\left(\frac{\sqrt{2}}{2}x' + \frac{\sqrt{2}}{2}y'\right) = 0.$$

Expanding these terms yields

$$\frac{1}{2}x'^2 - x'y' + \frac{1}{2}y'^2 + \frac{1}{2}x'^2 + x'y' + \frac{1}{2}y'^2 + x'^2 - y'^2$$

$$+ 2x' - 2y' - 2x' - 2y' = 0.$$

Collecting terms gives

$$2x'^2 - 4y' = 0$$

$$x'^2 - 2y' = 0 \qquad \text{Divide by 2.}$$

or, finally,

$$x'^2 = 2y',$$

the equation of a parabola. The graph is shown in Figure E.2.

Now Try Exercise 13

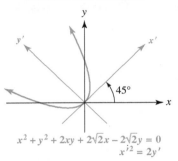

Rotation of a Parabola

$x^2 + y^2 + 2xy + 2\sqrt{2}x - 2\sqrt{2}y = 0$
$x'^2 = 2y'$

Figure E.2

We have graphed equations written in the form $Ax^2 + Cy^2 + Dx + Ey + F = 0$. As we saw in the preceding example, the rotation of axes eliminated the xy-term. Thus, to graph by hand an equation that has an xy-term, it is necessary to find an appropriate **angle of rotation** to eliminate the xy-term. The necessary angle of rotation can be determined by using the following result. The proof is quite lengthy and is not presented here.

ANGLE OF ROTATION

The xy-term is removed from the general equation

$$Ax^2 + Bxy + Cy^2 + Dx + Ey + F = 0$$

by a rotation of the axes through an angle θ, $0° < \theta < 90°$, where

$$\cot 2\theta = \frac{A - C}{B}.$$

This result can be used to find the appropriate angle of rotation, θ. To find the rotation equations, first find $\sin \theta$ and $\cos \theta$. The following example illustrates a way to obtain $\sin \theta$ and $\cos \theta$ from $\cot 2\theta$ without first identifying the angle θ.

EXAMPLE Rotating and graphing

Rotate the axes and graph $52x^2 - 72xy + 73y^2 = 200$.

SOLUTION Here $A = 52, B = -72$, and $C = 73$. By substitution,

$$\cot 2\theta = \frac{52 - 73}{-72} = \frac{-21}{-72} = \frac{7}{24}.$$

To find $\sin \theta$ and $\cos \theta$, use the trigonometric identities

$$\sin \theta = \sqrt{\frac{1 - \cos 2\theta}{2}} \quad \text{and} \quad \cos \theta = \sqrt{\frac{1 + \cos 2\theta}{2}}.$$

Sketch a right triangle and label it as in Figure E.3, to see that $\cos 2\theta = \frac{7}{25}$. (Recall that in the two quadrants with which we are concerned, $0° \le 2\theta \le 180°$, cosine and cotangent have the same sign.) Then

$$\sin \theta = \sqrt{\frac{1 - \frac{7}{25}}{2}} = \sqrt{\frac{9}{25}} = \frac{3}{5} \quad \text{and} \quad \cos \theta = \sqrt{\frac{1 + \frac{7}{25}}{2}} = \sqrt{\frac{16}{25}} = \frac{4}{5}.$$

Use these values for $\sin \theta$ and $\cos \theta$ to obtain

$$x = \frac{4}{5}x' - \frac{3}{5}y' \quad \text{and} \quad y = \frac{3}{5}x' + \frac{4}{5}y'.$$

Substituting these expressions for x and y into the original equation yields

$$52\left(\frac{4}{5}x' - \frac{3}{5}y'\right)^2 - 72\left(\frac{4}{5}x' - \frac{3}{5}y'\right)\left(\frac{3}{5}x' + \frac{4}{5}y'\right) + 73\left(\frac{3}{5}x' + \frac{4}{5}y'\right)^2 = 200.$$

This becomes

$$52\left(\frac{16}{25}x'^2 - \frac{24}{25}x'y' + \frac{9}{25}y'^2\right) - 72\left(\frac{12}{25}x'^2 + \frac{7}{25}x'y' - \frac{12}{25}y'^2\right)$$
$$+ 73\left(\frac{9}{25}x'^2 + \frac{24}{25}x'y' + \frac{16}{25}y'^2\right) = 200.$$

Combining terms gives

$$25x'^2 + 100y'^2 = 200.$$

Divide each side by 200 to get

$$\frac{x'^2}{8} + \frac{y'^2}{2} = 1, \quad \boxed{\text{New equation after rotation}}$$

an equation of an ellipse having x'-intercepts $\pm\sqrt{8}$ and y'-intercepts $\pm\sqrt{2}$. The graph is shown in Figure E.4. To find θ, use the fact that

$$\frac{\sin \theta}{\cos \theta} = \frac{\frac{3}{5}}{\frac{4}{5}} = \frac{3}{4} = \tan \theta,$$

from which $\theta = \tan^{-1}\frac{3}{4} \approx 37°$.

Now Try Exercise 17

Figure E.3

$\sin \theta = \frac{3}{5}$
$\cos \theta = \frac{4}{5}$
$\tan \theta = \frac{3}{4}$

$52x^2 - 72xy + 73y^2 = 200$
$\frac{x'^2}{8} + \frac{y'^2}{2} = 1$

Figure E.4

Summary of Conics with an *xy*-Term

The following summary enables us to use the general equation to decide on the type of graph to expect.

EQUATIONS OF CONICS WITH AN *XY*-TERM

If the general second-degree equation

$$Ax^2 + Bxy + Cy^2 + Dx + Ey + F = 0$$

has a graph, it will be one of the following:

(a) a circle or an ellipse (or a point) if $B^2 - 4AC < 0$;
(b) a parabola (or one line or two parallel lines) if $B^2 - 4AC = 0$;
(c) a hyperbola (or two intersecting lines) if $B^2 - 4AC > 0$;
(d) a straight line if $A = B = C = 0$ and $D \neq 0$ or $E \neq 0$.

E | Exercises

Exercises 1–6: Use the summary in this section to predict the graph of the second-degree equation.

1. $4x^2 + 3y^2 + 2xy - 5x = 8$

2. $x^2 + 2xy - 3y^2 + 2y = 12$

3. $2x^2 + 3xy - 4y^2 = 0$

4. $x^2 - 2xy + y^2 + 4x - 8y = 0$

5. $4x^2 + 4xy + y^2 + 15 = 0$

6. $-x^2 + 2xy - y^2 + 16 = 0$

Exercises 7–12: Find the angle of rotation θ that will remove the xy-term in the equation.

7. $2x^2 + \sqrt{3}xy + y^2 + x = 5$

8. $4\sqrt{3}x^2 + xy + 3\sqrt{3}y^2 = 10$

9. $3x^2 + \sqrt{3}xy + 4y^2 + 2x - 3y = 12$

10. $4x^2 + 2xy + 2y^2 + x - 7 = 0$

11. $x^2 - 4xy + 5y^2 = 18$

12. $3\sqrt{3}x^2 - 2xy + \sqrt{3}y^2 = 25$

Exercises 13–16: Use the given angle of rotation to remove the xy-term and graph the equation.

13. $x^2 - xy + y^2 = 6; \theta = 45°$

14. $2x^2 - xy + 2y^2 = 25; \theta = 45°$

15. $8x^2 - 4xy + 5y^2 = 36; \sin\theta = \dfrac{2}{\sqrt{5}}$

16. $5y^2 + 12xy = 10; \sin\theta = \dfrac{3}{\sqrt{13}}$

Exercises 17–24: Remove the xy-term from the equation by performing a suitable rotation. Graph the equation.

17. $3x^2 - 2xy + 3y^2 = 8$ **18.** $x^2 + xy + y^2 = 3$

19. $x^2 - 4xy + y^2 = -5$

20. $x^2 + 2xy + y^2 + 4\sqrt{2}x - 4\sqrt{2}y = 0$

21. $7x^2 + 6\sqrt{3}xy + 13y^2 = 64$

22. $7x^2 + 2\sqrt{3}xy + 5y^2 = 24$

23. $3x^2 - 2\sqrt{3}xy + y^2 - 2x - 2\sqrt{3}y = 0$

24. $2x^2 + 2\sqrt{3}xy + 4y^2 = 5$

Exercises 25–30: In the equation, remove the xy-term by rotation. Then translate the axes and sketch the graph.

25. $x^2 + 3xy + y^2 - 5\sqrt{2}y = 15$

26. $x^2 - \sqrt{3}xy + 2\sqrt{3}x - 3y - 3 = 0$

27. $4x^2 + 4xy + y^2 - 24x + 38y - 19 = 0$

28. $12x^2 + 24xy + 19y^2 - 12x - 40y + 31 = 0$

29. $16x^2 + 24xy + 9y^2 - 130x + 90y = 0$

30. $9x^2 - 6xy + y^2 - 12\sqrt{10}x - 36\sqrt{10}y = 0$

Bibliography

Acker, A., and C. Jaschek. *Astronomical Methods and Calculations.* New York: John Wiley and Sons, 1986.

Battan, L. *Weather in Your Life.* San Francisco: W. H. Freeman, 1983.

Beckmann, P. *A History of Pi.* New York: Barnes and Noble, 1993.

Bell, D. *Fundamentals of Electric Circuits,* Reston. Va.: Reston Publishing Company. 1981.

Benade, A. *Fundamentals of Musical Acoustics.* New York: Oxford University Press, 1976.

Beni, G., and S. Hackwood. *Recent Advances in Robotics.* New York: John Wiley and Sons, 1985.

Beranek, L. *Noise and Vibration Control.* Washington, D.C.: Institute of Noise Control Engineering, 1988.

Brearley, J., and A. Nicholas. *This Is the Bichon Frise.* Hong Kong: TFH Publication, 1973.

Brown, D., and P. Rothery. *Models in Biology: Mathematics, Statistics and Computing.* West Sussex, England: John Wiley and Sons, 1993.

Brown, F., J. Hastings, and J. Palmer. *The Biological Clock.* New York: Academic Press, 1970.

Carlson, T. "Über Geschwindigkeit und Grösse der Hefevermehrung in Würze." *Biochem. A.* 57:313–334.

Cheney, W., and D. Kincaid. *Numerical Mathematics and Computing.* 3rd ed. Pacific Grove, Calif.: Brooks/Cole Publishing Company, 1994.

Clime, W. *The Economics of Global Warming.* Washington, D.C.: Institute for International Economics, 1992.

Cole, F. *Introduction to Meteorology.* New York: Wiley, 1980.

Cooper, J., and R. Glassow. *Kinesiology.* 2nd ed. St. Louis: The C. V. Mosby Company, 1968.

Cotton, W., and R. Pielke. *Human Impacts on Weather and Climate.* Geophysical Science Series, vol. 2. Fort Collins, Colo.: *ASTeR Press, 1992.

Craig, J. *Introduction to Robotics: Mechanics and Control.* Reading, Mass.: Addison-Wesley Publishing Company, 1989.

Crownover, R. *Introduction to Fractals and Chaos.* Boston: Jones and Bartlett, 1995.

Duffet-Smith, P. *Practical Astronomy with Your Calculator.* New York: Cambridge University Press, 1988.

Eves, H. *An Introduction to the History of Mathematics.* 5th ed. Philadelphia: Saunders College Publishing, 1983.

Fletcher, N., and T. Rossing. *The Physics of Musical Instruments.* New York: Springer-Verlag, 1991.

Foley, J., A. van Dam, S. Feiner, J. Hughes, and R. Phillips. *Introduction to Computer Graphics.* Reading, Mass.: Addison-Wesley Publishing Company, 1994.

Foster, R., and J. Bates. "Use of mussels to monitor point source industrial discharges." *Environ. Sci. Technol.* 12:958–962.

Freebury, H. *A History of Mathematics.* New York: Macmillan, 1961.

Freedman, B. *Environmental Ecology: The Ecological Effects of Pollution, Disturbance, and Other Stresses.* 2nd ed. San Diego: Academic Press, 1995.

Garber, N., and L. Hoel. *Traffic and Highway Engineering*. Boston, Mass.: PWS Publishing Co., 1997.

Good, I. J. "What is the most amazing approximate integer in the universe?" *Pi Mu Epsilon Journal* 5 (1972): 314–315.

Grigg, D. *The World Food Problem*. Oxford: Blackwell Publishers, 1993.

Haber-Schaim, U., J. Cross, G. Abegg, J. Dodge, and J. Walter. *Introductory Physical Science*. Englewood Cliffs, N.J.: Prentice Hall, 1972.

Haefner, L. *Introduction to Transportation Systems*. New York: Holt, Rinehart and Winston, 1986.

Harker, J. *The Physiology of Diurnal Rhythms*. New York: Cambridge University Press, 1964.

Harrison, F., F. Hills, J. Paterson, and R. Saunders. "The measurement of liver blood flow in conscious calves." *Quarterly Journal of Experimental Physiology* 71:235–247.

Hartman, D. *Global Physical Climatology*. San Diego: Academic Press, 1994.

Heinz-Otto, P., H. Jürgens, and D. Saupe. *Chaos and Fractals: New Frontiers in Science*. New York: Springer-Verlag, 1993.

Hibbeler, R. *Structural Analysis*. Englewood Cliffs, N.J.: Prentice-Hall, 1995.

Hill, F. *Computer Graphics*. New York: Macmillan Publishing Company, 1990.

Hines, A., T. Ghosh, S. Loyalka, and R. Warder, Jr. *Indoor Air Quality and Control*. Englewood Cliffs, N.J.: Prentice-Hall, 1993.

Hoggar, S. *Mathematics for Computer Graphics*. New York: Cambridge University Press, 1993.

Hoppensteadt, F., and C. Peskin. *Mathematics in Medicine and the Life Sciences*. New York: Springer-Verlag, 1992.

Hosmer, D., and S. Lemeshow. *Applied Logistic Regression*. New York: John Wiley and Sons, 1989.

Howatson, A. *Electrical Circuits and Systems*. New York: Oxford University Press, 1996.

Howells, G. *Acid Rain and Acid Waters*. 2nd ed. New York: Ellis Horwood, 1995.

Huffman, R. *Atmospheric Ultraviolet Remote Sensing*. San Diego: Academic Press, 1992.

Huxley, J. *Problems of Relative Growth*. London: Methuen and Co., 1932.

Jarrett, J. *Business Forecasting Methods*. Oxford: Basil Blackwell, 1991.

Karttunen, H., P. Kroger, H. Oja, M. Poutanen, and K. Donner, eds. *Fundamental Astronomy*. 2nd ed. New York: Springer-Verlag, 1994.

Kerlow, I. *The Art of 3-D Computer Animation and Imaging*. New York: Van Nostrand Riehold, 1996.

Kissam, P. *Surveying Practice*. 3rd ed. New York: McGraw-Hill, 1978.

Kline, M. *The Loss of Certainty*. New York: Oxford University Press, 1980.

Kraljic, M. *The Greenhouse Effect*. New York: The H. W. Wilson Company, 1992.

Kress, S. *Bird Life—A Guide to the Behavior and Biology of Birds*. Racine, Wisc.: Western Publishing Company, 1991.

Lack, D. *The Life of a Robin*. London: Collins, 1965.

Lancaster, H. *Quantitative Methods in Biological and Medical Sciences: A Historical Essay*. New York: Springer-Verlag, 1994.

Loh, W. *Dynamics and Thermodynamics of Planetary Entry*. Englewood Cliffs, N.J.: Prentice-Hall, 1963.

Makridakis, S., and S. Wheelwright. *Forecasting Methods for Management*. New York: John Wiley and Sons, 1989.

Mandelbrot, B. *The Fractal Geometry of Nature*. New York: W. H. Freeman Company, 1982.

Mannering, F., and W. Kilareski. *Principles of Highway Engineering and Traffic Analysis*. New York: John Wiley and Sons, 1990.

Mar, J., and H. Liebowitz. *Structure Technology for Large Radio and Radar Telescope Systems*. Cambridge, Mass.: The MIT Press, 1969.

Mason, C. *Biology of Freshwater Pollution*. New York: Longman and Scientific and Technical, John Wiley and Sons, 1991.

Meeus, J. *Astronomical Algorithms*. Richmond, Va.: Willman-Bell, 1991.

Mehrotra, A. *Cellular Radio: Analog and Digital Systems*. Boston: Artech House, 1994.

Metcalf, H. *Topics in Classical Biophysics*. Englewood Cliffs, N.J.: Prentice-Hall, 1980.

Miller, A., and J. Thompson. *Elements of Meteorology.* 2nd ed. Columbus, Ohio: Charles E. Merrill Publishing Company, 1975.

Miller, A., and R. Anthes. *Meteorology.* 5th ed. Columbus, Ohio: Charles E. Merrill Publishing Company, 1985.

Moffitt, F. *Photogrammetry.* Scranton, Pa.: International Textbook Company, 1967.

Mortenson, M. *Computer Graphics: An Introduction to Mathematics and Geometry.* New York: Industrial Press Inc., 1989.

Motz, L., and J. Weaver. *The Story of Mathematics.* New York: Plenum Press, 1993.

Mueller, I., and K. Ramsayer. *Introduction to Surveying.* New York: Frederick Ungar Publishing Company, 1979.

National Council of Teachers of Mathematics. *Historical Topics for the Mathematics Classroom, Thirty-first Yearbook,* 1969.

Navarra, J. *Atmosphere, Weather and Climate.* Philadelphia: W. B. Saunders, 1979.

Nilsson, A. *Greenhouse Earth.* New York: John Wiley and Sons, 1992.

Pennycuick, C. *Newton Rules Biology.* New York: Oxford University Press, 1992.

Pielou, E. *Population and Community Ecology: Principles and Methods.* New York: Gordon and Breach Science Publishers, 1974.

Pierce, J. *The Science of Musical Sound.* New York: W. H. Freeman, 1992.

Pokorny, C., and C. Gerald. *Computer Graphics: The Principles behind the Art and Science.* Irvine, Calif.: Franklin, Beedle, and Associates, 1989.

Raggett, G. "Modeling the Eyam plague." *The Institute of Mathematics and Its Applications* 18: 221–226.

Resnikoff, H., and R. Wells, Jr. *Mathematics in Civilization.* New York: Dover Publications, Inc., 1984.

Riley, W., L. Sturges, and D. Morris. *Statics and Mechanics of Materials: An Integrated Approach.* New York: John Wiley and Sons, Inc., 1995.

Rist, Curtis. "The Physics of Foul Shots." *Discover,* October 2000.

Robert Wood Johnson Foundation. *Chronic Care in America: A 21st Century Challenge,* 1996.

Rodricks, J. *Calculated Risk.* New York: Cambridge University Press, 1992.

Roederer, J. *Introduction to the Physics and Psychophysics of Music.* New York: Springer-Verlag, 1973.

Rogers, E., and T. Kostigen. *The Green Book.* New York: Random House, 2007.

Ronan, C. *The Natural History of the Universe.* New York: MacMillan Publishing Company, 1991.

Ryan, B., B. Joiner, and T. Ryan. *Minitab Handbook.* Boston: Duxbury Press, 1985.

Sanders, D. *Statistics: A First Course.* 5th ed. New York: McGraw-Hill, 1995.

Schlosser, W. *Challenges of Astronomy.* New York: Springer-Verlag, 1991.

Semat, H., and J. Albright. *Introduction to Atomic and Nuclear Physics.* Austin, Tex.: Holt, Rinehart and Winston, 1972.

Sharov, A., and I. Novikov. *Edwin Hubble: The Discoverer of the Big Bang Universe.* New York: Cambridge University Press, 1993.

Sinkov, A. *Elementary Cryptanalysis: A Mathematical Approach.* New York: Random House, 1968.

Smith, R., and R. Dorf. *Circuits, Devices and Systems.* 5th ed. New York: John Wiley and Sons, Inc., 1992.

Socolow, R., and S. Pacala. "A Plan to Keep Carbon in Check." *Scientific American,* September 2006.

Stadler, W. *Analytical Robotics and Mechatronics.* New York: McGraw-Hill, Inc., 1995.

Stent, G. S. *Molecular Biology of Bacterial Viruses.* San Francisco: W. H. Freeman, 1963.

Thomas, D. *Swimming Pool Operators Handbook.* Washington, D.C.: National Swimming Pool Foundation, 1972.

Thomas, R. *The Old Farmer's 2012 Almanac.* Dublin, N.H.: The Old Farmer's Almanac, 2011.

Thomas, V. *Science and Sport.* London: Faber and Faber, 1970.

Thomson, W. *Introduction to Space Dynamics.* New York: John Wiley and Sons, 1961.

Triola, M. *Elementary Statistics.* Pearson Education, 2012.

Tucker, A., A. Bernat, W. Bradley, R. Cupper, and G. Scragg. *Fundamentals of Computing 1. Logic: Problem Solving, Programs, and Computers.* New York: McGraw-Hill, 1995.

Turner, R. K., D. Pierce, and I. Bateman. *Environmental Economics: An Elementary Approach.* Baltimore: The Johns Hopkins University Press, 1993.

Van Sickle, J. *GPS for Land Surveyors.* Chelsea, Mich.: Ann Arbor Press, 1996.

Varley, G., and G. Gradwell. "Population models for the winter moth." *Symposium of the Royal Entomological Society of London* 4:132–142.

Walker, A. *Observation and Inference: An Introduction to the Methods of Epidemiology.* Newton Lower Falls, Mass.: Epidemiology Resources, 1991.

Wang, Z. "Self-Powered Nanotech." *Scientific American,* January 2008.

Watt, A. *3D Computer Graphics.* Reading, Mass.: Addison-Wesley Publishing Company, 1993.

Webb, T. *Celestial Objects for Common Telescopes.* New York: Dover Publications Inc., 1962.

Weidner, R., and R. Sells. *Elementary Classical Physics,* vol. 2. Boston: Allyn and Bacon, 1965.

Wilcox, G., and C. Hesselberth. *Electricity for Engineering Technology.* Boston: Allyn and Bacon, 1970.

Williams, J. *The Weather Almanac 1995.* New York: Vintage Books, 1994.

Winter, C. *Solar Power Plants.* New York: Springer-Verlag, 1991.

Wolff, R., and L. Yaeger. *Visualization of Natural Phenomena.* New York: Springer-Verlag, 1993.

Wuebbles, D., and J. Edmonds. *Primer on Greenhouse Gases.* Chelsea, Mich.: Lewis Publishers, 1991.

Zeilik, M., S. Gregory, and D. Smith. *Introductory Astronomy and Astrophysics.* 3rd ed. Philadelphia: Saunders College Publishers, 1992.

Zhao, Y. *Vehicle Location and Navigation Systems.* Boston, Mass.: Artech House, 1997.

Answers to Selected Exercises

CHAPTER 1: Introduction to Functions and Graphs

SECTION 1.1 (pp. 8–10)

1. Rational number, real number   **3.** Rational number, real number   **5.** Real number   **7.** Natural number: $\sqrt{9}$; integers: $-3, \sqrt{9}$; rational numbers: $-3, \frac{2}{9}, \sqrt{9}, 1.\overline{3}$; irrational numbers: $\pi, -\sqrt{2}$ **9.** Natural numbers: none; integer: $-\sqrt{4}$; rational numbers: $\frac{1}{3}, 5.1 \times 10^{-6}, -2.33, 0.\overline{7}, -\sqrt{4}$; irrational number: $\sqrt{13}$ **11.** Rational numbers
13. Natural numbers   **15.** Integers   **17.** 51   **19.** -84
21. 0   **23.** 5   **25.** 8   **27.** -32 **29.** 4×10^1
31. 3.65×10^{-3} **33.** 2.45×10^3 **35.** 5.6×10^{-1}
37. -8.7×10^{-3} **39.** 2.068×10^2 **41.** 0.000001
43. 200,000,000   **45.** 156.7   **47.** 500,000   **49.** 4500
51. 67,000   **53.** 8×10^8; 800,000,000   **55.** 3.5×10^{-1}; 0.35
57. 2.1×10^{-3}; 0.0021   **59.** 5×10^{-3}; 0.005
61. 4.24×10^{19} **63.** 8.72×10^4 **65.** 7.67×10^{11}
67. 5.769   **69.** 0.058   **71.** 0.419   **73.** -1.235 **75.** 15.819
77. 1.4×10^{-1} watt   **79.** About 53,794 miles per hour
81. (a) 1.4%   (b) 3.9%   **83.** (a) 45,000,000 ft   (b) Yes
85. (a) $7.436\pi \approx 23.4$ in^3 (b) Yes

1.1 EXTENDED AND DISCOVERY EXERCISES (p. 11)

1. 2.9×10^{-4} cm   **3.** 0.25 feet, or 3 inches

SECTION 1.2 (pp. 22–25)

1. (a)
(b) Max: 6; min: -2 (c) Mean: $\frac{11}{6} = 1.8\overline{3}$
3. (a)
(b) Max: 30; min: -20 (c) Mean: 5
5.

-30	-30	-10	5	15	25	45	55	61

(a) Max: 61; min: -30
(b) Mean: $\frac{136}{9} \approx 15.11$; median: 15
7. $\sqrt{15} \approx 3.87$, $2^{2.3} \approx 4.92$, $\sqrt[3]{69} \approx 4.102$, $\pi^2 \approx 9.87$, $2^{\pi} \approx 8.82$, 4.1

$\sqrt{15}$	4.1	$\sqrt[3]{69}$	$2^{2.3}$	2^{π}	π^2

(a) Max: π^2; min: $\sqrt{15}$ (b) Mean: 5.95; median: 4.51
9. (a)
(b) Mean: 23.5; median: 23.95
The average area of the six largest lakes is 23,500 square miles. Half of these lakes have areas below 23,950 square miles and half have areas above.   (c) Lake Superior
11. 16, 18, 26; no

13. (a) $S = \{(-1, 5), (2, 2), (3, -1), (5, -4), (9, -5)\}$
(b) $D = \{-1, 2, 3, 5, 9\}$, $R = \{-5, -4, -1, 2, 5\}$
15. (a) $S = \{(1, 5), (4, 5), (5, 6), (4, 6), (1, 5)\}$
(b) $D = \{1, 4, 5\}$, $R = \{5, 6\}$
17. (a) $D = \{-3, -2, 0, 7\}$, $R = \{-5, -3, 0, 4, 5\}$
(b) x-min: -3; x-max: 7; y-min: -5; y-max: 5
(c) & (d)

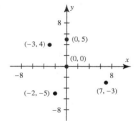

19. (a) $D = \{-4, -3, -1, 0, 2\}$, $R = \{-2, -1, 1, 2, 3\}$
(b) x-min: -4; x-max: 2; y-min: -2; y-max: 3
(c) & (d)

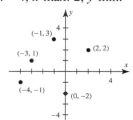

21. (a) $D = \{-35, -25, 0, 10, 75\}$,
$R = \{-55, -25, 25, 45, 50\}$
(b) x-min: -35; x-max: 75; y-min: -55; y-max: 50
(c) & (d)

23. Scatterplot   Line graph

25. 5 **27.** $\sqrt{29} \approx 5.39$ **29.** $\sqrt{41.49} \approx 6.44$ **31.** 8

33. $\frac{\sqrt{17}}{4} \approx 1.03$ **35.** $\frac{\sqrt{2}}{2} \approx 0.71$ **37.** 130 **39.** $\sqrt{a^2 + b^2}$

41. Yes

43. (a)

(b) $d = \sqrt{4100} \approx 64.0$ miles

45. 27 million units **47.** 9.5 seconds **49.** $(3, -0.5)$

51. $(10, 10)$ **53.** $(-2.1, -0.35)$ **55.** $(\sqrt{2}, 0)$ **57.** $(0, 2b)$

59. Center: $(0, 0)$; radius: 5 **61.** Center: $(0, 0)$; radius: $\sqrt{7}$

63. Center: $(2, -3)$; radius: 3 **65.** Center: $(0, -1)$; radius: 10

67. $(x - 1)^2 + (y + 2)^2 = 1$

69. $(x + 2)^2 + (y - 1)^2 = 4$

71. $(x - 3)^2 + (y + 5)^2 = 64$ **73.** $(x - 3)^2 + y^2 = 49$

75. $(x - 3)^2 + (y + 5)^2 = 50$

77. $(x + 2)^2 + (y + 3)^2 = 25$

79. $\left(x - \frac{7}{2}\right)^2 + (y - 3)^2 = \frac{25}{4}$

81.

83.

85.

87.

89.

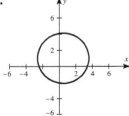

91. x-axis: 10; y-axis: 10 **93.** x-axis: 10; y-axis: 5

95. x-axis: 16; y-axis: 5

97. b **99.** a

101. $[-5, 5, 1]$ by $[-5, 5, 1]$

103. $[-100, 100, 10]$ by $[-100, 100, 10]$

105. (a) x-min: 2006; x-max: 2010; y-min: 6.1; y-max: 19.4

(b) $[2005, 2011, 1]$ by $[5, 20, 5]$ (answers may vary)

(c) (d)

107. (a) x-min: 2006; x-max: 2011; y-min: 180; y-max: 590

(b) $[2005, 2012, 1]$ by $[150, 600, 50]$ (answers may vary)

(c) (d)

CHECKING BASIC CONCEPTS FOR SECTIONS 1.1 AND 1.2 (p. 25)

1. (a) 9.88 (b) 1.28

3. (a) 3.485×10^8 (b) -1.2374×10^3 (c) 1.98×10^{-3}

5. $\left(1, \frac{5}{2}\right)$ **7.** Mean = 10,762.75; median = 12,941.5

SECTION 1.3 (pp. 38–41)

1. $(-2, 3)$ **3.** $f(7) = 8$

5.

7.

9.

11.

13.

15.

17.

19.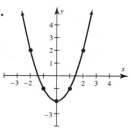

21. (a) $g = \{(-1, 0), (2, -2), (5, 7)\}$
(b) $D = \{-1, 2, 5\}, R = \{-2, 0, 7\}$
23. (a) $g = \{(1, 8), (2, 8), (3, 8)\}$
(b) $D = \{1, 2, 3\}, R = \{8\}$
25. (a) $g = \{(-1, 2), (0, 4), (1, -3), (2, 2)\}$
(b) $D = \{-1, 0, 1, 2\}, R = \{-3, 2, 4\}$
27. (a) $f(-2) = -8, f(5) = 125$ **(b)** All real numbers
29. (a) $f(-1)$ is undefined, $f(a + 1) = \sqrt{a + 1}$
(b) Nonnegative real numbers
31. (a) $f(-1) = 9, f(a + 1) = 3 - 3a$
(b) All real numbers
33. (a) $f(-1) = -2, f(a) = \frac{3a - 5}{a + 5}$ **(b)** $x \neq -5$
35. (a) $f(4) = \frac{1}{16}, f(-7) = \frac{1}{49}$ **(b)** $x \neq 0$
37. (a) $D =$ All real numbers; $R =$ All real numbers
(b) $g(-1) = -3; g(2) = 3$ **(c)** $g(-1) = -3; g(2) = 3$
39. (a) $D =$ All real numbers; $R = \{y \mid y \leq 2\}$
(b) $g(-1) = 1; g(2) = -2$ **(c)** $g(-1) = 1; g(2) = -2$
41. (a) $D = \{x \mid -2 \leq x \leq 2\}; R = \{y \mid -3 \leq y \leq 1\}$
(b) $g(-1) = -2; g(2) = 1$ **(c)** $g(-1) = -2; g(2) = 1$
43. $D = \{x \mid -3 \leq x \leq 3\}, R = \{y \mid 0 \leq y \leq 3\}$;
$f(0) = 3$
45. $D =$ all real numbers, $R = \{y \mid y \leq 2\}; f(0) = 2$
47. $D = \{x \mid x \geq -1\}, R = \{y \mid y \leq 2\}; f(0) = 0$
49. (a) $f(2) = 7$ **(b)** $f = \{(1, 7), (2, 7), (3, 8)\}$
(c) $D = \{1, 2, 3\}, R = \{7, 8\}$
51. (a) $[-4.7, 4.7, 1]$ by $[-3.1, 3.1, 1]$ **(b)** $f(2) = 1$
(c)

53. (a) $[-4.7, 4.7, 1]$ by $[-3.1, 3.1, 1]$ **(b)** $f(2) = 2$
(c)

55. Verbal: Square the input x.
Graphical:
$[-10, 10, 1]$ by $[-10, 10, 1]$

$f(2) = 4$

Numerical:

x	−2	−1	0	1	2
y	4	1	0	1	4

57. Verbal: Multiply the input by 2, add 1, and then take the absolute value.
Graphical:
$[-6, 6, 1]$ by $[-4, 4, 1]$

$f(2) = 5$

Numerical:

x	−2	−1	0	1	2
y	3	1	1	3	5

59. Verbal: Subtract x from 5.
Graphical:
$[-10, 10, 1]$ by $[-10, 10, 1]$

$f(2) = 3$

Numerical:

x	−2	−1	0	1	2
y	7	6	5	4	3

61. Verbal: Add 1 to the input and then take the square root of the result.
Graphical:
$[-6, 6, 1]$ by $[-4, 4, 1]$

$f(2) = \sqrt{3}$

Numerical:

x	−2	−1	0	1	2
y	—	0	1	$\sqrt{2}$	$\sqrt{3}$

63. Symbolic: $f(x) = 0.50x$
Graphical:

Numerical:

Miles	1	2	3	4	5	6
Cost	0.50	1.00	1.50	2.00	2.50	3.00

65. Yes. Domain and range include all real numbers.
67. No
69. Yes. $D: \{x \mid -4 \leq x \leq 4\}; R: \{y \mid 0 \leq y \leq 4\}$
71. (a) Yes
(b) Each real number has exactly one real cube root.
73. (a) No
(b) More than one student could have score x.
75. Yes, because IDs are unique. **77.** No **79.** Yes **81.** No
83. No **85.** Yes **87.** No **89.** Yes
91. $g(x) = 12x; g(10) = 120$; there are 120 inches in 10 feet.
93. $g(x) = \frac{x}{4}; g(10) = 2.5$; there are 2.5 dollars in 10 quarters.
95. $g(x) = 86,400x; g(10) = 864,000$; there are 864,000 seconds in 10 days.

97. (a) $V = \{(R, 37), (N, 30), (S, 17)\}$
(b) $D = \{N, R, S\}$, $R = \{17, 30, 37\}$
99. 200; 200 million tons of electronic waste will accumulate after 5 years.
101. $N(x) = 2200x$; $N(3) = 6600$; in 3 years the average person uses 6600 napkins.
103. Verbal: Multiply the input x by -5.8 to obtain the change in temperature.
Symbolic: $f(x) = -5.8x$.
Graphical: Numerical:

$[0, 3, 1]$ by $[-20, 20, 5]$

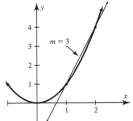

SECTION 1.4 (pp. 55–59)

1. $m = -2, b = 5$ **3.** $m = -8, b = 0$ **5.** $\frac{1}{2}$ **7.** -1
9. 0 **11.** -1 **13.** -8 **15.** Undefined
17. $-\frac{39}{35} \approx -1.1143$
19. Slope $= 2$; the graph rises 2 units for every unit increase in x.
21. Slope $= -\frac{3}{4}$; the graph falls $\frac{3}{4}$ unit for every unit increase in x, or equivalently, the line falls 3 units for every 4-unit increase in x.
23. Slope $= -1$; the graph falls 1 unit for every unit increase in x.
25. (a) Zero square feet of carpet would cost \$0.
(b) Slope $= 20$ **(c)** The carpet costs \$20 per square foot.
27. (a) $D(5) = 50$; after 5 hours the train is 50 miles from the station **(b)** -20; the train is traveling *toward* the station at 20 miles per hour.
29. (a) 150 miles **(b)** Slope $= 75$; the car is traveling *away* from the rest stop at 75 miles per hour.
31. Linear, but not constant **33.** Linear and constant
35. Nonlinear **37.** Nonlinear **39.** Yes, $m = 4$ **41.** No
43. (a) Slope: 2; y-int: -1; x-int: 0.5 **(b)** $f(x) = 2x - 1$
(c) 0.5
45. (a) Slope: $-\frac{1}{3}$; y-int: 2; x-int: 6 **(b)** $f(x) = -\frac{1}{3}x + 2$
(c) 6
47. $f(x) = -\frac{3}{4}x + \frac{1}{3}$ **49.** $f(x) = 15x$ **51.** $[5, \infty)$
53. $[4, 19)$ **55.** $[-1, \infty)$ **57.** $(-\infty, 1) \cup [3, \infty)$
59. $(-3, 5]$ **61.** $(-\infty, -2)$ **63.** $(-\infty, -2) \cup [1, \infty)$
65. Incr: never; decr: $(-\infty, \infty)$, $\left(\{x \mid -\infty < x < \infty\}\right)$
67. Incr: $(2, \infty)$, $\left(\{x \mid x > 2\}\right)$; decr: $(-\infty, 2)$, $\left(\{x \mid x < 2\}\right)$
69. Incr: $(-\infty, -2)$, $(1, \infty)$, $\left(\{x \mid x < -2\}, \{x \mid x > 1\}\right)$; decr: $(-2, 1)$, $\left(\{x \mid -2 < x < 1\}\right)$
71. Incr: $(-8, 0)$, $(8, \infty)$, $\left(\{x \mid -8 < x < 0\}, \{x \mid x > 8\}\right)$; decr: $(-\infty, -8)$, $(0, 8)$, $\left(\{x \mid x < -8\}, \{x \mid 0 < x < 8\}\right)$
73. Incr: $(-\infty, \infty)$, $\left(\{x \mid -\infty < x < \infty\}\right)$; decr: never
75. Incr: $(0, \infty)$, $\left(\{x \mid x > 0\}\right)$; decr: $(-\infty, 0)$, $\left(\{x \mid x < 0\}\right)$
77. Incr: $(-\infty, 1)$, $\left(\{x \mid x < 1\}\right)$; decr: $(1, \infty)$, $\left(\{x \mid x > 1\}\right)$

79. Incr: $(1, \infty)$, $\left(\{x \mid x > 1\}\right)$; decr: never
81. Incr: $(-3, \infty)$, $\left(\{x \mid x > -3\}\right)$; decr: $(-\infty, -3)$, $\left(\{x \mid x < -3\}\right)$
83. Incr: $(-\infty, \infty)$, $\left(\{x \mid -\infty < x < \infty\}\right)$; decr: never
85. Incr: $(-\infty, -2)$, $(2, \infty)$, $\left(\{x \mid x < -2\}, \{x \mid x > 2\}\right)$; decr: $(-2, 2)$, $\left(\{x \mid -2 < x < 2\}\right)$
87. Incr: $(-\infty, -1)$, $(0, 2)$, $\left(\{x \mid x < -1\}, \{x \mid 0 < x < 2\}\right)$; decr: $(-1, 0), (2, \infty)$, $\left(\{x \mid -1 < x < 0\}, \{x \mid x > 2\}\right)$
89. $(0, 2.4)$, $(8.7, 14.7)$, $(21, 27)$, $\left(\{x \mid 0 < x < 2.4\}, \{x \mid 8.7 < x < 14.7\}, \{x \mid 21 < x < 27\}\right)$
91. From -3 to -1: 1.2; from 1 to 3: -1.2
93. (a) 3 **(b)**

95. 7 **97.** 0.62 **99. (a)** From 1900 to 1940: 4.475; from 1940 to 1980: 11.25; from 1980 to 2010: about -10.57.
(b) From 1900 to 1940 cigarette consumption increased by 4.475 billion cigarettes per year, on average. The other rates may be interpreted similarly.
101.   **103.** Answers may vary.

105. (a) 3 **(b)** 0 **107. (a)** $2x + 2h + 1$ **(b)** 2
109. (a) $3x^2 + 6xh + 3h^2 + 1$ **(b)** $6x + 3h$
111. (a) $-x^2 - 2xh - h^2 + 2x + 2h$ **(b)** $-2x - h + 2$
113. (a) $2x^2 + 4xh + 2h^2 - x - h + 1$ **(b)** $4x + 2h - 1$
115. (a) $x^3 + 3x^2h + 3h^2x + h^3$ **(b)** $3x^2 + 3hx + h^2$
117. (a) $8t^2 + 16th + 8h^2$ **(b)** $16t + 8h$
(c) 64.4; the average speed of the car from 4 to 4.05 seconds is 64.4 feet per second.

1.4 EXTENDED AND DISCOVERY EXERCISES (p. 59)

1. (a) Yes; 2π inches per second **(b)** No; because the area function depends on the radius squared, the area function is not a linear function and does not increase at a constant rate.

CHECKING BASIC CONCEPTS FOR SECTIONS 1.3 AND 1.4 (p. 59)

1. Symbolic: $f(x) = 5280x$
Numerical:

x	1	2	3	4	5
$f(x)$	5280	10,560	15,840	21,120	26,400

Graphical:

3. $-\frac{3}{2}$ **5. (a)** $(-\infty, 5]$ **(b)** $[1, 6)$ **7.** -7

CHAPTER 1 REVIEW EXERCISES (pp. 63–65)

1. Natural number: $\sqrt{16}$; integers: $-2, 0, \sqrt{16}$; rational numbers: $-2, \frac{1}{2}, 0, 1.23, \sqrt{16}$; real numbers: $-2, \frac{1}{2}, 0, 1.23, \sqrt{7}, \sqrt{16}$

3. 1.891×10^6 **5.** 15,200 **7. (a)** 32.07 **(b)** 2.62 **(c)** 5.21 **(d)** 49.12 **9.** -41

11.

-23	-5	8	19	24

(a) Max: 24; min: -23

(b) Mean: 4.6; median: 8

13. (a) $S = \{(-15, -3), (-10, -1), (0, 1), (5, 3), (20, 5)\}$

(b) $D = \{-15, -10, 0, 5, 20\}$, $R = \{-3, -1, 1, 3, 5\}$

15. Not a function

$[-50, 50, 10]$ by $[-50, 50, 10]$

17. 10 **19.** $\left(2, -\frac{3}{2}\right)$ **21.** Yes

23. $(x - 2)^2 + (y - 5)^2 = 17$

25.

27.

29.

31.

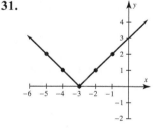

33. $f(x) = 16x$

$[0, 100, 10]$ by $[0, 1800, 300]$

x	0	25	50	75	100
$f(x)$	0	400	800	1200	1600

35. (a) $f(-3) = 5$, $f(1.5) = 5$ **(b)** All real numbers

37. (a) $f(-10) = 97$, $f(a + 2) = a^2 + 4a + 1$

(b) All real numbers

39. (a) $f(-3) = -\frac{1}{7}$, $f(a + 1) = \frac{1}{a - 3}$

(b) $D = \{x \mid x \neq 4\}$

41. No **43. (a)** Slope: -2; y-int: 6; x-int: 3

(b) $f(x) = -2x + 6$ **(c)** 3

45. Yes **47.** Yes **49.** 0 **51.** $-\frac{3}{4}$ **53.** 0 **55.** Linear

57. Nonlinear

59.

61. Yes; -4 **63.** 5 **65.** 760 seconds

67. (a) 198 feet **(b)** 1044 sq ft

69. (a) The data decrease rapidly, indicating a very high mortality rate during the first year.

$[-1, 5, 1]$ by $[0, 110, 10]$

(b) Yes **(c)** From 0 to 1: -90; from 1 to 2: -4; from 2 to 3: -3; from 3 to 4: -1. During the first year the population decreased, on average, by 90 birds. The other average rates of change can be interpreted similarly.

71. (a) $[1, 5, 1]$ by $[40, 70, 5]$

Nonlinear

(b) 2.5 **(c)** The average rate of change in outside temperature from 1 P.M. to 4 P.M. was 2.5°F per hour.

CHAPTER 1 EXTENDED AND DISCOVERY EXERCISES (pp. 65–66)

1. About 7.17 km

3. About 3.862

$[-3, 3, 1]$ by $[-2, 2, 1]$

5. About 4.039

$[-3, 3, 1]$ by $[-1, 3, 1]$

7. About 3.16; estimates will be less than the true value.

9. (a) Determine the number of square miles of Earth's surface that are covered by the oceans. Then divide the total volume of the water from the ice cap by the surface area of the oceans to get the rise in sea level. **(b)** About 25.7 feet

(c) Since the average elevations of Boston, New Orleans, and San Diego are all less than 25 feet, these cities would be under water without some type of dike system.

(d) About 238 feet

CHAPTER 2: Linear Functions and Equations

SECTION 2.1 (pp. 80–85)

1. $y = -2(x - 1) + 2$

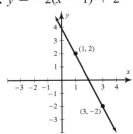
(1, 2)   (3, −2)

3. $y = \frac{3}{4}(x + 3) - 1$

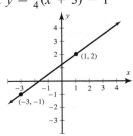
(1, 2)   (−3, −1)

5. $y = -2.4(x - 4) + 5$; $y = -2.4x + 14.6$;
$f(x) = -2.4x + 14.6$

7. $y = -\frac{1}{2}(x - 1) - 2$; $y = -\frac{1}{2}x - \frac{3}{2}$; $f(x) = -\frac{1}{2}x - \frac{3}{2}$

9. $y = \frac{3}{4}(x - 4) + 0$; $y = \frac{3}{4}x - 3$; $f(x) = \frac{3}{4}x - 3$

11. $y = \frac{2}{3}x - 1$ **13.** $y = -\frac{3}{5}x + \frac{3}{5}$ **15.** c

17. b   **19.** e   **21.** $y = 3x - 1$ **23.** $y = \frac{8}{3}x - \frac{17}{3}$

25. $y = -7.8x + 5$ **27.** $y = -\frac{1}{2}x + 45$

29. $y = -3x + 5$ **31.** $y = \frac{3}{2}x - 6$ **33.** $y = \frac{5}{18}x + \frac{11}{18}$

35. $y = 4x + 9$ **37.** $y = \frac{3}{2}x - 2960$ **39.** $y = \frac{2}{3}x - 2.1$

41. $y = \frac{1}{2}x + 6$ **43.** $y = x - 20$

45. $y = \frac{1}{2}x + \frac{9}{2}$ **47.** $y = -12x - 20$

49. $x = -5$; not possible   **51.** $y = 6$, $f(x) = 6$

53. $x = 4$; not possible   **55.** $x = 19$; not possible

57. x-int: 5; y-int: −4

59. x-int: 7; y-int: −7

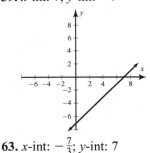

61. x-int: −7; y-int: 6

63. x-int: $-\frac{7}{3}$; y-int: 7

65. x-int: 4; y-int: 2

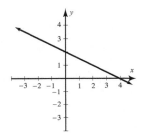

67. x-int: $\frac{5}{8}$; y-int: −5

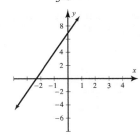

69. x-int: 5; y-int: 7; a and b represent the x- and y-intercepts, respectively.

71. x-int: $\frac{3}{2}$; y-int: $\frac{5}{4}$; a and b represent the x- and y-intercepts, respectively.   **73.** $\frac{x}{5} + \frac{y}{9} = 1$

75. (a) $y = 1.5x - 3.2$ **(b)** When $x = -2.7$, $y = -7.25$ (interpolation); when $x = 6.3$, $y = 6.25$ (extrapolation)

77. (a) $y = -2.1x + 105.2$ **(b)** When $x = -2.7$, $y = 110.87$ (extrapolation); when $x = 6.3$, $y = 91.97$ (interpolation).

79. (a) $f(x) = 7(x - 2008) + 3$, or $f(x) = 7x - 14,053$ (answers may vary); approximate   **(b)** −4%
(c) Extapolation; the result is negative, which is not possible.

81. (a) $y = \frac{12,000}{7}(x - 2003) + 25,000$, or
$y = \frac{12,000}{7}(x - 2010) + 37,000$; the cost of attending a private college or university is increasing by $\frac{12,000}{7} \approx \$1714$ per year, on average.   **(b)** About $31,857

83. (a) Leaving; 70 gallons   **(b)** x-int: 10, the tank is empty after 10 minutes; y-int: 100, the tank held 100 gallons initially.   **(c)** $y = -10x + 100$; the slope is −10, so the water is being drained at a rate of 10 gal/min.   **(d)** 5

85. (a) $y = -\frac{3}{7}(x - 1999) + 15$ or
$y = -\frac{3}{7}(x - 2013) + 9$ **(b)** Sales decreased, on average, by $\frac{3}{7} \approx \$0.43$ billion per year.   **(c)** $11.1 billion; this estimate is $0.7 billion high; interpolation

87. (a) $[\,2005, 2011, 1\,]$ by $[\,150, 450, 50\,]$

(b) Using the first and last points gives
$f(x) = 66.25(x - 2006) + 160$ (answers may vary).
(c) [2005, 2011, 1] by [150, 450, 50]

(d) The number of bankruptcies increased, on average, by 66,250 per year.
(e) 690,000 (answers may vary); extrapolation

89. (a) $y = -10.25x + 2000$ (answers may vary)
(b) Hours worked decreased, on average, by 10.25 hours per year.   **(c)** About 1549 hours (answers may vary)

91. [0, 3, 1] by [−2, 2, 1]

(a) No, the slope is not zero.   **(b)** The resolution of most calculator screens is not high enough to show the slight increase in the y-values.

93. (a) They do not appear to be perpendicular in the standard viewing rectangle (answers may vary for different calculators).

(b) In $[-15, 15, 1]$ by $[-10, 10, 1]$ and $[-3, 3, 1]$ by $[-2, 2, 1]$ they appear to be perpendicular.

$[-10, 10, 1]$ by $[-10, 10, 1]$

$[-15, 15, 1]$ by $[-10, 10, 1]$

$[-10, 10, 1]$ by $[-3, 3, 1]$

$[-3, 3, 1]$ by $[-2, 2, 1]$

(c) The lines appear perpendicular when the distance shown along the x-axis is approximately 1.5 times the distance along the y-axis.

95. $y_1 = x, y_2 = -x, y_3 = x + 2, y_4 = -x + 4$

97. $y_1 = x + 4, y_2 = x - 4, y_3 = -x + 4, y_4 = -x - 4$

99. $y \approx -0.789x + 0.526; r \approx -0.993$

$[-3, 4, 1]$ by $[-3, 3, 1]$

101. (a) Positive **(b)** $y = ax + b$, where $a = 3.25$ and $b = -2.45; r \approx 0.9994$ **(c)** $y = 5.35$

103. (a) Negative **(b)** $y = ax + b$, where $a \approx -3.8857$ and $b \approx 9.3254; r \approx -0.9996$ **(c)** $y \approx -0.00028$ (because of rounding, answers may vary slightly)

105. (a) $[-100, 1800, 100]$ by $[-1000, 28000, 1000]$

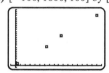

(b) $y = ax + b$, where $a \approx 14.680$ and $b \approx 277.82$
(c) 2500 light-years

107. (a) Positive

$[-5, 45, 5]$ by $[0, 6, 1]$

(b) $f(x) \approx 0.085x + 2.08$
(c) The number of passenger miles increased by about 0.085 trillion per year, on average.

$[-5, 45, 5]$ by $[0, 6, 1]$

(d) About 5.9 trillion

SECTION 2.2 (pp. 99–103)

1. One **3.** $4x - 1$ **5.** They are equal. **7.** Linear
9. Nonlinear **11.** Linear **13.** 4 **15.** -4

17. $\frac{32}{3}$ **19.** 4 **21.** 3 **23.** $\frac{1}{3}$ **25.** $\frac{4}{7}$ **27.** $-\frac{2}{19}$
29. -5 **31.** $\frac{17}{10}$ **33.** $\frac{7}{32}$ **35.** $\frac{5}{17}$ **37.** $\frac{400}{7}$
39. (a) No solutions **(b)** Contradiction
41. (a) $\frac{8}{3}$ **(b)** Conditional
43. (a) All real numbers **(b)** Identity
45. (a) No solutions **(b)** Contradiction
47. (a) All real numbers **(b)** Identity
49. 3 **51. (a)** 4 **(b)** 2 **(c)** -2
53. -1 **55.** 1 **57.** 4 **59.** 1.3 **61.** 0.675
63. 3.621 **65.** 2.294 **67.** 3 **69.** 8.6
71. 0.2 **73.** -1.2 **75.** 1 **77.** -4 **79.** 0.8
81. 2 **83.** $W = \frac{A}{L}$ **85.** $L = \frac{1}{2}P - W$
87. $y = 4 - \frac{3}{2}x$ **89.** $x = \frac{1}{4}y + \frac{3}{2}$
91. (a) $y = -2x + 8$ **(b)** $f(x) = -2x + 8$
93. (a) $y = \frac{1}{2}x + \frac{1}{4}$ **(b)** $f(x) = \frac{1}{2}x + \frac{1}{4}$
95. (a) $y = \frac{9}{8}x + \frac{9}{8}$ **(b)** $f(x) = \frac{9}{8}x + \frac{9}{8}$
97. 1989 **99.** About 1987
101. (a) For the graph of A, the percentage of people *against* legalization was decreasing at a rate of 1.6% per year. For the graph of F, the percentage of people *for* legalization was increasing at a rate of 1.5% per year.
(b) About 2011
103. $f(x) = 0.75x$; $42.18
105. (a) $0.048x$ **(b)** About 1,583,000
107. (a) About 2 hours (answers may vary)
(b) $\frac{15}{8} = 1.875$ hours
109. 3.2 hours at 55 mi/hr and 2.8 hours at 70 mi/hr
111. $\frac{1}{9}$ hour, or $6\frac{2}{3}$ minutes **113.** 41.25 feet
115. About 36.4 cubic feet **117.** About 8.33 liters
119. 36 inches by 54 inches
121. (a) $S(x) = 19x - 38,017$ **(b)** Sales increased, on average, by $19 billion per year. **(c)** 2013
123. $-40°F$ is equivalent to $-40°C$.
125. (a) f is linear because the amount of oil is mixed at a constant rate. **(b)** 0.48 pint; 0.48 pint of oil should be added to 3 gallons of gasoline to get the correct mixture.
(c) 12.5 gallons **127.** $\frac{80}{9} \approx 8.89$

2.2 EXTENDED AND DISCOVERY EXERCISES (p. 103)

1. (a) Yes; since multiplication distributes over addition, doubling the lengths gives double the sum of the lengths.
(b) No; for example, in the case of a square (a type of rectangle), the square of twice a side is four times the square of the side.
3. (a) $f(x) = 14,000x$ **(b)** About 1.9 hours

CHECKING BASIC CONCEPTS FOR SECTIONS 2.1 AND 2.2 (p. 104)

1. $y = -\frac{3}{4}x + \frac{7}{4}$; parallel: $y = -\frac{3}{4}x$;
perpendicular: $y = \frac{4}{3}x$ (answers may vary)
3. $y = -\frac{3}{2}x + \frac{1}{2}$ **5.** $-\frac{5}{3}$
7. (a) 2.5 **(b)** 2.5 **(c)** 2.5; The results are the same.

SECTION 2.3 (pp. 114–117)

1. $(-\infty, 2)$ **3.** $[-1, \infty)$ **5.** $[1, 8)$ **7.** $(-\infty, 1]$
9. $\{x \mid x \geq 2\}$, or $[2, \infty)$

11. $\{x \mid x < 10.5\}$, or $(-\infty, 10.5)$
13. $\{x \mid x \geq 13\}$, or $[13, \infty)$ **15.** $\{x \mid x < 0\}$, or $(-\infty, 0)$
17. $\{x \mid x \geq -10\}$, or $[-10, \infty)$
19. $\{x \mid x > 1\}$, or $(1, \infty)$
21. $\{x \mid x > \frac{7}{3}\}$, or $\left(\frac{7}{3}, \infty\right)$
23. $\{x \mid \frac{3}{2} < x \leq 3\}$, or $\left(\frac{3}{2}, 3\right]$
25. $\{x \mid -16 \leq x \leq 1\}$, or $[-16, 1]$
27. $\{x \mid -20.75 < x \leq 12.5\}$, or $(-20.75, 12.5]$
29. $\{x \mid -4 < x < 1\}$, or $(-4, 1)$
31. $\{x \mid \frac{9}{2} \leq x \leq \frac{21}{2}\}$, or $\left[\frac{9}{2}, \frac{21}{2}\right]$
33. $\{x \mid x \geq \frac{5}{3}\}$, or $\left[\frac{5}{3}, \infty\right)$
35. $\{x \mid -\frac{1}{2} < x \leq -\frac{1}{4}\}$, or $\left(-\frac{1}{2}, -\frac{1}{4}\right]$
37. $\{z \mid z \leq \frac{21}{19}\}$, or $\left(-\infty, \frac{21}{19}\right]$
39. $\{x \mid x \leq 2\}$ **41.** $\{x \mid x > 3\}$
43. $\{x \mid 0 \leq x \leq 2\}$ **45.** $\{x \mid -1 < x \leq 4\}$
47. (a) 2   **(b)** $\{x \mid x < 2\}$, or $(-\infty, 2)$
(c) $\{x \mid x \geq 2\}$, or $[2, \infty)$
49. (a) -2 **(b)** $\{x \mid x > -2\}$, or $(-2, \infty)$
(c) $\{x \mid x \leq -2\}$, or $(-\infty, -2]$
51. $\{x \mid x \leq 2\}$, or $(-\infty, 2]$
53. $\{x \mid x > 1\}$, or $(1, \infty)$
55. $\{x \mid x > 2.8\}$ **57.** $\{x \mid x \leq 1987.5\}$
59. $\{x \mid x > -1.82\}$
61. $\{x \mid 4 \leq x < 6.4\}$, or $[4, 6.4)$
63. $\{x \mid 4.6 \leq x \leq 15.2\}$, or $[4.6, 15.2]$
65. $\{x \mid 1 < x < 5.5\}$, or $(1, 5.5)$
67. (a) 8   **(b)** $\{x \mid x < 8\}$
69. $\{x \mid x < 4\}$; $\{x \mid x \geq 4\}$
71. $\{x \mid x < -\frac{3}{2}\}$, or $\left(-\infty, -\frac{3}{2}\right)$
73. $\{x \mid 1 \leq x \leq 4\}$, or $[1, 4]$
75. $\{x \mid -\frac{1}{20} \leq x < \frac{17}{20}\}$, or $\left[-\frac{1}{20}, \frac{17}{20}\right)$
77. $\{x \mid x \leq 31.4\}$, or $(-\infty, 31.4]$
79. $\{x \mid x > \frac{13}{2}\}$, or $\left(\frac{13}{2}, \infty\right)$
81. $\{x \mid x \leq 1.534\}$, or $(-\infty, 1.534]$
83. (a) Car A is traveling faster since its graph has the greater slope.   **(b)** 2.5 hours; 225 miles
(c) $0 \leq x < 2.5$
85. (a) $T(x) = 65 - 19x$ **(b)** $D(x) = 50 - 5.8x$
(c) Below 1.14 miles (approximately)
(d) Below 1.14 miles (approximately)
87. (a) Revenue increased, on average, by $0.86 billion per year.   **(b)** From 2012 to 2015
89. (a) $U(x) = 225x + 100$ **(b)** 2010 and after
91. (a) $V(x) = 7.6x - 15,212.6$
(b) About 2007 to 2009
93. About day 110 (April 19) to day 119 (April 28)
95. $3.98\pi \leq C \leq 4.02\pi$
97. (a) $f(x) = 3x - 1.5$ **(b)** $x > 1.25$
99. (a) $P(x) = 0.658x - 1290.76$ **(b)** Between 1989 and 2005   **(c)** Interpolation

2.3 EXTENDED AND DISCOVERY EXERCISES (p. 117)

1. $a < b \Rightarrow 2a < a + b < 2b \Rightarrow a < \dfrac{a + b}{2} < b$

SECTION 2.4 (pp. 127–133)

1. (a) $f(x) = \frac{x}{16}$ **(b)** $f(x) = 10x$
(c) $f(x) = 0.06x + 6.50$ **(d)** $f(x) = 500$
3. $f(x) = -\frac{1}{2}x + 3$ **5.** $f(x) = 2x + 5$ **7.** d   **9.** c
11. $B(t) = 1.2t + 27$; t represents years after 2010; $D = \{t \mid 0 \leq t \leq 4\}$ **13.** $T(t) = 0.5t + 0.4$; t represents months after January; $D = \{t \mid 0 \leq t \leq 11\}$
15. $P(t) = 21.5 + 0.6t$; t represents years after 1900; $D = \{t \mid 0 \leq t \leq 111\}$
17. (a) $W(t) = -10t + 300$ **(b)** 230 gal
(c) x-int: 30, the tank is empty after 30 minutes; y-int: 300, the tank contains 300 gallons of water initially.

(d) $D = \{t \mid 0 \leq t \leq 30\}$

19. (a) $f(x) = 0.04x + 1.2$ **(b)** 1,480,000
21. (a) $f(x) = 0.25x + 0.5$ **(b)** 1.125 inches
23. (a) 17; 17.2; 16.6   **(b)** $f(x) = 17x$
(c) The vehicle is getting 17 miles per gallon.

(d) $f(30) = 510$; the vehicle travels 510 miles on 30 gallons of gas.
25. (a) Max: 55 mi/hr; min: 30 mi/hr   **(b)** 12 miles
(c) $f(4) = 40, f(12) = 30, f(18) = 55$
(d) $x = 4, 6, 8, 12,$ and 16. The speed limit changes at each discontinuity.
27. (a) $P(1.5) = 1.10, P(3) = 1.30$; it costs $1.10 to mail 1.5 ounces and $1.30 to mail 3 ounces.
(b) $D = \{x \mid 0 < x \leq 5\}$

(c) $x = 1, 2, 3, 4$
29. (a) $f(1.5) = 30$; $f(4) = 10$
(b) $m_1 = 20$ indicates that the car is moving away from home at 20 mi/hr; $m_2 = -30$ indicates that the car is moving toward home at 30 mi/hr; $m_3 = 0$ indicates that the car is not moving; $m_4 = -10$ indicates that the car is moving toward home at 10 mi/hr.   **(c)** The driver starts at home and

drives away from home at 20 mi/hr for 2 hours until the car is 40 miles from home. The driver then travels toward home at 30 mi/hr for 1 hour until the car is 10 miles from home. Then the car does not move for 1 hour. Finally, the driver returns home in 1 hour at 10 mi/hr.
(d) Incr: $0 < x < 2$; decr: $2 < x < 3$ or $4 < x < 5$; const: $3 < x < 4$
31. (a) $-5 \le x \le 5$
(b) $f(-2) = 2, f(0) = 3, f(3) = 6$
(c)   **(d)** f is continuous.

33. (a) $-1 \le x \le 2$
(b) $f(-2) =$ undefined, $f(0) = 0, f(3) =$ undefined
(c)   **(d)** f is not continuous.

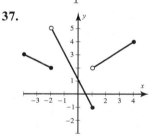

35. (a) $-3 \le x \le 3$
(b) $f(-2) = -2, f(0) = 1, f(3) = -1$
(c)   **(d)** f is not continuous.

37.

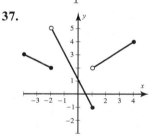

39. (a) $f(-3) = -10, f(1) = 4, f(2) = 4, f(5) = 1$
(b) $[1, 3]$ **(c)** f is not continuous.

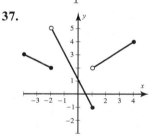

41. $xf(x) = \begin{cases} \frac{3}{4}x + 3, & \text{if } -4 \le x < 0 \\ -\frac{2}{3}x + 2, & \text{if } 0 \le x \le 3 \end{cases}$

43. (a)

(b) 700; there were 700 people for each housing start in 2009; small values **(c)** Yes
(d) Increasing: (2005, 2011); decreasing: (2000, 2005); constant: never
(e) $R(x) = \begin{cases} -9x + 18{,}225, & \text{if } 2000 \le x \le 2005 \\ 130x - 260{,}470, & \text{if } 2005 < x \le 2009 \\ 13.5x - 26{,}421.5, & \text{if } 2009 < x \le 2011 \end{cases}$

45. (a) $[-10, 10, 1]$ by $[-10, 10, 1]$

(b) $f(-3.1) = -8, f(1.7) = 2$
47. (a) $[-10, 10, 1]$ by $[-10, 10, 1]$

(b) $f(-3.1) = -7, f(1.7) = 3$
49. (a) $f(x) = 0.8[\![x/2]\!]$ for $6 \le x \le 18$
(b) $[6, 18, 1]$ by $[0, 8, 1]$

(c) $f(8.5) = \$3.20, f(15.2) = \$5.60$
51. 2.5 **53.** $\frac{9}{8}$ **55.** $k = 2.5, y = 20$ when $x = 8$
57. $k = 0.06, x = \$85$ when $y = \$5.10$
59. $\$1048, k = 65.5$ **61. (a)** $k = 0.01$ **(b)** 1.1 mm
63. (a) $k = \frac{15}{8}$ **(b)** $13\frac{1}{3}$ inches
65. (a) For $(150, 26)$, $\frac{F}{x} \approx 0.173$; for $(180, 31)$, $\frac{F}{x} \approx 0.172$; for $(210, 36)$, $\frac{F}{x} \approx 0.171$; for $(320, 54)$, $\frac{F}{x} \approx 0.169$; the ratios give the force needed to push a 1-pound box. **(b)** $k \approx 0.17$ (answers may vary)
(c) $[125, 350, 25]$ by $[0, 75, 5]$

(d) 46.75 pounds

67. (a) $S(x) \approx 3.974x - 14.479$ (answers may vary)
(b) About 5.15 cm
69. (a) $f(x) \approx 0.12331x - 244.75$ (answers may vary)
(b) \$3.0 million; interpolation **(c)** About 2017

2.4 EXTENDED AND DISCOVERY EXERCISES
(p. 133)

1. About 615 fish
3. Answers will vary.
5. (a) [1.580, 1.584, 0.001] by [−6.252, −6.248, 0.001]

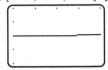

(b) A linear function would be a good approximation over a small interval.

CHECKING BASIC CONCEPTS FOR SECTIONS 2.3 AND 2.4 (p. 133)

1. $\{x \mid x > 3\}$
3. (a) 3 **(b)** $\{x \mid x > 3\}$ or $(3, \infty)$
(c) $\{x \mid x \le 3\}$ or $(-\infty, 3]$
5. $f(t) = 60t + 50$, where t is in hours

SECTION 2.5 (pp. 142–144)

1. −3, 3 **3.** $x < -3$ or $x > 3$, or $(-\infty, -3) \cup (3, \infty)$
5. It is V-shaped with the vertex on the x-axis. **7.** $|6a|$
9.

(a) −1 **(b)** Incr: $x > -1$, or $(-1, \infty)$; decr: $x < -1$, or $(-\infty, -1)$
11.

(a) $\frac{3}{2}$ **(b)** Incr: $x > \frac{3}{2}$, or $\left(\frac{3}{2}, \infty\right)$; decr: $x < \frac{3}{2}$, or $\left(-\infty, \frac{3}{2}\right)$
13. (a) **(b)**

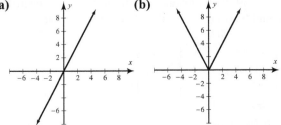

(c) 0

15. (a) **(b)**

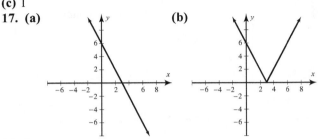

(c) 1
17. (a) **(b)**

(c) 3
19. −2, 2 **21.** 1, $\frac{9}{5}$ **23.** $-\frac{1}{2}$, 2 **25.** $-\frac{1}{3}$ **27.** $\frac{7}{16}$
29. No solutions **31.** $-\frac{23}{12}, \frac{19}{4}$ **33.** No solutions
35. $-1, \frac{17}{5}$ **37.** −1, 1 **39.** −3, 2
41. (a) −1, 7 **(b)** $-1 < x < 7$, or $(-1, 7)$
(c) $x < -1$ or $x > 7$, or $(-\infty, -1) \cup (7, \infty)$
43. (a) 1, 2 **(b)** $1 < x < 2$, or $(1, 2)$
(c) $x < 1$ or $x > 2$, or $(-\infty, 1) \cup (2, \infty)$
45. $-\frac{5}{2}, \frac{15}{2}$; $-\frac{5}{2} < x < \frac{15}{2}$, or $\left(-\frac{5}{2}, \frac{15}{2}\right)$
47. $\frac{7}{3}$, 1; $x < 1$ or $x > \frac{7}{3}$, or $\left(-\infty, 1\right) \cup \left(\frac{7}{3}, \infty\right)$
49. $-\frac{17}{21}, \frac{31}{21}$; $x \le -\frac{17}{21}$ or $x \ge \frac{31}{21}$, or
$\left(-\infty, -\frac{17}{21}\right] \cup \left[\frac{31}{21}, \infty\right)$
51. $-\frac{1}{3}, \frac{1}{3}$; $x < -\frac{1}{3}$ or $x > \frac{1}{3}$, or $\left(-\infty, -\frac{1}{3}\right) \cup \left(\frac{1}{3}, \infty\right)$
53. There are no solutions for the equation or inequality.
55. $\left(-\frac{7}{3}, 3\right)$, or $-\frac{7}{3} < x < 3$
57. $\left[-1, \frac{9}{2}\right]$, or $-1 \le x \le \frac{9}{2}$
59. $\left(-\frac{5}{2}, \frac{11}{2}\right)$, or $-\frac{5}{2} < x < \frac{11}{2}$
61. $(-\infty, 1) \cup (2, \infty)$, or $x < 1$ or $x > 2$
63. $\left(-\infty, \frac{5}{3}\right] \cup \left[\frac{11}{3}, \infty\right)$, or $x \le \frac{5}{3}$ or $x \ge \frac{11}{3}$
65. $(-\infty, -8) \cup (16, \infty)$, or $x < -8$ or $x > 16$
67. 6 **69.** $[-2, 4]$ **71.** $[0, \infty)$
73. Max: 75 mi/hr; min: 40 mi/hr
75. (a) $\frac{48}{19} \le x \le \frac{80}{19}$ **(b)** $\left|x - \frac{64}{19}\right| \le \frac{16}{19}$
77. (a) $19 \le T \le 67$ **(b)** The monthly average temperatures in Marquette vary between a low of 19°F and a high of 67°F. The monthly averages are always within 24 degrees of 43°F.
79. (a) $28 \le T \le 72$ **(b)** The monthly average temperatures in Boston vary between a low of 28°F and a high of 72°F. The monthly averages are always within 22 degrees of 50°F.
81. (a) $49 \le T \le 74$ **(b)** The monthly average temperatures in Buenos Aires vary between a low of 49°F (possibly in July) and a high of 74°F (possibly in January). The monthly averages are always within 12.5 degrees of 61.5°F.

83. (a) $|T - 10.5| < 0.5$ **(b)** $10.45 < T < 10.55$; The actual thickness must be greater than 10.45 mm and less than 10.55 mm.

85. (a) $|D - 2.118| \le 0.007$ **(b)** $2.111 \le D \le 2.125$; D must be greater than or equal to 2.111 inches and less than or equal to 2.125 inches.

87. $34.3 \le Q \le 35.7$

2.5 EXTENDED AND DISCOVERY EXERCISES (p. 144)

1. $|x - c| < \delta$

CHECKING BASIC CONCEPTS FOR SECTION 2.5 (p. 145)

1. $|2x|$ **3. (a)** $-2, 3$ **(b)** $[-2, 3]$, or $-2 \le x \le 3$; $(-\infty, -2) \cup (3, \infty)$, or $x < -2$ or $x > 3$ **5.** $-\frac{1}{3}, 1$

CHAPTER 2 REVIEW EXERCISES (pp. 148–152)

1. $y = \frac{1}{5}(x + 3) + 4$

3. $y = -\frac{7}{5}(x + 5) + 6$; $y = -\frac{7}{5}x - 1$; $f(x) = -\frac{7}{5}x - 1$

5. $y = \frac{2}{5}(x - 5) + 0$; $y = \frac{2}{5}x - 2$; $f(x) = \frac{2}{5}x - 2$

7. $f(x) = -2x - 1$

9. $y = 7x + 30$ **11.** $y = -3x + 2$

13. $y = -\frac{31}{57}x - \frac{368}{57}$

15. $x = 6$ **17.** $y = 3$ **19.** $x = 2.7$

21. x-int: 4; y-int: -5

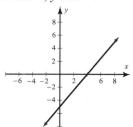

23. 6.4 **25.** $\frac{15}{7} \approx 2.143$ **27.** $\frac{5}{\pi} \approx 1.592$ **29.** -2.9

31. (a) All real numbers **(b)** Identity

33. (a) -3 **(b)** Conditional

35. $(-3, \infty)$ **37.** $\left[-2, \frac{3}{4}\right)$

39. $\{x \mid x \le 3\}$, or $(-\infty, 3]$

41. $\{x \mid -\infty < x < \infty\}$, or $(-\infty, \infty)$

43. $\left\{x \mid -1 < x \le \frac{7}{2}\right\}$, or $\left(-1, \frac{7}{2}\right]$

45. $\{x \mid x > -1\}$, or $(-1, \infty)$

47. (a) 2 **(b)** $x > 2$ **(c)** $x < 2$

49. (a) $f(-2) = 4, f(-1) = 6, f(2) = 3, f(3) = 4$ **(b)** f is continuous. **(c)** $x = -\frac{5}{2}$ or 2

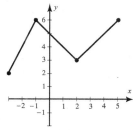

51. $-2, 7$ **53.** No solutions

55. ± 3; $x < -3$ or $x > 3$, or $(-\infty, -3) \cup (3, \infty)$

57. $\frac{17}{3}, -1$; $x < -1$ or $x > \frac{17}{3}$, or $(-\infty, -1) \cup \left(\frac{17}{3}, \infty\right)$

59. $-3 < x < 6$, or $(-3, 6)$

61. $x \le -\frac{5}{2}$ or $x \ge \frac{7}{2}$, or $\left(-\infty, -\frac{5}{2}\right] \cup \left[\frac{7}{2}, \infty\right)$

63. (a) $f(x) = 1060x + 17{,}700$ **(b)** Slope 1060 means that median income increased, on average, by about $1060 per year; y-intercept 17,700 means that in 1980 median income was $17,700 **(c)** $30,420; they are approximately equal. **(d)** About 2020; extrapolation

65. (a) $f(x) = 42.5x + 524$ **(b)** Slope 42.5 means that spending increased, on average, by about $42.5 billion per year; y-intercept 524 means that in 2010 spending was $524 billion. **(c)** $779 billion; interpolation **(d)** From 2014 to 2018

67. Initially the car is at home. After traveling 30 mi/hr for 1 hour, the car is 30 miles away from home. During the second hour the car travels 20 mi/hr until it is 50 miles away. During the third hour the car travels toward home at 30 mi/hr until it is 20 miles away. During the fourth hour the car travels away from home at 40 mi/hr until it is 60 miles away from home. During the last hour the car travels 60 miles at 60 mi/hr until it arrives home.

69. 155,590 **71.** 18.75 minutes

73. 0.9 hour at 7 mi/hr and 0.9 hour at 8 mi/hr

75. (a) $y = -1.2x + 3$

(b) $y = 4.8$ when $x = -1.5$, interpolation; $y = -1.2$ when $x = 3.5$, extrapolation **(c)** $\frac{17}{12}$

77. When $0 \le x \le 3$, the slope is 5, which means the inlet pipe is open and the outlet pipe is closed; when $3 < x \le 5$, the slope is 2, which means both pipes are open; when $5 < x \le 8$, the slope is 0, which means both pipes are closed; when $8 < x \le 10$, the slope is -3, which means the inlet pipe is closed and the outlet pipe is open.

79. The distance above the ground is between $1\frac{2}{3}$ kilometers and $3\frac{1}{3}$ kilometers.

81. Between 52.1431 feet and 52.4569 feet

CHAPTER 2 EXTENDED AND DISCOVERY EXERCISES (pp. 152)

1. (a) 62.8 inches

(b) [7, 15, 1] by [45, 75, 5]   [7, 15, 1] by [45, 75, 5]

Both sets of data are linear.

(c) Female: 3.1 inches; male: 3.0 inches

(d) $f(x) = 3.1(x - 8) + 50.4$; $g(x) = 3.0(x - 8) + 53$

(e) $55.67 \le$ female height ≤ 56.91; $58.1 \le$ male height ≤ 59.3

3. 3 miles

CHAPTERS 1–2 CUMULATIVE REVIEW EXERCISES (pp. 152–154)

1. 1.23×10^5; 5.1×10^{-3} **3.** 2.09

5. $(x + 2)^2 + (y - 3)^2 = 49$ **7.** $\sqrt{89}$

9. (a) $D = \{x \mid -\infty < x < \infty\}, R = \{y \mid y \geq -2\};$
$f(-1) = -1$
(b) $D = \{x \mid -3 \leq x \leq 3\}, R = \{y \mid -3 \leq y \leq 2\};$
$f(-1) = -\frac{1}{2}$
11. (a) $f(2) = 7; f(a - 1) = 5a - 8$
(b) $D = \{x \mid -\infty < x < \infty\}$
13. No. The graph does not pass the vertical line test.
15. 1   **17. (a)** $\frac{2}{3}; -2; 3$ **(b)** $f(x) = \frac{2}{3}x - 2$ **(c)** 3
19. $y = -\frac{11}{8}x - \frac{29}{8}$
21. $x = -1$ **23.** $y = 2x + 11$
25. x-int: -3; y-int: 2

27. 1   **29.** $-\frac{24}{17}$ **31.** 3   **33.** $(-\infty, 5)$
35. $(-\infty, -2) \cup (2, \infty)$
37. $\{x \mid x \leq \frac{5}{8}\}$, or $\left(-\infty, \frac{5}{8}\right]$
39. (a) 2   **(b)** $x < 2$ **(c)** $x \geq 2$
41. $-6, 4$ **43.** $-7, 7$
45. $\{x \mid 0 \leq x \leq 5\}$, or $[0, 5]$
47. (a) 770,000; it costs \$770,000 to manufacture 1500 computers.   **(b)** 500; each additional computer costs \$500 to manufacture; fixed costs are \$20,000.
49. (a) 9°F per hour   **(b)** On average, the temperature increased by 9°F per hour over this 2-hour period.
51. $\frac{60}{17} \approx 3.53$ hours
53. (a) $f(x) = \frac{28}{9}(x - 2001) + 56$
or $f(x) = \frac{28}{9}(x - 2010) + 84$ **(b)** About 100 pounds

CHAPTER 3: Quadratic Functions and Equations

SECTION 3.1 (pp. 167–172)

1. Quadratic; leading coefficient: 3; $f(-2) = 17$
3. Neither linear nor quadratic   **5.** Linear
7. (a) $a > 0$ **(b)** $(1, 0)$ **(c)** $x = 1$
(d) Incr: $x > 1$, or $(1, \infty)$; decr: $x < 1$, or $(-\infty, 1)$
(e) $D = (-\infty, \infty); R = [0, \infty)$
9. (a) $a < 0$ **(b)** $(-3, -2)$ **(c)** $x = -3$
(d) Incr: $x < -3$, or $(-\infty, -3)$; decr: $x > -3$, or $(-3, \infty)$
(e) $D = (-\infty, \infty); R = (-\infty, -2]$
11. The graph of g is narrower than the graph of f.
13. The graph of g is wider than the graph of f and opens downward rather than upward.
15. Vertex: $(1, 2)$; leading coefficient: -3;
$f(x) = -3x^2 + 6x - 1$
17. Vertex: $(4, 5)$; leading coefficient: -2;
$f(x) = -2x^2 + 16x - 27$
19. Vertex: $\left(-5, -\frac{7}{4}\right)$; leading coefficient: $\frac{3}{4}$;
$f(x) = \frac{3}{4}x^2 + \frac{15}{2}x + 17$

21. $f(x) = (x - 2)^2 - 2$ **23.** $f(x) = \frac{1}{2}(x - 2)^2 - 3$
25. $f(x) = -2(x + 1)^2 + 3$ **27.** $f(x) = -3(x - 2)^2 + 6$
29. $f(x) = (x + 2)^2 - 9$; vertex: $(-2, -9)$
31. $f(x) = \left(x - \frac{3}{2}\right)^2 - \frac{9}{4}$; vertex: $\left(\frac{3}{2}, -\frac{9}{4}\right)$
33. $f(x) = 2\left(x - \frac{5}{4}\right)^2 - \frac{1}{8}$; vertex: $\left(\frac{5}{4}, -\frac{1}{8}\right)$
35. $f(x) = \frac{1}{3}\left(x + \frac{3}{2}\right)^2 + \frac{1}{4}$; vertex: $\left(-\frac{3}{2}, \frac{1}{4}\right)$
37. $f(x) = 2(x - 2)^2 - 9$; vertex: $(2, -9)$
39. $f(x) = -3(x + 1.5)^2 + 8.75$; vertex: $(-1.5, 8.75)$
41. (a) $(0, 6)$ **(b)** Incr: $x < 0$, or $(-\infty, 0)$; decr: $x > 0$, or $(0, \infty)$
43. (a) $(3, -9)$ **(b)** Incr: $x > 3$, or $(3, \infty)$; decr: $x < 3$, or $(-\infty, 3)$
45. (a) $(1, -1)$ **(b)** Incr: $x > 1$, or $(1, \infty)$; decr: $x < 1$, or $(-\infty, 1)$
47. (a) $(0, 10)$ **(b)** Incr: $x > 0$, or $(0, \infty)$; decr: $x < 0$, or $(-\infty, 0)$
49. (a) $\left(\frac{1}{3}, -\frac{35}{12}\right)$ **(b)** Incr: $x < \frac{1}{3}$, or $\left(-\infty, \frac{1}{3}\right)$; decr: $x > \frac{1}{3}$, or $\left(\frac{1}{3}, \infty\right)$
51. (a) $\left(-\frac{1}{4}, \frac{15}{8}\right)$ **(b)** Incr: $x < -\frac{1}{4}$, or $\left(-\infty, -\frac{1}{4}\right)$; decr: $x > -\frac{1}{4}$, or $\left(-\frac{1}{4}, \infty\right)$
53. -6 **55.** $\frac{2}{3}$ **57.** $\frac{11}{4}$ **59.** $\frac{1}{4}$ **61.** $\frac{25}{4}$ **63.** $\frac{1}{3}$

65.

67.

69.

71.

73.

75.

77.

79.

81.   **83.**

85. -7 **87.** $6x + 3h - 2$ **89.** $f(x) = 2(x - 3)^2 + 1$
91. d   **93.** a   **95.** 250 ft by 250 ft
97. (a) $R(2) = 72$; the company receives \$72,000 for producing 2000 DVD players.   **(b)** 10,000   **(c)** \$200,000
99. (a) It is a parabola that opens upward.   **(b)** About 3.5¢ per copy when 7796 copies are made.
101. (a) 32 ft   **(b)** 34.25 ft
103. (a) $s(t) = -16t^2 - 66t + 120$
(b) Yes, because $s(2) < 0$.
105. 40 ft by 80 ft   **107.** 146 ft after 2.75 sec
109. 323 ft after 6.77 sec
111. $f(x) = \frac{1}{225}x^2 + 20$, or $f(x) \approx 0.0044x^2 + 20$
113. $f(x) = 2(x - 1)^2 - 3$
115. (a) $H(t) = 2(t - 4)^2 + 90$; $D = \{t \mid 0 \le t \le 4\}$
 (b) $H(1.5) = 102.5$ beats per minute
117. (a) $V(x) = 3.66x^2 + 1.5$ **(b)** 93 million
119. (a) $f(x) = 3.06(x - 1982)^2 + 1.6$ (answers may vary)
(b) [1980, 1996, 2] by [−50, 500, 100]

(c) About 250; by 1991 a total of about 250 thousand AIDS cases had been reported.
121. $f(x) = 3.125x^2 + 2.05x - 0.9$; $f(3.5) \approx 44.56$
123. (a) $f(x) \approx 0.055562x^2 - 220.05x + 217,886$
(b) About 49 thouand, which is 2 thousand too low
125. (a) $f(x) \approx 0.59462x^2 - 2350.82x + 2,323,895$
(b) About 454 thousand

3.1 EXTENDED AND DISCOVERY EXERCISES (p. 172)

1. (a)

x	1	2	3	4	5
$f(x)$	−2	1	6	13	22

(b) 3; 5; 7; 9   **(c)** $2x + h$; $2x + 1$
(d) 3; 5; 7; 9; the results are the same.

3. (a)

x	1	2	3	4	5
$f(x)$	0	−3	−10	−21	−36

(b) −3; −7; −11; −15
(c) $-4x + 3 - 2h$; $-4x + 1$
(d) −3; −7; −11; −15; the results are the same.

SECTION 3.2 (pp. 183–187)

1. $-4, 3$ **3.** 0, 2   **5.** $0, \frac{7}{3}$ **7.** $-1, \frac{15}{2}$ **9.** -3
11. $\frac{1}{2}$ **13.** $-5, \frac{1}{3}$ **15.** $\frac{1}{2}, \frac{5}{6}$ **17.** $-3 \pm \sqrt{5}$
19. $\pm \frac{\sqrt{13}}{2}$ **21.** No real solutions   **23.** $3 \pm 2\sqrt{2}$

25. $\frac{-1 \pm \sqrt{13}}{3}$ **27.** $\frac{1}{5}$ **29.** $\frac{5 \pm \sqrt{85}}{30}$ **31.** $-2, -1$
33. x-intercepts: $-\frac{5}{2}, \frac{1}{3}$; y-intercept: -5
35. x-intercept: $\frac{3}{2}$; y-intercept: -9
37. x-intercepts: $\frac{2}{3}, 3$; y-intercept: -6
39. $-2, 0$ **41.** $-2, 3$ **43.** $\pm\sqrt{3} \approx \pm 1.7$ **45.** 1.5
47. $-0.75, 0.2$ **49.** 0.7, 1.2   **51.** $-2 \pm \sqrt{10}$
53. $-\frac{5}{2} \pm \frac{1}{2}\sqrt{41}$ **55.** $1 \pm \frac{\sqrt{15}}{3}$ **57.** $4 \pm \sqrt{26}$
59. $\frac{3 \pm \sqrt{17}}{2}$ **61.** $\frac{3 \pm \sqrt{17}}{4}$ **63.** $\frac{-1 \pm \sqrt{97}}{12}$
65. $\{x \mid x \ne \sqrt{5}, x \ne -\sqrt{5}\}$
67. $\{t \mid t \ne -1, t \ne 2\}$ **69.** $y = \frac{-12x^2 + 1}{8}$; yes
71. $y = \frac{x}{5}$; yes   **73.** $y = 3 \pm \sqrt{9 - x^2}$; no
75. $y = \pm \frac{\sqrt{12 - 3x^2}}{2}$; no   **77.** $r = \pm \sqrt{\frac{3V}{\pi h}}$
79. $v = \pm \sqrt{\frac{2K}{m}}$ **81.** $b = \pm \sqrt{c^2 - a^2}$
83. $t = \frac{25 \pm \sqrt{625 - 4s}}{8}$
85. (a) $3x^2 - 12 = 0$ **(b)** $b^2 - 4ac = 144 > 0$. There are two real solutions.   **(c)** ± 2
87. (a) $x^2 - 2x + 1 = 0$ **(b)** $b^2 - 4ac = 0$. There is one real solution.   **(c)** 1
89. (a) $x^2 - 4x = 0$ **(b)** $b^2 - 4ac = 16 > 0$. There are two real solutions.   **(c)** 0, 4
91. (a) $x^2 - x + 1 = 0$ **(b)** $b^2 - 4ac = -3 < 0$. There are no real solutions.
93. (a) $2x^2 + 5x - 12 = 0$ **(b)** $b^2 - 4ac = 121 > 0$. There are two real solutions.   **(c)** $-4, \frac{3}{2}$
95. (a) $9x^2 - 36x + 36 = 0$ **(b)** $b^2 - 4ac = 0$. There is one real solution.   **(c)** 2
97. (a) $\frac{1}{2}x^2 + x + \frac{13}{2} = 0$ **(b)** $b^2 - 4ac = -12 < 0$. There are no real solutions.
99. (a) $3x^2 + x - 1 = 0$
(b) $b^2 - 4ac = 13 > 0$. There are two real solutions.
(c) $\frac{-1 \pm \sqrt{13}}{6}$
101. (a) $a > 0$ **(b)** $-6, 2$ **(c)** Positive
103. (a) $a > 0$ **(b)** -4 **(c)** Zero
105. 2.2 seconds   **107.** 2009   **109.** 8.5 in. by 11 in.; yes
111. 15 in. by 25 in.   **113.** About 1.49 in.
115. About 18.23 in.
117. 86 shirts   **119. (a)** $s(t) = -16t^2 + 160t + 32$
(b) About 10.2 sec
121. (a) $B(x) = 5.2(x - 1995)^2 + 180$ **(b)** 2005
123. (a) $I(x) = -2.277x^2 + 11.71x + 40.4$
(b) About 2005 and 2012
125. (a) $E(15) = 1.4$; in 2002 there were 1.4 million Walmart employees.
(b) $f(x) \approx 0.00474x^2 + 0.00554x + 0.205$ (answers may vary)
(c) [0, 25, 5] by [0, 2.6, 0.2]

(d) About 2011 (answers may vary)

3.2 EXTENDED AND DISCOVERY EXERCISES (pp. 187–188)

1. $676 = 26^2$; yes; $-\frac{5}{2}, \frac{3}{4}$ **3.** 69; no; $\frac{3 \pm \sqrt{69}}{10}$
7. $x^2 = k \Rightarrow \sqrt{x^2} = \sqrt{k} \Rightarrow |x| \Rightarrow \sqrt{k} \Rightarrow x = \pm\sqrt{k}$

CHECKING BASIC CONCEPTS FOR SECTIONS 3.1 AND 3.2 (p. 188)

1. Vertex; $(1, -4)$; axis of symmetry: $x = 1$;
x-intercepts: $-1, 3$

3. $f(x) = 2(x + 1)^2 + 3$
5. $f(x) = (x + 2)^2 - 7; (-2, -7); -7$
7. 11 in. by 15 in.

SECTION 3.3 (pp. 195–196)

1. $2i$ **3.** $10i$ **5.** $i\sqrt{23}$ **7.** $2i\sqrt{3}$ **9.** $3i\sqrt{6}$
11. $2 \pm 2i$ **13.** $-2 \pm 2i\sqrt{2}$ **15.** -5 **17.** -6
19. $-3\sqrt{2}$ **21.** $8i$ **23.** $-2 - i$ **25.** $5 - 21i$
27. $-1 + 6i$ **29.** $4 + 8i$ **31.** $5 - i$ **33.** $4 - 7i$
35. $-5 - 12i$ **37.** 4 **39.** $\frac{1}{2} - \frac{1}{2}i$ **41.** $\frac{19}{26} + \frac{9}{26}i$
43. $-\frac{2}{25} + \frac{4}{25}i$ **45.** $3i$ **47.** $\frac{1}{2} + i$
49. $-18.5 + 87.4i$ **51.** $8.7 - 6.7i$
53. $-117.27 + 88.11i$ **55.** $-0.921 - 0.236i$
57. -1 **59.** $-i$ **61.** 1 **63.** i
65. $\pm i\sqrt{5}$ **67.** $\pm i\sqrt{\frac{1}{2}}$ **69.** $\frac{3}{10} \pm \frac{i\sqrt{11}}{10}$ **71.** $2 \pm i$
73. $\frac{3}{2} \pm \frac{i\sqrt{11}}{2}$ **75.** $-1 \pm i\sqrt{3}$ **77.** $1 \pm \frac{i\sqrt{2}}{2}$
79. $\frac{5}{4} \pm \frac{i\sqrt{7}}{4}$ **81.** $\frac{11}{8} \pm \frac{i\sqrt{7}}{4}$
83. (a) Two real zeros **(b)** $-1, \frac{3}{2}$
85. (a) Two imaginary zeros **(b)** $-\frac{1}{2} \pm \frac{i\sqrt{7}}{2}$
87. (a) Two imaginary zeros **(b)** $\pm i\sqrt{2}$
89. $Z = 10 + 6i$ **91.** $V = 11 + 2i$ **93.** $I = 1 + i$

3.3 EXTENDED AND DISCOVERY EXERCISE (p. 196)

1. (a) $i^1 = i, i^2 = -1, i^3 = -i, i^4 = 1, i^5 = i, i^6 = -1,$
$i^7 = -i, i^8 = 1,$ and so on. **(b)** Divide n by 4. If the
remainder is r, then $i^n = i^r$, where $i^0 = 1, i^1 = i,$
$i^2 = -1,$ and $i^3 = -i$.

SECTION 3.4 (pp. 203–206)

1. (a) $(-\infty, -1) \cup (1, \infty)$, or $\{x \mid x < -1 \text{ or } x > 1\}$
(b) $(-1, 1)$, or $\{x \mid -1 < x < 1\}$
3. (a) $[-4, 4]$, or $\{x \mid -4 \le x \le 4\}$
(b) $(-\infty, -4] \cup [4, \infty)$, or $\{x \mid x \le -4 \text{ or } x \ge 4\}$
5. (a) $(-2, 2)$, or $\{x \mid -2 < x < 2\}$
(b) $(-\infty, -2) \cup (2, \infty)$, or $\{x \mid x < -2 \text{ or } x > 2\}$
7. (a) $-3, 4$ **(b)** $(-3, 4)$, or $\{x \mid -3 < x < 4\}$
(c) $(-\infty, -3) \cup (4, \infty)$, or $\{x \mid x < -3 \text{ or } x > 4\}$
9. (a) $\pm\sqrt{5}$ **(b)** $[-\sqrt{5}, \sqrt{5}]$, or
$\{x \mid -\sqrt{5} \le x \le \sqrt{5}\}$

(c) $(-\infty, -\sqrt{5}] \cup [\sqrt{5}, \infty)$, or
$\{x \mid x \le -\sqrt{5} \text{ or } x \ge \sqrt{5}\}$
11. (a) $-\frac{8}{3}, 0$ **(b)** $[-\frac{8}{3}, 0]$, or $\{x \mid -\frac{8}{3} \le x \le 0\}$
(c) $(-\infty, -\frac{8}{3}] \cup [0, \infty)$, or $\{x \mid x \le -\frac{8}{3} \text{ or } x \ge 0\}$
13. (a) $\frac{3}{2}$ **(b)** $(-\infty, \frac{3}{2}) \cup (\frac{3}{2}, \infty)$, or $\{x \mid x < \frac{3}{2} \text{ or } x > \frac{3}{2}\}$
(c) No solutions
15. (a) $\frac{2}{3}, \frac{5}{4}$ **(b)** $[\frac{2}{3}, \frac{5}{4}]$, or $\{x \mid \frac{2}{3} \le x \le \frac{5}{4}\}$
(c) $(-\infty, \frac{2}{3}] \cup [\frac{5}{4}, \infty)$, or $\{x \mid x \le \frac{2}{3} \text{ or } x \ge \frac{5}{4}\}$
17. (a) $-1 \pm \sqrt{2}$ **(b)** $(-1 - \sqrt{2}, -1 + \sqrt{2})$, or
$\{x \mid -1 - \sqrt{2} < x < -1 + \sqrt{2}\}$
(c) $(-\infty, -1 - \sqrt{2}) \cup (-1 + \sqrt{2}, \infty)$, or
$\{x \mid x < -1 - \sqrt{2} \text{ or } x > -1 + \sqrt{2}\}$
19. (a) $-3 < x < 2$ **(b)** $x \le -3 \text{ or } x \ge 2$
21. (a) $x = -2$ **(b)** $x \ne -2$
23. (a) No solutions **(b)** All real numbers
25. (a) $-\frac{5}{2}, -\frac{1}{2}$ **(b)** $(-\frac{5}{2}, -\frac{1}{2})$, or $\{x \mid -\frac{5}{2} < x < -\frac{1}{2}\}$
(c) $(-\infty, -\frac{5}{2}) \cup (-\frac{1}{2}, \infty)$, or $\{x \mid x < -\frac{5}{2} \text{ or } x > -\frac{1}{2}\}$
27. (a) $-1, \frac{7}{5}$ **(b)** $(-\infty, -1) \cup (\frac{7}{5}, \infty)$,
or $\{x \mid x < -1 \text{ or } x > \frac{7}{5}\}$ **(c)** $(-1, \frac{7}{5})$, or
$\{x \mid -1 < x < \frac{7}{5}\}$
29. (a) $x < -1 \text{ or } x > 1$ **(b)** $-1 \le x \le 1$
31. (a) $-6 < x < -2$ **(b)** $x \le -6 \text{ or } x \ge -2$
33. $-2 \le x \le -0.5$ **35.** $x < -3 \text{ or } x > 2$
37. $-2 \le x \le 2$ **39.** All real numbers
41. $x \le -2 \text{ or } x \ge 3$ **43.** $-\frac{1}{3} < x < \frac{1}{2}$
45. $-4 \le x \le 10$ **47.** No solutions
49. All real numbers except $\frac{2}{3}$ **51.** $x \le 0 \text{ or } x \ge 1$
53. $x \le -2 \text{ or } x \ge 3$ **55.** $-\sqrt{5} \le x \le \sqrt{5}$
57. $x \le \frac{23}{7} \text{ or } x \ge 22.4$ **59.** $2 \le x \le 7$
61. $x \le -2 \text{ or } x \ge 5$ **63.** All real numbers
65. $x < -2 - \sqrt{7} \text{ or } x > -2 + \sqrt{7}$
67. About 35 mi/hr, but not more than 38 mi/hr
69. $2 \le r \le 3$ (inches)
71. (a) $f(0) = 160, f(2) = 131.2$; initially the heart rate is
160 bpm, and after 2 minutes it is about 131 bpm.
(b) About $2.9 \le x \le 5$ (minutes)
73. From 1989 to 1992
75. From 2007 to 2008 and from 2009 to 2010

CHECKING BASIC CONCEPTS FOR SECTIONS 3.3 AND 3.4 (p. 206)

1. (a) $5i$ **(b)** $-3\sqrt{6}$ **(c)** $\frac{1}{2} \pm \frac{i\sqrt{2}}{2}$
3. (a) $[-3, 0]$, or $\{x \mid -3 \le x \le 0\}; (-\infty, -3) \cup (0, \infty)$,
or $\{x \mid x < -3 \text{ or } x > 0\}$
(b) $(-\infty, \infty)$, or $\{x \mid -\infty < x < \infty\}$; no solutions
5. (a) $(-\infty, -6] \cup [6, \infty)$, or $\{x \mid x \le -6 \text{ or } x \ge 6\}$
(b) $(-\infty, \infty)$, or $\{x \mid -\infty < x < \infty\}$
(c) $\left[\frac{1 - \sqrt{5}}{2}, \frac{1 + \sqrt{5}}{2}\right]$, or $\left\{x \mid \frac{1 - \sqrt{5}}{2} \le x \le \frac{1 + \sqrt{5}}{2}\right\}$

SECTION 3.5 (pp. 220–223)

1. $y = (x + 2)^2$ **3.** $y = \sqrt{x + 3}$
5. $y = |x + 2| - 1$
7. $y = \sqrt{x + 2} - 3$

9. $y = (x - 2)^2 - 3$
$[-10, 10, 1]$ by $[-10, 10, 1]$

11. $y = (x + 6)^2 - 4(x + 6) + 5$
$[-10, 10, 1]$ by $[-10, 10, 1]$

13. $y = \frac{1}{2}(x + 3)^2 + 2(x + 3) - 3$
$[-10, 10, 1]$ by $[-10, 10, 1]$

15. (a) $g(x) = 3(x + 3)^2 + 2(x + 3) - 5$
(b) $g(x) = 3x^2 + 2x - 9$
17. (a) $g(x) = 2(x - 2)^2 + 4$
(b) $g(x) = 2(x + 8)^2 - 5$
19. (a) $g(x) = 3(x - 2000)^2 - 3(x - 2000) + 72$
(b) $g(x) = 3(x + 300)^2 - 3(x + 300) - 28$
21. (a) $g(x) = -\sqrt{x - 4}$ **(b)** $g(x) = \sqrt{-x + 2}$
23. $(x - 3)^2 + (y + 4)^2 = 4$; center: $(3, -4)$; $r = 2$
25. $(x + 5)^2 + (y - 3)^2 = 5$;
center: $(-5, 3)$; $r = \sqrt{5}$

27. (a)

(b)

(c)

29. (a)

(b)

(c)

31. (a)

(b)

(c)

33. (a)

(b)

(c)

35. $y = -\sqrt{x} - 1$

Given function   x-axis reflection

37. $y = x^2 + x$

Given function   y-axis reflection

39. *x*-axis: *y*-axis:

41. *x*-axis: *y*-axis:

43. *x*-axis: *y*-axis:

45. Shift the graph of $y = x^2$ right 3 units and upward 1 unit.
47. Shift the graph of $y = x^2$ left 1 unit and vertically shrink it with factor $\frac{1}{4}$.
49. Reflect the graph of $y = \sqrt{x}$ across the *x*-axis and shift it left 5 units.
51. Reflect the graph of $y = \sqrt{x}$ across the *y*-axis and vertically stretch it with factor 2.
53. Reflect the graph of $y = |x|$ across the *y*-axis and shift it left 1 unit.

55.   **57.**

59.   **61.**

63.   **65.**

67.   **69.**

71.   **73.**

75.   **77.**

79.

x	1	2	3	4	5	6
g(*x*)	12	8	13	9	14	16

81.

x	−2	0	2	4	6
g(*x*)	5	2	−3	−5	−9

83.

x	0	1	2	3	4	5
g(*x*)	0	2	1	5	6	8

85.

x	−2	−1	0	1	2
g(*x*)	0	3	6	9	12

87. $(-12, 8)$, $(0, 10)$, and $(8, -2)$
89. $(-10, 7)$, $(2, 9)$, and $(10, -3)$
91. $(-12, -3)$, $(0, -4)$, and $(8, 2)$
93. $(6, 6)$, $(0, 8)$, and $(-4, -4)$
95. $f(x) = 7(x - 2008)^2 + 11.6$
97. $f(x) = 1.8(x - 2008)^2 + 22$
99. $g(x) = 0.00075(x - 1990)^2 + 0.17(x - 1990) + 44$
101. $y = -0.4(x - 3)^2 + 4$ (mountain)
$[-4, 4, 1]$ by $[0, 6, 1]$

103. (a) $y = \frac{1}{20}x^2 - 1.6$
$[-15, 15, 1]$ by $[-10, 10, 1]$

(b) $y = \frac{1}{20}(x - 2.1)^2 - 2.5$.
The front has reached Columbus by midnight.
$[-15, 15, 1]$ by $[-10, 10, 1]$

CHECKING BASIC CONCEPTS FOR SECTION 3.5 (p. 224)

1. (a) Shifted 4 units to the left
(b) Shifted 3 units down
(c) Shifted 5 units to the right and 3 units up
3. (a) $y = (x - 3)^2 - 4$ **(b)** $y = -x^2$
(c) $y = (-x + 6)^2$ **(d)** $y = (-(x + 6))^2$

5. (a)

x	-2	0	2	4	6
$g(x)$	4	6	9	11	12

(b)

x	-5	-3	-1	1	3
$h(x)$	-2	-6	-12	-16	-18

CHAPTER 3 REVIEW EXERCISES (pp. 228–229)

1. (a) $a < 0$ **(b)** $(2, 4)$ **(c)** $x = 2$
(d) Incr: $x < 2$, or $(-\infty, 2)$; Decr: $x > 2$, or $(2, \infty)$
3. $f(x) = -2x^2 + 20x - 49$; leading coefficient: -2
5. $f(x) = -(x + 1)^2 + 2$
7. $f(x) = (x + 3)^2 - 10$; vertex: $(-3, -10)$ **9.** $\left(\frac{1}{3}, -\frac{11}{3}\right)$

11.   **13.**

15. -29 **17.** $-4, 5$ **19.** $\pm\frac{\sqrt{7}}{2}$ **21.** $-\frac{7}{2}, 2$ **23.** $-2, 5$
25. $-1 \pm \sqrt{6}$ **27.** $\frac{3 \pm \sqrt{11}}{2}$ **29.** $y = \pm\sqrt{\frac{2x^2 - 6}{3}}$; no
31. (a) $4i$ **(b)** $4i\sqrt{3}$ **(c)** $-5\sqrt{3}$
33. (a) $-\frac{5}{2}, \frac{1}{2}$ **(b)** $-\frac{5}{2}, \frac{1}{2}$ **35.** $\pm\frac{3}{2}i$
37. (a) $-3 < x < 2$, or $(-3, 2)$
(b) $x \leq -3$ or $x \geq 2$, or $(-\infty, -3] \cup [2, \infty)$
39. $\{x \mid 1 \leq x \leq 2\}$, or $[1, 2]$
41. $\{x \mid x \leq -3 \text{ or } x \geq 5\}$, or $(-\infty, -3] \cup [5, \infty)$
43. $y = -f(x)$ $y = f(-x)$

45.   **47.**

49. 11 ft by 22 ft

51. (a) $h(0) = 5$; the stone was 5 ft above the ground when it was released.   **(b)** 117 ft   **(c)** 126 ft
(d) After 2 seconds and 3.5 seconds
53. 11 in. by 15 in.
55. $M(x) = 30(x - 2007)^2 + 60$

CHAPTER 3 EXTENDED AND DISCOVERY EXERCISES (p. 230)

1. (a) 23.32 ft/sec
(b) $[-1, 16, 1]$ by $[-1, 16, 1]$ Yes   **(c)** 12.88 ft

3. (a) $[-1, 8, 1]$ by $[-4, 4, 1]$

(b) The graph of $y = f(2k - x) = f(4 - x)$ is a reflection of $y = f(x)$ across the line $x = 2$.
5. (a) $[-15, 3, 1]$ by $[-3, 9, 1]$

(b) The graph of $f(2k - x) = f(-12 - x)$ is a reflection of $y = f(x)$ across the line $x = -6$.
7. (a) $[0, 1200, 100]$ by $[-800, 0, 100]$

The front reached St. Louis, but not Nashville.
(b) $g(x) = -\sqrt{750^2 - (x - 160)^2} - 110$
(c) $[0, 1200, 100]$ by $[-800, 0, 100]$

The cold front reached both cities in less than 12 hours.

CHAPTER 4: More Nonlinear Functions and Equations

SECTION 4.1 (pp. 238–242)

1. Yes; degree: 3; a: 2   **3.** No
5. Yes; degree: 4; a: -5 **7.** No
9. Yes; degree: 0; a: 22
11. (a) Local maximum: approximately 5.5; local minimum: approximately -5.5 **(b)** No absolute extrema
13. (a) Local maxima: approximately 17 and 27; local minima: approximately -10 and 24   **(b)** No absolute extrema

15. (a) Local maxima: approximately 0.5 and 2.8; local minimum: approximately 0 **(b)** Absolute maximum: 2.8; no absolute minimum

17. (a) Local maximum: 0; local minimum: approximately −1000 **(b)** No absolute maximum; absolute minimum: −1000

19. (a) Local maximum: 1; local minimum: −1
(b) Absolute maximum: 1; absolute minimum: −1

21. (a) No local maxima; local minimum: approximately −3.2 **(b)** Absolute maximum: 3; absolute minimum: approximately −3.2

23. (a) Local maxima: approximately 0.5 and 2; local minima: approximately −2 and −0.5 **(b)** Absolute maximum: 2; absolute minimum: −2

25. (a) No local maxima; local minimum: −2
(b) No absolute maximum; absolute minimum: −2

27. (a) No local extrema **(b)** No absolute extrema

29. (a) Local minimum: 1; no local maxima
(b) Absolute minimum: 1; no absolute maximum

31. (a) Local maximum: 4; no local minima
(b) Absolute maximum: 4; no absolute minimum

33. (a) Local minimum: $-\frac{1}{8}$; no local maxima
(b) Absolute minimum: $-\frac{1}{8}$; no absolute maximum

35. (a) Local minimum: 0; no local maxima
(b) Absolute minimum: 0; no absolute maximum

37. (a) No local extrema **(b)** No absolute extrema

39. (a) Local minimum: −2; local maximum: 2
(b) No absolute extrema

41. (a) Local maxima: 19, −8; local minimum: −13
(b) Absolute maximum: 19; no absolute minimum

43. (a) Local minimum: −8; local maximum: 4.5
(b) Absolute minimum: −8; no absolute maximum

45. (a) Local maximum: 8; no local minima
(b) Absolute maximum: 8; no absolute minimum

47. Neither **49.** Even

51. Odd **53.** Neither **55.** Even **57.** Even

59. Odd **61.** Neither **63.** Even

65. Even **67.** Even **69.** Neither **71.** Odd

73. Note that $f(0)$ can be any number.

x	−3	−2	−1	0	1	2	3
$f(x)$	21	−12	−25	1	−25	−12	21

75. $f(5) = 6$; $f(3) = -4$
77. Answers may vary.

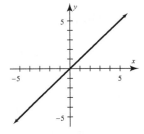

79. No. If $(2, 5)$ is on the graph of an odd function f, then so is $(-2, -5)$. Since f would pass through $(-3, -4)$ and then $(-2, -5)$, it could not always be increasing.

81. Answers may vary.

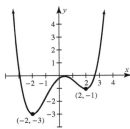

83. Answers may vary; yes, but it does not have to be quadratic.

85.

87.

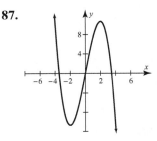

89. On $(0, 3)$; on $(3, 6)$

91. (a) Absolute maximum: 84°F; absolute minimum: 63°F; the high temperature was 84°F and the low was 63°F. **(b)** Local maxima: approximately 78°F and 84°F; local minima: approximately 63°F and 72°F
(c) $1.6 < x < 2.9$; $3.8 < x < 5$ (approximate)

93. (a) $F(1) \approx 69$; in January 2009, Facebook had about 69 million unique users. $F(12) \approx 132$; in December 2009, Facebook had about 132 million unique users. **(b)** No, F has no real extrema.

[0, 13, 2] by [0, 150, 25]

(c) $(1, 12)$ or $\{x \mid 1 < x < 12\}$

95. (a) Possible absolute maximum in January and absolute minimum in July **(b)** Absolute maximum: $140; absolute minimum: $15; the maximum cost, $140, occurs in January and the minimum cost, $15, occurs in July.

[1, 12, 1] by [0, 150, 10]   [1, 12, 1] by [0, 150, 10]

97. (a) Even **(b)** 83°F **(c)** They are equal. **(d)** Monthly average temperatures are symmetric about July. July has the highest average and January the lowest. The pairs June-August, May-September, April-October, March-November, and February-December have approximately the same average temperatures.

4.1 EXTENDED AND DISCOVERY EXERCISES (pp. 242–243)

1. The maximum area occurs when the figure is a rectangle with length about 4.24 and height about 2.12.
3. (a) About 1 hour 54 minutes **(b)** About 2 hours 8 minutes **(c)** About 1 hour 46 minutes

SECTION 4.2 (pp. 253–258)

1. (a) The turning points are approximately (1.6, 3.6), (3, 1.2), (4.4, 3.6). **(b)** After 1.6 minutes, the runner is 360 feet from the starting line. The runner turns and jogs toward the starting line. After 3 minutes, the runner is 120 feet from the starting line. The runner turns and jogs away from the starting line. After 4.4 minutes, the runner is again 360 feet from the starting line. The runner turns and jogs back to the starting line.
3. (a) 0; 0.5 **(b)** $a > 0$ **(c)** 1
5. (a) 3; $-6, -1$, and 6 **(b)** $a < 0$ **(c)** 4
7. (a) 4; $-3, -1, 0, 1$, and 2 **(b)** $a > 0$ **(c)** 5
9. (a) 2; -3 **(b)** $a > 0$ **(c)** 3
11. (a) 1; -1 and 2 **(b)** $a > 0$ **(c)** 2
13. (a) d **(b)** (1, 0) **(c)** 1 **(d)** No local maxima; local minimum: 0 **(e)** No absolute maxima; absolute minimum: 0
15. (a) b **(b)** $(-3, 27), (1, -5)$ **(c)** $x \approx -4.9$, $x = 0, x \approx 1.9$ **(d)** Local maximum: 27; local minimum: -5 **(e)** No absolute maximum; no absolute minimum
17. (a) a **(b)** $(-2, 16), (0, 0), (2, 16)$ **(c)** $x \approx -2.8$, $x = 0, x \approx 2.8$ **(d)** Local maximum: 16; local minimum: 0 **(e)** Absolute maximum: 16; no absolute minimum
19. (a) $[-10, 10, 1]$ by $[-10, 10, 1]$

(b) $(-3, 6), (3, -6)$ **(c)** Local minimum: -6; local maximum: 6
21. (a) $[-10, 10, 1]$ by $[-10, 10, 1]$

(b) There are three turning points located at $(-3, -7.025), (0, -5)$, and $(3, -7.025)$.
(c) Local minimum: -7.025; local maximum: -5
23. (a) $[-10, 10, 1]$ by $[-10, 10, 1]$

(b) $\left(\frac{1}{3}, \frac{2}{3}\right) \approx (0.333, 0.667)$
(c) Local minimum: $\frac{2}{3} \approx 0.667$; no local maximum
25. (a) $[-10, 10, 1]$ by $[-10, 10, 1]$

(b) $\left(-2, \frac{10}{3}\right) \approx (-2, 3.333), \left(1, -\frac{7}{6}\right) \approx (1, -1.167)$
(c) Local minimum: $-\frac{7}{6} \approx -1.167$; local maximum: $\frac{10}{3} \approx 3.333$
27. (a) Degree: 1; leading coefficient: -2
(b) Up on left end, down on right end; $f(x) \to \infty$ as $x \to -\infty$, $f(x) \to -\infty$ as $x \to \infty$
29. (a) Degree: 2; leading coefficient: 1 **(b)** Up on both ends; $f(x) \to \infty$ as $x \to -\infty$, $f(x) \to \infty$ as $x \to \infty$
31. (a) Degree: 3; leading coefficient: -2
(b) Up on left end, down on right end; $f(x) \to \infty$ as $x \to -\infty$, $f(x) \to -\infty$ as $x \to \infty$
33. (a) Degree: 3; leading coefficient: -1
(b) Up on left end, down on right end; $f(x) \to \infty$ as $x \to -\infty$, $f(x) \to -\infty$ as $x \to \infty$
35. (a) Degree: 5; leading coefficient: 0.1
(b) Down on left end, up on right end; $f(x) \to -\infty$ as $x \to -\infty$, $f(x) \to \infty$ as $x \to \infty$
37. (a) Degree: 2; leading coefficient: $-\frac{1}{2}$ **(b)** Down on both ends; $f(x) \to -\infty$ as $x \to -\infty$, $f(x) \to -\infty$ as $x \to \infty$
39. (a)

(b) Degree 3 **(c)** $a < 0$ **(d)** $f(x) = -x^3 + 8x$
41. (a)

(b) Degree 2 **(c)** $a > 0$ **(d)** $f(x) = x^2 - 2x - 1$
43. (a)

(b) Degree 4 **(c)** $a < 0$ **(d)** $f(x) = -x^4 + 3x^2 - 1$

45. Answers may vary.

47. Answers may vary.

49. Not possible
53. Answers may vary.

51. Not possible
55.

57. As the viewing rectangle increases in size, the graphs begin to look alike. Each formula contains the term $2x^4$, which determines the end behavior of the graph for large values of $|x|$.
(a) $[-4, 4, 1]$ by $[-4, 4, 1]$

(b) $[-10, 10, 1]$ by $[-100, 100, 10]$

(c) $[-100, 100, 10]$ by $[-10^6, 10^6, 10^5]$

59. For f: 1; for g: 0.5; for h: 0.25. On the interval $[0, 0.5]$, the higher the degree of the function, the smaller the average rate of change.
61. (a) 12.01 **(b)** 12.0001 **(c)** 12.000001
The average rate of change is approaching 12.
63. (a) $4.01\overline{6}$ **(b)** $4.0001\overline{6}$ **(c)** $4.000001\overline{6}$
The average rate of change is approaching 4.
65. $9x^2 + 9xh + 3h^2$ **67.** $-3x^2 - 3xh - h^2 + 1$
69. $f(-2) \approx 5, f(1) \approx 0$
71. $f(-1) \approx -1, f(1) \approx 1, f(2) \approx -2$
73. $f(-3) = -63, f(1) = 3, f(4) = 10$
75. $f(-2) = 6, f(1) = 7, f(2) = 9$
77. (a)

(b) f is not continuous. **(c)** ± 2

79. (a)

(b) f is continuous. **(c)** $\sqrt{2}$
81. (a)

(b) f is continuous. **(c)** $-\sqrt[3]{3}, \dfrac{\sqrt{17} + 1}{2}$
83. (a) $F(3) = 6$; 300 boats are able to harvest 6 thousand tons of fish. **(b)** Absolute max: 12; 12 thousand tons of fish is the maximum that can be caught.
85. (a) $H(-2) = 0; H(0) = 1; H(3.5) = 1$
(b)

87. (a) Approximately $(1, 13)$ and $(7, 72)$ **(b)** The low monthly average temperature of 13°F occurs in January. The high monthly average temperature of 72°F occurs in July.
89. (a) 4 seconds **(b)** From 0 to 4 seconds; from 4 to 7 seconds **(c)** $m = 36, a = -16, b = 144$
(d) $x \approx 2.8$ or $x \approx 5.7$; the height is 100 feet at about 2.8 seconds and at about 5.7 seconds.
91. (a) $f(x) \approx -0.0006296x^3 + 0.06544x^2 - 0.368x + 2.8$
(b) $[-5, 60, 10]$ by $[0, 80, 20]$

(c) $f(34) \approx 41.2; f(60) \approx 80.3$ **(d)** 1994 $(x = 34)$, interpolation; 2020 $(x = 60)$, extrapolation

4.2 EXTENDED AND DISCOVERY EXERCISES (pp. 258–259)

1. (a) $D = [0, 10]$, or $\{x \mid 0 \leq x \leq 10\}$
(b) $A(1) = 405$; after 1 min, the tank contains 405 gal of water. **(c)** Degree: 2; leading coefficient: 5 **(d)** No, more than half; yes, because the water will drain faster at first.

3. Conc. down: $(-\infty, \infty)$
5. Conc. up: $(1, \infty)$; conc. down: $(-\infty, 1)$
7. Conc. up: $(-2, 2)$; conc. down: $(-\infty, -2)$, $(2, \infty)$

CHECKING BASIC CONCEPTS FOR SECTIONS 4.1 AND 4.2 (p. 259)

1. (a) Incr: $(-2, 1)$, $(3, \infty)$, or $\{x \mid -2 < x < 1\}$, $\{x \mid x > 3\}$; decr: $(-\infty, -2)$, $(1, 3)$, or $\{x \mid x < -2\}$, $\{x \mid 1 < x < 3\}$
(b) Local maximum: approximately 3; local minima: approximately -13 and -2
(c) No absolute maximum; absolute minimum: approximately -13 **(d)** Approximately -3.1, 0, 2.2, and 3.6; they are the same values.
3. (a) Not possible
(b) Answers may vary.   **(c)** Answers may vary.

   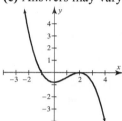

(d) Not possible
5. $f(x) \approx -1.01725x^4 + 10.319x^2 - 10$

SECTION 4.3 (pp. 266–267)

1. $\frac{x^3}{2} - \frac{3}{2x}$ **3.** $x - \frac{2}{3x} - \frac{1}{3x^3}$ **5.** $-\frac{1}{x^3} + \frac{1}{4}$ **7.** $5x - 10 + \frac{5}{3x}$
9. Quotient: $x^2 + x - 2$; remainder: 0
11. Quotient: $2x^3 - 9x^2 + 4x - 23$; remainder: 40
13. Quotient: $3x^2 + 3x - 4$; remainder: 6
15. $x^3 - 1$ **17.** $4x^2 + 3x - 2 + \frac{4}{x-1}$ **19.** $x^2 - x + 1$
21. $3x^2 + 4x - 2 + \frac{2}{2x-1}$ **23.** $x^3 + 2 + \frac{-2}{3x-7}$
25. $5x^2 - 12 + \frac{30}{x^2+2}$ **27.** $4x + 5$
29. $x^2 - 2x + 4 + \frac{-1}{2x^2+3x+2}$ **31.** $x^3 - 8x^2 + 15x - 6$
33. $(x-2)(x-1) - 1$ **35.** $(2x+1)(x^2-1) + 1$
37. $(x^2+1)(x-1) + 2$ **39.** $x^2 - 3x - 2$
41. $3x^2 + 4x + \frac{3}{x-5}$ **43.** $x^3 - x^2 - 6x$
45. $2x^4 - 2x^3 + 4 + \frac{1}{x+0.5}$ **47.** 3 **49.** -42
51. $L = 4x + 3$; 43 ft

SECTION 4.4 (pp. 278–282)

1. $(x+2)$, $(x+1)$, $(x-1)$
3. $(x+2)$, $(x+1)$, $(x-1)$, $(x-2)$
5. $f(x) = 2\left(x - \frac{11}{2}\right)(x-7)$
7. $f(x) = (x+2)(x-1)(x-3)$
9. $f(x) = -2(x+5)\left(x - \frac{1}{2}\right)(x-6)$
11. $f(x) = 7(x+3)(x-2)$
13. $f(x) = -2x(x+1)(x-1)$
15. $f(x) = (x+4)(x-2)(x-8)$
17. $f(x) = -1(x+8)(x+4)(x+2)(x-4)$
19. $f(x) = \frac{1}{2}(x+1)(x-2)(x-3)$
21. $f(x) = \frac{1}{2}(x+1)(x-1)(x-2)$
23. $f(x) = -2(x+2)(x+1)(x-1)(x-2)$

25. $f(x) = 10(x+2)\left(x - \frac{3}{10}\right)$
27. $f(x) = -3x(x-2)(x+3)$
29. $f(x) = x(x+1)(x+3)\left(x - \frac{3}{2}\right)$
31. $f(x) = (x-1)(x-3)(x-5)$
33. $f(x) = -4(x+4)\left(x - \frac{3}{4}\right)(x-3)$
35. $f(x) = 2x(x+2)\left(x + \frac{1}{2}\right)(x-3)$
37. Yes **39.** No
41. -2 (odd), 4 (even); minimum degree: 5
43. $f(x) = (x+1)^2(x-6)$
45. $f(x) = (x-2)^3(x-6)$
47. $f(x) = (x+2)^2(x-4)$
49. $f(x) = -1(x+3)^2(x-3)^2$
51. $f(x) = 2(x+1)^2(x-1)^3$
53. (a) x-int: -2, -1; y-int: 4
(b) -2 has multiplicity 1; -1 has multiplicity 2
(c)

55. (a) x-int: -2, 0, 2; y-int: 0
(b) 0 has multiplicity 2; -2 and 2 each have multiplicity 1
(c)

57. (a) $-3, \frac{1}{2}, 1$ **(b)** $f(x) = 2(x+3)\left(x - \frac{1}{2}\right)(x-1)$
59. (a) $-2, -1, 1, \frac{3}{2}$
(b) $f(x) = 2(x+2)(x+1)(x-1)\left(x - \frac{3}{2}\right)$
61. (a) $\frac{1}{3}, 1, 4$ **(b)** $f(x) = 3\left(x - \frac{1}{3}\right)(x-1)(x-4)$
63. (a) 1 **(b)** $f(x) = (x + \sqrt{7})(x-1)(x - \sqrt{7})$
65. Possible: 0 or 2 positive, 1 negative; actual: 0 positive, 1 negative
67. Possible: 1 positive, 1 negative; actual: 1 positive, 1 negative
69. Possible: 0 or 2 positive, 1 or 3 negative; actual: 0 positive, 1 negative
71. $-3, 0, 2$ **73.** $-1, 1$ **75.** $-2, 0, 2$ **77.** $-5, 0, 5$
79. ± 2 **81.** $-3, 0, 6$ **83.** 0, 1 **85.** $-\frac{1}{4}, 0, \frac{5}{3}$
87. $\pm \frac{2}{3}, \pm 1$ **89.** $-1, \pm \frac{\sqrt{3}}{2}$ **91.** $\pm 2, \frac{1}{2}$ **93.** $\pm \frac{3}{2}, \pm \frac{\sqrt{6}}{2}$
95. $-2, 3$ **97.** $-2.01, 0.12, 2.99$ **99.** $-4.05, -0.52, 1.71$
101. $-2.69, -1.10, 0.55, 3.98$
103. Because $f(2) = -1 < 0$ and $f(3) = 4 > 0$, the intermediate value property states that there exists an x-value between 2 and 3 where $f(x) = 0$.
105. Because $f(0) = -1 < 0$ and $f(1) = 1 > 0$, the intermediate value property states that there exists an x-value between 0 and 1 where $f(x) = 0$.

107. 4, 32; yes, by the intermediate value property

109. 12 A.M., 2 A.M., 4 A.M.

111. Approximately 11.34 cm

113. June 2, June 22, and July 12

115. (a) $f(x) \approx -0.184 (x + 6.01) (x - 2.15) (x - 11.7)$
(b) The zero of -6.01 has no significance. The zeros of $2.15 \approx 2$ and $11.7 \approx 12$ indicate that during February and December the average temperature is $0°F$.

117. (a) As x increases, C decreases.
(b) $C(x) \approx -0.000068x^3 + 0.0099x^2 - 0.653x + 23$
(c) [0, 70, 10] by [0, 22, 5]

(d) $0 \leq x < 32.1$ (approximately)

4.4 EXTENDED AND DISCOVERY EXERCISES (p. 282)

1. Dividing $P(x)$ by $x - 2$ synthetically results in the following bottom row: 1 1 5 2 12.
Since $2 > 0$ and the bottom row values are all nonnegative, there is no real zero greater than 2.

3. Dividing $P(x)$ by $x + 2$ synthetically results in the following bottom row: 1 -1 1 -2 7.
Since $-2 < 0$ and the bottom row values alternate in sign, there is no real zero less than -2.

5. Dividing $P(x)$ by $x - 1$ synthetically results in the following bottom row: 3 5 1 2 1.
Since $1 > 0$ and the bottom row values are all nonnegative, there is no real zero greater than 1.

CHECKING BASIC CONCEPTS FOR SECTIONS 4.3 AND 4.4 (p. 283)

1. $x^2 - 2x + 1$ **3.** $f(x) = -\frac{1}{2}(x + 2)^2 (x - 1)$; -2 has multiplicity 2; 1 has multiplicity 1.
5. The zeros are $-4, -1, 2,$ and 4;
$f(x) = (x + 4) (x + 1) (x - 2) (x - 4)$.

SECTION 4.5 (pp. 288–289)

1. Two imaginary zeros

3. One real zero; two imaginary zeros

5. Two real zeros; two imaginary zeros

7. Three real zeros; two imaginary zeros

9. (a) $f(x) = (x - 6i) (x + 6i)$ **(b)** $f(x) = x^2 + 36$

11. (a) $f(x) = -1(x + 1) (x - 2i) (x + 2i)$
(b) $f(x) = -x^3 - x^2 - 4x - 4$

13. (a) $f(x) = 10(x - 1) (x + 1) (x - 3i) (x + 3i)$
(b) $f(x) = 10x^4 + 80x^2 - 90$

15. (a) $f(x) = \frac{1}{2}(x + i) (x - i) (x + 2i) (x - 2i)$
(b) $f(x) = \frac{1}{2}x^4 + \frac{5}{2}x^2 + 2$

17. (a) $f(x) = -2(x - (1 - i)) (x - (1 + i)) (x - 3)$
(b) $f(x) = -2x^3 + 10x^2 - 16x + 12$

19. $\frac{5}{3}, \pm 5i$ **21.** $\pm 3i, \frac{1}{4} \pm \frac{i\sqrt{7}}{4}$

23. (a) $\pm 5i$ **(b)** $f(x) = (x - 5i) (x + 5i)$

25. (a) $0, \pm i$ **(b)** $f(x) = 3(x - 0) (x - i) (x + i)$, or $f(x) = 3x(x - i) (x + i)$

27. (a) $\pm i, \pm 2i$
(b) $f(x) = (x - i) (x + i) (x - 2i) (x + 2i)$

29. (a) $-2, \pm 4i$ **(b)** $f(x) = (x + 2) (x + 4i) (x - 4i)$

31. $0, \pm i$ **33.** $2, \pm i\sqrt{7}$ **35.** $0, \pm i\sqrt{5}$

37. $0, \frac{1}{2} \pm \frac{i\sqrt{15}}{2}$ **39.** $-2, 1, \pm i\sqrt{8}$ **41.** $-2, \frac{1}{3} \pm \frac{i\sqrt{8}}{3}$

SECTION 4.6 (pp. 302–305)

1. Yes; $D = \left\{x \mid x \neq \frac{5}{4}\right\}$

3. Yes; $D =$ all real numbers

5. No; $D = \{x \mid x \neq -1\}$

7. Yes; $D =$ all real numbers

9. No; $D = \{x \mid x \neq -1, x \neq 0\}$

11. Yes; $D = \{x \mid x \neq -1\}$

13. Horizontal: $y = 4$; vertical: $x = 2$; $D = \{x \mid x \neq 2\}$

15. Horizontal: $y = -4$; vertical: $x = \pm 2$; $D = \{x \mid x \neq 2, x \neq -2\}$

17. Horizontal: $y = 0$; vertical: none; $D =$ all real numbers

19. $y = 3$ **21.** Horizontal: $y = 2$; vertical: $x = 3$

23. Horizontal: $y = 0$; vertical: $x = \pm\sqrt{5}$

25. Horizontal: none; vertical: $x = -5$ or 2

27. Horizontal: $y = \frac{1}{2}$; vertical: $x = \frac{5}{2}$

29. Horizontal: $y = 3$; vertical: $x = 1$

31. Horizontal: none; vertical: none, since $f(x) = x - 3$ for $x \neq -3$ **33.** b **35.** d

37. $f(x) = \frac{x + 1}{x + 3}$ (answers may vary)

39. $f(x) = \frac{1}{x^2 - 9}$ (answers may vary)

41. Horizontal: $y = 0$; vertical: $x = 0$

43. Horizontal: $y = 0$; vertical: $x = 0$

45. $g(x) = f(x - 3)$

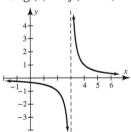

47. $g(x) = f(x) + 2$

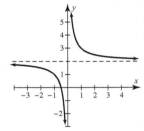

49. $g(x) = f(x + 1) - 2$

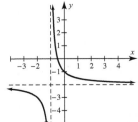

51. $g(x) = -2h(x - 1)$

53. $g(x) = h(x + 1) - 2$

55. (a) $D = \{x \,|\, x \neq 2\}$
   (b) $[-9.4, 9.4, 1]$ by
   $[-6.2, 6.2, 1]$

   (c) Horizontal: $y = 1$;
   vertical: $x = 2$
   (d)

57. (a) $D = \{x \,|\, x \neq 2,$
   $x \neq -2\}$
   (b) $[-9.4, 9.4, 1]$ by
   $[-6.2, 6.2, 1]$

   (c) Horizontal: $y = 0$;
   vertical: $x = \pm 2$
   (d)

59. (a) $D = \{x \,|\, x \neq 2,$
   $x \neq -2\}$
   (b) $[-9.4, 9.4, 1]$ by
   $[-9.3, 9.3, 1]$

   (c) Horizontal: $y = 0$;
   vertical: $x = \pm 2$
   (d)

61. (a) $D = \{x \,|\, x \neq 2\}$
   (b) $[-4.7, 4.7, 1]$ by
   $[-6.2, 6.2, 1]$

   (c) Horizontal: none;
   vertical: none, since
   $f(x) = x + 2$ for $x \neq 2$
   (d)

63.

65.

67.

69.

71.

73. (a) Slant: $y = x - 1$;
   vertical: $x = -1$
   (b)

75. (a) Slant: $y = \frac{1}{2}x - 3$;
   vertical: $x = -2$
   (b)

77. (a) Slant: $y = x + 3$;
   vertical: $x = 1$
   (b)

79. (a) Slant: $y = 2x + 1$;
   vertical: $x = \frac{1}{2}$
   (b)

81. -3 **83.** 1 **85.** $-\frac{1}{2}$

87.

89.

91.

93. (a) About 33%; the least active 98% post $\frac{1}{3}$ of the postings. **(b)** About 67%; the most active 2% post $\frac{2}{3}$ of the postings.

95. (a) 5%; at 1 second, there is a 5% chance that the visitor is abandoning the website. **(b)** About 1.8%; at 60 seconds, there is a 1.8% chance that the visitor is abandoning the website.

97. (a) $T(4) = 0.25$; when vehicles leave the ramp at an average rate of 4 vehicles per minute, the wait is 0.25 minute or 15 seconds. $T(7.5) = 2$; when vehicles leave the ramp at an average rate of 7.5 vehicles per minute, the wait is 2 minutes. **(b)** The wait increases dramatically.

99. (a) $N(20) = 0.5$, $N(39) \approx 38$
(b) It increases dramatically. **(c)** $x = 40$

101. (a) $y = 10$

[0, 14, 1] by [0, 14, 1]

(b) When $x = 0$, there are 1 million insects. **(c)** It starts to level off at 10 million. **(d)** The horizontal asymptote $y = 10$ represents the limiting population after a long time.

103. (a) $f(400) = \frac{2540}{400} = 6.35$ inches. A curve designed for 60 miles per hour with a radius of 400 ft should have the outer rail elevated 6.35 in. **(b)** As the radius x of the curve increases, the elevation of the outer rail decreases.

[0, 600, 100] by [0, 50, 5]

(c) The horizontal asymptote is $y = 0$. As the radius of the curve increases without bound ($x \to \infty$), the tracks become straight and no elevation or banking ($y \to 0$) is necessary. **(d)** 200 ft

4.6 EXTENDED AND DISCOVERY EXERCISES (p. 305)

1. $-\frac{1}{3}$; $-\frac{1}{x(x + h)}$ **3.** $-\frac{1}{2}$; $-\frac{3}{2x(x + h)}$

CHECKING BASIC CONCEPTS FOR SECTIONS 4.5 AND 4.6 (pp. 305–306)

1. $f(x) = 3(x - 4i)(x + 4i) = 3x^2 + 48$
3. $f(x) = (x - 1)(x - 2i)(x + 2i)$
5. (a) $D = \{x \mid x \neq 1\}$ **(b)** Vertical asymptote: $x = 1$; horizontal asymptote: $y = 2$

(c)

7. (a)

(b)

(c) 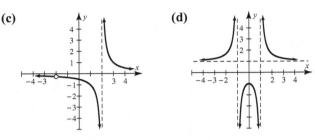 **(d)**

SECTION 4.7 (pp. 317–322)

1. -3 **3.** $\frac{1}{2}$, 2 **5.** $\frac{1}{2}$ **7.** -1 **9.** $\frac{13}{8}$ **11.** $\pm\sqrt{2}$ **13.** No real solutions **15.** 0, ± 2 **17.** $-\frac{5}{3}, \frac{7}{5}$ **19.** -14

21. No real solutions (extraneous: 2)
23. -3 (extraneous: 1) **25.** 1 (extraneous: -2)
27. No real solutions (extraneous: 1)
29. (a) -4, -2, or 2
(b) $(-4, -2) \cup (2, \infty)$, or $\{x \mid -4 < x < -2 \text{ or } x > 2\}$
(c) $(-\infty, -4) \cup (-2, 2)$, or $\{x \mid x < -4 \text{ or } -2 < x < 2\}$
31. (a) -4, -2, 0, or 2
(b) $(-4, -2) \cup (0, 2)$, or $\{x \mid -4 < x < -2 \text{ or } 0 < x < 2\}$
(c) $(-\infty, -4) \cup (-2, 0) \cup (2, \infty)$, or $\{x \mid x < -4 \text{ or } -2 < x < 0 \text{ or } x > 2\}$
33. (a) -2, 1, or 2 **(b)** $(-\infty, -2) \cup (-2, 1)$, or $\{x \mid x < -2 \text{ or } -2 < x < 1\}$
(c) $(1, 2) \cup (2, \infty)$, or $\{x \mid 1 < x < 2 \text{ or } x > 2\}$
35. (a) 0 **(b)** $(-\infty, 0) \cup (0, \infty)$, or $\{x \mid x < 0 \text{ or } x > 0\}$
(c) No solutions
37. (a) 0 or 1 **(b)** $(-\infty, 0) \cup (1, \infty)$, or $\{x \mid x < 0 \text{ or } x > 1\}$
(c) $(0, 1)$, or $\{x \mid 0 < x < 1\}$
39. (a) -2, 0, or 2
(b) $(-\infty, -2) \cup (2, \infty)$, or $\{x \mid x < -2 \text{ or } x > 2\}$
(c) $(-2, 0) \cup (0, 2)$, or $\{x \mid -2 < x < 0 \text{ or } 0 < x < 2\}$
41. $(-1, 0) \cup (1, \infty)$, or $\{x \mid -1 < x < 0 \text{ or } x > 1\}$
43. $[-2, 0] \cup [1, \infty)$, or $\{x \mid -2 \leq x \leq 0 \text{ or } x \geq 1\}$
45. $(-3, -2) \cup (2, 3)$, or $\{x \mid -3 < x < -2 \text{ or } 2 < x < 3\}$
47. $\left(-\infty, -\sqrt{2}\right) \cup \left(\sqrt{2}, \infty\right)$, or $\left\{x \mid x < -\sqrt{2} \text{ or } x > \sqrt{2}\right\}$
49. $[-2, 1] \cup [2, \infty)$, or $\{x \mid -2 \leq x \leq 1 \text{ or } x \geq 2\}$
51. $[-3, 2]$, or $\{x \mid -3 \leq x \leq 2\}$
53. $(-\infty, 1] \cup [2, 4]$, or $\{x \mid x \leq 1 \text{ or } 2 \leq x \leq 4\}$
55. $(-\infty, -1) \cup \left(0, \frac{4}{3}\right) \cup (2, \infty)$, or $\left\{x \mid x < -1 \text{ or } 0 < x < \frac{4}{3} \text{ or } x > 2\right\}$
57. $(-\infty, 0)$, or $\{x \mid x < 0\}$
59. $(-3, \infty)$, or $\{x \mid x > -3\}$
61. $(-2, 2)$, or $\{x \mid -2 < x < 2\}$
63. $(-\infty, 2)$, or $\{x \mid x < 2\}$

65. $(-\infty, -1) \cup \left(\frac{3}{2}, \infty\right)$, or $\left\{x \mid x < -1 \text{ or } x > \frac{3}{2}\right\}$

67. $(-\infty, -3) \cup (-1, 2)$, or $\{x \mid x < -3 \text{ or } -1 < x < 2\}$

69. $(-1, 1) \cup \left[\frac{5}{2}, \infty\right)$, or $\left\{x \mid -1 < x < 1 \text{ or } x \geq \frac{5}{2}\right\}$

71. $(3, \infty)$, or $\{x \mid x > 3\}$

73. $(-\infty, 0) \cup \left(0, \frac{1}{2}\right] \cup [2, \infty)$, or
$\left\{x \mid x < 0 \text{ or } 0 < x \leq \frac{1}{2} \text{ or } x \geq 2\right\}$

75. $(-2, 0) \cup [2, \infty)$, or $\{x \mid -2 < x < 0 \text{ or } x \geq 2\}$

77. (a) About 12.4 cars per minute **(b)** 3

79. Two possible solutions: width = 7 in., length = 14 in., height = 2 in.; width ≈ 2.266 in., length ≈ 4.532 in., height ≈ 19.086 in.

81. (a) $A(x) = \frac{x^2}{144} + \frac{3}{x}$ **(b)** $C(x) = 0.1\left(\frac{x^2}{144} + \frac{3}{x}\right)$
(c) 6 in. × 6 in. × 3 in.

83. (a) $D(0.05) \approx 238$; the braking distance for a car traveling at 50 miles per hour on a 5% uphill grade is about 238 ft.
(b) As the uphill grade x increases, the braking distance decreases, which agrees with driving experience.
(c) $x = \frac{13}{165} \approx 0.079$, or 7.9%

85. (a) $x \leq 36$ (approximately) **(b)** The average line length is less than or equal to 8 cars when the average arrival rate is about 36 cars per hour or less.

87. (a) The braking distance increases. **(b)** $0 < x \leq 0.3$

89. $\sqrt[3]{212.8} \leq x \leq \sqrt[3]{213.2}$, or (approximately) $5.97022 \leq x \leq 5.97396$ inches

91. $k = 6$ **93.** $k = 8$ **95.** $T = 160$ **97.** $y = 2$

99. Becomes half as much **101.** Becomes 27 times as much

103. $k = 0.5, n = 2$ **105.** $k = 3, n = 1$

107. 1.18 grams **109.** $\sqrt{50} \approx 7$ times as far

111. $\frac{2}{9}$ ohm **113.** F decreases by a factor of $\frac{\sqrt{2}}{2}$

SECTION 4.8 (pp. 333–336)

1. 4 **3.** $\frac{1}{8}$ **5.** -9 **7.** 27 **9.** 2 **11.** 9 **13.** $-\frac{1}{243}$

15. 16 **17.** $\frac{9}{4}$ **19.** $(2x)^{1/2}$ **21.** $z^{5/3}$ **23.** $\frac{1}{y^{3/4}}$

25. $x^{5/6}$ **27.** $y^{3/4}$ **29.** $\frac{\sqrt{b}}{\sqrt[4]{a^3}}$ **31.** $\sqrt{\sqrt{a} + \sqrt{b}}$

33. 4 **35.** 64 **37.** 5 **39.** -2

41.

43.

45.

47.

49.

51.

53. 7 **55.** -1 **57.** 2, 3 **59.** 4 **61.** 15 **63.** 8

65. -28 **67.** 2 **69.** 65,538

71. $50^{3/2} - 50^{1/2} \approx 346.48$ **73.** b

75.

77.

79.

81. 2 **83.** 81 **85.** ±32 **87.** ±8 **89.** $\sqrt[3]{16}$

91. $-1, -\frac{1}{2}$ **93.** $-\frac{1}{4}, \frac{5}{7}$ **95.** $-8, 27$ **97.** $\frac{1}{8}, \frac{64}{27}$

99. 1 **101.** $-1, \frac{1}{27}$

103. About 3.5; average speed is about 3.5 mi/hr.

105. $w \approx 3.63$ lb **107.** About 58.1 yr

109. (a) $a = 1960$ **(b)** $b \approx -1.2$
(c) $f(4) = 1960(4)^{-1.2} \approx 371$. If the zinc ion concentration reaches 371 milligrams per liter, a rainbow trout will survive, on average, 4 minutes.

111. (a) $f(2) \approx 1.06$ grams
(b) & (c) Approximately 1.1 grams

113. $a \approx 3.20, b \approx 0.20$

[1, 9, 1] by [0, 6, 1]

115. (a) $f(x) = 0.005192x^{1.7902}$ (Answers may vary.)
(b) About 2.6 million; too high; extrapolation
(c) About 1999

117. $a \approx 874.54, b \approx -0.49789$

4.8 EXTENDED AND DISCOVERY EXERCISES (p. 336)

1. The graph of an odd root function (not shown) is always increasing; the function is negative for $x < 0$, positive for $x > 0$, and zero at $x = 0$. It is an odd function.

3. $\dfrac{1}{\sqrt{x+h}+\sqrt{x}}$ **5.** $\dfrac{x+1}{x^{5/3}}$ **7.** $\dfrac{2-x}{3x^{1/3}(x+1)^2}$

9. (a) $20-x$

(b) $AP=\sqrt{x^2+12^2}$; $BP=\sqrt{(20-x)^2+16^2}$

(c) $f(x)=\sqrt{x^2+12^2}+\sqrt{(20-x)^2+16^2}$, $0<x<20$

(d) $[0, 20, 5]$ by $[0, 50, 10]$ **(e)** 8.57 ft; 34.41 ft

CHECKING BASIC CONCEPTS FOR SECTIONS 4.7 AND 4.8 (p. 336)

1. (a) $\frac{1}{2}$ **(b)** $-5, \frac{7}{3}$

(c) No real solutions (extraneous: -2)

3. $(-2, -1]\cup[1, \infty)$, or $\{x\,|-2<x\le-1 \text{ or } x\ge1\}$

5. (a) -8 **(b)** $\frac{1}{4}$ **(c)** 9   **7.** 8 (extraneous: 1)

9. $a=2, b=\frac{1}{2}$

CHAPTER 4 REVIEW EXERCISES (pp. 341–344)

1. Degree: 3; leading coefficient: -7

3. (a) Local minimum: -2; local maximum: 4.1

(b) No absolute minimum; no absolute maximum

5. Even   **7.** Odd   **9.** Odd

11. Answers may vary.

13. (a) 2; $-2, 0, 1$ **(b)** $a<0$ **(c)** 3

15. Up on left end, down on right end;

$f(x)\to\infty$ as $x\to-\infty$; $f(x)\to-\infty$ as $x\to\infty$

17. 7

19. (a)

f is continuous.

(b) $f(1)=2$; $f(3)=-1$ **(c)** $1, \sqrt{6}$

21. $2x^2-3x-1$ **23.** $2x^2-3x+1+\dfrac{1}{2x+3}$

25. $f(x)=\frac{1}{2}(x-1)(x-2)(x-3)$

27. $f(x)=\frac{1}{2}(x+2)(x-1)(x-3)$

29. $-3, \frac{1}{2}, 2$ **31.** $0, \pm\sqrt{3}$ **33.** $-1.88, 0.35, 1.53$

35. $0, \pm i$ **37.** $f(x)=4(x-1)(x-3i)(x+3i)$; $f(x)=4x^3-4x^2+36x-36$;

39. $f(x)=(x+i)(x-i)\left(x-\left(-\frac{1}{2}+\frac{i\sqrt{3}}{2}\right)\right)\times\left(x-\left(-\frac{1}{2}-\frac{i\sqrt{3}}{2}\right)\right)$

41. Horizontal: $y=\frac{2}{3}$; vertical: $x=\frac{1}{3}$

43.   **45.**

47. Answers may vary.

49. 4   **51.** No real solutions (extraneous: 2)

53. (a) $(-\infty, -4)\cup(-2, 3)$, or $\{x\,|\,x<-4 \text{ or } -2<x<3\}$

(b) $(-4, -2)\cup(3, \infty)$, or $\{x\,|-4<x<-2 \text{ or } x>3\}$

55. $(-3, 0)\cup(2, \infty)$, or $\{x\,|-3<x<0 \text{ or } x>2\}$

57. $(-\infty, -2)\cup\left(\frac{1}{2}, \infty\right)$, or $\left\{x\,|\,x<-2 \text{ or } x>\frac{1}{2}\right\}$

59. 216 **61.** 8 **63.** $x^{4/3}$ **65.** $y^{1/2}$

67. $D=\{x\,|\,x\ge0\}$; $f(3)\approx15.59$

69. 4 **71.** 6 **73.** $\frac{81}{16}$ **75.** 15 **77.** $-2, \frac{1}{3}$ **79.** $-1, 125$

81. (a) Dog: 148; person: 69 **(b)** 6.4 in.

83. (a) $81.5°F$ **(b)** 87.3; the ocean reaches a maximum temperature of about $87.3°F$ in late July. **85.** 4 sec

CHAPTER 4 EXTENDED AND DISCOVERY EXERCISES (pp. 344–345)

1. (a)

$f(t)=t^2$	$t_1=10$ $t_2=11$	$t_1=10$ $t_2=10.1$	$t_1=10$ $t_2=10.01$	$t_1=10$ $t_2=10.001$
average velocity (ft/sec)	21	20.1	20.01	20.001

(b) The velocity of the bike rider is 20 ft/sec at 10 sec.

3. (a)

f_1 in $[-10, 10, 1]$ by $[-10, 10, 1]$ f_2 in $[-10, 10, 1]$ by $[-10, 10, 1]$

f_3 in $[-10, 10, 1]$ by $[-10, 10, 1]$ f_4 in $[-10, 10, 1]$ by $[-10, 10, 1]$

(b) Neither the graph of each linear function nor the graph of its average rate of change has any turning points.

(c) For any linear function, the graph of its (average) rate of change is a constant function whose value is equal to the slope of the graph of the linear function.

5. (a)

f_1 in [−10, 10, 1] by [−10, 10, 1]

f_2 in [−10, 10, 1] by [−10, 10, 1]

f_3 in [−10, 10, 1] by [−10, 10, 1]

f_4 in [−10, 10, 1] by [−10, 10, 1]

(b) The graph of a cubic function has two turning points or none; the graph of its average rate of change has one turning point. The x-coordinate of a turning point of the function corresponds to an x-intercept on the graph of the average rate of change.

(c) For any cubic function, the graph of its average rate of change is a quadratic function. The leading coefficients of a cubic function and its average rate of change have the same sign.

CHAPTERS 1–4 CUMULATIVE REVIEW EXERCISES (pp. 345–347)

1. (a) $D = \{-3, -1, 0, 1\}$; $R = \{-2, 4, 5\}$ **(b)** No
3. $D = \{x \mid -2 \le x \le 2\}$; $R = \{x \mid 0 \le x \le 3\}$; $f(0) = 3$
5. $C(x) = 0.25x + 200$; $C(2000) = 700$; the cost of driving 2000 miles in one month is $700. **7.** 18
9. $y = -\frac{9}{5}x + \frac{7}{5}$ **11.** $y = -5$ **13.** Each radio costs $15 to manufacture. The fixed cost is $2000. **15.** $\frac{3}{5}$ **17.** $0, \frac{8}{3}$
19. $-2, \frac{5}{7}$ **21.** $\frac{1}{27}$; -8 **23.** $\frac{4}{5}$ **25.** No solutions; contradiction
27. $\left(-\infty, -\frac{1}{2}\right)$, or $\left\{x \mid x < -\frac{1}{2}\right\}$
29. $\left(-\infty, \frac{4}{5}\right] \cup [2, \infty)$, or $\left\{x \mid x \le \frac{4}{5} \text{ or } x \ge 2\right\}$
31. $(-\infty, -3] \cup [0, 3]$, or $\{x \mid x \le -3 \text{ or } 0 \le x \le 3\}$
33. (a) $-3, -1, 1, 2$ **(b)** $(-\infty, -3) \cup (-1, 1) \cup (2, \infty)$, or $\{x \mid x < -3 \text{ or } -1 < x < 1 \text{ or } x > 2\}$
(c) $[-3, -1] \cup [1, 2]$, or $\{x \mid -3 \le x \le -1 \text{ or } 1 \le x \le 2\}$

35. (a)

(b)

(c)

(d)

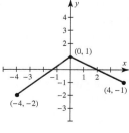

37. (a) Incr: $(-\infty, -2), (1, \infty)$, or $\{x \mid x < -2\}, \{x \mid x > 1\}$; decr: $(-2, 1)$, or $\{x \mid -2 < x < 1\}$
(b) Approximately -3.3, 0, and 1.8
(c) $(-2, 3)$ and $(1, -1)$ **(d)** Local maximum: 3; local minimum: -1
39. Answers may vary.

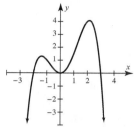

41. (a) $a - 2 + \frac{3}{a^2}$ **(b)** $2x^2 + 2x - 2 + \frac{-1}{x - 1}$
43. $f(x) = 4(x + 3)(x - 1)^2(x - 4)^3$ **45.** $-\frac{1}{2} + \frac{7}{2}i$
47. $D = \{x \mid x \ne -1, x \ne 4\}$; vertical: $x = -1, x = 4$; horizontal: $y = 0$
49. $m_1 = 20$ thousand: the pool is being filled at a rate of 20 thousand gallons per hour. $m_2 = 10$ thousand: the pool is being filled at a rate of 10 thousand gallons per hour. $m_3 = 0$: the pool is neither being filled nor being emptied. $m_4 = -15$ thousand: the pool is being emptied at a rate of 15 thousand gallons per hour.
51. 3.75 liters **53.** 400 thousand toy figures
55. (a) $C(t) = t(805 - 5t) = 805t - 5t^2$ **(b)** 25, 136; the cost is $17,000 when either 25 or 136 tickets are purchased. **(c)** $32,400 when 80 or 81 tickets are sold
57. $r \approx 1.7$ in., $h \approx 3.5$ in.

CHAPTER 5: Exponential and Logarithmic Functions

SECTION 5.1 (pp. 359–365)

1. 7 **3.** $4x^3$ **5.** The cost of x square yards of carpet
7. (a) -5 **(b)** -5 **(c)** -3 **(d)** $-\frac{1}{3}$
9. (a) $\frac{11}{2}$ **(b)** 0 **(c)** $\frac{9}{4}$ **(d)** Undefined
11. (a) $(f + g)(x) = 2x + x^2$; all real numbers
(b) $(f - g)(x) = 2x - x^2$; all real numbers
(c) $(fg)(x) = 2x^3$; all real numbers
(d) $(f/g)(x) = \frac{2}{x}$; $D = \{x \mid x \ne 0\}$
13. (a) $(f + g)(x) = 2x^2$; all real numbers
(b) $(f - g)(x) = -2$; all real numbers
(c) $(fg)(x) = x^4 - 1$; all real numbers
(d) $(f/g)(x) = \frac{x^2 - 1}{x^2 + 1}$; all real numbers
15. (a) $(f + g)(x) = 2x$; $D = \{x \mid x \ge 1\}$
(b) $(f - g)(x) = -2\sqrt{x - 1}$; $D = \{x \mid x \ge 1\}$
(c) $(fg)(x) = x^2 - x + 1$; $D = \{x \mid x \ge 1\}$
(d) $(f/g)(x) = \frac{x - \sqrt{x - 1}}{x + \sqrt{x - 1}}$; $D = \{x \mid x \ge 1\}$
17. (a) $(f + g)(x) = 2\sqrt{x}$; $D = \{x \mid x \ge 0\}$
(b) $(f - g)(x) = -2$; $D = \{x \mid x \ge 0\}$
(c) $(fg)(x) = x - 1$; $D = \{x \mid x \ge 0\}$
(d) $(f/g)(x) = \frac{\sqrt{x} - 1}{\sqrt{x} + 1}$; $D = \{x \mid x \ge 0\}$

19. (a) $(f + g)(x) = \frac{4}{x + 1}; D = \{x | x \neq -1\}$

(b) $(f - g)(x) = -\frac{2}{x + 1}; D = \{x | x \neq -1\}$

(c) $(fg)(x) = \frac{3}{(x + 1)^2}; D = \{x | x \neq -1\}$

(d) $(f/g)(x) = \frac{1}{3}; D = \{x | x \neq -1\}$

21. (a) $(f + g)(x) = \frac{x + 1}{2x - 4}; D = \{x | x \neq 2\}$

(b) $(f - g)(x) = \frac{1 - x}{2x - 4}; D = \{x | x \neq 2\}$

(c) $(fg)(x) = \frac{x}{(2x - 4)^2}; D = \{x | x \neq 2\}$

(d) $(f/g)(x) = \frac{1}{x}; D = \{x | x \neq 0, x \neq 2\}$

23. (a) $(f + g)(x) = x^2 - 1 + |x + 1|$; all real numbers

(b) $(f - g)(x) = x^2 - 1 - |x + 1|$; all real numbers

(c) $(fg)(x) = (x^2 - 1)|x + 1|$; all real numbers

(d) $(f/g)(x) = \frac{x^2 - 1}{|x + 1|}; D = \{x | x \neq -1\}$

25. (a) $(f + g)(x) = \frac{(x - 1)(2x^2 - 2x + 5)}{(x + 1)(x - 2)}$;

$D = \{x | x \neq -1, x \neq 2\}$

(b) $(f - g)(x) = \frac{-3(x - 1)(2x - 1)}{(x + 1)(x - 2)}$;

$D = \{x | x \neq -1, x \neq 2\}$

(c) $(fg)(x) = (x - 1)^2; D = \{x | x \neq -1, x \neq 2\}$

(d) $(f/g)(x) = \frac{(x - 2)^2}{(x + 1)^2}$;

$D = \{x | x \neq 1, x \neq -1, \text{and } x \neq 2\}$

27. (a) $(f + g)(x) = \frac{x^2 + 4x - 1}{(x - 1)^2(x + 1)}$;

$D = \{x | x \neq 1, x \neq -1\}$

(b) $(f - g)(x) = \frac{-x^2 - 3}{(x - 1)^2(x + 1)}$;

$D = \{x | x \neq 1, x \neq -1\}$

(c) $(fg)(x) = \frac{2}{(x - 1)^3}; D = \{x | x \neq 1, x \neq -1\}$

(d) $(f/g)(x) = \frac{2(x - 1)}{(x + 1)^2}; D = \{x | x \neq 1, x \neq -1\}$

29. (a) $(f + g)(x) = x^{1/2}(x^2 - x + 1); D = \{x | x \geq 0\}$

(b) $(f - g)(x) = x^{1/2}(x^2 - x - 1); D = \{x | x \geq 0\}$

(c) $(fg)(x) = x^2(x - 1); D = \{x | x \geq 0\}$

(d) $(f/g)(x) = x(x - 1); D = \{x | x > 0\}$

31. (a) 2   **(b)** 4   **(c)** 0   **(d)** $-\frac{1}{3}$

33. (a) 2   **(b)** -3 **(c)** 2   **(d)** -2

35. (a) -5 **(b)** -2 **(c)** 0   **(d)** Undefined

37. (a) 5   **(b)** 5   **(c)** 0   **(d)** Undefined

39.

x	-2	0	2	4
$(f + g)(x)$	6	5	5	15
$(f - g)(x)$	-6	5	9	5
$(fg)(x)$	0	0	-14	50
$(f/g)(x)$	0	—	-3.5	2

41. (a) $g(-3) = -5$ **(b)** $g(b) = 2b + 1$

(c) $g(x^3) = 2x^3 + 1$ **(d)** $g(2x - 3) = 4x - 5$

43. (a) $g(-3) = -4$ **(b)** $g(b) = 2(b + 3)^2 - 4$

(c) $g(x^3) = 2(x^3 + 3)^2 - 4$

(d) $g(2x - 3) = 8x^2 - 4$

45. (a) $g(-3) = -\frac{11}{2}$ **(b)** $g(b) = \frac{1}{2}b^2 + 3b - 1$

(c) $g(x^3) = \frac{1}{2}x^6 + 3x^3 - 1$ **(d)** $g(2x - 3) = 2x^2 - \frac{11}{2}$

47. (a) $g(-3) = 1$ **(b)** $g(b) = \sqrt{b + 4}$

(c) $g(x^3) = \sqrt{x^3 + 4}$ **(d)** $g(2x - 3) = \sqrt{2x + 1}$

49. (a) $g(-3) = 14$ **(b)** $g(b) = |3b - 1| + 4$

(c) $g(x^3) = |3x^3 - 1| + 4$

(d) $g(2x - 3) = |6x - 10| + 4$

51. (a) $g(-3)$ is undefined.   **(b)** $g(b) = \frac{4b}{b + 3}$

(c) $g(x^3) = \frac{4x^3}{x^3 + 3}$ **(d)** $g(2x - 3) = \frac{2(2x - 3)}{x}$

53. (a) 3   **(b)** 4   **55. (a)** 18   **(b)** 23

57. (a) $(f \circ g)(x) = (x^2 + 3x - 1)^3$; all real numbers

(b) $(g \circ f)(x) = x^6 + 3x^3 - 1$; all real numbers

(c) $(f \circ f)(x) = x^9$; all real numbers

59. (a) $(f \circ g)(x) = x^4 + x^2 - 3x - 2$; all real numbers

(b) $(g \circ f)(x) = (x + 2)^4 + (x + 2)^2 - 3(x + 2) - 4$; all

real numbers   **(c)** $(f \circ f)(x) = x + 4$; all real numbers

61. (a) $(f \circ g)(x) = 2 - 3x^3$; all real numbers

(b) $(g \circ f)(x) = (2 - 3x)^3$; all real numbers

(c) $(f \circ f)(x) = 9x - 4$; all real numbers

63. (a) $(f \circ g)(x) = \frac{1}{5x + 1}; D = \{x | x \neq -\frac{1}{5}\}$

(b) $(g \circ f)(x) = \frac{5}{x + 1}; D = \{x | x \neq -1\}$

(c) $(f \circ f)(x) = \frac{x + 1}{x + 2}; D = \{x | x \neq -1, x \neq -2\}$

65. (a) $(f \circ g)(x) = \sqrt{4 - x^2} + 4$;

$D = \{x | -2 \leq x \leq 2\}$

(b) $(g \circ f)(x) = \sqrt{4 - (x + 4)^2}$;

$D = \{x | -6 \leq x \leq -2\}$

(c) $(f \circ f)(x) = x + 8$; all real numbers

67. (a) $(f \circ g)(x) = \sqrt{3x - 1}; D = \{x | x \geq \frac{1}{3}\}$

(b) $(g \circ f)(x) = 3\sqrt{x - 1}; D = \{x | x \geq 1\}$

(c) $(f \circ f)(x) = \sqrt{\sqrt{x - 1} - 1}; D = \{x | x \geq 2\}$

69. (a) $(f \circ g)(x) = x$; all real numbers

(b) $(g \circ f)(x) = x$; all real numbers

(c) $(f \circ f)(x) = 25x - 4$; all real numbers

71. (a) $(f \circ g)(x) = x; D = \{x | x \neq 0\}$

(b) $(g \circ f)(x) = x; D = \{x | x \neq 0\}$

(c) $(f \circ f)(x) = x; D = \{x | x \neq 0\}$

73. (a) -4 **(b)** 2   **(c)** -4

75. (a) -3 **(b)** -2 **(c)** 0

77. (a) 5   **(b)** Undefined   **(c)** 4   **79.** 4; 2

Answers may vary for Exercises 81–93.

81. $f(x) = x - 2, g(x) = \sqrt{x}$

83. $f(x) = x + 2, g(x) = \frac{1}{x}$

85. $f(x) = 2x + 1, g(x) = 4x^3$

87. $f(x) = x^3 - 1, g(x) = x^2$

89. $f(x) = x + 2, g(x) = -4|x| - 3$

91. $f(x) = x - 1, g(x) = \frac{1}{x^2}$

93. $f(x) = x^{1/4}, g(x) = x^3 - x$

95. $P(x) = 10x - 12{,}000; P(3000) = \$18{,}000$

97. (a) $I(x) = 36x$ **(b)** $C(x) = 2.54x$

(c) $F(x) = (C \circ I)(x)$ **(d)** $F(x) = 91.44x$

99. (a) $s(x) = \frac{11}{6}x + \frac{1}{9}x^2$ **(b)** $s(60) = 510$; it takes 510

feet to stop when traveling 60 mi/hr.

101. (a) $(g \circ f)(1) = 5.25$; a 1% decrease in the ozone

layer could result in a 5.25% increase in skin cancer.

(b) Not possible using the given tables

103. (a) 4.5%   **(b)** $(g \circ f)(x)$ computes the percent

increase in peak electrical demand during year x.

105. (a) $(g \circ f)(1960) = 1.98$
(b) $(g \circ f)(x) = 0.165(x - 1948)$
(c) $f, g,$ and $g \circ f$ are all linear functions.
107. (a) $(g \circ f)(2) \approx 25°C$ **(b)** $(g \circ f)(x)$ computes the Celsius temperature after x hours.
109. (a) $A(4s) = 16\frac{\sqrt{3}}{4}s^2 = 16A(s)$; if the length of a side is quadrupled, the area increases by a factor of 16.
(b) $A(s + 2) = \frac{\sqrt{3}}{4}(s^2 + 4s + 4) = A(s) + \sqrt{3}(s + 1)$; if the length of a side increases by 2, the area increases by $\sqrt{3}(s + 1)$.
111. $A = 36\pi t^2$
113. (a)

x	1990	2000	2010	2020	2030
$h(x)$	32	35.5	39	42.5	46

(b) $h(x) = f(x) + g(x)$
115. $h(x) = 0.35x - 664.5$
117. (a) $M(20) = 50$; $N(20) = 140$; the median income was $50 thousand in 2010, while the 90th percentile was $140 thousand.
(b) $D(x) = -0.15x^2 + 3.9x + 72$; $D(x)$ gives the household income difference between the 90th percentile and the median.
(c) $D(20) = 90$; the household income difference between the 90th percentile and the median in 2010 was $90 thousand.
119. Let $f(x) = ax + b$ and $g(x) = cx + d$. Then $f(x) + g(x) = (ax + b) + (cx + d) = (a + c)x + (b + d)$, which is linear.
121. (a) $(f \circ g)(x) = k$; a constant function
(b) $(g \circ f)(x) = ak + b$; a constant function

SECTION 5.2 (pp. 375–379)

1. Closing a window
3. Closing a book, standing up, and walking out of the classroom
5. Subtract 2 from x; $x + 2$ and $x - 2$
7. Divide x by 3 and then add 2; $3(x - 2)$ and $\frac{x}{3} + 2$
9. Subtract 1 from x and cube the result; $\sqrt[3]{x} + 1$ and $(x - 1)^3$ **11.** Take the reciprocal of x; $\frac{1}{x}$ and $\frac{1}{x}$
13. One-to-one **15.** Not one-to-one
17. Not one-to-one
19. Not one-to-one; does not have an inverse
21. One-to-one; does have an inverse
23. One-to-one **25.** Not one-to-one
27. Not one-to-one **29.** Not one-to-one
31. Not one-to-one **33.** Not one-to-one
35. One-to-one **37.** No **39.** Yes
41. $f^{-1}(x) = x^3$ **43.** $f^{-1}(x) = -\frac{1}{2}x + 5$
45. $f^{-1}(x) = \frac{x + 1}{3}$ **47.** $f^{-1}(x) = \sqrt[3]{\frac{x + 5}{2}}$
49. $f^{-1}(x) = \sqrt{x + 1}$ **51.** $f^{-1}(x) = \frac{1}{2x}$
53. $f^{-1}(x) = -\frac{2(x - 3)}{5}$ **55.** $f^{-1}(x) = -\frac{2x}{x - 1}$
57. $f^{-1}(x) = \frac{x + 1}{x - 2}$ **59.** $f^{-1}(x) = \frac{1}{x + 3}$
61. $f^{-1}(x) = \sqrt[3]{\frac{1 + x}{x}}$
63. If the domain of f is restricted to $x \ge 0$, then $f^{-1}(x) = \sqrt{4 - x}$.

65. If the domain of f is restricted to $x \ge 2$, then $f^{-1}(x) = 2 + \sqrt{x - 4}$.
67. If the domain of f is restricted to $x \ge 0$, then $f^{-1}(x) = (x - 1)^{3/2}$.
69. If the domain of f is restricted to $0 \le x \le \frac{3}{\sqrt{2}}$, then $f^{-1}(x) = \sqrt{\frac{9 - x^2}{2}}$.
71. $f^{-1}(x) = \frac{x + 15}{5}$; D and R are all real numbers.
73. $f^{-1}(x) = x^3 + 5$; D and R are all real numbers.
75. $f^{-1}(x) = 4x + 5$; D and R are all real numbers.
77. $f^{-1}(x) = x^2 + 5$; $D = \{x \mid x \ge 0\}$ and $R = \{y \mid y \ge 5\}$
79. $f^{-1}(x) = \frac{1}{x} - 3$; $D = \{x \mid x \ne 0\}$ and $R = \{y \mid y \ne -3\}$
81. $f^{-1}(x) = \sqrt[3]{\frac{x}{2}}$; D and R are all real numbers.
83. $f^{-1}(x) = \sqrt{x}$; D and R include all nonnegative real numbers.
85.

x	5	7	9
$f^{-1}(x)$	1	2	3

For f: $D = \{1, 2, 3\}$, $R = \{5, 7, 9\}$;
for f^{-1}: $D = \{5, 7, 9\}$, $R = \{1, 2, 3\}$
87.

x	0	4	16
$f^{-1}(x)$	0	2	4

For f: $D = \{0, 2, 4\}$, $R = \{0, 4, 16\}$;
for f^{-1}: $D = \{0, 4, 16\}$, $R = \{0, 2, 4\}$
89.

x	0	2	4	6
$f^{-1}(x)$	0	$\frac{1}{2}$	1	$\frac{3}{2}$

91. 1 **93.** 3 **95.** 5 **97.** 1
99. (a) $f(1) \approx 110$ dollars **(b)** $f^{-1}(110) \approx 1$ year
(c) $f^{-1}(160) \approx 5$ years; $f^{-1}(x)$ computes the years necessary for the account to accumulate x dollars.
101. (a) 2 **(b)** 3 **(c)** 1 **(d)** 3
103. (a) 4 **(b)** 0 **(c)** 9 **(d)** 4
105.

107.

109.

111.

113.

115.
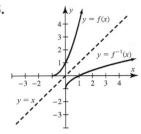

117. $Y_1 = 3X - 1$, $Y_2 = (X + 1)/3$, $Y_3 = X$
$[-4.7, 4.7, 1]$ by $[-3.1, 3.1, 1]$

119. $Y_1 = X^3/3 - 1$, $Y_2 = \sqrt[3]{(3X + 3)}$, $Y_3 = X$
$[-4.7, 4.7, 1]$ by $[-3.1, 3.1, 1]$

121. (a) Yes **(b)** The radius r of a sphere with volume V
(c) $r = \sqrt[3]{\dfrac{3V}{4\pi}}$ **(d)** No. If V and r were interchanged, then r would represent the volume and V would represent the radius. **123. (a)** 135.7 pounds **(b)** Yes
(c) $h = \dfrac{7}{25}\left(W + \dfrac{800}{7}\right) = \dfrac{7}{25}W + 32$ **(d)** 74; the maximum recommended height for a person weighing 150 lb is 74 in. **(e)** The inverse formula computes the maximum recommended height for a person of a given weight.
125. (a) $(F \circ Y)(2) = 10,560$ represents the number of feet in 2 miles. **(b)** $F^{-1}(26,400) = 8800$ represents the number of yards in 26,400 ft. **(c)** $(Y^{-1} \circ F^{-1})(21,120) = 4$ represents the number of miles in 21,120 ft.
127. (a) $(Q \circ C)(96) = 1.5$ represents the number of quarts in 96 tbsp. **(b)** $Q^{-1}(2) = 8$ represents the number of cups in 2 qt. **(c)** $(C^{-1} \circ Q^{-1})(1.5) = 96$ represents the number of tablespoons in 1.5 qt.

5.2 EXTENDED AND DISCOVERY EXERCISES (p. 379)

1. (a) $f^{-1}(x)$ computes the elapsed time in seconds when the rocket was x ft above the ground. **(b)** The solution to the equation $f(x) = 5000$ is the elapsed time in seconds when the rocket reached 5000 ft above the ground. **(c)** Evaluate $f^{-1}(5000)$.

CHECKING BASIC CONCEPTS FOR SECTIONS 5.1 AND 5.2 (p. 380)

1. (a) $(f + g)(1) = 1$ **(b)** $(f - g)(-1) = 3$
(c) $(fg)(0) = 2$ **(d)** $(f/g)(2)$ is undefined.
(e) $(f \circ g)(2) = -2$ **(f)** $(g \circ f)(-2) = -1$
3. (a) $(f + g)(x) = x^2 + 6x - 3$
(b) $(f/g)(x) = \dfrac{x^2 + 3x - 2}{3x - 1}, x \neq \dfrac{1}{3}$
(c) $(f \circ g)(x) = 9x^2 + 3x - 4$

5. (a) Yes; yes; $f^{-1}(x) = x - 1$ **(b)** No; no
7. (a) 0 **(b)** 2

SECTION 5.3 (p. 393–398)

1. $\dfrac{1}{8}$ **3.** 6 **5.** -18 **7.** 2 **9.** 1 **11.** 5
13. Linear; $f(x) = -1.2x + 2$
15. Exponential; $f(x) = 8(\dfrac{1}{2})^x$
17. Exponential; $f(x) = 5(2^x)$
19. Linear; $f(x) = 3.5x - 2$
21. Exponential; $f(x) = 81(\dfrac{1}{3})^x$
23. $f(x) = 2^x$ **25.** $f(x) = 2x + 1$
27. $C = 5, a = 1.5$ **29.** $C = 10, a = 2$
31. $C = 3, a = 3$ **33.** $C = \dfrac{1}{2}, a = \dfrac{1}{3}$
35. $f(x) = 4x + 4; g(x) = 4(2)^x$
37. $f(x) = -\dfrac{7}{2}x + 5; g(x) = 3(\dfrac{1}{2})^x$
39. $C = 5000, a = 2$; x represents time in hours.
41. $C = 200,000, a = 0.95$; x represents the number of years after 2000.
43. About 11 pounds per square inch
45. 71.2571 **47.** -0.7586

49.

51.

53.

55.
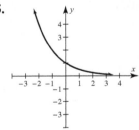

57. $C = 1, a = \dfrac{1}{2}$ **59.** $C = \dfrac{1}{2}, a = 4$
61. (a) D: $(-\infty, \infty)$ or $\{x \mid -\infty < x < \infty\}$; R: $(0, \infty)$ or $\{x \mid x > 0\}$ **(b)** Decreasing **(c)** $y = 0$
(d) y-intercept: 7; no x-intercept **(e)** Yes; yes
63. (i) b **(ii)** d **(iii)** a **(iv)** c

65. (a)

(b)

(c)

(d)

67.

69.

71.

73. $841.53   **75.** $1730.97   **77.** $4451.08
79. $1652.83   **81.** $14,326.78   **83.** Annually
85. (a) $B(x) = 2.5(3)^x$
(b) About 13 million per milliliter
87. (a) About 1.5 watts per square meter
(b) The y-intercept indicates that the intensity is 300 watts
per square meter at the surface.
$[-5, 50, 5]$ by $[0, 350, 50]$

89. About 7.2 million
91. (a) $C \approx 0.72, a \approx 1.041$ (answers may vary slightly)
(b) 1.21 ppb (answers may vary slightly)
93. (a) About 6,214,000 bacteria per milliliter
(b) There will be 10 million *E. coli* bacteria per milliliter
after about 214 min, or about 3.6 hr.
95. (a) About 92%   **(b)** About 0.83 min
97. $T(t) = 100\left(\frac{1}{2}\right)^{t/2.8}; T(5.5) \approx 25.6\%$
99. (a) $P(x) = 95(0.9)^x$ **(b)** About 11.5%
(c) About 6.6 feet   **101.** About 18,935 yr
103. About 27.3%
105. (a) $C = 2.5, a = 0.7$ **(b)** 1.225 ppm
107. (a) $H(30) \approx 0.42$; about 0.42 horsepower is required
for each ton pulled at 30 mi/hr.
(b) About 2100 horsepower   **(c)** 2

5.3 EXTENDED AND DISCOVERY EXERCISES (p. 398)

1. The formulas are equivalent.   **3.** $12,914.64
5. (a) About 1.0005   **(b)** 1   **(c)** They are very similar.
7. (a) About 0.6068   **(b)** About 0.6065
(c) They are very similar.
9. The average rate of change near x and the value of the
function at x are approximately equal.

SECTION 5.4 (pp. 410–414)

1.

x	10^0	10^4	10^{-8}	$10^{1.26}$
$\log x$	0	4	-8	1.26

3. (a) Undefined   **(b)** -2 **(c)** $-\frac{1}{2}$ **(d)** 0
5. (a) 1   **(b)** 4   **(c)** -20 **(d)** -2
7. (a) 2   **(b)** $\frac{1}{2}$ **(c)** 3   **(d)** Undefined
9. (a) $n = 1, \log 79 \approx 1.898$
(b) $n = 2, \log 500 \approx 2.699$ **(c)** $n = 0, \log 5 \approx 0.699$
(d) $n = -1, \log 0.5 \approx -0.301$
11. (a) $\frac{3}{2}$ **(b)** $\frac{1}{3}$ **(c)** $-\frac{1}{5}$ **(d)** -1
13. $\{x \mid x > -3\}$, or $(-3, \infty)$
15. $\{x \mid x < -1 \text{ or } x > 1\}$, or $(-\infty, -1) \cup (1, \infty)$
17. $\{x \mid -\infty < x < \infty\}$, or $(-\infty, \infty)$
19. $\{x \mid x < 2\}$, or $(-\infty, 2)$
21. -5.7 **23.** $2x, x > 0$ **25.** 64
27. -4 **29.** π **31.** $x - 1$ for $x > 1$
33. 6   **35.** $\frac{1}{2}$ **37.** -3 **39.** 2   **41.** 2   **43.** -2
45. -1 **47.** 0   **49.** -4
51.

x	6	7	21
$f(x)$	0	2	8

53. (a) $4x = \log_7 4$ **(b)** $x = \ln 7$ **(c)** $x = \log_c b$
55. (a) $x = 8^3$ **(b)** $2 + x = 9^5$ **(c)** $b = k^c$
57. (a) -2 **(b)** $\log 7 \approx 0.85$ **(c)** No solutions
59. (a) -2 **(b)** $\ln 2 \approx 0.69$ **(c)** 3
61. (a) 0   **(b)** $\frac{1}{2}$ **(c)** $\frac{1}{3}$
63. $-\ln 3 \approx -1.10$ **65.** 2   **67.** $\frac{2}{3}$
69. $\frac{\log 13}{4} \approx 0.28$ **71.** $\log_3 4 \approx 1.26$ **73.** $\ln 23 \approx 3.14$
75. $\log_2 14 \approx 3.81$ **77.** $\ln\left(\frac{18}{5}\right) \approx 1.28$ **79.** 8
81. (a) $10^2 = 100$ **(b)** $10^{-3} = 0.001$
(c) $10^{1.2} \approx 15.8489$
83. (a) $2^6 = 64$ **(b)** $3^{-2} = \frac{1}{9}$ **(c)** $e^2 \approx 7.3891$
85. $2^{1.2} \approx 2.2974$ **87.** $\frac{49}{2}$ **89.** 1000   **91.** 20
93. $e^{3/4} \approx 2.1170$ **95.** $e^{7/5} \approx 4.0552$ **97.** 16
99. $\frac{1}{2} e^{6/5} \approx 1.6601$ **101.** 8   **103.** $a = 5, b = 2$
105. $f^{-1}(x) = \ln x$ **107.** $f^{-1}(x) = 2^x$

109. Decreasing

111. (a)

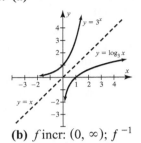

(b) f incr: $(0, \infty)$; f^{-1}
incr: $(-\infty, \infty)$

113. $x = 2$

115. $x = 0$

117. $x = 0$

119. $x = 1$

121. $D = \{x \mid x > -1\}$
$[-6, 6, 1]$ by $[-4, 4, 1]$

123. $D = \{x \mid x < 0\}$
$[-6, 6, 1]$ by $[-4, 4, 1]$

125. 120 dB **127. (a)** $L(100) = 6$; a 100-thousand-pound plane needs 6000 feet of runway. **(b)** No. It increases by 3000 ft. **(c)** If the weight increases tenfold, the runway length increases by 3000 ft.
129. (a) 4.7 **(b)** $10^{3.5} \approx 3162$
131. (a) Yugoslavia: $x = 1,000,000$;
Indonesia: $x = 100,000,000$ **(b)** 100
133. (a) $f(0) = 27$, $f(100) \approx 29.2$. At the eye, the barometric air pressure is 27 in.; 100 mi away, it is 29.2 in.
(b) The air pressure increases rapidly at first and then starts to level off.
$[0, 250, 50]$ by $[25, 30, 1]$

(c) About 7 miles
135. (a) About $49.4°C$ **(b)** About 0.69 hr, or 41.4 min
137. (a) About 0.189, or an 18.9% chance
(b) $x = -3 \ln (0.3) \approx 3.6$ min
139. $a = 7$, $b = 4$; about 178 km^2
141. (a) $C = 3$, $a = 2$ **(b)** After about 2.4 days

5.4 EXTENDED AND DISCOVERY EXERCISES (p. 414)

1. (a) 1.00 **(b)** 0.50 **(c)** 0.33 **(d)** 0.25
3. (a) $T(x) = 6.5 \ln (1.3 \cdot 1.005^x)$; $T(100) \approx 4.95$.
The average global temperature may increase by 4.95°F by the year 2100.
(b) $[0, 200, 50]$ by $[0, 1000, 100]$ $[0, 200, 50]$ by $[0, 10, 1]$

The carbon dioxide level graph is exponential, whereas the average global temperature graph is linear. **(c)** Average global temperature rises by a constant amount each year.

CHECKING BASIC CONCEPTS FOR SECTIONS 5.3 AND 5.4 (pp. 414–415)

1. 1752.12; 1754.74
3. $\log_2 15$ represents the exponent k such that $2^k = 15$. No.
5. (a) $\ln 5 \approx 1.609$ **(b)** $\log 25 \approx 1.398$
(c) $10^{1.5} \approx 31.623$ **7. (a)** About 38.1 million; in 2012 California's population was about 38.1 million. **(b)** 37.3; in 2010 California's population was about 37.3 million. **(c)** About 1% **(d)** 2017

SECTION 5.5 (pp. 421–423)

1. 1.447; Product rule **3.** 2.197; Quotient rule
5. 3.010; Power rule **7.** $\log_2 a + \log_2 b$
9. $\ln 7 + 4 \ln a$ **11.** $\log 6 - \log z$
13. $2 \log x - \log 3$ **15.** $\ln 2 + 7 \ln x - \ln 3 - \ln k$
17. $2 + 2 \log_2 k + 3 \log_2 x$
19. $2 + 3 \log_5 x - 4 \log_5 y$
21. $4 \ln x - 2 \ln y - \frac{3}{2} \ln z$
23. $-1 + 3 \log_4 (x + 2)$ **25.** $3 \log_5 x - 4 \log_5 (x - 4)$
27. $\frac{1}{2} \log_2 x - 2 \log_2 z$ **29.** $\frac{1}{3} \ln (2x + 6) - \frac{5}{3} \ln (x + 1)$
31. $\frac{1}{3} \log_2 (x^2 - 1) - \frac{1}{2} \log_2 (1 + x^2)$
33. $\log 6$ **35.** $\ln 5^{-3/2}$ **37.** $\log 2$
39. $\log 6$ **41.** $\log_7 5k^2$ **43.** $\ln x^3$ **45.** $\log x^{3/2}$
47. $\ln \frac{x^3 z^4}{\sqrt{y^3}}$ **49.** $\ln \frac{2}{e}$ **51.** $\ln \frac{x^2 \sqrt{z}}{y^4}$
53. $\log (4 \sqrt{x^5})$ **55.** $\log \frac{(x^2 - 1)^2 (x - 2)^4}{\sqrt{y}}$
57. (a) Yes **(b)** By the product rule:
$\log 3x + \log 2x = \log (3x \cdot 2x) = \log 6x^2$
59. (a) Yes **(b)** By the quotient rule:
$\ln 2x^2 - \ln x = \ln \left(\frac{2x^2}{x}\right) = \ln 2x$
61. (a) Yes **(b)** By the power rule:
$\ln x^4 - \ln x^2 = 4 \ln x - 2 \ln x = 2 \ln x$
63.

65.

67. $\frac{\log 25}{\log 2} \approx 4.644$ **69.** $\frac{\log 130}{\log 5} \approx 3.024$

71. $\frac{\log 5}{\log 2} + \frac{\log 7}{\log 2} \approx 5.129$ **73.** $\sqrt{\frac{\log 46}{\log 4}} \approx 1.662$

75. $\frac{\log 12 / \log 2}{\log 3 / \log 2} = \frac{\log 12}{\log 3} \approx 2.262$ **77.** 4.714

79. ± 2.035 **81.** $L(x) = \frac{3 \ln x}{\ln 10}$; $L(50) \approx 5.097$; yes

83. 10 decibels   **85.** $I = I_0\, e^{-kx}$

87. (a) $x = 100 \ln \frac{P}{37.3}$ (b) About 7; the population is expected to reach 40 million during 2017.

89. $t = \frac{\ln \frac{A}{P}}{r}$

91. $\log(1 \cdot 2^2 \cdot 3^3 \cdot 4^4 \cdot 5^5) = \log 86{,}400{,}000$

SECTION 5.6 (pp. 431–435)

1. (a) About 2   (b) $\ln 7.5 \approx 2.015$
3. (a) About 2   (b) $5 \log 2.5 \approx 1.990$
5. $\ln 1.25 \approx 0.2231$ **7.** $\log 20 \approx 1.301$
9. $-\frac{5}{6} \ln 0.4 \approx 0.7636$ **11.** $\frac{\ln 0.5}{\ln 0.9} \approx 6.579$
13. $1 + \frac{\log 4}{\log 1.1} \approx 15.55$ **15.** 1   **17.** $\frac{1}{5}$ **19.** 1, 2
21. No solutions   **23.** $2 + \frac{\log(1/3)}{\log(2/5)} \approx 3.199$
25. $\frac{\log 4}{\log 4 - 2 \log 3} \approx -1.710$ **27.** $\frac{3}{1 - 3 \ln 2} \approx -2.779$
29. $\frac{\log(64/3)}{\log 1.4} \approx 9.095$ **31.** $1980 + \frac{\log(8/5)}{\log 1.015} \approx 2012$
33. -3 **35.** $0, -1$ **37.** 1   **39.** $\frac{6}{7}$ **41.** $-\frac{12}{5}$
43. $10^{2/3} \approx 4.642$ **45.** $\frac{1}{2} e^5 \approx 74.207$
47. $\pm \sqrt{50} \approx \pm 7.071$ **49.** 6   **51.** -39
53. 10^{-11} **55.** $e \approx 2.718$ **57.** $2^{2.1} \approx 4.287$
59. $\sqrt{50} \approx 7.071$ **61.** $-\frac{998}{3}$ **63.** $2 \left(\text{extraneous } -\frac{5}{3} \right)$
65. $1 + \sqrt{2} \approx 2.414$ (extraneous $1 - \sqrt{2}$)
67. 2 (extraneous -2)   **69.** 2 (extraneous -4)
71. 4 (extraneous -4)   **73.** 0.31   **75.** 1.71   **77.** 2.10
79. 2018   **81.** $\frac{\ln 0.25}{-0.12} \approx 11.55$ ft
83. (a) $T(x) = 2300(2)^{x/2}$ (b) $T(40) \approx 2{,}411{,}724{,}800$; in 2011 there were about 2.4 billion transistors on an integrated circuit.   (c) About 1995   **85.** (a) About 0.88; the Human Development Index is 0.88.   (b) 3.9
87. About 1981   **89.** (a) $C = 1$, $a \approx 1.01355$
(b) $P(2010) \approx 1.14$ billion   (c) About 2030
91. (a) $T_0 = 32$, $D = 180$, $a \approx 0.045$ (b) About 139°F
(c) About 1 hr   **93.** (a) About 16.7°C   (b) About 1.09 hr
95. About 2.8 acres   **97.** $100 - 10^{1.16} \approx 85.5\%$
99. (a) $\frac{\ln 1.15}{6} \approx 0.0233$ (b) About 1.45 billion per liter
(c) About 2.36%   **101.** 8.25 yr   **103.** (a) $\frac{\ln 1.5}{0.03} \approx 13.5$
(b) \$500 invested at 3% compounded continuously results in \$750 after 13.5 years.   **105.** About 8633 yr
107. $-2 \ln 0.5 \approx 1.39$ min   **109.** About 3.6 hr
111. About 13.5 yr   **113.** (a) 11 milligrams/liter
(b) About 2.11 hr
115. $t = \frac{\log(A/P)}{n \log(1 + r/n)}$

5.6 EXTENDED AND DISCOVERY EXERCISE (p. 435)

1. $f(x) = Ce^{x \ln a}$ and $g(x) = e^{x \ln 2}$; that is, $k = \ln a$.

CHECKING BASIC CONCEPTS FOR SECTIONS 5.5 AND 5.6 (p. 435)

1. $2 \log x + 3 \log y - \frac{1}{3} \log z$ **3.** (a) $\frac{\log(29/5)}{\log(1.4)} \approx 5.224$

(b) $\frac{1}{3}$ **5.** (a) It levels off at 80°F.   (b) 17 min

SECTION 5.7 (pp. 441–443)

1. Logarithmic   **3.** Exponential
5. Exponential: $f(x) = 1.2(1.7)^x$
7. Logarithmic: $f(x) = 1.088 + 2.937 \ln x$
9. Logistic: $f(x) = \frac{9.96}{1 + 30.6e^{-1.51x}}$
11. (a) Quadratic: $V(x) = 3.55x^2 + 0.21x + 1.9$
(b) 91.7 million   **13.** $f(x) = 9.02 + 1.03 \ln x$
15. (a) $f(x) = 1.4734(0.99986)^x$
(b) Approximately 0.55 kg/m³
17. (a) $f(x) = \frac{4.9955}{1 + 49.7081 e^{-0.6998x}}$
(b) About 5 thousand per acre
19. (a) $C(x) = \frac{0.94}{1 + 17.97 e^{-0.862x}}$ (b) About 0.93 billion
21. (a) $A(w) = 101 w^{0.662}$
(b) $[0, 20, 2]$ by $[100, 700, 50]$

(c) About 11.2 lb
23. (a) 3 ft; after 5 years, the tree is 3 feet tall.
(b) $H(x) = \frac{50.2}{1 + 47.4 e^{-0.221x}}$
(c) $[0, 45, 5]$ by $[0, 55, 5]$

(d) About 17.4 yr   **(e)** Interpolation
25. (a) The data are not linear.
$[-2, 32, 5]$ by $[0, 80, 10]$

(b) $f(x) = 12.42(1.066)^x$ (c) $f(39) \approx 150$; fertilizer use increased but at a slower rate than predicted by f.

5.7 EXTENDED AND DISCOVERY EXERCISE (p. 443)

1. (a) $f(x) = 0.0904(0.844)^x$ (regression) or $f(x) \approx 0.128(0.777)^x$ (trial and error)
(b) About 4.6 min   (c) Answers may vary.

CHECKING BASIC CONCEPTS FOR SECTION 5.7 (p. 444)

1. Exponential: $f(x) = 0.5(1.2)^x$
3. Logistic: $f(x) = \frac{4.5}{1 + 277 e^{-1.4x}}$

CHAPTER 5 REVIEW EXERCISES (pp. 447–450)

1. (a) 8 **(b)** 0 **(c)** −6 **(d)** Undefined
3. (a) 7 **(b)** 1 **(c)** 0 **(d)** $-\frac{9}{2}$
5. (a) 2 **(b)** 1 **(c)** 2 **7. (a)** $\sqrt{6}$ **(b)** 12
9. $(f \circ g)(x) = \left(\frac{1}{x}\right)^3 - \left(\frac{1}{x}\right)^2 + 3\left(\frac{1}{x}\right) - 2; D = \{x \mid x \neq 0\}$
11. $(f \circ g)(x) = x$; all real numbers
13. $f(x) = x^2 + 3, g(x) = \sqrt{x}$ (answers may vary)
15. Subtract 6 from x and then multiply the result by 10; $\frac{x}{10} + 6$ and $10(x - 6)$ **17.** f is one-to-one. **19.** f is not one-to-one.
21.

x	6	4	3	1
$f^{-1}(x)$	−1	0	4	6

For $f: D = \{-1, 0, 4, 6\}$ and $R = \{1, 3, 4, 6\}$;
for $f^{-1}: D = \{1, 3, 4, 6\}$ and $R = \{-1, 0, 4, 6\}$
23. $f^{-1}(x) = \frac{x + 5}{3}$
25. $(f \circ f^{-1})(x) = f\left(\frac{x + 1}{2}\right) = 2\left(\frac{x + 1}{2}\right) - 1 = x$;
$(f^{-1} \circ f)(x) = f^{-1}(2x - 1) = \frac{(2x - 1) + 1}{2} = x$
27. 1 **29.** $f^{-1}(x) = x^2 - 1, x \geq 0$;
for $f: D = \{x \mid x \geq -1\}$ and $R = \{y \mid y \geq 0\}$;
for $f^{-1}: D = \{x \mid x \geq 0\}$ and $R = \{y \mid y \geq -1\}$
31. $C = 3, a = 2$
33. **35.**

D = all real numbers $D = \{x \mid x < 0\}$

37. $C = 2, a = 2$ **39.** \$1562.71 **41.** $\ln 19 \approx 2.9444$
43. 3 **45.** −21 **47.** 2 **49.** 1 **51.** 2.631
53. $\log 125 \approx 2.097$ **55.** $10 \ln 5.2 \approx 16.49$
57. $-\frac{1}{\log 5} \approx -1.431$ **59.** $10 + \frac{\log(29/3)}{\log(0.78)} \approx 0.869$
61. $f(x) = 1.5(2)^x$ **63.** $10^{1.5} \approx 31.62$
65. $e^{3.4} \approx 29.96$ **67.** $\log 30x$ **69.** $\ln y - 2\ln x$
71. $10^{1/4} \approx 1.778$ **73.** $\frac{100,000}{3} \approx 33,333$

75. 1 (extraneous −4)
77. The x-intercept is b. If $(0, b)$ is on the graph of f, then $(b, 0)$ is on the graph of f^{-1}.
79. (a) 11,022/mL **(b)** About 1.86 hr **81.** $h(x) = 15x$
83. $x \approx 2.74$; the fish weighs 50 milligrams at about 3 weeks. **85.** About 3.8 min
87. Logistic: $f(x) = \frac{171.4}{1 + 18.4e^{-0.0744x}}$
89. $a \approx 3.50, b \approx 0.74$

[0, 5, 1] by [0, 3, 1]

CHAPTER 5 EXTENDED AND DISCOVERY EXERCISES (pp. 450–451)

1. The data points $(\ln x, \ln y)$ seem to be almost linear. Using linear regression gives the equation $y = 1.5x - 8.5$. Since $b = 1.5$ and $a = e^{-8.5} \approx 0.0002$, we get the power function $f(x) = 0.0002x^{1.5}$.
3. (a) 163.00000000000000000000000000000232; it is not an integer.

CHAPTER 9: Systems of Equations and Inequalities

SECTION 9.1 (pp. 714–719)

1. 20; the area of a triangle with base 5 and height 8 is 20.
3. 13 **5.** −18 **7.** $\frac{4}{5}$ **9.** $f(x, y) = y + 2x$
11. $f(x, y) = \frac{xy}{1 + x}$ **13.** $x = \frac{4y + 7}{3}; y = \frac{3x - 7}{4}$
15. $x = y^2 + 5; y = \pm\sqrt{x - 5}$ **17.** $x = 2y; y = \frac{x}{2}$
19. (2, 1); linear **21.** (4, −3); nonlinear **23.** (2, 2)
25. $\left(\frac{1}{2}, -2\right)$ **27.** Consistent with solution (2, 2)
29. Inconsistent; no solutions

31. **33.**

No solutions; inconsistent   (2, −1); consistent, independent

35. **37.**

(−2, 2); consistent, independent $\{(x, y) \mid 2x - y = -4\}$; consistent, dependent

39. (−2, 1) **41.** $\left(\frac{1}{2}, 2\right)$ **43.** (6, 8)
45. $\{(x, y) \mid 3x - 2y = 5\}$ **47.** No solutions **49.** (4, 3)
51. (−2, 4), (0, 0) **53.** (2, 4), (4, 2) **55.** (2, 4), (−2, −4)
57. No real solutions **59.** $\{(x, y) \mid 2x^2 - y = 5\}$
61. (−2, 0), (2, 0) **63.** (−2, −2), (0, 0), (2, 2)
65. $x - y = 2, 2x + 2y = 38$, where x is width and y is height; 10.5 in. wide, 8.5 in. high
67. $x + y = 75, 4x + 7y = 456$, where x is the number of child tickets and y is the number of adult tickets; 23 child tickets, 52 adult tickets **69.** $l = 7, w = 5$ **71.** (14, 6); consistent, independent **73.** (1, 3); consistent, independent
75. $\{(x, y) \mid x + y = 500\}$; consistent, dependent
77. No solutions; inconsistent
79. $\left(-\frac{11}{7}, \frac{12}{7}\right)$; consistent, independent
81. (2, −4) **83.** $\{(x, y) \mid 7x - 3y = -17\}$

85. No solutions **87.** (10, 20) **89.** (2, 1)
91. (−5, −4) **93.** (3, 3), (−3, 3)
95. (4, 3), (−4, 3), (3, 4), (−3, 4) **97.** (2, 0), (−2, 0)
99. $(-\sqrt{8}, -\sqrt{8}), (\sqrt{8}, \sqrt{8})$ **101.** (6, 2), (−2, −6)
103. (1, −1) **105.** (1, 2)
107. (−1.588, 0.239), (0.164, 1.487), (1.924, −0.351)
109. (1.220, 0.429) **111.** (0.714, −0.169)
113. (a) $x + y = 670, x - y = 98$
(b) (384, 286) (c) Consistent; independent
115. $W_1 = \dfrac{300}{1 + \sqrt{3}} \approx 109.8$ lb,

$W_2 = \dfrac{300\sqrt{3}}{\sqrt{6} + \sqrt{2}} \approx 134.5$ lb

117. $r \approx 1.538$ in., $h \approx 6.724$ in.
119. 12 by 12 by 4 in. or 9.10 by 9.10 by 6.96 in.
121. (a) $x + y = 11{,}693, x - y = 437$
(b) & (c) (6065, 5628)
123. (a) $x + y = 3000, 0.08x + 0.10y = 264$
(b) $1800 at 8%; $1200 at 10%
125. There are no solutions. If loans totaling $3000 are at 10%, then the interest must be $300.
127. Airplane: 520 mi/hr; wind speed: 40 mi/hr
129. (a) $l = 13$ ft, $w = 7$ ft (b) $A = 20w - w^2$
(c) 100 ft^2; a square pen will provide the largest area.
131. (a) First model: about 245 lb; second model: about 253 lb (b) Models agree when $h \approx 65.96$ in.
(c) First model: 7.46 lb; second model: 7.93 lb
133. About 1.77 m^2 **135.** $S(60, 157.48) \approx 1.6$ m^2
137. 0.51 **139.** 32.4 **141.** Approximately 10,823 watts
143. Approximately 2.54 cords
145. $S(w, h) = 0.0101w^{0.425}h^{0.725}$

APPENDIX C: Partial Fractions (p. AP-29)

1. $\dfrac{5}{3x} + \dfrac{-10}{3(2x + 1)}$ **3.** $\dfrac{6}{5(x + 2)} + \dfrac{8}{5(2x - 1)}$

5. $\dfrac{5}{6(x + 5)} + \dfrac{1}{6(x - 1)}$

7. $\dfrac{-2}{x + 1} + \dfrac{2}{x + 2} + \dfrac{4}{(x + 2)^2}$ **9.** $\dfrac{4}{x} + \dfrac{4}{1 - x}$

11. $\dfrac{15}{x} + \dfrac{-5}{x + 1} + \dfrac{-6}{x - 1}$ **13.** $1 + \dfrac{-2}{x + 1} + \dfrac{1}{(x + 1)^2}$

15. $x^3 - x^2 + \dfrac{-1}{3(2x + 1)} + \dfrac{2}{3(x + 2)}$

17. $\dfrac{1}{9} + \dfrac{-1}{x} + \dfrac{25}{18(3x + 2)} + \dfrac{29}{18(3x - 2)}$

19. $\dfrac{-3}{5x^2} + \dfrac{3}{5(x^2 + 5)}$ **21.** $\dfrac{-2}{7(x + 4)} + \dfrac{6x - 3}{7(3x^2 + 1)}$

23. $\dfrac{1}{4x} + \dfrac{-8}{19(2x + 1)} + \dfrac{-9x - 24}{76(3x^2 + 4)}$

25. $\dfrac{-1}{x} + \dfrac{2x}{2x^2 + 1} + \dfrac{2x + 3}{(2x^2 + 1)^2}$

27. $\dfrac{-1}{x + 2} + \dfrac{3}{(x^2 + 4)^2}$

29. $5x^2 + \dfrac{3}{x} + \dfrac{-1}{x + 3} + \dfrac{2}{x - 1}$

APPENDIX D: Percent Change and Exponential Functions (pp. AP-34–AP-36)

1. (a) 0.35 (b) −0.0007 (c) 7.21 (d) 0.003
3. (a) −0.055 (b) −0.0154 (c) 1.2 (d) 0.0015
5. (a) 37% (b) −9.5% (c) 190% (d) 35%
7. (a) −12.1% (b) 140% (c) 320% (d) −25%
9. (a) 100% (b) −50%
11. (a) 2.36% (b) −2.31%
13. (a) 44.44% (b) −30.77%
15. (a) $1800 (b) $3300 (c) 2.2
17. (a) −$2200 (b) $1800 (c) 0.45
19. (a) −$4500 (b) $3000 (c) 0.4
21. $f(x) = 9500(0.65)^x$ **23.** $f(x) = 2500(1.05)^x$
25. $f(x) = 1000(0.935)^x$
27. $C = 8, a = 1.12, r = 0.12$ or 12%
29. $C = 1.5, a = 0.35, r = -0.65$ or −65%
31. $C = 1, a = 0.55, r = -0.45$ or −45%
33. $C = 7, a = e, r = e - 1$ or about 171.8%
35. $C = 6, a = \frac{1}{3}, r = -\frac{2}{3}$ or about −66.7%
37. $f(t) = 35{,}000(1.098)^{t/2}$; about 44,215
39. $f(t) = 1000(3)^{t/7}$; about 5620
41. $f(t) = I_0\left(\frac{2}{3}\right)^{t/2}$; about $0.418I_0$
43. $f(t) = 5000(4)^{t/35}$; $6864.10
45. 10 years; $4027.51 **47.** 3.5 years; $1006.88
49. 2.8 years; $3020.63 **51.** 1.75% **53.** 2% **55.** 1%
57. About 2.21% **59.** They are equal. **61.** $7.39
63. About 2.56%

APPENDIX E: Rotation of Axes (p. AP-40)

1. Circle or ellipse or a point
3. Hyperbola or two intersecting lines
5. Parabola or one line or two parallel lines
7. 30° **9.** 60° **11.** 22.5°
13.

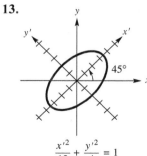

$$\dfrac{x'^2}{12} + \dfrac{y'^2}{4} = 1$$

15.

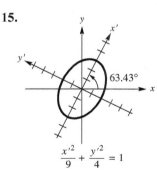

$$\dfrac{x'^2}{9} + \dfrac{y'^2}{4} = 1$$

17.

$$\frac{x'^2}{4} + \frac{y'^2}{2} = 1$$

19.

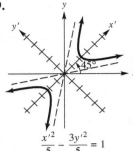

$$\frac{x'^2}{5} - \frac{3y'^2}{5} = 1$$

25.

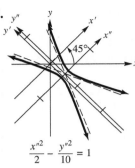

$$\frac{x''^2}{2} - \frac{y''^2}{10} = 1$$

27.

$$x''^2 \approx -8.94y''$$

21.

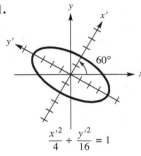

$$\frac{x'^2}{4} + \frac{y'^2}{16} = 1$$

23.

$$y'^2 = x'$$

29.

$$x''^2 = -6y''$$

Photo Credits

Index of Applications

Index

Math 103
Algebraic Reasoning

Activities Manual

Barbara Edwards, Charisse Hake, Ching-chia Ko,
Stephanie Bowers, Gulden Karakok, Jessica Cohen

Table of Contents

<u>Activities</u>

MATH 103
INTRODUCTIONS

GOALS: This activity has two goals:
- To meet each other.
- To explore ideas about displaying data and the three measures of central tendency – mean (average), median and mode.

Part I. Introductions

Go around the group and introduce yourselves.
Each person should say:
a) his/her name and
b) an interesting fact about him/herself.
Take notes, since you will later be responsible for introducing the person to your right to the entire class.

Part II. Data Collection

Collect and record the following data for your group. Put your group's answers to each of the seven questions on separate slips of paper.

1. How many miles is it between campus and your home town? Record your answers.
Then calculate the mean, median and mode for this data. (Formulas are on the next page if you need them.) Which of these three measures best describes your group?

2. How tall are you (in inches)? Record your answers and then calculate the mean, median and mode for this data. Which of these three measures best describes your group?

3. How many books (other than text books or reading assigned in a course) did you read last year? Record your answers and then calculate the mean, median and mode for this data. Which of these three measures best describes your group?

4. What is your favorite spectator sport?

5. What is your **least** favorite vegetable?

6. In what month were you born?

7. How many pets do you have and what are they?

Part III. Data Analysis and Representation

At the appropriate time, each of the seven groups will collect all the data slips from all the groups for one question. Group one will collect all the data slips for question 1; Group two will collect all the data for question 2; etc.

After you have all the data for your specified question you must decide how to **best represent** the data for your question so that your representation best describes the class as a whole on this question. Your choices of representation are:

- Pie Chart
- Bar Chart
- Line Plot
- Table
- Scatter Plot

Groups 1, 2, and 3 will need to decide if they should use the raw data or the means, medians, and modes from each group. If using the means, medians and modes, would it be better to recalculate the mean, median and mode from the original data for the entire class?

Part IV. Reporting

Each group will present to the class. Your presentation will include:

- Introduce the person on your right and share their interesting fact discussed in part I.
- Show your chart/graph to the class.
- Explain why you chose to make that kind of graph for your specific data set.

Review of Mean, Median, and Mode:

Calculating Mean (Average): Calculate by adding all data points and dividing by the number of data points. Example for data points: 10, 2, 5, 7, 14, 3, 5 the sum is 46. Divide by 7 and the result is 6.57 (rounded).

Calculating Median: The median of a set of numerical data is the middle number when the data is listed in numerical order. If the set contains an even number of entries, the median is the average (mean) of the two midmost numbers. In the example from above, arrange as 2, 3, 5, 5, 7, 10, 14. The median is 5 because 2, 3, 5 come before and 7, 10, 14 come after the second 5.

Calculating Mode: The mode of a data set is an entry or entries that occur as many times or more times as any other entry in the set. In the example above the mode is 5.

MATH 103
BLOOD ALCOHOL CONCENTRATION ACTIVITY

Below is some information on the effects of drinking alcohol on the concentration of alcohol in the blood. Blood Alcohol Concentration (BAC) is given as a percentage of the amount of alcohol in a sample of blood. For example, in a certain sample of blood a BAC of .10 means that one-tenth of a percent of the blood is alcohol – or somewhat simplistically, that .001 parts are alcohol and .999 parts are "pure" blood.

Alcohol affects individuals differently. Your blood alcohol level is affected by your age, weight, gender, time of day, physical condition, prior amount of food consumed, other drugs or medication taken, and a multitude of other factors. In addition, different drinks may contain different amount of alcohol, so it is important to know how much and the concentration of alcohol that is consumed. The body metabolizes alcohol at the rate of about one drink per hour.

Below are two tables – one for women and one for men. Again, these values are **estimates,** so the actual BAC for a given individual may vary.

Blood Alcohol Concentration Estimate – for Men

Drinks[1]	Body Weight in Pounds								Influence[2]
	100	120	140	160	180	200	220	240	
1	.04	.03	.02	.02	.02	.02	.02	.02	Possibly
2	.08	.06	.05	.05	.04	.04	.03	.03	
3	.11	.09	.08	.07	.06	.06	.05	.05	Impaired
4	.15	.12	.11	.09	.08	.08	.07	.06	
5	.19	.16	.13	.12	.11	.09	.09	.09	DUI
6	.23	.19	.16	.14	.13	.11	.10	.09	
7	.26	.22	.19	.16	.15	.13	.12	.11	
8	.30	.25	.21	.19	.17	.15	.14	.13	
9	.34	.28	.24	.21	.19	.17	.15	.14	
10	.38	.31	.27	.23	.21	.19	.17	.16	

---

[1] One drink is 1.25 oz. of 80 proof liquor, 12 oz. beer, or 5 oz. of wine.
[2] Subtract .01 for each hour from onset of drinking.

Blood Alcohol Concentration Estimate – for Women

Drinks[3]	Body Weight In Pounds								Influence[4]
	90	100	120	140	160	180	200	220	
1	.05	.05	.04	.03	.03	.03	.02	.02	Possibly
2	.10	.09	.08	.07	.06	.05	.05	.04	
3	.15	.14	.11	.10	.09	.08	.07	.06	Impaired
4	.20	.18	.15	.13	.11	.10	.09	.08	
5	.25	.23	.19	.16	.14	.13	.11	.10	DUI
6	.30	.27	.23	.19	.17	.15	.14	.12	
7	.35	.32	.27	.23	.20	.18	.16	.14	
8	.40	.36	.30	.26	.23	.20	.18	.17	
9	.45	.41	.34	.29	.26	.23	.20	.19	
10	.51	.45	.38	.32	.28	.25	.23	.21	

[Information from Greater Dallas Council on Alcohol & Drug Abuse – www.gdcada.org.]

There are specific effects related to BAC. These may differ due to individual variation and some users may become intoxicated at a much lower BAC, however the following gives the effects for an "average" individual.

- 0.02-0.03 BAC: No loss of coordination, slight euphoria and loss of shyness. Depressant effects are not apparent.
- 0.04-.06 BAC: Feeling of well-being, relaxation, lower inhibitions, sensation of warmth. Euphoria. Some minor impairment of reasoning and memory, lowering of caution.
- 0.07-0.09 BAC: Slight impairment of balance, speech, vision, reaction time, and hearing. Euphoria. Judgment and self-control are reduced, and caution, reason and memory are impaired. In Oregon it is illegal to operate a motor vehicle at this level of intoxication.

---

[3] One drink is 1.25 oz. of 80 proof liquor, 12 oz. beer, or 5 oz. of wine.
[4] Subtract .01 for each hour of drinking.

- 0.10-0.125 BAC: Significant impairment of motor coordination and loss of good judgment. Speech may be slurred; balance, vision, reaction time and hearing will be impaired. Euphoria.
- 0.13-0.15 BAC: Gross motor impairment and lack of physical control. Blurred vision and major loss of balance. Euphoria is reduced and dysphoria (anxiety, restlessness) is beginning to appear.
- 0.16-0.20 BAC Dysphoria predominates, nausea may appear. The drinker has the appearance of a "sloppy drunk."
- 0.25 BAC: Needs assistance in walking; total mental confusion. Dysphoria with nausea and some vomiting.
- 0.30 BAC: Loss of consciousness.
- 0.40BAC and up: Onset of coma, possible death due to respiratory arrest.

[Information from www.indiana.edu/-adic/effects.html.]

Questions:

For each question in Part A and Part B, write down an **answer** AND write down a **verbal explanation of why** that answer is correct. Write your answers on a separate piece of paper in your notebook.

If you need to do any calculations to determine an answer, include those as part of your written explanation.

Part A.
1. If a 90 pound female drank two drinks in one hour could she legally drive in Oregon? Why or why not?
2. Suppose she drank two drinks and one cup of coffee in one hour; could she legally drive? Why or why not?
3. How many drinks could cause the appearance of dysphoria in a 160 pound male?
4. Suppose a 180 pound male drinks eight 12 oz. beers beginning at 6 pm. What time will it be when he can legally drive?
5. The information in the first two tables shows Blood Alcohol Concentration Estimates as a result of (or dependent upon) what variables?
6. Would it be possible to construct one graph (with x-axis and y-axis) containing all the information from the first two tables? If you say yes, draw a sketch of the graph. If you say no, explain in detail why not.

Part B.

7. Concentrate on two specific cases – a 100 pound woman and a 180 pound man. Construct an accurate graph for each case that gives you the BAC level as it depends upon the number of drinks consumed per hour. (Make sure to label the axes with verbal descriptions, units, and an accurate scale.)

8. Compare your graphs. What differences do you notice? Explain in your own words what information you get and what conclusions you can draw from these graphs.

9. How many 12 oz. beers would each person in #7 have to drink before his or her BAC reaches 0.30? [Hmmm…. How can you figure this out for the 180 pound man?]

10. Compare the BAC information for a 120 pound man with that of a 120 pound woman. What is the difference between their BAC levels if they each have two drinks?

11. Does that difference remain constant as they each drink three, four or more drinks?

12. Plot these differences on a graph with the vertical axis labeled "BAC Difference" and the horizontal axis labeled "Number of Drinks." Note: There is more than one correct way to do this. After you complete #10-12 compare your graphs with those of other groups.

13. Answer questions 10 through 12 for a 200 pound man and a 200 pound woman.

14. Compare all of your graphs. Explain in your own words what information they give you. Be as detailed as possible in your conclusions.

15. Do you think BAC is more heavily dependent upon a person's gender or a person's weight? Justify your answer using your graphs and/or other mathematical reasoning from your work in part B.

MATH 103
STEEPNESS

Observe the following wheelchair ramp:

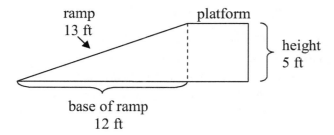

Write complete answers, with verbal explanations given and any necessary calculations shown, for each question.

1. a. Write a description of how you can measure the steepness of the ramp. Try to think of a couple different ways and list everything your group comes up with.
    b. Does the ramp have the same steepness throughout or is the steepness changing? Explain your answer.

2. a. What quantities affect steepness?
    b. Would increasing or decreasing the length of the platform while keeping the ramp the same length affect steepness? Explain your answer.
    c. Would increasing or decreasing the length of the ramp while keeping the ramp the same height affect steepness? Explain your answer.

3. a. Draw two different ramps with the same steepness.
    b. How do you know they have the same steepness? Include calculations and a verbal explanation.
    c. How are the two ramps similar and how are they different?

4. a. Create as many ramps as possible with the same steepness as a ramp with a height of 3 cm and base length of 12 cm. Use a ruler to make careful drawings. Label your dimensions for each ramp.

    b. How can you describe the relationship between the dimensions of the ramps you drew in part (a) and the dimensions of the ramp with a height of 3 cm and base length of 12 cm?

    c. Create a ramp with the same steepness as in #4(a), but with a base length of 1 cm.

    d. Explain how you could change the height of the original ramp if you increased its base length from 12 cm to 13 cm but wanted the new ramp to have the same steepness as the original in #4(a).

5. a. Find the slope of the following line. Show what you did to compute the slope.

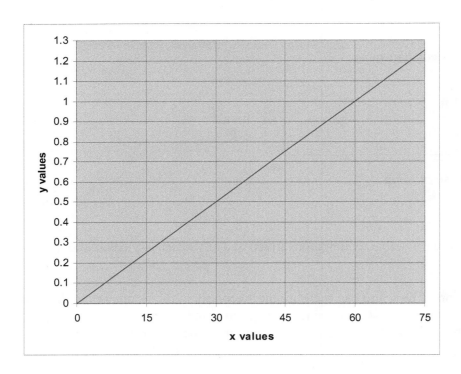

b. What does the slope of the line represent?

This activity is adapted from the 2002 NCTM Yearbook article, "Developing Understanding of Ratio-as-Measure as a Foundation for Slope". Lobato & Thanheiser

SPEED

6. a. How can you determine if two people are walking at the same speed? What quantities need to be taken into account?

     b. If two people take the same number of steps in the same time period, are they walking at the same speed?

     c. If one person takes more steps than the other person in a given time interval, can it be determined who is walking faster with only this information?

     d. If a person walks 6 feet every 3 seconds, this means they are walking how many feet each second? If the person walked the same speed, how many feet would they walk in 9 seconds?

This activity is adapted from the 2002 NCTM Yearbook article, "Developing Understanding of Ratio-as-Measure as a Foundation for Slope". Lobato & Thanheiser

SLOPE

7. In #5 above you computed the slope of the graph of the line shown below. Now consider the following situation:

Carmen sets out on foot from home on her way to school. Suppose the graph above shows the distance (in miles) that Carmen has traveled from home at time t (in minutes).

a. How is Carmen's speed related to the slope of the line?

b. What is her speed in miles per hour?

8. A leaky faucet drips water into a measuring cup. The graph below shows the water level in the measuring cup over time. The cup started out with some water in it before the dripping began.

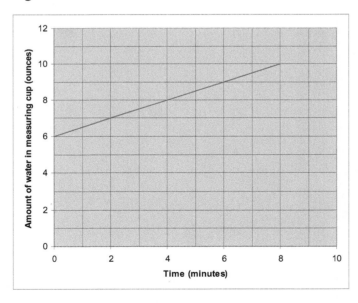

a) What does the point (0, 6) on the graph of the line tell you **about the situation**? Include values and units in your explanation.

b) What can you say about how the water level is changing over time? Include values and units in your explanation. Explain how you get this information from the graph.

9. Suppose Susan is traveling in her wheelchair (set at a certain speed) up the ramp given below. Sketch two different graphs below to accurately represent this situation.

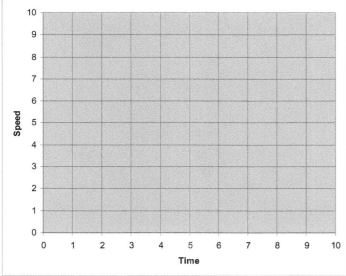

This activity is adapted from the 2002 NCTM Yearbook article, "Developing Understanding of Ratio-as-Measure as a Foundation for Slope". Lobato & Thanheiser

13

MATH 103
WALKING THE DOG

Part 1: Your friend is doing a study of how much people exercise in their normal daily activities. Part of this study involves making graphical representations of distances and speeds of typical activities. You volunteer to help, using a perfect example from the previous weekend:

You went for a walk with your Great Dane early on a beautiful Saturday morning. For the first five minutes, you strolled along together peacefully, 3½ blocks down the road, until the dog found a fire hydrant and insisted on stopping for a minute. You continued to stroll along again for another two blocks when a squirrel jumped out in front of you and led you on a merry chase: for two minutes you went forward and back, forward and back about a block each time, before the squirrel finally ran up a tree. It took you another three minutes before you could persuade the dog to leave the tree. By that time, you were late for lunch and hurried back home arriving breathless 20 minutes from the time that you set out.

(Review your work from Steepness Activity #9 and create the same two kinds of graphs to accurately represent the situation above.)

Part 2: Tell a story whose events could be represented by the following graph

Time (sec.)	distance (miles)
0	0
25	0.1
75	0.433
100	0.60
125	0.70
150	0.70
175	0.75
275	1.25
300	1.30

MATH 103
DISTANCE GRAPHS

Part 1

Answer the following questions about the graph shown below.

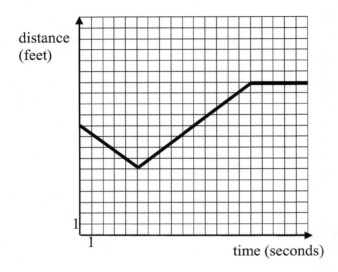

1. Is this a total distance graph or a distance from home graph? Explain how you determined this.

2. How far from home is this person when he/she begins moving? Explain how you determined this.

3. Does this person ever get home during the time period shown on the graph? Explain how you determined this.

Part 2

Your instructor will assign your group one of the following problems.

GROUP 1

a. Write a story to match this graph. Explain how each part of your story matches to a part of the graph.
b. Draw an accurate speed vs. time graph to go with your story. Show all your speed calculations.

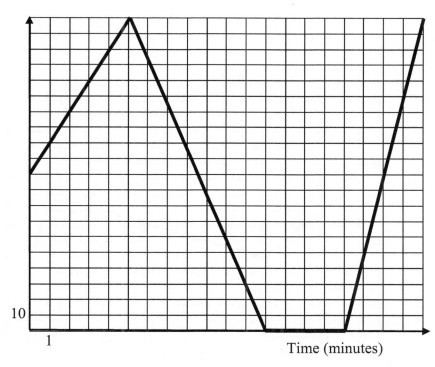

Distance
From
Coffee Shop
(meters)

10

1

Time (minutes)

GROUP 2

a. Write a story to match this graph. Explain how each part of your story matches to a part of the graph.
b. Draw an accurate speed vs. time graph to go with your story. Show all your speed calculations.

Distance From Class (feet)

5

1

Time (minutes)

GROUP 3

a. Write a story to match this graph. Explain how each part of your story matches to a part of the graph.
b. Draw an accurate speed vs. time graph to go with your story. Show all your speed calculations.

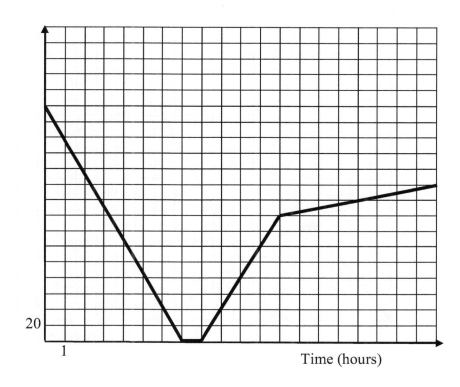

Distance From Home (miles)

20

1

Time (hours)

GROUP 4

a. Write a story to match this graph. Explain how each part of your story matches to a part of the graph.
b. Draw an accurate speed vs. time graph to go with your story. Show all your speed calculations.

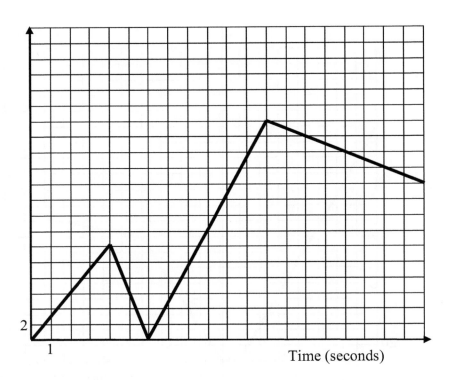

Distance
From
Library
(meters)

2

1

Time (seconds)

GROUP 5

a. Write a story to match this graph. Explain how each part of your story matches to a part of the graph.
b. Draw an accurate speed vs. time graph to go with your story. Show all your speed calculations.

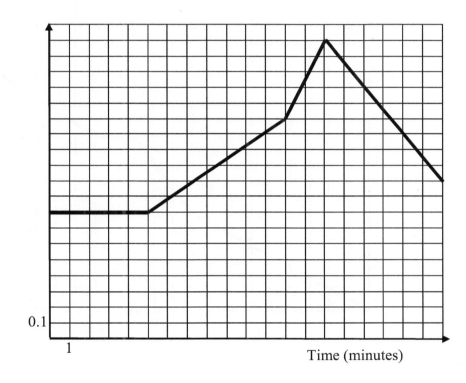

Distance From Home (km)

0.1

1

Time (minutes)

GROUP 6

a. Write a story to match this graph. Explain how each part of your story matches to a part of the graph.

b. Draw an accurate speed vs. time graph to go with your story. Show all your speed calculations.

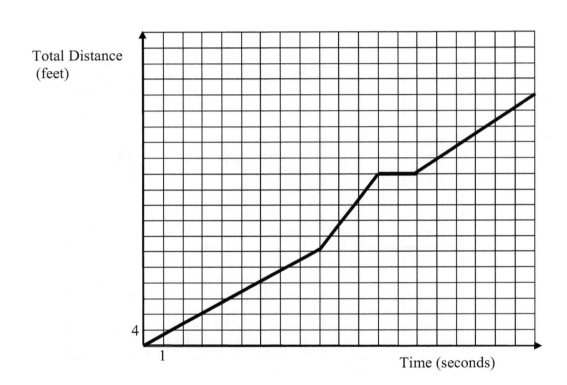

GROUP 7

a. Write a story to match this graph. Explain how each part of your story matches to a part of the graph.

b. Draw an accurate speed vs. time graph to go with your story. Show all your speed calculations.

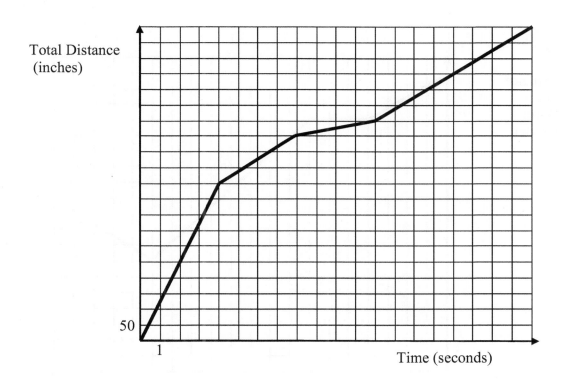

GROUP 8

a. Write a story to match this graph. Explain how each part of your story matches to a part of the graph.
b. Draw an accurate speed vs. time graph to go with your story. Show all your speed calculations.

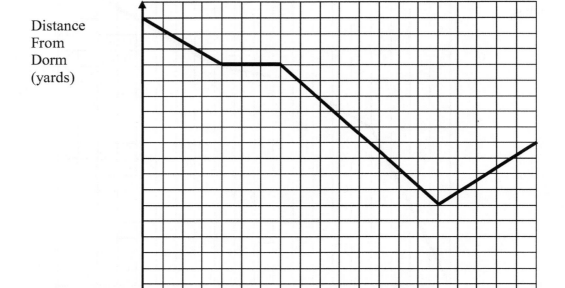

Distance
From
Dorm
(yards)

2

1

Time (minutes)

MATH 103
UNDERSTANDING LINEAR EQUATIONS

1. Many real life relationships can be described mathematically using numbers, graphs, and equations. Consider the case of two boys, Dan and Travis, where Dan is two years older than Travis.

   a) Is there a dependency relation between the two boys' ages as described? Which of these two ages would be the independent variable, and which would be the dependent variable? Why?
   b) Make a table of data points for the two boys' ages. Be sure to include a sufficient range of ages to give a good picture of the relationship.
   c) Use the data points from your table to plot the points in a graph. Be sure that your graph corresponds to your decisions in part a) about independent and dependent variables.
   d) What shape do the points in your graph make? Does it make sense to connect them? Why or why not?
   e) If Travis gets one year older, what happens to Dan? Where does this relationship appear in your graph?
   f) When Travis was born, how old was Dan? Where does this appear in your graph?
   g) Write an equation showing the relationship between the two boys' ages. Be sure to define your variables (what letter you are using to represent what data) and that your equation reflects the decisions you made about independent and dependent variables.
   h) Consider your responses to parts e) and f). Where do those relationships appear in your equation?

2. The following table shows data about the ages of two boys, Jonathan and Mike.

Jonathan's Age	Mike's Age
2	5
4	7
5	8
7	10
10	13

   a) Graph the data points from the table. What did you choose as your independent variable? As your dependent variable? Why?
   b) Write an equation for the relationship between Jonathan's and Mike's ages. Be sure you define your variables and that your choice of independent and dependent variables correspond to your graph.
   c) If Jonathan gets one year older, what happens to Mike? Where do you see this relationship in your graph? In your equation? How do you know?
   d) When Jonathan was born, was Mike already born? If so, how old was he? How do you know?
   e) Consider and compare your answers to questions 1e) and 2c). Would it have been possible for this answer to be 1/2? Or 2? Or -3? Why or why not?

3. Tom's father was four times as old as Tom in 2000. In 2010, Tom's father will be 5 years less than three times Tom's age.
a) Develop a single equation showing the relationship between Tom's age and his father's age.
b) Let f denote the age of Tom's father. Give a real world interpretation of the f-intercept.

4. The Austin Community Profile" published by the Greater Austin Chamber of Commerce (1996) includes the following bar chart with the statement, "Austin's population has doubled about every 20 years."

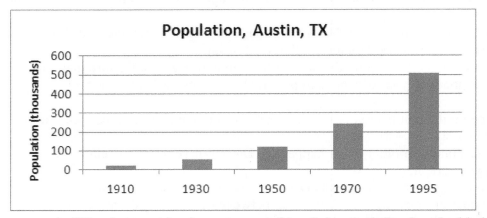

a) What is meant by the statement, "Austin's population has doubled about every 20 years?"
b) Can the statement, "Austin's population has doubled every 20 years" be converted to a linear equation? Explain why or why not.
c) Plot the data given by the bar chart, with an accurate scale. Be sure that you choose your independent and dependent variables in a way that makes sense for the data.
d) Do the points lie on a straight line? If so, determine the equation of the line.
e) Write a short paragraph summarizing the Greater Austin Chamber of Commerce's statement that "Austin's population has doubled about every 20 years." and how this does or does not illustrate a linear relationship.

5. Determine a linear equation that represents the set of points whose distance from the *x*-axis is 4 times its distance from the *y*-axis. Is the equation you came up with the only one which will work? Explain.

Adapted from Small, D. (2005). *Contemporary College Algebra: Data, Functions, Modeling*

1. Find the *x*-intercept and *y*-intercept of each line shown in the graphs below. **Write each intercept as a coordinate point.** Then use these to answer question 2.

a.

b.

c.

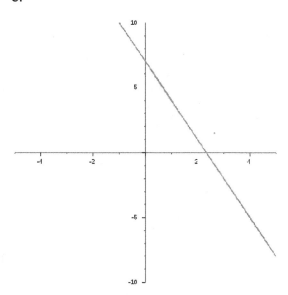

2. a. Compare the coordinate points for all three *x*-intercepts above. In what way are they <u>exactly</u> the same?

b. Now compare the coordinate points for all three *y*-intercepts above. In what way are they <u>exactly</u> the same?

3. **Use symbolic algebra** and **your answers from #2** on the previous page to find the x-intercept and y-intercept of the graph created by each linear equation below.

Show all steps of work.   Give exact values.   Write each intercept as a coordinate point.

a) $4y - 5x = -3$

b) $y = -\dfrac{3}{8}x + \dfrac{9}{4}$

c) $y = 100x$

d) $y = -45$

4. Find the exact values of the *x*-intercept and *y*-intercept of the graph created by the line whose table of values is given. Explain and show how you found the intercepts. Write each intercept as a coordinate point.

x	-3	-2	-1
y	2.5	4.4	6.3

5. Suppose the velocity of a ball that is thrown straight up into the air is given by $v = 128 - 32t$, where v is the velocity in feet per second and t is the number of seconds since the ball was thrown.

a) Use symbolic algebra to find the *v*-intercept on the graph created by the given equation. Write it as a coordinate point.

b) Explain what the *v*-intercept point means *in the context of the situation*. Remember to include units in your explanation.

c) Find the *t*-intercept on the graph created by the given equation. Write it as a coordinate point.

d) Explain what the *t*-intercept point means *in the context of the situation*. Remember to include units in your explanation.

MATH 103
EXPLORING RATE OF CHANGE

1. Suppose water is poured at the same constant rate into the four containers shown below, which all have the same height. For each container, sketch a graph of the height of the water in the container versus time. Explain how the graph and the shape of the container are related.

a.

Explanation:

b.

Explanation:

c.

Explanation:

d.

Explanation:

2. The two containers shown below have the same total height and the same width at the widest part. Suppose water is poured at the same constant rate into the containers.

a. For each container, sketch a graph of the height of the water in the container versus time.

b. Compare and contrast the two graphs. Explain completely.

3. The three containers shown below have the same total height and the same width at the widest part. Suppose water is poured at the same constant rate into the containers.

  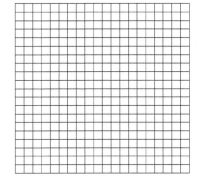

a. For each container, sketch a graph of the height of the water in the container versus time.

b. Compare and contrast the three graphs. Explain completely.

4. Suppose you are given following graphs of the height of water versus time. Draw a possible container for each graph. Completely justify your drawing in each case, making sure to explain how each part of the graph relates to each part of the container.

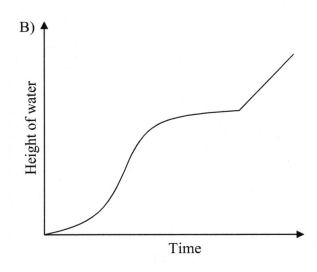

Container A:

Explanation:

Container B:

Explanation:

5. A girl on a bicycle rides along flat ground at a constant rate, going as fast as she can. After awhile she gets to a hill. She rides up the hill and down the other side. Then she continues on flat ground at the same constant rate as at the beginning.

Draw a graph of her **speed** versus time. Explain in detail how your graph relates to the situation.

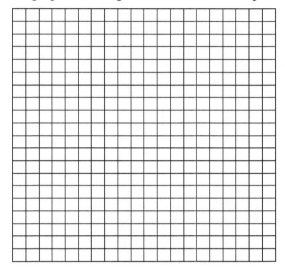

Explanation:

6. A little bit of stress often makes a person perform better. Athletes and entertainers channel this nervous energy into delivering a better performance. But having too much stress will usually make a person perform worse. The higher the stress level the faster the level of performance will go down.

a. Draw a graph of performance level versus amount of stress. Choose and label a scale on both axes.

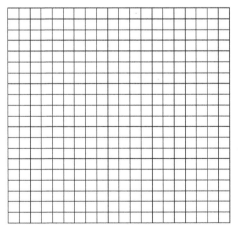

b. Which part of your graph shows where stress level is highest? How is performance level at that point?

c. Which part of your graph shows where performance level is highest? How is stress level at that point?

d. For which part of your graph is performance level increasing?

e. At what stress level is performance increasing the fastest? Explain how this is shown in the graph.

f. At what stress level is performance increasing the slowest? Explain.

g. For what stress levels is performance decreasing?

MATH 103
STUDY TABLE

Every Tuesday afternoon five friends – Michael, Jose, Katrina, Tolanda and Chen – meet at The Beanery to study math together. This study group started last spring when they all were in high school together. We can identify a relationship between each of these students and the number of credit hours for which each is enrolled this term at Oregon State – but we may not know everything there is to know about these friends; in fact, they may not know certain things about each other! We know the following

- Jose is registered for sixteen credit hours this term.
- Tolanda is registered for seventeen hours.
- Chen is registered for sixteen hours.
- Katrina is registered for fifteen hours.

What we don't know is that Katrina, who is very bright and energetic, is also registered for thirteen hours under another name and is being paid by that other person to take classes – definitely not legal! And sadly, we also know that Michael is no longer registered at all at Oregon State but he doesn't want to tell his friends about this.

If we must associate each name with one number between 1 and 23 (representing credit hours), can we do this with this particular group of friends? Why or why not? Discuss this in your group.

This particular relationship, between a student at OSU and a number between 1 and 23 illustrates an important idea in mathematics called **_function_**. Look up a definition for function. Does this tale of a group of friends studying together represent a function? Why or why not?

MATH 103
FUNCTIONS

DEFINITIONS
- A **relation** from one set to another is a pairing of the elements in the first set with the elements in the second set.
- A **dependency relation** is a relation where the values of one variable depend on the values of the other.
- An **ordered pair** is a pair of points related to one another through a relation.
  - For example, the set {(2, 4), (5, 25), (0, 0), (-13, 169)} is a set of ordered pairs relating the first set of elements, {2, 5, 0, -13}, with the second set of elements, {4, 25, 0, 169}.
- A **function** is a relation linking two sets so that each input corresponds to exactly one output.
  - i.e. for every x value, there is only one corresponding y value

1. Which of the following relations are dependency relations? For those that <u>are</u> dependency relations, identify the independent and dependent variables.
   a. The outside temperature at your school measured over a day.
   b. Names in a telephone book and telephone numbers
   c. A mother and her child.
   d. The amount of a person's education and the person's salary.
   e. The amount of interest paid on a credit card and the credit card balance.
   f. The day of the year and the number of hours of daylight.
   g. Postage required for a first class letter and the weight of the letter.
   h. An individual and her social security number.

2. For the relations in question 1, give an example of an ordered pair from each.
3. For the relations in question 1, which are functions? Justify your answer.
4. Does the relation described in the definition of an ordered pair at the top of the page represent a function? Why or why not?

DEFINITION: The **domain** is the set of all possible inputs of a function, and the **range** is the set of all possible outputs.

5. For the relations from question 1 which you determined were functions, describe the domain and range.

6. a. Is y a function of x in the relation $y = 2x - 3$? Develop **TWO** different arguments to support your position.
   b. Write a set of 4 ordered pairs for $y = 2x - 3$
   c. If you decided $y = 2x - 3$ is a function, describe the domain and range.

7. Which, if any, linear relations are functions? Justify your answer.

8. Make up two relations, each consisting of six ordered pairs, such that the first is a function and the second is not. Display each of your relations graphically and numerically (with a table).

9. Sketch five different graphs, two that display functions and three that display relations that are not functions. Explain why your graphs meet the criteria.

10. For each relation shown below, determine if y is or is not a function of x. Justify each answer using the definition of function.
    Then identify the domain and range, and plot the relation.
    a)

x	1	3	0	-1	2
y	2	3	1	5	4

    b)

x	1	3	-2	1	5
y	2	4	5	4	2

    c)

x	-1	2	0	-1	-3
y	2	0	1	2	1

11. For each of the following conditions, make up an example or explain why no example can exist.
    a) A function whose domain is {1, 2, 3, 4} and whose range is {2, 3}
    b) A relation that is not a function but whose domain is {1, 2, 3, 4} and whose range is {2, 3}
    c) An increasing function (a function whose graph rises from left to right)
    d) A decreasing function (a function whose graph falls from left to right)
    e) A function that is neither increasing or decreasing
    f) A function whose graph looks like a horseshoe opening to the right

12. Suppose the function c(d) gives as an output the number of dozens of cookies that can be made from d pounds of dough.
a) Translate the statement c(7) = 8 into a coordinate point that would be on the graph of c.
b) Explain in words, including values and units, what c(7) = 8 means in the context of the situation.
c) If 13 dozen cookies can be made from 11 pounds of dough, write this information using function notation and also write it as a coordinate point on the graph of c.

MATH 103
DOMAIN AND RANGE

The **domain** is the set of all possible inputs of a function, and the **range** is the set of all possible outputs.

A function is a relationship which we can represent in various ways so that it can be analyzed and interpreted. In this activity we will represent some functions in a number of different ways to help us study and determine their domains and ranges.

FUNCTION #1: $f(x) = 2x - 3$

a) Complete the table of values. For each x-value listed, record the related $f(x)$-value. If any x-value does not relate to an $f(x)$-value draw a line through the box.

x	-5	-4	-3	-2	-1	0	1	2	3	4	5
$f(x)$											

b) Use the table above to help you create an accurate graph of the function. If the graph extends beyond the viewing window, indicate that by putting an arrow on the graph. If the graph ends, clearly show an endpoint on the graph.

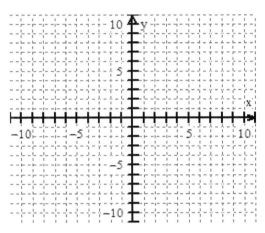

Use the graph and table you made above to help you answer parts c and d.

c) Any x-value that corresponds to a specific $f(x)$-value is in the domain of the function f. On the number line below, shade all x-values that are in the domain of f. If any x-values are not in the domain, leave them unshaded.

d) Any $f(x)$-value that is possible to obtain as an output from the function is in the range of the function. On the number line below, shade all $f(x)$-values that are in the range of f. If any values are not in the range, leave them unshaded.

FUNCTION #2: $f(x) = 5 - x^2$

a) Complete the table of values. For each x-value listed, record the related $f(x)$-value. If any x-value does not relate to an $f(x)$-value draw a line through the box.

x	-5	-4	-3	-2	-1	0	1	2	3	4	5
$f(x)$											

b) Use the table above to help you create an accurate graph of the function. If the graph extends beyond the viewing window, indicate that by putting an arrow on the graph. If the graph ends, clearly show an endpoint on the graph.

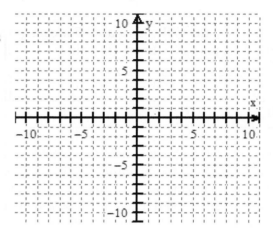

Use the graph and table you made above to help you answer parts c and d.

c) Any x-value that corresponds to a specific $f(x)$-value is in the domain of the function f. On the number line below, shade all x-values that are in the domain of f. If any x-values are not in the domain, leave them unshaded.

d) Any $f(x)$-value that is possible to obtain as an output from the function is in the range of the function. On the number line below, shade all $f(x)$-values that are in the range of f. If any values are not in the range, leave them unshaded.

FUNCTION #3: $f(x) = x^3 + 3x - 2$

a) Complete the table of values. For each x-value listed, record the related $f(x)$-value. If any x-value does not relate to an $f(x)$-value draw a line through the box.

x	-5	-4	-3	-2	-1	0	1	2	3	4	5
$f(x)$											

b) Use the table above to help you create an accurate graph of the function. If the graph extends beyond the viewing window, indicate that by putting an arrow on the graph. If the graph ends, clearly show an endpoint on the graph.

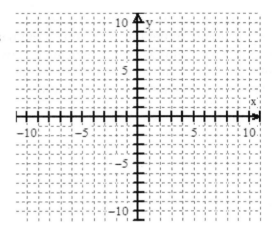

Use the graph and table you made above to help you answer parts c and d.

c) Any x-value that corresponds to a specific $f(x)$-value is in the domain of the function f. On the number line below, shade all x-values that are in the domain of f. If any x-values are not in the domain, leave them unshaded.

d) Any $f(x)$-value that is possible to obtain as an output from the function is in the range of the function. On the number line below, shade all $f(x)$-values that are in the range of f. If any values are not in the range, leave them unshaded.

FUNCTION #4: $f(x) = \sqrt{x+3}$

a) Complete the table of values. For each *x*-value listed, record the related *f(x)*-value. If any *x*-value does not relate to an *f(x)*-value draw a line through the box.

x	-5	-4	-3	-2	-1	0	1	2	3	4	5
f(x)											

b) Use the table above to help you create an accurate graph of the function. If the graph extends beyond the viewing window, indicate that by putting an arrow on the graph. If the graph ends, clearly show an endpoint on the graph.

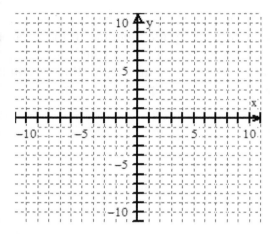

Use the graph and table you made above to help you answer parts c and d.

c) Any *x*-value that corresponds to a specific *f(x)*-value is in the domain of the function *f*. On the number line below, shade all *x*-values that are in the domain of *f*. If any *x*-values are not in the domain, leave them unshaded.

d) Any *f(x)*-value that is possible to obtain as an output from the function is in the range of the function. On the number line below, shade all *f(x)*-values that are in the range of *f*. If any values are not in the range, leave them unshaded.

40

FUNCTION #5: $f(x) = \sqrt{16 - x^2}$

a) Complete the table of values. For each *x*-value listed, record the related *f*(x)-value. If any *x*-value does not relate to an *f*(x)-value draw a line through the box.

x	-5	-4	-3	-2	-1	0	1	2	3	4	5
f(x)											

b) Use the table above to help you create an accurate graph of the function. If the graph extends beyond the viewing window, indicate that by putting an arrow on the graph. If the graph ends, clearly show an endpoint on the graph.

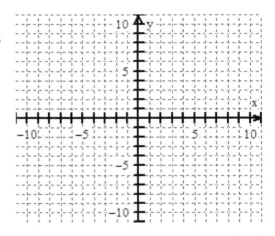

Use the graph and table you made above to help you answer parts c and d.

c) Any *x*-value that corresponds to a specific *f*(x)-value is in the domain of the function *f*. On the number line below, shade all *x*-values that are in the domain of *f*.   If any *x*-values are not in the domain, leave them unshaded.

d) Any *f*(x)-value that is possible to obtain as an output from the function is in the range of the function. On the number line below, shade all *f*(x)-values that are in the range of *f*.   If any values are not in the range, leave them unshaded.

41

FUNCTION #6: $f(x) = \dfrac{3}{x} - 2$

a) Complete the table of values. For each x-value listed, record the related $f(x)$-value. If any x-value does not relate to an $f(x)$-value draw a line through the box.

x	-5	-4	-3	-2	-1	0	1	2	3	4	5
$f(x)$											

b) Use the table above to help you create an accurate graph of the function. If the graph extends beyond the viewing window, indicate that by putting an arrow on the graph. If the graph ends, clearly show an endpoint on the graph.

** Notice in this table there is a single x-value for which $f(x)$ does not exist. To create an accurate graph near this point, you will need to make another table with some x-values closer to this point and/or use a graphing calculator to help you determine what happens to the left and right of this point on the graph. **

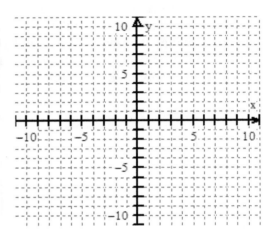

Use the graph and table you made above to help you answer parts c and d.

c) Any x-value that corresponds to a specific $f(x)$-value is in the domain of the function f. On the number line below, shade all x-values that are in the domain of f. If any x-values are not in the domain, leave them unshaded.

d) Any $f(x)$-value that is possible to obtain as an output from the function is in the range of the function. On the number line below, shade all $f(x)$-values that are in the range of f. If any values are not in the range, leave them unshaded.

FUNCTION #7: $f(x) = \dfrac{1}{x+3}$

a) Complete the table of values. For each x-value listed, record the related $f(x)$-value. If any x-value does not relate to an $f(x)$-value draw a line through the box.

x	-5	-4	-3	-2	-1	0	1	2	3	4	5
$f(x)$											

b) Use the table above to help you create an accurate graph of the function. If the graph extends beyond the viewing window, indicate that by putting an arrow on the graph. If the graph ends, clearly show an endpoint on the graph.

As in the last problem, you will likely need to do additional work to make an accurate graph.

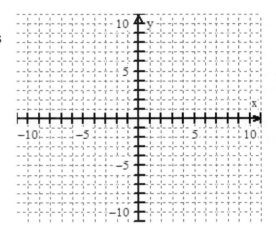

Use the graph and table you made above to help you answer parts c and d.

c) Any x-value that corresponds to a specific $f(x)$-value is in the domain of the function f. On the number line below, shade all x-values that are in the domain of f. If any x-values are not in the domain, leave them unshaded.

d) Any $f(x)$-value that is possible to obtain as an output from the function is in the range of the function. On the number line below, shade all $f(x)$-values that are in the range of f. If any values are not in the range, leave them unshaded.

43

FUNCTION #8: $f(x) = \dfrac{5}{x^2 + 2x - 8}$

a) Complete the table of values. For each x-value listed, record the related $f(x)$-value. If any x-value does not relate to an $f(x)$-value draw a line through the box.

x	-5	-4	-3	-2	-1	0	1	2	3	4	5
$f(x)$											

b) Use the table above to help you create an accurate graph of the function. If the graph extends beyond the viewing window, indicate that by putting an arrow on the graph. If the graph ends, clearly show an endpoint on the graph.

As in the last problem, you will likely need to do additional work to make an accurate graph.

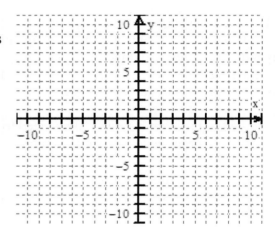

Use the graph and table you made above to help you answer parts c and d.

c) Any x-value that corresponds to a specific $f(x)$-value is in the domain of the function f. On the number line below, shade all x-values that are in the domain of f. If any x-values are not in the domain, leave them unshaded.

d) Any $f(x)$-value that is possible to obtain as an output from the function is in the range of the function. On the number line below, shade all $f(x)$-values that are in the range of f. If any values are not in the range, leave them unshaded.

Now that you have looked at each function in multiple representations and have shaded each domain and range on a number line, you can also write each domain and range in words and symbolically.

For example:
- If the domain of a function includes all x-values, in words we can say "all real numbers" and in symbols we can write $(-\infty, \infty)$.
- If the range of a function includes all y-values except -3 and 5, in words we can say "all real numbers except -3 and 5" and in symbols we can write either $y \neq -3, 5$ or $(-\infty, -3) \cup (-3, 5) \cup (5, \infty)$.
- If the domain of a function includes all x-values between 4 and infinity, in words we can say "from 4 to infinity" and in symbols we can write $x \geq 4$ or $[4, \infty)$.

Look back at your shaded number lines for each function and fill in the table below.

Function	Domain in words	Domain in symbols	Range in words	Range in symbols
$f(x) = 2x - 3$				
$f(x) = 5 - x^2$				
$f(x) = x^3 + 3x - 2$				
$f(x) = \sqrt{x + 3}$				
$f(x) = \sqrt{16 - x^2}$				
$f(x) = \dfrac{3}{x} - 2$				
$f(x) = \dfrac{1}{x + 3}$				
$f(x) = \dfrac{5}{x^2 + 2x - 8}$				

Adapted from the 2005 activity from the National Council of Teachers of Mathematics
http://illuminations.nctm.org/lessondetail.aspx?id=L621

MATH 103
SYSTEMS OF EQUATIONS

1. Many real life relationships are more complicated than can be modeled with a single linear equation. For example, consider the scenario described here:

   Two math 103 groups are working on their group projects in the MLC and decide to take a break together. Group A buys 1 can of soda and 4 bottles of water for $2.60 and Group B spends $2.80 on 3 cans of soda and 2 bottles of water. How much does a group member who asked for a soda owe? How much does a group member who asked for a bottle of water owe?

   a) What are the unknowns in this situation? Use variables to represent each unknown, and be very careful that you describe the variable completely.
   b) Use the variables to write an equation representing the purchases made by Group A.
   c) Use the variables to write an equation representing the purchases made by Group B.
   d) Are these equations linear or non-linear? How do you know? (You may need to review the definition of linear equation.)

   Next you will explore three different methods for solving systems of equations.

   e) **Substitution Method** (Solve for a variable in one equation and substitute for that variable in the other equation.)
      1. Isolate one variable in the equation for Group A (**Hint:** Choose the variable that is easiest to isolate)
      2. Replace that variable in the equation for Group B with the result from step 1. This will result in only one variable in your equation for Group B.
      3. Solve for the remaining variable in the Group B equation. What does this result mean?
      4. Replace the variable in the original Group A equation with the value you found in step 4 and solve for the other variable. What does this result mean?

   f) **Graphical Method** (Plot both equations and determine their point of intersection)
      1. Isolate the same variable in both of your original equations for Group A and Group B (i.e. get each equation into a $y = mx + b$ form – although your variables may be different letters)
      2. Use your graphing calculator to plot both equations together. What do you notice about the graphs?
      3. Use the trace function on your calculator to determine where your lines intersect. What is that point? How does it relate to your answer in (e)?
      4. What is the downside to this method? Explain.

g) **Elimination Method** (Multiply one equation by an appropriate number and add it to the other equation in order to eliminate a variable. Repeat this process until a solution is determined)
1. Start with the two original equations. Your equations will probably look like these below, although your variables may be different and the order may be different. You should keep your variables the same as what you chose above, but you must arrange your terms in the same order.
$$s + 4w = \$2.60$$
$$3s + 2w = \$2.80$$
2. Multiply the first equation by -3 (this means multiply *every* term by -3) and add the first equation to the second. This will leave you with one equation, which will have only one variable.
3. Solve the resulting equation for the remaining variable. What does this value mean?
4. Choose one of the original equations and replace the variable you found in step 3 with the value you determined. Solve for the remaining variable. What does this value mean?

2. How do your solutions in each of the three methods compare?

3. Is it possible to have two lines that don't intersect? If so, what does that imply about the solution of the corresponding system of equations?

4. Is it possible for a system of two equations to have two solutions? Three? Infinitely many? How do you know? If it is possible, what does that imply about the graphs of the equations?

5. Solve the following using all three methods: A sundae is being made from 98% fat-free frozen yogurt and 80% fat-free dessert topping. How many ounces of each should be used if we wish to have a 10-ounce, 90% fat-free sundae?

6. Solve the following using all three methods: Mark is 11 times older than his son Benjamin. In 27 years, Benjamin will be ½ the age of his father. How old are they now?

7. Solve the following using any method (or combination of methods) you choose: A booth at the farmer's market had a mix-and-match sale on apples, pears, and grapes. They offered the following three options, each for $6.
   Option 1: 24 apples, 12 pears, 1 bunch of grapes
   Option 2: 12 apples, 18 pears, 1 bunch of grapes
   Option 3: 8 apples, 8 pears, 3 bunches of grapes
Based on this sale, determine the price for a single apple, a single pear, and one bunch of grapes.

Adapted from Small, D. (2005). *Contemporary College Algebra: Data, Functions, Modeling*

MATH 103
FUNCTION SORTING TASK

In the following pages you will find twelve graphs and twelve tables. Your task will be to do the following.

1. In your group decide which graphs "resemble" each other or have some common feature and sort the graphs into different piles. Your group may decide to sort in any way that makes sense to you, but after you have sorted the graphs you will write one or two sentences describing your sorting strategy.

2. Next, your group should match each of the twelve tables of values with the matching (or most closely matching) graph. Think about your graph sorting strategy. Would you sort the graphs with their tables in another way? If so, revise your two sentences and resort your graphs.

GRAPH 1

GRAPH 2

GRAPH 3

GRAPH 4

GRAPH 5

GRAPH 6

GRAPH 7

GRAPH 8

GRAPH 9

GRAPH 10

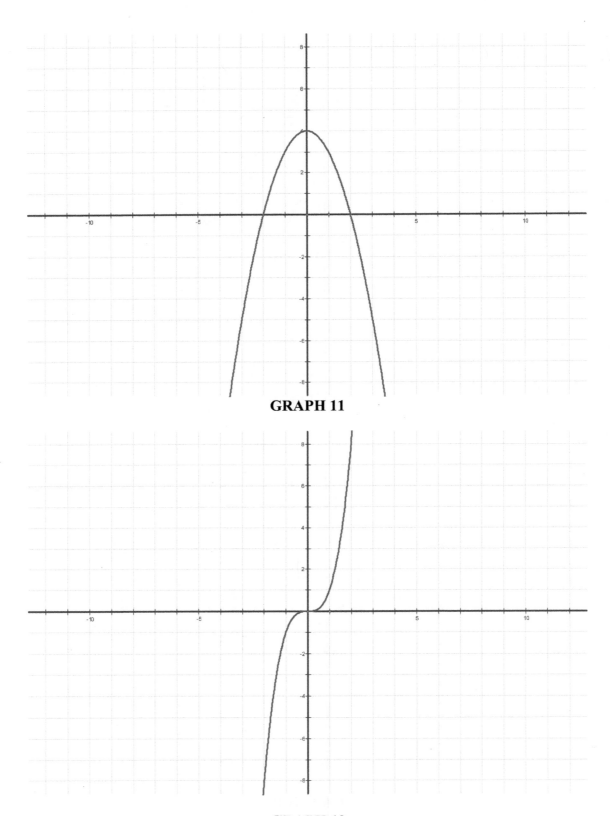

GRAPH 11

GRAPH 12

TABLE 1

x	y
0	2
1	2
2	3
3	3
4	4
5	4
8	6

TABLE 2

x	y
-2	-0.91
-1	-1.88
0	0
1	0.88
2	0.87
3	0.04
4	-0.74

TABLE 3

x	y
-2	-1.7
-1	-0.58
0	0
1	0.55
2	1.72
3	13.0

TABLE 4

x	y
-2	1.9
-1	2.5
0	3.1
1	3.7
2	4.3
3	4.9
4	5.1

TABLE 5

x	y
0	0
1	1
2	1
3	2
4	2
5	3
6	3

TABLE 6

x	y
-2	4.8
-1	4.3
0	3.8
1	3.3
2	2.8
3	2.3
4	1.8

TABLE 7

x	y
-3	81
-2	8
-1	1
0	0
1	1
2	8
3	81

TABLE 8

x	y
-3	3
-2	2
-1	1
0	0
1	1
2	2
3	3

TABLE 9

x	y
-3	2.75
-2	2.5
-1	2.0
0	1.0
1	-1.0
2	-5.0

TABLE 10

x	y
-3	-5
-2	0
-1	3
0	4
1	3
2	0
3	5

TABLE 11

x	y
-3	-1.88
-2	-1.75
-1	-1.50
0	-1.0
1	0.0
2	2.0
3	6.0

TABLE 12

x	y
-3	-27.0
-2	- 8.0
-1	- 1.0
0	0
1	1.0
2	8.0
3	27.0

MATH 103
INFLUENCE OF PARAMETERS IN THE QUADRATIC

One of the most common families of functions found in College Algebra textbooks is the Quadratic Function family. The general form of this family is given as

$$f(x) = ax^2 + bx + c$$

In this form x is the **variable** for the function and a, b, and c are **parameters**.

Example: Suppose $g(x) = 3x^2 - 2x + 7$ is a function *in* x (that means x is the variable which can be any real number in this case) and a, b, and c are parameters with $a = 3$, $b = -2$, and $c = 7$.

1. For the function g, create both a table of input/output pairs and a graph.

x	$g(x)$
-3	
-2	
-1	
0	
1	
2	
3	

You will explore the affect of the general parameters a, b, and c on the graphs and tables of the members of the quadratic function family. It will be a good idea to look at various different values for these parameters, but it should be done in an organized way.

2. In pairs, devise a plan for attacking this problem. First, state in your own words what you want to find out   Second, state in your own words what your strategy will be.
3. Share your ideas with one other pair and revise your plan if you think it is necessary.
    a. How does the parameter a influence the graph of a quadratic function? Explain and give at least two examples of equations and graphs that support your conclusions.
    b. How does the parameter b influence the graph of a quadratic function? Explain and give at least two examples of equations and graphs that support your conclusions.
    c. How does the parameter c influence the graph of a quadratic function? Explain and give at least two examples of equations and graphs that support your conclusions.

MATH 103
DORITOS

You're at a party with a bunch of friends. After the first rush at the chip bowl, the rate at which people are eating the chips starts declining.

1. What does the last sentence above tell you? How is the number of chips changing with time?

2. One of your friends suggests that the Doritos are experiencing exponential decay. You don't quite remember what exponential decay is, so the next day your friend has you perform the following investigation:

    Suppose the following pictures show the chip bowl at different times during the party.

    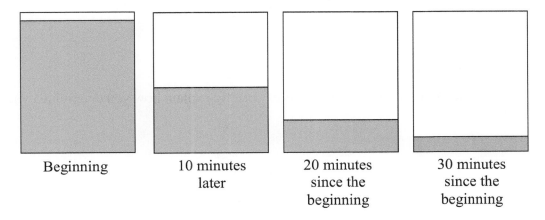

    Beginning   10 minutes later   20 minutes since the beginning   30 minutes since the beginning

    Construct a table of 8 data points consistent with these pictures and plot them. Be sure to include a scale and units for each axis.

    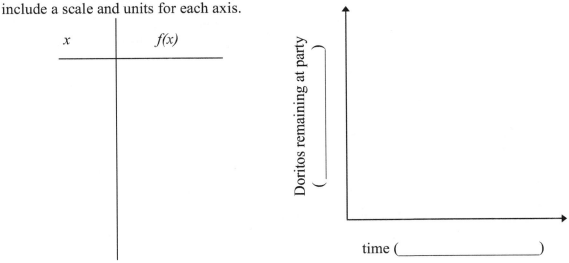

3. How long until there's half of what you started with? How long until there is 1/64 of what you started with?

4. Can you write an equation of the form $y = mx + b$ that fits your data? Explain your answer.

5. Write an equation for the Doritos function. Briefly explain how you determined your answer.

6. We know the rate of change of a linear function is constant. Describe the rate of change of the Doritos function. Use your graph or table to justify your answer.

7. In your own words, explain exponential decay.

MATH 103
BABYSITTING

1. The Jones family pays a certain rate per hour for babysitting.

   a. Write a sentence explaining how you would determine your pay.
   b. Use variable(s) to write an equation for this situation and explain what each part of your equation represents.
   c. In your own words, write what you think the word "variable" means in mathematics. Are all of the symbols you wrote in your equation in part (b) variables? Why or why not?

2. Now suppose you have been hired to babysit the Jones children next Saturday night at a rate of $8 per hour.

   a. Their parents aren't sure how long they will be gone, but it will be anywhere from 2 to 5 hours. Using the definition of function, explain why this babysitting situation represents a function.

   b. Now make a careful graph that represents this situation. Be sure to label your units and scale.

   c. Explain how your graph in part (b) supports the statement that the relationship between the amount of time you spend babysitting and your total pay is a function.

   d. What is the domain and what is the range of the babysitter function? Justify your answer.

3. Now suppose the Jones's always round up to the nearest quarter hour when paying you for babysitting (for example, if you babysat for 4 hours and 40 minutes, they'd pay you for 3 hours and 45 minutes, but if you babysat for 2 hours and 50 minutes, they'd pay you for 3 hours).

a. You will babysit the Jones children for anywhere from 2 to 5 hours on Saturday night. Make a careful, labeled graph that represents this situation.

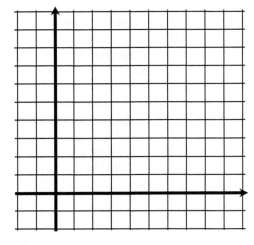

b. Is the relationship between the amount of time you spend babysitting and your total pay a function? If so, what is the domain and what is the range? Justify all of your answers.

Trigonometric Functions and Identities

Right Triangle Trigonometry

$$\sin \theta = \frac{\text{side opposite}}{\text{hypotenuse}} \qquad \cos \theta = \frac{\text{side adjacent}}{\text{hypotenuse}}$$

$$\csc \theta = \frac{\text{hypotenuse}}{\text{side opposite}} \qquad \sec \theta = \frac{\text{hypotenuse}}{\text{side adjacent}}$$

$$\tan \theta = \frac{\text{side opposite}}{\text{side adjacent}}$$

$$\cot \theta = \frac{\text{side adjacent}}{\text{side opposite}}$$

The Unit Circle and Special Angles

The Unit Circle

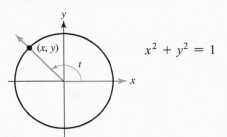

$$x^2 + y^2 = 1$$

$$\sin t = y \qquad \cos t = x \qquad \tan t = \frac{y}{x}$$

$$\csc t = \frac{1}{y} \qquad \sec t = \frac{1}{x} \qquad \cot t = \frac{x}{y}$$

Pythagorean

$$\sin^2 \theta + \cos^2 \theta = 1$$

$$1 + \tan^2 \theta = \sec^2 \theta$$

$$1 + \cot^2 \theta = \csc^2 \theta$$

Sum and Difference

$$\cos (\alpha + \beta) = \cos \alpha \cos \beta - \sin \alpha \sin \beta$$

$$\cos (\alpha - \beta) = \cos \alpha \cos \beta + \sin \alpha \sin \beta$$

$$\sin (\alpha + \beta) = \sin \alpha \cos \beta + \cos \alpha \sin \beta$$

$$\sin (\alpha - \beta) = \sin \alpha \cos \beta - \cos \alpha \sin \beta$$

$$\tan (\alpha + \beta) = \frac{\tan \alpha + \tan \beta}{1 - \tan \alpha \tan \beta}$$

$$\tan (\alpha - \beta) = \frac{\tan \alpha - \tan \beta}{1 + \tan \alpha \tan \beta}$$

Reciprocal

$$\sin \theta = \frac{1}{\csc \theta} \qquad \cos \theta = \frac{1}{\sec \theta} \qquad \tan \theta = \frac{1}{\cot \theta}$$

$$\csc \theta = \frac{1}{\sin \theta} \qquad \sec \theta = \frac{1}{\cos \theta} \qquad \cot \theta = \frac{1}{\tan \theta}$$

Quotient

$$\tan \theta = \frac{\sin \theta}{\cos \theta} \qquad \cot \theta = \frac{\cos \theta}{\sin \theta}$$

Negative-Angle

$$\sin (-\theta) = -\sin \theta \qquad \csc (-\theta) = -\csc \theta$$

$$\cos (-\theta) = \cos \theta \qquad \sec (-\theta) = \sec \theta$$

$$\tan (-\theta) = -\tan \theta \qquad \cot (-\theta) = -\cot \theta$$

Double-Angle

$$\sin 2\theta = 2 \sin \theta \cos \theta$$

$$\cos 2\theta = \cos^2 \theta - \sin^2 \theta$$

$$= 2 \cos^2 \theta - 1$$

$$= 1 - 2 \sin^2 \theta$$

$$\tan 2\theta = \frac{2 \tan \theta}{1 - \tan^2 \theta}$$

Power-Reducing

$$\sin^2 \theta = \frac{1 - \cos 2\theta}{2}$$

$$\cos^2 \theta = \frac{1 + \cos 2\theta}{2}$$

$$\tan^2 \theta = \frac{1 - \cos 2\theta}{1 + \cos 2\theta}$$

Half-Angle

$$\sin \frac{\theta}{2} = \pm \sqrt{\frac{1 - \cos \theta}{2}} \qquad \cos \frac{\theta}{2} = \pm \sqrt{\frac{1 + \cos \theta}{2}}$$

$$\tan \frac{\theta}{2} = \frac{1 - \cos \theta}{\sin \theta} \qquad \tan \frac{\theta}{2} = \frac{\sin \theta}{1 + \cos \theta}$$

Formulas from Geometry

Rectangle

$A = LW$

$P = 2L + 2W$

Triangle

$A = \frac{1}{2}bh$

$P = a + b + c$

Pythagorean Theorem

$c^2 = a^2 + b^2$

Circle

$C = 2\pi r$

$A = \pi r^2$

Equilateral Triangle

$A = \dfrac{\sqrt{3}}{4}s^2$

$P = 3s$

Parallelogram

$A = bh$

$P = 2a + 2b$

Trapezoid

$A = \frac{1}{2}(a + b)h$

$P = a + b + c + d$

$\dfrac{x^2}{a^2} + \dfrac{y^2}{b^2} = 1$ $(0, b)$

$(-a, 0)$ $(a, 0)$

$(0, -b)$

Ellipse

$A = \pi ab$

$P \approx 2\pi\sqrt{\dfrac{a^2 + b^2}{2}}$

Sum of the Angles in a Triangle

$A + B + C = 180°$

Sum of the Angles in a Quadrilateral

$A + B + C + D = 360°$

Rectangular (Parallelepiped) Box

$V = LWH$

$S = 2LW + 2LH + 2WH$

Cylinder

$V = \pi r^2 h$

$S = 2\pi rh + 2\pi r^2$

Sphere

$V = \frac{4}{3}\pi r^3$

$S = 4\pi r^2$

Cone

$V = \frac{1}{3}\pi r^2 h$

$S = \pi r^2 + \pi r\sqrt{r^2 + h^2}$

Formulas from Algebra

Basic Properties

$a + b = b + a$

$ab = ba$

$(a + b) + c = a + (b + c)$

$(ab)c = a(bc)$

$a(b + c) = ab + ac$

$\dfrac{a}{c} + \dfrac{b}{c} = \dfrac{a + b}{c}$

$\dfrac{a}{b} \times \dfrac{c}{d} = \dfrac{ac}{bd}$

Exponents

$a^m a^n = a^{m+n}$

$(a^m)^n = a^{mn}$

$(ab)^n = a^n b^n$

$\left(\dfrac{a}{b}\right)^n = \dfrac{a^n}{b^n}$

$\dfrac{a^m}{a^n} = a^{m-n}$

$a^{-n} = \dfrac{1}{a^n}$

$\dfrac{a^{-m}}{a^{-n}} = \dfrac{a^n}{a^m}$

$\left(\dfrac{a}{b}\right)^{-n} = \left(\dfrac{b}{a}\right)^n$

Logarithms

$\log_a x = k \quad \text{means} \quad x = a^k$

$\log_a 1 = 0 \quad \text{and} \quad \log_a a = 1$

$\log_a m + \log_a n = \log_a mn$

$\log_a m - \log_a n = \log_a \dfrac{m}{n}$

$\log_a m^r = r \log_a m$

$\log_a a^x = x$

$a^{\log_a x} = x$

$\log_a x = \dfrac{\log_b x}{\log_b a} \text{ (change of base)}$

Radicals

$a^{1/n} = \sqrt[n]{a}$

$a^{m/n} = \sqrt[n]{a^m}$

$a^{m/n} = \left(\sqrt[n]{a}\right)^m$

$\sqrt[n]{ab} = \sqrt[n]{a} \cdot \sqrt[n]{b}$

$\sqrt[n]{\dfrac{a}{b}} = \dfrac{\sqrt[n]{a}}{\sqrt[n]{b}}$

Special Factoring

$a^2 - b^2 = (a - b)(a + b)$

$a^2 + 2ab + b^2 = (a + b)^2$

$a^2 - 2ab + b^2 = (a - b)^2$

$a^3 + b^3 = (a + b)(a^2 - ab + b^2)$

$a^3 - b^3 = (a - b)(a^2 + ab + b^2)$

Constants

$\pi \approx 3.141593$

$e \approx 2.718282$

$i = \sqrt{-1}$

$i^2 = -1$

Distance Formula

$d = \sqrt{(x_2 - x_1)^2 + (y_2 - y_1)^2}$

Midpoint Formula

$M = \left(\dfrac{x_1 + x_2}{2}, \dfrac{y_1 + y_2}{2}\right)$

Quadratic Formula

$x = \dfrac{-b \pm \sqrt{b^2 - 4ac}}{2a}$

Slope of a Line

$m = \dfrac{\Delta y}{\Delta x} = \dfrac{y_2 - y_1}{x_2 - x_1}$

Average Rate of Change of f from x_1 to x_2

$\dfrac{y_2 - y_1}{x_2 - x_1} \quad \text{or} \quad \dfrac{f(x_2) - f(x_1)}{x_2 - x_1}$

Slope-Intercept Form

$y = mx + b$

Point-Slope Form

$y = m(x - x_1) + y_1$

$y - y_1 = m(x - x_1)$

Horizontal Line

$y = b$

Vertical Line

$x = k$

Vertex Formula

$x = -\dfrac{b}{2a}$

Vertex (Standard) Form

$y = a(x - h)^2 + k$

Standard Equation of a Circle

$(x - h)^2 + (y - k)^2 = r^2$